42nd European Photovoltaic Solar Energy Conference and Exhibition (EU PVSEC 2025)

Bilbao, Spain
22-26 September 2025

Volume 1 of 6

ISBN: 979-8-3313-2987-7

42nd European Photovoltaic Solar Energy Conference and Exhibition (EU PVSEC 2025)

Bilbao, Spain
22-26 September 2025

Volume 1 of 6

42nd European Photovoltaic Solar Energy Conference and Exhibition

Proceedings of the International Conference

22 September – 26 September 2025

Edited by:

C. DEL CAÑIZO
Solar Energy Institute
UPM
Spain

R. KENNY
European Commission
Joint Research Centre
Italy

J. BERGMILLER
WIP Renewable Energies
Germany

J. DE GREGORIO
WIP Renewable Energies
Germany

Edition Team:

B. Yildiz
L. Großhans
A. Michaelsen
U.E. Birgi
WIP Renewable Energies
Germany

Photos at:

Coordination of the Technical Programme:

European Commission Joint Research Centre
Via E. Fermi 1
21020 Ispra (VA)
Italy

Institutional Support:

European Commission

Institutional PV Industry Cooperation:

SolarPower Europe
ESMC – European Solar Manufacturing Council

Supporting Organisations:

AUSTRALIAN PV INSTITUTE
ASOM – Alliance for Solar Mobility
BASQUE ENERGY CLUSTER
BILBAO CONVENTION BUREAU
EASE – European Association for Storage of Energy
ETIP PV – European Technology & Innovation Platform PV
GÜNDER – Turkish Solar Energy Society
IEA PVPS - IEA Photovoltaic Power Systems Programme
INSTITUTO SOLAR DE ENERGÍA SOLAR
LDES – Long Duration Energy Storage Council
NSEFI – National Solar Energy federation of India
NUS /SERIS – National University of Singapore / Solar Energy Research Institute of Singapore
UPM - Polytechnic University of Madrid

Supporting Associations:

EERA – European Energy Research Aliance
EREF – European Renewable Energies Federation
EUREC – The Association of European Renewable Energy Research Centres
VDMA Photovoltaic Equipment

Local Support:
ENTE VASCO DE LA ENERGÍA
EUH – University of the Basque Country

EU PVSEC 2025 realised by:

WIP Renewable Energies
Sylvensteinstr. 2, 81369 Munich, Germany
Tel: +49 89 720 12 735, Fax: +49 89 720 12 791
Email: pv.conference@wip-munich.de
www.eupvsec.org
www.wip-munich.de

Proceedings produced and published by:

WIP Renewable Energies
Sylvensteinstr. 2, 81369 Munich, Germany
Tel: +49 89 720 12 735, Fax: +49 89 720 12 791
Email: pv.conference@wip-munich.de
www.eupvsec.org
www.wip-munich.de

42nd EUROPEAN PHOTOVOLTAIC SOLAR ENERGY CONFERENCE AND EXHIBITION
22 SEPTEMBER – 26 SEPTEMBER 2025

EU PVSEC 2025 COMMITTEES

INTERNATIONAL SCIENTIFIC ADVISORY COMMITTEE (ISAC)

Chair

P. Szymanski, European Commission Joint Research Centre, Director of Energy, Transport and Climate, Petten, The Netherlands

Committee Members

V. Bermúdez Benito, Founder & Principal Consultant, Berbetin, Antibes, France

G.C. Eder, OFI, Vienna, Austria

P. Frankl, Head of the Renewable Energy Division, International Energy Agency, France

M. Getsiou, European Commission, DG RTD, Brussels, Belgium

S.W. Glunz, Head of Division Photovoltaics - Research, Fraunhofer ISE, Freiburg, Germany

N.M. Haegel, Director of the National Center for Photovoltaics, NREL, Golden, USA

R. Kenny, European Commission Joint Research Centre, Directorate for Energy and Transport and Climate, Ispra, Italy

S. Nowak, Managing Director of NET Nowak Energy & Technology, St. Ursen, Switzerland

R. Schlatmann, Chairman of ETIP PV, Head of the Solar Energy Division at Helmholtz-Zentrum Berlin, Germany

W.C. Sinke, TNO Energy Transition, The Netherlands

M. Topič, Head of Laboratory of Photovoltaics and Optoelectronics of the University of Ljubljana, Slovenia

P. Verlinden, Director at Amrock, Visiting Professor at Sun Yat-Sen University, Guangzhou, China

E. Voroshazi, Head of PV module process laboratory, CEA, Le Bourget-du-Lac, France

J. Bergmiller, Managing Director Events & Knowledge Transfer, WIP Renewable Energies, Munich, Germany

J. de Gregorio, Head of Unit, Scientific Services and Cooperation, WIP Renewable Energies, Munich, Germany

CONFERENCE EXECUTIVE COMMITTEE

Conference General Chair

C. del Cañizo, UPM, Madrid, Spain

Technical Programme Chair

R. Kenny, European Commission Joint Research Centre, Directorate for Energy and Transport and Climate, Ispra, Italy

Committee Members

W.C. Sinke, Program Development Manager, TNO Energy Transition, The Netherlands

S. Nowak, Managing Director of NET Nowak Energy & Technology, St. Ursen, Switzerland

M. Topič, Head of Laboratory of Photovoltaics and Optoelectronics of the University of Ljubljana, Slovenia

V. Bermúdez Benito, BERBETIN, France

E. Voroshazi, Head of PV Module Process Laboratory, CEA, Le Bourget-Du-Lac France

H. Ossenbrink, Former European Commission Joint Research Centre, Germany

J. Bergmiller, Managing Director Events & Knowledge Transfer, WIP Renewable Energies, Munich, Germany

J. de Gregorio, Head of Unit, Scientific Services and Cooperation, WIP Renewable Energies, Munich, Germany

2025 SCIENTIFIC COMMITTEE

Programme Technical Chair

R. Kenny, European Commission, Joint Research Centre, Italy

Topic Chairs

Topic 1: Silicon Materials and Cells

F. Schindler, Fraunhofer ISE, Germany

Topic 2: Thin Films and New Concepts

I. Gordon, imec, Belgium

Topic 3: Photovoltaic Modules and BoS Components

T. Barnes, NREL, USA

Topic 4: PV Systems Engineering, Integrated/Applied PV

A.M. Gracia Amillo, FUNDACION CENER, Spain

Topic 5: PV in the Energy Transition

C. Agraffeil, CEA / INES, France

Topic Organisers and Paper Review Experts

Topic 1: Silicon Materials and Cells

F. Schindler, Fraunhofer ISE, Germany

C. Fischer, Wacker Chemie, Germany

G. Hahn, University of Konstanz, Germany

K. Ding, Forschungszentrum Jülich, Germany

P. Roca i Cabarrocas, CNRS-LPICM, France

A. W. Weeber, TNO Energy Transition, The Netherlands

D. Muñoz, CEA / INES, France

S. W. Glunz, Fraunhofer ISE, Germany

K. Bothe, ISFH, Germany

M. Topic, University of Ljubljana, Slovenia

P. Fath, RCT-Solutions, Germany

S. Peters, Hanwha Q CELLS, Germany

M.P. Bellmann, SINTEF, Norway

A. Ciesla, UNSW, Australia

C. Hagendorf, Freiberg Instruments, Germany

X. Yu, Zhejiang University, China

J.S. Lee, KIER, South Korea

R. Brendel, ISFH, Germany

T. Dullweber, ISFH, Germany

J. Horzel, Fraunhofer ISE, Germany

W. Nemeth, NREL, United States of America

R. Turan, METU, Türkiye

F. Menchini, ENEA, Italy

W. Favre, CEA, France

J. Meier, Meier Technologies, Switzerland
J. Schmidt, ISFH, Germany
M. Wright, University of Oxford, United Kingdom
J. Zhao, CSEM, Switzerland
A. Morisset, CSEM, Switzerland
A. Richter, Fraunhofer ISE, Germany
J. Linke, ISC Konstanz, Germany
B. Geerligs, TNO Energy Transition, The Netherlands
S. Dubois, CEA, France
M. Hermle, Fraunhofer ISE, Germany
B. Terheiden, University of Konstanz, Germany
P. Delli Veneri, ENEA, Italy
T. Matsui, AIST, Japan
Y. Ohshita, Toyota Technological Institute, Japan
E. Bruhat, HOLOSOLIS, France
A. Augusto, Dalarna University, Sweden
F. Ferrazza, ENI S.p.A., Italy
A. Otaegi, UPV/EHU, Spain
M.C. Schubert, Fraunhofer ISE, Germany
H. Duman, KalyonPV, Türkiye
N. Usami, Nagoya University, Japan
Y. Zhu, UNSW, Australia
D. Brunner, RENA Technologies, Germany
A. Danel, CEA, France
C. Gerardi, 3Sun, Italy
H.J. Nonnenmacher, Meyer Burger, Germany
P. Verlinden, AMROCK, Australia
Q. Wang, Wang, Qi, China
W. Zhang, Zhang, Weiming, China
Y. Chen, Trina Solar Energy, China
E. Krassowski, CE Cell Engineering, Germany
M. Foti, 3Sun, Italy
D.L. Bätzner, Meyer Burger Research, Switzerland

Topic 2: Thin Films and New Concepts
I. Gordon, imec, Belgium
J.C. Goldschmidt, Marburg University, Germany
F. Schoofs, Oxford PV, United Kingdom
N. Kyranaki, Hasselt University, Belgium
S. Veenstra, TNO Energy Transition, The Netherlands
T. Aernouts, imec, Belgium
A.N. Tiwari, SOLTIWA, Switzerland
G. Siefer, Fraunhofer ISE, Germany
M. Edoff, Uppsala University, Sweden
A. Marti Vega, UPM, Spain
J. Poortmans, imec, Belgium
I. Ramiro, UPM, Spain
T. Magorian Friedlmeier, ZSW, Germany

S. Albrecht, HZB, Germany
S. Berson, CEA, France
P. Carroy, CEA, France
C. Case, Oxford PV, United Kingdom
G. Coletti, FuturaSun, Italy
S. De Wolf, KAUST, Saudi Arabia
U.W. Paetzold, KIT, Germany
H. Sivaramakrishnan Radhakrisnan, imec, Belgium
P. Schulze, Fraunhofer ISE, Germany
L. Wang, Technology Innovation Institute, United Arab
    Emirates
Y. Smirnov, Applied Materials, United States of America
B. Stannowski, HZB, Germany
F. Fertig, Hanwha Q CELLS, Germany
L. Lancellotti, ENEA, Italy
S. Cros, CEA, France
S. Hayase, The University of Electro-Communications, Japan
S. Huang, Macquarie University, Australia
M. Khenkin, HZB, Germany
C. Lin, National Taiwan University, Taiwan

M.S.H. Norton, University of Cyprus, Cyprus
P. Pistor, Pablo de Olavide University, Spain
W. Tress, Zurich University of Applied Sciences,
    Switzerland
A. Aguirre, imec, Belgium
D. Lan, UNSW Sydney, China
M. Saliba, University of Stuttgart, Germany
P. Manshanden, TNO Energy Transition, The Netherlands
L. Vesce, University of Rome II, Italy
I. Dogan, TNO Solliance, The Netherlands
Y. Kuang, imec, Belgium
M. Al Katrib, IPVF, France
M.I. Hossain, QEERI, Qatar
W.H. Chiu, Chang Gung University, Taiwan
C. Chen, Ming Chi University of Technology, Taiwan
C. Fell, CSIRO Energy Technology, Australia
G. Brammertz, imec, Belgium
T. Dalibor, Avancis, Germany
S. Ishizuka, AIST, Japan
A. Redinger, University of Luxembourg, Luxembourg
A. Romeo, University of Verona, Italy
V. Sittinger, Fraunhofer IST, Germany
M. Theelen, TNO/Solliance, The Netherlands
G. Timò, RSE, Italy
A. Kanevce, ZSW, Germany
A. Pérez-Rodríguez, IREC, Spain
R. Gutzler, ZSW, Germany
W. Witte, ZSW, Germany
T. Nishimura, Tokyo Institute of Technology, Japan
C. Qian, University of New South Wales, Australia
J.P. Connolly, CentraleSupelec, France
J.P. Kleider, CNRS/GeePs, France
I. Konovalov, University of Applied Sciences Jena, Germany
Y. Okada, University of Tokyo, Japan
M. Rusu, HZB, Germany
H. Meddeb, DLR, Germany
E. Saucedo, Universitat Politècnica de Catalunya (UPC),
    Spain
P. Vidal-Fuentes, FUNDACIÓ INSTITUT DE RECERCA
    EN ENERGIA DE CATALUNYA, Spain
C. Malerba, ENEA, Italy
C. Becker, HZB, Germany
D. Kuciauskas, NREL, United States of America
M. Ochoa, University of Cantabria, Spain
T. Tayagaki, AIST, Japan
S. Wasmer, WAVELABS Solar Metrology Systems,
    Germany
S. Zandi, UNSW, Australia
C. Messmer, University of Freiburg, Germany
J.B. Puel, Institut Photovoltaïque d'Ile de France (IPVF),
    France
S. Ternes, University of Rome II, Italy

Topic 3: Photovoltaic Modules and BoS Components
V. Bermúdez Benito, BERBETIN, France
R. Preu, Fraunhofer ISE, Germany
R. Gottschalg, Fraunhofer CSP, Germany
T. Barnes, NREL, United States of America
G. Friesen, SUPSI, Switzerland
G. Bardizza, TÜV Rheinland Solar, Italy

V. Barth, CEA, France
A. Faes, CSEM, Switzerland
A. Lennon, Sundrive Solar, Australia
M. Mittag, Fraunhofer ISE, Germany
M.A. Muñoz-García, UPM, Spain
H. Nagel, Fraunhofer ISE, Germany
S. Pietralunga, CNR, Italy
T. Timofte, ISC Konstanz, Germany

S. Feldbacher, PCCL, Austria
A. Halm, ISC Konstanz, Germany
H. Hanifi, AESOLAR, Germany
E. Warren, NREL, United States of America
S. Zhang, Trina Solar Energy, China
X. Zhen, Canadian Solar, China
G. Beaucarne, Dow Silicones Belgium, Belgium
T. Bejat, CEA, France
C. Camus, LayTec, Germany
U. Jahn, Fraunhofer CSP, Germany
G. Oreski, PCCL, Austria
M. Pander, Fraunhofer CSP, Germany
T. Sample, European Commission JRC, Italy
A. Morlier, imo-imomec, Belgium
C. Barretta, PCCL, Austria
P. Gebhardt, Fraunhofer ISE, Germany
C. Sen, UNSW, Australia
O. Arriaga Arruti, CSEM, Switzerland
X. Gu, NIST, United States of America
C. Xiao, Chinese Academy of Sciences, United States of
America
R. Aninat, TNO/Solliance, The Netherlands
S. Mitterhofer, NIST, United States of America
B. Hoex, UNSW, Australia
E. Özkalay, SUPSI, Switzerland
M. Bokalič, University of Ljubljana, Slovenia
S. Bordihn, ISFH, Germany
M. Despeisse, CSEM, Switzerland
J. Govaerts, imec, Belgium
J. Lopez-Garcia, STS-Certified, Spain
M. Pravettoni, Technology Innovation Institute, United Arab
Emirates
T. Stoyanova Lyubenova, Joint Research Centre, Italy
C. Ulbrich, HZB, Germany
J. Moereke, Avancis, Germany
Y.S. Long, ITRI, Taiwan
D. Pavanello, European Commission JRC, Italy
A.K. Vidal de Oliveira, UFSC, Brazil
J. Bengoechea, CENER, Spain
M. Ernst, ANU, Australia
H. Ellis, European Commission JRC, Italy
B. Mihaylov, European Commission JRC, Italy
G. Chowdhury, 3E, Belgium
B. Aissa, QEERI - Qatar Environment and Energy Research
Institute, Qatar

Topic 4: PV Systems Engineering, Integrated/Applied PV
A. Gracia Amillo, CENER, Spain
W.G.J.H.M. van Sark, Utrecht University, The Netherlands
K. Lappalainen, Tampere University, Finland
J.M. Almeida Serra, University of Lisbon, Portugal
I. Tsanakas, CEA, France
C. Buerhop-Lutz, HI ERN, Germany
D. Moser, Becquerel Institute Italia, Italy
F. Frontini, SUPSI, Switzerland
G.C. Eder, OFI, Austria
A. Scognamiglio, ENEA, Italy
A. Chatzipanagi, European Commission JRC, Italy
I. Antón Hernández, UPM, Spain
R.M.E. Valckenborg, TNO, The Netherlands
T. Reindl, SERIS, Singapore
J.R. Gonzalez, European Space Agency, The Netherlands
G. Mütter, Gerhard Mütter e.U., Austria
T. Merdzhanova, Forschungszentrum Jülich, Germany

V. Lara-Fanego, Solargis, Spain
A. Louwen, Eurac Research, Italy
A. Martinez Fernandez, European Commission JRC, Italy
T. Oozeki, AIST, Japan

J. Remund, Meteotest, Switzerland
M. Sengupta, NREL, United States of America
M. Zehner, Rosenheim Technical University of Applied
Sciences, Germany
B. Nouri, German Aerospace Center, Spain
S. Poddar, UNSW, Australia
D. Bachour, HBKU/ Qatar Foundation, Qatar
J. Yang, NREL, United States of America
S. Bouguerra, imo-imomec, Belgium
C. Alonso-Tristán, UBU, Spain
M. Carbone, ENEL Green Power, Italy
M. Dennenmoser, BayWa r.e. Solar Projects GmbH,
Germany
C.W. Hansen, Sandia National Laboratories, United States of
America
A. Neubert, DNV Maritime Software GmbH, Germany
D. Berrian, Belectric, Germany
M. Oliosi, PVsyst, Switzerland
J. Moschner, KU Leuven / EnergyVille, Belgium
C. Bucher, BUAS, Switzerland
B. Wittmer, PVsyst SA, Switzerland
M. Bolen, SB Energy, United States of America
D. Daßler, Fraunhofer CSP, Germany
R. Einhaus, ZSW, Germany
P. Hacke, NREL, United States of America
A. Heimsath, Fraunhofer ISE, Germany
J. Lin, PV Guider, Taiwan
A. Migan-Dubois, GeePs, France
M. Rinio, University of Karlstad, Sweden
J.S. Stein, Sandia National Laboratories, United States of
America
D. Stellbogen, ZSW, Germany
M. Theristis, Sandia National Laboratories, United States of
America
A. Virtuani, CSEM, Switzerland
A. Driesse, PV Performance Labs, Germany
M. Øgaard, IFE, Norway
A. Nobre, SERIS, Singapore
T. Trupke, UNSW, Australia
C. Cornaro, University of Rome II, Italy
G. A. dos Reis Benatto, DTU, Denmark
S. Malik, Fraunhofer CSP, Germany
S. Lindig, Univers SAS, France
M.M. Nygård, Institute for Energy Technology, Norway
P. Alonso Gomez, BayWa r.e., Germany
Y. Assoa, CEA, France
P. Bonomo, SUPSI, Switzerland
V. D'Ambrosio, University of Naples Federico II, Italy
E. Román Medina, Tecnalia, Spain
L.H. Slooff, TNO Energy Transition, The Netherlands
S. Villa, TNO, The Netherlands
M. La Rosa, Glass to Power, Italy
T. Del Caño, Onyx Solar Energy, Spain
X. Zhihao, AIST, Japan
P. Sharif, ODTU-GUNAM, Türkiye
K. Umeda, TAISEI CORPORATION, Japan
S. Boddaert, CSTB, France
N. Lysgaard Andersen, DTU, Denmark
K. Meyer, ISFH, Germany
T. Biel, NET Nowak Energy & Technology, Switzerland
F. Colucci, ENEA, Italy
A. Pascaris, NREL, United States of America
C. Dupraz, INRAE, France
C. Alonso-García, CIEMAT, Spain
A. Lefort, BayWa, Germany
H.N. Riise, IFE, Norway
M.A. Schüler, Next2Sun Technology GmbH, Germany
P.J. Pérez-Higueras, University of Jaén, Spain
K. Oda, Agritree,

M. Berwind, Fraunhofer ISE, Germany
M. Dörenkämper, TNO, The Netherlands
M. Heinrich, Fraunhofer ISE, Germany
B. Newman, Lightyear, The Netherlands
A. Reinders, Eindhoven University of Technology, The Netherlands
T. Tanahashi, AIST, Japan
J. Leloux, LuciSun, Belgium
E. Shirazi, University of Twente, The Netherlands
K. Araki, University of Miyazaki, Japan
K. Nishioka, University of Miyazaki, Japan
R. Campesato, CESI, Italy
V. Khorenko, Azur Space, Germany
G. Kakoulaki, European Commission Joint Research Centre, Italy
H. Toyota, JAXA, Japan
P. Garcia-Linares, UPM, Spain
I. Weiss, Weiss, Ingrid, Germany
A. Hensel, Fraunhofer ISE, Germany
J.S. da Fernandes, Hochschule Offenburg, Germany
Y. Ueda, Tokyo University of Science, Japan
J. Braid, Sandia National Laboratories, United States of America

Topic 5: PV in the Energy Transition
J. Stierstorfer, WIP Renewable Energies, Germany
R. Pestana, R&D Nester, Portugal
P.J. Alet, CSEM, Switzerland
C. Agraffeil, CEA, France
K. WAMBACH, Wambach-Consulting, Germany
C. del Cañizo, UPM, Spain
L. Großhans, WIP Renewable Energies, Germany
M. Getsiou, European Commission DG RTD, Belgium
S. Nowak, NET Nowak Energy & Technology, Switzerland
C. Breyer, LUT University, Finland
I. Kaizuka, RTS Corporation, Japan
G. Masson, Becquerel Institute, Belgium
P. Baliozian, VDMA, Germany
L. Großhans, WIP Renewable Energies, Germany
C. Candelise, Bocconi University, Italy
S. Caneva, WIP Renewable Energies, Germany

G. Barchi, Eurac Research, Italy
R. Bründlinger, AIT, Austria
V. Efthymiou, University of Cyprus, Cyprus
M. Centeno Brito, University of Lisbon, Portugal
F. Carigiet, ZHAW, Switzerland
B. Gaiddon, HESPUL, France
F.Z. Ouchani, Green Energy Park, Morocco
M. Rennhofer, AIT, Austria
G. Adinolfi, ENEA, Italy
W. Schaffer, Salzburg Netz, Austria
A. Haber, e-control, Austria
G. Heilscher, Technische Hochschule Ulm, Germany
A. Anctil, Michigan State University, United States of America
S. Arancón, Plug and Play, Spain
S. Capaccioli, ETA - Florence Renewable Energies, Italy
V. Fthenakis, Columbia University, United States of America
G. Heath, NREL, United States of America
K. Komoto, Mizuho Research & Technologies, Ltd., Japan
W. Palitzsch, LuxChemtech, Germany
S. Ovaitt, NREL, United States of America
M. de Wild-Scholten, SmartGreenScans, The Netherlands
S. Herceg, Fraunhofer ISE, Germany
C. Polacchi, Eurac Research, Italy
N. Espinosa, Universidad de Murcia, Spain
E. Drahi, TotalEnergies OneTech, France
S. Guastella, RSE, Italy

H. Ossenbrink, Band Gap, Germany
D. Polverini, European Commission DG GROW, Belgium
N. Taylor, European Commission JRC, Italy
K.A. Weiß, Fraunhofer ISE, Germany
I. Kafedjiska, Helmholtz Zentrum Berlin, Germany
P. Malbranche, Solar Action, France
S. De Iuliis, ENEA, Italy
T. Haarberg, BNW-Energy, Norway
A. Nayfeh, Khalifa University, United Arab Emirates
E. Vartiainen, Fortum Renewables Oy, Finland
E. Veronese, Eurac Research, Italy
P. Sanchez-Friera, Solkeys, Spain
N. Cherradi, Desert Technologies, Saudi Arabia
S. Nold, Fraunhofer ISE, Germany
H.J.J. Yu, CEA, France
M. Beck, U.S. Department of Energy, United States of America
M. Woodhouse, NREL, United States of America
A.B. Cristóbal, UPM, Spain
G. Ruggieri, Insubria University, Italy
S. Tay, NUS, Singapore

Awards Coordinators

Student Awards Coordinator
A.H.M. Smets, Delft University of Technology, The Netherlands

Student Awards Committee
R. Kenny, EU PVSEC Technical Programme Chair, Italy
C. del Canizo, Conference Chair, UPM, Spain
E. Voroshazi, CEA, France
J. Poortmans, imec, Belgium
P.J. Alet, CSEM, Switzerland
S. Caneva, WIP Renewable Energies, Germany
A. Romeo, University of Verona, Italy
G. Friesen, SUPSI, Switzerland
F. Schindler, Fraunhofer ISE, Germany
J.C. Goldchmidt, Marburg University, Germany
D. Moser, Becquerel Institute, Italy
K. Ding, FZJ, Germany
W.C. Sinke, TNO Energy Transition, The Netherlands
M. Topic, University of Ljubljana, Slovenia
R. Schlatman, HZB, Germany
S. Glunz, Fraunhofer ISE, Germany
A.M. Vega, UPM, Spain
I. Kaizuka, RTS, Japan
P.D. Veneri, ENEA, Italy
J. Bengoechea, CENER, Spain

Poster Awards Coordinator
P. Malbranche, Solar Action, France

Poster Awards Committee
R. Kenny, European Commission JRC, Italy
C. del Canizo, UPM, Spain
W. van Sark, Utrecht University, The Netherlands
I. Tsanakas, CEA INES, France
L. Miranda, Oxford PV, United Kingdom
D. Munoz, CEA INES, France
I. Gordon, imec, Belgium
E. Roman, Tecnalia, Spain
G. Eder, OFI, Austria
I. Antón, UPM, Spain
S. Veenstra, TNO, The Netherlands
J.M. Almeida Serra, University of Lisbon, Portugal
T. Magorian Friedlmeier, ZSW, Germany
J. Stierstorfer, WIP Renewable Energies, Germany

SUBJECT INDEX

Silicon Materials and Cells

Sessions 1CP.1, 1EP.3, 1AO.4, 1AO.5, 1AO.6, 1BO.1, 1BO.2, 1BO.3, 1BO.4, 1DO.9, 1BV.5, 1CV.2

Thin Films and New Concepts

Sessions 2CP.2, 2BO.1, 2CO.1, 2CO.2, 2DO.9, 2DO.6, 2DO.7, 2DO.8, 2AO.2, 2AO.3, 2AO.1, 2BO.8, 2BO.9, 2BO.10, 2BV.1, 2BV.2, 2CV.3

Photovoltaic Modules and BoS Components

Sessions 3CP.1, 3CP.3, 3CO.10, 3CO.11, 3DO.12, 3DO.16, 3DO.19, 3DO.20, 3BO.11, 3BO.12, 3BO.14, 3BO.15, 3AV.1, 3AV.2, 3AV.3

PV Systems Engineering, Integrated/Applied PV

Sessions 4AP.1, 4AO.7, 4AO.8, 4AO.9, 4DO.1, 4DO.3, 4BO.6, 4BO.7, 4CO.8, 4CO.9, 4DO.10, 4DO.17, 4BO.5, 4BO.16, 4BO.17, 4DO.2, 4DO.4, 4DO.5, 4CO.3, 4EO.2, 4BV.3, 4BV.4, 4CV.1, 4DV.1, 4DV.4,

PV in the Energy Transition

Sessions 5CP.1, 5CP.2, 5DO.14, 5DO.15, 5CO.4, 5CO.5, 5CO.6, 5DO.18, 5CO.4, 5CO.5, 5CO.6, 5DO.18, 5EO.3, 5EO.1, 5DV.2, 5DV.3,

FOREWORD

The European Photovoltaic Solar Energy Conference and Exhibition (EU PVSEC) stands as the World's leading and most renowned forum for PV research and development and the biggest conference on PV solar energy. In 2025, celebrating its 42nd edition, the EU PVSEC was the essential meeting and exchanging point for global PV experts from research, development, and industry.

Held from 22–26 September 2025 in Bilbao, Spain, the EU PVSEC 2025 was a resounding success, showcasing a wide range of cutting-edge research results. Bringing together both the Conference and the Exhibition, this edition attracted more than 1600 participants from 61 countries who contributed over 1000 presentations across various fields of science and technology. The event provided an essential platform for the exchange of knowledge and ideas on photovoltaic research, innovations, and applications. In the exhibition area 51 companies from all parts of the world welcomed visitors and presented their products and services.

Conference Highlights

The EU PVSEC covered a broad range of topics with an extensive programme that offers an opportunity for workers from across the entire field of photovoltaics to share their findings, as well as an opportunity for multidisciplinary learning. Rapid advances in materials, designs, and manufacturing processes reflect the accelerating expansion of the global PV market. The programme was arranged into 5 topics as follows:
- Silicon Materials and Cells;
- Thin Films and New Concepts;
- Photovoltaic Modules and Balance of System Components;
- PV Systems Engineering, Integrated/Applied PV;
- PV in the Energy Transition.

Communicating the key messages from the conference, not only to participants, but also to other researchers, key stakeholders, policy makers and the general public was an important added value. We thank the Highlights Committee, composed of selected members of the Scientific Committee, as well as the Session Chairs, for providing a comprehensive summary of the findings and state of the art research that were delivered during this year's event. Some key highlights are listed below, while further details may be found in the dedicated highlights presentation in the annex of these proceedings.

Cross-cutting themes:

- Demonstrated the versatility of solar technologies, spanning traditional and emerging application areas.
- Sustainability and circularity remain central, with research focused on reducing material use, such as replacing silver with copper, and advancing end-of-life management of modules.
- Ensuring long-term stability and predictable energy yield is equally essential, with many examples of studies on degradation mechanisms and efforts to elucidate their root-causes, such as in the case of UVID.

- The role of artificial intelligence across the PV value chain is rapidly expanding, from design to operations and maintenance, including among many others drone applications.

Latest Solar Innovations in Materials, Cells, Modules and PV Systems:

While silicon solar cells remain the cornerstone of PV technology, perovskite solar cells continue to stand out as the leading complementary technology to silicon, both as standalone devices and in tandem configurations. Research efforts are increasingly focused on enhancing stability, understanding degradation mechanisms, improving durability and scalability, and ensuring full industrial compatibility.

Many companies presented impressive results on industrial-size single-junction perovskite modules as well as perovskite-based tandem modules, and several new efficiency records were announced during the event. The rapid pace of innovation in cell and module architecture underscores the need for accelerated and more robust testing and qualification methodologies. Both the industry and the research community are moving swiftly to assess and improve reliability in this fast-evolving PV landscape.

A major focus in module research remains the optimisation of materials and packaging to ensure long lifetimes and predictable energy yields from high-efficiency cells. In parallel, many innovative advances in the operation and maintenance (O&M) of PV systems were presented and discussed.

Applications, Grid Integration and Storage

"PV can be deployed everywhere": from space applications to agrivoltaics, PV noise barriers, building-integrated photovoltaics (BIPV), floating PV systems, and even vehicles. Among these, agrivoltaics is gaining momentum as a promising dual land use approach, offering economic benefits for farmers while increasing resilience to climate change.

Flexibility solutions, particularly through battery storage, were recognised in many technical presentations as essential to accommodate higher PV penetration levels and to reduce energy curtailment. At the same time, strengthening grid infrastructure and enhancing grid management capabilities remain critical to enable the next phase of large-scale PV integration.

Photovoltaics in the Energy Transition

Options for re-establishing competitive module manufacturing in Europe were extensively analysed, including detailed policy recommendations for industrial support and market growth. Currently, a mismatch persists between global PV module installation rates and production rates, resulting in growing inventories and sharply reduced prices.

Finally, inclusiveness, diversity, citizen participation, awareness, education, and social engagement were underlined as vital dimensions of the sector's long-term sustainability and innovation capacity.

EU PVSEC 2025 Proceedings

Selection for inclusion in the conference was made by the Scientific Committee's paper review experts and topic organisers (see the listing on pages 010002-001-005), to whom we express our sincere gratitude for their comprehensive review work and overall contribution to the success of the conference.

The EU PVSEC 2025 Proceedings contain the full papers covering most of the highlights described above and more. The Proceedings provide a comprehensive overview of the PV solar sector, its current status and future prospects in science, research, innovation, development and deployment extending to 3,750 pages. In addition to the 299 submitted papers, the proceedings include 101 presentations (slides) shown during the plenary and oral presentations as well as 176 poster files of the visual presentations. In total this amounts to 576 publications.

The Conference Proceedings are published as downloadable files and are also fully accessible online. A DOI code (Digital Object Identifier) has been assigned to each paper. This ensures unequivocal and permanent identification and full citability. The EU PVSEC 2025 papers can be viewed and downloaded in a full free open access from the EU PVSEC's Proceedings website https://userarea.eupvsec.org/proceedings.

The proceedings of the EU PVSEC 2025 strengthen the commitment to providing quick and open access to high quality scientific results. This is a powerful source for targeted and quick information search and retrieval, enabling you to search by topic, keywords, paper title, DOI, author, or organization.

We are confident that these Proceedings will play an important role in providing a comprehensive overview of the current actors and activities in the global PV sector and that they will disseminate information on the state-of-the-art of technologies and applications. This can generate further research, add momentum to innovation and promote interest in PV worldwide.

We would like to cordially thank all authors and participants of the EU PVSEC 2025 for their contributions and look forward to welcoming you in Rotterdam, The Netherlands from 14 – 18 September 2026 at the EU PVSEC 2026, the 43rd European Photovoltaic Solar Energy Conference and Exhibition

The Editors

TABLE OF CONTENTS OF EU PVSEC 2025 PROCEEDINGS PAPERS

[1] Anhalt University of Applied Sciences, Köthen, Germany; [2] Fraunhofer CSP, Halle, Germany

Oral SESSION 2AO.2 Advances in Chalcogenide Devices

2AO.2.3 A New Method for Sb-doped CdSeTe/CdTe Devices with Superior Stability   020057

Elisa Artegiani[1], Mariyam Mukhtar[1], Alessandro Romeo[1]
[1] University of Verona, Verona, Italy

Oral SESSION 2AO.3 III-V Based Devices | Tandem and Perovskite Solar Cells

2AO.3.3 Micro-Crystal GaAs Array Sub-Cells for Si Tandem Solar Cells   020058

James Patrick Connolly[1], Ahmed Nejim[2], Alexandre Jaffré[1], José Alvarez[1],
Jean-Paul Kleider[1], Denis Mencaraglia[1], Laurie Dentz[3], Géraldine Hallais[3],
Frederic Hamouda[3], Laetitia Vincent[3], Daniel Bouchier[3], Charles Renard[3]
[1] CNRS, Gif-sur-Yvette, France; [2] SILVACO, St. Ives, United Kingdom; [3] CNRS, Palaiseau, France

2AO.3.5 Multiscale Models for Perovskite Optimisation   020060

Philippe Baranek[1], James Patrick Connolly[2], Antoine Gissler[1], Philip Schulz[3],
Michel Rerat[4], Roberto Dovesi[5]
[1] EDF R&D, Palaiseau, France; [2] CNRS, Gif-sur-Yvette, France; [3] IPVF, Palaiseau, France;
[4] IPREM, Pau, France; [5] Academy of Sciences of Turin, Torino, Italy

2AO.3.6 Modelling Recovery in Perovskite Solar Cells under Light and Dark to   020062
Address Stability Challenges

Guillem Álvarez-Pérez[1], Jean Baptiste Puel[1], Jean François Guillemoles [1]
[1] IPVF, Palaiseau, France

Oral SESSION 2BO.10 Advanced Modelling and Characterisation of Perovskite Solar Cells

2BO.10.2 On Perimeter Losses in Perovskite Top- and Poly-Si-Passivated Silicon   020063
Bottom Cells – Do Small Area Tandems Reveal the Full Efficiency Potential?

Felix Haase[1], Lukas Brockmann[1], Annika Raugewitz[1], Verena Steckenreiter[1],
Verena Barnscheidt[1], Roland Clausing[1], Sara Baumann[1], Joachim
Vollbrecht[1], Welmoed Veurman[1], Johannes Löhr[1], Dongyang Liu[1], Mircea
Turcu[1], Lasse Nasebandt[1], Udo Römer[1], David Sylla[1], Jessica Strey[1], Martha
Löhning[1], Larissa Mettner[1], Renate Winter[1], Anja Christ[1], Heike
Kohlenberg[1], Cornelia Marquardt[1], Emanuel Brueckner[1], Hossein Rabiei[1],
Michael Rienäcker[1], Sarah Kajari-Schröder[1], Tobias Wietler[1], Robby Peibst[1]
[1] ISFH, Emmerthal, Germany

2BO.10.5 In-depth Characterization and Simulation Approach for the Understanding of   020064
In- and Outdoor Degradation of Perovskite Solar Cells

Jonathan Parion[1], Amit Kumar Harit[1], Elias Peraticos[2], Vasiliki Paraskeva[2],
Maria Hadjipanayi[2], Aranzazu Aguirre[1], Filip Duerinckx[1], Hariharsudan

Sivaramakrishnan Radhakrishnan[1], Jef Poortmans[1], Johan Lauwaert[3], Bart Vermang[1]
[1] *Hasselt Unversity, Genk, Belgium;* [2] *University of Cyprus, Nicosia, Cyprus;* [3] *Ghent University, Ghent, Belgium*

Oral SESSION 2BO.8 Advanced Conversion Devices

Visual SESSION 2BV.1 New Materials, Devices and Conversion Concepts | New Modelling and Characterisation Techniques

Nathan Roosloot[1], Harsha Walpita[2], Christoph Seiffert[1], Jean Thomas[3], Maarten Dörenkämper[4], Minne M. de Jong[4], Josefine H. Selj[1], Gaute Otnes[1]
[1] *Institute for Energy Technology, Kjeller, Norway;* [2] *University of Oslo, Kjeller, Norway;* [3] *Ciel et Terre, Lille, France;* [4] *TNO, Eindhoven, The Netherlands*

Visual SESSION 3AV.3 PV Modules Characterisation and Performances Assessment

3CO.11.5 Indoor Characterization and Analysis of Reverse Breakdown Behavior of   020223
Solar Cells with Different Cell Architectures

Bengt Jaeckel[1], Jens Froebel[1], Matthias Pander[1], Andreas Maixner[2], Hamed Hanifi[2]
[1] Fraunhofer CSP, Halle, Germany; [2] AESOLAR, Koenigsbrunn, Germany

Plenary SESSION 3CP.1 Si PV Manufacturing: Pushing the Limits of Performance

3CP.1.2   IBC4EU: European Back Contact Technology   020225

Florian Buchholz[1], Daniel Tune[1], Tobias Meßmer[1], Jonathan Linke[1], Manjunath Prasad[1], Valentin D. Mihailetchi[1], Juras Ulbikas[2], Arne Dahle[3], Martijn Meereboer[4], Francesca Fabris[5], Erik Eikelboom[5], Tom Borgers[6], Rik Van Dyck[6], Filip Duerinckx[7], Hariharsudan Sivaramakrishnan Radhakrishnan[7], Timea Bejat[8], Samuel Harrison[8], Ashish Binani[9], Nicolas Guillevin[9], Jan Kroon[9], Yevgeniya Larionova[10], Thorsten Dullweber[10], Ofer Shochet[11], Isaac Rosen [11], Ingo Röver [12], Wolfram Palitzsch[12], Yasmin Zaror[13], Johannes Stierstorfer[14], Aurimas Radzevicius[15], Julius Denafas[16], Tuomas Vanhanen [17], Tuukka Savisalo[17], Maximilian Pospischil [18], Marian Breitenbücher [18], Özlem Coşkun[19], Melodie de l`Epine [20], Philippe Macé[20], Ian Kenchington[20]

[1] ISC Konstanz, Konstanz, Germany; [2] Protechnology, Vilnius, Lithuania; [3] Norsun, Oslo, Norway; [4] Energyra, Westknollendam, The Netherlands; [5] Futurasun, Citadella, Italy; [6] IMEC, Genk, Belgium; [7] Hasselt Unversity, Genk, Belgium; [8] CEA, Le Bourget-du-Lac, France; [9] TNO, Petten, The Netherlands; [10] ISFH, Emmerthal, Germany; [11] Copprint, Jerusalem, Israel; [12] LuxChemTech, Freiberg, Germany; [13] WIP Renewable Energies, Munich, Germany; [14] WIP - Renewable Energies, Munich, Germany; [15] Valoe Cells, Vilnius, Lithuania; [16] Solitek, Vilnius, Lithuania; [17] Valoe, Mikkeli, Finland; [18] Highline Technologies, Freiburg, Germany; [19] Kalyon PV, Ankara, Türkiye; [20] Becquerel Institute, Brussels, Belgium

Plenary SESSION 3CP.3 Perovskite – Silicon Tandems: Towards Commercialisation | PV Stability in the Field

3CP.3.4   Outdoor Performance and Reliability of Perovskite (Pk)-Silicon (Si)   020226
Tandems: >1 year of Monitoring in the NEXUS Project

Atse Louwen[1], Jordi Veirman[1], Alexander Astigarraga[1], Juan José Stivanello[1], David Moser[2], Perrine Carroy[3], Vincent Barth[3], Delfina Muñoz[3], Markus Lenz[4], Anika Sidler[4], Jorge Ferrando[5], Maximiliano Alejandro Senno[5], Henk J. Bolink[5], Talat Özden[6], Hisham Nasser[6], Shuaifeng Hu[7], Xinyi Shen[7], Henry Snaith[7]
[1] Eurac Research, Bolzano, Italy; [2] Becquerel Institute Italy, Trento, Italy; [3] CEA / INES, Le Bourget-du-Lac, France; [4] School of Life Sciences FHNW, Muttenz, Switzerland; [5] University of Valencia, Paterna, Spain; [6] ODTÜ-GÜNAM, Ankara, Türkiye; [7] University of Oxford, Oxford, United Kingdom

Oral SESSION 3DO.12 Innovative Encapsulation Materials

Nikolina Pervan[1], Jutta Geier[1], Christian Veas[1], Gernot Oreski[1]
[1] PCCL, Leoben, Austria

Oral SESSION 4AO.7 Solar Resource Assessment

Oral SESSION 4AO.8 Solar Irradiance Forecasting

Oral SESSION 4AO.9 Irradiance for PV Design | Shading and Glare Mitigation

Oral SESSION 4DO.1 PV Tracking and Simulation

*Marcus Rennhofer[1], Philipp Mayer-Ullmann[1], Diana Maria Krainer[1],
Gusztav Ujvari[1], Janine Lichtenberger[1], Konrad Kainz[1], Vassilissa Neussl[1],
Bernhard Kubicek[1]*
[1] AIT, Vienna, Austria

Visual SESSION 4DV.4 PV System Engineering

Visual SESSION 5DV.3 Grid Integration and Flexibility Enablers | Global, Country- and Application-Specific Analysis of PV Deployment Aspects | Costs, Economics, Finance and Markets

This presentation was selected by the Sc. Committee of the EU PVSEC 2025 for submission of a full paper to one of the EU PVSEC's collaborating peer-reviewed journals.

ENHANCING BROADBAND ANTIREFLECTION PERFORMANCE OF SILICON SOLAR CELLS USING GRASS-LIKE ALUMINA VIA ATOMIC LAYER DEPOSITION

Jiahui Xu[1*], Yuxuan Li[2], Wenjing Zhang[1], Geng Zhang[3], Pierre Verlinden[1], Cui Liu[2], Zhenjue Shen[1], Xiao Yuan[1]

[1] Yangtze institute for solar technology (YIST), Jiangyin, Jiangsu, 214400, China

[2] School of Materials Science and Engineering, East China University of Science and Technology, Shanghai, 200237, China

[3] Jolywood (ShanXi) Solar Technology Co., Ltd, Taiyuan, ShanXi, 030000, China

*Corresponding author: telephone: (+86)17621183653, email: xujh@yist.org.cn

ABSTRACT: Nano grass-like alumina structures were fabricated on the front surface of tunnel oxide passivated contact (TOPCon) silicon solar cells to improve broadband antireflection performance. Under the AM1.5G and AM0 spectra from 300 to 1180 nm wavelengths, the nano grass-like alumina structures reduces the weighted reflectance by 0.9%abs and 1.1%abs. The integrated short-circuit current density increases by 0.7 mA/cm² and 1 mA/cm², respectively. These photocurrent gains are primarily caused by reducing the front-side reflection losses at short wavelengths. Additional benefits arise from reduced front-side escape losses at medium and long wavelengths. No additional surface recombination is observed after nano grass-like alumina structures integration, supported by minority carrier lifetime and IV measurements. The nano grass-like alumina structures also exhibit excellent low optical reflection loss at high incident angles. Finally, post-encapsulation reflectance measurements confirmed that the nano grass-like alumina structures retained superior broadband antireflective properties.
Keywords: antireflection, glass-like alumina, nanostructures, silicon solar cell

1 INTRODUCTION

Recent advances in crystalline silicon (c-Si) solar cells have boosted power efficiency and cut manufacturing costs, accelerating the adoption of photovoltaics [1]. Research is generally focused on new structures and materials to reach the theoretical efficiency limit of c-Si solar cells. Passivated contacts, like amorphous silicon heterojunctions (SHJ) and tunnel oxide passivated contacts (TOPCon), are enabling to reach efficiencies closer theoretical limits and, therefore, are drawing significant attention. A large-area hybrid interdigitated-back-contact (HIBC) solar cell, for instance, has achieved a record efficiency of 27.8% [2]. Regardless of their specific design, a key research goal for c-Si solar cells is to reduce surface recombination and optical absorption losses. These cells typically use micron-scale pyramid textures with antireflection layers. However, front-side short-wavelength reflection losses still accounts for a large portion of power loss and represent a major limitation for further efficiency improvement [3, 4].

Various methods have been developed to minimize front-side optical reflection. One method is using nanostructured silicon textures, also known as black silicon. The sub-wavelength feature sizes of black silicon can scatter light and greatly reduce reflectance across a broadband, with an average reflectance below 2% [5]. But black silicon creates many surface defects, causing severe recombination of photogenerated carriers [6]. The trade-off between optical gains and electrical losses is difficult to resolve within the "coupled surface structures" framework, where light trapping and surface passivation are linked. Another strategy is to engineer multilayer antireflection coatings. This can achieve ultra-low reflection at specific wavelengths by adjusting the refractive index and thickness of the films [7]. However, it is expensive and difficult to achieve broad-spectrum antireflection while maintaining high-quality passivation with this method [8].

To solve this trade-off, decoupled structures have been proposed, where sub-wavelength structure coatings are applied on top of passivation layers. This allows light trapping and surface passivation to be optimized independently. Research on external light-trapping for gallium arsenide (GaAs) solar cells offers insights for c-Si solar cells. GaAs solar cells have high optical absorption, so surface texturing has limited benefits, and their crystal structure is not easily etched. For instance, Liu et al. [9] used SiO_2 nanopillars on GaAs solar cells, which reduced average reflectance to 5.5%, but the constant porosity limited the refractive index gradient and performance. In contrast, Reuna et al. [10] created a grass-like Al_2O_3 layer that lowered average reflectance to 2.8% and preserved electrical performance, showing promise.

In this study, nano grass-like alumina (NGLA) was applied to standard TOPCon solar cells using atomic layer deposition (ALD) for the first time. This reduced the weighted reflectance under the AM1.5G spectrum from 5.38% to 4.52%. Measurements of saturation current density (J_0) and open-circuit voltage (V_{oc}) confirmed that photocurrent was enhanced without harming passivation, leading to a 0.7% absolute increase in efficiency. The process is also compatible with current TOPCon solar cell manufacturing equipment, making it suitable for industrial use.

2 EXPERIMENTAL

2.1 Sample preparation

Industrial bifacial TOPCon solar cells and non-metallized "blue wafers" were cut to 50 mm × 50 mm using a laser to fit the ALD chamber. The TOPCon solar cells were soldered with busbar wires for consistent electrical measurements before and after the NGLA process. The samples were placed in a thermal ALD system with the front surface facing up. Trimethylaluminum (TMA) and deionized (DI) water were used as precursors with nitrogen as a carrier and purge gas. Amorphous ALD Al_2O_3 films were deposited at 150 °C over 400 cycles. The NGLA structures were then formed by immersing the samples in 80 °C DI water for 30 minutes. Finally, a simplified encapsulation with silicone and cover glass was performed to test the stability of the NGLA structures in a module-like environment.

2.2 Characterization

A scanning electron microscope (SEM) with an energy dispersive spectrometer (EDS) was used to analyze the morphology and elemental composition of the NGLA structures. Reflectance and transmittance spectra were measured with a spectrophotometer. Effective minority carrier lifetime (τ_{eff}), implied V_{oc} (iV_{oc}), and J_0 were measured on non-metallized wafers using transient photoconductivity decay. A spectral response system was used for external quantum efficiency (EQE) characterization. Current-voltage (IV) curves and electrical parameters were measured with a class A+A+A+ steady-state AM1.5G & AM0 solar simulator and an IV measurement system.

3 RESULTS AND DISCUSSIONS

3.1 Surface morphology and optical property

Figure 1 shows the SEM images of NGLA morphologies on the TOPCon solar cell front surface. Figures 1a and 1c show top-views of textured and metallized finger regions at 20.0 K magnification, with higher magnification views in Figures 1b and 1d. Cross-section images are shown in Figures 1e and 1f. The NGLA structures are made of randomly stacked Al_2O_3 nano-flakelets, about 10 nm thick and 100 nm high, consistent with other reports [11]. The structure has a graded porosity, decreasing from the air towards the c-Si substrate, which is crucial for creating a smooth refractive index profile. The ALD process ensures uniform coverage, a benefit over other techniques. Figure 1f shows the NGLA layer is about 140 nm thick, roughly three times the original film thickness. The transformation is believed to result from differing dissolution rates of amorphous Al_2O_3 and AlOOH species in DI water, followed by recrystallization into $Al(OH)_3$ during the hydrothermal process [12].

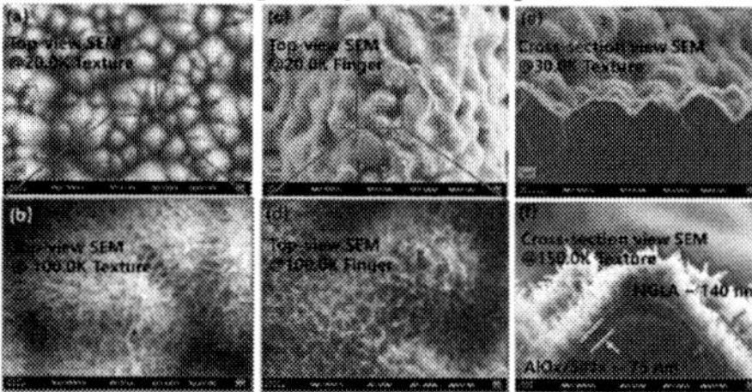

Figure 1: Top-view and cross-section view SEM images of NGLA morphologies.

Figure 2 demonstrates the optical performance of the NGLA structures. Weighted average reflectance (R_{ave}) values were calculated for AM1.5G and AM0 spectra. Figures 2a and 2b show that NGLA structures significantly reduced reflectance at short (300 ~ 535 nm) and medium-long (740 ~ 1050 nm) wavelengths, providing excellent broadband antireflection. This is due to the graded porosity, which creates a gradual refractive index transition from 1.0 (air) to 1.65 (ALD Al_2O_3), reducing Fresnel reflections. The three-dimensional nano-flakelet structure also increases light path length through multiple scattering and refraction, enhancing absorption.

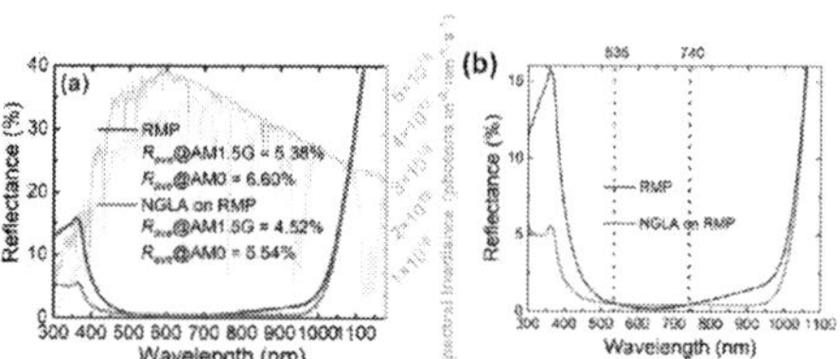

Figure 2: (a) Reflectance and (d) amplified reflectance spectra of conventional RMP TOPCon solar cells and NGLA TOPCon solar cells from 300 to 1180 nm wavelengths.

A slight reflectance increase was seen in the mid-wavelength range (535-740 nm) because the NGLA structures interfere with the original antireflection design. Overall, NGLA integration reduced the R_{ave} from 5.38% to 4.52% under AM1.5G spectrum, and it dropped from 6.60% to 5.54% under AM0 spectrum. This proves NGLA structures improve broadband optical absorption. This characteristic is especially suitable for solar cells designed for space applications that includes a stronger short-wavelength radiation and usually untextured solar cell surface.

3.2 Passivation property

High-quality surface passivation is critical for high efficiency. Unlike black silicon, which results in poor surface passivation [13], NGLA structures do not degrade the quality of passivation. Measurements on non-metallized wafers and soldered solar cells were conducted to evaluate the effect of the NGLA fabrication process on passivation. Figures 3a-3c show that after NGLA formation on non-metallized wafers, the τ_{eff} reached 3196 µs, iV_{oc} was 740 mV, and J_0 was reduced to 8.7 fA/cm², indicating no degradation. These results further confirm that the NGLA process does not harm surface recombination parameters, and may even improve passivation quality, possibly by passivating edges damaged by laser cutting. Similar edge passivation effects by ALD Al_2O_3 films have been reported previously [14, 15].

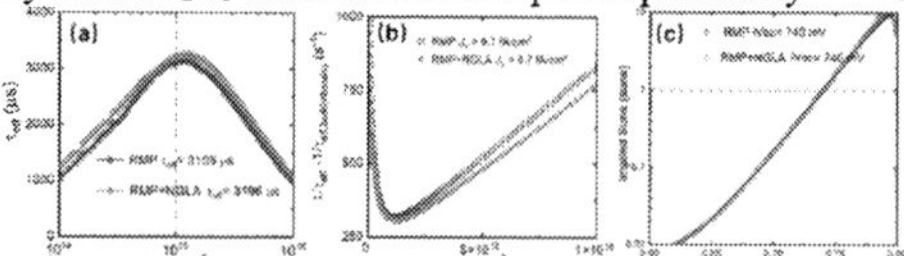

Figure 3: Comparison of passivation properties before and after NGLA structure formation. (a) The τ_{eff}, (b) iV_{oc} and (c) J_0 of non-metallized TOPCon blue wafers with RMP textures and NGLA on top of RMP textures.

3.3 Solar cell performance

The optical improvements from NGLA structures were assessed at the device level. Reflectance and EQE curves were measured on a soldered TOPCon solar cell. As shown in Figure 4, the NGLA TOPCon solar cells had reduced reflectance and improved EQE in the 300 ~ 500 nm range, while the internal quantum efficiency (IQE) remained unchanged. This confirms the EQE improvement is due to enhanced front reflectance, not better carrier collection. In the 500 ~ 750 nm range, reflectance, EQE, and IQE were similar between both structures. In the 750-1000 nm range, NGLA TOPCon solar cells had slightly lower reflectance and higher EQE, while IQE remained high, indicating that the graded refractive index suppresses long-wavelength reflection and improves light trapping. For the 1000 ~ 1180 nm range, NGLA TOPCon solar cells had similar reflectance but higher EQE and IQE. This is likely due to enhanced light trapping and unintentional Al_2O_3 deposition on the rear side. The superior antireflection and slight passivation improvement led to an integrated J_{sc} increase from 41.1 mA/cm² to 42.1 mA/cm², whcih is a 2.4% relative improvement under AM1.5G spectrum. And under the AM0 spectrum, the integrated J_{sc} increase from 50.5 mA/cm² to 51.5 mA/cm², which is a 2% relative improvement.

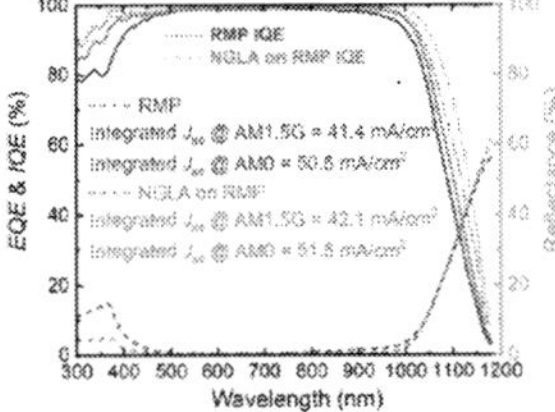

Figure 4: EQE (solid lines), reflectance (dash lines) and IQE (dotted lines) spectra of conventional RMP TOPCon solar cell and one of soldered NGLA TOPCon solar cell.

Table 1 shows the IV data for three soldered solar cells (A1–A3) before and after NGLA process. The V_{oc} of all three solar cells remained stable, with an average improvement of about 1 mV, confirming that passivation quality was not degraded. Significant increases in J_{sc} were observed, confirming the broadband antireflection benefit at the device level. Due to inconsistent fill factor (FF) values, efficiency results varied; A1 had a slight drop, while A2 and A3 improved by 0.9% and 0.7%, respectively. Further work with full-size solar cells is planned to get a more accurate evaluation.

Table 1: The IV parameters of three conventional RMP TOPCon solar cells before and after the NGLA process.

Cell Name	V_{oc} (mV)	FF (%)	J_{sc} (mA/cm²)	Eff (%)	$R_{sh}(\Omega)$
A1	723	72.0	40. 6	21.1	89
A1@ NGLA	722	70.0	41.5	21.0	22
A2	718	68.6	40.5	19.9	8
A2@ NGLA	719	70.4	41.1	20.8	14
A3	719	77.4	40.8	22.7	527
A3@ NGLA	721	76.8	42.2	23.4	202

Nanostructured textures on c-Si solar cells generally reduce angular sensitivity, which is beneficial for fixed or vertically mounted modules. We measured EQE curves at different incident angles. The EQE of RMP solar cells decreased significantly, especially in short and mid-to-long wavelengths. The NGLA solar cells showed a smaller EQE reduction. At a 60° incidence angle, the integrated J_{sc} of NGLA solar cells was 98.3% of the normal-incidence value, while RMP solar cells only retained 95.6%. This confirms that NGLA structures improve both broadband antireflection and angular stability.

3.4 PV module performance

The optical performance of the NGLA structures was also tested at the module level. Blue wafers with and without NGLA were encapsulated with silicone and glass,

and their reflectance was measured. Figure 5a shows that the NGLA structures maintained excellent broadband antireflection after encapsulation, with R_{ave} decreasing by 0.6% under both AM1.5G and AM0 spectra. Cross-section SEM images (Figure 5b) showed that some NGLA structures collapsed or folded during encapsulation. The silicone also infiltrated the porous nano-flakelets, which weakened the graded refractive index profile. These changes account for the slight reduction in antireflective performance observed at the module level.

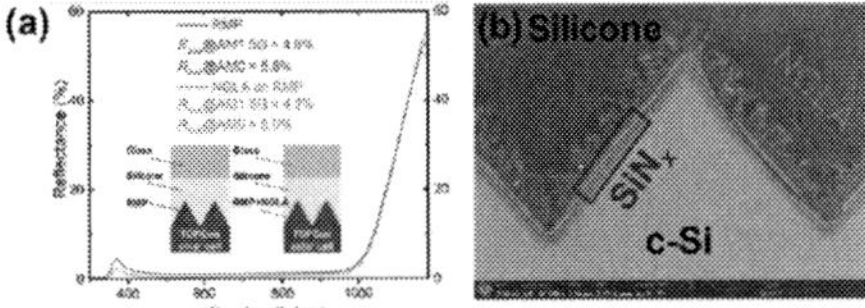

Figure 5: (a) Reflectance spectrum of encapsulated RMP and NGLA TOPCon PV modules. (b) Cross-sectional SEM image of the encapsulated NGLA TOPCon PV modules.

4 CONCLUSIONS

This study presents the direct integration of the NGLA structures based on ALD technique on the front surface of standard textured TOPCon solar cells. The NGLA was fabricated via low-temperature ALD followed by a DI water treatment. This structure composed of Al2O3 nano-flakelets with a graded porosity, establishes a gradual refractive index transition from air to the underlying passivation layer. This significantly reduces broadband reflection. Experimental results indicate that NGLA structure enhances the Jsc of TOPCon solar cells by more than 0.6 mA/cm2. This enhancement occurs without compromising passivation quality, thereby contributing to a notable improvement in efficiency. Additionally, the NGLA TOPCon solar cells exhibit greater stability in light absorption under varying incident angles. Although partial structural collapse was observed after encapsulation, the NGLA structure still maintains superior anti-reflective performance compared to conventional RMP textures. The fabrication process is fully compatible with existing TOPCon production lines, highlighting its strong potential for industrial-scale application.

5 ACKNOWLEDGMENTS

This work was supported by the Yangtze Institute for Solar Technology (Y20240202-RD). We thank Jolywood Solar Technology Co., Ltd for the help of TOPCon solar cell. We thank JITRI Advanced Materials R&D Co. Ltd. for the help with SEM analysis and cross sections.

6 REFERENCE

[1] Li W, Xu Z, Yan Y, Zhou J, Huang Q, Xu S, Zhang X, Zhao Y, Hou G. Advanced Energy Materials 14 (2024)
[2] Green Martin A, Dunlop Ewan D, Yoshita M, Kopidakis N, Bothe K, Siefer G, Hao X, Jiang Jessica Y. Progress in Photovoltaics: Research and Applications 33 (2025) 795-810

[3] Fung T H, Pasanen T P, Zhang Y, Soeriyadi A, Vähänissi V, Scardera G, Payne D, Savin H, Abbott M. Solar Energy Materials and Solar Cells 210 (2020)

[4] Wang G, Su Q, Tang H, Wu H, Lin H, Han C, Wang T, Xue C, Lu J, Fang L, Li Z, Xu X, Gao P. Nature Communications 15 (2024) 8931

[5] Hsu C-H, Liu S-M, Wu W-Y, Cho Y-S, Huang P-H, Huang C-J, Lien S-Y, Zhu W-Z. Arabian Journal of Chemistry 13 (2020) 8239-8274

[6] Otto M, Algasinger M, Branz H, Gesemann B, Gimpel T, Füchsel K, Käsebier T, Kontermann S, Koynov S, Li X, Naumann V, Oh J, Sprafke A N, Ziegler J, Zilk M, Wehrspohn R B. Advanced Optical Materials 3 (2015) 147-164

[7] Selj J H, Mongstad T T, Sondenå R, Marstein E S. Solar Energy Materials and Solar Cells 95 (2011) 2576-2582

[8] Ji C X, Liu W, Bao Y D, Chen X L, Yang G Q, Wei B, Yang F H, Wang X D. Photonics 9 (2022)

[9] Liu S, Qian Y, Lin Y, Sun L, Zhu Y, Li D. Solar Energy Materials and Solar Cells 266 (2024) 112679

[10] Reuna J, Hietalahti A, Aho A, Isoaho R, Aho T, Vuorinen M, Tukiainen A, Anttola E, Guina M. Acs Applied Energy Materials 5 (2022) 5804-5810

[11] An Z, Hao J, Sun S, Su J-a, Yang C, Wang S, Cheng S, Dong B. Langmuir 40 (2024) 21644-21655

[12] Willis S A, McGuinness E K, Li Y, Losego M D. Langmuir 37 (2021) 14509-14519

[13] Özkol E, Procel P, Zhao Y, Mazzarella L, Medlin R, Šutta P, Isabella O, Zeman M. Physica Status Solidi RRL: Rapid Research Letters 14 (2019)

[14] Baliozian P, Al-Akash M, Lohmüller E, Richter A, Fellmeth T, Münzer A, Wöhrle N, Saint-Cast P, Stolzenburg H, Spribille A, Preu R. IEEE Journal of Photovoltaics 10 (2020) 390-397

[15] Lohmüller E, Baliozian P, Gutmann L, Kniffki L, Beladiya V, Geng J, Wang L, Dunbar R, Lepert A, Hofmann M, Richter A, Huyeng J D. Solar Energy Materials and Solar Cells 258 (2023) 112419

Enhancing Broadband Antireflection Performance of Silicon Solar Cells Using Grass-Like Alumina via Atomic Layer Deposition

Jiahui Xu, Yuxuan Li, Wenjing Zhang, Geng Zhang, Pierre Verlinden, Cui Liu, Xiao Yuan

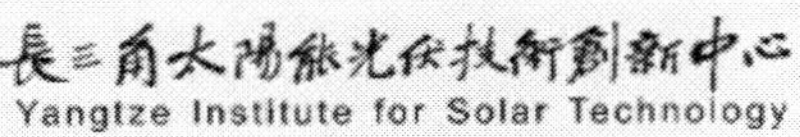

1. Introduction

YiST

- **Conventional c-Si solar cell**

- **Objective of this research**
  - **Developing a decoupling surface offering better antireflection and light-trapping while maintaining low surface recombination and excellent J_0.**

  - **Decoupling surface**

020002-002

2. Experimental

- Nano grass-like Al_2O_3 (NGLA) via (ALD + DIW treatment)

✓ Anti-reflectance

✓ Passivation

✓ Compatibility

✓ Cost

Ref : https://aalto.zoom.us/j/66890081498

020002-003

2. Experimental

YIST

Process of NGLA solar cell

Bifacial TOPCon solar cell & Non-metallized TOPCon wafer
(182 mm *182 mm)

Laser cutting

Bifacial TOPCon solar cell
(50 mm * 50 mm)

Non-metallized TOPCon wafer
(50 mm * 50 mm)

Soldering

SEM, IV, R_F, EQE, $SunsVoc$

τ_{eff}, J_0, iV_{oc}

Thermal ALD Al_2O_3 : TMA + H_2O, 150 °C

DI treatment: 80 °C, 30 min

SEM, IV, R_F, EQE, $SunsVoc$

τ_{eff}, J_0, iV_{oc}

Encapsulation

020002-004

3. Results

3.1 Surface morphology

YiST

NGLA
TOPCon solar cell

- SEM top-view @ 100.0K
- SEM cross-section view @150.0K

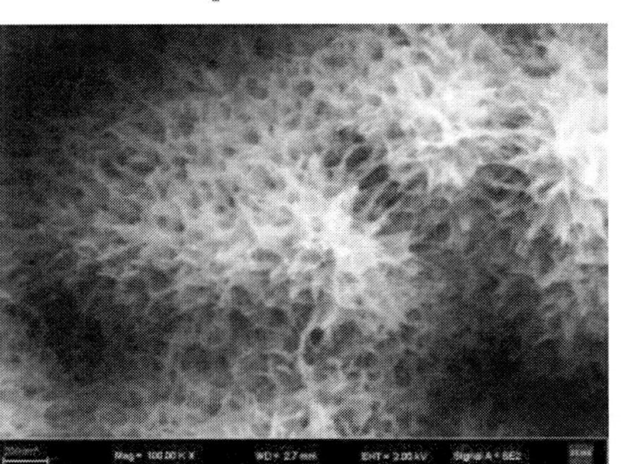

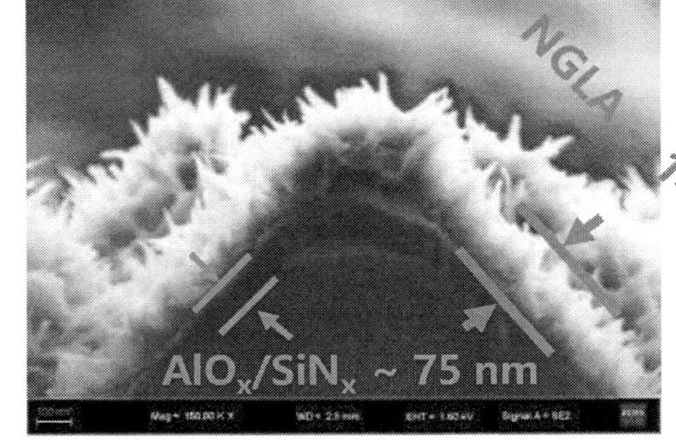

- Disorganized grass-like structure
- Conformal coverage
- Sub-wavelength feature sizes
- Gradually decreasing porosity

020002-005

3. Results

3.2 Optical property ■ Reflectance spectra and weighted averaged values

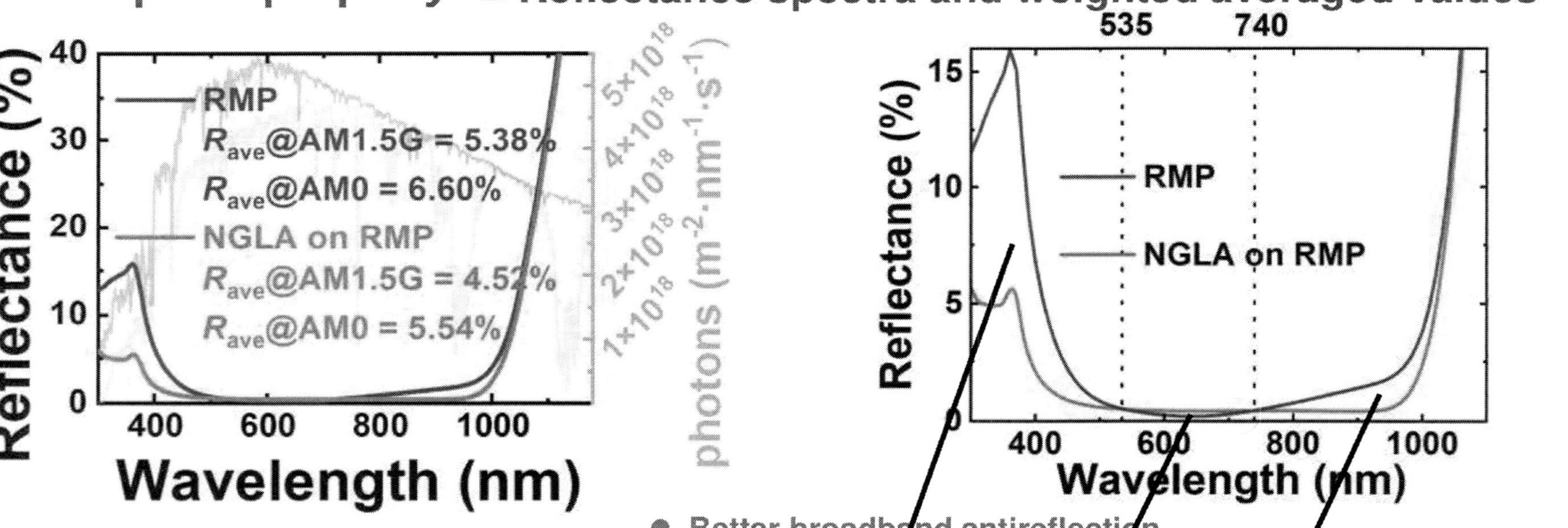

- Better broadband antireflection

① R_{ave} from 5.38% to 4.52% @ AM1.5G

② R_{ave} from 6.60% to 5.54% @ AM0

① Significantly decrease (300 ~ 535 nm, 5.4×10^{20} photons m^2/s)

② Slight increase (535 ~ 740 nm, 9.3×10^{20} photons m^2/s)

③ Significantly decrease(740 ~ 1050 nm, 10.8×10^{20} photons m^2/s)

020002-006

3. Results

3.3 Passivation property

YiST

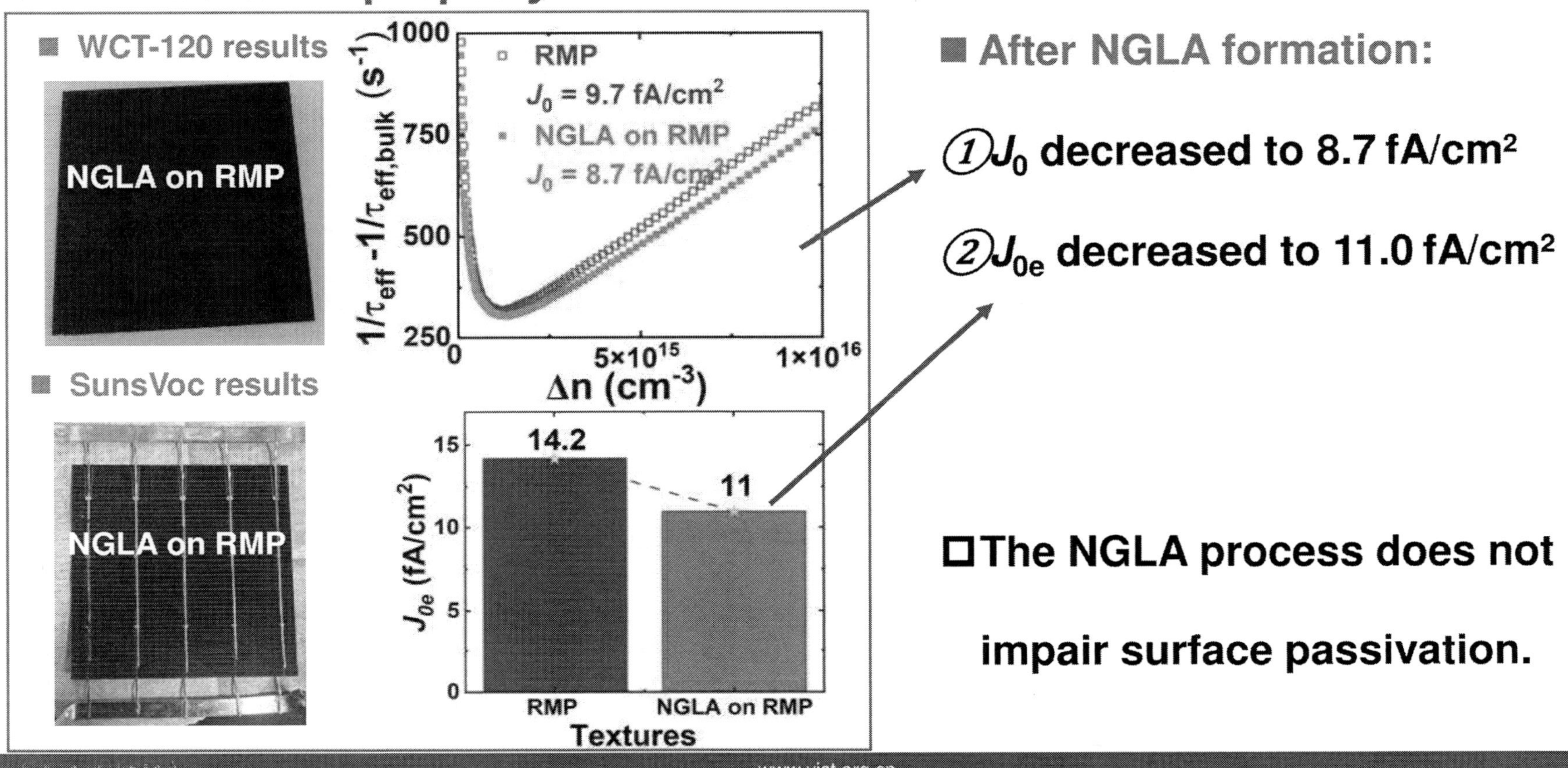

■ After NGLA formation:

① J_0 decreased to 8.7 fA/cm^2

② J_{0e} decreased to 11.0 fA/cm^2

☐ The NGLA process does not impair surface passivation.

3. Results

3.4 EQE & IQE

	AM 1.5G	0.1 mA/cm²	0.1 mA/cm²	0.5 mA/cm²
	AM 0	0.3 mA/cm²	0.2 mA/cm²	0.5 mA/cm²

- EQE measurements

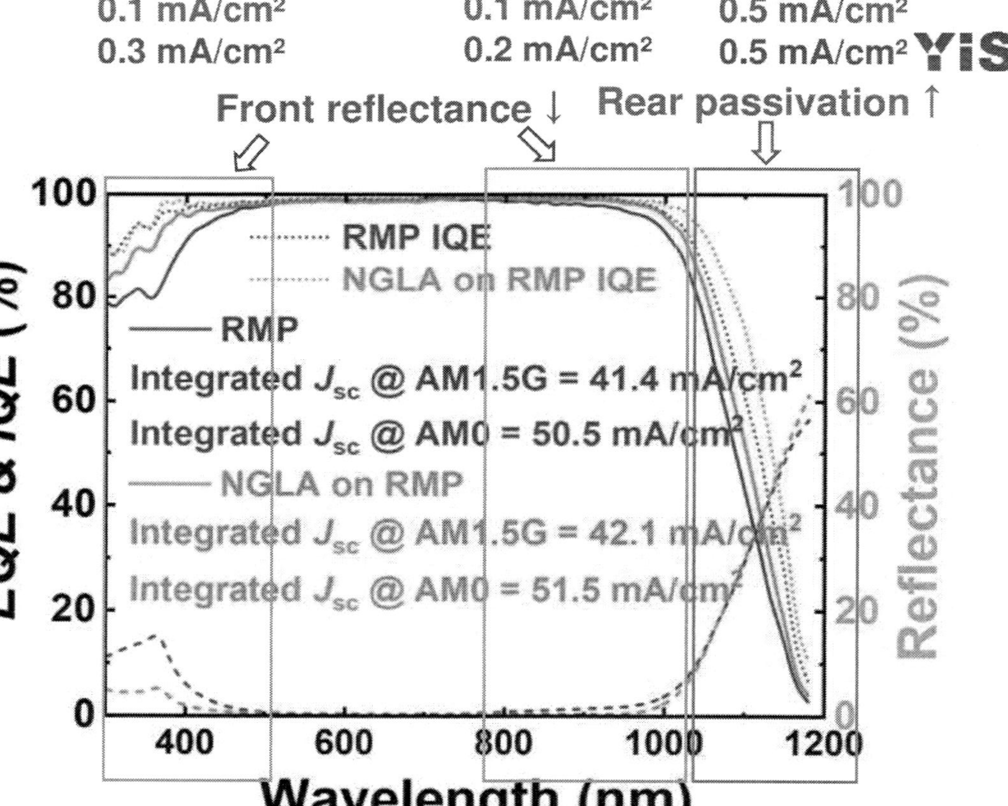

> The integrated J_{sc} increased from 41.4 mA/cm² to 42.1 mA/cm² , a 2.4% relative improvement @ AM1.5G

> The integrated J_{sc} increased from 50.5 mA/cm² to 51.5 mA/cm² , a 2.0% relative improvement @ AM0

3. Results
3.5 Solar cell performance

YiST

Cell Name	V_{oc} (mV)	Improvement (%)	J_{sc} (mA/cm^2)	Improvement (%)
A1	723	/	40. 6	/
A1@NGLA	722	- 0.1	41.5	+ 2.2
A2	718	/	40.5	/
A2 @ NGLA	719	+ 0.1	41.1	+ 1.5
A3	719	/	40.8	/
A3 @NGLA	721	+ 0.3	42.2	+ 3.4

■ IV measurements:

① The NGLA did not degrade passivation.

② The NGLA enhanced J_{sc} over 1.5% improvement at solar cell level.

➢ Additional full-size solar cells will be fabricated.

020002-009

3. Results

YiST

3.6 Angular sensitivity in spectral response

- EQE curves and integrated J_{sc} at different incidence angles

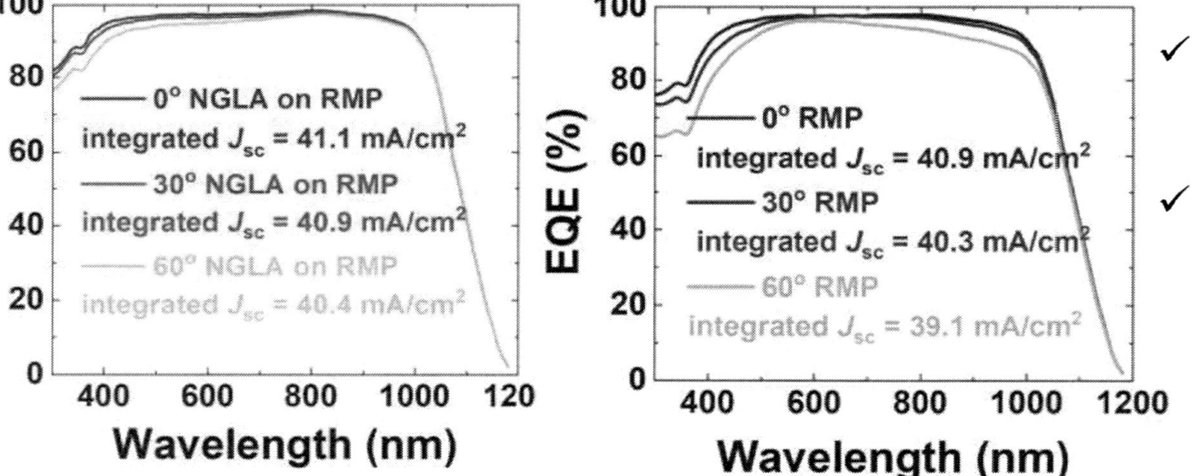

✓ The NGLA shows wide-angle antireflection

✓ Better for fixed angles PV applications

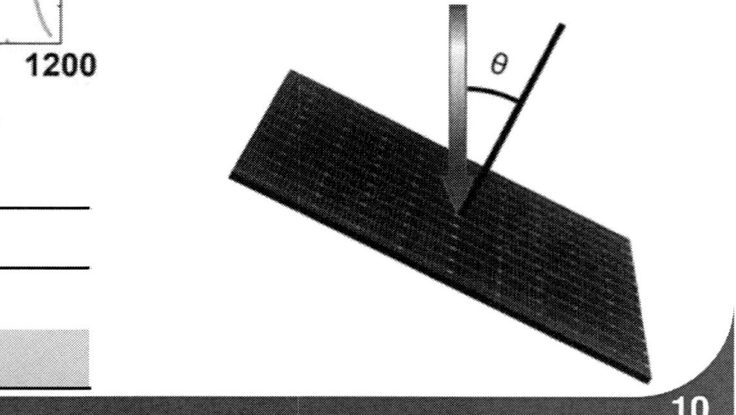

- $J_{sc} (\theta) / J_{sc} (\theta = 0)$ (%)

Sample	0°	30°	60°
RMP	100	98.7	95.6
NGLA on RMP	100	99.5	98.3

020002-010

3. Results
3.7 PV module performance

- Reflectance spectra, weighted averaged values and SEM cross-section view after encapsulation

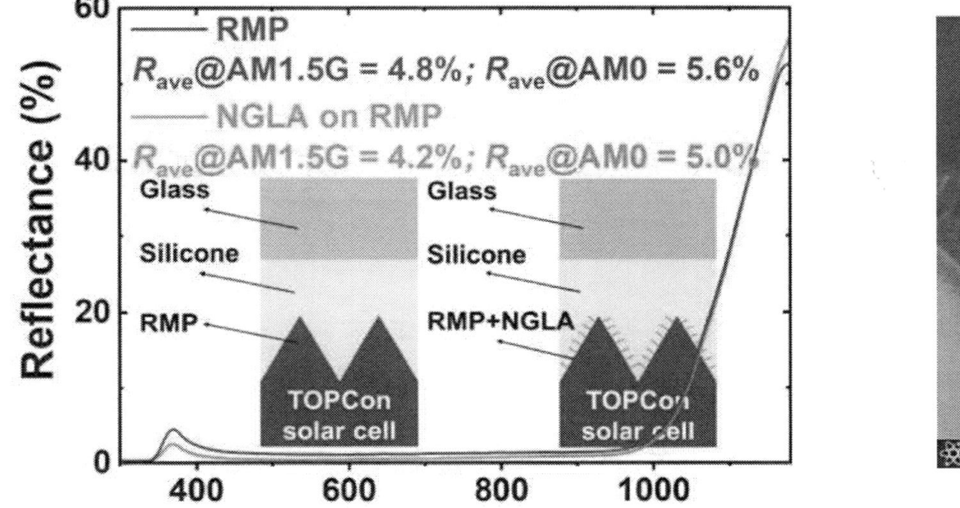

① R_{ave} all decreased by 0.6% @ AM1.5G & AM0 spectrum.

② The NGLA structures collapsed or folded during encapsulation

③ The NGLA retain broadband antireflection after encapsulation.

020002-011

4. Summary

✓ The NGLA structures show wide-angle broadband antireflection.

✓ The NGLA structures enhance the J_{sc} of TOPCon solar cells over 0.6 mA/cm^2, without degrading the surface passivation and the J_0.

✓ The open-circuit voltage is preserved.

✓ The NGLA structures maintain antireflection and light-trapping performance after encapsulation.

➢ Next steps: Transfer results from small structures to large-size solar cells.

5. Outlook

YiST

- Potential application : untextured (flat surface) devices with advantage of lowering J_0

● Perovskite/silicon tandem solar cells ● Untextured silicon solar cells ● Multijunction III-V solar cells

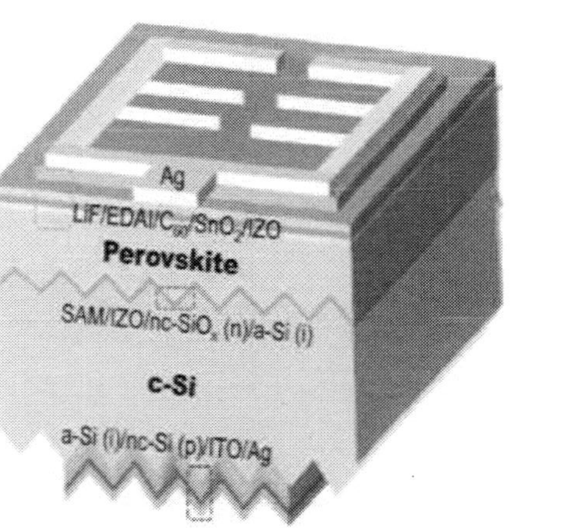

Jia, L. *Nature* 644, 2025

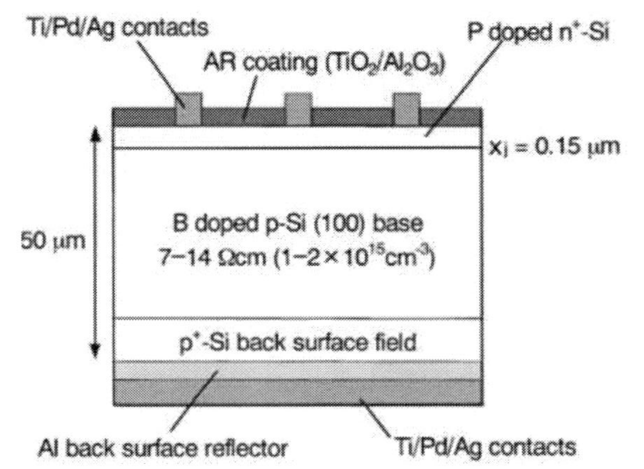

Yamaguchi, M. *Solmat* 68, 2001

contact	ARC	contact
n-AlInP	Window	0.1μm
n-GaInP	Emitter	0.1μm
p-GaInP	Base	0.7μm
p-GaInP	BSF	0.1μm
Tunnel Junction		
n-AlInP	Window	0.1μm
n-InGaAs	Emitter	0.1μm
p-GaInP	Base	2.0μm
p-GaInP	BSF	0.1μm
Tunnel Junction		
n-AlInP	Window	0.1μm
n-Ge	P-diffusion	30μm
p-Ge	Substrate	145μm
Back contact		

Weinan, Z. *Solener* 217, 2021

020002-013

長三角太陽能光伏技術創新中心
Yangtze Institute for Solar Technology

YiST

Jiahui Xu

Email: xujh@yist.org.cn

Thank you

ORCID:

https://yist.org.cn

Screen Printed Cu-TOPCon Cells With Reduced Ag Consumption

Jan Lossen, Justus Carstens, Mertcan Comak, Apoorva Gattu, Dominik Rudolph, Pirmin Preis, Lejo Koduvelikulathu

EU-PVSEC Bilbao 2025

22.09.2025

ISC
research
for a sunny future

Go for Gold?

We were very happy that the German team won the gold medal at EuroBasket.

Comment of my turkish collegue: „You are stupid – investing in silver gives much better returns".

020003-002

Development of Ag price

From https://www.bullionbypost.eu, downloaded on 21.09.2025

- Silver price has increased 120% in only 3 years.

- The price is now very close to its last record high from 2011

- (but also Gold is on an all-time high)

Ag consumption by PV

Record 597 GW of global solar capacity added in 2024; slower but steady 33% annual growth

Annual solar PV installed capacity 2000-2024

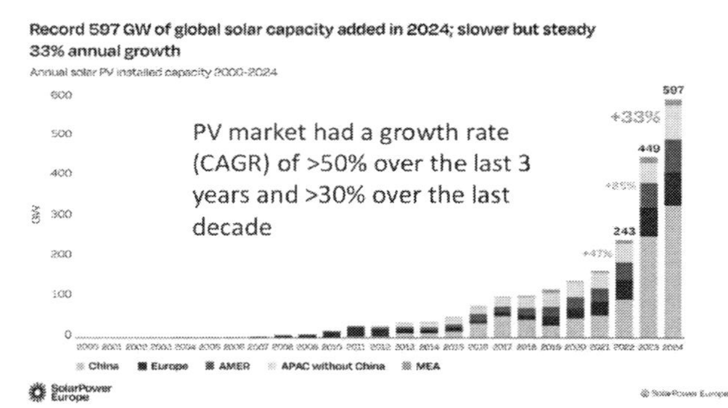

Annual TW solar market likely to be reached by 2030

Global cumulative solar PV market scenarios 2025-2030

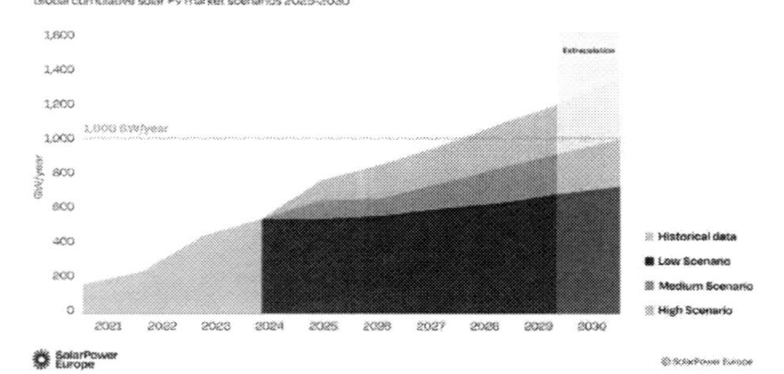

- PV market has increased 14-fold over the past decade [1].

- Even if growth slows down, a production of > 1 TWp/y is likely to be reached in 2030 [2].

- At current Ag consumtion (~12 mg/Wp) 1 TWp of PV would equal to ~41% of world Ag supply [3]

-> better to reduce dependency on silver!

[1] IEA PVPS, 2025 Snapshot of Global PV Markets, April 2025
[2] Solar Power Europe, Global Market Outlook for Solar Power 2025-2029, 6 May 2025
[3] The Silver Institute and Metals Focus, Word Silver Survey 2025, April 2025.

020003-004

Cu-TOPCon Approach

Objective
- Fully screen printed TOPCon solar cell
- Replace as much silver as possible
- Without compromising efficiency

Approach:
- Use Ag paste only for FS fingers and RS contact layer
- Cu- paste for RS conduction layer and BB's

020003-005

Cu-TOPCon Approach

Objective
- Fully screen printed TOPCon solar cell
- Replace as much silver as possible
- Without compromising efficiency

Approach:
- Use Ag paste only for FS fingers and RS contact layer
- Cu- paste for RS conduction layer and BB's
- Use same number of printers (4x)

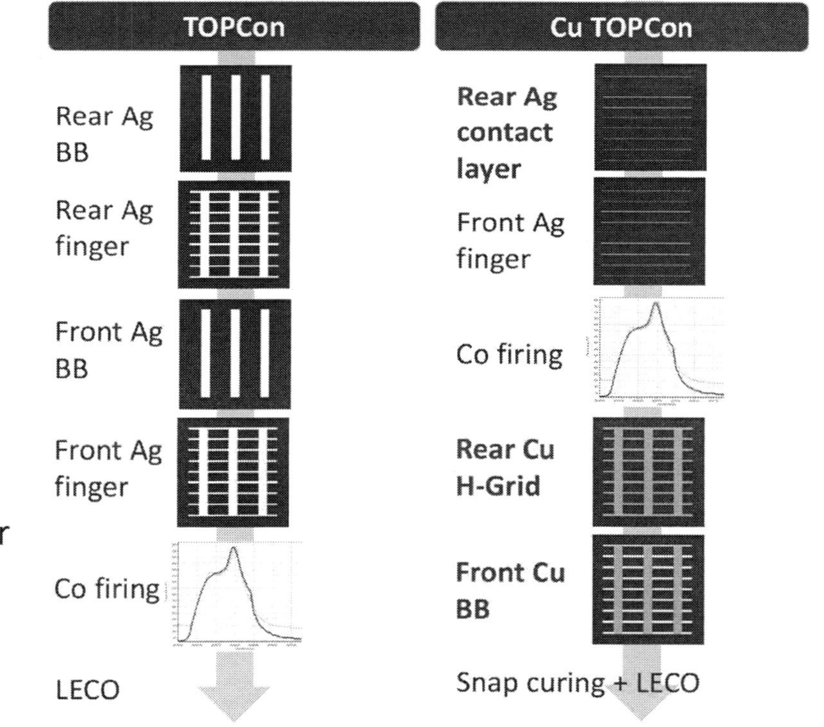

Status technology development

- N. Chen demonstrated ZEBRA IBC cells with Hybrid-Ag-Cu fingers in 2022. [4]
- We demonstrated first Cu-TOPCon cells at SiliconPV2024. [5]
- Yuchao Zhuan from USNW published several papers on TOPCon cells with Ag dash contacts and Cu/Al printed fingers. [6],[7]
- DKEM claims first TOPCon mass production with high-Cu paste (using Ag-coated Cu-particles).[8]

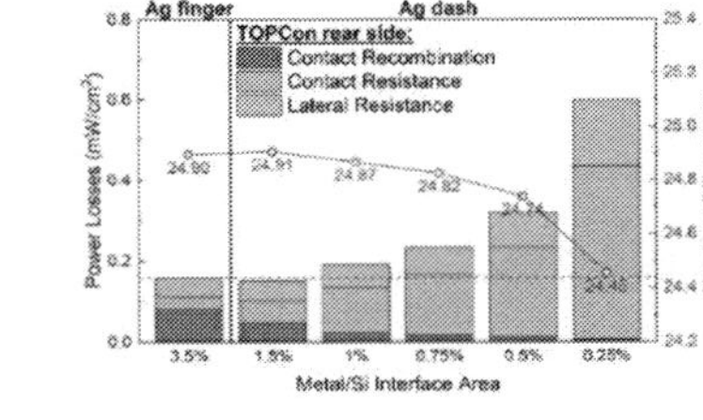

Cross section of Ag-Cu finger on ZEBRA IBC cell [4]

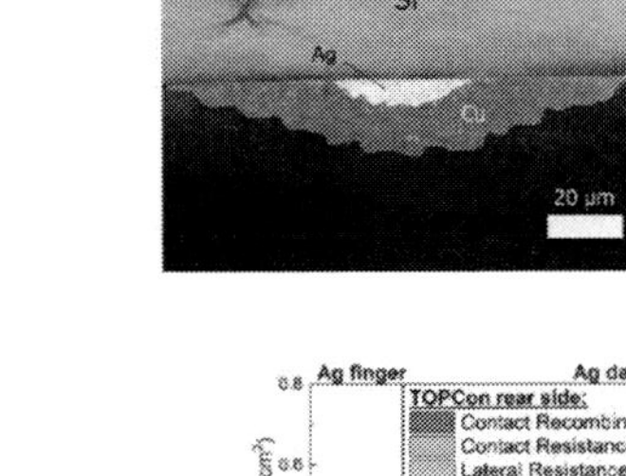

Slide from DKEM talk [8]

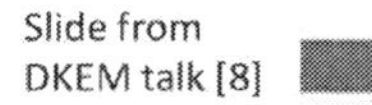

Simulated efficiencies and power losses from contact recombination, contact resistance and lateral resistance in TOPCon solar cells with standard Ag fingers and Ag dashes [7].

[4] N. Chen, et al. Screen printed copper paste for metallization of IBC solar cells, SiliconPV 2022, AIP Conf. Proc. 2023
[5] J. Lossen, et al., Proceedings of Silicon PV 2024, https://doi.org/10.52825/siliconpv.v2i.1316
[6] Y. Zhang, et. al., Ultra-Lean Silver Screen-Printing for Sustainable Terawatt-Scale Photovoltaic. Sol. RRL, 8: 2400478. https://doi.org/10.1002/solr.202400478
[7] Y. Zhang, et al., Silver-lean screen-printing metallisation for industrial TOPCon solar cells: Enabling an 80 % reduction in silver consumption, SOLMAT288, 2025, https://doi.org/10.1016/j.solmat.2025.113654.
[8] F. Guo, TaiyangNews Cell & Module Production Equipment & Processing Materials Conference, Sep. 2, 2025.

020003-007

Copper paste from Copprint

- Based on a blend of Cu micro and nano particles

- Rapid curing at low temperature (~300°C)

- Sintering agent prevents oxidation

020003-008

Challenges addressed in this work

- Validate efficiency potential and cost savings

- Confirm feasibility of print-on-print approach

- Optimize curing process towards shorter process time

- Demonstrate solderability

020003-009

Cell experiment

- Experiment on M10R industrial TOPCon precursor, all printings at ISC

- Ag-Ref-cells vs. Cu-TOPCon cells with 2 different contact layers

	Ag Ref	CuTOPCon Line Contact („Cu Line")	CuTOPCon Point contact („Cu Point")
Opening	18 µm	8 µm	8 µm, 50/150
Pr. line width	30 µm	23 µm	19 µm
Cross section	188 µm²	63.6 µm²	12.8 µm²
Ag-Laydown L1	**70.6 mg**	**23.2 mg**	**5 mg**
Cu-Print L2	-	40 µm	40 µm
Total Ag Laydown (with FS and BB)	194 mg	73 mg	55 mg
Ag saving		**-62% (-46%*)**	**-72% (-60%*)**

(* Considering lower Ag-BB laydown in Reference)

Ag Ref

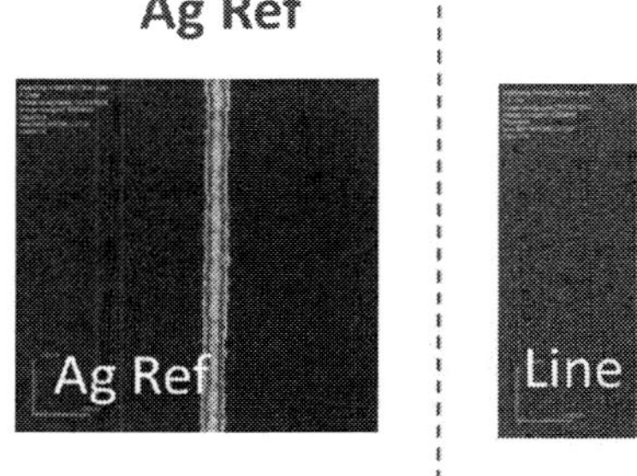

Cu -TOPCon

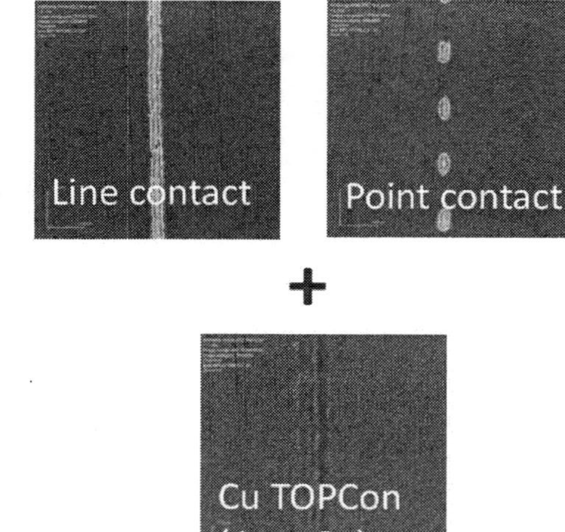

020003-010

IV parameter of cells

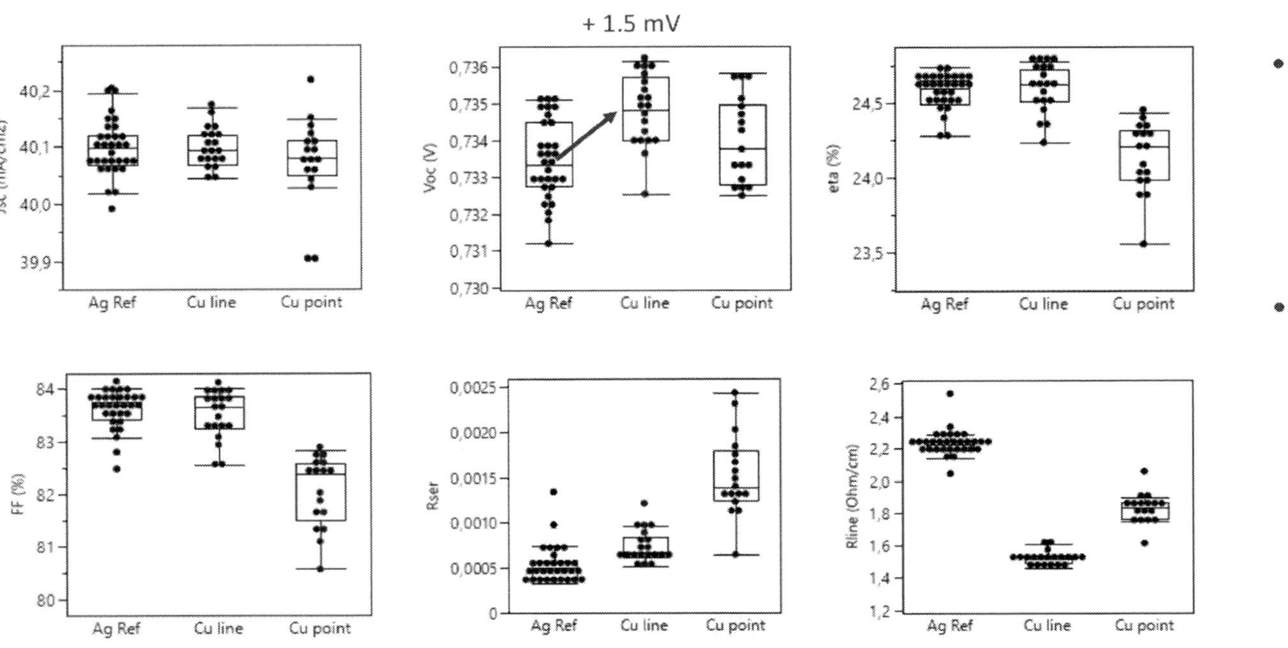

- Best group: Cu line
  - **+1,5 mV gain in Voc**
  - Increased Rser, with marginal effect on FF
- Cu Point group exhibits clearly reduced FF
  - Line resistance is still low
  - Contact area probably too small -> increase of contact resistance loss, in agreement to [7]

[7] Y. Zhang, et al., SOLMAT288, 2025, https://doi.org/10.1016/j.solmat.2025.113654

Cost saving potential

- Lab experiment yielded **equal efficiency** for cells with **46% Ag reduction**

- A demonstration run with an industrial partner showed **similar IV characteristics at efficiency level 25.3%** with lower Ag and Cu laydown

- **Cost saving** calculated for different scenarios based on typical industrial paste laydown[9]

  - With Ag-Price at 1350 USD/kg even most conservative scenario results in savings of ~**0.25 USD ct/Wp**

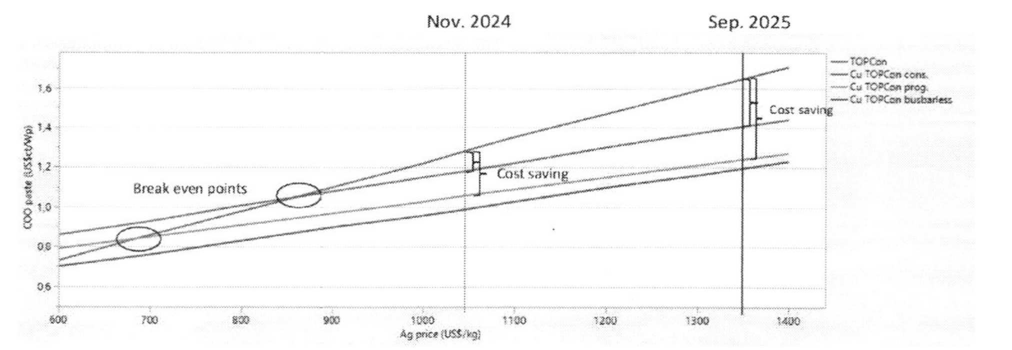

[9] P. Preis et al., Silver paste reduction for TOPCon solar cells using a hybrid Cu and Ag screen printing metallization, PVSEC-35, 2024, Numazu, Japan

020003-012

Feasibility of print-on-print

First layer with < 10 µm line width need knotless screens

Mertcan Comak investigated the expansion of knotless screens during usage[10]

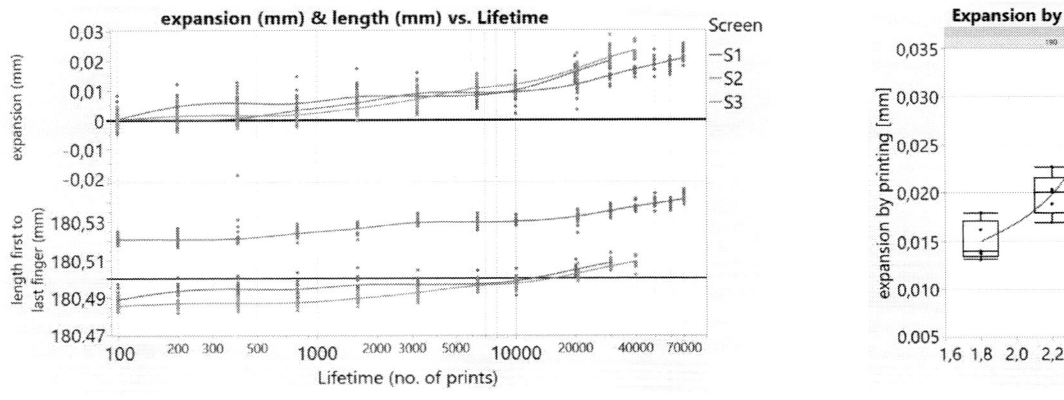

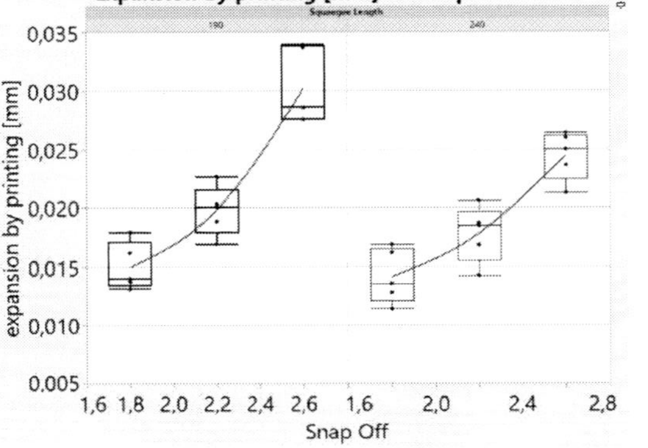

Conclusion: print-on-print of 40 µm Cu line on 10 µm Ag line is feasible!

[10] M. Comak, et al., Distortion of knotless printing screens in solar cell mass-production, SOLMAT 294, 2025, https://doi.org/10.1016/j.solmat.2025.113894.

020003-013

Optimization of Cu-curing process

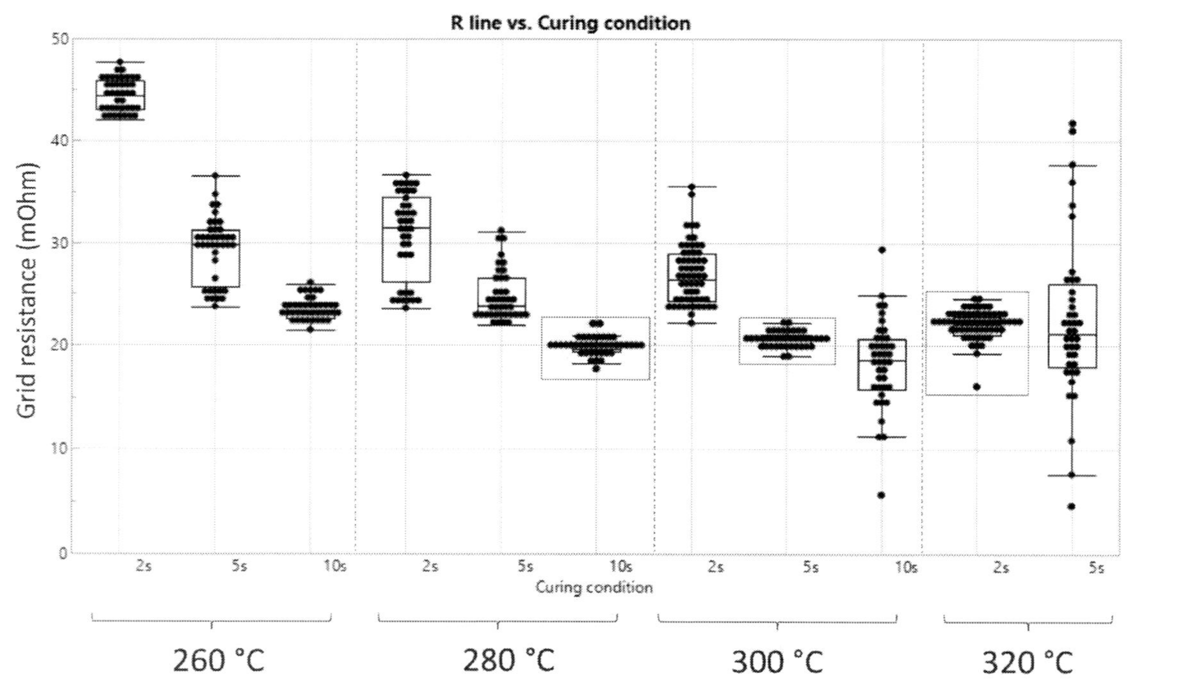

- Cu-Curing is performed as snap curing between two hot plates or rollers

- Lowest grid resistance achieved for:
  - 280°C, 10s
  - 300°C, 5s
  - 320°C, 2s

-> acceleration to process time of 2s is possible

020003-014

Soldering on Cu BBs

Peel tests after soldering on TT stringer (using Ribbon BS 0.8x0.24 SnPb):

- Peel force initially low (adhesion low on paste surface)
- Modification of paste and introduction of chemical pre-treatment substantially increased peel force,
- Now cohesive breakage

Paste 2, no pre treatment

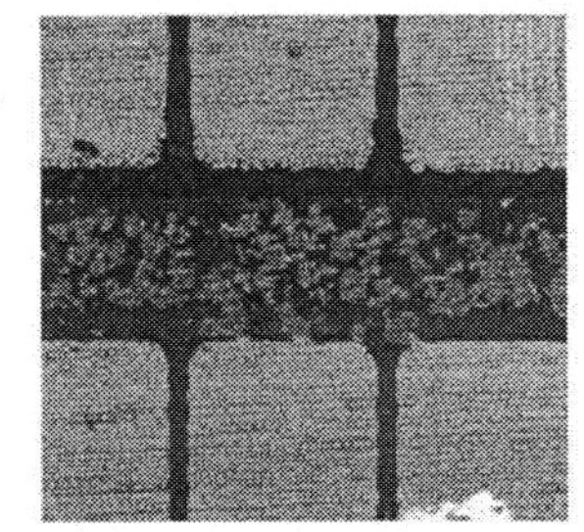
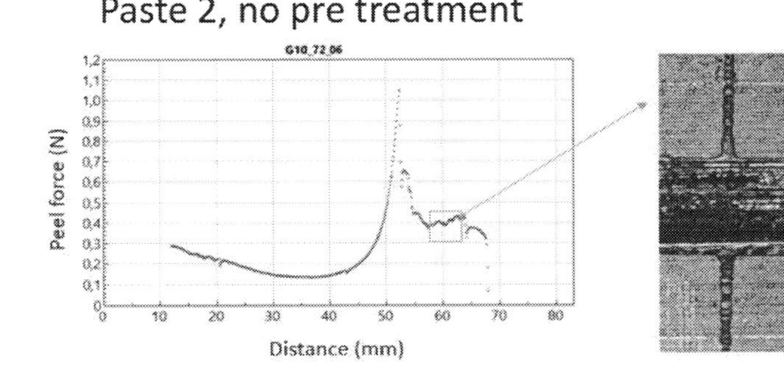

Paste 2, chem. pre treatment A

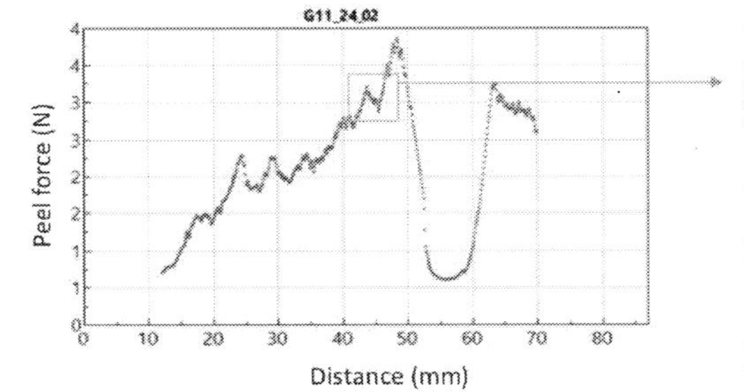
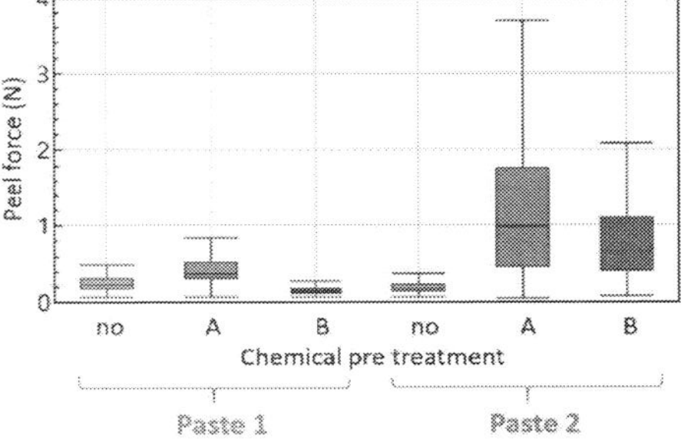

Summary and outlook

- **Same efficiency for Cu-TOPCon**, with headroom for further increase
  - If rhoC can be decreased further, even smaller contact area can be used and Voc improves further.
- Remaining challenges could be adressed successfully
  - Print-on-print on rear side feasible
  - **Fast curing process demonstrated** -> High throughput pilot tool under development with German machine builder
  - **Soldering on Cu-BB with high peel force demonstrated**
- Massive cost savings already for **partially** replacing Ag by Cu
- Let's leave to the gold and silver to the athletes and use more copper on the solar cells

020003-016

© ISC Konstanz e.V.   Lossen et al., Screen Printed Cu-TOPCon Cells With Reduced Ag Consumption, EUPVSEC 2025

Thank you

For the attention

This work has received funding from the German Federal ministry of Economic Affairs and Energy under the project "KONTRAST" with grant agreement 03EE1128A and project "BuKuMu" with grant agreement 03EE1225E

Copprint

We thank Copprint for supplying Cu-pastes and discussion of results

Supported by:

Federal Ministry for Economic Affairs and Energy

on the basis of a decision by the German Bundestag

Visit ISC Konstanz — 21st – 24th October 2025

020003-018

Back-up slides

Cost reduction potential for industrial M10 TOPCon solar cell

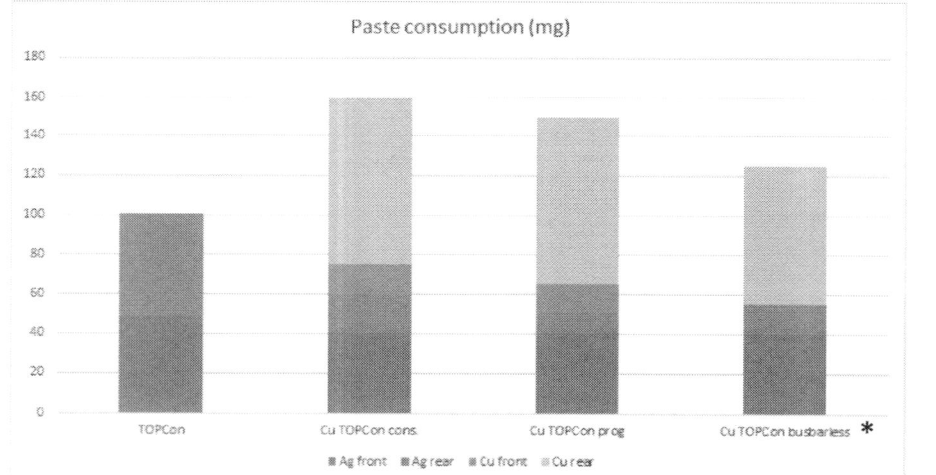

Paste consumption	TOPCon	Cu TOPCon cons.	Cu TOPCon prog.	Cu TOPCon busbarless
Total Ag paste (mg)	101 mg	60 mg	50 mg	55 mg
Total Cu paste (mg)	-	100 mg	100 mg	70 mg
Ag consumption mg/Wp	12.2	7.3	6.1	6.7

Assumptions:

- 3 different Ag reduction scenarios

- Assumed efficiency 25% / 8.25 Wp

- Price Cu paste 350 US$/kg

- Busbarless cell requires alternative module interconnection with might be attributed with different costs for module manufacturing (f.e. SmartWire or TECC-Wire[14])

*under development

[14] Jonas Marten et al.; 11th Metallization and Interconnection Workshop 2023; TECC Wire: A new technology for interconnecting temperature sensitive solar cells

020003-020

COO calculation metallization pastes

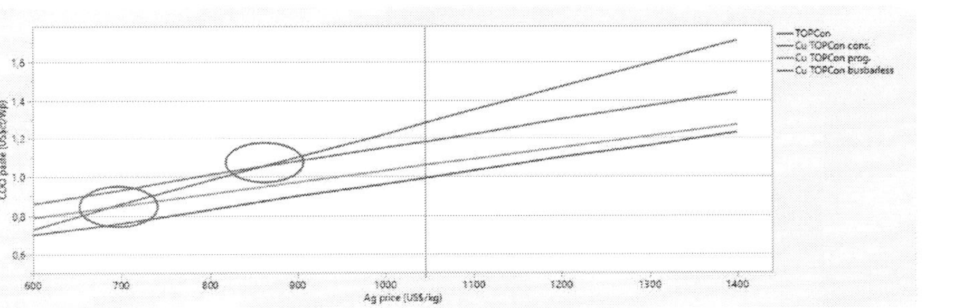

- Break even at silver price of 700 US$/kg or 850 US$/kg, depending on scenario

- Current silver price of 1045 $/kg: cost advantage of **0.1 - 0.22 US$ct/Wp** is possible

- Potential cost saving for 2GW TOPCon factory: **2.0Mio — 4.4 Mio US$/year**

- Even lower metallization costs can be achieved with busbarless approach, but module manufacturing costs will be different

020003-021

Cell experiment Cu TOPCon

Experiment on M10R industrial TOPCon precursor, all printings at ISC

Ag-Ref-cells vs. Cu-TOPCon cells with 2 different contact layers

	Ag Ref	CuTOPCon Line Contact	CuTOPCon Point contact
Opening	18 µm	8 µm	8 µm, 50/150
Pr. line width	30 µm	23 µm	19 µm
Cross section	188 µm²	63.6 µm²	12.8 µm²

Group	Ref	Ref_Corr	Cu line	Cu point	Comment
	(mg)	(mg)	(mg)	(mg)	comment
FS Finger	49,8	49,8	49,8	49,8	
FS Ag-BB	36,4	8			(excessive)
FS Cu-BB			46	46	
RS Finger	70,6	70,6	23,2	5	
RS Cu finger			98	98	
RS BB	37,1	8			(excessive)
RS Cu BB			40	40	
Sum Ag	193,9	136,4	73	54,8	
Sum Cu			184	184	
mg/Wp		16,4	8,8	6,6	
Ag-Saving			-46%	-60%	(-

020003-022

Cell experiment Cu TOPCon

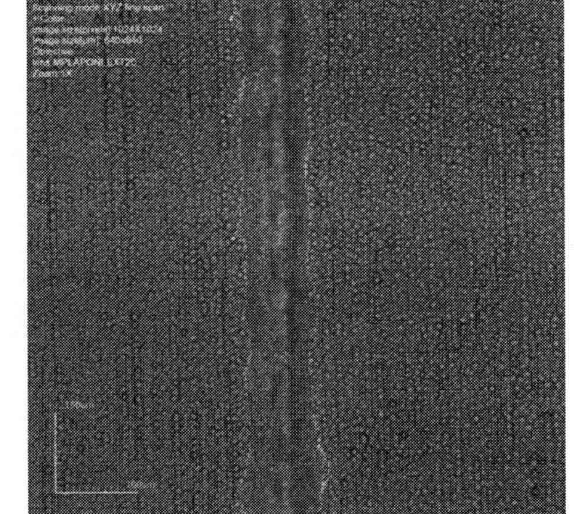

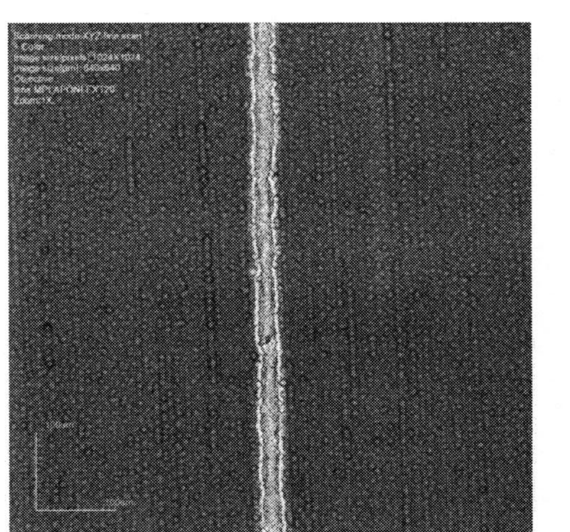

	Line Contact, Ag Layer	Line Contact, Ag + Cu Layer
Opening	8 µm	40 µm (Cu Layer)
Pr. line width	23 µm	66 µm
Cross section	63.6 µm2	238 µm2

020003-023

ISC
research
for a sunny future

Fraunhofer
CSP

EU-PVSEC 2025

DETECTING LOCAL LASER-DOPING VARIATIONS BY (HYPER-)SPECTRAL IMAGING AND MACHINE LEARNING MODELS

Marko Turek[1], **Stefan Eiternick**[1], **Jonathan Linke**[2], **Jan Hoß**[2]

(1) Fraunhofer Center for Silicon Photovoltaics CSP, Halle, Germany
(2) ISC-Konstanz e.V., Konstanz, Germany

Supported by:

Federal Ministry
for Economic Affairs
and Climate Action

on the basis of a decision
by the German Bundestag

LASER DOPING FOR REAR CONTACT SOLAR CELLS – (HYPER-)SPECTRAL IMAGING

Overview of the presentation

I. **Introduction and objective: Alignment assessment of p-/n-contacts**
- ISC polyZEBRA cell concept and local laser-activation of (p+) stripe pattern

II. **Approach: Optical hyperspectral imaging (HSI)**
- Data acquisition: Combining spatial and spectral information
- Data analysis: Pre-processing and classification

III. **Result: Separation of (p+) from (p) layers in HSI-data**
- Classification of (p+) vs. (p) pixels in image by advanced data processing

IV. **Conclusion: Fast imaging of doping patterns possible**

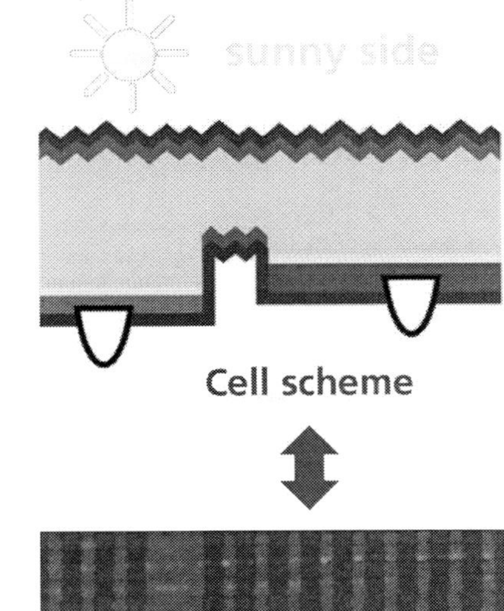

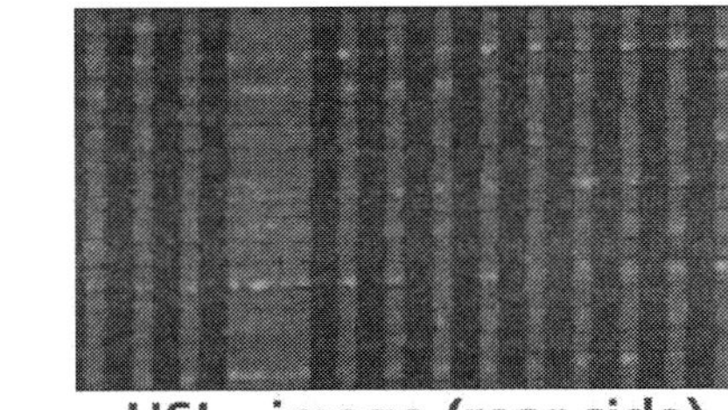

Fraunhofer
CSP

INTRODUCTION

Back-contact solar cells and "polyZEBRA" cell concept

Back-contact solar cells

- Reduced front-side shading → higher cell currents [1]
- TOPCon approach: no polycrystalline silicon (poly-Si) for contact passivation on front side needed [1,2]
- Efficiencies: cell > 27.8% [3] and module > 25%

[1] J. Linke et. al., EPJ PV 16 (2025); [2] R. Kopecek et. al., pv-tech.org/why-tbc-will-follow-shortly-after-topcon/: [3] nrel.gov/pv/cell-efficiency

Fraunhofer
CSP

020004-003

INTRODUCTION

Back-contact solar cells and "polyZEBRA" cell concept

Back-contact solar cells

- Reduced front-side shading → higher cell currents [1]
- TOPCon approach: no polycrystalline silicon (poly-Si) for contact passivation on front side needed [1,2]
- Efficiencies: cell > 27.8% [3] and module > 25%

ISC "polyZEBRA" cell concept [1]

- IBC patterning via laser processing
- Poly-Si on interfacial oxide (SiO_x) for both contacts
- Processes compatible with industrial technologies

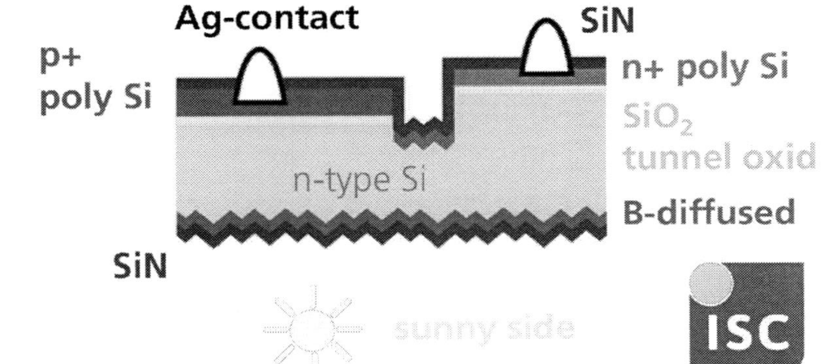

[1] J. Linke et. al., EPJ PV 16 (2025); [2] R. Kopecek et. al., pv-tech.org/why-tbc-will-follow-shortly-after-topcon/: [3] nrel.gov/pv/cell-efficiency

Fraunhofer
CSP

020004-004

INTRODUCTION

"polyZEBRA" cell concept: Laser activation as major process step

Laser-activation (doping) of p+ poly Si

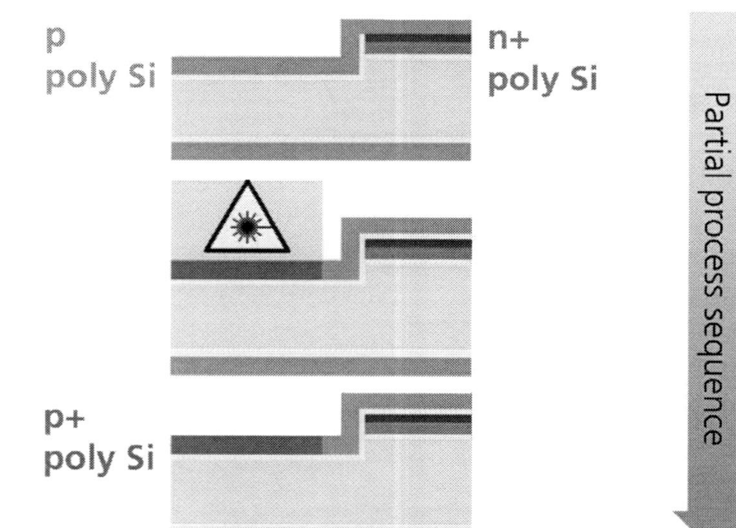

ISC "polyZEBRA" cell concept [1]

➢ IBC patterning via laser processing

➢ Poly-Si on interfacial oxide (SiO_x) for both contacts

➢ Processes compatible with industrial technologies

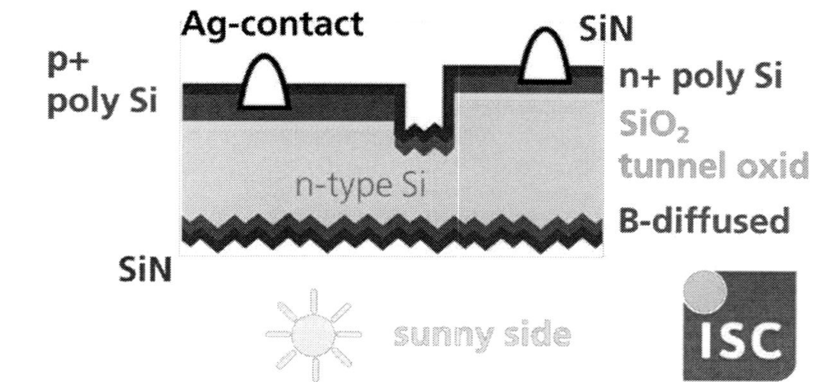

27.08.2025   © Fraunhofer CSP

- public information -

Fraunhofer CSP

020004-005

INTRODUCTION

"polyZEBRA" cell concept: Laser activation as major process step

Laser-activation (doping) of p+ poly Si

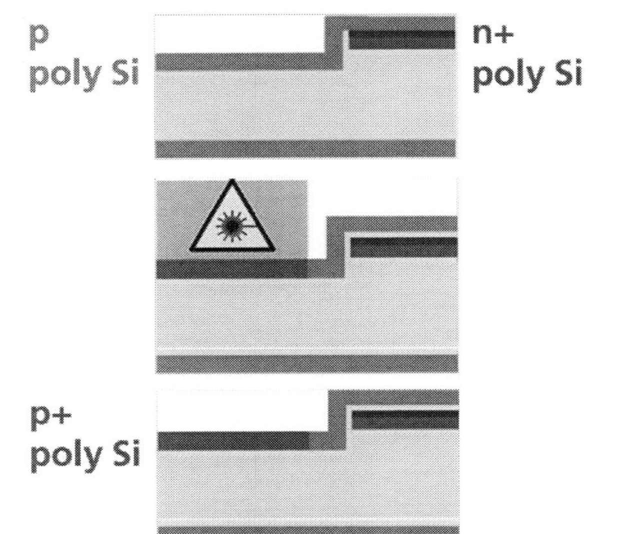

Rear-side pattern with fine structure

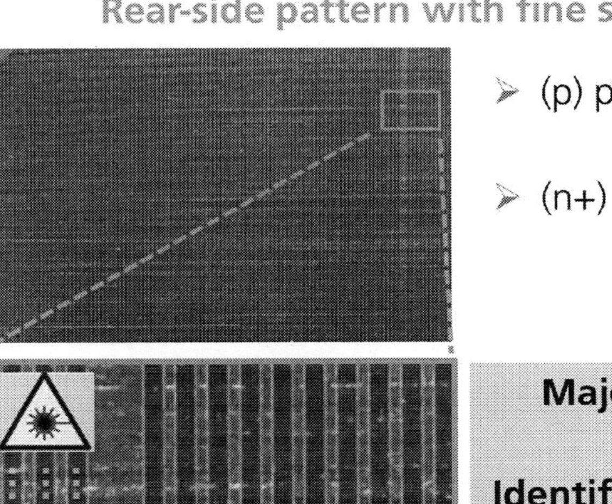

➢ (p) poly: ~ 500 µm

➢ (n+) poly: ~250 µm

Major challenge

Identification of laser mis-alignment

27.08.2025 © Fraunhofer CSP

- public information -

Fraunhofer
CSP

020004-006

INTRODUCTION

"polyZEBRA" cell concept: Laser activation as major process step

Requirements for quality control

- Inspection directly after laser activation
- Method suited for fast inline application
- Contactless, non-destructive

Rear-side pattern with fine structure

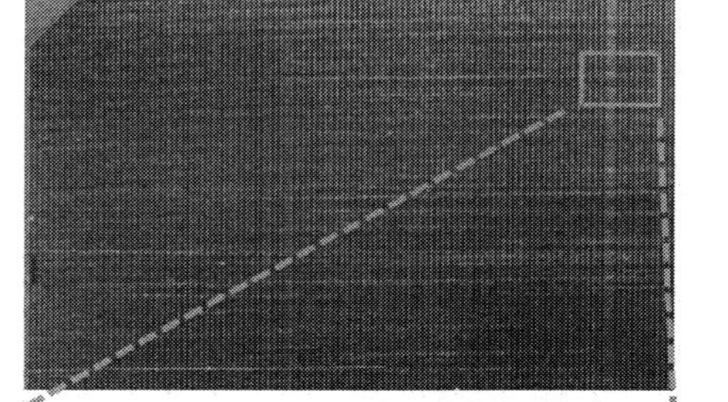

- (p) poly: ~ 500 µm
- (n+) poly: ~250 µm

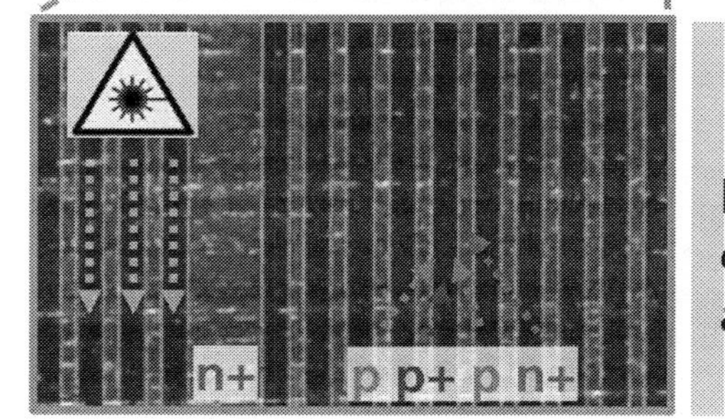

Major challenge

Identification of laser mis-alignment

Fraunhofer CSP

020004-007

INTRODUCTION

"polyZEBRA" cell concept: Quality control of laser-activation step

Requirements for quality control

- Inspection directly after laser activation
- Method suited for fast inline application
- Contactless, non-destructive

Simpler test structure for new approach:

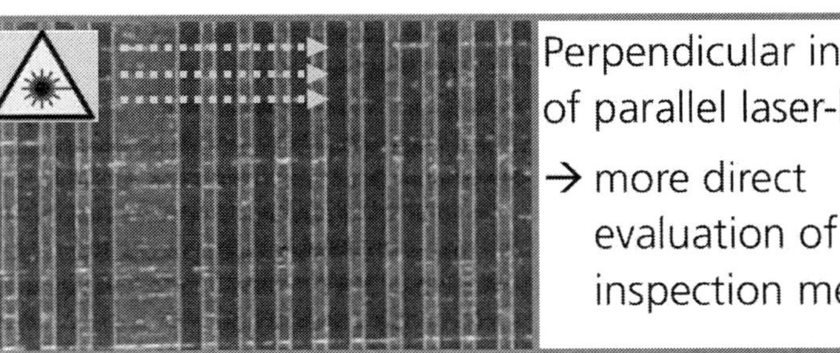

Perpendicular instead of parallel laser-lines:

→ more direct evaluation of inspection method

Rear-side pattern with fine structure

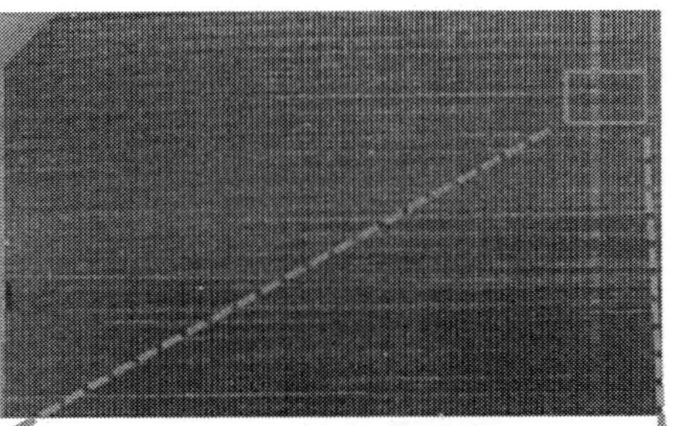

- (p) poly: ~ 500 µm
- (n+) poly: ~250 µm

Major challenge

Identification of laser mis-alignment

Fraunhofer
CSP

020004-008

INTRODUCTION

"polyZEBRA" cell concept: Quality control of laser-activation step

Requirements for quality control

- Inspection directly after laser activation
- Method suited for fast inline application
- Contactless, non-destructive

Simpler test structure for new approach:

Perpendicular instead of parallel laser-lines:

→ more direct evaluation of inspection method

Identification of laser mis-alignments:

Can laser-activated (p+) regions be separated from (p) regions by hyperspectral imaging?

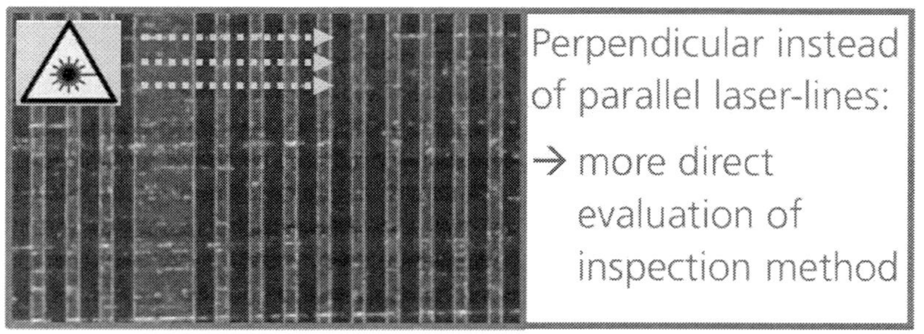

27.08.2025 © Fraunhofer CSP

Fraunhofer CSP

020004-009

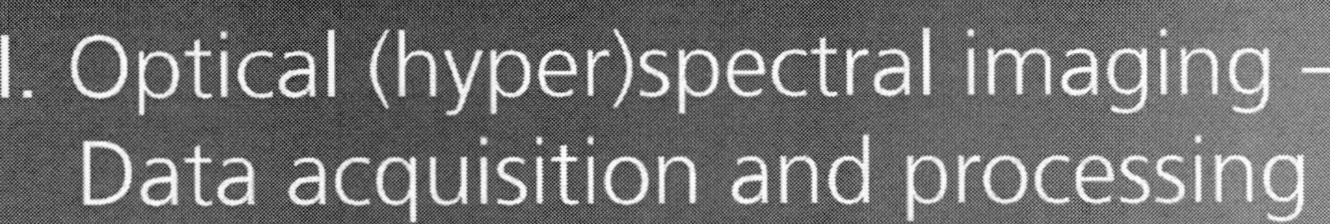

II. Optical (hyper)spectral imaging – Data acquisition and processing

APPROACH: HSI – DATA ACQUISITION

Combining spatial imaging with spectral information

HSI camera technology

- Yields spatial and spectral information at the same time

- In general, applicable to inline implementation

- **Many images generated: one image for each wavelength 400 .. 1000 nm**

Test structure – rear side
(horizontal laser pattern!)

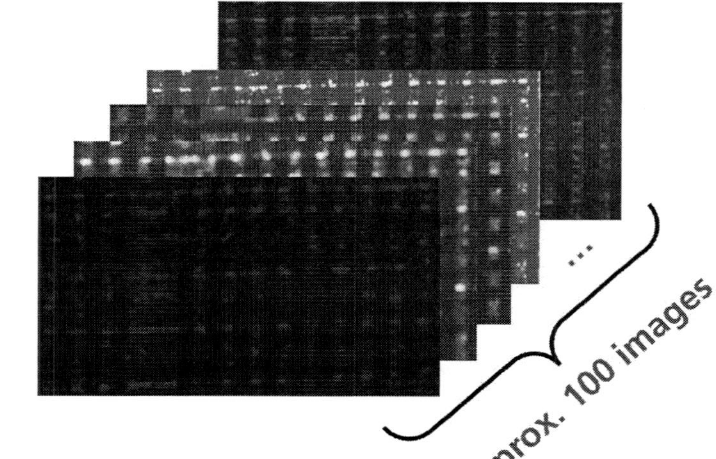

photograph

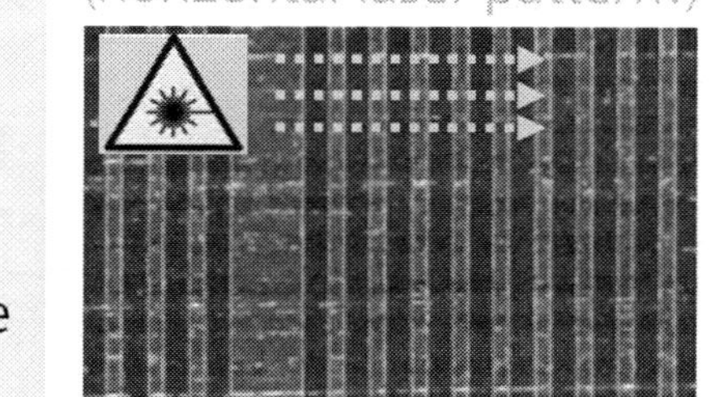

HSI – "RGB" image

Hyperspectral imaging

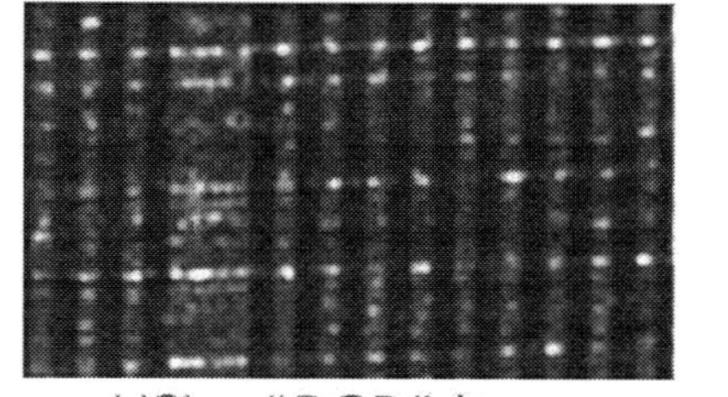

approx. 100 images

Fraunhofer
CSP

APPROACH: HSI – DATA ACQUISITION

Combining spatial imaging with spectral information

HSI camera technology

➢ Yields spatial and spectral information at the same time

➢ In general, applicable to inline implementation

➢ Each pixel contains entire optical spectrum

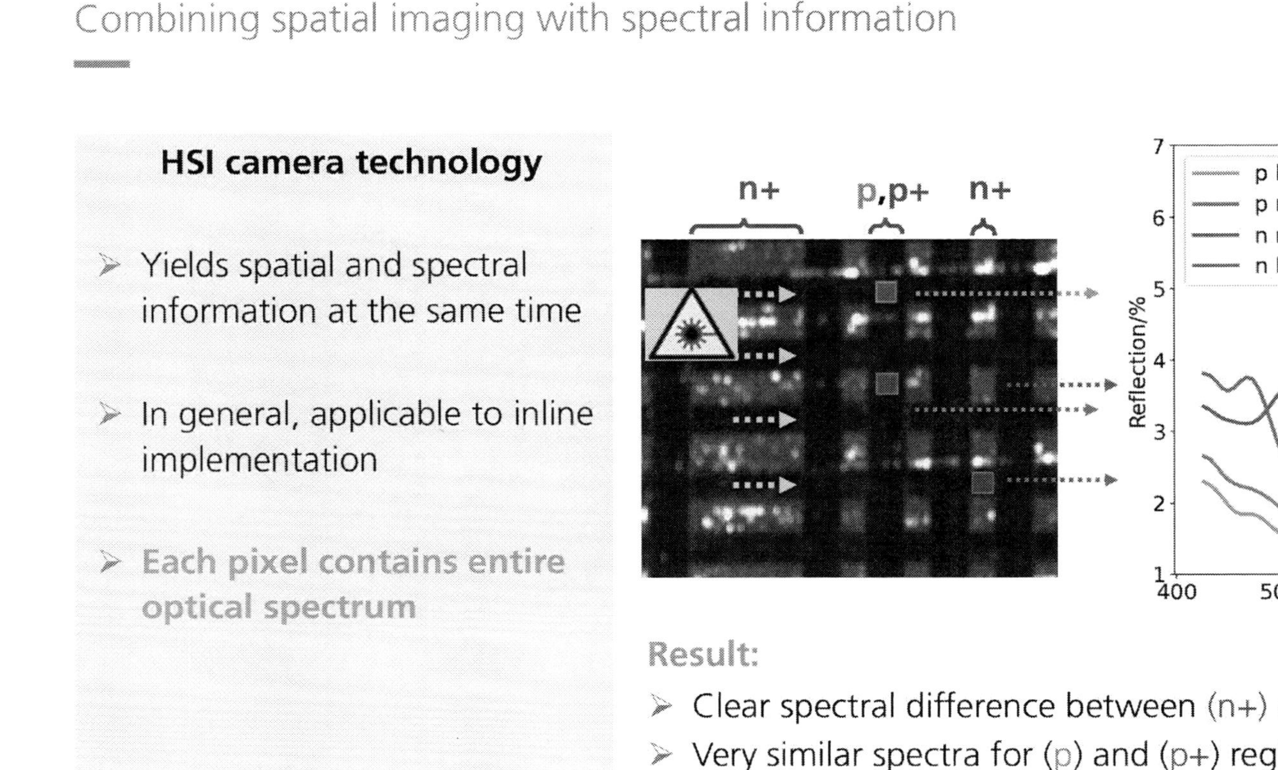

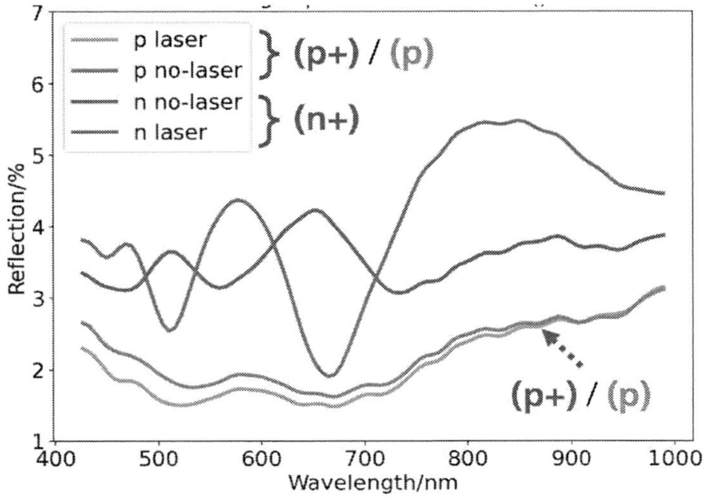

Result:

➢ Clear spectral difference between (n+) and (p, p+) region

➢ Very similar spectra for (p) and (p+) region → need to be separated

Fraunhofer CSP

020004-012

APPROACH: HSI – DATA ACQUISITION

Combining spatial imaging with spectral information

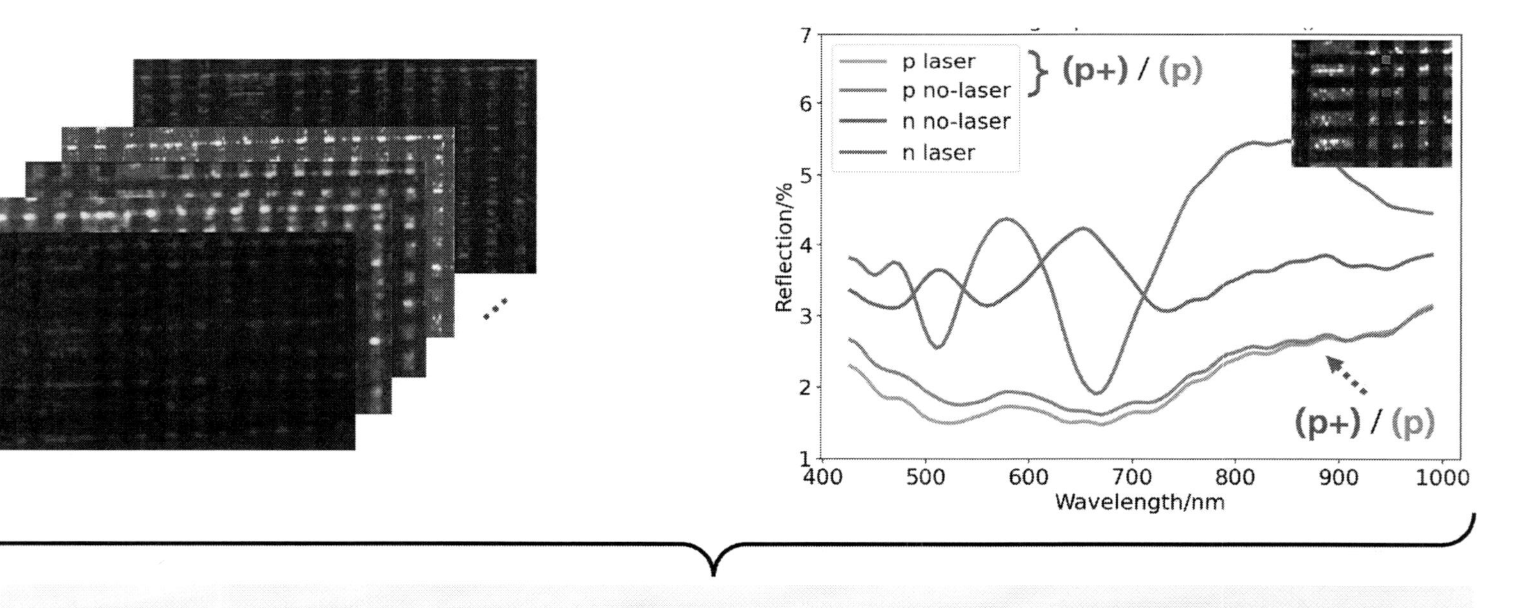

Extensive data set → Automated data-preprocessing and analysis to separate (p+) vs. (p)

27.08.2025   © Fraunhofer CSP   - public information -

Fraunhofer
CSP

020004-013

APPROACH: HSI – DATA PRE-PROCESSING: "NORMALIZATION"

Material-independent algorithms – extracting relevant spectral finger-prints

Data pre-processing step 1[*]: **Correction of local illumination variations** (e.g. sample-to-sample)

HSI raw data → Pixel-wise intensity correction

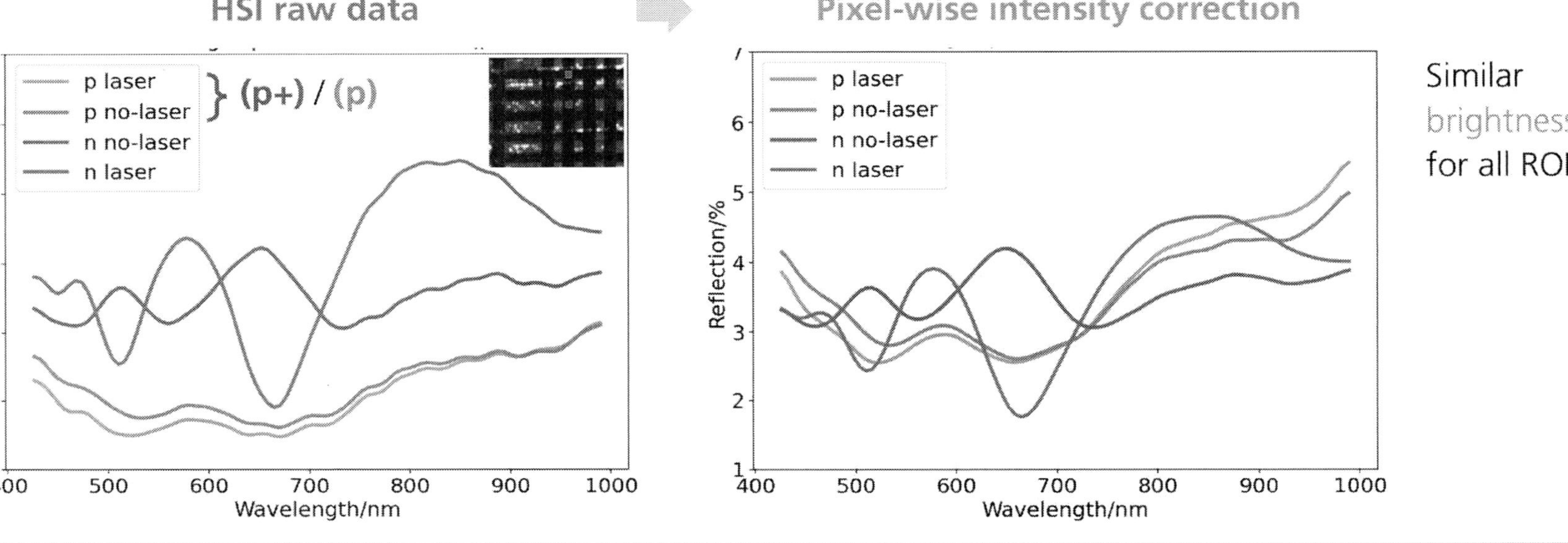

(*) e.g. A. C. Müller and S. Guido: Introduction to machine learning with Python. O'Reilly Media Inc. (2018)

Fraunhofer
CSP

020004-014

APPROACH: HSI – DATA PRE-PROCESSING: "FEATURE SCALING"

Material-independent algorithms – extracting relevant spectral finger-prints

Data pre-processing step 2[(*)]: **Correction of local contrast variations**

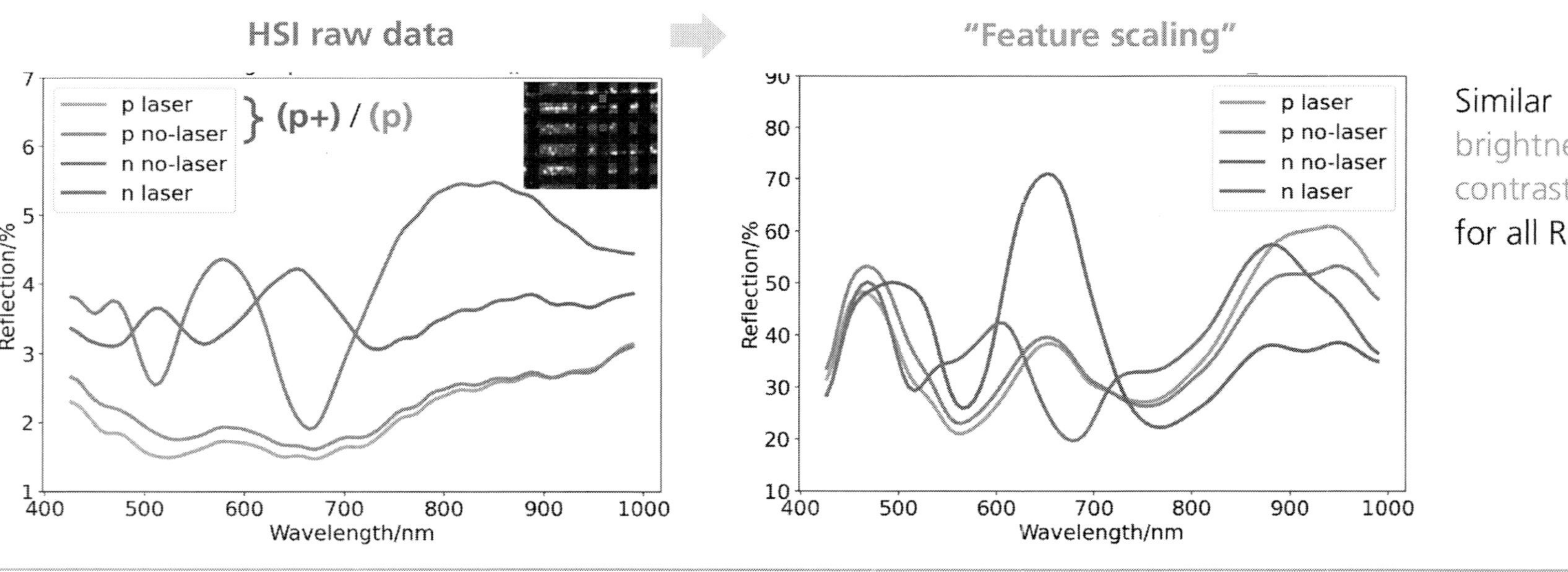

(*) e.g. A. C. Müller and S. Guido: Introduction to machine learning with Python. O'Reilly Media Inc. (2018)

020004-015

APPROACH: HSI – DATA PRE-PROCESSING: "DIMENSIONALITY REDUCTION"

Material-independent algorithms – extracting relevant spectral finger-prints

Data pre-processing step $3^{(*)}$: **Reducing the data set** to accelerate sub-sequent algorithms

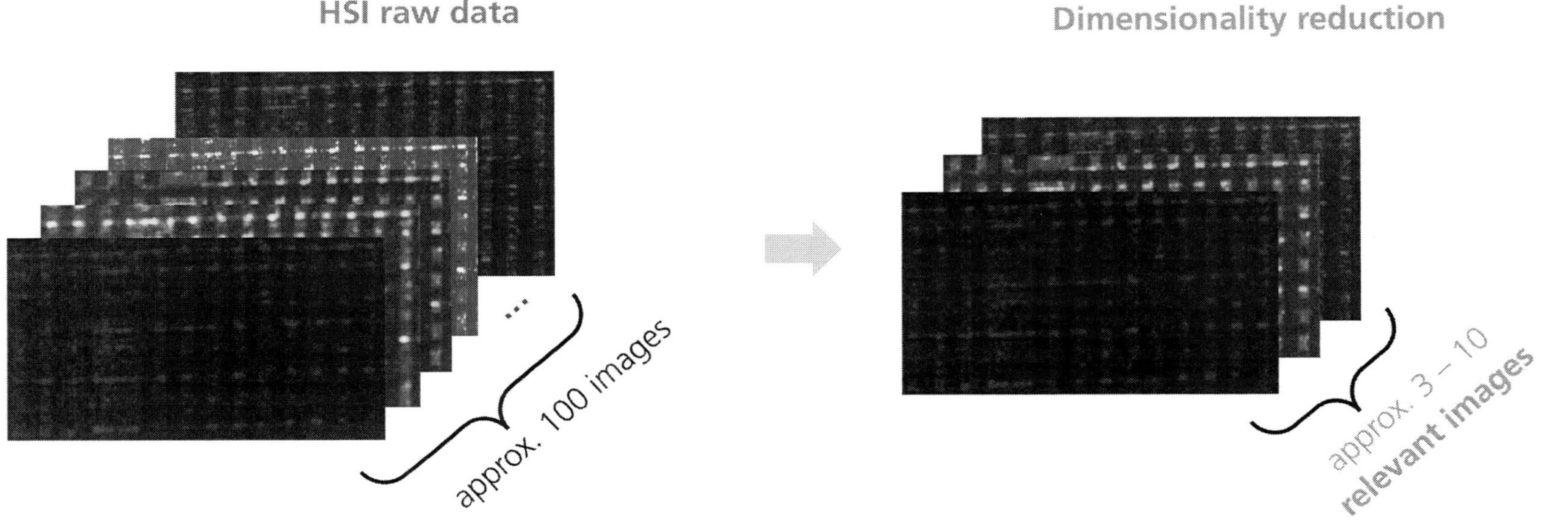

(*) e.g. A. C. Müller and S. Guido: Introduction to machine learning with Python. O'Reilly Media Inc. (2018)

Fraunhofer
CSP

020004-016

III. Identification and classification of rear side pattern

RESULTS: HSI – DATA PRE-PROCESSING

Material-independent algorithms – extracting relevant spectral finger-prints

Result of data pre-processing → Drastically reduced data set containing most significant information

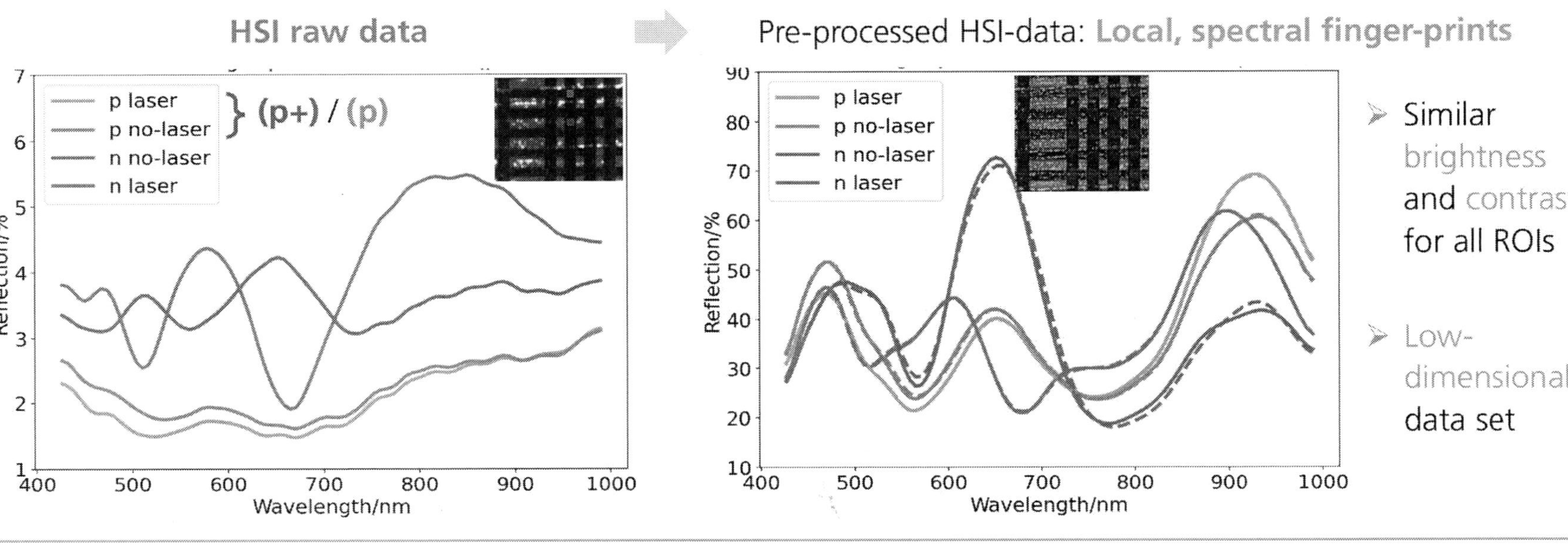

27.08.2025   © Fraunhofer CSP   - public information -   Fraunhofer CSP   020004-018

RESULTS: HSI – DATA PRE-PROCESSING

Material-independent algorithms – extracting relevant spectral finger-prints

Result of data pre-processing → Drastically reduced data set containing most significant information

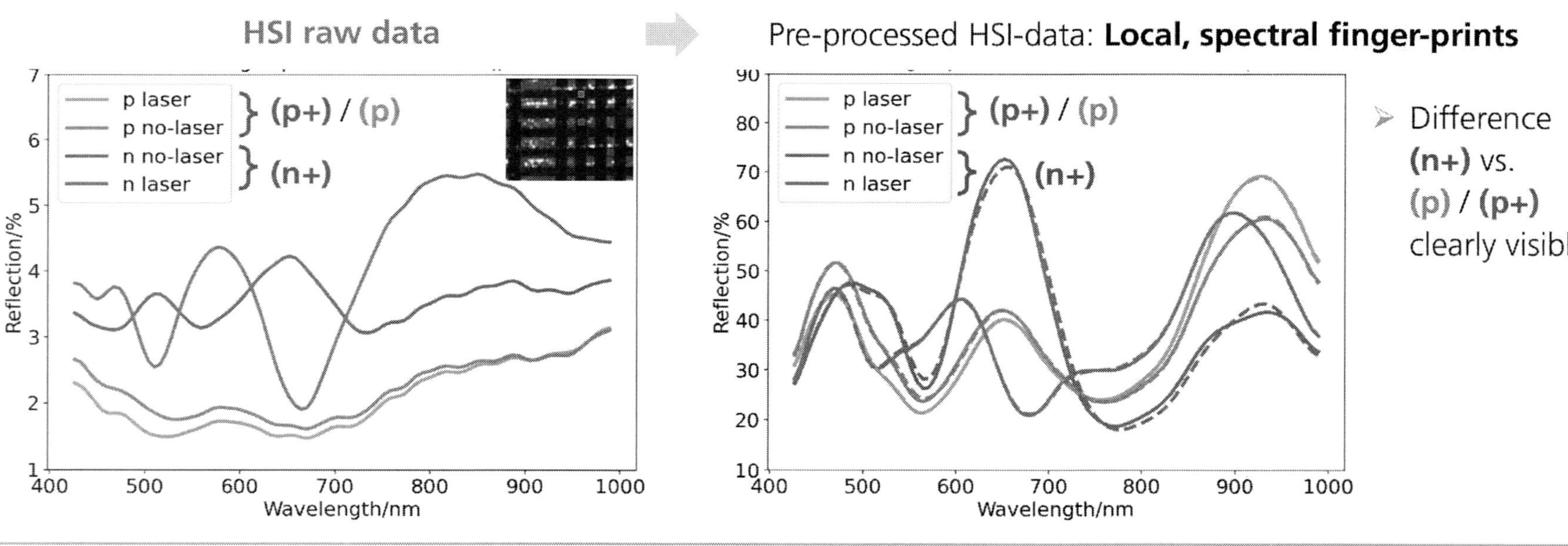

27.08.2025   © Fraunhofer CSP   - public information -   020004-019

Fraunhofer
CSP

RESULTS: HSI – DATA PRE-PROCESSING

Material-independent algorithms – extracting relevant spectral finger-prints

Result of data pre-processing → Drastically reduced data set containing most significant information

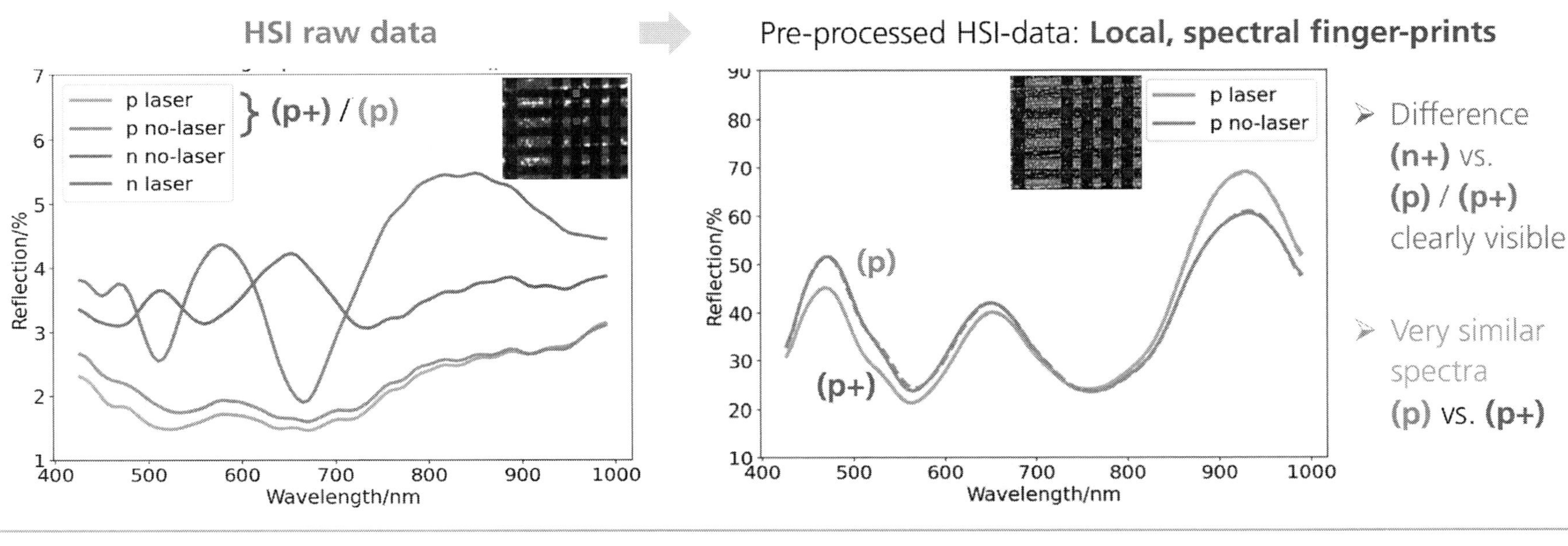

020004-020

RESULTS: HSI – DATA PREPROCESSING

Material-independent algorithms – classification of pixels requires further data analysis

Identification of laser mis-alignments:

Can laser-activated (p+) regions be separated from (p) regions by hyperspectral imaging?

- public information -

Fraunhofer
CSP

020004-021

RESULTS: HSI – DATA PREPROCESSING

Material-independent algorithms – classification of pixels requires further data analysis

Identification of laser mis-alignments:

Can laser-activated (p+) regions be separated from (p) regions by hyperspectral imaging?

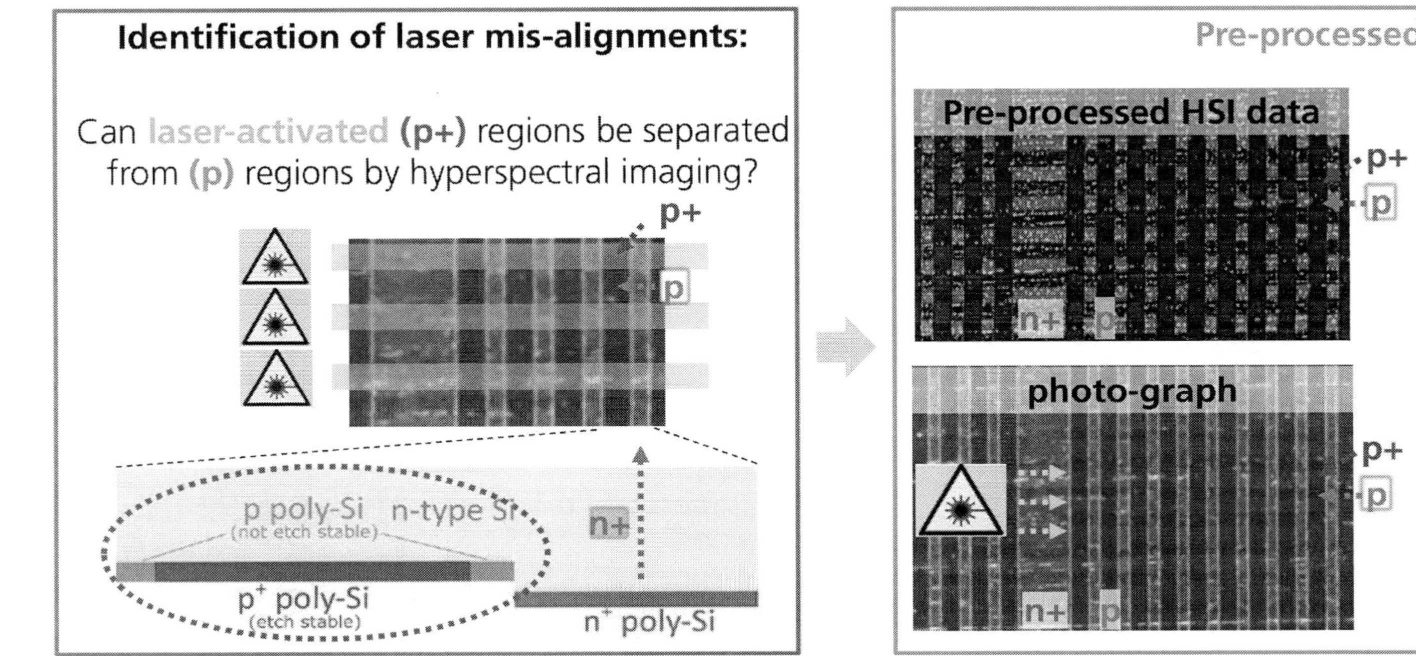

Pre-processed data

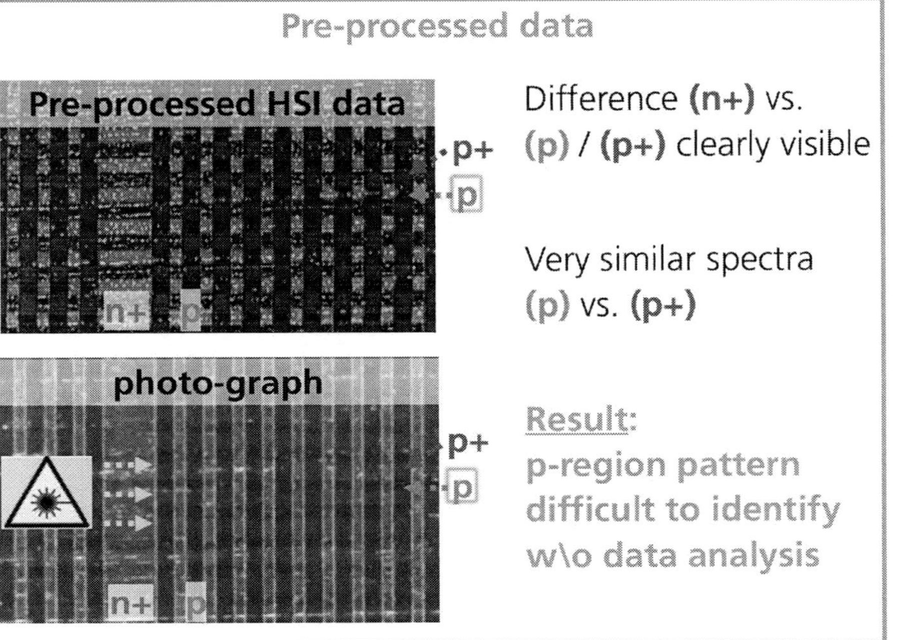

Difference (n+) vs. (p) / (p+) clearly visible

Very similar spectra (p) vs. (p+)

Result:
p-region pattern difficult to identify w\o data analysis

020004-022

RESULTS: HSI – DATA ANALYSIS

Material-independent algorithms – classification of pixels

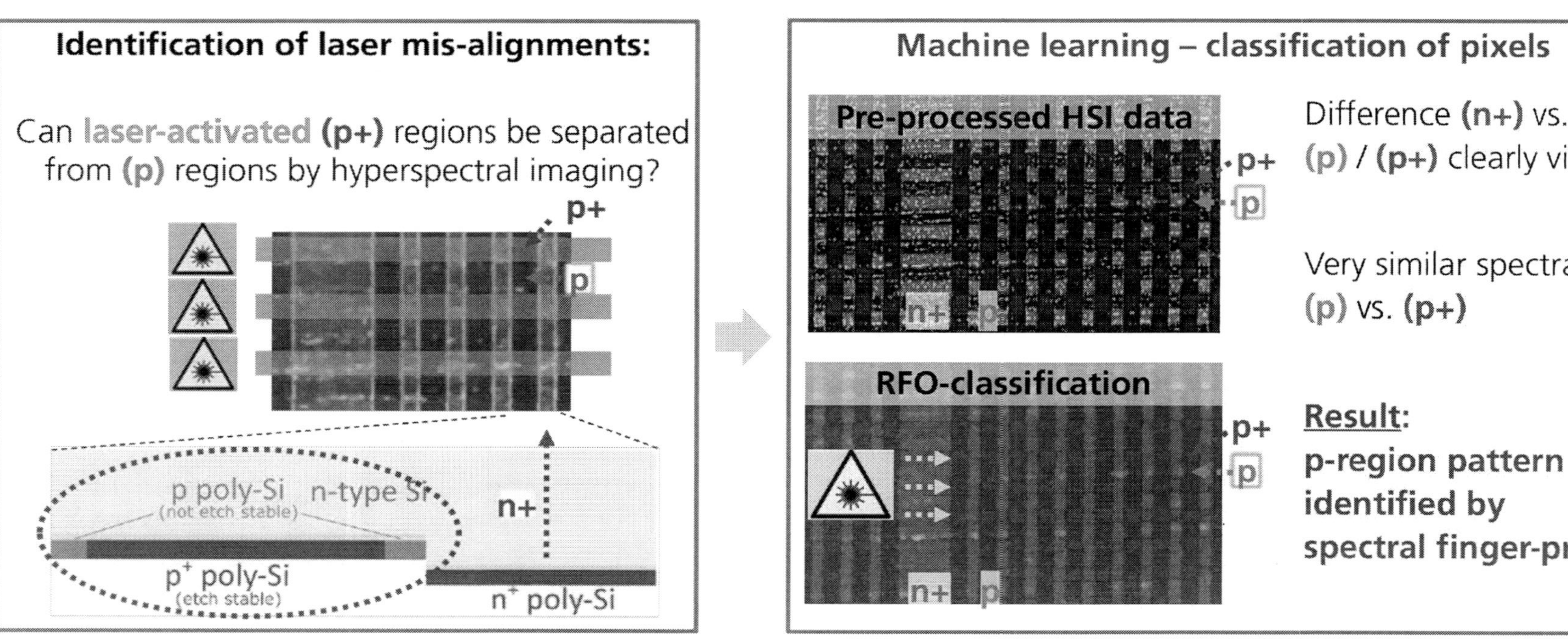

OUTLOOK: SIMPLIFIED APPROACH FOR SPECTRAL IMAGING

LED sun-simulator combined with mono-chrome camera

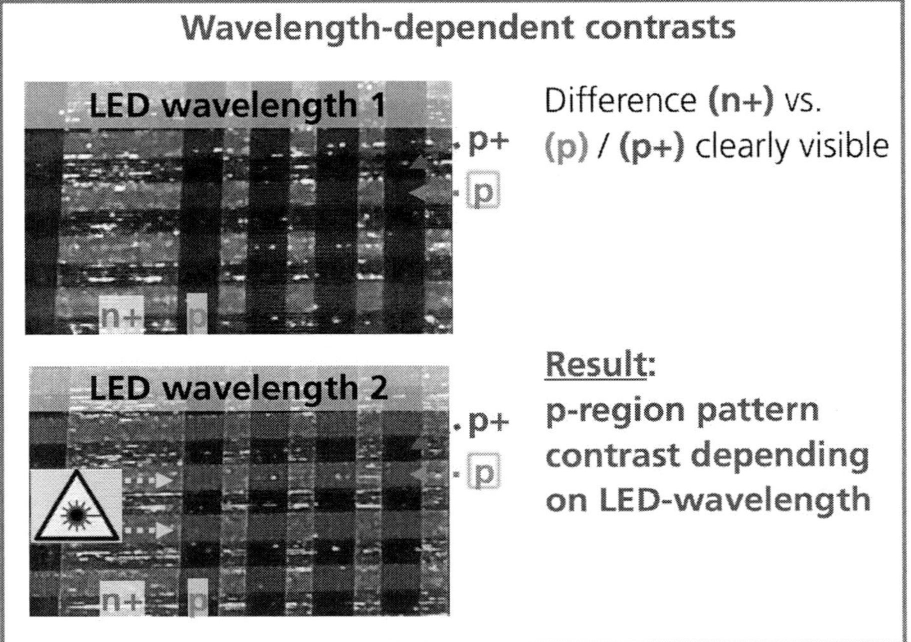

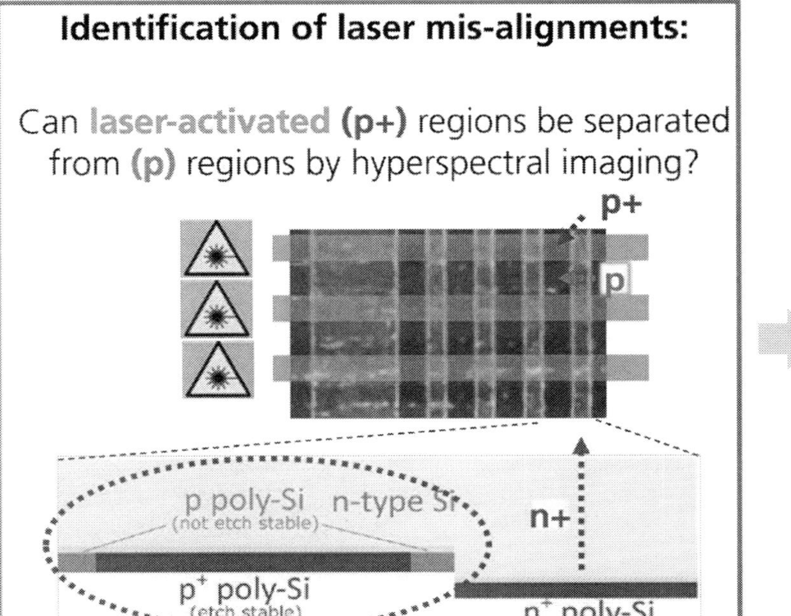

27.08.2025   © Fraunhofer CSP   - public information -

Fraunhofer CSP

020004-024

SUMMARY: INLINE QUALITY CONTROL FOR BACK-CONTACT SOLAR CELLS

Rapid imaging of rear side pattern by combining spectral with spatial information

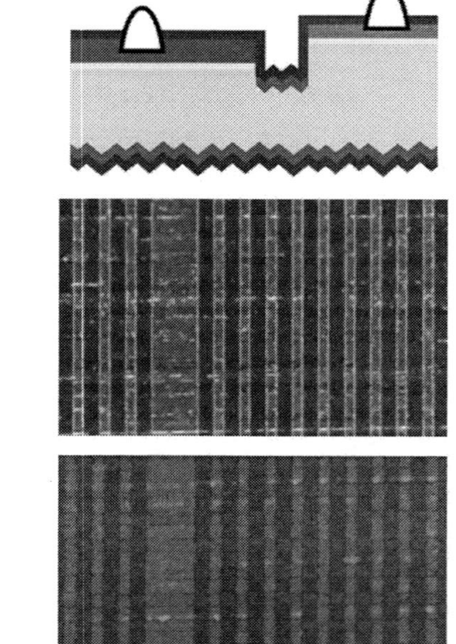

Results of (optical) HSI approach:

1. Test structures with local laser-doped regions investigated by spectral imaging
2. Local spectral finger-prints → only minor differences between (p+) vs. (p)
3. Automated training and classification results in separation of (p+) from (p)

Outlook:

➢ Simplified "LED-approach" based on identified relevant wavelengths
➢ Increase of spatial resolution for "real" patterns with dimensions below 20μm

Conclusion: Optical hyperspectral imaging (HSI) can serve as fast and sensitive quality control technique for IBC solar cells

020004-025

isc research
for a sunny future

Thank you for your attention!

Marko Turek
Tel. +49 345 5589 5121
marko.turek@csp.fraunhofer.de

Fraunhofer CSP
Otto-Eißfeldt- Straße 12
06120 Halle (Saale)
www.csp.fraunhofer.de

**Funded within
project "SelFi"
(FKZ 03EE1138B)**

Supported by:

Federal Ministry
for Economic Affairs
and Climate Action

on the basis of a decision
by the German Bundestag

RCT
solutions

Photovoltaic
Services & Technology
Solutions Partner

Pathway to TBC: Process, Design, and Cost
Implications for new PERC & TOPCon Lines

Group of companies
RCT   RCT   RCT
power hydrogen

Julian Reichle* Sraisth, Mehul Raval, Gourab Das, Andreas Teppe, Wolfgang Jooss and Peter Fath
RCT Solutions GmbH, Line – Eid – Str. 1, 78467 Konstanz, Germany
With support of Wolfgang Herbst from ViridisIQ GmbH, Germany
*E-mail: julian.reichle@rct-solutions.com

Motivation for TBC Solar Cells
Next phase of production expansion indicates TBC

Market Share of Cell Technologies

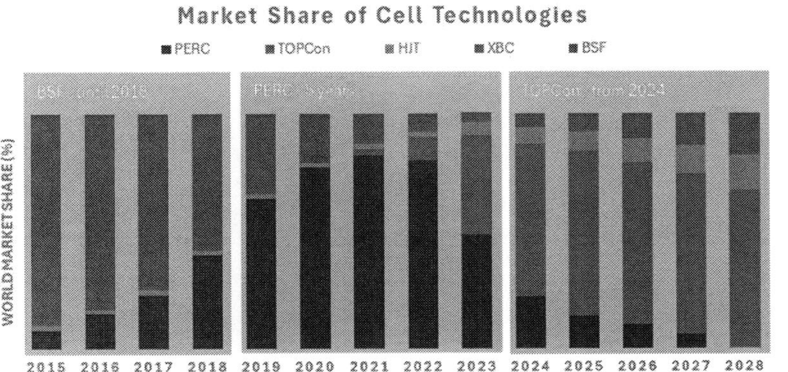

Challenge:

- Advanced technologies like TOPCon and PERC
- Building new factories takes time, while solar cell tech lasts only 5–7 years
- How to future-proof, enable updates, and design adaptable systems?

+ Based on same equipment's as PERC and TOPCon

+ Back contacts – no front side metallization

- Enhanced light absorption improves cell efficiency [1]. → Higher module yield.
- Simplifies the metallization process, as only one side needs to be processed [2]
- Easier to apply low-cost copper metalization
- TBC structures supports tandem cell configurations, enabling future advancements in solar technology [3]

+ Adopting advanced passivation methods

- Lowering recombination losses on both polarity surfaces

[1] F. Haase, C. Hollemann, S. Schäfer, M. Merkle, M. Rienäcker, J. Krugener, R. Brendel and R. Peibst, "Laser contact openings for local poly-Si-metal contacts enabling 26.1%-efficient POLO-IBC solar cells.," Sol. Energy Mater. Sol. Cells, p. 186:184–193, 2018;.

[2] M. K. Mat Desa et al., "Silicon back contact solar cell configuration: A pathway towards higher efficiency," Renewable and Sustainable Energy Reviews, vol. Volume 60, pp. 1516–1532, 2016.

[3] Erkan Aydin et al., "Pathways toward commercial perovskite/silicon," Science, no. 383, 2024.

020005-002

The RCT Group at a Glance

RCT solutions

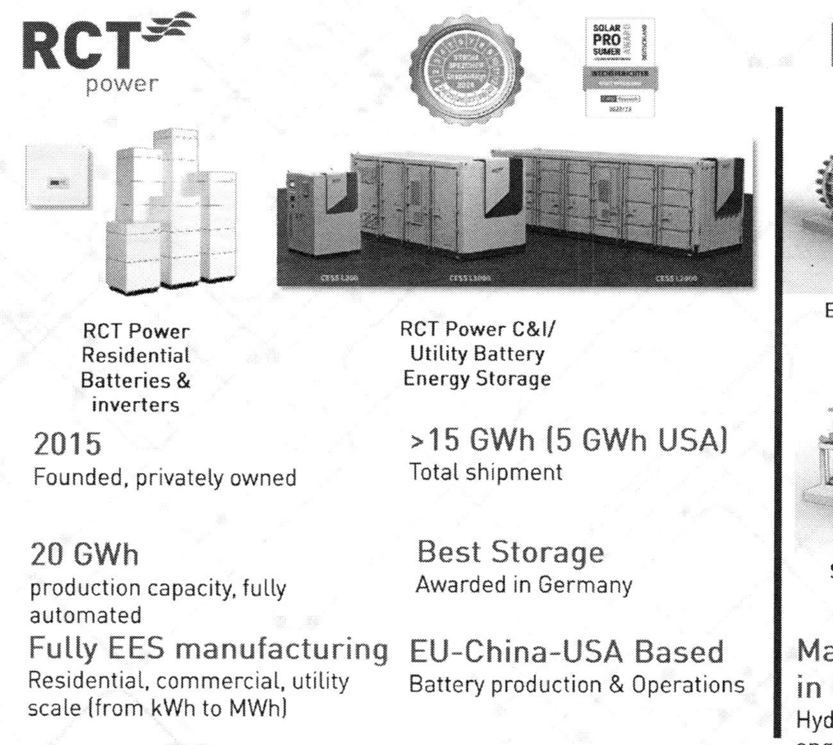

RCT solutions

2012
Founded, privately owned

≈ 100 GW
Supporting PV manufacturing capacity

26+
Countries

62
Factories worldwide

World's First
Fully integrated giga-scale factory installation

76 GW
Ingot & Wafer integration

RCT power

2015
Founded, privately owned

20 GWh
production capacity, fully automated

Fully EES manufacturing
Residential, commercial, utility scale (from kWh to MWh)

>15 GWh (5 GWh USA)
Total shipment

Best Storage
Awarded in Germany

EU-China-USA Based
Battery production & Operations

RCT hydrogen

Made/Engineered in Germany
Hydrogen equipment & engineering service

Factory Output
250MW (Target)

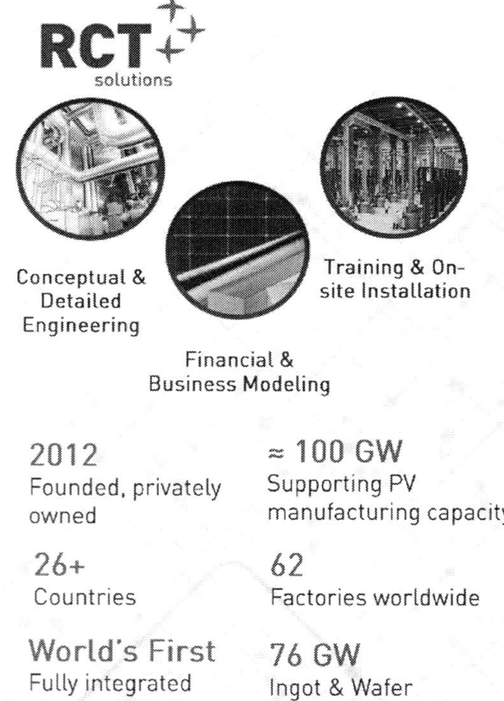

020005-003

Aim and Approach
Application of the conceptional engineering approach

Technology Selection → **Process Flow Decision** → **Conceptional Engineering** → **Cost of Ownership** → **Summary and Outlook**

Technology Selection
- Baseline Technology
- Upgrade Technology

Process Flow Decision
- Process Routes
- Line Balancing

Conceptional Engineering
- Layout & Room book
- Facility Utility Matrix
- Mass & Load Balance
- HR-Plan

Cost of Ownership
- Equipment CAPEX
- Utility, Facility and Building CAPEX
- OPEX
- Sensitivity

020005-004

Technology Selection
Solar cell efficiency limits & status

Potential & production efficiency for different solar cell technologies

020005-005

Technology Selection
Scenarios considered for TBC upgrade route

Case	A-0	A-1	A-2	B-0	B-1	B-2	C-0
Baseline Technology	PERC Reference 5.0 GW	PERC 5.0 GW		TOPCon Reference 5GW	TOPCon 5.5 GW		TBC Reference 5.6 GW
End technology		TBC 5.6 GW	TBC 4.3 GW		TBC 5.6 GW	TBC 4.8GW	
Considerations	N/A	• Space • Utilities	• Utilities	N/A	• Space • Utilities	• Utilities	

- Reference cases for PERC, TOPCon and TBC cell production
- PERC and TOPCon as baseline technology
- PERC was selected, as there are some IP related risks
- Upgrade to TBC from PERC and from TOPCon
- Each upgrade scenario considers complete utility buildout from the beginning
- Two different cases for each technology combination **with and without space provision.**

020005-006

Process Flow and Cell Design
TOPCon to TOPCon Back Contact (TBC) upgrade

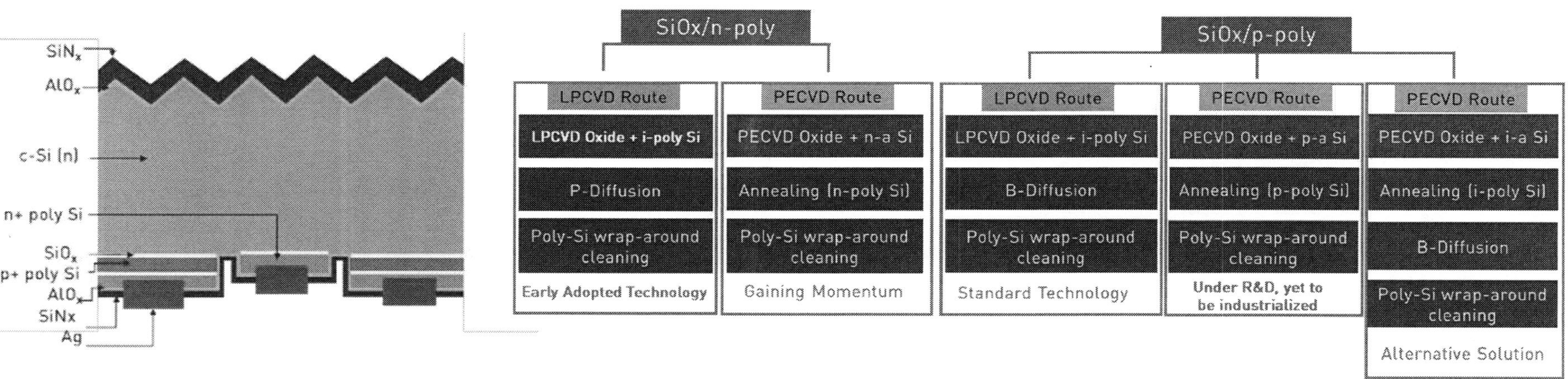

- TBC requires **p-type and n-type poly-Si passivated contacts**
- For in-situ B-doped a-Si, B-atoms migrate easily towards tunnel-oxide upon annealing, creating defects & leads to degradation in the passivating quality
- Thereby LPCVD route adopted for TBC by big players already
- Though in R&D, **p-poly Si (B)** is being developed in **PECVD** process, but the process window is much more narrow as compared to n-poly Si (P)
- PECVD equipment from upgrade available ´→ **Ex-situ diffusion** of PECVD deposited a-Si is an alternative solution

020005-007

Process Flow and Cell Design
More process steps require more space

TOPCon Back Contact (TBC) – OPT A

- SDE + Cleaning
- Tunnel Oxide + i-Poly Si Deposition (RS) LPCVD F2F
- B-Diffusion (RS) (F2F Loading)
- Laser Ablation (RS)
- p-poly-Si Etching (Ablated part) + Cleaning
- Tunnel Oxide + i-poly Si Deposition LPCVD F2F
- P-Diffusion (RS) (F2F Loading)
- Laser Isolation (to avoid n-and p-doped shunting)
- Alkaline Texturization (FS)
- AlO_x (Both Side)
- SiN_x ARC (FS) and Capping (RS)
- Printing, Firing & Testing

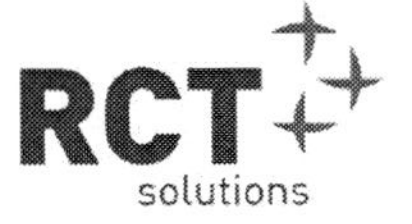

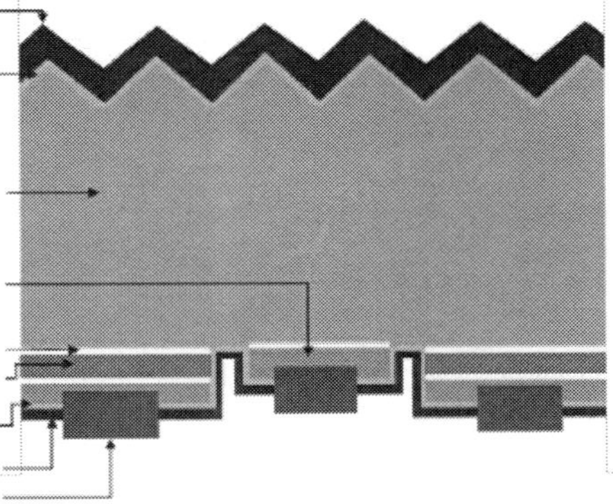

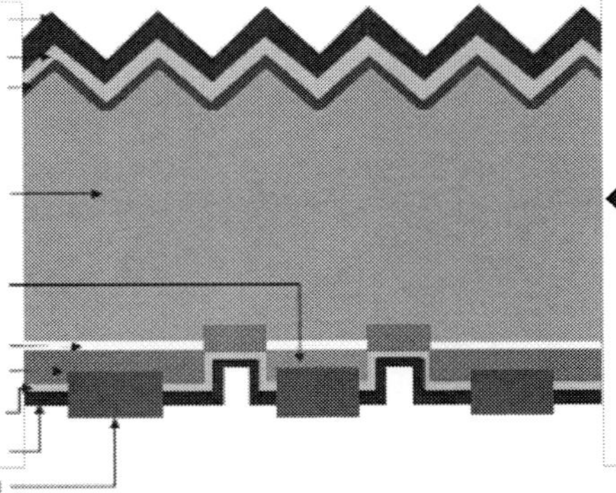

TOPCon Back Contact (TBC) – OPT B

- SDE + Cleaning
- Tunnel Oxide + i-poly Si Deposition (PECVD)
- P-Diffusion
- SiNx Capping layer
- Laser Ablation
- Tunnel Oxide and n-Poly-Si Dtching + Cleaning
- Tunnel Oxide + i-poly Si Deposition (PECVD)
- B-Diffusion (BSG Formation)
- Local Laser Doping
- Alkaline Texturization
- B-Diffusion (Gap & FS)
- AlOx + SiNx Deposition (BS)
- Printing, Firing & Testing

Conceptional Engineering
More process steps required for TBC

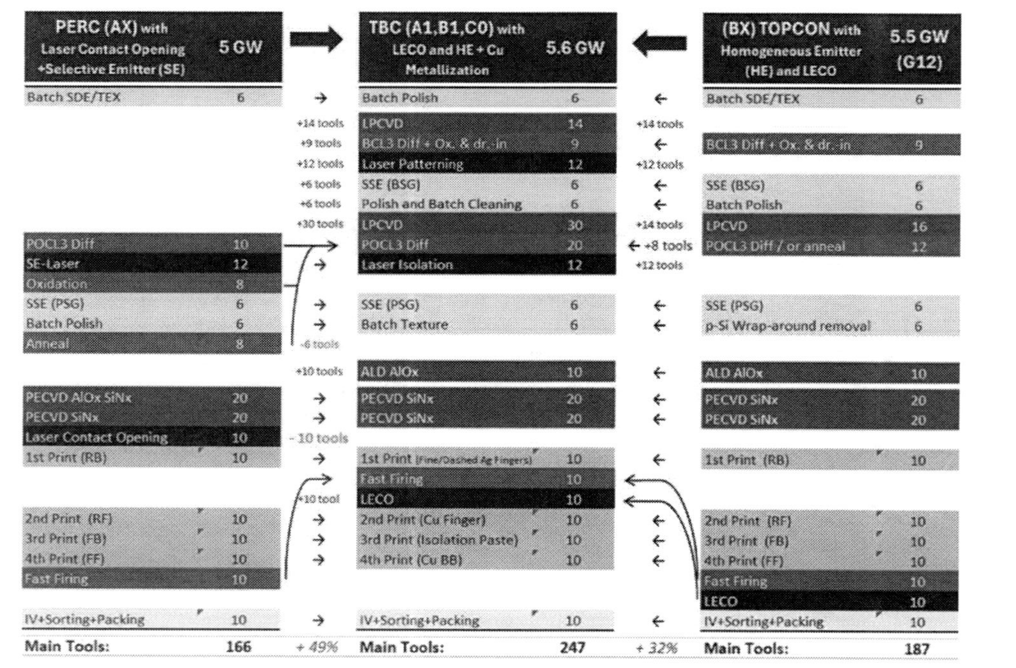

- Upgrade scenario 1 – covers space and utility provision.
- Extra TBC steps raise CAPEX, labor, and complexity.
- Most TOPCon tools are reusable.
- Some minor PERC tools will be removed.
- TBC process flow is still early and expected to evolve.

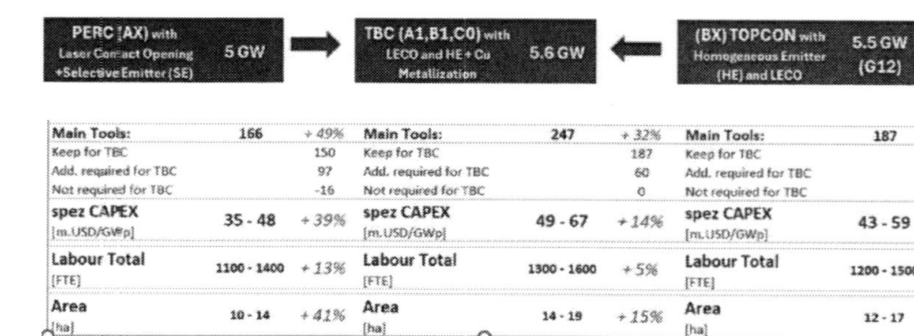

Main Tools:	166	+ 49%	Main Tools:	247	+ 32%	Main Tools:	187
Keep for TBC		150	Keep for TBC		187	Keep for TBC	
Add. required for TBC		97	Add. required for TBC		60	Add. required for TBC	
Not required for TBC		-16	Not required for TBC		0	Not required for TBC	
spez CAPEX [m.USD/GWp]	35 - 48	+ 39%	spez CAPEX [m.USD/GWp]	49 - 67	+ 14%	spez CAPEX [m.USD/GWp]	43 - 59
Labour Total [FTE]	1100 - 1400	+ 13%	Labour Total [FTE]	1300 - 1600	+ 5%	Labour Total [FTE]	1200 - 1500
Area [ha]	10 - 14	+ 41%	Area [ha]	14 - 19	+ 15%	Area [ha]	12 - 17

020005-009

Conceptional Engineering–
Layout – Reserve space within each equipment cluster

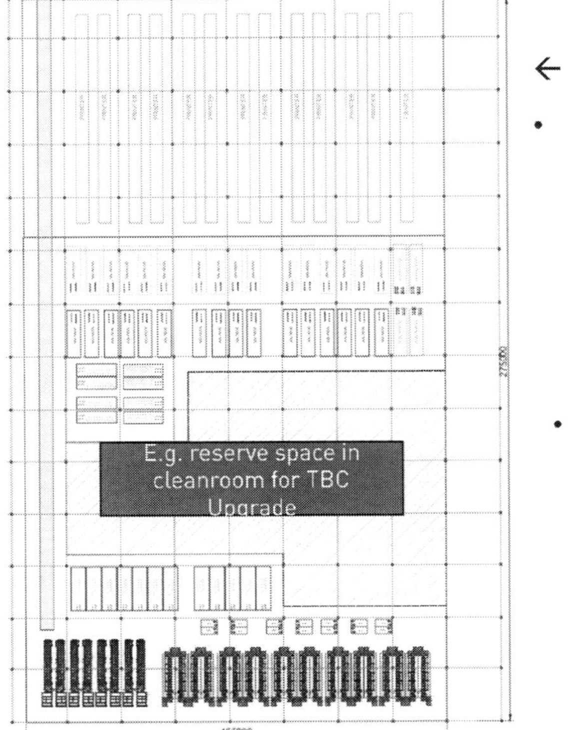

← Option1 : Separated Reserve Space for Upgrade

- Easier to temporary close or separate (OPEX reduction of cleanroom or renting out temporarily)

Option 2: Reserve Space Inside the Factory in each Cluster: →

- Piping can be reduced

- Improved material and personnel flow after process or technology upgrade

Option 2 was considered

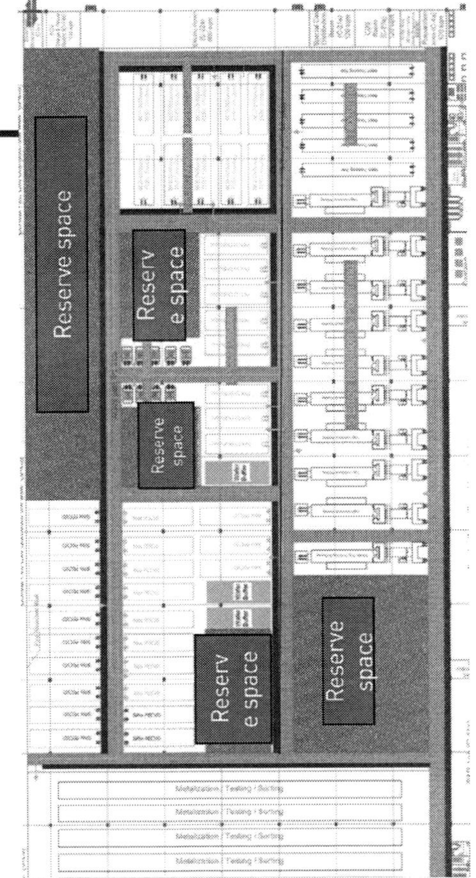

020005-010

Conceptional Engineering–
Often Overseen – Utility, Facility and Building Design

- New technologies → often increased CAPEX
- Utility and facility CAPEX are frequently underestimated.
- E.g. switching gases or liquids, like from Phosphoroxychlorid (POCl3) to Phosphine (PH3), → careful evaluation due to major differences.

Non-Process Packages
Civil
Architectural
Infrastructure
Structural
Rainwater System
General HVAC
Sewage Treatment
LV Power Distribution
MV Power Distribution
Lightning System
Emergency Power System (DG, UPS)

Process Packages
Process Cooling Water
High Side Water Generation/Chilled Water
Waste Water Treatment
Waste Gas Treatment
Bulk Gas Distribution
Process Gas Distribution
Process Chemical Distribution
DI Water
Compressed Dry Air/ Compressed Air
Facility Monitoring & Controlling System
Clean Room Design

020005-011

Cost of Ownership
Before and after the Upgrade compared to no Upgrade

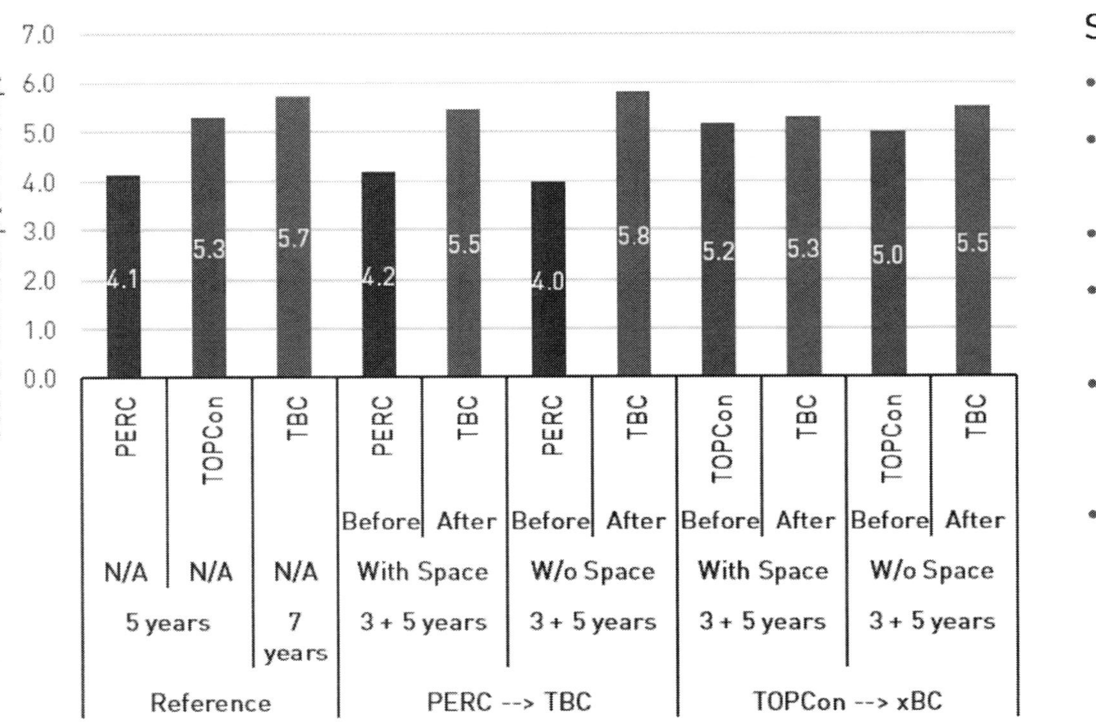

Reference			PERC --> TBC				TOPCon --> xBC			
PERC	TOPCon	TBC	PERC	TBC	PERC	TBC	TOPCon	TBC	TOPCon	TBC
			Before	After	Before	After	Before	After	Before	After
N/A	N/A	N/A	With Space		W/o Space		With Space		W/o Space	
5 years		7 years	3 + 5 years		3 + 5 years		3 + 5 years		3 + 5 years	

Summary of Ownership Cost Analysis

- Different lifetime assumed.
- Calculate ownership costs before and after upgrade
- References w/o upgrade also included
- Lower initial cost for PERC and TOPCon with utilities only
- Include expansion space increasing upfront cost, but still lower as reference if longer
- TBC Upgrade cost lower, if longer operating can be expected and no equipment needs to be removed or replaced e.g. TOPCon to TBC

* **Key assumptions CoO:** Depreciation: Equipment 5 - 7 years – Utilities 10 years – Building 20 years – Western Location – 2000 USD/sqm building cost reference – Cumulative interest 3.8%

020005-012

Summary of the Upgrade Scenarios results

Case	A1	A2	B1	B2
Start Up Technology	PERC 5.0 GW		TOPCon 5.5 GW	
Upgrade Technology	TBC 5.6 GW	TBC 4.3 GW	TBC 5.6 GW	TBC 4.8 GW
Provision	• Space • Utilities	• Utilities	• Space • Utilities	• Utilities
CAPEX [mUSD] Start + Upgrade	723 + 146	587 + 109	795 + 31	723 + 31
CoO [USDct/Wp]	PERC: 4.2 TBC: 5.5	PERC: 4.0 TBC: 5.8	TOPCon: 5.2 TBC: 5.3	TOPCon: 5.0 TBC: 5.5
Removed and added tools for upgrade	-16 tools + 97 tools	-46 tools +72 tools	-0 tools + 60 tools	-12 tools +50
Result	+ Competitive TBC cost + Moderate CAPEX increase	+ Lowest CAPEX Option	+ Simplest Upgrade options (no tool removal) + Most competitive TBC cost	+ Moderate CAPEX + Competitive TOPCon and TBC Cost
Targeted Developer or investor	• Balanced developer • Long-term cost efficiency and stable production output with low TOPCon IP Confidence	• Developers with CAPEX constraints, hesitant adding space for TBC expansion • With low IP Confidence in TOPCon	• Minimal disruptions to existing production lines. • Technological advantage	• New developers seek market-leading technology • Limited confidence in TBC's IP landscape, making them cautious about large-scale investments.

020005-013

Summary and Outlook

Key Points:

- **Technology cycles lasts 5–7 years,** so western factories with longer setup times should be upgradeable.

- TBC (TOPCon Back Contact) cells are **likely the next evolution.**

- **Various upgrade options** differ in capacity, space, and utility needs.

- Upgrading to TBC requires **more CAPEX and complexity**

- Cost of ownership favors providing utilities only initially (before upgrade) but **allocating extra space reduces future costs (after upgrade).**

→ RCTs recommendation – reserving space for future upgrades.

Outlook:

Excess space can be also utilized for:

- **Debottlenecking:** Increase line capacity by debottlenecking. Changes in throughput requirements of certain process steps might change.

- **Equipment Upgrade:** Based on existing solar cell concept (comparable to selective emitter in PERC / TOPCon cells, LECO, etc.)

- **Innovation platform** for equipment builders, initial testing of next generation solar cell concepts („pilot line" for next phase extension)

Changes in Module Design to be addressed → Addressed in tomorrows 3CO.11.3 *"Techno-Economic Analysis of Suitable Module BOM for Different Climatic Conditions"* by Sraisth

TBC comes with higher resource demands → addressed in my Sesson tomorrow 5CO.4.4 *"LCA Learning Curve for Crystalline Silicon Solar Technologies based on Technology Improvements"*

020005-014

Thank you to all RCT Solutions colleagues – Join us at Konstanz

Gefördert durch:

Bundesministerium
für Wirtschaft
und Energie

aufgrund eines Beschlusses
des Deutschen Bundestages
Project PV Pilot - FKZ 03EE1219

020005-015

RCT Solutions GmbH
Line-Eid-Strasse 1
D-78467 Konstanz, Germany

Phone +49 7531 58470 12
info@rct-solutions.com
http://www.rct-solutions.com

Regd. HRB 708952,
Executive Board: Dr. Peter Fath

Confidential

Thank you

Group of companies

RCT solutions   **RCT** power   **RCT** hydrogen

42nd European Photovoltaic Solar Energy Conference and Exhibition

This presentation was selected by the Sc. Committee of the EU PVSEC 2025 for submission of a full paper to one of the EU PVSEC's collaborating peer-reviewed journals.

INDUSTRIAL IMPLEMENTATION OF 24%-EFFICIENT POLO IBC SOLAR CELLS AND FUTURE UPGRADE TO 26%-EFFICIENT POLO2 IBC

Thorsten Dullweber[1,*], Yevgeniya Larionova[1], Philip Jäger[1], Verena Mertens[1], Sabrina Schimanke[1], Melanie Ripke[1], Ulrike Baumann[1], Alaa Osman[1], Udo Römer[1], Robby Peibst[1], Rolf Brendel[1,2], Özlem Coşkun[3], Gamze Çekerek[3], Meriç Çalışkan Arslan[3], Geoffrey Gregory[4], Erik Hoffmann[4], and Massimo Centazzo[4]

[1] Institute for Solar Energy Research Hamelin (ISFH), Am Ohrberg 1, 31860 Emmerthal, Germany
[2] Institute of Solid-State Physics, Leibniz Universität Hannover, Appelstrasse 2, 30167 Hannover, Germany
[3] Kalyon PV, Başkent OSB Şadi Türk Bulvarı 23 Malıköy, Ankara, Türkiye
[4] EnPV GmbH, Durlacher Allee 93, 76131 Karlsruhe, Germany

ABSTRACT: IBC solar cells have gained tremendous interest in the PV industry as next-generation technology. ISFH has developed a lean manufacturing process sequence for POLO IBC solar cells applying p-type Cz wafers, an Al-BSF base contact and local PECVD deposition of the SiO_xN_y/n-type polysilicon emitter through a glass shadow mask. In this paper, we report a new best POLO IBC cell efficiency of 24.3% processed at ISFH on M2 wafer size. In 2024, we started to transfer the POLO IBC process from the ISFH SolarTeC to the Kalyon PV manufacturing line using their M10 sized p-type Ga-doped Cz wafers and cell production tools. With Kalyon PV's wet chemistry and PECVD AlO_x/SiN tools good surface passivation is demonstrated by obtaining an iV_{oc} up to 727 mV using textured, rear side polished AlO_x/SiN passivated test wafers. Kalyon PV targets to process first M10-sized POLO IBC solar cells till end of 2025. However, the POLO IBC efficiency will be limited to below 25.5% by the carrier recombination at the Al-BSF base contact. To overcome this limitation, ISFH is applying a SiO_x/p-type polysilicon layer stack to a novel industrial processing sequence for the $POLO^2$ IBC solar cell. We use M2-sized n-type Cz wafers, deposit both polysilicon layers in-situ-doped full-area and laser-structure both polysilicon polarities in a novel and lean IBC trench patterning process. We obtain a measured implied V_{oc} = 735 mV and implied FF = 86.0% of $POLO^2$ IBC cell precursors processed without metal contacts. Since the polysilicon contacts minimize carrier recombination at metal contacts, the implied V_{oc} value demonstrates the high V_{oc} potential of this promising new $POLO^2$ IBC manufacturing process thereby indicating a conversion efficiency potential above 26%.

Keywords: silicon solar cells, IBC, back contact, passivating contacts, polysilicon

1 INTRODUCTION

In the past years ISFH has developed a lean manufacturing process sequence for POLO IBC solar cells applying p-type wafers, an Al-BSF base contact and a local PECVD deposition of the SiO_xN_y/n-poly-Si emitter through a glass shadow mask [1,2,3]. In this paper, we report a new best POLO IBC cell efficiency of 24.3% processed at ISFH on M2 wafer size using industry-type processing equipment at the ISFH SolarTeC. The POLO IBC process with shadow masks at ISFH is very similar to the typical industrial bifacial PERC+ mass production sequence as e.g. applied by Kalyon PV in their cell production line, allowing to re-use most of the existing PERC+ production tools [2,3]. To convert a PERC+ production line to POLO IBC, only the $POCl_3$ furnace and laser doping tool have to be replaced by a new PECVD tool for local SiO_xN_y/n-poly-Si deposition [2,3]. In 2024, Kalyon PV and ISFH signed a technology licensing agreement and started to transfer the POLO IBC process from the ISFH SolarTeC to the Kalyon PV PERC+ manufacturing line using their M10 sized Ga-doped Cz wafers [4] and their PERC+ cell production tools. In this paper, we publish first promising POLO IBC test wafer results processed at Kalyon PV obtaining implied V_{oc} values up to 727 mV demonstrating a suitable passivation quality of Kalyon PVs wet chemistry and PECVD AlO_x/SiN tools.

However, the POLO IBC efficiency will be limited to below 25.5% by the carrier recombination at the Al-BSF base contact [5]. To overcome this limitation aiming at n-type polysilicon (n-poly-Si) / p-type polysilicon (p-poly-Si) $POLO^2$ IBC cell efficiencies beyond 26%, in collaboration with EnPV a carrier selective SiO_x/p-poly-Si layer stack has been developed at ISFH using industrial tools for the wet chemically grown SiO_x and the in-situ doped p-poly-Si deposited by LPCVD. Last year, we have published a best J_0 = 2.3 fA/cm^2 [6]. ISFH is applying the SiO_x/p-poly-Si layer stack to develop a novel industrial processing sequence for the $POLO^2$ IBC solar cell [7]. We deposit both poly layers in-situ-doped full-area on M2-sized n-type Cz wafers and laser-structure both poly-Si polarities in a novel IBC trench layout targeting very cost-effective processes for etch barrier formation and poly-Si etching [7]. In this paper, we present first promising test wafer results demonstrating an implied V_{oc} up to 735 mV for $POLO^2$ IBC solar cell precursors without metal contacts processed with industrial tools in the ISFH SolarTeC.

This EUPVSEC conference paper is a shortened version of a corresponding invited full manuscript submitted to EPJ Photovoltaics.

2 24% POLO IBC CELLS BY ISFH AND TECHNOLOGY TRANSFER TO KALYON PV

The POLO IBC process flow is published in detail in previous papers [2,3,8] and yielded a previously best POLO IBC cell efficiency of 23.9% [4]. In this paper, we report a new best POLO IBC cell efficiency of 24.1% independently confirmed by ISFH CalTeC with the current-voltage (IV) parameters summarized in Tab. 1. The high open circuit voltage V_{oc} = 723 mV demonstrates the good surface passivation quality of the AlO_x/SiN and SiO_x/n-poly-Si layers with saturation current densities J_0 around 3 fA/cm^2 [9]. The efficiency improvement from 23.9% to 24.1% was obtained by applying a 25°C lower n-poly-Si annealing temperature which is now optimized for the wet chemical SiOx.and which increased the V_{oc} from 720 mV to 723 mV, see Table I. In addition, integrating contact pads in the busbars and applying a new IV test chuck with contact pins ensured a more precise contacting thereby reducing the series resistance from 0.8 to 0.67 $m\Omega cm^2$ as shown in Table I. This new IV test chuck was qualified for high-precision IV test at ISFH CalTeC enabling an independent certified efficiency measurement. Subsequently, we optimized the anti-reflection coating applying a triple-layer AlO_x/SiN/SiON stack instead of the AlO_x/SiN layer which reduces the average reflectance from 1.7% to 0.9% thereby increasing the J_{sc} by 0.4 mA/cm^2 leading to a new best POLO IBC efficiency of 24.3% displayed in Table I. As can be seen in Table 1, the POLO IBC series resistance $R_s = 0.67$ Ωcm^2 is still relatively high thereby limiting the FF to 81.3%. The high R_s is caused by a high Ag to n-poly contact resistance of 25 $m\Omega cm^2$ as published in Ref. 8 which is subject to further optimization.

Table I: IV parameters of the best POLO IBC solar cells at ISFH with M2 p-type wafer size. The 23.9% efficient cell is our previously best cell published in [4]. The 24.1% cell was independently confirmed by ISFH CalTeC. The 24.3% cell applies our latest process improvement and is measured in-house while ISFH CalTeC certification is pending.

Efficiency [%]	V_{oc} [mV]	J_{sc} [mA/cm²]	FF [%]	Rs [mΩcm²]
23.9	720	41.1	80.5	0.80
24.1	723	40.8	81.5	0.67
24.3	723	41.4	81.3	0.67

Kalyon PV has processed the first M10-sized p-type Ga-doped test wafers to apply and optimize the PERC+ production recipes for alkaline texturing, acidic polishing, wet chemical cleaning, and AlO_x/SiN front and rear passivation for POLO IBC. Double-sided textured and AlO_x/SiN-passivated wafers exhibit iV_{oc} values up to 731 mV. When adding rear polishing after texturing to the test wafer process sequence, first test wafers achieved an iV_{oc} value of only 687 mV. By optimizing the existing cleaning process post polishing and by selecting higher resistivity wafers with higher bulk lifetimes, the median iV_{oc} improves to 717 mV with a best iV_{oc} value of 727 mV as shown in Fig. 1. Hence, the iV_{oc} values obtained with Kalyon PV wet chemistry and AlO_x/SiN production tools are approaching the best POLO IBC iV_{oc} values of 740 mV obtained at ISFH SolarTeC [4,8]. As a next future step, Kalyon PV will process first complete POLO IBC solar cells using their M10 sized Cz wafers and PERC+ processing equipment with support by ISFH and assess the manufacturability via a small-scale pilot production.

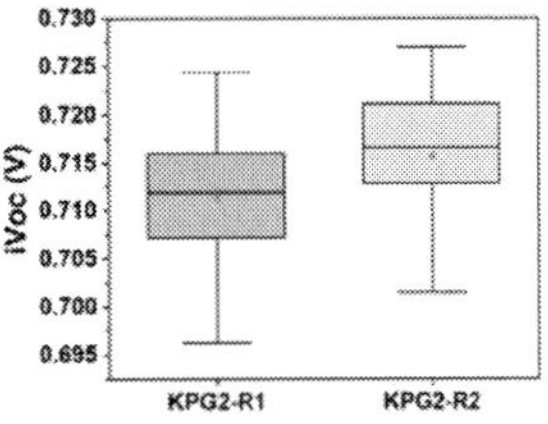

KPG2-R1: Wafer resistivity range is 1.0 Ωcm – 1.09 Ωcm

KPG2-R2: Wafer resistivity range is 1.1 Ωcm – 1.3 Ωcm

Figure 1: QSSPC measurement results of POLO IBC lifetime precursors processed at Kalyon PV using their Ga-doped M10 Cz wafers and their PERC+ mass production tools for wet chemistry, PECVD AlO_x/SiN, and firing. The lifetime samples achieve an implied V_{oc} up to 727 mV demonstrating a suitable surface passivation quality of the industrial process tools.

3 FUTURE UPGRADE TO 26% EFFICIENT POLO2 IBC CELLS

The POLO IBC cell efficiency is limited to below 25.5% by carrier recombination at the alloyed Al-BSF base contact as simulated in [5] and as evident from the large gap between $iV_{oc} = 740$ mV published in Ref. 4 and $V_{oc} = 723$ mV in Table 1. Hence, ISFH is developing an industrial $POLO^2$ IBC design with carrier selective n-poly-Si and p-poly-Si contacts.

ISFH applies the SiO_x/p-poly-Si process of Ref. 6 to develop a novel $POLO^2$ IBC solar cell processing sequence. Using mostly lab-type tools and p-type float zone silicon wafers, a small-area $POLO^2$ IBC solar cell with 25.5% efficiency has been developed at ISFH [9]. In this paper, we report for the first time results obtained with a novel industrial $POLO^2$ IBC process sequence displayed in Fig. 2 [7]. For this industrial approach, we choose M2-sized n-type Cz wafers due to their higher tolerance to Fe contamination and LeTID degradation and use solely industrial processing tools at the ISFH SolarTeC. We grow the SiO_x wet chemically and deposit the p-poly-Si layer in-situ-doped by LPCVD full-area (process steps 1 and 2 in Fig. 2). During the high-temperature poly-anneal in step 3 we use O_2 and hence grow a thin oxide layer on the p-poly-Si. We laser ablate the oxide and apply a KOH etch in steps 4 and 5 to locally remove the p-poly-Si and a few micrometer of the silicon substrate. The final HF dip in step 5 fully removes the barrier oxide. Afterwards we wet chemically grow the second interfacial oxide (step 5) and deposit the n-poly-Si in-situ doped by LPCVD (step 6). In the future, we plan to replace these two steps by an in-situ PECVD SiON/n-poly-Si deposition as published in [3]. In the subsequent high-temperature poly-Si anneal in step 7 we again use O_2 and grow a thin barrier oxide layer on the n-poly-Si. We remove the oxide layer from the front by a single sided etching step 8 and laser ablate the oxide on the rear side at the edges of the p-poly-Si in step 9. Hence, the following texture (step 10) removes the two poly-Si layers and interfacial oxide layers and textures the front side as well as the rear side where the barrier oxide has been removed. Thereby we form a textured trench region on the rear side where all poly layers are fully removed hence insulating the two solar cell polarities.

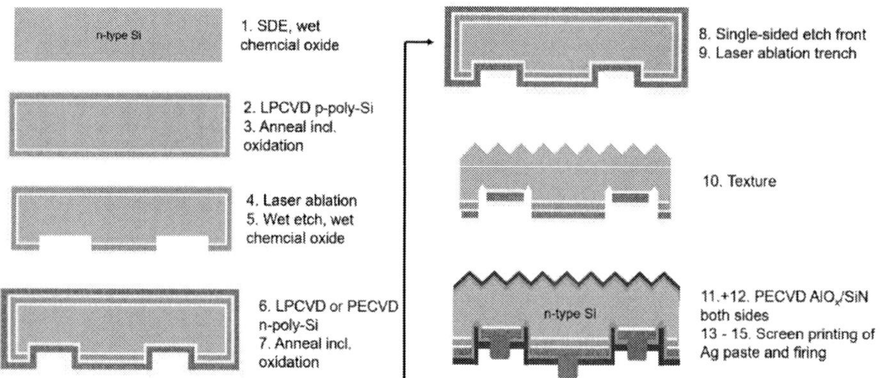

Figure 2: Schematic drawing of the novel industrial POLO^2 IBC process sequence [7]. We apply an oxide barrier formed in the n-poly-Si anneal, a subsequent laser ablation of the oxide barrier at the p-poly edges followed by a texture etch to remove the poly-Si layers in a narrow trench region in order to insulate the n-poly-Si base contact layer from the p-poly-Si/n-poly-Si emitter tunneling contact.

In the p-poly-Si emitter region the interfacial oxide and n-poly-Si layer form a tunneling contact with the p-poly-Si layer. The final HF dip post texture (step 10) removes the remaining barrier oxide from the rear side. Afterwards, we deposit AlO$_x$/SiN layer stacks on both sides (steps 11 + 12) and screen print Ag contacts on the rear side and fire the cells at around 800°C set temperature (steps 13 – 15).

We find the POLO^2 IBC process sequence in Fig. 2 to be a rather short and hence potentially cost-effective process sequences for manufacturing IBC solar cells with n-poly-Si and p-poly-Si passivating contacts. In addition, the trench insulation in steps 9 and 10 requires to laser only about 10% of the rear side wafer area whereas other IBC process sequences e.g. in Refs. 9, 10, 11 have to laser about 50% of the rear side area which is challenging in terms of laser process time and production throughput. Another benefit is that the novel POLO^2 IBC process sequence in Fig. 2 allows to use UV or alternatively cheaper green or IR lasers where the latter may create silicon defects at the wafer surface which are removed by the texture etch. In contrast, IBC process sequences e.g. in Refs. 9, 10, 11 laser on top of poly-Si layers without etching these layers and hence they have to strictly avoid creating laser damage in the silicon substrate which may limit the choice of suitable laser sources. Finally, both poly-Si polarities in Fig. 2 terminate with an n-poly-Si layer which allows to use the same screen printing paste for both solar cell metal polarities, e.g. an industry-typical TOPCon Ag paste.

To assess the passivation quality and V_{oc} potential of the novel industrial POLO^2 IBC process flow, we process test wafers as POLO^2 IBC solar cell precursors with the process sequence in Fig. 2 but without metal contacts using solely industrial processing tools at the ISFH SolarTeC. The test wafers mostly contain the IBC-typical interdigitated finger layout as sketched in Fig. 2. We add two 4 × 4 cm^2 areas on the wafer where we change the laser patterning processes to obtain a field representing the n-poly-Si base contact (top left) and another field representing the p-poly-Si/n-poly-Si emitter contact (bottom right). Figure 3 shows a photoluminescence (PL) image of the measured carrier lifetime t at an illumination intensity of 0.78 suns of the resulting test wafer with the POLO^2 IBC finger layout including the vertical busbar regions as well as the n-poly-Si only (top left) and p-poly-Si/n-poly-Si only (bottom right) fields. In these three different areas, we also measure the injection dependent lifetime by QSSPC thereby determining iV_{oc}, iFF and the surface J_0.

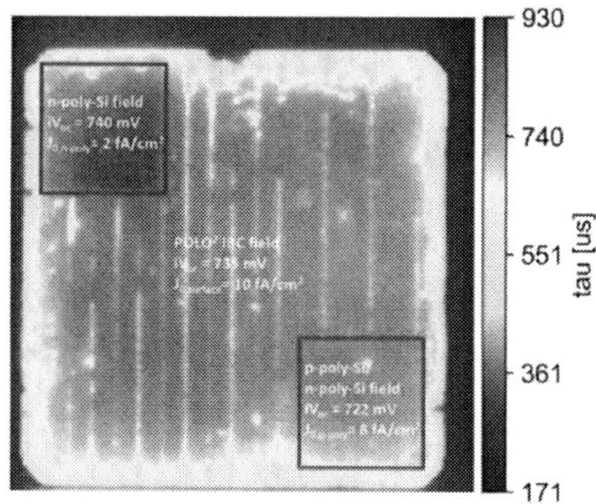

Figure 3: Photoluminescence (PL) mapping of the carrier lifetime τ of a M2-sized n-type Cz test wafer representing a POLO^2 IBC solar cell without metal contacts applying the novel process sequence in Fig. 2 revealing a promising iV_{oc} = 735 mV. The n-poly-Si field reveals an excellent $J_{0,n-poly}$ = 2 fA/cm^2 of the n-poly-Si base area. The p-poly-Si/n-poly-Si field corresponding to the p-poly-Si/n-poly-Si emitter area yields a $J_{0,p-poly}$ = 8 fA/cm^2 which is a bit higher than the best values Ref. 6.

As shown in Fig. 3, the POLO^2 IBC area yields an iV_{oc} up to 735 mV which is in-between the n-poly-Si field with iV_{oc} = 740 mV and the p-poly-Si/n-poly-Si field with 722 mV. The implied fill factor iFF of the POLO^2 IBC area ranges up to $iFF = 86.0\%$. To estimate the efficiency potential of the novel industrial $POLO^2$ IBC process sequence, we calculate the so-called implied efficiency $i\eta$ as follows

$$i\eta = iV_{oc} \times iFF \times J_{sc} / P_{light}$$
$$= 735 \text{ mV} \times 86.0\% \times 41.7 \text{ mA/cm}^2 / 100 \text{ mW/cm}^2$$
$$= 26.4\%$$

Here, we assume a $J_{sc} = 41{,}7$ mA/cm^2 which has been simulated for a $POLO^2$ IBC solar cell in Ref. 5. Due to the nature of the passivating poly-Si contacts, we target to maintain the good iV_{oc} value as V_{oc} value in the $POLO^2$ IBC cell when including screen-printed metal contacts by stopping the metal contact alloying within the poly-Si keeping the SiO_x passivation intact. However, the fill factor of the $POLO^2$ IBC cell including screen-printed metal contacts will be lower than the iFF due to additional resistive losses of the metallization. Nevertheless, we assess the measured iV_{oc} and iFF values in Fig. 3 as promising indication of an $POLO^2$ IBC efficiency potential of about 26%.

4 CONCLUSIONS

By optimizing the poly-Si annealing temperature, introducing contact pads for the IV test, and optimizing the anti-reflective coating, we obtained a new best POLO IBC cell efficiency of 24.3% processed at ISFH on M2-sized p-type wafers. With support by ISFH, Kalyon PV is currently transferring and implementing the POLO IBC process to their PERC+ cell manufacturing line using their in-house M10-sized Ga-doped Cz wafers. Textured, rear side polished and AlO_x/SiN passivated test wafers obtain an iV_{oc} up to 727 mV demonstrating a suitable passivation quality of Kalyon PVs wet chemistry and PECVD AlO_x/SiN production tools. Kalyon PV targets to process first M10-sized POLO IBC solar cells till end of 2025.

As a next IBC technology upgrade aiming at 26% efficiency, ISFH is currently developing a novel industrial processing sequence for $POLO^2$ IBC solar cells with n-poly-Si and p-poly-Si carrier selective contacts. The novel industrial processing sequence includes in-situ doped and full-area deposited poly-Si layers and laser-structuring of both poly-Si polarities in a novel IBC trench layout. Using solely industrial processing tools in our ISFH SolarTeC, M2 sized n-type Cz wafers, we measured $iV_{oc} = 735$ mV and $iFF = 86.0\%$ of $POLO^2$ IBC cell precursors processed without metal contacts. Since the poly-Si contacts minimize carrier recombination at metal contacts, the iV_{oc} value demonstrates the V_{oc} potential and an efficiency potential of up to 26.4% of this promising new $POLO^2$ IBC manufacturing process.

Acknowledgments

The authors thank the companies LPKF Laser & Electronics SE, Germany, for manufacturing the glass shadow masks, and TOYO ALUMINIUM K.K., Japan, for providing the aluminum paste. We thank Jan Krügener, Leibniz University Hannover, Germany, for support with LPCVD depositions. We thank our ISFH colleagues Karsten Bothe and Gerrit Lange for support with IV test chuck optimization, Tobias Neubert for laser recipe setup, and Welmoed Veurman for Quokka 3 simulations.

References

[1] T. Dullweber et al., presented at the SNEC Conference, Shanghai, China, 2021.
[2] V. Mertens et al., Proc. 38th Europ. Photovolt. Solar Energy Conf. (2021), pp. 135 - 139
[3] T. Dullweber et al., Proc. 8th World Conference on Photovoltaic Energy Conversion (2022), pp. 35 – 39
[4] T. Dullweber et al., Proc. 41st Europ. Photovolt. Solar Energy Conf. (2024), p. 020008
[5] C. N. Kruse et al., Scientific Reports, **11**, 996 (2021)
[6] E. Hoffmann et al., Proc. 41st Europ. Photovolt. Solar Energy Conf. (2024), p. 020020
[7] ISFH patents pending
[8] V. Mertens et al., Solar RRL **8**, 2300919 (2024)
[9] U. Römer et al, presented at the Silicon PV Conference (2025)
[10] J. Linke et al., Proc. 8th World Conference on Photovoltaic Energy Conversion (2022), pp. 102 – 106
[11] Aiko press release July 2025 available at: https://aikosolar.com/en/the-worlds-most-efficient-solar-technology/

USING A SHADOW MASK DURING GAS-PHASE ETCHING: A ONE-STEP PATTERNING METHOD FOR POLY-SILICON LAYERS

Laurent F. CLOCHARD[1], Yevgeniya LARIONOVA[2], Thorsten DULLWEBER[2]
[1] Nines Photovoltaics, Synergy Centre, TUD Tallaght Campus, D24A386 DUBLIN, Ireland
[2] ISFH, Institut für Solarenergieforschung GmbH Am Ohrberg 1, D-31860 Emmerthal, Germany

Abstract – This paper presents a convenient poly-silicon layer patterning technique, using a shadow mask during a gas-phase etching process. The etching is carried out at atmospheric pressure and delivers high throughput, single side processing and high selectivity, preserving the mask for multiple use and with potential for industrial application. This work was carried out in the context of the development of solar cell architectures beyond the standard TOPCon, where more sophisticated etching steps are required to accurately pattern poly-silicon layers across the wafer surface, in particular for the application of back contacted cells.
Keywords: silicon, solar cell, etching, manufacturing, patterning, IBC

1 Introduction

There is a strong interest in developing patterning processes for solar cells, enabling new cell architectures and increased efficiency. Passivated contacts have been successfully adopted by the industry in the standard TOPCON (Tunnel Oxide Passivated Contacts) process. In that scheme, the rear contacts are passivated using a tunnel oxide and doped poly-silicon stack across the whole wafer surface. Poly-Si layers lead to parasitic absorption, while the TOPCON stack is only needed under the contacts ; hence the requirement for accurate patterning of the layers. Similarly, IBC cells also require localized interdigitated poly-silicon layers at the rear side. Existing patterning processes can be cumbersome, using multiple steps, typically involving the deposition of a masking layer, that subsequently needs to be removed. This paper explores a simplified, single step patterning process.

We investigate the patterning of poly-Si using a shadow mask within a single sided gas-phase etching process, to locally remove the poly-Si from the unwanted areas. This gaseous etching process, referred as ADE (for Atmospheric Dry Etching) has been used previously for texturing applications of multi-crystalline wafer [1], and for the poly-Si wrap-around removal produced by industrial deposition tools such as LPCVD and PECVD tools [2] and was originally designed to suit the industrial requirements of cell manufacturing (low cost, high throughput). In a recent publication [3], we have shown that this etching process has very high selectivity, and that this characteristic can be leveraged to devise several methods and strategies for patterning. The figure below summaries the various options.

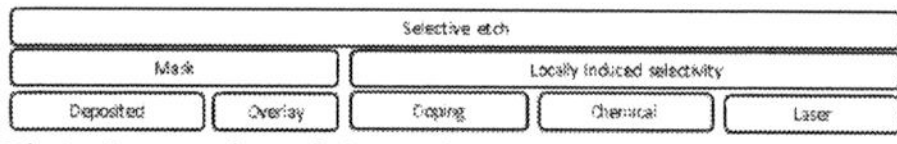

Fig1. Summaries of the various routes toward patterning with gas-phase etch ADE

The process options can be divided in two main strands: schemes using masks, and schemes designed to locally induce etching selectivity. In this work, we will focus on the use of a mask. Our previous publication [3] showed results from a deposited SiOx mask, while this time we will focus on using a physical overlay, commonly referred as "shadow mask", as sometimes used in deposition processes: the mask creates a shadow, protecting specific areas of the substrate from deposition. In our etching application, we will rely on the mask to preserve an existing layer from being etched away. To generate the same patterning outcome, the etch mask design should therefore be the negative version of the deposition mask design (cf fig 2).

Potential advantages of using a shadow mask within an etching process when compared to deposition include : the mask can be used a large number of time (providing the material is selected to provide high etch selectivity), and does not need to be cleaned; for very small narrow area of removal, it might be more efficient to etch ; the inline nature of the process enables easy application/removal of the masks on the wafer, resulting in easier handling and less breakage. The choice of one method or another will depend on the overall impacts of these factors.

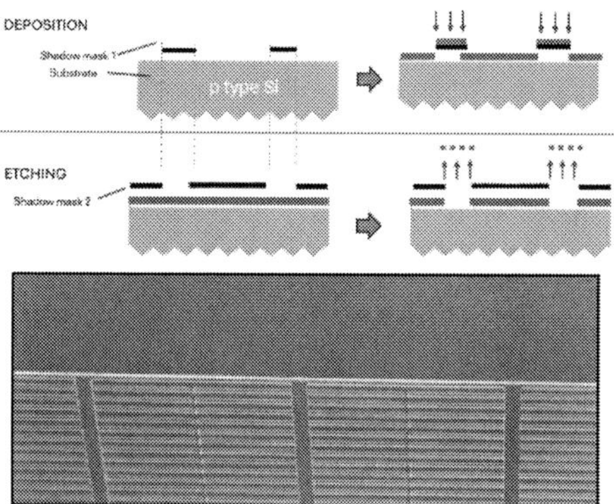

Fig.2 Schematic of shadow mask usage in deposition process (a) and etching process (negative version)(b) and a picture of the mask pattern (c).

2 Materials and method

The shadow mask is made of glass. The mask was provided and used by ISFH in previous publications [4] and originally made by the German company LPKF AG, using their proprietary Laser-Induced Deep Etching glass structuring technology [5]. The thinnest branches of the mask had a 250um width, while the larger branches were in the 950um range. The openings had a width of 750um (fig.2c). Although the mask pattern for etching should be the negative version of a mask designed for deposition, we used the same deposition mask in these experiments.

For this set of experiments, p-type Cz wafers of M2 sizes

were used. After saw damage removal, an 80nm layer of SiNx was deposited (PECVD, Centrotherm) at the front side of the wafer. Then both side were deposited with approximately 150nm of a-Si:H. The presence of the SiNx layer at the front gives the wafer a vivid color, with variations directly proportional to the a-Si:H layer thickness. It can be seen (fig 3.) that the deposition was not fully uniform (color variation from pink to green).

Prior to ADE etching, the wafers are pre-cleaned in a 5%HF solution for 1 minutes, followed by 5 minutes D.I. rinsing, and 10 minutes drying in a 95%Nitrogen gas flow at 80degC, to remove any native oxide or mild contaminations.

The mask was manually positioned directly on top of the wafer, then the ensemble is placed on the conveyor belt of the gas-phase etching tool, held by vacuum suction. The wafer is then conveyed inside the process chamber and etched through the Atmospheric Dry Etching reactor (ADE). The etch rate is directly affected by temperature and gas concentration. We used a low concentration of 2%F2 in N2 carrier gas in order to better control the process, and a reactor temperature of 190 degC while varying the time of etching.

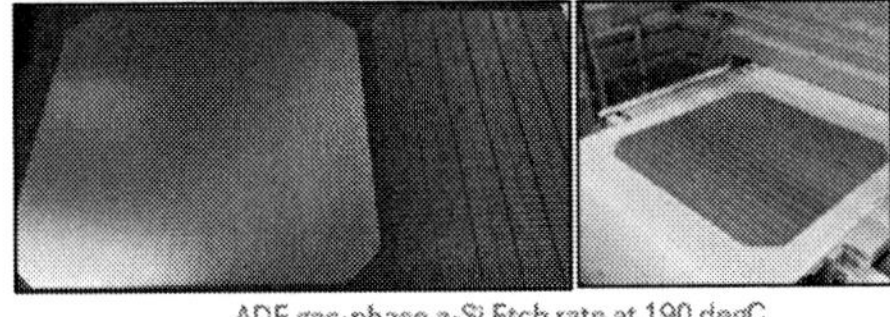

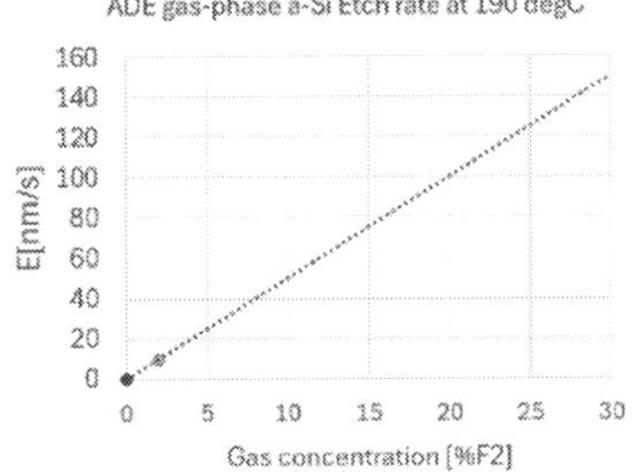

Fig.3 a)Wafer before etching (left), and shadow mask(right) b) ADE process etch rate vs gas concentration c) Wafer + mask positioned on belt before entering the ADE reactor

3 Results

Wafers were initially etched without mask to find the duration required for full removal of the layer. Partially etched wafers were used to highlight the color variation range. After some process tunning adjusting the etch process duration, patterns started to appear. Results below are for etching time of approximately 16 seconds. The SiNx layer underneath the poly layer provides a good contrast and enables straightforward visual inspection of the sample. The area with remaining poly can clearly be seen, and any color variation indicates a variation of the a-Si:H thickness layer. The SiNx layer appears as a dark yellow color.

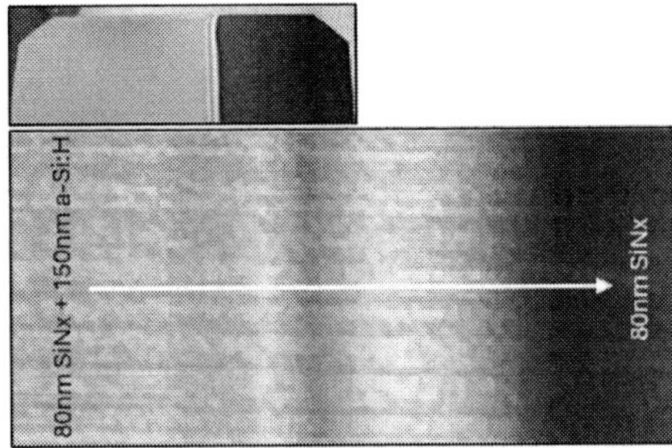

Fig. 4 Partially etched wafers, showing a range of colors related to the a-Si:H layer thickness

The etching time is varied in order to avoid over or under etching, and identify the process window. The wafer was analyzed with optical microscope imaging, and the variation of the remaining a-Si "fingers" width were measured across various areas.

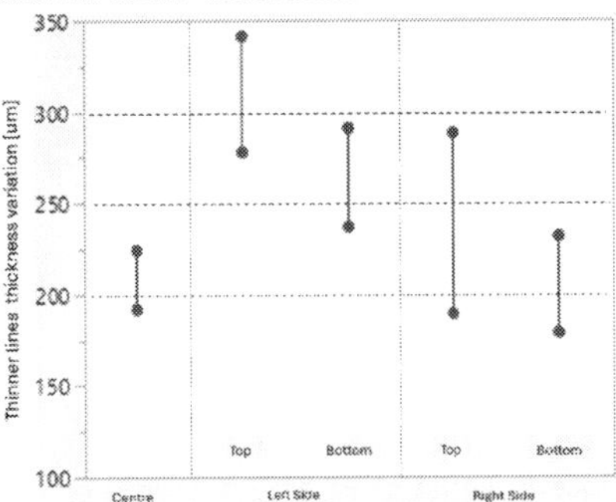

Fig.7 Width variations of the thinner masked section (250um), for the SiNx+a-Si:H stack

Fig.6 optical microscope images of the patterned a-Si:H layer post etching showing larger and thinner masked sections ; Areas on the patterned wafer with 80nm SiNx + 150nm a-Si:H stack

3 Discussion

There are some obvious variations across the wafers that are related to a number of aspects including: homogeneity of the a-Si:H starting layer, homogeneity of the gas flow, flatness of the wafer surface and flatness of the mask (both at the microscopic level and across the wafer width).

One would expect that since the ADE gas-phase process is anisotropic in the conditions used in this experiment, the amount of lateral etching should be comparable to the overall thickness of the a-Si:H layer removed (vertical etching). However, the measured width variation of the thinner masked section is several order of magnitude larger (~50um) compared to the thickness of the a-Si layer being etched (150nm). We also noted that the thinner features disappeared very quickly if the process duration was extended. We therefore look at understanding the impact of the SiNx layer.

Impact of the SiNx under-layer:

The SiNx layer has a much lower etch rate than a-Si:H(~200 times less), and acts as an etch stop. We can divide the process into 2 phases, before and after the etch stop has been reached and analyze the process conditions. In the first phase, there is a large area of a-Si:H exposed through the opening of the mask. During that phase, we can assume both vertical and lateral etch rates are equal (anisotropic), with a given etch rate E1 (fig.9). When the process reaches the SiNx layer, the area that can react with the gas is suddenly dramatically reduced, only the vertical sides of the remaining a-Si located under the glass mask are being etched. Since the incoming etching gas flow has not changed when compared to phase 1, there is now much more unreacted gas molecules available to react with the sidewall area. This directly impact the etch rate. We can therefore argue that in this second phase, the etch rate is higher.

Fig. 9 Schematic describing the two process phases and impact on etch rates and width of features

Taking a single unit of the mask and assuming vertical walls, we calculated a theoretical ratio of more than 2,000 between the exposed area of the two etch phases. If we apply that factor to the overall average etch rate of 10 nm/s measured (based on the a-Si:H layer thickness and the process duration), this would mean that the fingers side walls could be etched at a rate close to 20,000 nm/s during Phase 2 of the etch process. This order of magnitudes tally with the range of finger width variations we have measured.

This artefact from the SiNx layer can therefore have a significant impact on our results. We conclude that although using SiNx as an underlayer is convenient to easily visualize the a-Si:H etch thickness variation, it is not suitable to assess the suitability of the process of delivering consistent feature width. We expect a much wider process window, and lower impact on sidewalls, when the a-Si under-layer has similar etch rates as the poly-Si itself. Additional experiments (fig.10) were conducted on wafers with only a layer of a-Si:H directly on top of c-Si and even though a systematic analysis was not carried out at the time of writing, visual inspection seems to confirm that the finger width is much more consistent in that case, and that the process window can be extended. Visual inspection is less straightforward without the underlying SiNx layer, but the pattern can be observed under low angle light exposure.

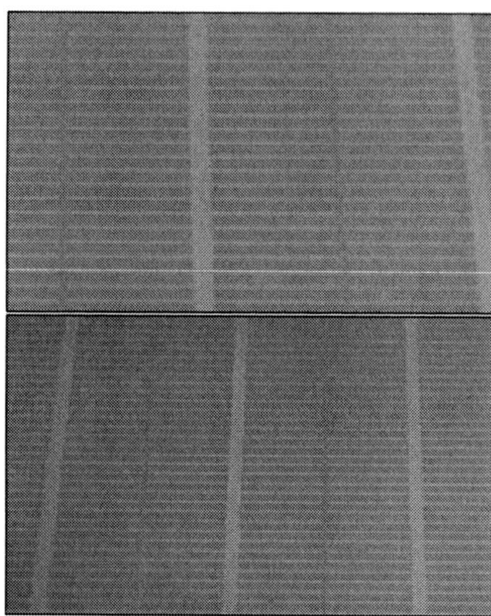

Fig. 10 Patterning obtained from wafers with a-Si:H deposited on c-Si wafers (without SiNx underlayer)

Passivated contacts typically have a thin tunnel oxide layer locate below the poly-Si layer, but this should not in principle be an issue as such layers have pinholes and previous experiments have shown that they can be etched away by the ADE gas-phase process [6]. Follow on experiment will still need to be confirming the impact of such layer in the context of this work however.
Shadowing Efficiency: The etching gas is still reaching across the whole surface of the wafer, since the color is changing when compared to the unetched sample. We can also observe that the wider features of the glass tend to protect better the poly-layer, indicating that there is an edge effect from the glass feature, that is not proportional to the glass width. The chamfer applied to the glass edges might also impact the corner sharpness of the masking.
The surface of the wafer itself would also have an impact on how easily the gas can diffuse below the mask. The wafer used had a typical saw damaged removal surface, presenting large shallow square pits leftover of inverted pyramids created by the KOH wet process. A more polished surface would improve the masking efficiency, but it remains to be seen if it has an impact on the cell device performance.

4 Conclusion
A single side gas-phase etching process was evaluated, using a thin glass mask to pattern a poly-silicon layer for advanced solar cell architecture applications. A pattern could be created in a single process step, in less than 20 seconds. The influence of an underlying 80nm thick SiNx layer on the resulting feature width was analyzed, and found to be detrimental. Further experiments are required to qualify the process at a cell level.

References
[1] B. Kafle, T. Freund, S. Werner, J. Schon, A. Lorenz, A. Wolf, L. Clochard, E. Duffy, P. Saint-Cast, M. Hofmann, J. Rentsch, IEEE J. Photovoltaics. 2017 7, 136, DOI: 10.1109/JPHOTOV.2016.2626921.

[2] Kafle B., Mack S., Teßmann C., Bashardoust S.,

Clochard L., Duffy E., Wolf A., Hofmann M. and Rentsch J. 2022 Sol. RRL 6 2100481

[3] Clochard l. & al, GAS PHASE, SELECTIVE ETCHING OF POLY-SILICON FOR LAYER PATTERNING, Proceedings of the European Photovoltaic Solar Energy Conference and Exhibition, 2024

[4] Verena Mertens & al., LOCAL PECVD SIOXNY/N-POLY-SI DEPOSITION THROUGH A SHADOW MASK FOR POLO IBC SOLAR CELLS, Proceeding of the 38th European Photovoltaic Solar Energy Conference and Exhibition, 2021

[5] M. Stöhr et al., Proc. 37th EUPVSEC, 521-524 (2020).

[6] PATTERNING BY SELECTIVE ETCHING OF POLY-SILICON USING A HIGH ETCH RATE SINGLE SIDED GASEOUS PROCESS, L. Clochard, D. Young, Mingzhe Yu, S. Bonilla, 2024, DOI: 10.52825/siliconpv.v2i.1317

UV STABLE PASSIVATION STACK WITH PLASMA-ENHANCED ATOMIC LAYER DEPOSITION OF ALUMINIUM OXIDE FROM AN INDUSTRIAL TUBE-TYPE DIRECT PLASMA-ENHANCED CHEMICAL VAPOR DEPOSITION SYSTEM

B. Min[1], C. Hollemann[1], S. Junge[1], V. X. Nguyen[2], T. Pernau[2], D. Seiffert[2], H. Haverkamp[2], T. Dullweber[1], V. Mertens[1], H. Schulte-Huxel[1] and R. Brendel[1, 3]

[1]Institute for Solar Energy Research Hamelin (ISFH), 31860 Emmerthal, Germany
[2]centrotherm international AG, 89143 Blaubeuren, Germany
[3]Dep. Solar Energy, Inst. Solid-State Physics, Leibniz University of Hannover, 30167 Hannover, Germany

ABSTRACT: We implement the plasma-enhanced atomic layer deposition (PEALD) of AlO_x layers in an industrial tube-type plasma-enhanced chemical vapor deposition (PECVD) system with a direct plasma source. Its surface passivation qualities on the boron-diffused textured surface of n-type silicon wafers and on the undiffused textured surface of p-type silicon wafers are investigated by varying the process parameters. The study shows that the number of ALD cycles is one of the essential parameters for achieving high passivation quality on the boron-diffused textured surface of n-type wafers. We achieve a surface recombination current density J_{0s} of 3.6 fA/cm^2, extracted from lifetime measurements with a device simulation by considering a measured electrically active dopant depth profile. In contrast, the number of ALD cycles shows no impact on the surface passivation quality on the undiffused textured surface of p-type wafers. In both cases, we achieve a passivation quality which is on the same level as our reference with a PEALD AlO_x layer, deposited with a lab-scale ALD tool. Our tube-type PEALD AlO_x/PECVD SiN_y passivation stack is integrated at the cell front side of a p-type back junction (BJ) solar cell featuring n^+-type passivating polysilicon on oxide (POLO) contacts. Its cell performance is on the same level as the reference group with PECVD AlO_x/SiN_y passivation stack. The UV stability is investigated by exposing cell precursors to ultraviolet light with a dose of 4.5 kWh/m^2. While the PECVD AlO_x/SiN_y passivation stack shows a significant degradation of the measured effective lifetime and the implied open-circuit voltage, the passivation quality of tube-type PEALD AlO_x/PECVD SiN_y passivation stack is stable.
Keywords: PECVD, aluminum oxide, surface passivation, passivating contacts, poly-Si, UV stability, TOPCon

1 INTRODUCTION

The plasma-enhanced atomic layer deposition (PEALD) is currently widely applied for the deposition of aluminum oxide (AlO_x) to passivate the surface of highly efficient industrial solar cells such as TOPCon (tunnel oxide passivated contact) solar cells. Its unique advantages are, in particular, precise thickness control, excellent uniformity and conformity compared to other deposition techniques [1].

On the other hand, the tube-type plasma-enhanced chemical vapor deposition (PECVD) tool is the most used and well-established equipment in PV industry, especially for the deposition of silicon nitride (SiN_y) or also for the deposition of poly-Si layers to fabricate passivating contacts.

The realization of PEALD AlO_x deposition with the tube-type PECVD tool is a very attractive idea for the PV industry, since it will use all the advantages of the ALD technique combined with the benefits of the tube-type PECVD tool such as lower equipment cost and high throughput. Furthermore, no ALD system will be needed in the production line, which reduces the investment cost, maintenance efforts as well as the wafer breakage between different systems. Liao et al. demonstrated the implementation of PEALD AlO_x deposition in an industrial tube-type PECVD tool (LeadMicro, ZR5000), achieving 24.3 % as the best efficiency of their fabricated TOPCon solar cells [1].

In this work, we independently validate the implementation of PEALD AlO_x deposition in an industrial tube-type PECVD system (centrotherm, cPLASMA 2600) from a different equipment manufacturer. Compared to the previous publication of Liao et al., we investigate the impact of the number of

ALD cycles on the passivation quality, different surfaces, such as undiffused textured p-type wafer surfaces, and the application of the combination of PEALD AlO_x and PECVD AlO_x to reduce the process duration. Finally, the developed passivation stack is applied in the fabrication of p-type back junction (BJ) solar cells featuring n^+-type passivating polysilicon on oxide (POLO) contacts and its UV stability is investigated.

2 EXPERIMENTAL

For the first part of this work, we investigate the passivation quality by fabricating symmetric lifetime samples on phosphorus-doped and gallium-doped Cz-Si wafers featuring boron-diffused and undiffused random-pyramid-textured surfaces, respectively. After a firing step at a set temperature of 800 °C, the samples are characterized using a Sinton lifetime tester (WCT-120). We measure each wafer at five different positions (center and four corners). In the second part of the paper, we fabricate POLO BJ solar cells using gallium-doped p-type Cz-Si wafers to validate the developed tube-type PEALD AlO_x/PECVD SiN_y passivation stack. Its UV stability is investigated by measuring the lifetimes of POLO BJ solar cell precursors (cells without metallization) before and after exposition to UV light.

3 RESULTS

3.1 Passivation quality on n-type Cz-Si wafers with boron-diffused textured surfaces

Figure 1 shows the effective carrier lifetimes (τ_{eff}) at an injection level Δn of 10^{15} cm^{-3} and the emitter

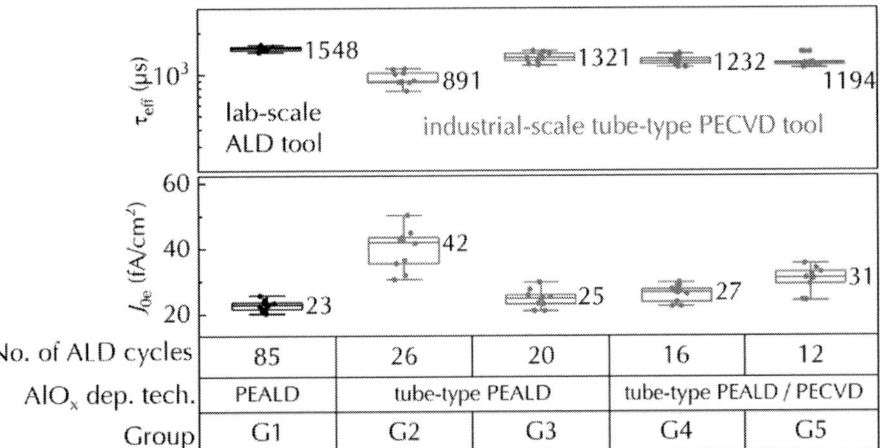

Figure 1 τ_{eff} at the injection level of $\Delta n = 10^{15}$ cm^{-3} and J_{0e} of symmetric n-type Cz-Si samples with boron-diffused random-pyramid-textured surfaces.

recombination current densities (J_{0e}) of symmetric lifetime samples with boron-diffused textured surfaces on n-type wafers. The box height spans from the first to the third quartile (also known as interquartile range [IQR]), and the whiskers indicate the maximum and minimum of 1.5×IQR beyond the box. The numbers next to the boxes give the median values. The colors of boxplots indicate different equipment for the AlO$_x$ deposition. The reference group G1 is passivated with 10-nm-thick PEALD AlO$_x$ layers deposited with a lab-scale ALD tool (FlexAL ALD, Oxford instruments) which is our best-known method with this tool. The groups G2 – G5 receive PEALD AlO$_x$ layer deposited with an industrial tube-type PECVD tool (centrotherm, cPLASMA 2600). The deposition rate is 0.125 nm/cycle, the pulse duration for TMA and O$_2$ plasma is 4 s. We apply various number of ALD cycles between 12 – 26 as indicated in Figure 1. For the groups G4 and G5 we deposit additionally a 2 nm-thick PECVD AlO$_x$ layer on top of tube-type PEALD AlO$_x$ layer. Finally, we then deposit 75-nm-thick SiN$_y$ layer on all samples using the same PECVD tool. With 20 ALD cycles of tube-type PEALD AlO$_x$, we achieve 20.9 fA/cm^2 as the lowest J_{0e} value in the group G3. In order to distinguish the contribution of the emitter bulk and the textured surface to the measured J_{0e} value, we first measure the depth profile of the boron emitter with electrochemical capacitance-voltage profiler (WEP, CVP21) as shown in Figure 2 with a sheet resistance of 140 Ω/□. Subsequently, we apply it in the simulation software EDNA 2 from PV Lighthouse. We then vary the surface recombination current density J_{0s} [2] to reproduce the measured J_{0e} value. The simulation results in a J_{0s} value of 3.6 fA/cm^2, indicating the excellent surface passivation quality of developed tube-type PEALD AlO$_x$/PECVD SiN$_y$ passivation stack on boron-diffused textured surfaces.

Based on the simulation analysis, we optimize as the next step our boron diffusion process by adjusting the BBr$_3$ flow, deposition temperature, temperature and duration of the drive-in and post-oxidation step. Figure 2 shows the measured electrically active boron dopant concentration before and after our optimization of the boron diffusion process with a sheet resistance (R_{sheet}) of 140 Ω/□ and 350 Ω/□, respectively. The peak boron concentration at surface is successfully reduced from $4×10^{19}$ cm^{-3} to $\sim10^{19}$ cm^{-3}. Figure 3 shows the measured τ_{eff} and J_{0e} of symmetric textured n-type Cz-Si samples with optimized boron emitter. Herein, we apply the PEALD AlO$_x$ from the lab-scale ALD tool as a reference and tube-type PEALD AlO$_x$ from the industrial PECVD tool which corresponds the groups G1 and G3 in the previous section.

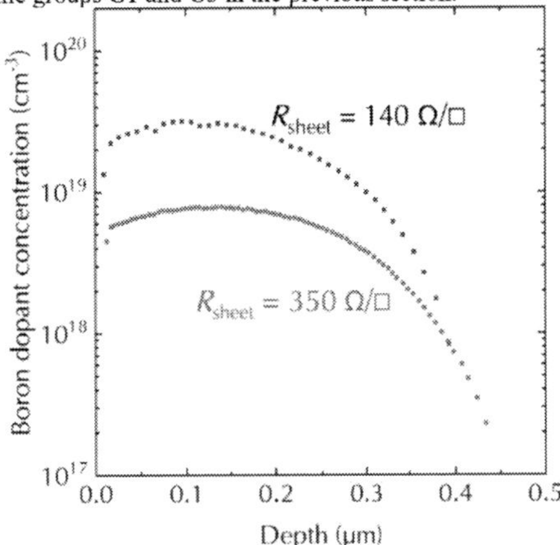

Figure 2: Measured electrically active boron dopant concentrations before and after boron diffusion optimization with a sheet resistance of 140 Ω/□ and 350 Ω/□, respectively.

Compared to our previous results, as depicted as G3 in Figure 1, the surface passivation quality improves by nearly 50 % with the optimized boron emitter. The median J_{0e} value reduces from 25 fA/cm^2 to 13 fA/cm^2 and the median τ_{eff} increases from 1321 μs to 2455 μs. Furthermore, the comparison with the reference demonstrates that the passivation quality of the tube-type PEALD AlO$_x$ is on the same level as that of the PEALD AlO$_x$ layer fabricated with a lab-scale tool.

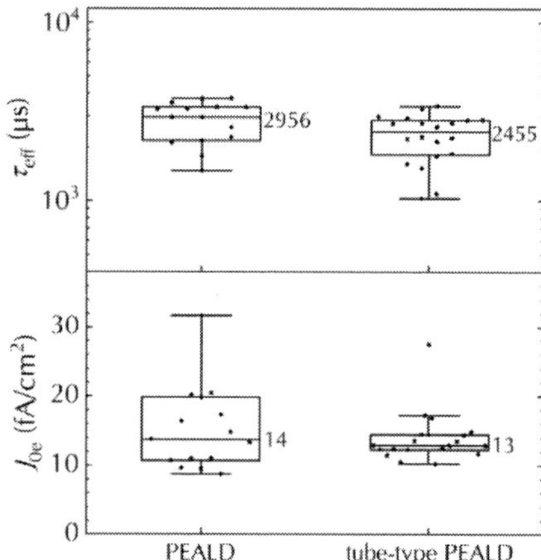

Figure 3: τ_{eff} at the injection level of $\Delta n = 10^{15}$ cm^{-3} and J_{0e} of symmetric textured n-type Cz-Si samples with optimized boron emitter

3.2 Passivation quality on p-type wafers with undiffused textured surfaces

Figure 4**Fehler! Verweisquelle konnte nicht gefunden werden.** shows the measured τ_{eff} at an injection level of 10^{15} cm^{-3} and J_{0s} values of p-type wafers on undiffused textured surfaces. It is to note that J_{0s} is equal to J_{0e} in this case since the samples have no diffused emitter. The resistivity of the Ga-doped p-type Cz-Si wafers is 0.85 Ωcm. Hence, the well-known slope method by Kane and Swanson [3] cannot be applied since the base is in low injection during illumination with the flash lamp from the Sinton lifetime tester. We therefore extract the J_{0s} values by reproducing the measured injection-dependent lifetime curves with the device simulation software Quokka 3. We vary the SRH lifetime parameters in the bulk and the J_{0s} until we achieve an agreement between measured and simulation lifetime curve for an injection level range between 2×10^{14} cm^{-3} and 2×10^{16} cm^{-3}. All

groups with tube-type PEALD AlO$_x$ show J_{0s} values on the same level as the reference group G1. The median J_{0s} values corresponds well with J_{0s} values extracted from n-type samples with boron-diffused textured surface in the previous section. However, the τ_{eff} values of the groups with tube-type PEALD AlO$_x$ are slightly lower than that of the reference group. In contrast to the results with n-type samples, the iV_{oc} values are nearly unaffected by different numbers of ALD cycles. Also, the additional PECVD AlO$_x$ layer on top of the tube-type PEALD AlO$_x$ layer seems to have no impact on the passivation quality.

3.3 Cell results

We fabricate POLO back junction (BJ) solar cells as depicted in Figure 5. More details and the advantage of this cell concept were presented in our previous work [4]. The busbarless cells are measured with a LOANA tool from pv-tools applying a contacting scheme that neglects the resistance of the metal grid [5].

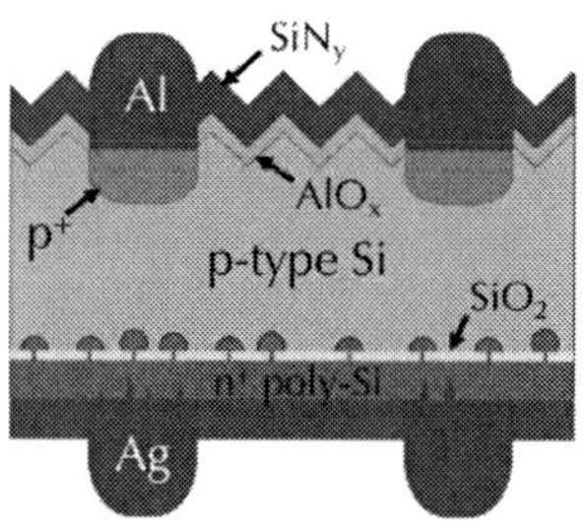

Figure 5: Schematic of a POLO BJ solar cell [3]

Figure 6 shows the IV parameters of POLO BJ solar cells featuring tube-type PEALD AlO$_x$/PECVD SiN$_y$ passivation stack depicted as black box plot. As a reference, the red box plot shows the IV parameters of POLO BJ solar cells featuring PECVD AlO$_x$/SiN$_y$ passivation stack. The efficiencies of both groups are on the same level while the group with tube-type PEALD AlO$_x$/PECVD SiN$_y$ shows slightly higher open-circuit

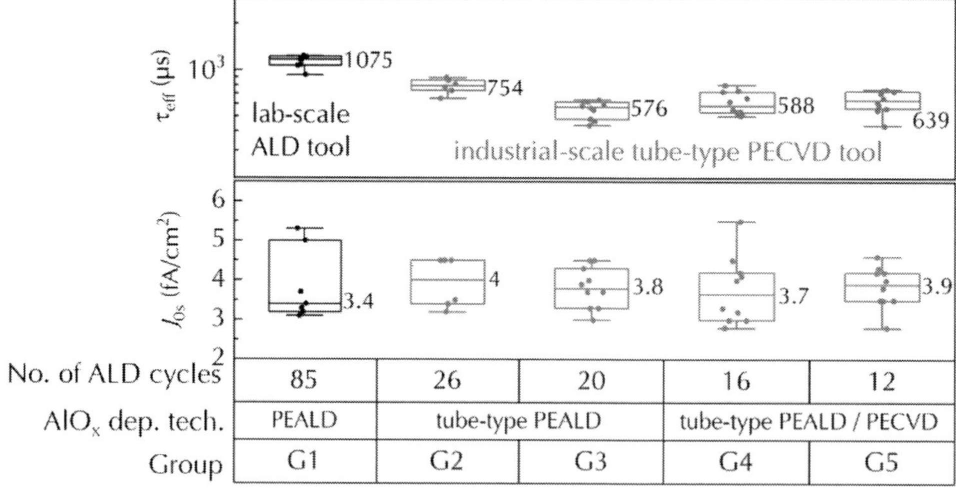

	G1	G2	G3	G4	G5
No. of ALD cycles	85	26	20	16	12
AlO$_x$ dep. tech.	PEALD	tube-type PEALD		tube-type PEALD / PECVD	
Group	G1	G2	G3	G4	G5

Figure 4 τ_{eff} at the injection level of $\Delta n = 10^{15}$ cm^{-3} and J_{0s} of symmetric p-type samples with undiffused textured surfaces

voltage (V_{oc}) and short-circuit current density (J_{sc}).

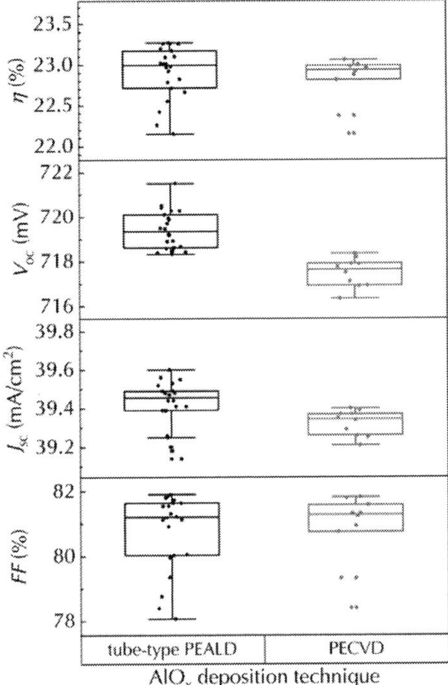

Figure 6: Measured *IV* parameters of POLO BJ solar cells featuring an AlO$_x$ layer deposited with tube-type PEALD and PECVD deposition techniques.

It is worth to note that both groups show excellent surface passivation qualities with a median iV_{oc} of 735 mV and 733 mV, respectively, measured on cell precursors (cells without metallization) using the Sinton lifetime tester as shown in Figure 1. In the finished solar cell, the V_{oc} is about 15 mV lower and hence the efficiencies are also decreased. One reason for the decrease is a strong deterioration of passivating POLO contacts at the rear side due to Ag-spiking, as depicted in the schematic in Figure 5. We are currently working on the avoidance such Ag-spiking by applying different Ag pastes and by adjusting the dielectric layer thickness. This optimization has already been successfully carried out in our previous work with a different Ag paste [6].

3.4 UV stability

The UV stability of the developed passivation stack is investigated by exposing the cell precursors (cells without metallization) to UV light for 24 hours, which corresponds to a UV dose of 4.5 kWh/m². The wavelengths range from 290 nm to 400 nm. The cell precursors are fabricated together with the solar cells presented in Figure 6. The samples were not encapsulated and not covered with any glass pane, hence the UV exposure to the cell is much stronger than the usual standard test with modules. Figure 7 shows the measured τ_{eff} and iV_{oc} values of POLO BJ cell precursors before and after UV exposure. The POLO BJ precursors featuring PECVD AlO$_x$/SiN$_y$ show a strong degradation in τ_{eff} as well as in iV_{oc}. In contrast, the values of the samples with tube-type PEALD AlO$_x$/PECVD SiN$_y$ are nearly unchanged, demonstrating their strongly

improved UV stability. More detailed studies on the UV stability on the module level will be presented in a separate publication [7].

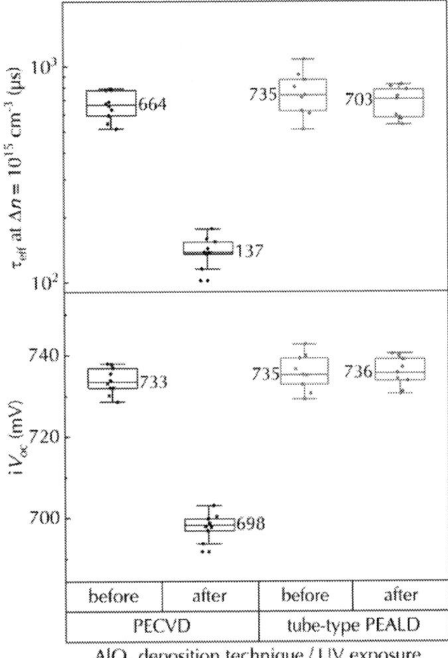

Figure 7: Impact of UV exposure on POLO BJ cell precursors without metallization featuring PECVD AlO$_x$/PECVD SiN$_y$ and tube-type PEALD AlO$_x$/PECVD SiN$_y$ front side passivation stack

4   CONCLUSIONS

We have demonstrated the application of tube-type PEALD AlO$_x$/PECVD SiN$_y$ passivation stacks for the application to high efficiency silicon solar cells. We investigated the impact of the number of ALD cycles on the passivation quality on textured surfaces of n-type and p-type Cz-Si wafers. In addition, we showed that the combination of the tube-type PEALD AlO$_x$ and PECVD AlO$_x$ is an attractive option to reduce the processing time.

On boron-diffused textured surfaces of n-type wafers, the number of ALD cycles is a crucial parameter to achieve a high passivation quality. By applying 20 ALD cycles, we achieve a median J_{0e} value of 13 fA/cm² with an optimized boron emitter featuring a sheet resistance of 350 Ω/□. In contrast to this, the number of ALD cycles shows no impact on the passivation quality on undiffused textured surfaces on p-type silicon wafers, resulting a median J_{0s} values around 4 fA/cm².

The developed tube-type PEALD AlO$_x$/PECVD SiN$_y$ passivation stack was successfully implemented into POLO BJ solar cells. Our development led to a notable increase in V_{oc} and J_{sc} compared to the PECVD AlO$_x$/PECVD SiN$_y$ passivation stack.

Finally, the UV exposure of the cell precursors shows that the tube-type PEALD AlO$_x$ layer is UV stable, while the PECVD AlO$_x$ layer degrades strongly under UV exposure.

Our development enables the reduction of cell

fabrication cost as well as the increase of PV module energy yield, since it is more UV stable. This can reduce the fabrication cost of all solar cells with AlO_x layer on the front side (e.g. POLO BJ or TOPCon solar cells).

[1] B. Liao, X. Wu, W. Wu, C. Liu, S. Ma, S. Wang, T. Xie, Q. Wang, Z. Du, W. Shen, X. Li, W. Li, B. Hoex. "Tube-type plasma-enhanced atomic layer deposition of aluminum oxide: Enabling record lab performance for the industry with demonstrated cell efficiencies >24%", Prog. Photovoltaics 31, 52-61 (2023).

[2] K.R. McIntosh, L.E. Black. "On effective surface recombination parameters", J. Appl. Phys. 116, - (2014).

[3] D. Kane, R. Swanson. "Measurement of the emitter saturation current by a contactless photoconductivity decay method", Proc. of the 18th IEEE Photovoltaic Specialist Conference, New York, 1985, pp. 578-583.

[4] B. Min, V. Mertens, Y. Larionova, T. Pernau, H. Haverkamp, T. Dullweber, R. Peibst, B. R. "24.2 %-efficient POLO back junction solar cell with industrial PECVD AlO_x/SiN_y passivation", Proc. of the 40th European Photovoltaic Solar Energy Conference and Exhibition, Lisbon, Portugal, 2023.

[5] K. Bothe, C. Kruse, D. Hinken. "Contacting of busbarless solar cells for accurate I-V measurements", Proc. of the 37th European Photovoltaic Solar Energy Conference and Exhibition, Online event, 2020.

[6] B. Min, N. Wehmeier, T. Brendemuehl, F. Haase, Y. Larionova, L. Nasebandt, H. Schulte-Huxel, R. Peibst, R. Brendel. "716 mV Open-Circuit Voltage with Fully Screen-Printed p-Type Back Junction Solar Cells Featuring an Aluminum Front Grid and a Passivating Polysilicon on Oxide Contact at the Rear Side", Solar RRL 5, 2000703 (2021).

[7] C. Hollemann, B. Min, V.X. Nguyen, T. Pernau, D. Seiffert, H. Haverkamp, R. Brendel, H. Schulte-Huxel. "UV Stability of Aluminum Oxide Fabricated with Tube-Type Plasma-Enhanced Atomic Layer Deposition", Solar RRL n/a, 202500510 (2025).

UV stable passivation stack with PEALD aluminum oxide from an industrial tube-type PECVD system

B. Min[1], C. Hollemann[1], S. Junge[1], V. X. Nguyen[2], T. Pernau[2], D. Seiffert[2], H. Haverkamp[2], T. Dullweber[1], V. Mertens[1], H. Schulte-Huxel[1] and R. Brendel[1, 3]

[1]Institute for Solar Energy Research Hamelin (ISFH), Germany

[2]centrotherm international AG, Germany

[3]Dep. Solar Energy, Inst. Solid-State Physics, Leibniz University Hannover, Germany

Motivation

**Plasma-enhanced
atomic layer deposition (PEALD) technique**

- Widely applied for AlO_x deposition
- Precise thickness control and excellent uniformity and conformity

**Tube-type plasma-enhanced
chemical vapor deposition (PECVD) equipment**

- Most used and well-established equipment in PV industry (SiN_y, poly-Si, …)
- Low equipment cost and high throughput

020009-002

Tube-type PEALD

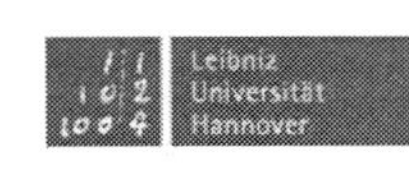

Plasma-enhanced atomic layer deposition (**PEALD**) technique

- Widely applied for AlO_x deposition
- Precise thickness control and excellent uniformity and conformity

Tube-type plasma-enhanced chemical vapor deposition (**PECVD**) equipment

- Most used and well-established equipment in PV industry (SiN_y, poly-Si, …)
- Low equipment cost and high throughput

PEALD AlO_x deposition with the tube-type PECVD tool (**tube-type PEALD**)

- PEALD & PECVD with a same tool → no need for ALD system in the production
- Less investment cost, maintenance efforts as well as the wafer breakage between different systems
- First demonstration by Liao et al. with (LeadMicro, ZR5000), 24.3 %-efficient TOPCon solar cell[1]

[1] B. Liao et al., Prog. Photovoltaics 31, 52-61 (2023)

020009-003

Aim of this work

  ISFH

- **Independent validation** with a system from a different equipment manufacturer (centrotherm, cPLASMA 2600)

- **Impact of the number of ALD cycles** on passivation quality

- **Different surfaces**
  - Boron-diffused textured surface of n-type wafers (TOPCon front side)
  - Undiffused textured surface of p-type wafers

- **Combination of tube-type PEALD** AlO_x **and PECVD** AlO_x to reduce the process duration

- Investigation on **UV stability**

020009-004

4 Leibniz Universität Hannover

n-type wafers with boron-diffused textured surfaces

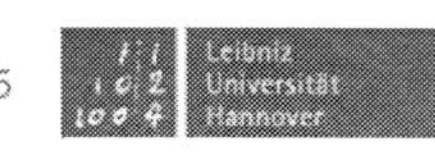

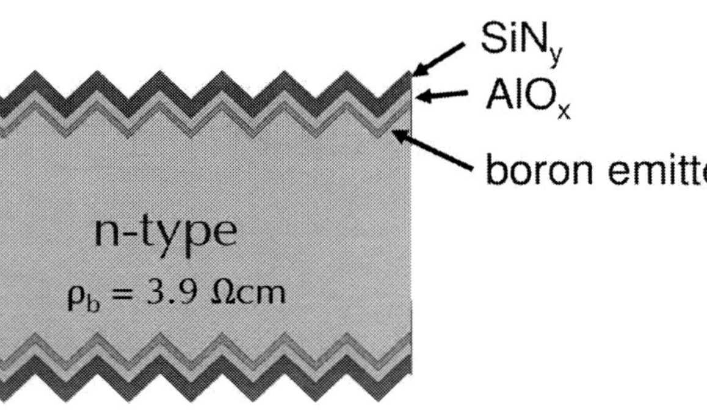

No. of ALD cycles	85	26	20	16	12
AlO$_x$ dep. tech.	PEALD	tube-type PEALD		tube-type PEALD / PECVD	
Group	G1	G2	G3	G4	G5

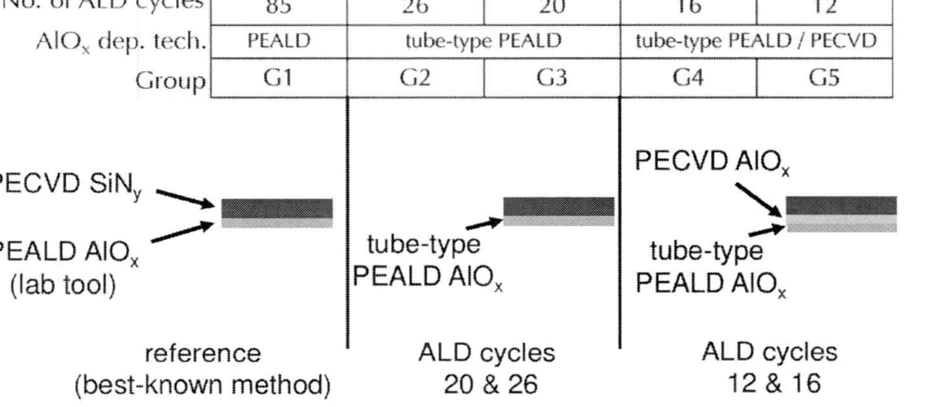

- Equivalent to TOPCon front side

- All samples fired at 800 °C

- Measurement at five wafer positions (center, 4 corners)

020009-005

n-type wafers with boron-diffused textured surfaces

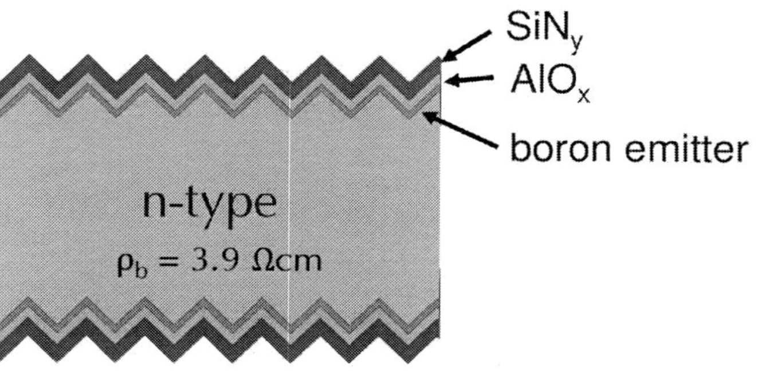

No. of ALD cycles	85	26	20	16	12
AlO_x dep. tech.	PEALD	tube-type PEALD		tube-type PEALD / PECVD	
Group	G1	G2	G3	G4	G5

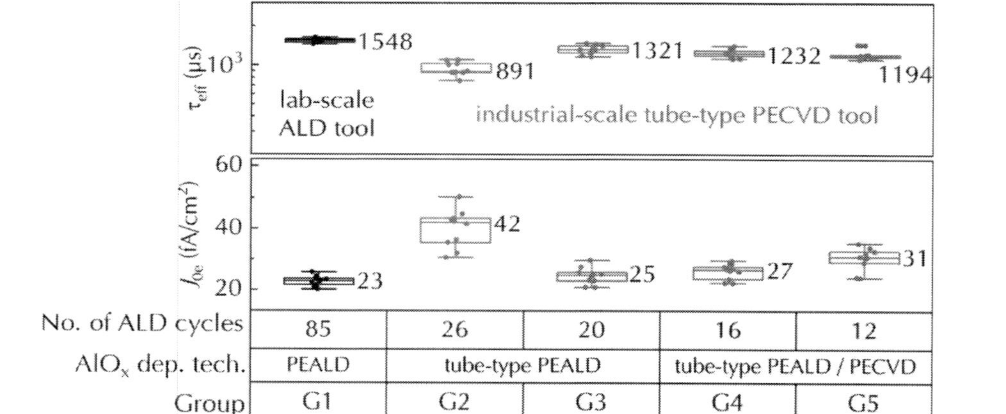

- **Strong impact of number of ALD cycles (G2 vs. G3)**

- 20 ALD cycles leads to the best passivation quality, same level as the reference

- Tube-type PEALD AlO_x / PECVD AlO_x (G4 & G5): promising option with 16 ALD cycles

Separation between J_0 in the emitter bulk & surface

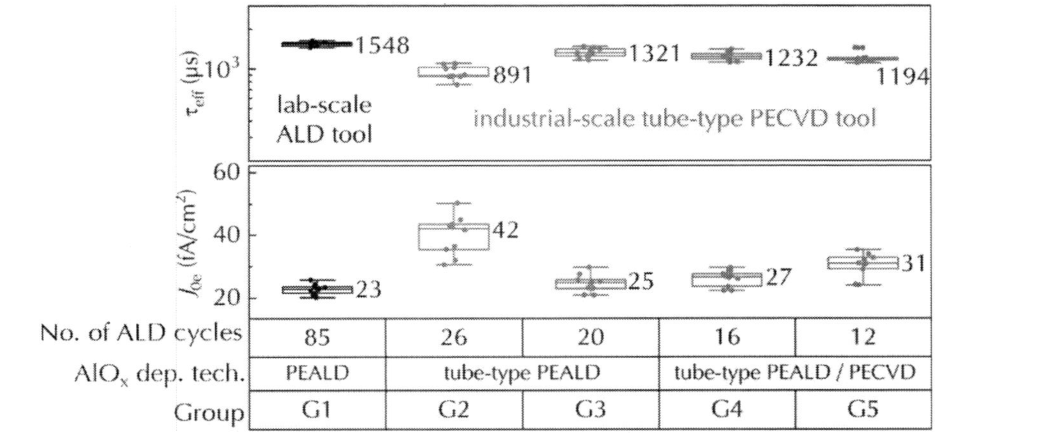

Group	G1	G2	G3	G4	G5
AlO$_x$ dep. tech.	PEALD	tube-type PEALD		tube-type PEALD / PECVD	
No. of ALD cycles	85	26	20	16	12

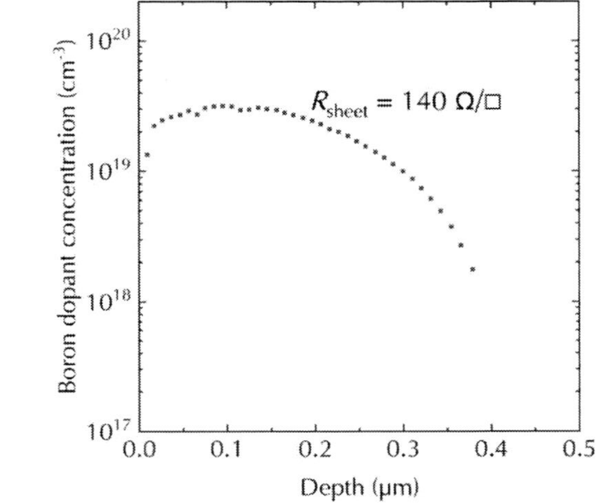

- $J_{0e} = J_{0e,b}$ (Auger in the emitter bulk) + J_{0s} (SRH at surface)

- Separation between $J_{0e,b}$ and J_{0s} with EDNA2[1] & ECV profile as input

- Best result in G3 with tube-type PEALD: J_{0e} = 20.9 fA/cm² = 17.3 fA/cm² + **3.6 fA/cm²**

  → Auger in the emitter bulk dominates J_{0e} currently

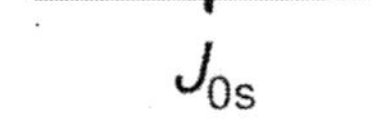

[1] K.R. McIntosh and P.P. Altermatt, 35th IEEE PVSEC (2010)

n-type wafers with improved boron emitter

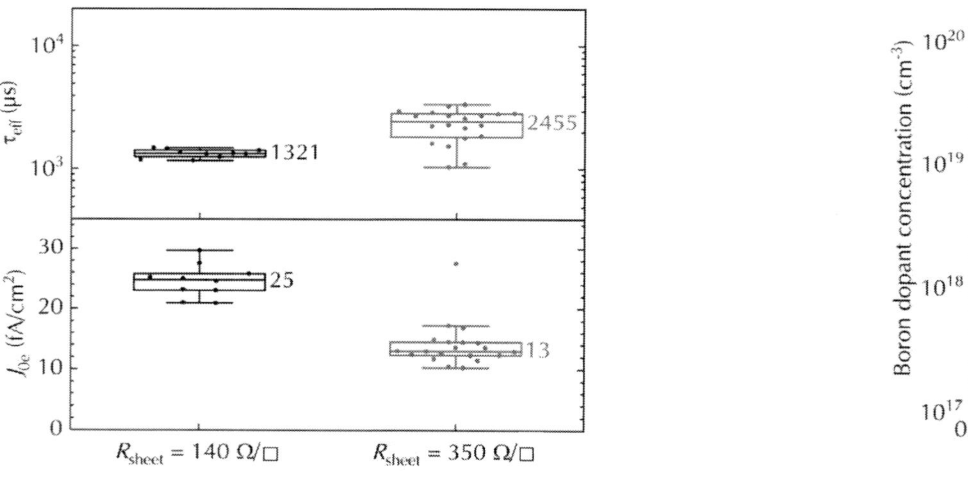

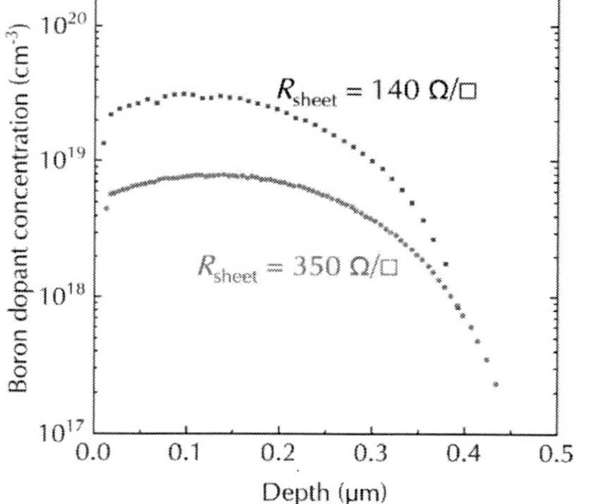

- Improved boron emitter with R_{sheet} = 350 Ω/□

- 20 ALD cycles for tube-type PEALD AlO$_x$ as in G3

- J_{0e} (median) decreases from 25 fA/cm^2 to **13 fA/cm^2**

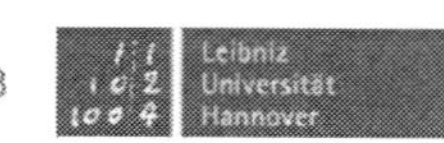

020009-008

p-type wafers with undiffused textured surfaces

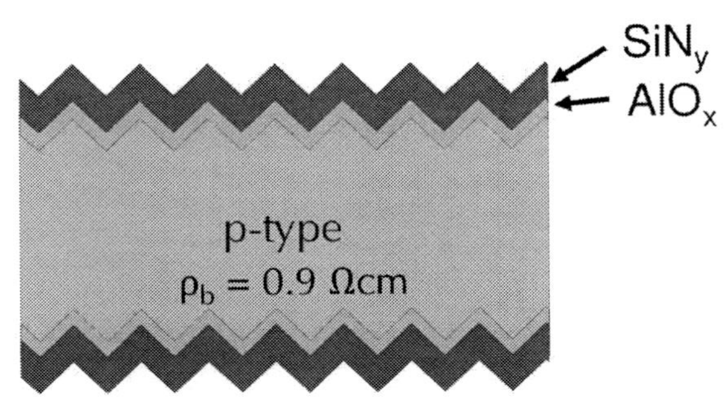

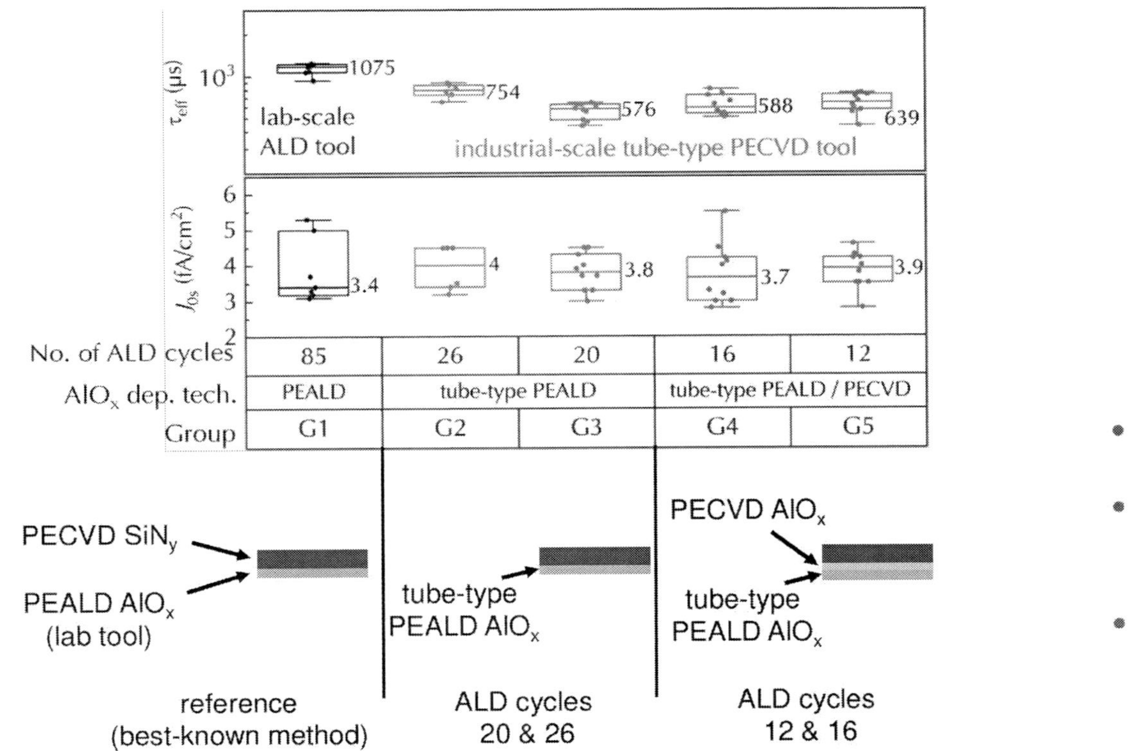

- All samples fired at 800 °C

- Measurement at five wafer positions (center, 4 corners)

- Only J_{0s} since no emitter exists

B. Min et al., 42nd EU PVSEC, 23rd September 2025, 1BO.3.6

p-type wafers with undiffused textured surfaces

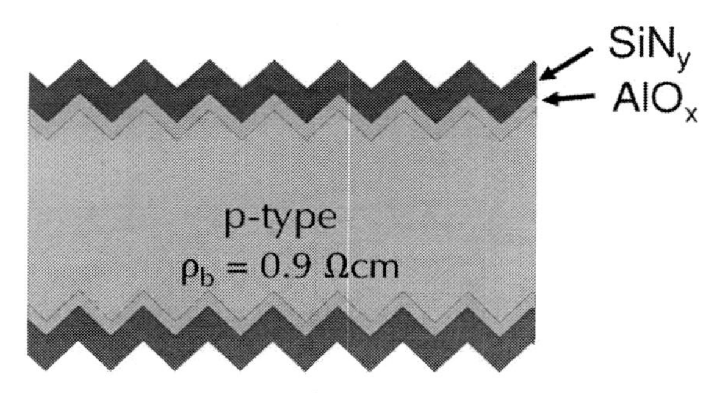

No. of ALD cycles	85	26	20	16	12

No. of ALD cycles	85	26	20	16	12
AlO$_x$ dep. tech.	PEALD	tube-type PEALD		tube-type PEALD / PECVD	
Group	G1	G2	G3	G4	G5

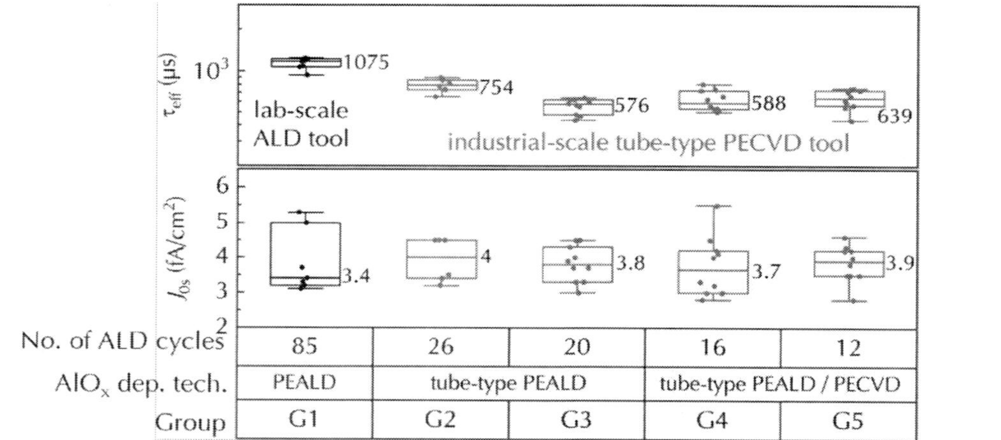

- Notable differences in τ_{eff}, could be also caused by bulk effects

- **No impact of number of ALD cycles on J_{0s}**

- Passivation quality of all groups are on the same level as the reference

- Median J_{0s}: 3.7 – 4 fA/cm², corresponds well with J_{0s} from n-type wafer surface (J_{0s} = 3.6 fA/cm²)

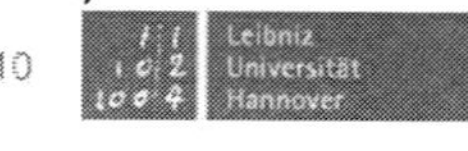

020009-010

POLO Back Junction (BJ) and its advantages

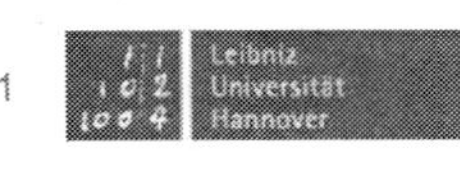

POLO BJ[1]

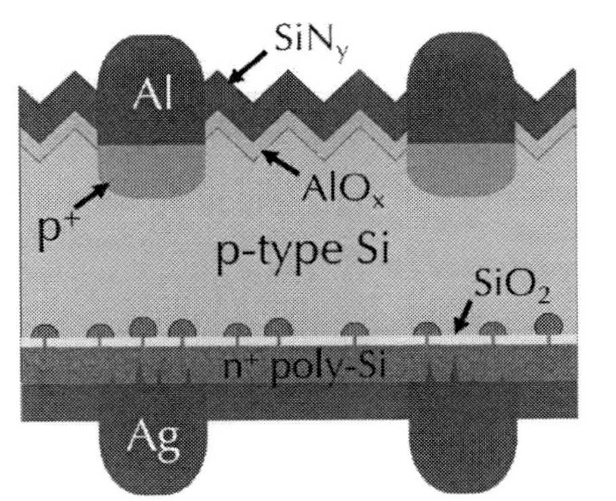

- n$^+$-type passivating poly-Si on oxide (POLO) rear contacts

- **Leaner process flow** compared to TOPCon (less process steps, no boron diffusion)

- Up to **50% less Ag consumption** compared to TOPCon & HJT

- Best efficiency so far[2]: 24.2% with a V_{oc} of 725 mV

- Ag-free metallization[3] is also possible

- Ag-free interconnection (Brinkmann et al. 3CO.10.1, Wednesday, 3:15 pm)

- Detailed cost analysis of POLO BJ (Gomez Trilos et al. 5DO.11.6, Thursday, 8:30 am)

[1] R. Brendel et al., 35th EUPVSEC (2018)
[2] B. Min et al., Prog Photovolt Res Appl., 1-9 (2024)
[3] B. Min et al., 40th EUPVSEC (2023)

020009-011

Integration of tube-type PEALD AlO$_x$ in solar cells

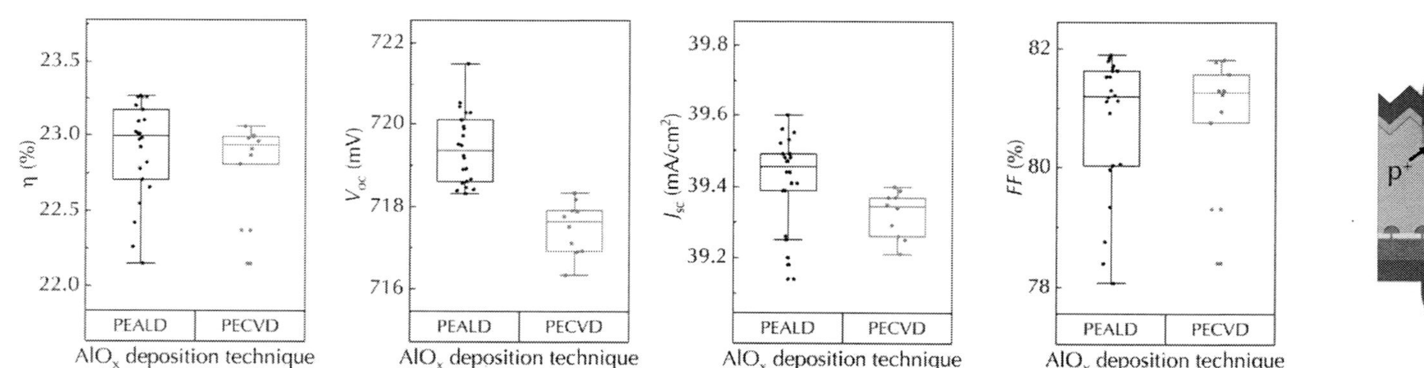

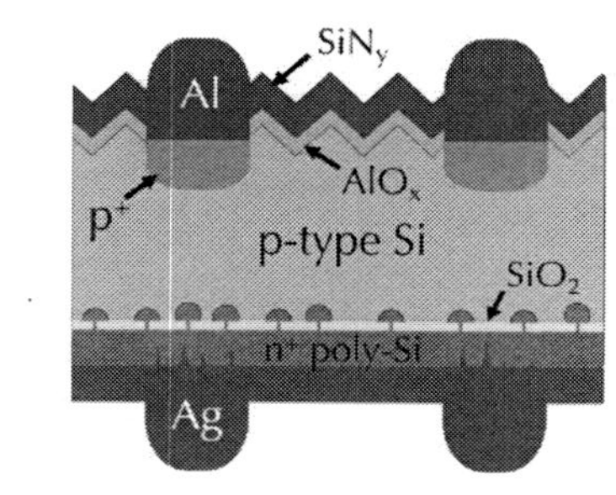

- Reference (red box plot) POLO BJ solar cells featuring PECVD AlO$_x$/SiN$_y$ passivation stack

- The efficiencies of both groups are on the same level

- Tube-type PEALD AlO$_x$/PECVD SiN$_y$ shows notably higher V_{oc} and J_{sc}

B. Min et al., 42nd EU PVSEC, 23rd September 2025, 1BO.3.6

020009-012

Tube-type PEALD AlO$_x$ / PECVD SiN$_y$ is UV stable

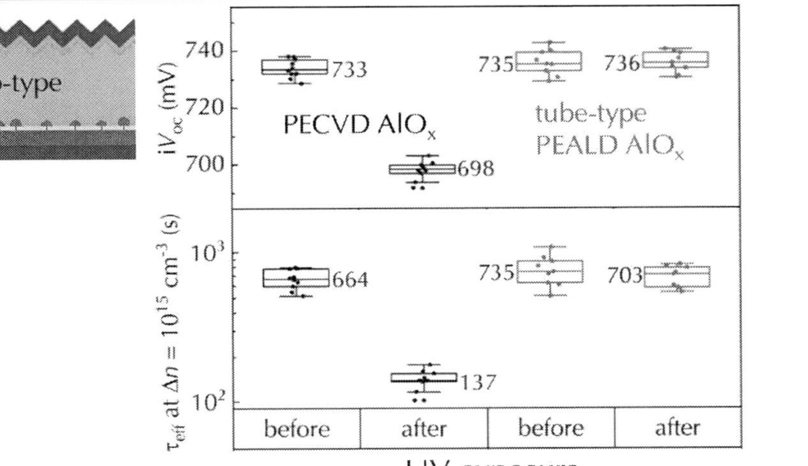

- Undiffused textured surface of p-type wafer

- UV dose of 4.5 kWh/m^2, λ = 290 – 400 nm

- PECVD AlO$_x$ / PECVD SiN$_y$ degrades significantly

More details in C. Hollemann et al., Solar RRL, 2025, https://doi.org/10.1002/solr.202500510

Tube-type PEALD AlO$_x$ / PECVD SiN$_y$ is UV stable

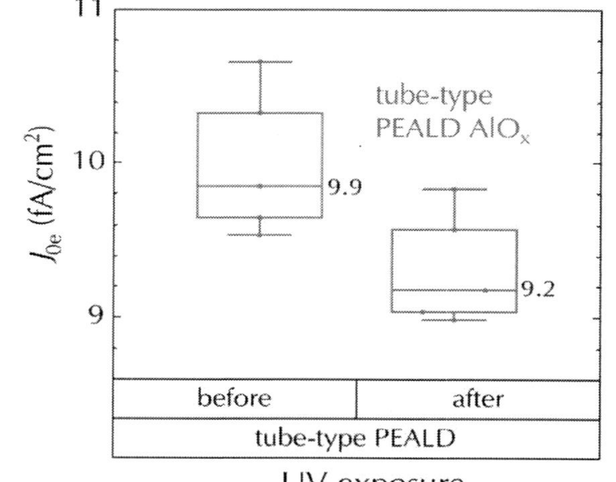

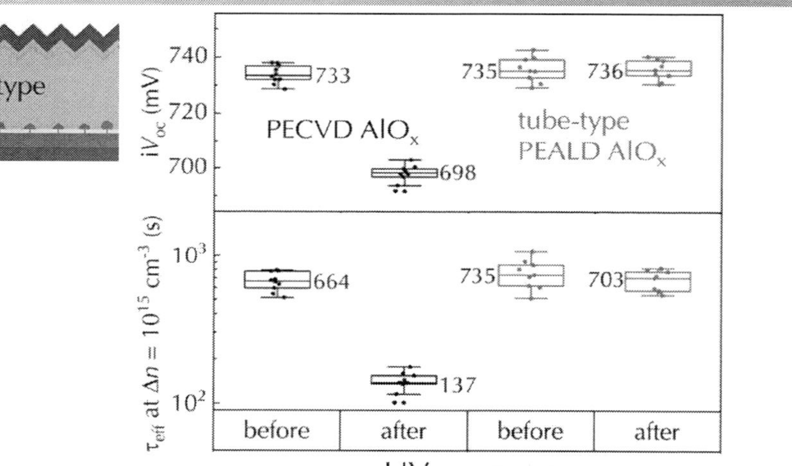

- Undiffused textured surface of p-type wafer
- UV dose of 4.5 kWh/m^2, λ = 290 − 400 nm
- PECVD AlO$_x$ / PECVD SiN$_y$ degrades significantly

- Boron-diffused textured surface of n-type wafer
- UV dose of 9 kWh/m^2, λ = 290 − 400 nm

More details in C. Hollemann et al., Solar RRL, 2025, https://doi.org/10.1002/solr.202500510

Summary

- Successful validation of tube-type PEALD AlO_x with cPLASMA 2600, centrotherm

- Tube-type PEALD AlO_x shows excellent surface passivation quality

- Number of ALD cycles is crucial for boron-diffused textured surface of n-type wafers

- Combination of the tube-type PEALD AlO_x and PECVD AlO_x is an attractive option

- Tube-type PEALD AlO_x is UV stable, while the PECVD AlO_x degrades strongly under UV exposure.

- Reduction of cell fabrication cost as well as the increase of PV module energy yield of all solar cells with AlO_x on the front side (e.g. POLO BJ or TOPCon solar cells)

020009-015

Acknowledgments

The authors thank to **M. Pollmann**, **B. Gehring**, **L. Spasówka**, **S. Spätlich**, **T. Brendemühl**, **T. Friedrich**, **T. Neubert** and **D. Sylla** for processing solar cells (all ISFH), **M. Dhamrin** and **K. Tsuji** from Toyo Aluminium K. K. for their supports regarding Al pastes.

This work was financially supported by the German Federal Ministry for Economic Affairs and Energy (BMWE) under contact number 03EE1150A (APOLON) and by the German State of Lower Saxony for the project ARTEMIS through the special assets fund for economic development, ecological sector, chapter 5157.

Supported by:

Federal Ministry
for Economic Affairs
and Energy

on the basis of a decision
by the German Bundestag

Leibniz
Universität
Hannover

020009-016

ADVANCEMENTS ON POST-PROCESSING OF HIGH EFFICIENCY CELLS: DATA FROM MASS PRODUCTION AND EXPERIMENTAL ROADMAP

Alessandro Voltan[1], Francesco Dalla Torre[1], Bertrand Hladys[2], Pedro Jeronimo[2], Grazia Litrico[3], Alessandro Furnari[3], Alfredo Di Matteo[3], Marcello Sciuto[3], Jonas De Rose[4]

[1]Applied Materials, Via Postumia Ovest, 244, 31048, Olmi di San Biagio di Callalta, TV, Italy
[2]Univ Grenoble Alpes, CEA, LITEN, DTS, INES, F-38000, Grenoble, France
[3]Enel Green Power, Contrada Blocco Torrazze, Zona Industriale, 95121, Catania, Italy
[4]Fraunhofer Institute for Solar Energy Systems ISE, Heidenhofstr. 2, 79110 Freiburg, Germany

The power output and conversion efficiency of solar cells can change after exposure to illumination, with increases or decreases depending on the cell structure. According to the literature, high-intensity light exposure combined with controlled heating can enhance the performance of amorphous-crystalline silicon heterojunction (HJT) solar cells and modules [1]. This efficiency improvement is attributed to simultaneous defect recovery and reductions in series resistance. In this work, we present a rapid post-treatment process for HJT solar cells, utilizing an LED-based oven jointly designed by Applied Materials (AMAT, Italy) and CEA-INES (France), in collaboration with 3Sun (Enel Group, Italy). The architecture of the developed Fast Light Soaking (LS) solution is described in detail in [2]. Using the Fast Light Soaking process at lab scale, we achieved an efficiency gain of up to +0.6%, with open-circuit voltage (Voc) and fill factor (FF) generally being the main contributors to this improvement [2].

In this paper, we provide an overview of the latest achievements obtained with the Fast Light Soaking process, including: i) data collected in mass production, ii) the effect of the Light Soaking process on cells from different efficiency classes, and iii) a detailed degradation analysis after LS. The impact of Light Soaking on different metallization processes, using various silver- and copper-based pastes, will also be reported.

Preliminary results on the effect of the Light Soaking process on HJT cells with an nc-Si:H n-doped silicon layer, as well as on TOPCon cells, will be presented as part of our experimental roadmap.

Keywords: Heterojunction, Light Soaking, TOPCon, In-line post processing

1 INTRODUCTION

The behavior of HJT cells under Light Soaking and the related defect recovery is still actively investigated in literature. The main requirements for successful post processing are in any case intensive illumination and cell temperature controlled below the cell damage threshold (<250°C) even in localized regions [2].

Based on process requirements, a dedicated Fast Light Soaking oven has been developed using high power LEDs light sources and released in mass production [Fig. 1]. During the R&D testing an efficiency gain up to +0.6%abs has been obtained with 12s exposure time on small batches.

In this work we will focus on deployment of Light Soaking in mass production at 3Sun, including:

1) Effect of Light Soaking process on cells belonging to different efficiency classes;

2) Degradation of HJT cells after Light Soaking process and impacted IV parameters;

3) Light Soaking combined with different metallization processes at lab scale.

Further tests are planned at 3Sun to better quantify the effect of Light Soaking exposure on additional process steps including: i) deposition of an intrinsic amorphous silicon layer on the front side of the cell, using dedicated gases to increase the energy gap, with a benefit in terms of the transparency to the incident light; ii) deposition of a nano-crystalline n-doped silicon layer; iii) deposition of a transparent conductive oxide on the back side of the cell with high mobility, high working function and high transparence values.

To evaluate the applicability of the Light Soaking process to other cell structures, a batch of TOPCon cells was treated after firing using various Light Soaking recipes at high temperature. In all cases, a significant efficiency gain was observed, laying the groundwork for further investigations. These future studies will primarily focus on the combined effects of Light Soaking and LECO (Laser-Enhanced Contact Optimization [3]) on TOPCon cells.

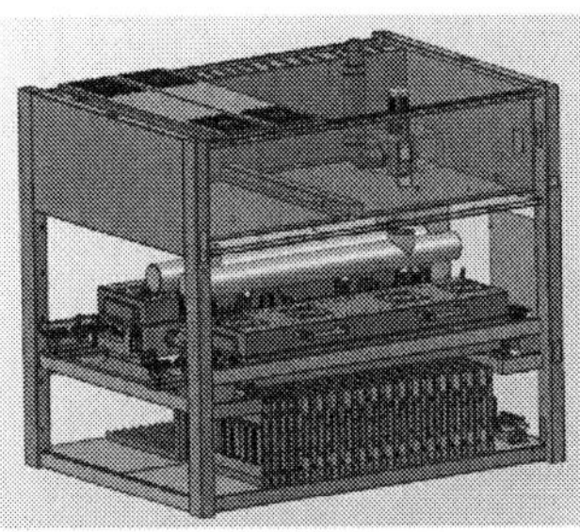

Figure 1: Fast Light Soaking design (a) and final installation in mass production at 3Sun-ENEL (b)

2 RESULTS FROM MASS PRODUCTION

In order to quantify the benefit of Light Soaking process in mass production, a lot of 2k bifacial HJT cells with standard a-Si:H (n) layer has been measured and subdivided in 10 Efficiency classes with a range of +0.2% abs each. The distribution of cells in efficiency classes is reported in Fig. 2. After the measurements, all the cells have been processed and exposed to the same light soaking recipe using the in-line oven reported in Fig 1 and then remeasured. The average efficiency gain for the most representative classes is reported in Table I, where, as expected, the higher gain is obtained on lower classes. An average gain of +0.6%abs is obtained also on the highest classes, confirming the results previously achieved at lab scale. Also in this case (Fig. 3) the efficiency gain is mainly due to the combination of Voc improvement (+6mV average) and FF (+1.5% Average), while the impact on Isc can be considered negligible. The Voc improvements are the results of enhanced passivation properties of the substrate surfaces while the FF gain comes from both series and sheet resistance enhancement.

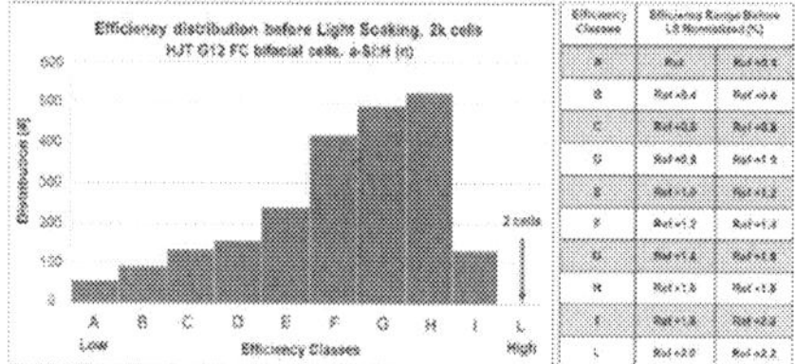

Figure 2: Distribution of Efficiency classes, HJT G12 FC bifacial cells, a-Si:H (n) at 3Sun

Table 1: Average Efficiency gain for representative classes

Efficiency gain after Light Soaking [abs]					
Class	A	C	G	H	I	L
Average	+1.12%	+1.01%	+0.61%	+0.60%	+0.59%	+0.56%

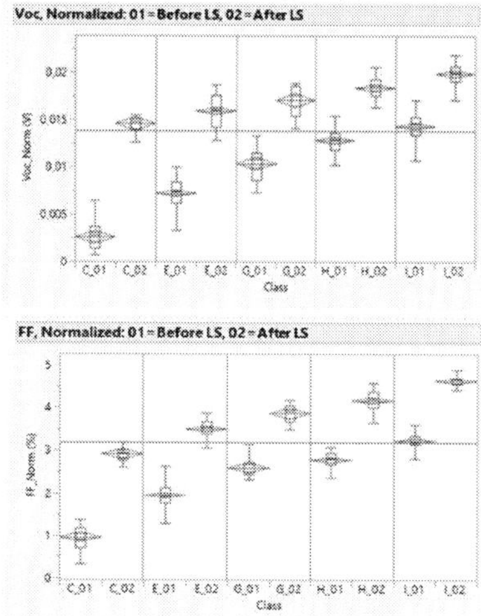

Figure 3: Voc and FF gain for representative classes

Beside the immediate effect on electrical properties due to Light Soaking process on HJT cells, the degradation mechanism during standard dark storage conditions has been investigated. Cells belonging to Class H (Fig. 2) have been selected for this purpose and re-measured multiple times. In Table 2 we report the results of cumulative losses respectively after 11 and 34 days of storages. From Table II it visible that the degradation process in dark condition can be considered stabilized after 11 days with an efficiency loss <0.15%abs starting from an initial gain of +0.64%, with a net stabilized gain of +0.5%abs efficiency, +5mV Voc and +1.3%abs FF. Efficiency losses are partially due to cells handling.

Table II: Cumulative losses during dark storage

CLASS H: weekly monitoring, cumulative losses					
	Voc (mV)	Isc (mA)	Pmax (W)	FF (%)	Eff (%)
Δ (pre/postLS)	+ 6	+ 30	+ 0.28	+ 1.47	+ 0.64
Δ (after 11 Days)	- 1	- 30	- 0.06	- 0.19	- 0.13
Δ (after 34 Days)	- 1	- 39	- 0.06	- 0.19	- 0.15

The Light Soaking process has been fully implemented in mass production and is now running continuously. The process is closely monitored, and the average efficiency gain is periodically checked, consistently confirming the results reported in Table I.

3 EXPERIMENTAL ROADMAP

In order to better understand the Light Soaking mechanics and fully quantify the benefit on high efficiency cells, additional tests have been planned. In this paragraph we report the main results achieved on HJT cells comparing impact of Light Soaking with i) different metallization processes and ii) different layers structure. For what concerning the first point, main results are reported on Fig. 4 where 4 batches of same M2 precursors have been screen printed using 4 different pastes and then exposed at the same Light Soaking process. The four cases represented in Fig. 4 relates respectively to i) Ag-Cu paste provided by Vendor A, ii) Silver paste with Nano particles, iii) Ag-Cu paste provided by Vendor B and iv) Standard Reference Silver paste.
Beside the different starting efficiency, all the batches showed similar results with a clear improvement of data distribution.
Average gain is in good agreement with results reported in previous paragraph and summarized in Table III.

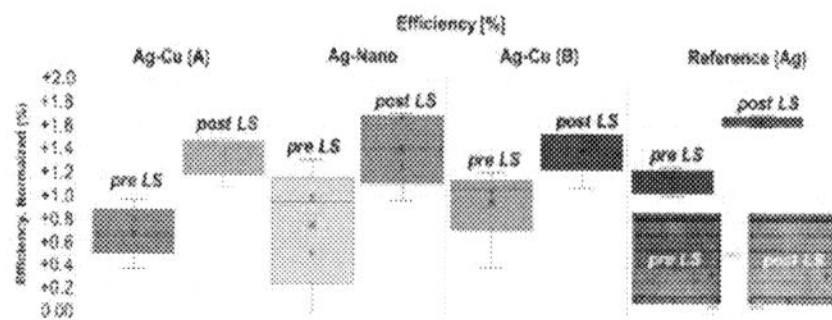

Figure 4: Effect of LS on different metallization processes, HJT cells.

Table III: Average gain after LS using different metallization processes

Δ (pre/postLS)	Isc (mA)	Voc (mV)	Pmax (W)	FF (%)	Eff (%)
AVERAGE	+40	+5.2	+0.14	+1.14	+0.56

Furthermore, effects of Light Soaking on different HJT structures have been investigated comparing cells with n-doped nc-Si:H layer thickness instead of reference a-Si:H (n) layer. Several tests have been performed with different n-doped nc-Si:H layer thickness (15, 19 and 22nm) showing decreasing efficiency with increasing layer thickness. Best results have been achieved with 15nm n-doped nc-Si:H layer, comparable with Class H a-Si:H (n) reported in previous Fig. 2.

After Light Soaking (Table IV), higher Efficiency gain was achieved on 15nm nc-Si:H cells compared with nc-Si:H HJT cell with same starting efficiency (+0.9%abs vs +0.6%abs). To be noticed the Isc increase in case of nc-Si:H cells probably due to improved nc-Si:H layers crystallinity and better interfaces between amorphous and nc layers after Light Soaking.

Table IV: Gain after LS, comparison between a-Si:H (n) and 15nm nc-Si:H HJT cell with same starting efficiency

Gain after Light Soaking				
	Voc [mV]	Isc [mA]	FF (%)	Eff (%)
CLASS H, a-Si:H (n)	+6	+30	+1.4	+0.6
DOE2, 15nm nc-Si:H	+12	+194	+0.9	+0.9

4 POST FIRING ANNEALING OF TOPCON CELLS

Continuing with the experimental roadmap, the Light Soaking tool has been used for the Post-Firing Anneal (PFA) process on TOPCon solar cells. For this purpose, a dedicated LED-based mock-up oven (FIG. 6) was employed, capable of reaching higher temperatures and maintaining them for longer durations than the standard HJT Light Soaking oven.

Based on existing knowledge, PFA is expected to provide "additional hydrogenation" [4], further passivating remaining defects via hydrogen atoms. By reducing recombination effects, increases in open-circuit voltage (Voc), fill factor (FF), and efficiency (η) are generally observed after PFA on TOPCon cells, while also removing any excess hydrogen that could otherwise lead to further degradation.

For testing purpose, 2 groups of cells (respectively fired at 770°C and 810°C peak Temperature) provided by Fraunhofer ISE, without any additional PFA, have been exposed at 3 different LS processes: i) Recipe_A (400°C for 35s) ii) Recipe_B (400°C for 20s) iii) LSK_STD (Standard Light Soaking Recipe used for HJT cells).

Promising results have been achieved with both Recipe_A and Recipe_B due to increased peak temperature compared with LSK_STD Recipe (Table V). Respect to HJT cells, impact on Voc can be considered negligible.

After Light Soaking, cells have been shipped back to Fraunhofer ISE where they have been exposed to LECO (Laser-enhanced contact optimization, [3]). Results of TOPCon cells processed with Recipe A and reprocessed with LECO are reported in Table VI and Fig. 7. No further improvements after LECO have been obtained on

TOPCon cells fired at 810°C, showing equivalence between the two processes. On the other hand, highest Uoc (710mV vs 702mV) and Efficiency (23.3% vs 23.1%) have been obtained adding Light Soaking and LECO on cells fired at 770°C. Additional tests are planned for further process optimization and understanding.

Figure 6: Mock-up Light Soaking Oven used for PFA of TOPCon cells

Table V: PFA on TOPCon cell using different Light Soaking recipes.

Cells fired at (°C)	Average Gain (Recipe A ~35s)		
	Voc [mV]	FF [%]	Eff [abs%]
770	+1.0	+3.0	+0.93
810	+1.5	+1.3	+0.43

Cells fired at (°C)	Average Gain (Recipe B ~20s)		
	Voc [mV]	FF [%]	Eff [abs%]
770	+0.5	+3.4	+1.05
810	+1.4	+1.5	+0.48

Cells fired at (°C)	Average Gain (Recipe LSK_STD ~20s)		
	Voc [mV]	FF [%]	Eff [abs%]
770	+0.1	+0.04	+0.01
810	+1.4	+0.20	+0.12

Table VI: IV data after Light Soaking and LECO

IV data: Firing Recipe 770 °C (average)				
	Uoc [mV]	Jsc [mA/cm2]	FF [%]	Eff [%]
After LS, Recipe A	711	40.3	76.9	22.1
After (LS+LECO)	710	40.3	81.3	23.3

IV data: Firing Recipe 810 °C (average)				
	Uoc [mV]	Jsc [mA/cm2]	FF [%]	Eff [%]
After LS, Recipe A	702	40.2	81.5	23
After (LS+LECO)	702	40.2	81.8	23.1

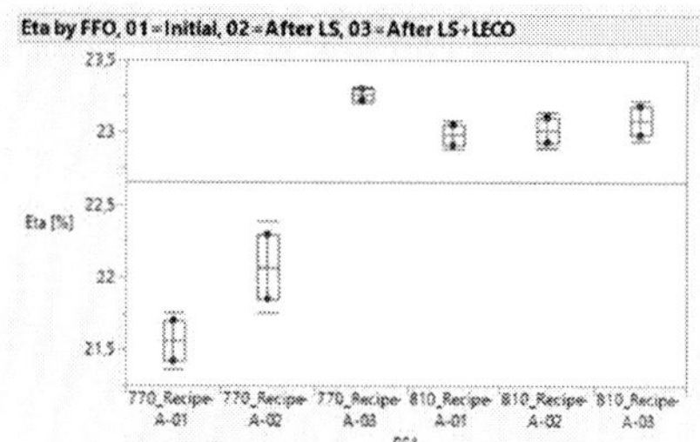

Figure 7: Efficiency results after PFA (Recipe A) and LECO

5 CONCLUSIONS

This work demonstrates the successful industrialization of Fast Light Soaking (LS) for high-efficiency HJT solar cells, confirming lab-scale efficiency gains up to +0.6% can be reliably reproduced in mass production. The process delivers consistent improvements in Voc and FF across different efficiency classes and metallization schemes, with negligible impact on Isc. Degradation studies indicate that the efficiency gain is largely retained after dark storage, supporting the process's robustness. The experimental roadmap further highlights the versatility of LS, showing promising results on HJT cells with nc-Si:H layers and on TOPCon cells, especially when combined with post-firing annealing and LECO treatments. The LED-based oven developed enables both static and dynamic processing, paving the way for flexible integration in industrial lines. Preliminary results suggest that further optimization of LS parameters and cell architectures could unlock additional performance gains. Overall, Fast Light Soaking emerges as a scalable, reliable post-processing step for next-generation silicon solar cells, supporting higher module efficiencies and improved manufacturing yield. Future work will focus on process optimization for advanced cell structures and long-term stability assessment under real-world conditions.

6 ACKNOWLEDGEMENTS

This work was partially supported by the European Union through the Horizon Europe project Shine PV under grant agreement No 101172902

References

[1] M. Wright et al., "High-Intensity Illuminated Annealing of Industrial SHJ Solar Cells: A Pilot Study," in IEEE Journal of Photovoltaics, vol. 12, no. 1, pp. 267-273, Jan. 2022.

[2] A. Voltan et al., "Progress on the design of a tool for the post-treatment of HJT cells : from prototyoe to in-line industrial tool", Proceeding of 40th EUPVSEC conference, 2023, Lisbon

[3] Xie Yi-Bo et al., Influence of Laser-Induced Sintering on Contact Performance of TOPCon Solar Cells, Acta Physica Sinica, 2024

[4] R. Chen et al., "24.58% efficient commercial n-type silicon solar cells with hydrogenation", Progress in Photovoltaics: Research and Applications, https://doi.org/10.1002/pip.3464, 2021

SOLAR PV SILICON RECYCLING VIA CHEMICAL AND VACUUM REFINING TECHNIQUES

Jonas Låstad*, Kai Tang**, Alexander Ulyashin**, Xiang Ma**, Jafar Safarian*
*NTNU, **SINTEF

ABSTRACT: The rapid expansion of global photovoltaic (PV) installations will inevitably result in large quantities of silicon-rich waste as early-generation modules reach their end of life. Recovering this silicon is critical for maintaining a sustainable solar value chain and reducing dependence on high-energy primary production. However, solar-grade silicon requires a purity level of 99.9999 wt% (6N), posing a significant challenge for recycling processes. Within the framework of the Apollo project, a combined chemical and vacuum refining route has been developed to recover and purify silicon from spent PV wafers. The integrated process sequence—acid leaching, alkaline leaching, and vacuum refining—reduces total impurity levels from 33,000 ppm in untreated material to 16 ppm in the final refined silicon. Chemical leaching steps remove adherent glass and metal contaminants, while vacuum refining efficiently eliminates volatile elements such as Ag and Cu. The final material reaches approximately 5N purity, with remaining impurities dominated by Ca and Zn. Minor carbon diffusion from the graphite crucible was detected but not included in the purity assessment. The results demonstrate the complementarity of the processes and suggest that further optimization of refining conditions could enable closed-loop silicon recycling for next-generation PV manufacturing.
Keywords: Solar silicon, PV recycling, Vacuum refining, Alkaline leaching,

1 INTRODUCTION

Global installed photovoltaic capacity has increased exponentially over the past two decades, and projections indicate that solar electricity will constitute a dominant share of renewable power generation within the next ten years. While this represents a major environmental success, it also introduces a new materials challenge: the generation of large volumes of end-of-life PV modules. As most first-generation installations approach the end of their 20–30 year lifetimes, silicon waste streams are expected to exceed several million tons annually.

Recycling these modules is essential for both resource efficiency and environmental stewardship. The silicon contained in solar cells represents more than half of the embodied energy of a module and recovering it could drastically lower the carbon footprint of future PV production. However, the recovery of solar-grade silicon requires achieving purities of 99.9999 wt% (6N) or higher. Such purity is necessary to ensure the low defect densities and long minority-carrier lifetimes that underpin photovoltaic efficiency.

The challenge is compounded by the complex structure of PV wafers, which typically contain doped regions, metallic conductors, and glassy encapsulants. These layers introduce a variety of contaminants—both chemical and structural—that must be eliminated without excessive material loss. Traditional metallurgical refining alone cannot achieve the required purity, while purely chemical processes are often limited by reagent consumption and waste generation.

The Apollo project aims to develop an integrated recycling framework that combines physical separation, chemical purification, and metallurgical refining. This work focuses on the latter stages: the purification of recovered silicon using a combination of acid leaching, alkaline leaching, and vacuum refining. The goal is to demonstrate a viable, scalable route to recover high-purity silicon suitable for reintroduction into the solar manufacturing cycle.

2 EXPERIMENTAL PROCEDURE

2.1 Sample origin and composition

The starting material consisted of mixed silicon fragments obtained from dismantled PV modules. Because these originated from real installations, the feedstock included wafers of different manufacturers, crystal structures, and dopant types. Most of the material was polycrystalline p-type silicon, reflecting the historical dominance of boron-doped cells in commercial production. Small quantities of n-type material were likely present but not separately analyzed. The recovered silicon pieces exhibited surface contamination from encapsulant residues, silver and aluminum metallization, and glass fragments. These features reflect typical characteristics of industrial PV waste, making the samples representative of actual recycling feedstock rather than laboratory-synthesized analogs.

2.2 Acid leaching

The initial chemical purification was performed by Fraunhofer CSP using a multi-step acid leaching process. Their process effectively removed most of the contacts and metallic impurities. The process also aided in removing the antireflective coating and thin glass layers present on the cell surfaces. After leaching, the samples were thoroughly rinsed with deionized water and dried.

2.3 Alkaline leaching

Following acid treatment, an alkaline leaching step was conducted at 25 °C for up to six hours using 1 M NaOH in a stirred beaker reactor. The objective was to dissolve residual glass (SiO_2) and oxide layers that may trap or encapsulate impurities. Sodium hydroxide reacts with SiO_2 to form soluble silicates, effectively etching the wafer surface and exposing cleaner bulk material.

This process also mechanically dislodged metallic inclusions, which were then removed during rinsing. While effective, the use of NaOH introduced trace sodium contamination in the treated samples, which must be carefully managed in future scale-up.

2.4 Vacuum refining

The purified silicon was subsequently refined in a vacuum induction furnace using a graphite crucible at 1500 °C and 5 Pa for 60 minutes. At this temperature, the silicon was fully molten, and volatile impurities such as Na, Mg, P, Zn, Ag, and Cu evaporated preferentially due to their higher vapor pressures relative to silicon. The process was designed to minimize silicon loss while enhancing impurity segregation through vaporization. During refining, carbon diffusion from the graphite crucible into the melt was detected, indicating slight contamination. Although this carbon was not included in the total impurity figures, its presence highlights a design consideration for future furnace materials or coatings to prevent back-diffusion.

2.5 Sample analysis

Elemental analyses were performed by Glow Discharge Mass Spectrometry (GDMS). The results represent surface-layer composition, considered representative of the bulk given the thin samples (~100 μm). Single-sample analyses were used for each process stage. The leachate solution from alkaline leach was also analyzed using Inductively Coupled Plasma Mass spectroscopy. The combined analysis provided insight to the mass flows of the leaching process.

3 RESULTS

3.1 Impurity reduction sequence

The sequential refining route achieved a marked reduction in total impurity concentration. The untreated PV silicon exhibited roughly 33,000 ppm total impurities, dominated by aluminum and copper. After the acid leaching, the impurity concentration dropped to 69 ppm, demonstrating the effectiveness of the nitric-hydrochloric mixture in removing metal-rich surface layers. The alkaline leach provided a further reduction to 24 ppm, primarily by dissolving glass and oxide residues. Despite a minor introduction of sodium from the NaOH reagent, the overall purity improvement confirmed the complementary role of acid and base leaching. Finally, vacuum refining lowered the impurity concentration to 16 ppm, corresponding to approximately 5N purity. This stage efficiently removed volatile elements such as Ag, Cu, and Mn, while also decreasing phosphorus and magnesium levels.

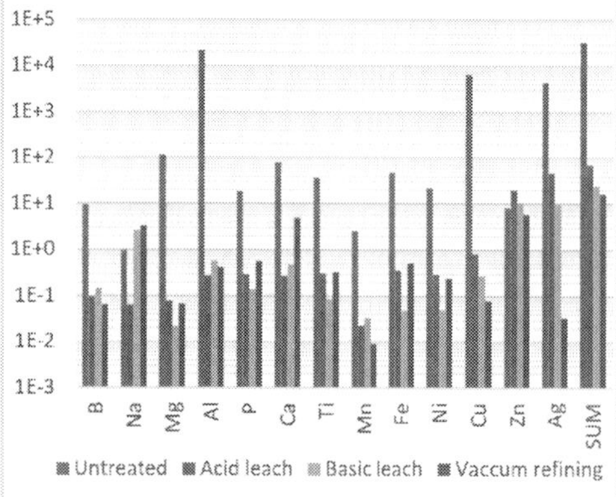

Figure 1: Impurity concentrations for selected elements from GDMS analysis

The trend in total impurities clearly demonstrates the progressive removal of contaminants through each process step. Chemical leaching primarily eliminates external and surface-bound impurities, while vacuum refining targets volatile elements within the silicon bulk. Carbon contamination from the crucible was detected as was expected.

4 DISCUSSION

4.1 Complementarity of chemical and vacuum refining

The experimental results underscore the synergistic interaction between chemical and metallurgical purification. The acid and alkaline leaching stages remove adherent and glassy impurities that would otherwise hinder mass transfer during vacuum refining. Once these layers are removed, the molten silicon surface becomes more active, facilitating impurity evaporation and reducing kinetic barriers.

The vacuum refining stage complements chemical cleaning by removing impurities that cannot be dissolved or dislodged chemically. Its efficiency relies on the difference in vapor pressure between silicon and the impurity elements. This difference allows volatile species to evaporate selectively under low pressure, leading to bulk purification without excessive silicon loss.

4.2 Mechanistic considerations

During the nitric-hydrochloric acid leach, transition metals are oxidized and complexed as soluble chlorides, while the alkaline step promotes the dissolution of silica and disintegration of adherent oxide films. In contrast, vacuum refining depends on mass transfer and vapor-liquid equilibrium, where impurity diffusion from the bulk to the melt surface governs removal efficiency.

The current refining parameters 1500 °C and 5 Pa— represent a balance between impurity volatility and silicon retention. Increasing temperature or reducing pressure further would enhance removal kinetics at the risk of silicon evaporation and contamination from crucible walls. Detailed kinetic modeling is planned to identify the optimal operating window.

4.3 Implications for PV recycling

The near-complete removal of silver and copper confirms the high efficiency of vacuum refining for volatile metals. The persistence of zinc and calcium, which remain as the dominant impurities, indicates their lower volatility and possible formation of stable silicides. Boron remains a key limitation due to its strong affinity for silicon and low vapor pressure; alternative removal methods such as gas-phase slag refining or oxidative treatments could be explored.

4.4 Process integration

The theoretically achieved purity of 5N aligns with reported requirements for feedstock in the Czochralski process for monocrystalline silicon production. This indicates that recycled silicon can feasibly re-enter the production chain without compromising material quality. Importantly, the combined refining route achieves this with moderate process complexity and without resorting to high reagent consumption or multiple refining cycles.

Within the Apollo project, these findings contribute to the broader goal of establishing a closed-loop PV recycling process that integrates mechanical separation, chemical leaching, and metallurgical refining. Such integration could enable recovery of glass, metals, and high-purity silicon from complete modules, supporting both environmental and economic sustainability.

5 FUTURE WORK

Future activities will focus on scaling and optimization. Laboratory-scale experiments will be extended to pilot-scale refining to assess throughput, silicon yield, and impurity removal consistency. Particular attention will be given to refining kinetic models for impurity evaporation, enabling better prediction of removal rates under varying temperature and pressure.

Parallel work will address crucible design and material selection, seeking coatings that prevent carbon diffusion while maintaining thermal conductivity and chemical inertness. Additionally, expanded analytical characterization, including ICP-MS depth profiling and SIMS mapping will verify homogeneity of purity across the silicon bulk.

On the process integration level, the Apollo consortium will explore coupling this refining route with mechanical module disassembly and glass recovery. The aim is to achieve an end-to-end circular recycling pathway where recovered silicon can directly replace virgin feedstock in crystal pulling or wafer casting.

Ultimately, the development of scalable, low-waste refining processes will be key to meeting the material demands of a growing global PV industry while minimizing its environmental footprint.

6 Conclusions

A combined chemical and vacuum refining route were demonstrated for the purification of silicon recovered from spent photovoltaic modules. Sequential treatments reduced impurities from 33,000 ppm in the untreated feedstock to 16 ppm following vacuum refining, corresponding to roughly 5N purity. The chemical leaching steps effectively removed surface contaminants and glass residues, while the vacuum refining stage eliminated volatile metallic elements. Together, these processes act in a complementary manner, addressing both surface and bulk impurities.

Minor carbon contamination from the graphite crucible was observed, suggesting a need for crucible optimization in future testing and upscaling. Besides this, the final material meets the purity criteria for reuse as feedstock in solar-cell manufacturing. The results confirm the feasibility of integrating chemical and metallurgical refining into closed-loop recycling systems, advancing the goal of sustainable, circular photovoltaic production.

REFERENCES

[1] APOLLO Project. (2025). https://www.apolloproject.eu

[2] Gangopadhyay, U. (2012). IOSR Journal of Engineering, 2(8), 41–48.

[3] Safarian, J., & Tangstad, M. (2012). Metallurgical and Materials Transactions B, 43(6), 1427–1445.

[4] Bathey, B. R., & Cretella, M. C. (1982). Journal of Materials Science, 17(11), 3077–3096.

Solar PV silicon recycling via chemical and vacuum refining techniques

Jonas Låstad*, Kai Tang**, Alexander Ulyashin**, Xiang Ma**, Jafar Safarian*
*NTNU, **SINTEF

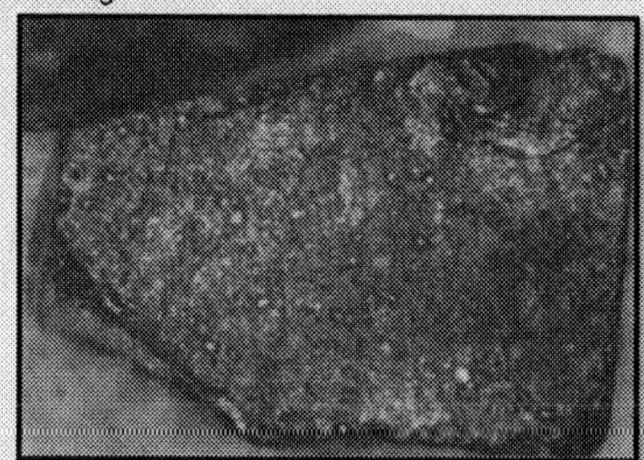

Exponential growth of solar panel deployment, combined with short lifetime, will cause major waste streams, which will require processing. The goal of the Apollo project to achieve complete recycling of solar panels demands solving the problem of Silicon recovery. This problem is difficult because of the high Si purity requirement of 99.9999wt% (6N) or higher. The unique structure and composition of waste poses unique challenges and advantages for recycling. [1]

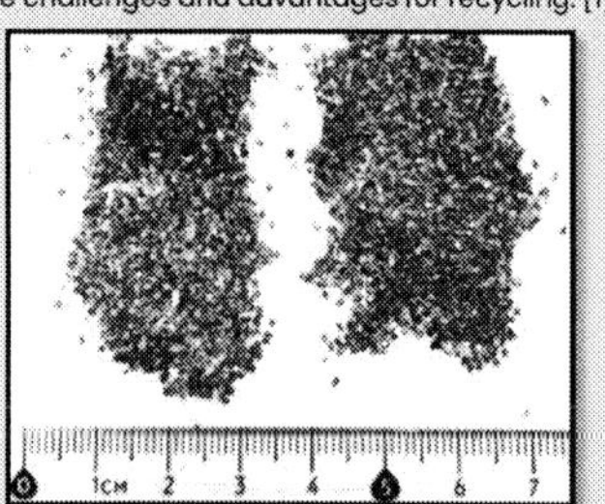

Recovered silicon samples. Left: acid leached, Right: untreated

The Apollo project attempts an improved recycling process, employing additional alkaline-leaching and vacuum refining steps. While the alkaline leach can remove the surface layers and glass impurities, the vacuum refining step is useful for separating volatile elements, such as phosphorus. Other elements suited for vacuum refining are Na, Mg, P, Zn, Ga, Ag, Sn, Sb, Pb, and Bi. The vacuum refining process occurs in 5 distinct steps, where silicon has a low mass transfer rate compared to most associated impurities. The kinetics of vacuum refining needs to be further studied for more development of the previous models about silicon refining. [3]

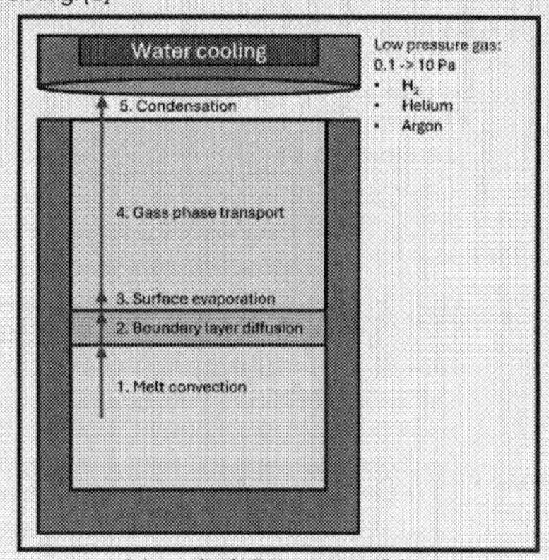

Schematic of NTNU vacuum refining process in lab scale

Surface digestion of the top and bottom wafer surface enables elimination of correlated impurities from the emitter and back surface layers. The structure of PV-wafers allows for this processes. N-type and P-type refer to the positive and negative doping of the different layers. Most impurities can be removed by this process, and selective removal of problematic impurities are possible depending on cell structure.

P-type dopants: **Boron, Aluminum, Gallium**
N-type dopants: **Phosphorous, Arsenic, Antimony**
Conductors: **Silver, Aluminum, Copper**
Emitter and BSF layer:
500 nm thick, 10¹⁸ cm⁻³ doping density
Bulk silicon layer:
200 μm thick, 10¹⁶ cm⁻³ doping density [2]

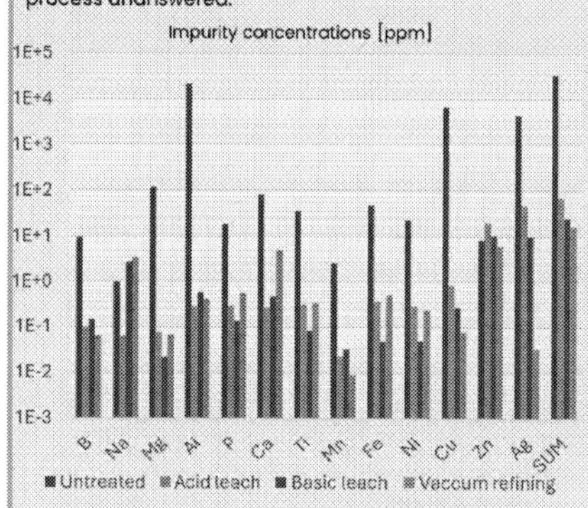

Schematic over PV-cell structure

Vacuum refining proved highly efficient at removing Cu and Ag, while also being promising for Mn. Both techniques yielded improved purity achieving 16 PPM or 5N purity. Alkaline leaching provided a reduction in metallic impurities; these seem to have been dislodged by the alkaline leaching and separated during rinsing. The combined results indicate the refining processeses are complementary. Contamination issues with the final vacuum sample leave the result of the combined process unanswered.

The resulting purity after vacuum refining is within the specifications provided by Bathey and Cretella (1982) [4] and would therefore be applicable for recycling as feedstock in the Czochralski process. The only remaining challenging impurity is B, but expected design changes in the PV-cell structure will eliminate this issue.

Glass and metal particles were observed attached on the surface of the recovered PV-silicon with as seen in the figure below. These contaminants remained after the acid leaching process. An alkaline leaching step was introduced primarily to remove these particles as the glass would be digested, and the metal would dislodged. A secondary benefit was found in the form of surface digestion.

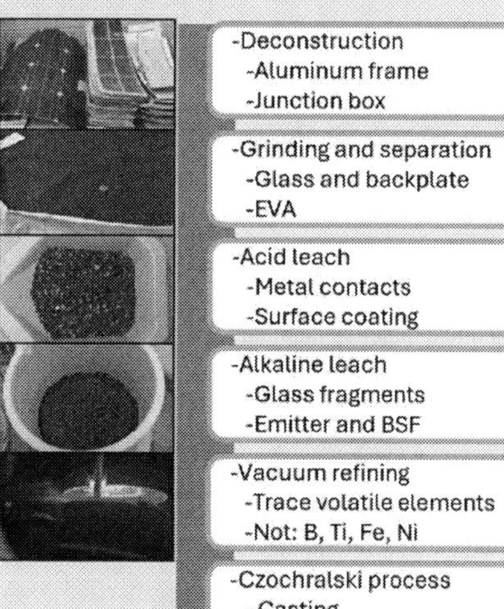

Polarized light image of acid leached PV-Si grain, with impurities

The separation and acidic leaching were initially performed by our partners. The alkaline leaching was performed in a dedicated stirring beaker reactor with 1 M NaOH at 25 °C for up to 6 hours. The vacuum refining was performed at 1500 °C and 5 Pa for 60 minutes. Both using the samples provided by Fraunhofer.

- Deconstruction
  - Aluminum frame
  - Junction box
- Grinding and separation
  - Glass and backplate
  - EVA
- Acid leach
  - Metal contacts
  - Surface coating
- Alkaline leach
  - Glass fragments
  - Emitter and BSF
- Vacuum refining
  - Trace volatile elements
  - Not: B, Ti, Fe, Ni
- Czochralski process
  - Casting
  - Not: B, C, P, As

Schematic of Si recycling path, including vacuum refining process

[1] APOLLO. (n.d.). APOLLO. Taken 12 may 2025, from https://www.apolloproject.eu
[2] Gangopadhyay, U. (2012). Comparative simulation study between n- type and p- type Silicon Solar Cells and the variation of efficiency of n- type Solar Cell by the application of passivation layer with different thickness using AFORS HET and PC1D. *IOSR Journal of Engineering, 02*(08), 41–48. https://doi.org/10.9790/3021-02814148
[3] Safarian, J., & Tangstad, M. (2012). Vacuum refining of molten silicon. *Metallurgical and Materials Transactions B, 43*(6), 1427–1445. https://doi.org/10.1007/s11663-012-9728-1
[4] Bathey, B. R., & Cretella, M. C. (1982). Solar-grade silicon. *Journal of Materials Science, 17*(11), 3077–3096. https://doi.org/10.1007/BF01203469

PARTNERS

Fraunhofer · NEW · EPFL · IPN · kalyon · MINESPIDER · MGG metrex · ODTU GUNAM · NSG · FENIX.TNT · NTNU · SAULE · SINTEF · UNIVERSITY OF LEICESTER · soltven · University of Glasgow

FUNDING

UKRI · Innovate UK

Project funded by

Co-funded by the European Union

NOVEL PV CONVERSION MECHANISMS
IN CRYSTALLINE SILICON FILLED
WITH CONDITIONED AMORPHIZED GRAINS

Z.T. KUZNICKI
SEGTON Advanced Technology
Address: 99 Boulevard de la REINE, 78000 VERSAILLES, France
Email: zbig.kuznicki@segton.com

ABSTRACT: Our research reveals a novel mechanism for low-energy generation and multiplication of secondary electrons in silicon nanostructures, specifically triggered by the UV component of the solar spectrum. By harnessing the additional kinetic energy of hot electrons, we introduce a complementary photovoltaic (PV) conversion pathway to surpass the Shockley-Queisser efficiency limit of 30% in silicon solar cells. These experimental findings, along with their theoretical interpretation, were developed within the LEEMONS Project. They directly informed the innovative design and architecture of the hidden tandem demonstrators, which were subsequently fabricated to meet stringent performance requirements.
Keywords: Silicon Solar Cell, High-Efficiency, Interfaces and Nanocomponents, Hot Electrons, Low-energy Secondary Generation and Multiplication.

1 INTRODUCTION

Amorphized grains have been built-in into crystalline silicon lattice by the ion implantation, their controlled amorphization and thermodynamic conditioning. Such an immersion is unfortunately always accompanied by postimplant defects with highly active recombination centers that completely obscures the desired effects of photogeneration.

This work presents the spectacular revelation of a phenomenon triggered by hard UVs in a transformed Si wafer; the secondary generation in highly hostile environment, see Fig. 1.

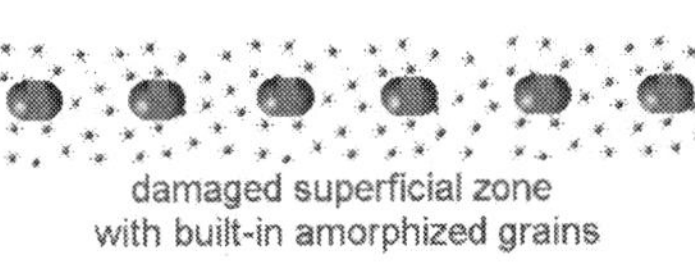

Figure 1: Built-in amorphized nanograins in unifacial silicon test device with a near-perfectly passivated front face (artist's view).

2 EXPERIMENT

FIG. 2 presents an optical view of built-in nanosystem of amorphized grains while FIGs. 3 and 4 show TEM image of amorphized grain cross section and the positions of the two built-in SEG-Matter nanolayers that are well-visualized on the SIMS fluorine profile; upper, at a depth greater than **19.5 nm** and lower, at a depth greater than **28 nm**.

Significant changes in the spectral response measurement conditions enable insight into the generation-recombination (G-R) balance even in the presence of strong recombination activity at well-defined zones.

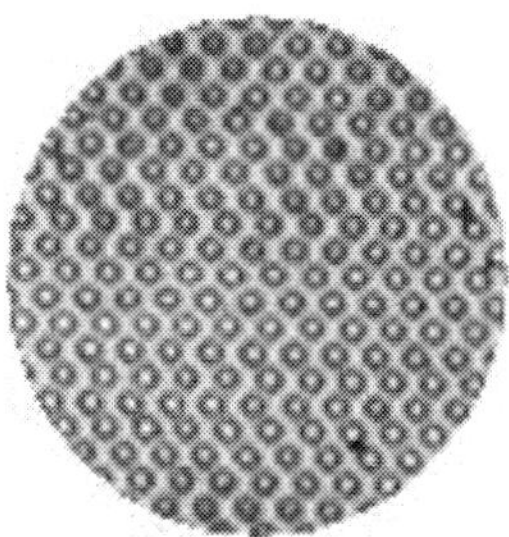

Figure 2: A nanosystem featuring 2 μm amorphized grains built-in into a crystalline silicon wafer, visualized by optical microscopy.

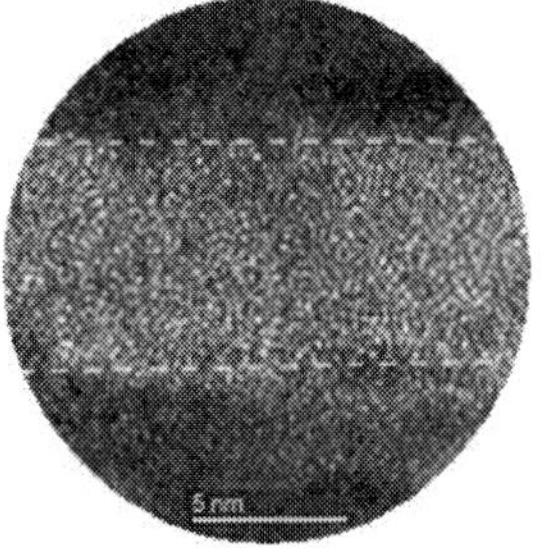

Figure: 3: TEM image of a cross-section illustrating the geometric structure of buried amorphized grains, the layers from top to bottom: upper crystalline, middle amorphous, and lower crystalline.

It should be emphasized that both defects and the secondary generation centers are localized at the superficial zone of the wafer. FIG. 1 illustrates the defected area, in which are plunged the generation centers that are internal to a Si metamaterial, named SEG-Matter.

Indeed, the precise positions of the two built-in SEG-Matter nanolayers appear in SIMS measurements, as shows the related fluorine profile, see FIG. 4.

The active surface coverage of SEG-Matter is limited to that of amorphized grains.

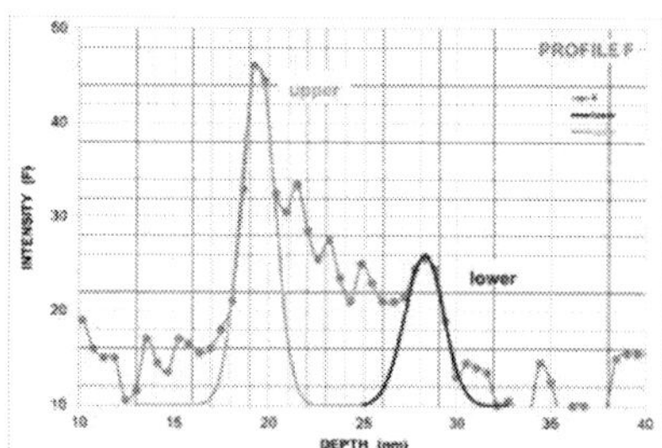

Figure 4: The positions of the two built-in SEG-Matter nanolayer appear clearly on the SIMS fluorine profile: the upper layer at a depth exceeding 19.5 nm and the lower layer at a depth exceeding 28 nm.

2.1 Experimental Protocol and Strategy

An optimized experimental protocol enables direct visualization of light-induced phenomena in silicon-embedded nanostructures. The protocol for our spectral response measurements is designed to deliberately manipulate the G-R balance to achieve defect saturation.

Spectral response measurements, under steady-state and time-resolved excitation, reveal abundant secondary electron generation, even in the presence of strong internal recombination. This secondary generation, localized at the wafer surface, is made observable through near-perfect electron transport and dynamic control of the G-R balance.

2.2 Methods for Achieving Defect Saturation

Saturation of the near-surface recombination centers can be achieved in two ways:

(i) By applying a continuous, broad-spectrum white light optical bias to maintain a steady-state population of free carriers that fill the defect states.

(ii) By increasing the flux of the monochromatic probe beam itself, so that it is intense enough to simultaneously generate collectable free carrier population that is enable to saturate the defects.

2.3 Key Challenges

The main obstacle is isolating the intrinsic optoelectronic activity of SEG-Matter nanostructures, which are integrated into crystalline silicon via ion implantation. The near-surface region, where UV absorption occurs, suffers from high-localized recombination due to surface states and postimplant defect zone, usually masking the useful photogeneration.

2.4 Solution

To observe the specific electronic activity of SEG-Matter under so adverse conditions, it is necessary to suppress or passivate the recombination pathways associated with the postimplant defects localized close to the surface zone.

This is possible to achieve this by employing an **optical bias** technique and different conditions of spectral response measurements.

3 RESULTS

Figure 6 shows the measured spectral response across the entire spectral range, highlighting a distinct feature in the long-wavelength range (800–1100 nm).

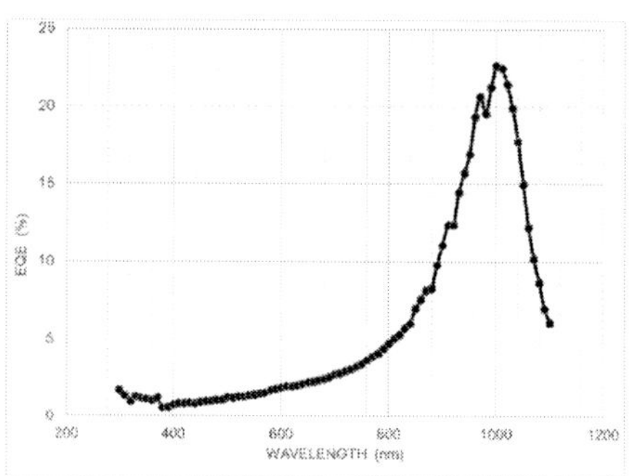

Figure 5: The dark-measured spectral response across the full range highlights a specific long-wavelength region (800–1100 nm), where external circuit collection is observed.

Longer-wavelength light penetrates deeper into the wafer, beyond the defect-rich near-surface region, generating a primary population of electron-hole pairs in the "clean" bulk of the semiconductor. Here, recombination from postimplant defects is negligible. However, a second harmful effect persists: the "sink effect," which causes internal recombination of photocarriers generated in the bulk. These carriers can diffuse back toward the defect-laden near-surface region and be annihilated before collection in the external circuit.

This leakage recombination acts as a powerful sink, ensuring that the overall G-R balance remains dominated by near-surface defects. As a result, the photogenerated carrier population is insufficient to overcome this sink, preventing net current collection in the external circuit at middle wavelengths (400–800 nm).

In general, recombination occurs at front-defects or rear-side contacts. Whereas in the wavelength range between 800 and 1100 nm, useful recombination on contacts predominates. Figure 1 illustrates the device structure, showing how the sink effect drives internal carrier recombination within the surface-damaged zone surrounding amorphized grains.

3.1 Spatial differentiation of photogeneration and recombination areas

Spatial segregation of G-R dynamics, both near the surface and in the bulk, as well as near and far from defects, enables targeted investigation of carrier photogeneration in the short-wavelength range (250–400 nm) via efficient carrier collection, as evidenced by short-circuit current measurements.

At UV, photogeneration remains confined to the shallow depth of light penetration. The "sink effect", where bulk-generated carriers diffuse back and recombine at near-surface defects, is absent, since free carrier generation does not occur in the bulk. Instead, the generation-recombination balance and net current collection are governed exclusively by the superficial zone.

3.2 Carrier collection

Carrier collection was first observed in the long-wavelength range (800–1000 nm), as shown in Fig. 6. This phenomenon arises from the spatial localization of absorption sites and the relative proximity of the collecting contacts, enabling effective collection of electron-hole pairs. .

Under the established experimental conditions (detailed experimental protocol), efficient carrier collection should be observed in the short-wavelength UV range. Indeed, the high photogeneration rate saturates defect-related recombination centers, while the near-perfect quality of the wafer ensures excellent carrier transport.

3.3 Time-resolved measurements

Time-resolved photogeneration experiments focused on the surface region reveal critical insights. When the photogeneration intensity exceeds a threshold, internal recombination is dynamically suppressed, as shown in FIG. 6.

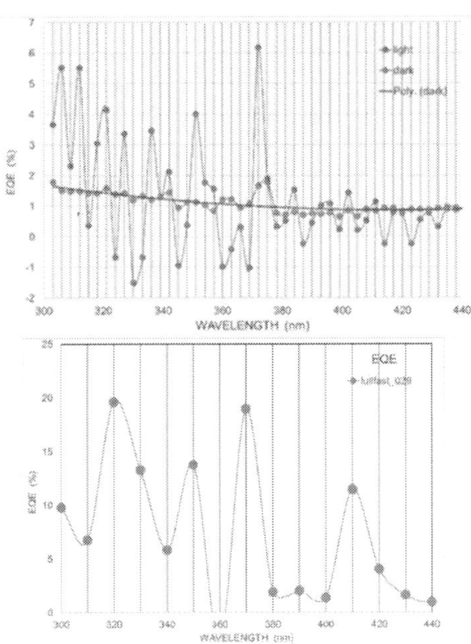

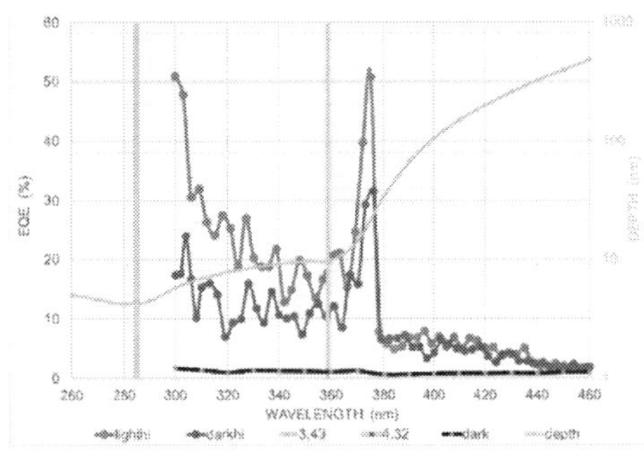

Figure 6: Dynamic EQE in a highly recombinant environment, the G-R balance. Results show in:
upper graph, a shorter 3 nm wavelength spread indicated by thin blue vertical lines. Comparison of curves acquired under two distinct conditions: i) without optical bias (orange) and ii) with optical bias (blue);
lower graph, a larger 10 nm wavelength spread of the measurement points.
Conditions: concentrated spot, acquisition time 1 sec/pt, average over three measurements per point.

The suppression of the recombination activity allows measurements to track the evolution of free electron populations and precisely locate secondary generation centers under UV excitation.

A wavelength-dependent scan further exposes the interplay between beneficial (contact-mediated) and detrimental (defect-driven) recombination processes.

Slow-scan UV measurements, highlight dynamic shifts in the G-R balance. This approach enables real-time observation of transient free electron populations in nanostructured silicon wafers, capturing their formation, electron transport and decay.

3.4 Abundant secondary generation

The experimental approach created conditions that allowed observation of abundant secondary carrier generation in the short-wavelength range (250–400 nm), even in the presence of highly active recombination centers, by dynamically modulating the G-R balance.

All observed data result from two recombination mechanisms: beneficial recombination at contacts and detrimental recombination at defects.

Surpassing a certain generation intensity threshold indicated complete dynamic suppression of internal recombination.

Moreover, UV illumination enables precise spatial mapping of these secondary generation sites, see FIG. 7.

Figure 7: Collection of hard UV conversion in a silicon test device measured in different conditions.

The thresholds of two direct bandgaps are marked by vertical lines: first (green line) at 3.43 eV (358.6 nm) and second (blue line) at 4.32 eV (284.7 nm). The penetration depth of light into crystalline silicon is shown for comparison.

Three spectral responses are shown: dark curve, usual in the dark; blue curve, usual in the dark but with a stronger incident beam; rose curve, measured with optical bias.

4 CONCLUSIONS

Through our experimental approach, we established conditions to improve the detection of secondary generation, even amidst particularly adverse G-R balances. This measurement methodology will be used as part of LEEMONS project to improve solar cell characterization understanding.

A time-resolved equilibrium between generation and recombination was distinctly evident. Elevated photogeneration, driven by well-integrated secondary generation centers, temporarily neutralizes recombination activity under UV excitation.

All observed data are attributable to two recombination mechanisms: beneficial recombination occurring at contacts and detrimental recombination associated with defects.

References

[1] Application of innovations grouped under the name giant photoconversion, Z.T. Kuznicki, P. Meyrueis, M. Hosatte; M. Basta, Proc. SPIE 12150 Photonics for Solar Energy Systems IX, 121500A (24 May 2022; doi:10.1117/12.2620963.

[2] Hidden Tandem Solar Cells, Z.T. Kuźnicki, 8th World Conference on Photovoltaic Energy Conversion (WCPEC-8), September 26-30, 2022, Milan, Italy. M. Smith, A. Miller, Proceedings 17th European Photovoltaic Solar Energy Conference, Vol. I (2022) 903.

Acknowledgements

The author thanks Dr. Mikael Hosatte for experimental support and Mr. Brice Rouffie for coordinating sample production (SEGTON AdT), as well as Dr. Damien Lachenal for providing the experimental platform and Dr. Pierre Papet for the spectral response measurements (Meyer Burger).

Analysis of Cu-Associated Defects in Silicon through Lifetime Spectroscopy

Dasilva-Villanueva N.[1], Fuertes Marrón D.[1], del Cañizo C.[1]

Instituto de Energía Solar, ETSI Telecomunicación, Universidad Politécnica de Madrid, Avenida Complutense 40 (28040), Madrid, Spain

Lifetime spectroscopy (LS):
determination of defect parameters from carrier lifetime measurements (Rein, Springer, 2005)

$$\tau_{SRH} = \tau_{n0} \frac{p_0 + p_1 + \Delta n}{n_0 + p_0 + \Delta n} + \tau_{p0} \frac{n_0 + n_1 + \Delta n}{n_0 + p_0 + \Delta n}$$

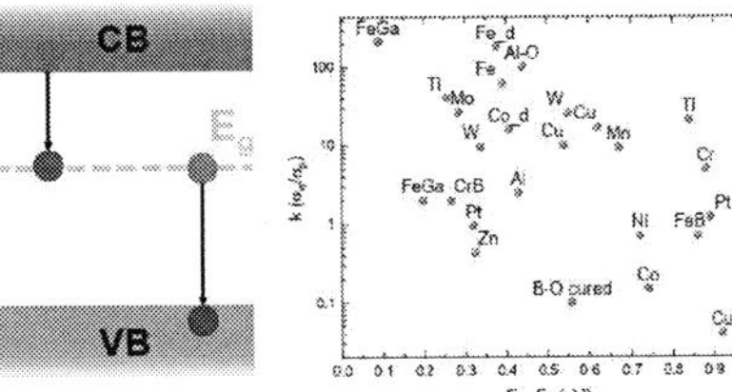

- SRH recombination characterized by defect **energy level** (E_t) and **ratio of capture cross-sections** (σ_n/σ_p, k)
- If SRH recombination **is dominant**: **defect identification through LS**
- Useful for low defect concentration: **undetectable through compositional techniques**

Step 1. Determination of carrier lifetime (LT) contributions:
- LT measurement (PCD)
- Determination of intrinsic and surface contributions
- Determination of SRH contribution

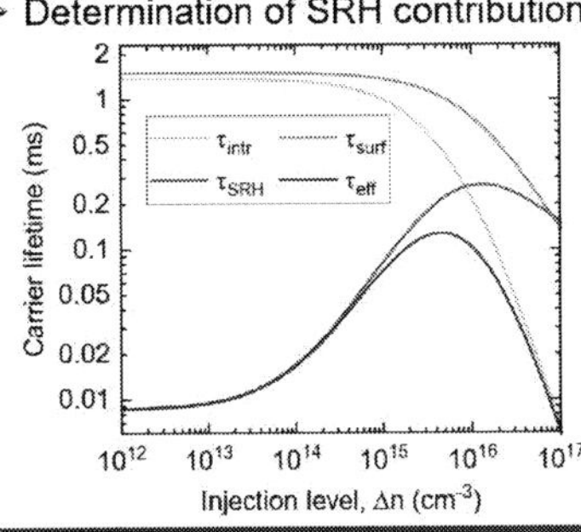

Step 2. Fit of the SRH contribution:
- Change Δn variable to X (n/p) in p-type or Y (p/n) in p-type
- Fit to the harmonic sum of n straight lines, corresponding to n defects
- Extraction of the slope and intercept

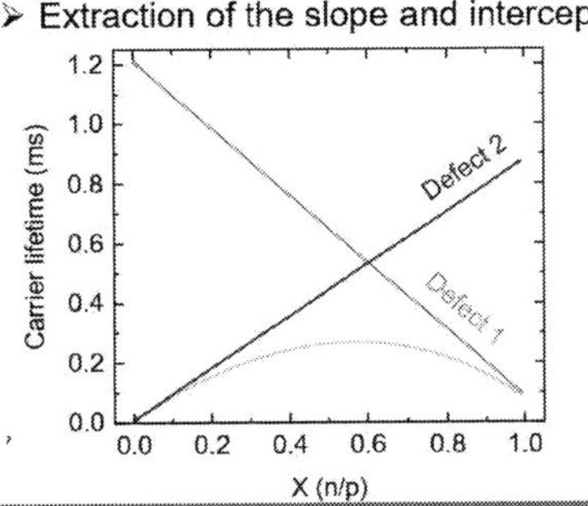

Step 3. Obtain defect parameters:
- Analytical expressions for E_t-k curves from fitting parameters
- Comparison of the curves obtained with the defect map

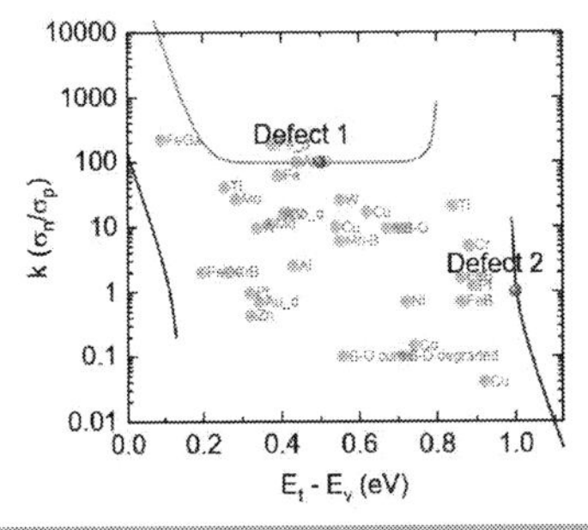

Case study:
- Two p-type mc solar-grade Si wafers, different effective carrier lifetimes, resistivity ~1Ω·cm

LS analysis:
- Difference in carrier lifetime between samples: different nature and/or defect concentration
- Compositional and metaestable analysis: rules out the presence of Fe, Cr and Ni
- LS analysis: two levels associated to Cu precipitates [1, 2]

[1] Inglese et al., Energy Procedia, 2016
[2] Lindroos J., Phd Thesis, 2015

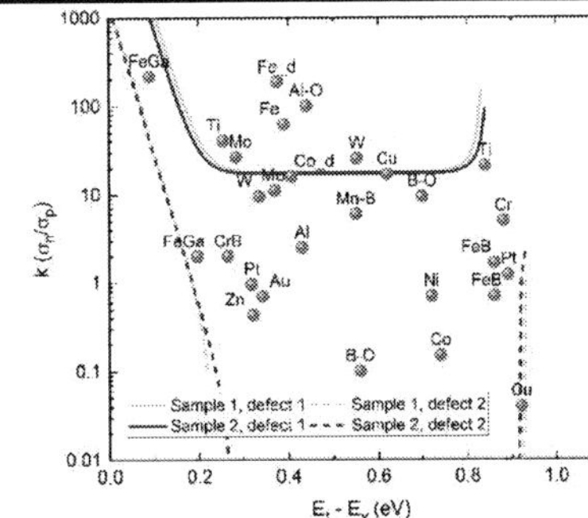
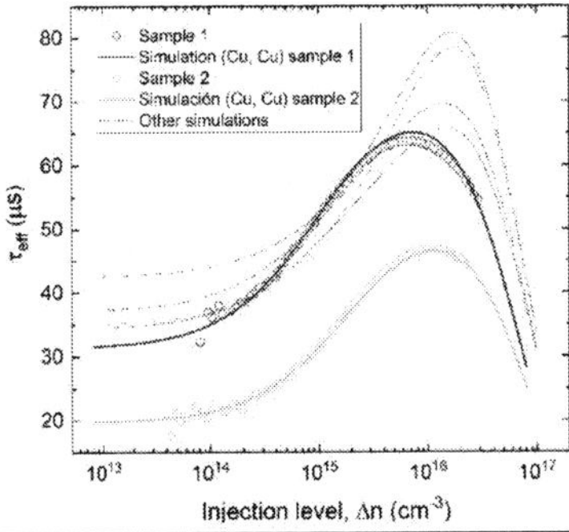

Multi-level defects:
- Some impurities introduce **more than one level**: Cu precipitates reported in literature as a **two-level defect** [2]
- Recombination rate associated to *a two-level defect* **different** from the recombination rate associated to *two defects acting simultaneously*
- **Complex lifetime expression**, 6-variable equation:

$$\tau_{SRH} = \frac{1 + \left(\frac{\sigma_{n1}v_{the}n_1 + \sigma_{p1}v_{thh}p}{\sigma_{p1}v_{thh}p_1 + \sigma_{n1}v_{the}n}\right) + \left(\frac{\sigma_{p2}v_{thh}p_2 + \sigma_{n2}v_{the}n}{\sigma_{n2}v_{the}n_2 + \sigma_{p2}v_{thh}p}\right)}{N_t(n_0 + p_0 + \Delta n)\left[\left(\frac{\sigma_{n1}\sigma_{p1}v_{the}v_{thh}}{\sigma_{p1}v_{thh}p_1 + \sigma_{n1}v_{the}n}\right) + \left(\frac{\sigma_{n2}\sigma_{p2}v_{the}v_{thh}}{\sigma_{n2}v_{the}n_2 + \sigma_{p2}v_{thh}p}\right)\right]}$$

- Fit performed with 4 parameters for each (E_{t1}, E_{t2}) data pair [3]
- **Fitting residuals** shown in contour plot: minimum value indicates **"true"** solution
- Good agreement with reported Cu precipitate states [2]: two-level defect, deep level with $E_c - E_t = 0.5$ eV and k = 22.4, shallow level with $E_c - E_t = 0.96$ eV and k = 0.042.

[3] Zhu et al., Solar Energy Materials and Solar Cells, 2020

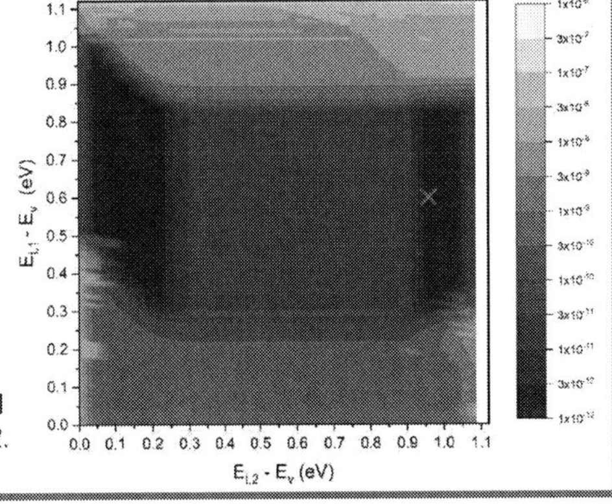

Conclusions

Acknowledgements. This research was funded by CETPartnership, the Clean Energy Transition Partnership under the 2023 joint call for research proposals, co-funded by the European Commission (GA N°101069750) and with the Spanish Research Agency MICIU/AEI10.13039/501100011033 through the TANDEM Project, (PCI2024-155056-2) Financial support from Grant No. PID2023-148369OB-C41 funded by the Spanish Research Agency is also acknowledged.

- Lifetime spectroscopy analysis **applied to SoG-Si wafers**
- **Computational analysis** for the SRH-equation based on a dual-level defect
- **Solution through fitting residual analysis** shows **good agreement** with reported values for Cu precipitates in literature
- **Identification of the dual-level introduced by Cu precipitates** as dominating SRH recombination in **SoG-Si wafers**

INVESTIGATION OF PROCESS PARAMETERS ON THE DISTRIBUTION OF THE MATERIAL PARAMETERS IN CZ-CRYSTALS DOPED WITH ANTIMONY

F. Mosel[1], N. Schüler[2]
[1] PVA Crystal Growing Sytems GmbH, Im Westpark 10-12, 35435 Wettenberg, Germany
[2] Freiberg Instruments GmbH, Delfter Straße 6, 09599 Freiberg, Germany
e-mail: frank.mosel@pvatepla.com
phone: +49 64168690-125, fax: +49 64168690-822

ABSTRACT: The market share of Cz mono-Si for the industrial mass production of solar cells has grown steadily in recent years. Casted Si has practically disappeared from the market. At the same time, a clear trend from p-type to n-type base material can be observed due to a progressive transition from PERC technology based on p-type cells to TOPCon solar cell structures based on n-type material (Fig.1). Phosphorus (P), arsenic (As), and antimony (Sb) are doping elements for n-type crystals, but until now, P-doped substrate crystals are standard. Here, too, a substitution of phosphorus with antimony as a doping element is emerging, similar to p-type substrate crystals, where the doping element boron was replaced with gallium. The advantage of Sb-doped crystals is the possibility of producing crystals with an almost axial homogeneous distribution of the specific resistivity by selecting appropriate process parameters. We examined the influence of the evaporation behavior of antimony during the crystal growth of Cz mono-Si in the resistivity range of interest for solar cells. We will present our main results in this conference contribution.
Keywords: resistivity distribution, antimony-doping, Czochralski process, evaporation

1 INTRODUCTION

For the c-Si module market the mass production of Si mono-wafers using the Czochralski (Cz) growth technique with recharging is the most economical production method.

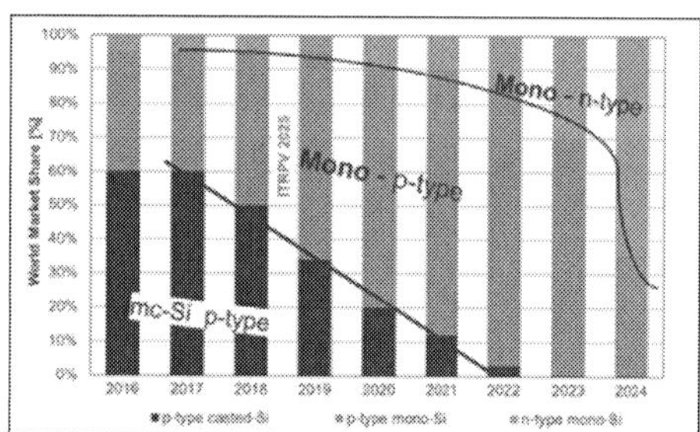

Figure 1: Market share for different wafer types [1]

For technological and economic reasons, the substrate crystals should have homogeneous material properties, both in axial and radial dimensions. The specific resistivity and the minority carrier lifetime are the outstanding material properties for a high solar cell efficiency. All doping elements in silicon have a distribution coefficient $k < 1$. This inevitably leads to a dopant enrichment in the melt during crystal growth, resulting in axial and radial inhomogeneous dopant incorporation. In addition to the segregation effect, some dopants exhibit a noticeable evaporation behavior from the silicon melt. Thus, with these dopants, two physical phenomena occur independently of each other. First, the dopant is incorporated into the growing crystal according to Scheil's law with the distribution coefficient of the dopant used. This means that the melt is continuously enriched with the dopant during the crystal growth process. Second, the dopant evaporates across the free melt surface. This means that the melt volume is permanently depleted of the dopant. Ideally, both effects can be balanced by varying the growth parameters in that way that a nearly constant dopant supply is maintained in the melt volume during the crystal growth process.

Boron was used as dopant for p-type crystals for a long time, but has been replaced by gallium due to its better stability with respect to LID. But also, for n-type crystals there are signs for a transition from phosphorus to antimony as dopant. The reason for this lies in the possibility of controlling the antimony content in the melt to a certain extent by varying the process atmosphere, despite the significantly less favorable distribution coefficient of antimony (k_{Sb}=0.023) compared to phosphorus (k_P=0.35). The effects of dopant enrichment and dopant depletion in the melt during the Cz-process are discussed in this paper.

2 APPROACH

2.1 Crystal growth

The crystal growth experiments presented in this paper were performed in a Cz-puller from PVA Crystal Growing Systems GmbH. Several 8-inch crystals were grown under identical growth conditions, except for the applied process pressure. To ensure comparability of the radial homogeneity of the grown crystals, the same rotation rates of crystal and crucible were applied. All samples examined in this work were grown from solar-grade polysilicon. As dopant antimony of 5N-quality was added as element to the silicon melt during its homogenization phase. Here too, the same time sequence was guaranteed for all crystal growth experiments which were successfully completed in the first attempt, i.e. no remelting due to structure loss was necessary. Six slices were sawn out of each crystal for characterization as shown in Fig.2. Evaporation coefficients were determined in separate experiments in a stagnant silicon melt.

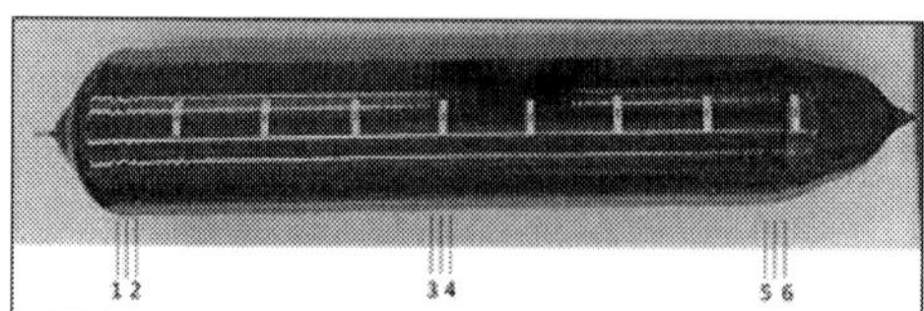

Figure 2: 8-inch Sb-doped Cz-silicon crystal

2.2 Axial distribution of the specific resistivity in Sb-doped Si-crystals

Crystal growth experiments were carried out with different initial dopant concentrations (Sb) at different Ar-process pressures. The applied process pressures are given in the legend of Fig.3 and Fig.4. With one exception, the pressures were constant during the growth experiments. In one special case, the process pressure was reduced from 30 mbar to 25 mbar during the body growth. Argon was used as the process gas in all crystal growth experiments at a flow rate of 30 l/min. The axial resistivity distributions were measured on the untreated surface of the grown crystals. Fig.3 shows the axial curves of the specific resistivity fitted to the measured data. For a better comparability of the results, Fig.4 shows the resistivity curves normalized to a starting value of 1 Ωcm at the top of the crystal body. Additionally, the axial resistivity distribution at a pressure of 20 mbar is plotted as a dashed line, as it would be expected theoretically applying a segregation coefficient of Sb (k_{Sb}=0.023), but without evaporation loss of antimony.

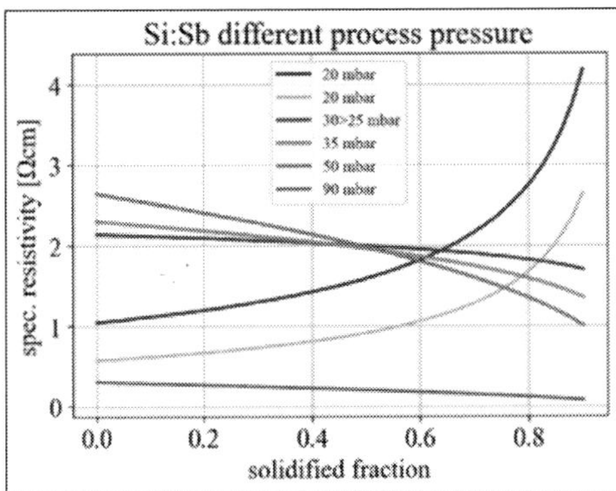

Figure 3: Axial resistivity distributions for different Ar-process pressures

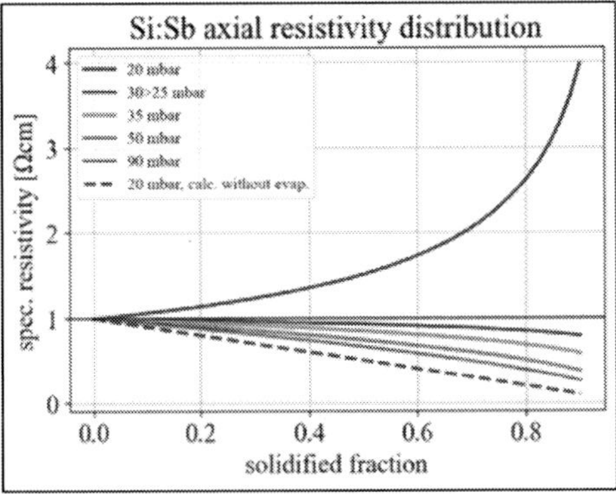

Figure 4: Axial resistivity distributions for different Ar-process pressures, normalized to 1 Ωcm at body start

Fig.4 shows that, under the applied growth parameters, merely an appropriate process gas control should be sufficient to achieve an axial homogeneous resistivity distribution in the Cz-crystal. The extreme sensitivity of the Ar-process pressure in the range between 20 mbar and 30 mbar is evident.

We therefore performed a crystal growth experiment according to Zulehner [2] with a continuously decreasing Ar-pressure from 60 mbar to 18 mbar to investigate the critical pressure range more precisely. Therefore, we previously modeled the limited process data from Fig.4 using a neural network with two hidden layers, as shown in Fig.5.

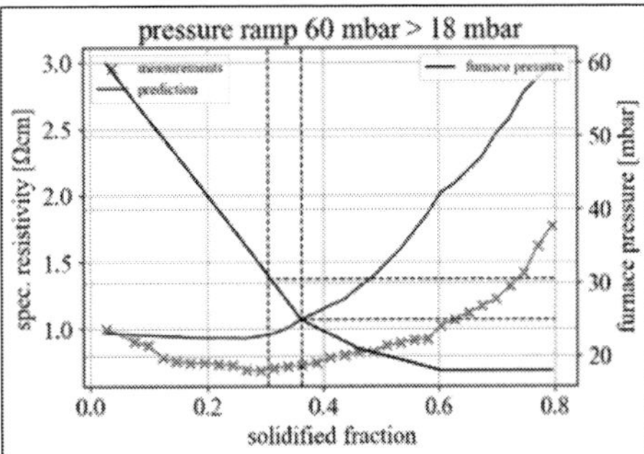

Figure 5: Theoretical and measured axial resistivity distribution of the Si:Sb crystal grown under a descending Ar-pressure of 60 mbar > 18 mbar

The calculated (=prediction) and measured (x) axial resistivity distributions are shown in Fig.5. Although there is a significant discrepancy between the calculated and measured data due to the limited amount of available data, it can be concluded that a control of the Sb-evaporation rate under the present crystal growth conditions in the pressure range between 30 mbar and 25 mbar should be applicable to balance the Sb evaporation in the melt with the Sb-enrichment near the crystallization front. Below 25 mbar the Sb-loss by evaporation across the free melt surface outweighs the segregation effect of the Sb-enrichment at the crystallization front causing an increase of the specific resistivity.

2.3 Radial distribution of the specific resistivity and minority carrier lifetime in Sb-doped Si-crystals

All crystal growth experiments shown in Fig.3 and Fig.4 are characterized by means of spatially resolved measurements of the specific resistivity and minority carrier lifetime on the corresponding crystal wafers as sketched in Fig.1. The measurement tool was the MDPpro from Freiberg Instruments GmbH [3] operating with a resolution of 1 mm. The resistivity is measured via an eddy current sensor and the lifetime is determined by means of MDP (Microwave Detected Photoconductivity) technique using a 980 nm laser for excitation with a penetration depth of 500 μm and duration of excitation pulse of 1000 μs. The measurements were performed on the as-sawn surface of the slices. Fig.6 - Fig.9 show the results of the mappings of the two crystal growth experiments, which were grown under a constant process pressure of 20 mbar (ingot A) and a decreasing process pressure of 30 mbar to 25 mbar (ingot B).

A comparison of Fig.7 with Fig.9 shows a drastic optimization in the axial resistivity distribution. In contrast, the process pressure does not appear to have any noticeable influence on the radial resistivity distribution.

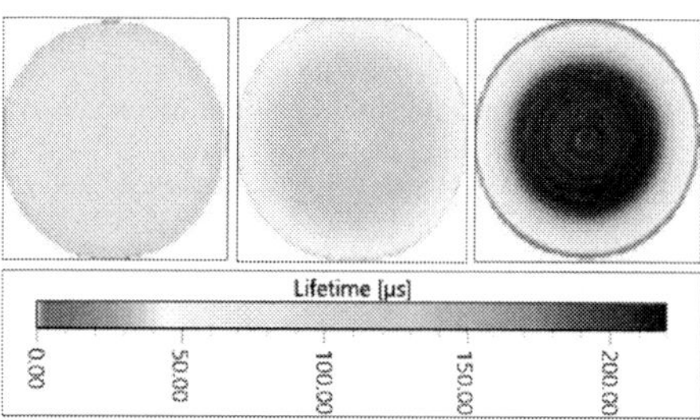

Figure 6: Lifetime maps of top-, middle-, tail-wafer of Ingot A, grown under a constant Ar-pressure of 20 mbar

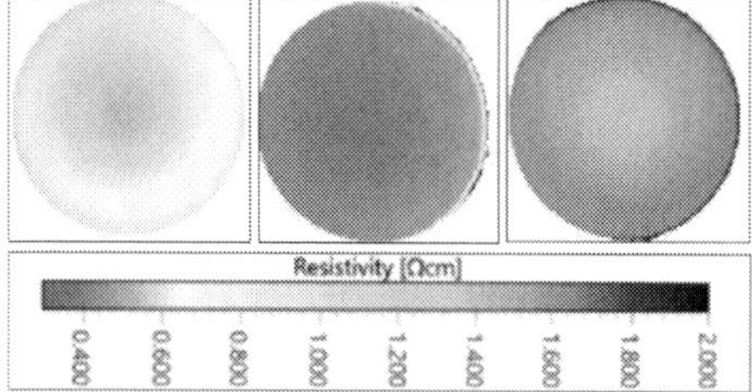

Figure 7: Resistivity maps of top-, middle-, tail-wafer of Ingot A, grown under a constant Ar-pressure of 20 mbar

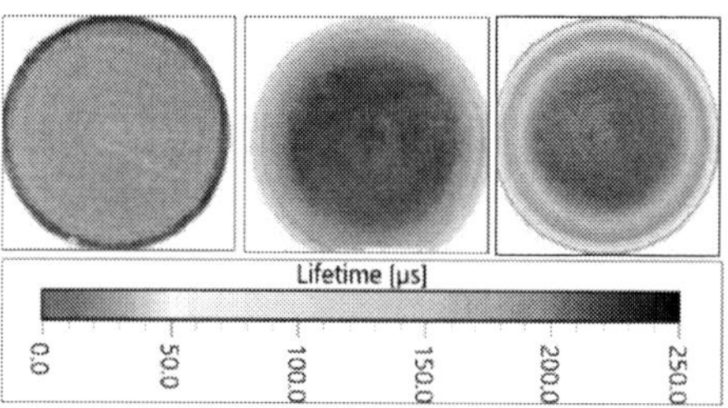

Figure 8: Lifetime maps of top-, middle-, tail-wafer of Ingot B, grown under a descending Ar-pressure of 30 mbar > 25 mbar

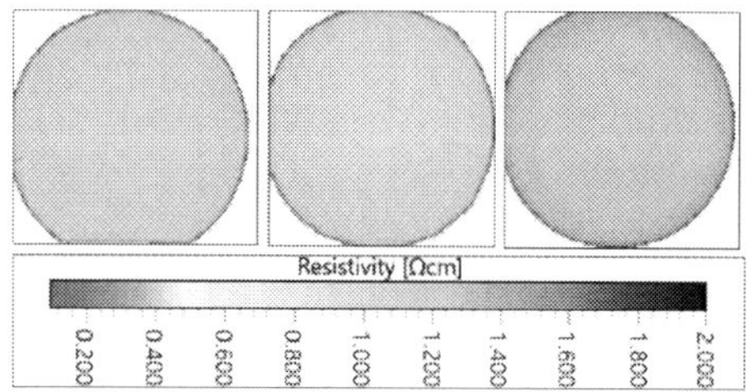

Figure 9: Resistivity maps of top-, middle-, tail-wafer of Ingot B, grown under a descending Ar-pressure of 30 mbar > 25 mbar

2.4 Influence of the growth parameters on the axial and radial Sb-distribution in the grown crystals

The dopant incorporation during the Cz batch process can described by the differential equation [4]:

$$\frac{dC_l}{dt} = \frac{C_l}{m_l}\frac{dm_x}{dt} - \frac{kC_l}{m_l}\frac{dm_x}{dt} - \frac{\gamma A_s}{m_l}C_l \quad (DGL)$$

with: C_l: dopant concentration in the melt, m_l: mass of the melt, m_x: mass of the crystal, k: distribution coefficient, γ: coefficient of evaporation rate, A_s: free melt surface

The following terms in (DGL) mean:

$$\frac{C_l}{m_l}\frac{dm_x}{dt} \quad (I)$$

Removal of melt (concentration of dopant) due to crystal growth

$$\frac{kC_l}{m_l}\frac{dm_x}{dt} \quad (II)$$

Removal of dopant due to crystal growth

$$\frac{gA_s}{m_l}C_l \quad (III)$$

Removal of dopant due to evaporation

Solving the DGL without considering the dopant reduction in the melt due to evaporation (III), applying the corresponding initial conditions, results in the well-known Scheil equation [5]:

$$C_l = C_0\left(1 - {m_x}/{m_0}\right)^{k-1} \quad (Scheil)$$

The two key parameters in the DGL that primarily influence the dopant incorporation during the Cz-batch process are the distribution coefficient k and the evaporation rate γ. The possibilities for influencing both parameters are described here:

2.4.1 Evaporation rate γ

The evaporation coefficient γ, also known as the evaporation rate, depends on a variety of factors, which are not all quantitatively accessible [6]. The evaporation rate depends, among other parameters, on the concentration of the evaporating element in the melt, the A/V ratio (A: free melt surface, V: melt volume), the process atmosphere (gas flow, gas pressure, gas type), the design of the hotzone, and the concentration of the elements or molecules which may be also involved in the evaporation process (e.g. oxygen).

Evaporation occurs in four sequential steps as sketched in Fig.10:

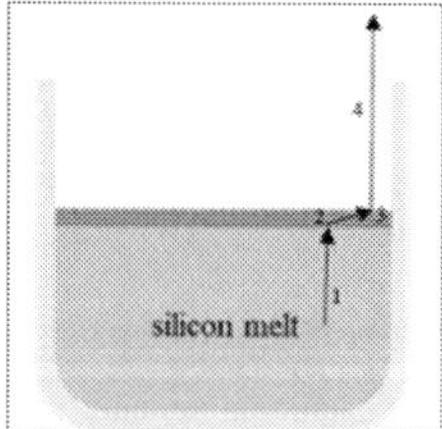

Figure 10: Sketched sequence of evaporation

1) Transport of the doping element or the oxygen compound of the doping element in the melt volume to a boundary layer, 2) Transport through the melt/gas boundary layer, 3) Physical evaporation process, 4) Removal through the gas phase. The time dependence of the evaporation process results from the four sub steps. The transport in the melt volume is dominated by the convection phenomena in the melt volume. The transport in the boundary layer is determined by convection and diffusion of the solute. The physical evaporation process

can be described by the Hertz-Knudsen equation. The transport through the gas phase is essentially influenced by the gas flow, chamber pressure, and nature of the gas (mass of the noble gas).

2.4.2 Determination of the evaporation rate using a 2-point measurement method [7]

For the determination of the evaporation rates at different process pressures, two crystal samples weighing approximately 40 g were taken from a stagnant melt as shown in Fig.11.

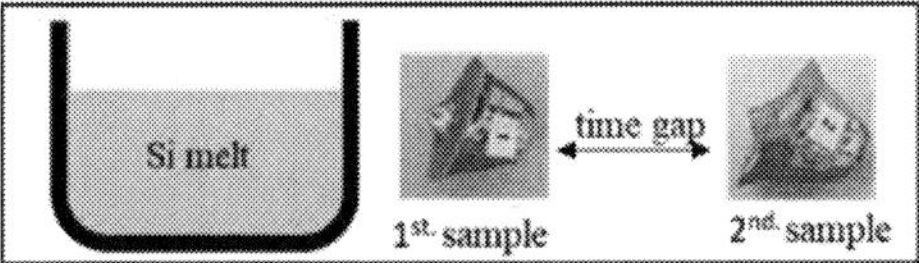

Figure 11: Principle of evaporation experiments

The chemical content of antimony in the samples was measured by means of ICP-MS (Inductively Coupled Plasma Mass Spectrometry). The main process conditions for the different evaporation experiments are given in the legend of Fig.12.

The evaporation of volatile elements can be described by a first-order kinetic reaction [6], i.e. by eq. (IV)

$$-\frac{dC}{C} = \gamma \frac{A}{V} dt \quad or \quad ln\left(\frac{C_t}{C_0}\right) = -\gamma \frac{A}{V} t \quad (IV)$$

where C_t, C_0, γ, A, V, t denote the actual doping element concentration [at/cm³], initial doping element concentration [at/cm³], evaporation rate constant [cm/s], free melt surface [cm²], melt volume [cm³], and process time [s], respectively.

The diagram shows the evaporation rates determined for antimony in a stagnant silicon melt without a growing crystal under the applied process conditions plotted versus the initial Sb concentration in the melt.

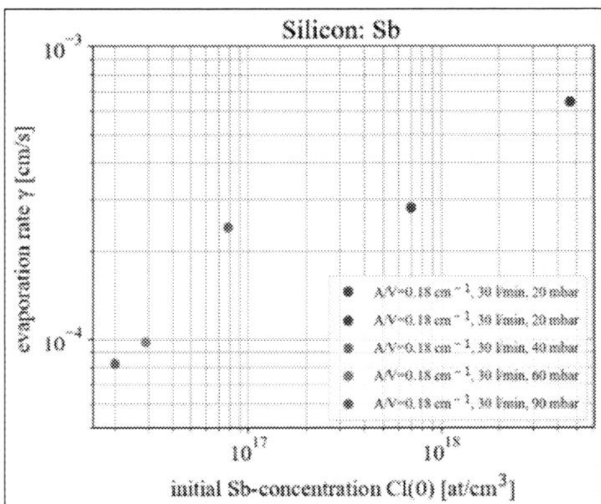

Figure 12: Overview of the evaporation coefficients γ of Sb in silicon melt

The graph illustrates that the evaporation rate γ of antimony in silicon melt is strongly influenced by the pressure of the Ar-process gas.

2.4.3 Segregation coefficient k:

Scheil's model with the segregation coefficient k as material parameter applies to a closed system without material exchange with the environment (evaporation).

$$\frac{C_S}{C_0} = k(1-g)^{k-1} \quad (Scheil)$$

with: C_S: dopant concentration in the crystal at the solidified fraction g, C_0: initial dopant concentration in the melt, k: segregation coefficient, g: solidified fraction

Since directional Cz-solidification is a dynamic process, the segregation coefficient k in Scheil's law is replaced by an effective segregation coefficient k_{eff}.

The dynamics of crystal growth (translation of the phase boundary) are described by the model of Burton, Prim, and Slichter introducing the concept of the effective segregation coefficient k_{eff} [8]:

$$k_{eff} = \frac{k_0}{k_0 + (1-k_0)exp\left(-\frac{f\delta}{D}\right)} \quad (BPS)$$

$$\delta = 1,61 D^{1/3} \nu^{1/6} \omega^{-1/2}$$

with: k_0: equilibrium distribution coefficient, f: freezing velocity, δ: extension of a boundary layer, D: diffusion constant of the dopant in the melt, v: kinematic viscosity of the melt, angular velocity of the crystal

The parameter δ in the BPS-equation is often interpreted as a boundary layer thickness in front of the crystallization interface that is enriched with dopant. The extent of this layer is mainly determined by the convection conditions in the melt. Outside of this fictitious boundary layer, the melt is completely mixed. δ should be understood as a fit parameter that considers the influence of melt convection at the phase boundary. Fig.13 shows the influence of pulling speed and crystal rotation on the effective distribution coefficient of Antimony k_{Sb}.

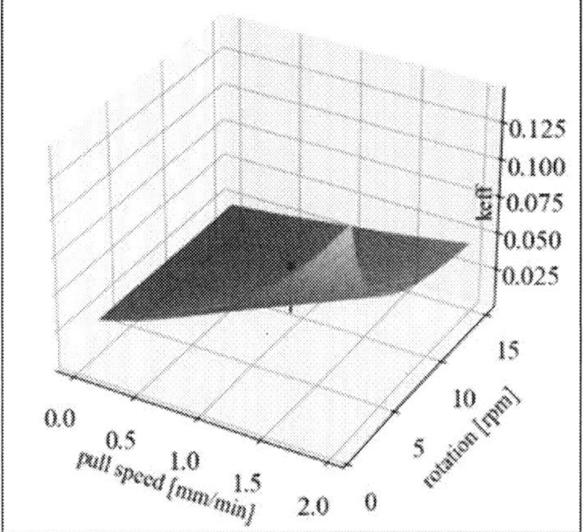

Figure 13: Segregation coefficient k_{eff} of Sb (k_{Sb}) versus average pull speed and crystal rotation. The marker (x) indicates the applied conditions.

Fig.14 illustrates the range of the BPS-parameter (v*δ/D) affecting the effective distribution coefficient of n-type dopants. The black symbols in Fig. 14 indicate the pulling parameters we apply in our 8-inch crystal growth experiments, while the red symbols represent their realistic upper limits.

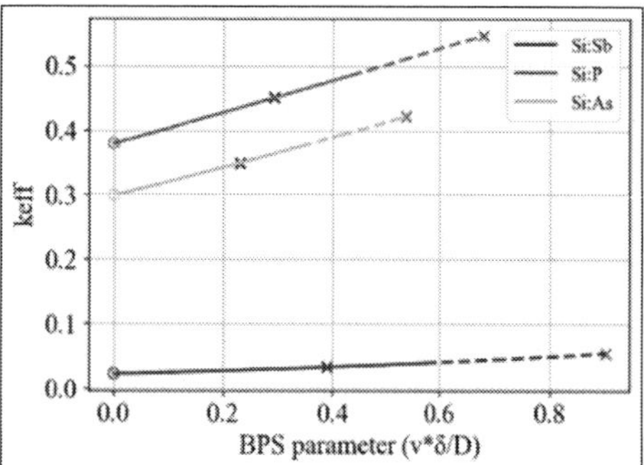

Figure 14: Segregation coefficient k_{eff} for n-type dopants versus BPS parameter. The symbols show the applied conditions ($\mathbf{x}$) and a theoretical upper limit (x).

The figures clearly show that adjusting the pulling parameters in a realistic range only have a very limited influence on the distribution coefficient and thus on the dopant incorporation.

2.5 Discussion of the radial resistivity distribution

Whereas the axial Sb-distribution in the crystal can be adjusted by controlling the process pressure during the Cz-process in order to obtain a satisfactory axial resistivity profile, the radial distribution of the resistivity does not seem to be affected and should be discussed more precisely. For that, we prepared line scans from the resistivity maps of Ingot A grown under a constant Ar-pressure of 20 mbar and Ingot B grown under a descending Ar-pressure of 30 mbar > 25 mbar and compared the measured data with theoretical values obtained from an analytical model published by H. Lee [9]. The main root causes of a radially inhomogeneous dopant incorporation are the formation of a curved interphase during crystal growth and a variation in the dopant supply at the crystallization front due to convection phenomena in the melt. The deflection of the solidification front under the applied growth conditions was measured on a crystal slice taken from the middle part of a reference crystal by means of LPS (Lateral Photovoltage Scanning) measurements [10] as shown in Fig.15. The determined deflection of the interface shape is shown in Fig.16.

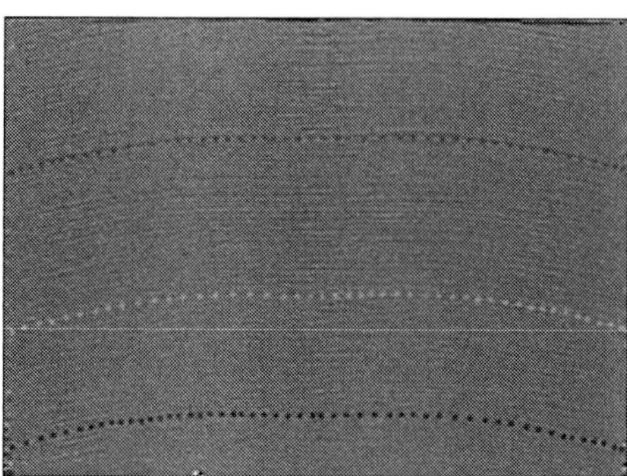

Figure 15: Interface deflection measured by means of LPS on the midlle part of the reference crystal (coloured lines)

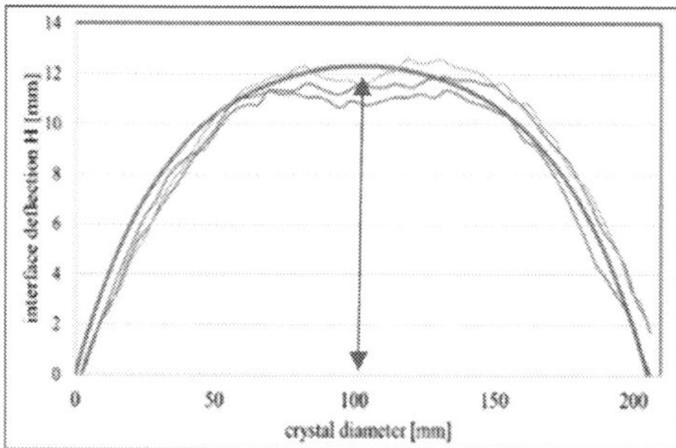

Figure 16: Interface deflection measured by means of LPS on the midlle part of the reference crystal (coloured lines) and the corresponding simulation results obtained by means of FEM simulation (blue line)

According to the model of H. Lee, the radial dopant distribution is approximated by a cubic function that reflects the rotational symmetry of the growth conditions in the Czochralski process. The different flow mechanisms resulting from forced convection (rotation conditions) and buoyancy convection are considered by a radial-dependent dopant concentration at the interface and different segregation coefficients at the center and the rim of the growing crystal. The deflection of the phase boundary is introduced in the model by its deviation from a flat interface in the crystal center (Fig.16). A detailed description of the model can be found in the corresponding literature [9]. In the following figures, the measured resistivity data are marked with blue symbols (x), the colored lines show the calculated curves according to the following theoretical assumptions:

Red curve: inhomogeneous diffusion boundary layer δ, concave interface

Green curve: inhomogeneous diffusion boundary layer δ, flat interface

Magenta curve: homogeneous diffusion boundary layer δ, concave interface

The term "diffusion boundary layer" is established in the BPS theory of the effective segregation coefficient as a descriptive interpretation of the convection conditions at the crystallization front.

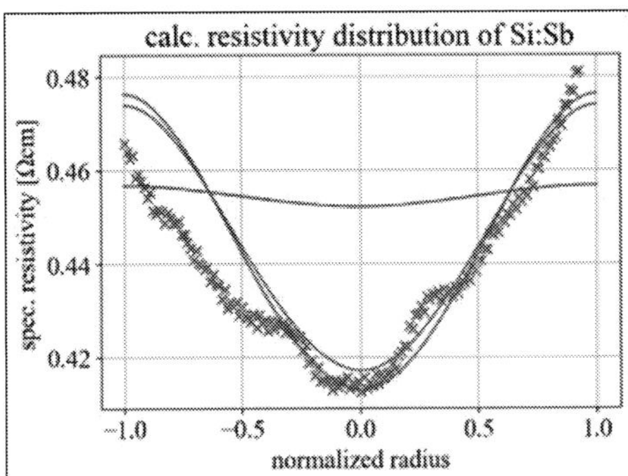

Figure 17: Measured (x) and calculated (colored lines) radial resistivity distribution at the top of ingot A, grown under a constant Ar-pressure of 20 mbar

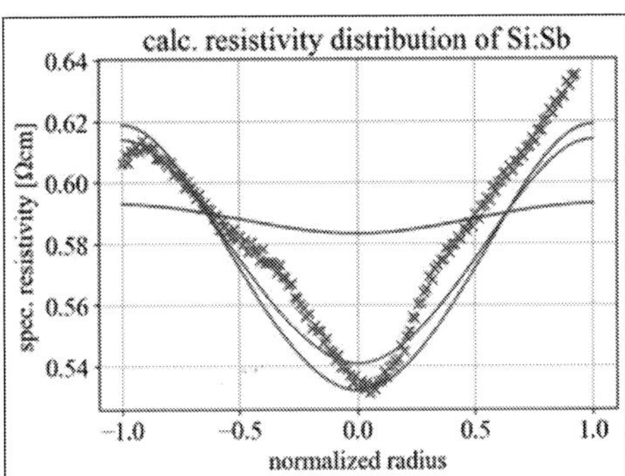

Figure 18: Measured (x) and calculated (colored lines) radial resistivity distribution in the middle of ingot A, grown under a constant Ar-pressure of 20 mbar

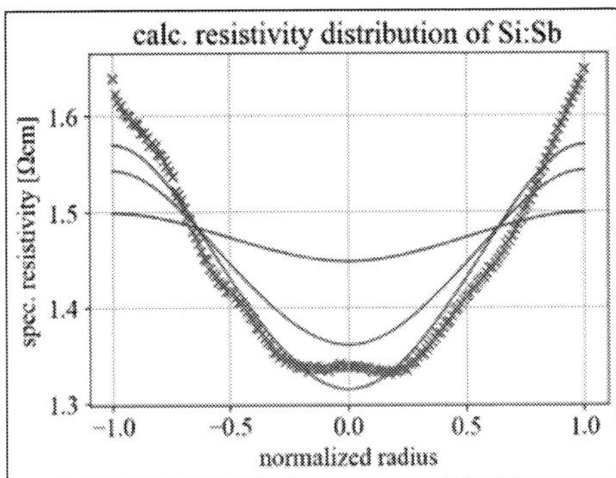

Figure 19: Measured (x) and calculated (colored lines) radial resistivity distribution at the tail of ingot A, grown under a constant Ar-pressure of 20 mbar

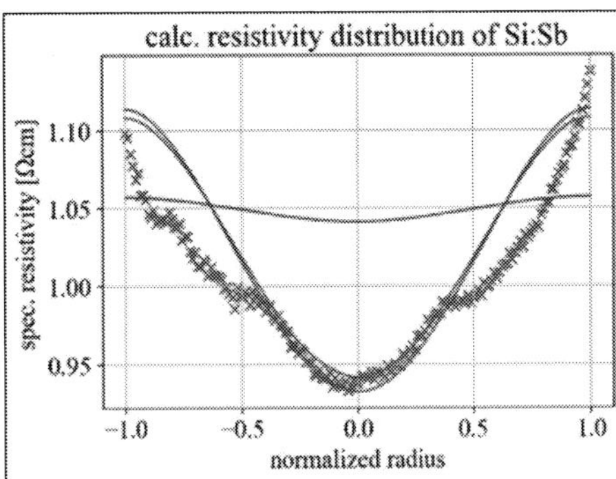

Figure 20: Measured (x) and calculated (colored lines) radial resistivity distribution at the top of ingot B, grown under a descending Ar-pressure of 30 mbar > 25 mbar

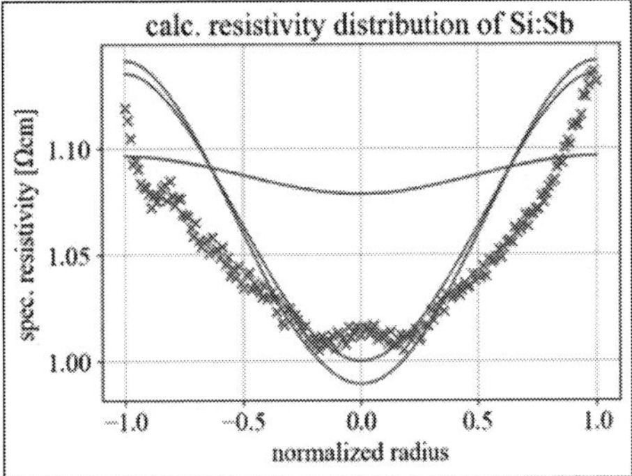

Figure 21: Measured (x) and calculated (colored lines) radial resistivity distribution in the middle of ingot B, grown under a descending Ar-pressure of 30 mbar > 25 mbar

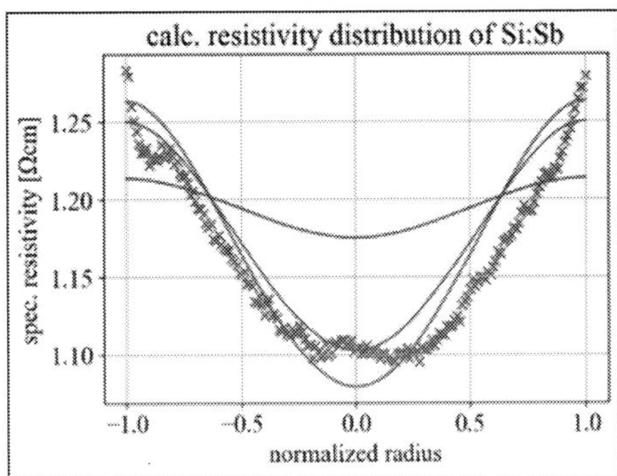

Figure 22: Measured (x) and calculated (colored lines) radial resistivity distribution at the tail of ingot B, grown under a descending Ar-pressure of 30 mbar > 25 mbar

A comparison of the radial resistivity distributions of crystal A (Fig.17–Fig.19) with crystal B (Fig.20-Fig.22) shows that the process pressure under the applied crystal growth conditions has no noticeable influence on the resistivity distribution, which is equivalent to the dopant distribution. The factors influencing the radial dopant incorporation are outlined in Fig. 23 according to the model of H. Lee.

Fig.23 shows the radial Sb-distributions derived from Fig.22 for the theoretical assumptions shown in the legend. The theoretical case of a flat phase boundary with a homogeneous dopant distribution on the melt side of the crystallization front is also plotted as dashed line (curve d). The comparison between the radial homogeneous distribution on a curved interface (curve c) with the conditions of radial inhomogeneous distributions (curve a and curve b) is intended to illustrate the dominant influence of the melt convection pattern on the dopant incorporation at the crystallization front. The influence of the deflection alone is rather low.

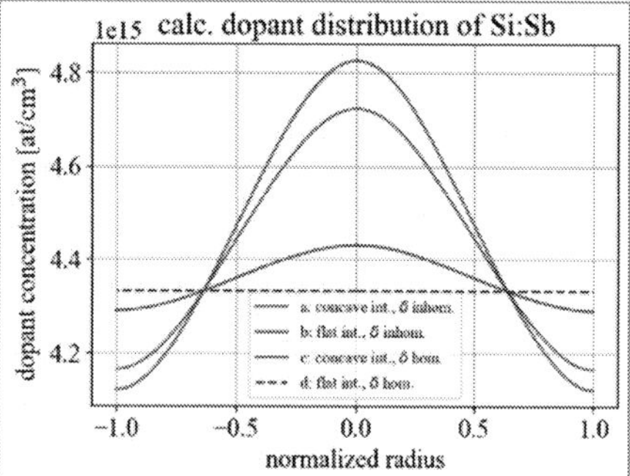

Figure 23: Theoretical Sb-distributions derived from the calculated resistivity distributions in Fig.22

2.6 Remarks on the nature of the volatile species in Sb-doped Cz-mono crystals

Doping elements may react with the oxygen dissolved in the silicon melt to form oxides. In the case of Ga-evaporation from the melt, it is evident that Ga_2O_3 is the dominant volatile species [7]. In the case of antimony evaporating from the melt, the facts are still unclear. Liu and Carlberg show by means of theoretical calculations that the formation of antimony oxide at the melt surface is rather negligible [11]. There are reports in the literature of reduced oxygen incorporation in Sb-doped Cz crystals. This effect is more pronounced in highly Sb-doped Si crystals compared to low Sb-doped Si crystals. The question of whether the oxygen loss is directly correlated with the evaporation process of antimony in the form of Sb_2O_3, or whether antimony evaporates as element and catalyzes the increased oxygen loss, is not clarified [12].

3 SUMMARY

- A precise control of the gas pressure during the Cz-process enables the possibility to grow Sb-doped Cz-mono crystals with an approximately constant axial distribution of the specific resistivity.
- In radial direction, the electronic properties are mainly influenced by an inhomogeneous dopant supply at the crystallization front due to a complex interaction of convection phenomena.

4 ACKNOWLEDGEMENTS

This work was supported by the German Federal Ministry for Economy Affairs and Climate Action under contract number 03EE1126B

5 REFERENCES

[1] M. Fischer, presentation at PV CellTech, Frankfurt am Main, March 11 2025

[2] Zulehner W, Huber D, Crystals, vol. 8, Berlin, Springer 1982 p.36

[3] www.freiberginstruments.com

[4] John P. DeLuca et al., Silicon Single Crystal doped with Gallium, Indium, or Aluminum, Patent Publication No. US 9,051,1659 B2 (2015)

[5] E. Scheil, Bemerkungen zur Schicht-kristallbildung, Z. Metallkunde **34**, (1942), 70-72

[6] Jafar Safarian, Merete Tangstad, Vacuum refining of molten silicon, Metallurgical and Materials Transactions B, Vol. 43B, 2012, 1427-1445

[7] F. Mosel, K. Hess, B. Klipp, M. Trempa, J. Friedrich, Investigation of process parameters on the distribution of the specific resistivity in Ga-doped Cz-crystals; Proceedings 40th European Photovoltaic Solar Energy Conf., Lisbon, (2023), 020024 001-007

[8] J.A. Burton, R.C. Prim, W.P. Slichter, The distribution of solute in crystals grown from the melt. Part I, Theoretical, J.Chem. Phys. **21** (1953), 1987-1991

[9] Hong H. Lee, A "freezing relation" for radial impurity distribution in Czochralski-grown crystakl, J. Cryst. Growth, **83**, (1987), 610-614

[10] F. Mosel, A.V. Denisov, K. Hess, B. Klipp, N. Sennova, C. Kranert, M. Trempa, C. Reimann, J. Friedrich, Influence of an active crystal cooling device on the shape of the phase boundary in mono ingots grown by the Czochralski technique; Proceedings 38th European Photovoltaic Solar Energy Conf., online, (2021), 339-346

[11] Z. Liu and T. Carlberg, On the mechanism of oxygen content reduction by antimony doping of Czochralski silicon melts, J. Electrochem. Soc., Vol.138, 1488-1492, (1991)

[12] K. Izunome et al., Evaluation of evaporated species from silicon melt surface during Sb-doped Czochralski silicon crystal growth, Jpn. J. Appl. Phys.,Vol. 34, (1995), pp L1635-L1637

INVESTIGATION OF PROCESS PARAMETERS ON THE DISTRIBUTION OF THE MATERIAL PARAMETERS IN CZ-CRYSTALS DOPED WITH ANTIMONY

Crystal Growing Systems

Freiberg Instruments

F. Mosel[1], N. Schüler[2]
[1] PVA Crystal Growing Sytems GmbH, Im Westpark 10-12, 35435 Wettenberg, Germany
[2] Freiberg Instruments GmbH, Delfter Straße 6, 09599 Freiberg, Germany
e-mail: frank.mosel@pvatepla.com
tel: +49 64168690-125, fax: +49 64168690-822

Introduction

The market share of Cz mono-Si for the mass production of solar cells has grown steadily in recent years. Casted Si has practically disappeared from the market. At the same time, a trend is emerging from p-type to n-type base material due to technology reasons.

Phosphorus (P), arsenic (As), and antimony (Sb) are doping elements for n-type crystals, but until now, P-doped substrate crystals are standard. Here, too, a substitution of phosphorus with antimony as a doping element is emerging, similar to p-type substrate crystals, where the doping element boron was replaced with gallium. The advantage of Sb-doped crystals is the possibility of growing crystals with an almost axial homogeneous distribution of the specific resistivity despite the unfavorable segregation coefficient of antimony (k_{Sb}=0.023) compared to phosphorus (k_P=0.38). The main advantage of Sb doping is the possibility of balancing the permanent enrichment of the melt with Sb due to the distribution coefficient with a controlled evaporation of Sb from the melt due to the evaporation coefficient, in order to get an axial homogenous resistivity distribution. However, this does not significantly affect the radial inhomogenous dopant incorporation.

Axial distribution of the specific resistivity in p-type Cz-ingots (measured on the as-grown surface)

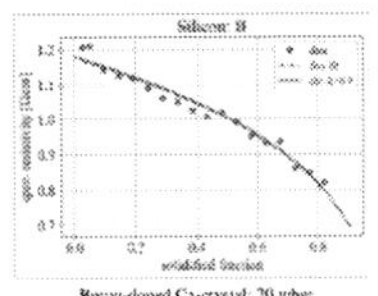

Boron-doped Cz-crystal: 20 mbar

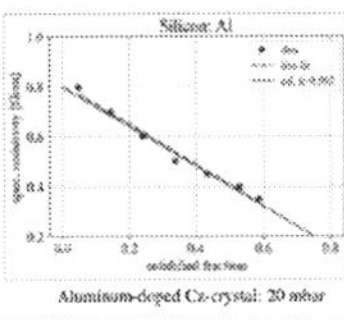

Aluminum-doped Cz-crystal: 20 mbar

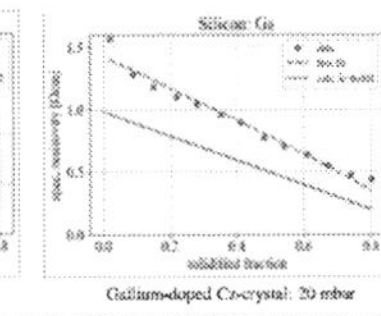

Gallium-doped Cz-crystal: 20 mbar

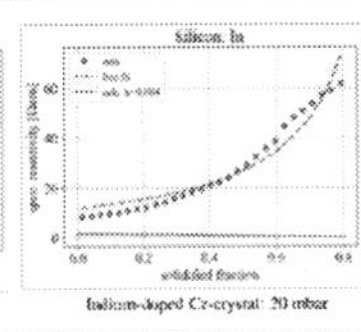

Indium-doped Cz-crystal: 20 mbar

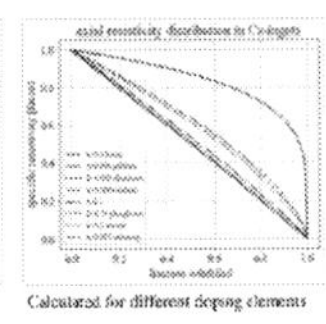

Calculated for different doping elements

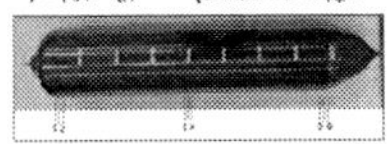

The axial resistivity distribution was measured by means of Semilch RT-1200

$$\rho = \rho_0 (1-g)^{(1-k)} \quad \text{parameter free fit: } \rho_0, k$$

The radial resistivity distribution was measured via an eddy current sensor and the lifetime was determined by means of MDP (Microwave Detected Photoconductivity) technique using the MDPpro system from Freiberg Instruments GmbH operating with a resolution of 1 mm.

Axial distribution of the specific resistivity in n-type Cz-ingots (measured on the as-grown surface)

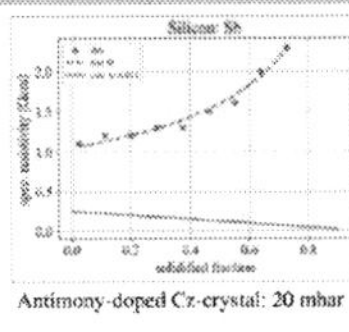

Phosphorus-doped Cz-crystal: 20 mbar

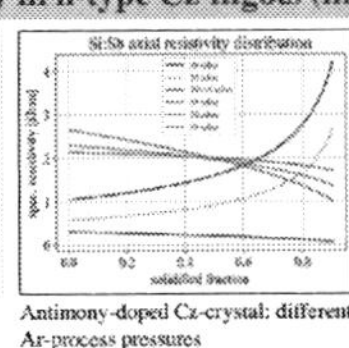

Arsenic-doped Cz-crystal: 20 mbar

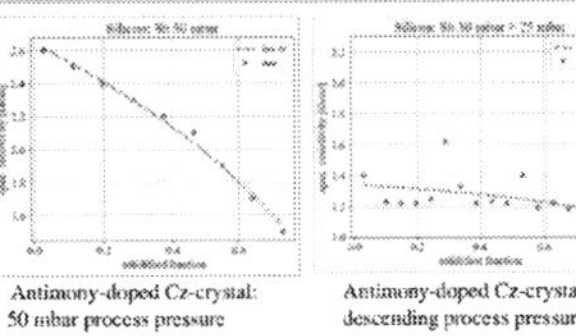

Antimony-doped Cz-crystal: 20 mbar

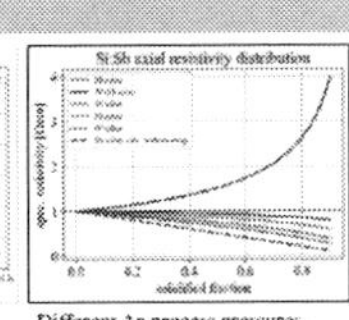

Antimony-doped Cz-crystal: different Ar-process pressures

Antimony-doped Cz-crystal: 50 mbar process pressure

Antimony-doped Cz-crystal: descending process pressure

Different Ar-process pressures, normalized to 1 Ωcm at body start

Radial resistivity and lifetime distribution in Sb-doped Cz-ingots (measured on the as-sawn slices)

Si:Sb-ingot grown under a constant Ar-pressure of 20 mbar

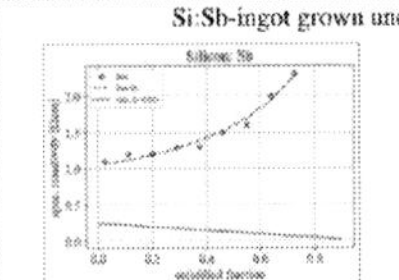

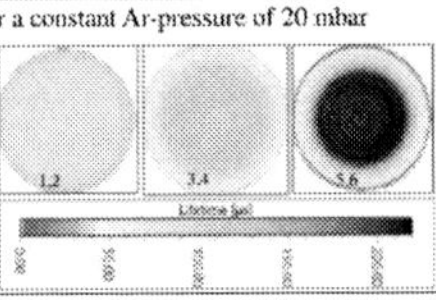

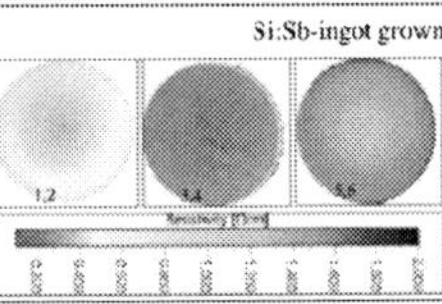

Si:Sb-ingot grown under a constant Ar-pressure of 20 mbar

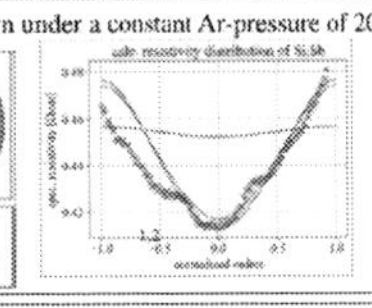

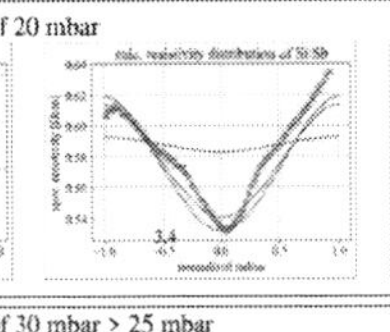

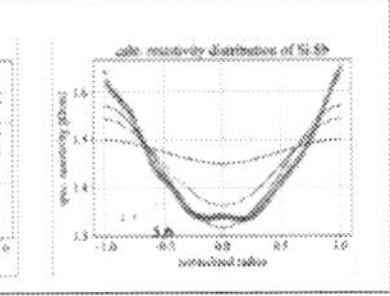

Si:Sb-ingot grown under a descending Ar-pressure of 30 mbar > 25 mbar

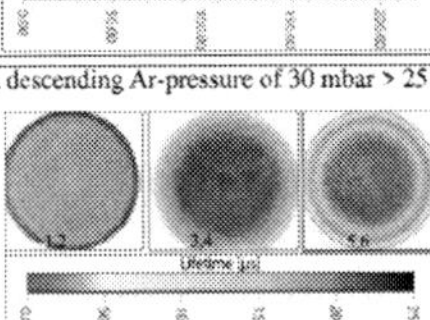

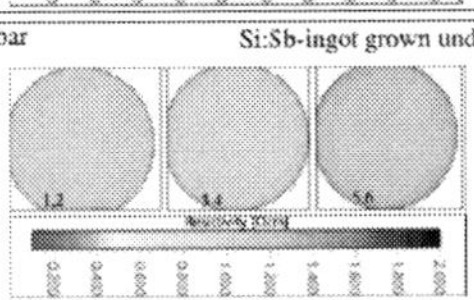

Si:Sb-ingot grown under a descending Ar-pressure of 30 mbar > 25 mbar

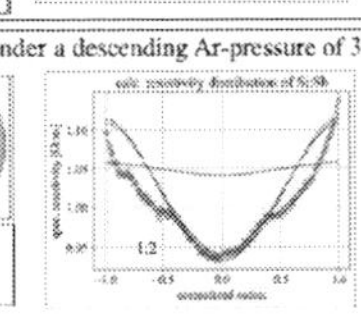

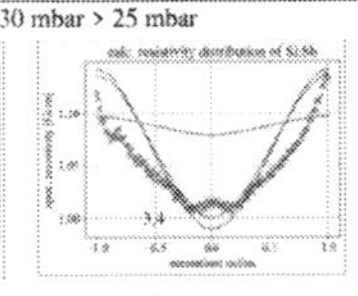

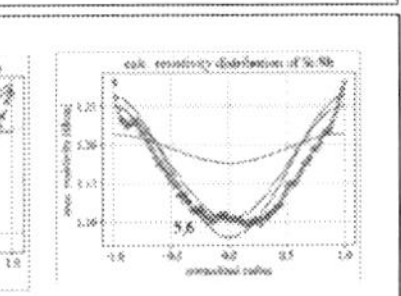

Influence of the growth parameters (k_{eff} and γ) on the axial and radial Sb-distribution in Cz-grown crystals

The dopant incorporation during the Cz batch process can be described by the differential equation [4]:

$$\frac{dC_l}{dt} = \frac{C_l}{m_l}\frac{dm_A}{dt} - \frac{kC_l}{m_l}\frac{dm_s}{dt} - \frac{\gamma A_s}{m_l}C_l \quad (DGL)$$

with: C_l: dopant concentration in the melt, m_l: mass of the melt, m_s: mass of the crystal, k: distribution coefficient, γ: coefficient of evaporation rate, A_s: free melt surface

The following terms in (DGL) mean:

$\frac{C_l}{m_l}\frac{dm_A}{dt}$ (I)
Removal of melt concentration of dopant)

due to crystal growth
$\frac{kC_l}{m_l}\frac{dm_s}{dt}$ (II)
Removal of dopant due to crystal growth

$\frac{\gamma A_s}{m_l}C_l$ (III)
Removal of dopant due to evaporation

Solving the DGL without considering the dopant reduction in the melt due to evaporation (III), results in the well-known Scheil equation [5]:

$$\frac{C_s}{C_0} = k(1-g)^{k-1} \quad (Scheil)$$

The two key parameters in the DGL that primarily influence dopant incorporation during the Cz batch process are the distribution coefficient k_{eff} and the evaporation rate γ.

Experimental investigations of the evaporation rate γ

Sketched sequence of evaporation [6]

1. Transport of the volatile element in the melt volume to the melt boundary layer (convection)
2. Transport through the boundary layer to the melt/gas interface (convection and diffusion)
3. Physical evaporation process of the volatile element at the free melt surface (Hertz-Langmuir-Knudsen equation)
4. Mass transport of the volatile element by the process gas flow and gas pressure

The evaporation of volatile elements or compounds is represented by a reaction of first order.

$$-\frac{dC}{C} = \gamma \frac{A}{V}dt$$

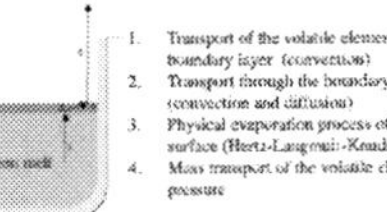

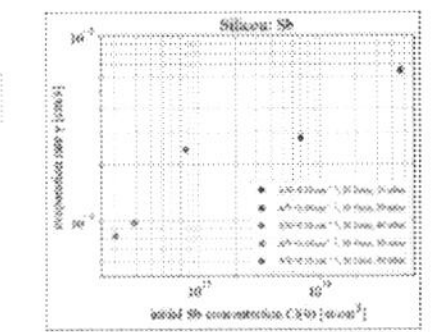

Estimation of the evaporation rate γ for different process conditions by means of 2-point calculation (2-sample estimation, t = time gap)

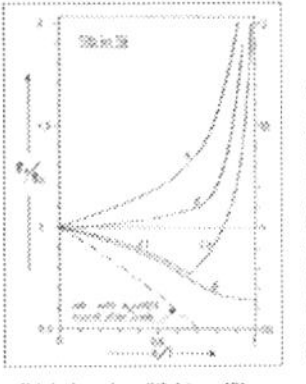

Original caption of Zulehner [2]

Axial resistivity variations in antimony-doped Cz Si single-crystals. The initial doping concentration (=0.018 Ωcm), melt volume and crystal diameter were the same for all curves. Due to the high vapour pressure of Sb, a great variety of axial resistivity profiles can be realized by applying different pressure and gas flow conditions. Curves A and B: Same pressure of 11 mbar but different gas flow characteristics. Curve C: 67 mbar in region C1, 11 mbar in region C2. Curve D: 25 mbar.

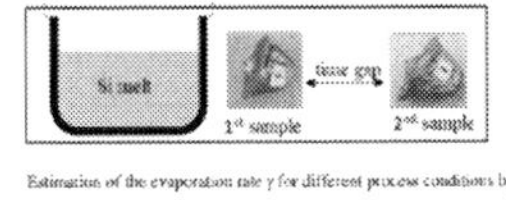

Theoretical and measured axial resistivity distribution of the Si:Sb crystal grown under a descending Ar-pressure of 60 mbar > 18 mbar

According to Zulehner [2] we performed a crystal growth experiment with a continuously decreasing Ar-pressure from 60 mbar to 18 mbar to investigate the critical pressure range more precisely. Therefore we previously modeled the limited process data using a neural network with two hidden layers, as shown. Although there is a significant discrepancy between the calculated (-) and measured (x) data due to the limited amount of available data, it can be concluded that a control of the Sb-evaporation rate under the present crystal growth conditions in the pressure range between 30 mbar and 25 mbar should be applicable to balance the Sb evaporation in the melt with the Sb-enrichment near the crystallization front. Below 25 mbar the Sb-loss by evaporation across the free melt surface outweighs the segregation effect of the Sb enrichment at the crystallization front causing an increase of the specific resistivity.

Theoretical considerations on the segregation coefficient k_{eff}

Model of Burton, Prim and Slichter (radial impurity distribution in Cz-grown crystals [8])

Scheil's model with the segregation coefficient k as material parameter applies to a closed system without material exchange with the environment (evaporation). The model of Burton, Prim, and Slichter describes the dynamics of crystal growth (translation of the phase boundary) introducing the effective segregation coefficient k_{eff} [8]. The parameter δ in the BPS-equation is often interpreted as a boundary layer thickness in front of the crystallization interface that is enriched with dopant, depending on the melt convection

$$k_{eff} = \frac{k_0}{k_0 + (1 - k_0)\exp\left(-\frac{f\delta}{D}\right)} \qquad \delta = 1.61 D^{1/3}\nu^{1/6}\omega^{-1/2}$$

with: k_0: equilibrium distribution coefficient, f: freezing velocity, δ: extension of a boundary layer, D: diffusion constant of the dopant in the melt, ν: kinematic viscosity of the melt, angular velocity of the crystal

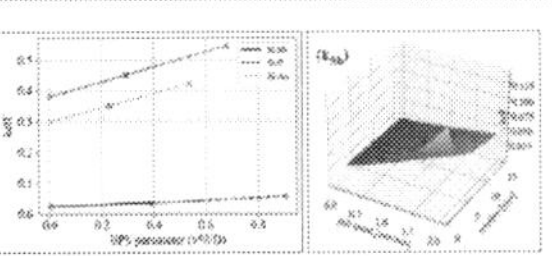

Segregation coefficient k_{eff} versus BPS-parameter (left) and k_{eff} (Sb) versus average pull speed and crystal rotation (right); the marker (x) indicates the applied conditions.

Model of Hong H. Lee (radial impurity distribution in Cz-grown crystals [9])

According to the model of H. Lee, the radial dopant distribution is approximated by a cubic function that reflects the rotational symmetry of the growth conditions during the Czochralski process. The different flow mechanisms resulting from forced convection (rotation conditions) and buoyancy convection are considered by a radial-dependent dopant concentration at the interface and different segregation coefficients at the center and the rim of the growing crystal. The deflection of the phase boundary is introduced in the model by its deviation from a flat interface in the crystal center.

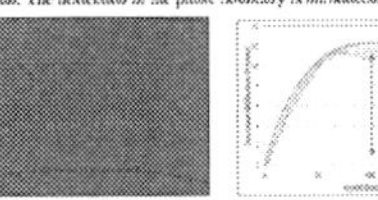

Interface deflection measured by means of LPS (coloured lines)

LPS results and the corresponding FEM simulation (blue line)

Radial resistivity distribution: measured (x) and calculated (lines)

Theo. Sb-distributions derived from the resistivity distributions

Results

references are given in the corresponding conference paper

- A precise control of the gas pressure during the Cz-process enables the possibility to grow Sb-doped Cz-mono crystals with an approximately constant axial resistivity distribution
- In radial direction, the electronic properties are mainly influenced by an inhomogeneous dopant supply at the crystallization front due to a complex interaction of convection phenomena.

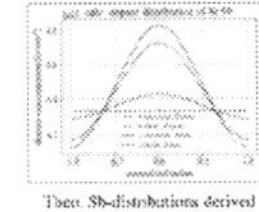

ELLIPSOMETRY CHARACTERIZATION AND MODELLING OF POROUS SILICON LAYERS: UTILIZING DIFFERENT ABSORPTION DEPTHS TO AID MODELLING

Per-Anders Hansen*, Junjie Zhu
Institute for Energy Technology, Norway
*per-anders.hansen@ife.no

Ellipsometry is a powerful and establish characterization tool for porous silicon (PS) and other thin film materials on silicon substrates. PS is often made through electrochemical etching in an HF-containing solution. Etch rates, pore dimensions, porosity level variations in the etch direction etc. depends on the electrical current and the chemistry of the solution among other. In many cases, this leads to interface layers towards the substrate-PS and air-PS interfaces, gradients and even optical anisotropy if the pore dimensions are large enough. In this work, we show that we can utilize the large wavelength-dependent variations in absorption depths to model the different parts of such samples independently, simplifying the modelling process and allows us to solve some aspects of the sample structure without being required to solve the whole structure which can be complex. Ellipsometry data and modelling of one such sample having both porosity gradients, interface layers and a thin and denser layer towards the surface is shown below. Such complexities for PS layers are well-known in literature, but can still be challenging to solve compared to a simple homogeneous film. We show that both the UV-blue and NIR ranges are necessary for a complete solution, but also that these ranges can be used to solve the top and bulk depths independently.

1 INTRODUCTION

Ellipsometry is well established for PS layers, which have been investigated by the PV community both as anti-reflective coatings [1, 2] and production of solar wafers through epitaxial growth [3, 4]. It is well-known in literature that varying electrical parameters and chemical components in the electrolyte solutions can result in porosity profiles that range from simple homogeneous layer to complex structures with interface structures and graded profiles [5, 6]. By utilizing the different probing depths of the shallowly penetrating UV-blue and deep penetrating NIR, the different sections of an overall complex sample structure can be reduced to more simpler components. This can aid modelling of samples with unknown structures, and understanding the different wavelengths ranges penetration depths could also strongly reduce the necessary measurement time. By minimizing the wavelength range and resolution in addition to the number and values of measurement angles, time-consuming measurements such as full-wafer mapping can be done much more efficient with the same or better modelling accuracy.

The aim of this work is to establish a modelling approach that utilizes the large variations in absorption depths in different wavelength ranges to probe different depths into complex sample structures independently. We exemplify our approach with a known and complex porosity profile that show porosity variations in both top, bulk and bottom depths [7, 8]. Without any knowledge of the samples optical structure, it can be challenging to model such samples as all aspects have to be represented well before a good fit can be achieved. In our approach, the different depths can be probed and modelled independently before combining them and establishing the complete sample structure.

2 EXPERIMENTAL

We use a Variable Angle Spectroscopic Ellipsometer (VASE) from J. A. Woollam for data collection and the CompleteEASE software for modelling. Our VASE is equipped with an x-y translation stage for wafer mapping and can be equipped with focusing probes to reduce the measurement spot-size. Measurements cover the 260 – 1700 nm range, and are generally obtained at 70-75 ° incident angle. Full-range and partial-range modelling uses the following parts of the data: Full-range (280 – 1650 nm); UV-blue range (280 – 500 nm); Vis-NIR range (700 – 1650 nm). The wafers and PS layers in this work was provided by NexWafe GmbH in the Horizon-EU project EMPOWER.

3 RESULTS AND DISCUSSIONS

3.1 Absorption depths at different wavelengths

The absorption depths (also called penetration depth) tells us how deep into a material light of a given wavelength can travel before being reduced to $1/e$ (~37 %) due to absorption. If the light entering the material is I_0, then the intensity $I(x)$ at depth x is defined by Eq.1.

$$I(x) = I_0 e^{-\alpha x} \qquad \text{Eq.1}$$

The absorption depth δ is then defined as Eq. 2.

$$\delta = \alpha^{-1} \qquad \text{Eq.2}$$

Through ellipsometry modelling one obtains the materials wavelength-dependent refractive index an extinction coefficient, $n(\lambda)$ and $k(\lambda)$. $k(\lambda)$ and $\alpha(\lambda)$ is related through Eq. 3, which allows calculations of δ directly from ellipsometry results.

$$\alpha(\lambda) = \frac{4\pi}{\lambda} k(\lambda) \qquad \text{Eq.3}$$

The absorption depth into silicon at different wavelengths is shown in Figure 1. Note the logarithmic y-scale. Silicon is a indirect bandgap material with the fundamental bandgap at around 1100 nm (1.12 eV). In addition, silicon has two higher direct bandgaps at approximately 265 nm and 295 nm (3.4 and 4.2 eV). The absorption coefficient near the two direct bandgaps is much higher than in the Vis-NIR range that only experience indirect bandgap absorption. This translates into an absorption depth that is 3-4 orders of magnitude smaller in the UV-blue range than in the Vis-NIR range.

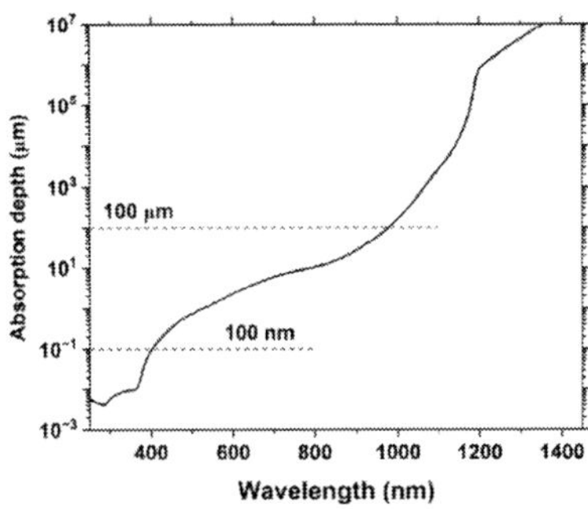

Figure 1: The absorption depth into silicon as a function of probing light wavelength. The very strong absorption in the UV-blue range leads to very shallow absorption depths. Note the logarithmic y-scale.

In ellipsometry, the effective "probing depth", i.e. the sample depth that can contribute significantly to the collected data, is significantly smaller than the absorption depth. This is due to two factors: The light hits the material at an angle, usually 40-80°, which increases the effective optical path. In addition, the light also has to reflect from an interface and travel back up to the surface. If the light intensity that exits the surface this way is insignificant compared to the primary specularly reflected beam, ellipsometry will effectively not "see" this depth. This is illustrated in Figure 2. The short-wavelength UV-blue light will only have significant contributions from structures in the top ~50 nm. On the other hand, the long-wavelength Vis-NIR can probe up to a hundred microns and even further for sub-bandgap light. This light will have contributions from the full sample structure.

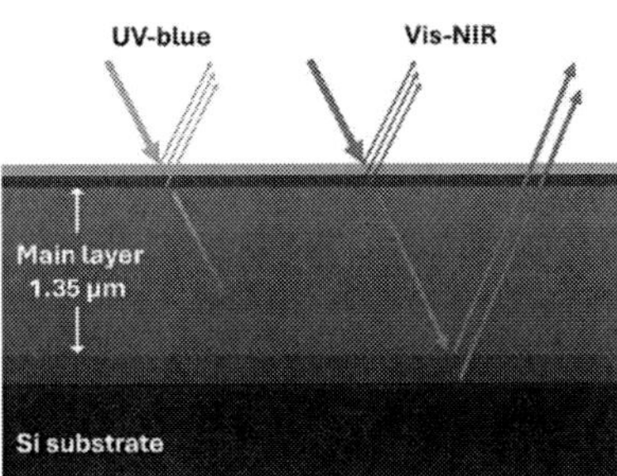

Figure 2: Illustration showing that strongly absorbed light effectively probes exclusively the top sample layers, while poorly absorbed (or not absorbed at all) light contains contributions from the full sample structure.

3.2 ELLIPSOMETRY MODELS

PS layers can be well-represented in ellipsometry through the effective media approximation (EMA) material model, combining crystalline silicon and air [9, 10]. In this model, the percentage of air, i.e. the porosity, is the only material variable. In ellipsometry investigations, material models can also include other elements such as small levels of amorphous silicon [11] or

anisotropy [10, 12]. However, in this work, the simple Si/air EMA model was sufficient. In addition to the material model, the data modelling includes sample parameters (number of layers, thicknesses, gradients) and instrument parameters.

Conceptually, the sample consists of a single 1.35 µm porous silicon (PS) layer. However, modelling this as a simple single-layer structure yields a poor fit to the ellipsometry data. To improve the model, two commonly used additions are included: a surface roughness layer and an interface layer between the PS and the silicon substrate (labelled "Si/PS" in Figure 4). These additions significantly enhance the fit, though the result remains only moderately satisfactory. To further refine the model, two additional features are introduced: a gradient in the main PS layers porosity, and a thin low-porosity surface layer. These additions results in a model that fits the data well, as seen in Figure 3.

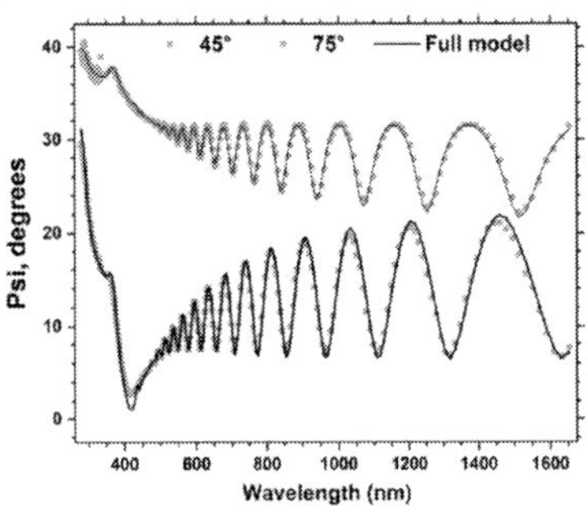

Figure 3: Ellipsometry Psi data and model fit, using the full model and the full data range.

The full ellipsometry model is shown in Figure 4, including the four layer features: Silicon substrate / PS layer interface (Si/PS), a graded-porosity main PS layer, a thin porosity dip layer and finally a surface roughness layers. All these features are known for such samples [7, 8].

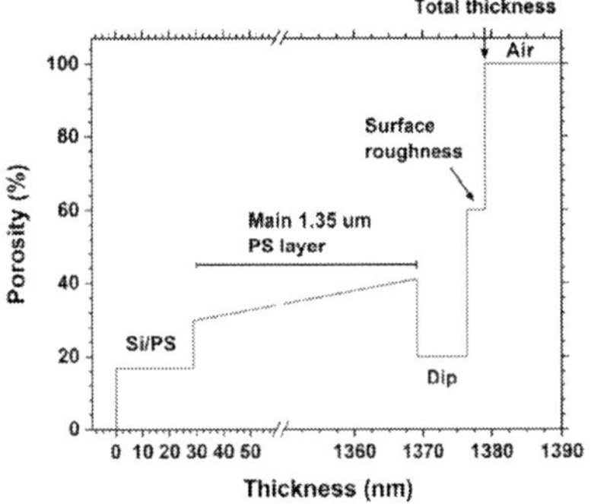

Figure 4: Full ellipsometry model for this PS sample. The model is similar to that reported by Selj et al [7, 8].

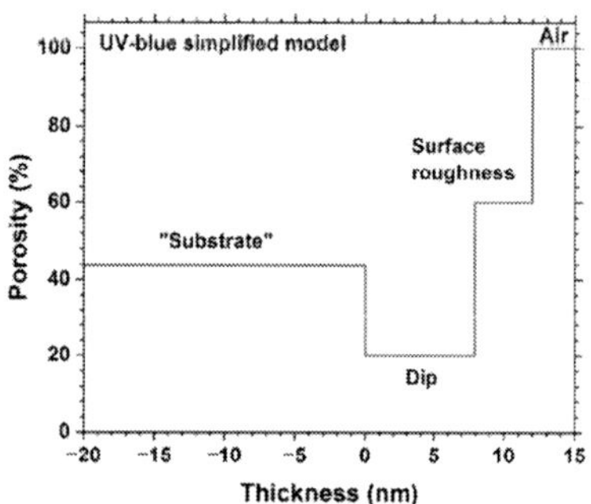

Figure 5: The UV-blue model, treating the top of the main PS layer as a "substrate", as this light cannot probe any deeper than this interface.

3.3 SOLVING THE MODEL STRUCTURE

If we are presented with ellipsometry data from new sample with a (partially) unknown sample structure, constructing the complete model structure can be challenging. In order to solve the full-range data, the complete sample structure must be used and all aspects of the samples must be well-represented before we can obtain a reasonable fit to sample variables such as layer thicknesses and porosities.

Figure 6 shows the mean square error (MSE) of the modelled thickness value for the thin top porosity dip layer as a function of model (full vs UV-blue) and the data range used in the fit. It is seen that the full model (Figure 4) with the full data range (black curve) gives equal thickness value and equal uniqueness ("V" shape) as the simplified UV-blue model (Figure 5) using only the shallow-penetrating (short-wavelength) part of the data (green curve). In the case of an unknown sample structure, the full model would struggle until all aspects of the sample is found and accurately represented. Before that is achieve, it can be challenging to discover these aspects from the ellipsometry data alone, in particular for complex samples. There are many combinations of parameters for the material and sample models that can lead to equally mediocre fits, so freely searching for new aspects to add to improve the fit can lead down a wrong path. On the other hand, there is generally only few-to-one sets of parameters that lead to good fits. The simplified UV-blue model significantly simplifies the number of sample aspects that must be represented to obtain a good fit. This reduces the chance of the model over-compensating with other parameters and the user over-compensating with additional sample aspects that might not be present. Through this approach, we can model the top part individually and accurately, and then add and lock this part into the full model that we are building.

We can also attempt to solve only this top part with the full model using only the shallow-penetration data (yellow curve), as the model for the deeper structures in theory should not affect the fit. However, it is seen that the accuracy is significantly lower (less clear V-shape) and the obtained value is also slightly thicker. The reason for this is that although the deeper-lying structures don't affect the data in this range directly, the porosity immediately below the dip layer (the "substrate" in Figure 5) is part of the deeper-level structure. The full model then still has to fit

this parameters as part of the deeper structures which has no correlation with this data range. Effectively, this adds uncertainty and the possibility for unrealistic over-compensation from other parameters. Trying to model the top dip layer with the full model and only the deep-penetrating data results in a nearly flat MSE curve, i.e. this cannot resolve the top structure at all.

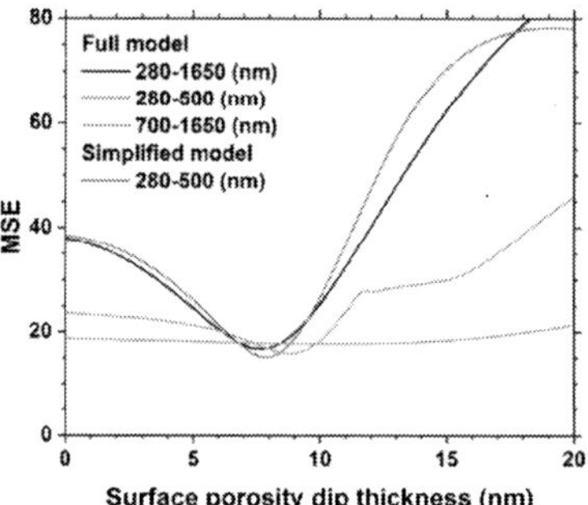

Figure 6: Thickness accuracy of the top porosity dip layer as a function of model and data wavelength range.

Similarly, it is possibly to do simplifications of the deeper structures as well. The Vis-NIR data is of course affected by the top sample structure, but the impact is much smaller. As seen in Figure 2, the contribution to the measured data from the deeper level has very different optical path differences than the contributions from the shallow top layers. The contributions from the deeper structures leads to the short-wavelength oscillations in Figure 3, while the top layer contribution will be very long-wavelength due to the few 10's nm total thickness. This will only contribute as an almost-constant modulation of these short-wavelength oscillations. The top layers can then be approximated as a single "effective" surface layer having the same impact in the Vis-NIR range. We exemplify this through the thickness values of the main 1.35 µm PS layer.

Figure 7 shows the MSE of the thickness of the main PS layer as a function of model and wavelength range. The full model with the full data range (black curve) gives an accurate value for this parameters. In fact, and contrary to the top layers, this parameter can be accurately modelled with the full model and narrowing the data to only the Vis-NIR range (yellow curve). However, this still means that the full model has to be provided. Also, modelling only the Vis-NIR range with the full model results in nearly fully correlated (i.e. inaccurate) values for the top layers (as exemplified in Figure 6). Although an accurate value for the main PS layer thickness can be obtained, it is not good practice to have models with strong correlations among other parameters. What we instead can do is to simplify the top layer structure as a single effective roughness layer. Using this simplified model with only the Vis-NIR range (blue curve, nearly fully overlapping with yellow) yields an accurate fit for the main PS layer thickness, while removing the parameter correlations of the full model.

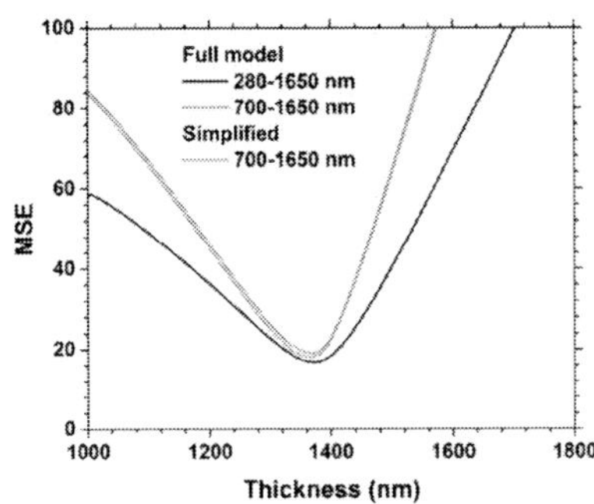

Figure 7: Thickness accuracy of the 1.35 µm main PS-layer as a function of model and data wavelength range.

Through these two simplifications and choice of data range, we can first investigate and establish the top layers and the deeper layers independently, and then afterwards combine them into a full sample model .

4 CONCLUSIONS

In this work, we have showed that by utilizing the large differences in absorption depth in silicon, it is possible to model shallow surface structures and deep bulk layers independently. The NIR range is insignificantly affected by the surface structures details, while the UV-blue range will not have contributions from any of the structures below some tens of nanometers. By approaching these two ranges independently, it is much easier to solve a complex sample structure with multiple interface and grading aspects. This approach is not limited to porous silicon, but rather general for samples that has large differences in absorption depths for different wavelength ranges.

5 ACKNOWLEDGEMENTS

This project has received funding from the European Union's Horizon Europe research and innovation program under grant agreement No 101172767.

6 REFERENCES

[1] Selj, J.H., et al., *Optimization of multilayer porous silicon antireflection coatings for silicon solar cells.* Journal of Applied Physics, 2010. **107**(7).

[2] Ge, D., et al., *Optimization of porous silicon structure as antireflective material.* The European Physical Journal D, 2022. **76**(2): p. 27.

[3] Karim, M., et al., *Tuning of strain and surface roughness of porous silicon layers for higher-quality seeds for epitaxial growth.* Nanoscale Research Letters, 2014. **9**(1): p. 348.

[4] Rittmann, C., et al., *Epitaxially Grown p-type Silicon Wafers Ready for Cell Efficiencies Exceeding 25%.* Solar RRL, 2023. **7**(8): p. 2200698.

[5] Stefan Reber, K.S., US10975490, *Apparatus and method for etching one side of a semiconductor substrate.* 2016

[6] Pettersson, L.A.A., L. Hultman, and H. Arwin, *Porosity depth profiling of thin porous silicon layers by use of variable-angle spectroscopic ellipsometry: a porosity graded-layer model.* Applied Optics, 1998. **37**(19): p. 4130-4136.

[7] Selj, J., et al., *Ellipsometric study of the influence of chemical etching on thin porous silicon structures.* Thin Solid Films, 2011. **519**(9): p. 2998-3001.

[8] Selj, J.H., et al., *Thin Porous Silicon Films Displaying a Near-Surface Dip in Porosity.* ECS Transactions, 2011. **33**(16): p. 181.

[9] Rossow, U., et al., *Influence of the formation conditions on the microstructure of porous silicon layers studied by spectroscopic ellipsometry.* Thin Solid Films, 1995. **255**(1): p. 5-8.

[10] Golovan', L.A., P.K. Kashkarov, and V.Y. Timoshenko, *Form birefringence in porous semiconductors and dielectrics: A review.* Crystallography Reports, 2007. **52**(4): p. 672-685.

[11] Strashnikova, M.I., et al., *Optical properties of porous silicon.* Journal of Experimental and Theoretical Physics, 2001. **93**(2): p. 363-371.

[12] Kovalev, D., et al., *Strong in-plane birefringence of spatially nanostructured silicon.* Applied Physics Letters, 2001. **78**(7): p. 916-918.

Ellipsometry characterization and modelling of porous silicon layers:
Utilizing different absorption depths to aid modelling

Per-Anders Hansen, Junjie Zhu

Institute for Energy Technology

Corresponding author: per-anders.hansen@ife.no

INTRODUCTION

Ellipsometry is an excellent tool for porous silicon **(PS)** layers in photovoltaics, explored for anti-reflective coatings and epitaxial wafer growth. By tuning electrolyte conditions, porosities range from uniform to complex structures. This makes ellipsometry modelling challenging. By combining the difference in probing depths of UV-blue and Vis-NIR light, we decompose such structures into simpler components, aiding modelling and interpretation. Samples for this work was provided by NexWafe GmbH in the Horizon-EU project EMPOWER.

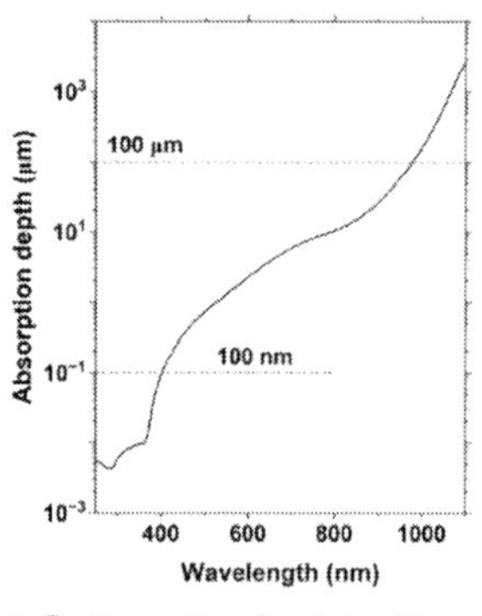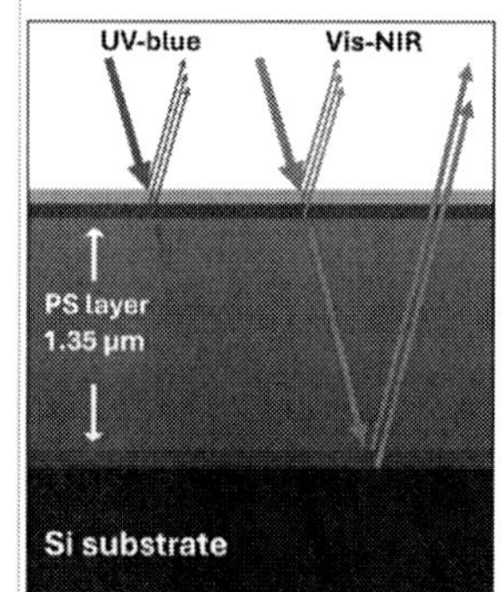

Left: Absorption depth in silicon as a function of wavelength.
Right: An illustration of the different probe depths in ellipsometry.

Ellipsometry model

We demonstrate our approach using a sample with a known porosity profile, featuring a substrate/PS-layer interface, porosity gradient, surface roughness, and a distinct near-surface porosity dip. This structure is documented in literature and by our group [1].

Without prior knowledge of the optical structure, building a complete ellipsometry model is challenging, as all features must be accurately represented for a good fit. Our method uses differing probing depths of UV-blue and Vis-NIR light to model surface layers independently before constructing the full sample structure.

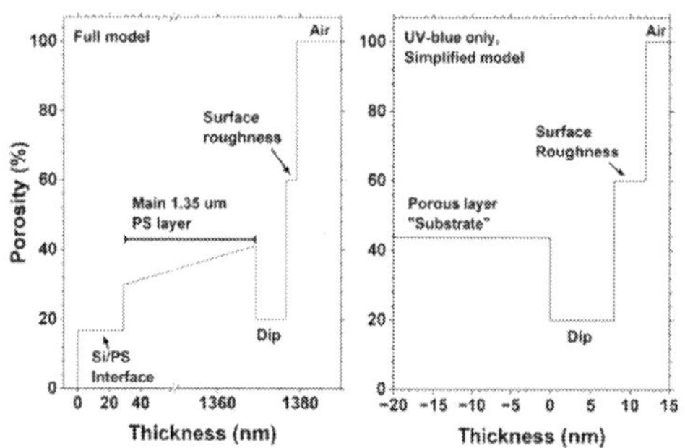

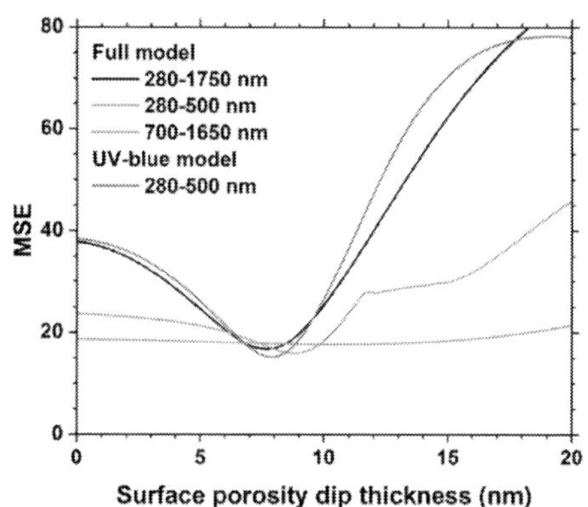

Mean square error (MSE) of the modelled near-surface porosity dip as a function of model complexity and data wavelength range.

Simplifying the modelling

A *parameter uniqueness plot* shows how certain a parameter value is in the model. A sharp V-shape indicates high certainty; a flat curve means other values give equally good fits.

We show that our simplified model **(green)**, using only UV-blue data, achieves similar parameter uniqueness for the near-surface porosity dip as the full-complexity model using the full UV-Vis-NIR range **(black)**.

In contrast, the full-complexity model using only shallow UV-blue data **(yellow)** reduces modelling certainty, over-compensating with many other parameters. Using only deep Vis-NIR data, this model fails to fit the top layer entirely **(blue)**.

A similar simplification is possible for deeper layers. Since Vis-NIR data is nearly unaffected by the top 50 nm, deeper layers can be modelled independently. In this case (not shown), the top multi-layer structure can be simplified to a single "effective surface roughness" layer.

Conclusions

In this work, we present an approach for modelling ellipsometry data of complex layers. By exploiting the large differences in penetration depth across wavelength ranges, surface and bulk structures can be resolved independently. This enables solving parts of the structure sequentially, before assembling the complete model from the simpler components.

REFERENCES

[1] Selj, J.H., *et al.*, Thin Porous Silicon Films Displaying a Near-Surface Dip in Porosity. **ECS Transactions, 2011.** 33(16), p. 181

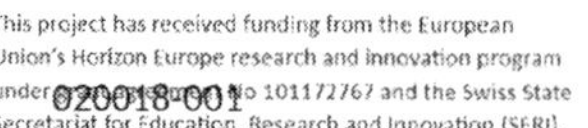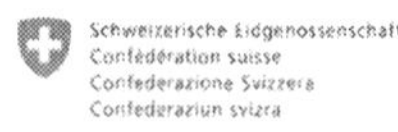

This project has received funding from the European Union's Horizon Europe research and innovation program under grant agreement no 101172767 and the Swiss State Secretariat for Education, Research and Innovation (SERI).

Schweizerische Eidgenossenschaft
Confédération suisse
Confederazione Svizzera
Confederaziun svizra
Swiss Confederation

Federal Department of Economic Affairs, Education and Research EAER
State Secretariat for Education, Research and Innovation SERI

SUSTAINABLE, HIGH-THROUGHPUT, INDUSTRY-READY, NEXT-GENERATION TECHNOLOGY FOR EUROPEAN MANUFACTURING LEADERSHIP IN PHOTOVOLTAICS (SHINE PV)

Nicola Frasson[1], Marco Galiazzo[1], Sven Kluska[2], Vincent Barth[3], Jonathan Govaerts[4], Frank Lenzmann[5], Giovanni Paolo Borzi[6], Betina Debastiani Benato[7] and Victor Acinas[8]

[1]Applied Materials Italia srl,
[2]Fraunhofer ISE - Gesellschaft zur Forderung der Angewandten Forschung EV
[3]CEA-INES- Commissariat a l Energie Atomique et aux Energies Alternatives
[4]IMEC - Interuniversitair Micro-Electronica Centrum
[5]TNO - Nederlandse Organisatie voor toegepast-natuurwetenschappelijk onderzoek
[6]Enginsoft SpA
[7]AMIRES, the Business Innovation Management Institute z.ú.
[8]Applied Materials Ireland Ltd.

ABSTRACT: The SHINE PV project, funded by the European Commission [1], aims to revolutionize the photovoltaic manufacturing landscape in Europe by developing alternative technological routes to mainstream production. This initiative, which started in January 2025 and will last four years, focuses on enhancing the competitiveness of European manufacturers by reducing production costs and simultaneously increasing efficiency.
To drive technological innovation in the photovoltaic (PV) industry, it is essential to explore alternative technological routes for Silicon Heterojunction (SHJ) and Tunnel Oxide Passivated Contact (TOPCon) solar cells. SHINE PV focuses on key steps in back-end manufacturing, such as metallization, post-processing, and interconnection. By introducing high-volume manufacturing (HVM) processes like parallel dispensing and plating, we can replace traditional screen-printing methods. For post processing, the project will develop both edge-repassivation and light soaking processes and equipment, with the aim of recovering or enhancing cell efficiency after laser separation. For the module making step both TWILL interconnection and shingling will be developed, to increase the resilience of the modules in reliability testing and decrease costs. These advancements will not only enhance the efficiency of solar cells and modules but also streamline the manufacturing process, making it more sustainable and economically viable.
In terms of efficiency and cost reduction, the goal is to increase solar cell efficiency by 0.5% absolute compared to the reference process. This improvement, coupled with a 4-10% reduction in the cost of ownership (CoO), can be achieved through reduced material costs and increased equipment productivity. Establishing a robust European PV innovation and production base is crucial for sustainability and competitiveness [2] [3] [4]. Demonstrating complete back-end PV manufacturing lines will reinforce the sustainability of the European PV value chain, enhancing the resilience and diversity of the domestic energy sector industrial base.

1 INTRODUCTION

SHINE PV project will address three manufacturing steps of solar cell production, applied both to TOPCon and SHJ precursors (Figure 1). For each step two different technologies will be evaluated, the process variables will be identified with design of experiments and a dedicated production equipment (TRL7) will be produced.

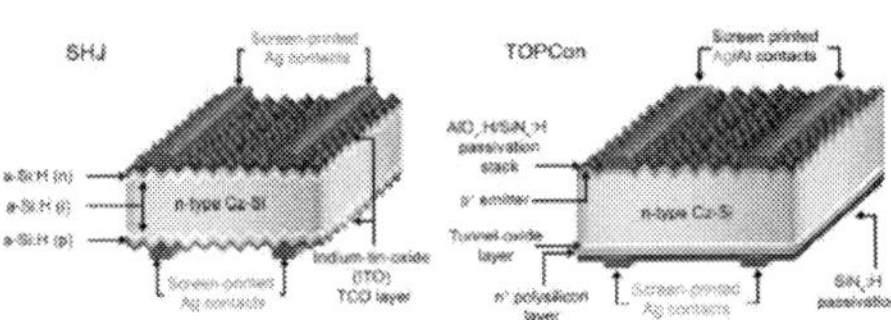

Figure 1 Representation of SHJ (left) and TOPCon (right) cell structures [5].

Parallel dispensing and plating will be evaluated as alternatives to traditional screen printing. These approaches will also enable the partial or complete replacement of silver with copper/silver coated copper materials, which are more cost-effective and abundant.
Post-processing techniques play a crucial role in enhancing the performance and long-term stability of solar cells. The application of Light Soaking (LS) processes in HVM helps to increase the performance of solar cells. Additionally, recovering cutting-induced losses through Edge Re-Passivation (ERP) is essential for maintaining the efficiency of the cells. These processes can restore the electrical properties and overall performance of solar cells after laser cutting or with intrinsic defects which can cause a loss in efficiency.

Innovations in interconnection methods, such as Twill and Shingling processes, are pivotal in optimizing the metallization and post-processing steps. These methods improve the electrical properties, aesthetics, reliability, and compatibility of solar cells with premium module designs. Twill interconnection involves weaving conductive materials in a specific pattern to enhance electrical connectivity and reduce resistance. On the other hand, shingling involves overlapping and gluing solar cells to create a seamless and aesthetically pleasing surface, which also improves the module efficiency by reducing the gaps between cells. By integrating these innovative interconnection techniques, manufacturers can produce solar modules that not only perform better but also meet the aesthetic and reliability demands of the market. More details on the different technologies are discussed later in the paper.

2 PARTNERS

The key metrics of the project are presented in Figure 2 in a matrix structure, where the three key aspects of the manufacturing process are investigated, with several KPIs respectively for efficiency gain, CoO and overall sustainability and exploitation.

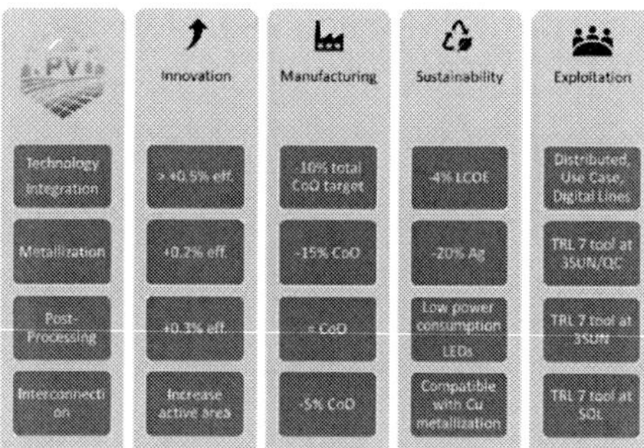

Figure 2 Principal KPI matrix for the SHINE PV project.

Overall project goals are reported in the top row in blue. Regarding the demonstration of the integrated process steps, there will be multiple sites where the equipment modules or the processes will be tested in a manufacturing plant or a research center (Figure 3).

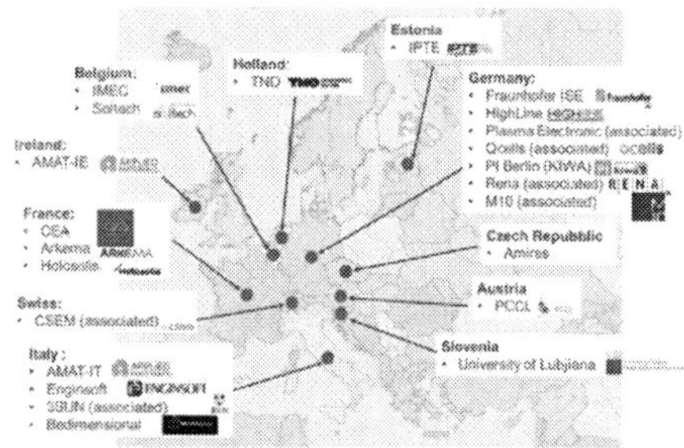

Figure 3 Partners distribution in Europe.

Finally, the process results will be combined by specific experiments and by digital tools that will simulate the production conditions for a full SHINE PV line (Figure 4).

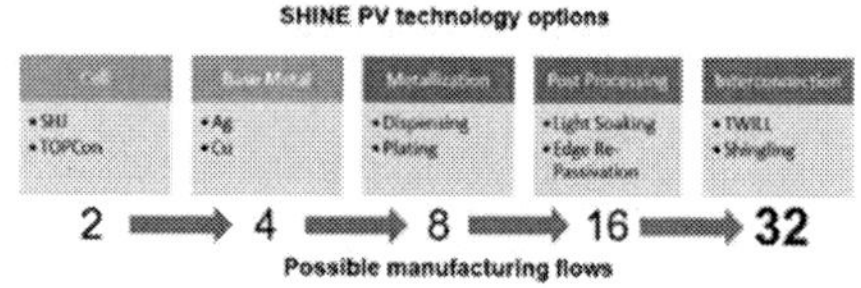

Figure 4 Possible manufacturing sequences generated withing the SHINE PV project.

3   TECHNOLOGICAL INNOVATION

Partners will lead and work on different work-packages (WPs) according to their experience in the different fields (Figure 5) and deliver results to the consortium.

Figure 5 WPs structure and WP leaders.

WP1 focuses on the integration and optimization of dispensing [6] [7] [8] and plating processes [9] [10] for solar cells metallization. Also, a preliminary simulation phase is necessary to establish the best metallization grid pattern over the two cell surfaces, front and back. Dispensing and plating can be further coupled with laser sintering processes to accelerate the curing process and optimize the throughput but also integrate materials like copper which are entering the market and need ad-hoc process conditions. With this purpose, paste developments are also ongoing to find more suitable silver and non-silver pastes that can be compatible with these new metallization technologies, especially on the dispensing side. WP2 aims at developing post-processing technologies that can restore or enhance the cell properties like edge repassivation [11] [12] and light-soaking [13], targeting small defects in the cell that are no longer negligible when pushing the energy efficiency to the physical limit. Part of the work will also include the identification of all potential process-related limitations and provide clear feedback to all equipment providers for hardware or process specific adaptation. WP3 instead focuses on the development of novel interconnection technologies like TWILL [14] [15] and shingling [16] [17] to provide reliable, design flexible and efficient solar modules. Also, the modelling of thermo-mechanical stresses and failure modes for these modules is studied. Finally, the development of an easy-release encapsulant to be used in module manufacturing is studied to permit a more facilitated end-of-life disassembly of module components. In the WP4 the design, development, assembly and validation of different tools is targeted including dispensing, plating, light-soaking, edge-repassivation, shingling and semi-automated foil-making and pick&place for TWILL tools. WP5 aims at creating tools that can simulate and then optimize individual process steps according to Industry 4.0 approaches and technologies and so create a fully digital infrastructure to assess and evaluate the efficiency, compatibility and overall performance of SHINE PV equipment. Furthermore, these tools can be also used to perform reliability and outdoor testing for PV modules produced using SHINE PV processes and equipment, collect data and share it within the consortium and the public. Finally, WP6 and WP7 regard the communication, dissemination, management and coordination of the whole project including the analysis and evaluation of environmental and social impacts of advanced PV manufacturing solutions, new business models and events participation.

4   PRELIMINARY RESULTS
-    WP1 (Metallization)

Grid model and simulations studies are initially proposed by University of Ljubljana (UL) to describe cell properties for both SHJ and TOPCon substrates by developing and validating one or more models via Spice, PVMOS, Griddler, COMSOL, Sentaurus T-CAD or a combination thereof. First phase outcomes provided a 7D model that considers the number of shingles, number of fingers on front/back side and the fingers height/width on the two sides in the description of the solar cell. Main issues are related to the description of the cost function (Figure 6) and further discussions are ongoing between partners including Applied Materials (AMAT), CEA-INES and Fraunhofer-ISE (Fh-ISE).

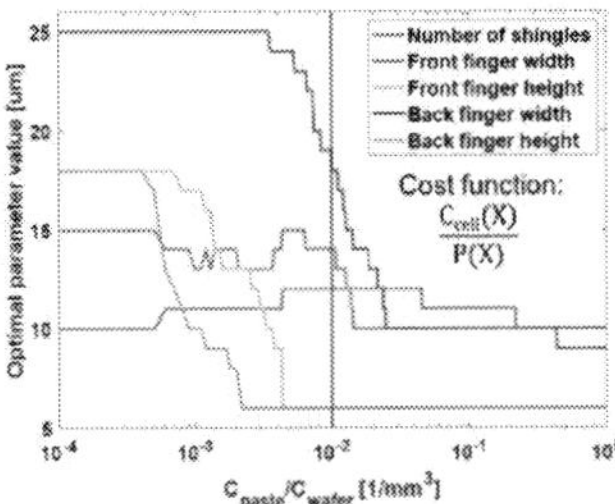

Figure 6 Cost function description.

However, the simulations already reached a good level of accuracy for a given set of parameters (Figure 7).

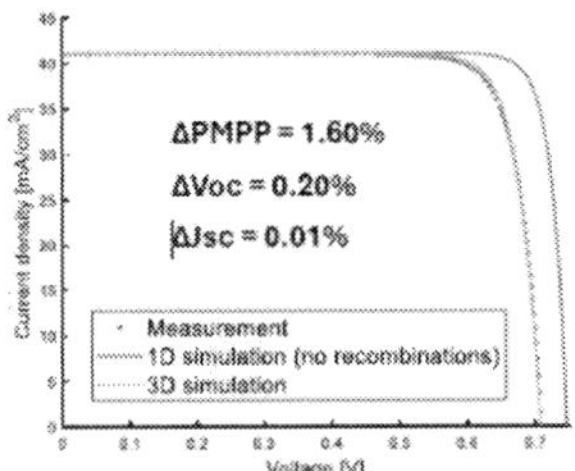

Figure 7 Comparison of simulated and measured IV curves of a TOPCon solar cell.

On the equipment side, the parallel dispensing kit has also been developed by HighLine (HL) and FH-ISE and the integration on a HVM tool (Applied Materials Tempo Presto) is ongoing with main issues solved like head leaks and hardware/software integration of the new printing head (Figure 8). The most crucial point in technology validation is related to the paste sourcing and/or development to match the required properties from a high-performance dispenser.

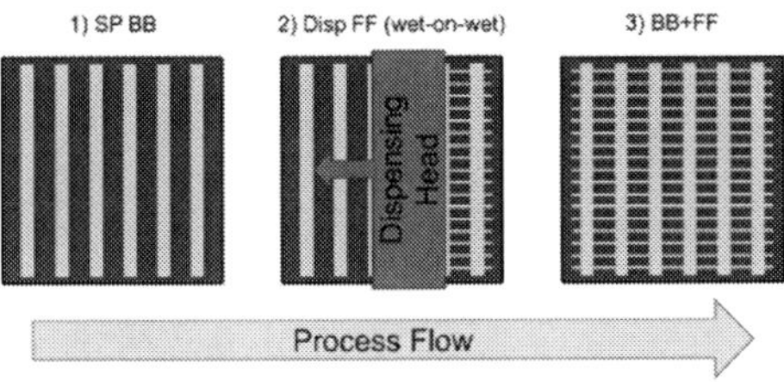

Figure 8 Screen printing and dispensing combined in the cell metallization flow.

Together with BeDimensional (BeD), FH-ISE and HL are working on new stable and compatible formulations for both low and high-temperature processes. On the plating process development and plating for SHJ/TOPCon side, CSEM, FH-ISE and RENA are working on Ni-Cu-Ag or Ni-Cu-Sn processes and a Ni-seed followed by Cu and Ag plating metallization process has already provided promising results. Main discussions include the footprint of the tool, the tool stability and the cost-of-ownership (CoE) of this technology. Also, copper or silver-coated copper particles can be used as seed layers and dispensed to obtain a thin line of around 14 microns (Figure 9).

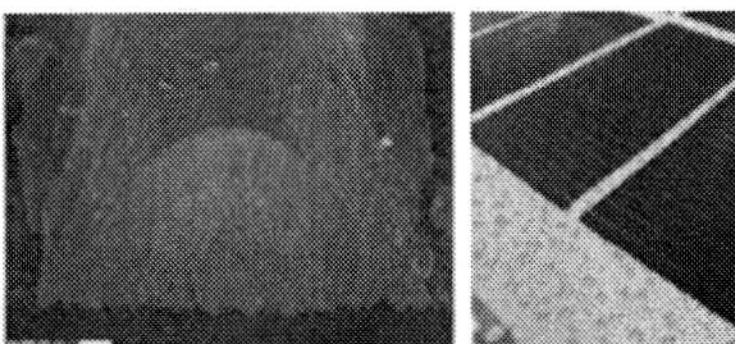

Figure 9 Left, copper plating over silver paste used as seed layer. Right, TOPCon half-cut cells after copper plating.

This last approach has demonstrated the potential to reach the outstanding < 1 mg/watt result.
Also, the development of plated metallization processes for TOPCon solar cells focusses on optimization of laser ablation parameters to achieve a laser contact opening (LCO) and inline plating deposition process scalable for mass production and is mainly driven by FH-ISE/RENA. To complete the WP1, laser sintering is also introduced as concept, evaluating the use of a laser scan over low temperature curing pastes to accelerate the curing process and permit the curing of copper formulations and so minimizing thermal impact on the a-Si interface in SHJ and preventing Cu in-diffusion into silicon while avoiding degradation of the seed grid-c-Si in TOPCon. This laser process might be compatible with the LS process presented in the WP2 so cross-experiments are planned.

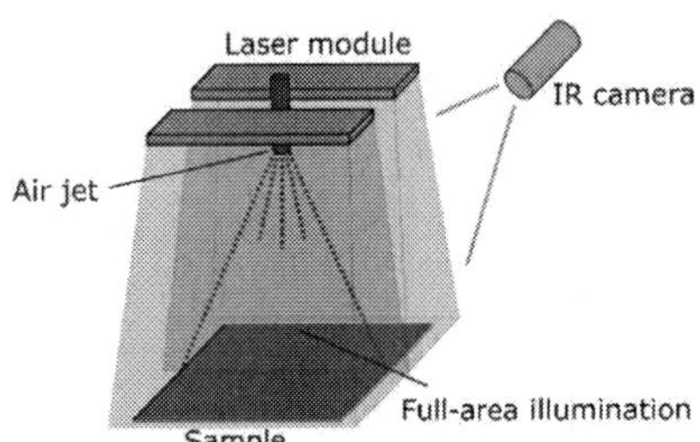

Figure 10 Laser sintering concept with VCSEL laser diode (977nm) and controlled air jet flow for temperature control.

- WP2 (Post Processing)
The LS tool is developed by CEA-INES and AMAT and the procedure consists in the cell exposure to high intensity light source (50 Suns) by using a tool that exposes HJT solar cells to high-intensity, multi-wavelength LED light and controlled heating for rapid post-treatment, enhancing cell performance by reducing defects and improving series resistance. FH-ISE and CSEM will instead focus on light-soaking with TOPCon substrates. The tool is already installed and working at different sites, 2 internal partners and 1 external partner. With this purpose, multiple data can be achieved and analyzed, both from HVM and R&D environments for thermal profiles design and IV characterization (Figure 11, Table 1).

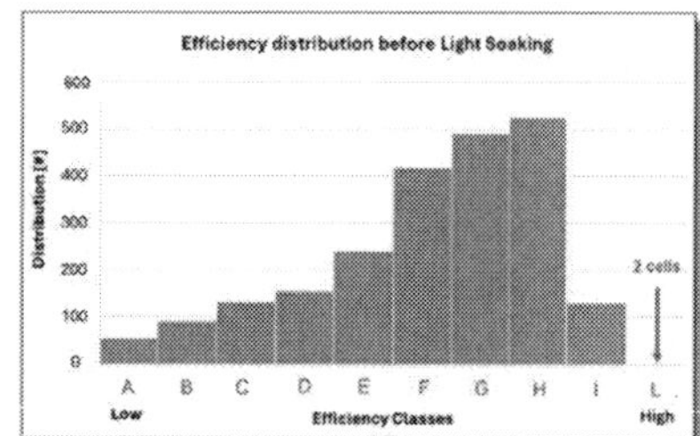

Figure 11 Efficiency classes from SHJ production data.

Efficiency class	Efficiency Gain %
A (low)	+1.12 %
E-F (mid)	+0.60 %
L (high)	+0.56 %

Table 1 LS efficiency gains on SHJ solar cells, HVM data.

Data will be then provided to UL to improve the understanding of LS impact on different depths of the samples via device modelling and to help provide clear guidelines for further process optimization. With the light soaking procedure, an average of +0.5% efficiency gain is recorded and even higher values are measured when exposing low-lifetime and low-grade substrates, meaning that a greater recovery is performed. Further experiments will be done to study the effects of the high-intensity light on the metal grid, contact resistance and line resistance. LS is also compatible with TOPCon solar cells in which an average gain of 0.3% has been already demonstrated (Figure 12).

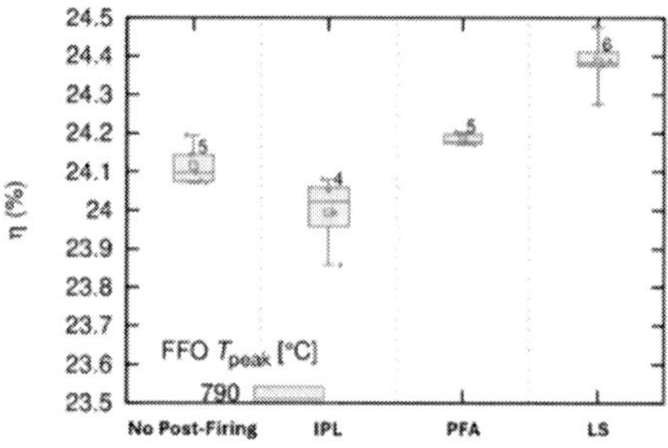

Figure 12 Light Soaking (LS) compared to Intense Pulse Light and Laser Post Firing Anneal post-processes.

On the ERP side, an 80% recovery of the pre-laser cell properties is shown by using AlOx as capping layer on the edge at laboratory scale with SHJ solar cells. The use of ERP has been demonstrated to be valid on both SHJ and TOPCon substrates in which FH-ISE is mostly involved. The process has been validated on shingle configuration (Figure 13).

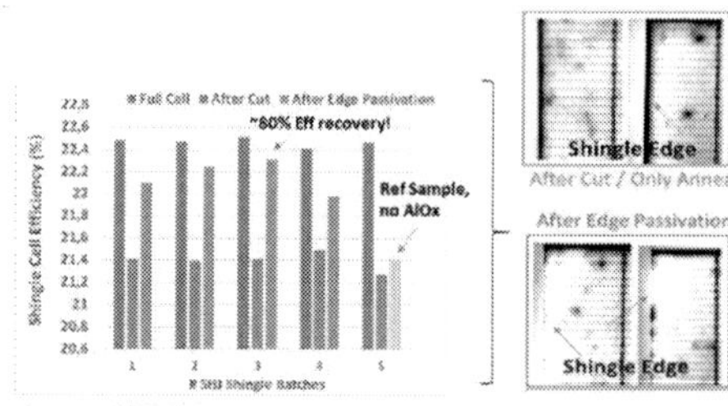

Figure 13 ERP results on SHJ substrates (shingles).

Next steps involving edge-repassivation will include high-throughput tools like plasma-enhanced atomic layer deposition (PE-ALD), study of the best annealing condition and the long-term impact on module (reliability testing) while also evaluating the CAPEX impact of a HVM tool. Also, it will be important to understand if ERP process can impact interconnection quality and/or final module reliability.

- WP3 (Interconnection)

Simulation trials by PCCL and UL and FH-ISE will help in getting insights on the thermomechanical and electrical behaviour of the cells when interconnected and under reliability testing. Also, models have been developed on the encapsulants to be used considering key parameters like thickness and hot-spot resilience. Finite Element Modeling (FEM, Figure 14) of different cell interconnection technologies (shingling and TWILL) has already been started to identify possible fabrication routes and loading related failures but also to compute the temperature distribution, deformation and thermomechanical stress during the shingling.

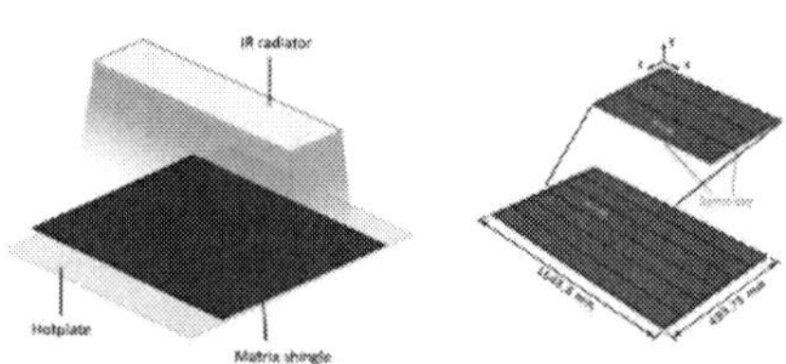

Figure 14 FEM models' principles to study temperature distribution and stress on shingles (let) and develop process and loading failures (right).

About shingling simulations, FH-ISE will focus on the matrix shingling interconnection using COMSOL Multiphysics and determine the minimum encapsulant thickness by a parameter sensitivity study. More data will be provided by partners during the development and scale-up of these alternative interconnection technologies. TWILL consists of a multiple wire interconnection method embedding conductive copper wires in polymeric carrier foils in which the metal interconnection occurs during lamination, eliminating the need of a separate stringing step (Figure 15). This method will be scaled to M10-G12 half-cut by IMEC, IPTE and ARK and reliability testing with different encapsulants and cells is ongoing.

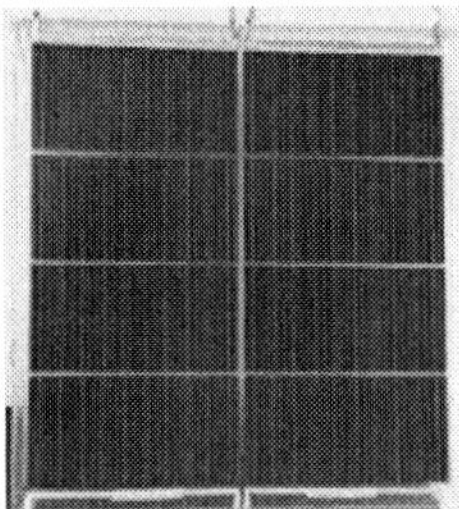

Figure 15 Twill mini module after lamination and curing optimization.

Shingling instead consists of interconnecting solar shingles via electrically conductive adhesives (ECA) to form flexible, any length, ribbon connected solar strings and so provide a certain degree of flexibility in the module design and size. In the shingling process development, partners will focus on shingle overlap reduction, reduction of Ag usage at the ECA level (either by ECA reduction or by usage of low content Ag ECA) and improvement in handling of thin wafers with AMAT/CEA-INES mainly focusing on SHJ and FH-ISE/M10 on TOPCon and matrix shingling. TNO will investigate an easy-release encapsulant to enable the recycling of all constituting materials of the device at end-of-life. This material has been preliminary tested on the front and rear side of solar cells showing that the two surfaces can be separated after material activation. Crucial steps in the development of this material are the lamination step (local delamination points) and the reliability testing according to the IEC61215 standard: single cell glass-glass modules have been made and the reliability testing is ongoing on release encapsulant and release encapsulant combined with TPO samples. Next steps will include the scale up to 4-cell mini-modules. The release encapsulant material properties and consistency will be analyzed in LCA study. The release encapsulant will be also tested for its re-use potential adding information for the LCA study.

-    WP4 (Equipment)
WP4 activities are strongly dependent on previous WPs and some of the activities are ongoing in parallel development like the dispensing kit integration as well as the TWILL and ERP tools design. AMAT, HL and FH-ISE will continue to work on the dispensing integration on HVM tool (Figure 16) which in principle will be used for both SHJ and TOPCon.

Figure 16 Dispensing kit mounted on screen-printing tool head

The upscaling potential of the plating process on SHJ and TOPCon will be evaluated on a pilot plating line from

RENA installed at FH-ISE to uncover potential limitations and shortcomings. AMAT will also continue to contribute to the development of a light-soaking tool that can demonstrate an efficiency gain entitlement on SHJ cells of 0.3% in industrial cells, with yield of 98% and uptime of 92%. Also, significant efforts will be spent on the upgrade of the shingling tool to scale up to G12 formats and add more flexibility in cell dimension, ribbon shape and string length. Singulus (SING) will develop an equipment platform for the ERP. IPTE will instead first upgrade a semi-automated foil-making tool and a pick-and-place tool and then focus on building a high-TPT, fully automated and flexible roll-to-stack foil-making machine (Figure 17), with a targeted speed of <5s/foil/line, and an availability (>92%) and yield (>97%). This work will be conducted in parallel with IMEC and ARK which will provide encapsulant foils.

Figure 17 Equipment concept for high-volume integrated production with TWILL interconnection concept

-    WP5 (Integration and Line Demonstration)
Previous WPs will provide the data and contribute to providing a starting point in the simulation of all the processing steps (Figure 18). As the amount of data will increase, Enginsoft (ENG) will oversee the making of a model that can include all the process variables, individual manufacturing steps performance (e.g. yield, TPT) and process variability that will be used to describe the SHINE PV line and progressively validate it. The final goal will be also creating and making available 2D and 3D models representing the production layout and material flows of a production line. Such models will support the different demonstrators as well as provide a virtual demonstration environment for the project results to assess and evaluate the efficiency, compatibility and overall performance of SHINE PV equipment.

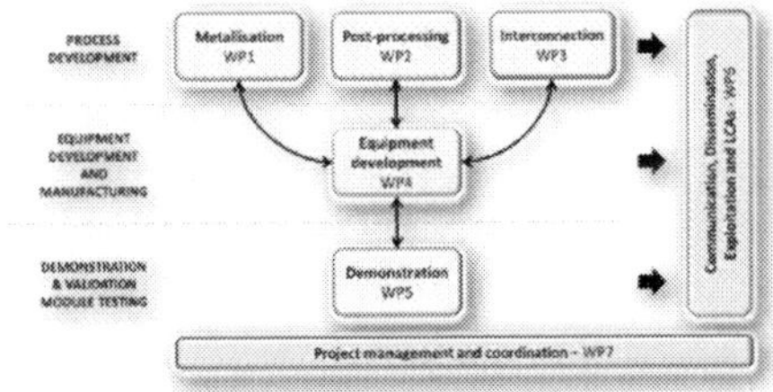

Figure 18 WPs contributions to WP5 and data flow

Also, the assessment and validation of solar modules will be studied via models, providing insights on aggregated raw data from the consortium, periodic metric measurements along long-term testing of installed modules and assessment of performance and seasonality effects.

- WP6-7 (LCA, Exploitation, Management)
Developing new supply chains and business models is crucial when working on alternative technological routes to mainstream advanced photovoltaic production and while trying to be competitive with the Asian market (Figure 19). Diversified EU manufacturing, circular, sustainable materials, job creation & tech leadership and energy security & autonomy are the most important factors to consider while working on a strategy.

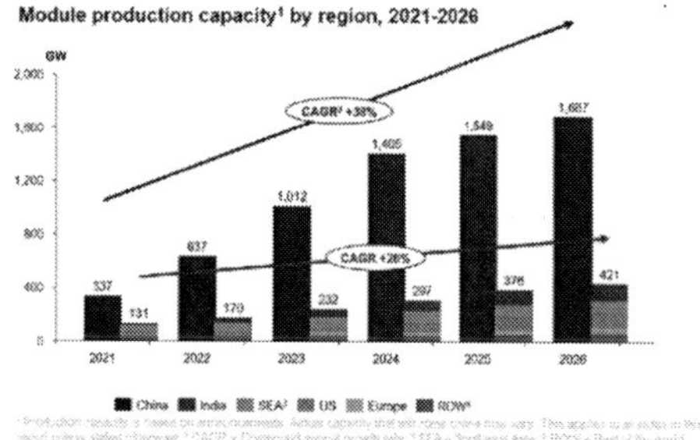

Figure 19 PV production capacity of Asia compared to Europe and rest of the world

SHINE PV supports the EU's goal of strategic autonomy in clean energy, while ensuring sustainable, resilient, and competitive PV production by promoting the adoption of standards (ISO 14044, Semi-35 Standard [18]) and performing circularity assessments like life cycle assessments (LCA, Figure 20).

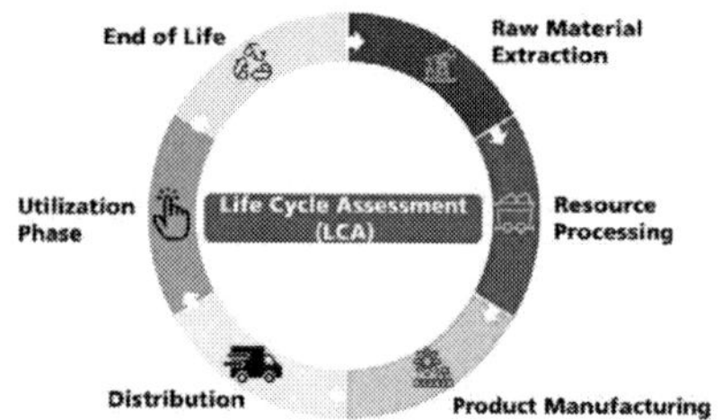

Figure 20 Data requirements for the entire supply chain flow

Some work has already been done on the communication side by introducing the project to the web, social and by creating cloud infrastructure for data sharing and reporting.

5 CONCLUSIONS

Despite the early phase of the project, interesting results have been already achieved especially on the WP2 part in which significant advantages in using the tools developed under the SHINE PV project have been demonstrated at both laboratory and HVM scales. Also, WP3 provided interesting outputs on the use of copper and plating as an alternative to standard silver pastes, providing a more sustainable and efficient route for PV. Some of the WPs are still on hold and will start to contribute to the next months but all the activities, periodic meetings and preliminary test or phases are in place and ready.

The SHINE PV consortium will continue to bring together the key industry expertise in both research and equipment, developing complete solutions for advanced manufacturing and more results will come in the following months.

More on the project and the partners can be found out at the following link: https://shinepv.eu/about/

6 AUTHOR CONTRIBUTIONS

AMAT-Italy for paper writing and submission, all the partners for reviewing and contributing.

7 FUNDING

This project has received funding from the European Union's Horizon Europe research and innovation programme under grant agreement No 101172902.

8 ACKNOWLEDGEMENTS

We would like to thank all the partners who have contributed to the making of this paper and the SHINE PV project.

9 REFERENCES

[1] EU-Funding&Tenders, "Sustainable, High-throughput, Industry-ready, Next-generation technology for European manufacturing leadership in PV (SHINE PV)," HORIZON-CL5-2024-D3-01, 01 01 2025. [Online]. Available: https://ec.europa.eu/info/funding-tenders/opportunities/portal/screen/how-to-participate/org-details/897837918/project/101172902/program/43108390/details. [Accessed 01 01 2025].

[2] W. Mackenzie, "How will China's expansion affect global solar module supply chain," Wood Mackenzie, 01 Month 2023. [Online]. Available: https://go.woodmac.com/l/131501/2023-11-10/317ftc/131501/1699609270p9l75YZ9/WOODMA_1.PDF. [Accessed 01 September 2025].

[3] P. J. Verlinden, "Future challenges for photovoltaic manufacturing at the terawatt level," *Journal of Renewable and Sustainable Energy*, vol. 12, no. 2020, p. 053505, 2020.

[4] R. Rossi, "SolarPower Europe," SolarPower Europe, 01 01 2023. [Online]. Available: https://www.solarpowereurope.org/insights/outlooks/eu-market-outlook-for-solar-power-2023-2027. [Accessed 01 01 2025].

[5] Y. Zhang, "Design considerations for multi-terawatt scale manufacturing of existing and future photovoltaic technologies: challenges and opportunities related to silver, indium and bismuth consumption," *Energy & Environmental Science*, vol. 14, no. 11, pp. 5587-5610, 2021.

[6] S. Pordan, "Optimizing solar cell metallization by parallel dispensing," *Solar Energy Materials and Solar Cells*, vol. 266, no. 2024, p. 112685, 2024.

[7] K. Gensowski, "Filament stretching during parallel dispensing – A way to reduce silver consumption in SHJ metallization," *Solar Energy Materials and Solar Cells,* vol. 245, no. 2022, p. 111871, 2022.

[8] K. Gensowski, "Filament stretching during micro-extrusion of silver pastes enables an improved fine-line silicon solar cell metallization," *Scientific Reports,* vol. 12, no. 2022, p. 12318, 2022.

[9] A. Lachowiz, "Aging tests of mini-modules with copper-plated heterojunction solar cells and pattern-transfer-printing of copper paste," *EPJ Photovolt.,* vol. 11, no. 2024, p. 7, 2024.

[10] B. Grubel, "Progress of plated metallization for industrial bifacial TOPCon silicon solar cells," *Progress in Photovoltaics,* vol. 30, no. 6, pp. 615-621, 2022.

[11] S. Harrison, "How to Combine SHJ Cell-Edge Passivation and Module Reliability?," in *SiliconPV Conference Proceedings,* Chambery, 2024.

[12] E. Lohmüller, "Thermal laser separation and high-throughput layer deposition for edge passivation for TOPCon shingle solar cells," *Solar Energy Materials and Solar Cells,* vol. 258, no. 2023, p. 112419, 2023.

[13] A. Voltan, "Advancements on post-processing of high efficiency cells: data from mass production and experimental roadmap," in *Proceeding of 42nd EUPVSEC,* Bilbao, 2025.

[14] J. Govaerts, "Encapsulant-Integrated Interconnection of Bifacial Solar Cells for BIPV Applications: Latest Results in the Twill-BIPV Project," in *Proceedings of the EU PVSEC 2020,* Online, 2020.

[15] J. Govaerts, "Interconnection and lamination technologies towards ubiquitous integration of photovoltaics," *Progress in Photovoltaics,* vol. 31, no. 11, pp. 1114-1129, 2023.

[16] M. Foti, "22% efficiency module combining Silicon Heterojunction Solar and Shingle interconnection," in *49th Photovoltaics Specialists Conference (PVSC),* Philadelphia, 2022.

[17] N. Klasen, "Performance of shingled solar modules under partial shading," *Progress in Photovoltaics,* vol. 30, no. 4, pp. 325-338, 2021.

[18] SPIE, "SPIE Digital Library," SPIE, 29 08 2017. [Online]. Available: https://www.spiedigitallibrary.org/conference-proceedings-of-spie/10313/1031353/Analyzing-component-manufacturing-costs-using-the-SEMI-E35-standard-for/10.1117/12.2283979.short. [Accessed 01 01 2025].

BEYOND SILVER: COMPARATIVE PERFORMANCE ANALYSIS OF ALTERNATIVE METALLIZATION STRATEGIES IN SILICON SOLAR CELLS

Seda Kilickaya[1], Melisa Korkmaz Arslan[1], Esma Alloji[2], Serdar Akbayrak[3] and Veysel Unsur[1,3,*]

[1] Center for Solar Energy Research and Application (ODTU-GUNAM), Ankara, Turkiye
[2] Nanoscience and Nano-Engineering, Necmettin Erbakan University, Konya, Turkiye
[3] Department of Fundamental Sciences in Engineering, Necmettin Erbakan University, Konya, Turkiye
* veysel.unsur@odtugunam.org

ABSTRACT: The photovoltaic industry's reliance on silver (Ag) for silicon solar cell metallization faces critical challenges due to Ag scarcity, cost volatility, and sustainability concerns. This study systematically evaluates advanced metallization strategies to reduce or eliminate Ag usage while maintaining high-performance solar cell operation. We investigate fine-line printing, hybrid/core-shell architectures, and alternative materials such as copper (Cu), aluminum (Al), and nickel (Ni). Fine-line printing enables Ag finger widths as narrow as 10–15 μm, reducing front-side Ag consumption by up to 25% (9 mg/W) without compromising efficiency. However, sub-10 μm finger widths introduce printability challenges and increased series resistance. Hybrid and core-shell pastes, such as Cu-core/Ag-shell configurations, mitigate Cu's oxidation and diffusion risks at low temperatures but face limitations in high-temperature processes (>750°C) required for TOPCon and IBC cells. To address this, Ag-doped Ni pastes (4% Ag) demonstrate a breakthrough, achieving power conversion efficiencies comparable to traditional Ag contacts while slashing Ag usage to <0.5 mg/Wp. In parallel, Cu-only pastes are explored for their ultra-low cost and high conductivity, yet require advanced barrier layers (e.g., Ni, Ti) to suppress Cu diffusion into silicon during high-temperature firing. Recent optimizations in rapid thermal annealing processes enable Cu paste stability at industrial scales, achieving efficiencies of ~22.5%. Meanwhile, Al-only pastes, while limited by higher contact resistance, show promise for rear-side metallization if used with Al/(boron doped)Si or Al/Ge alloy mixtures.

Keywords: Si solar cells, metallization, alternative materials, Cu contact, Ni contacts

1 INTRODUCTION

The rapid growth of the photovoltaic (PV) industry, driven by global decarbonization efforts, has intensified concerns over the scarcity of silver (Ag), a critical material for silicon solar cell metallization. The limited supply of Ag along with fluctuating cost threatens the sustainability and scalability of PV manufacturing, particularly as screen printing remains the dominant metallization technique.

To address this challenge, significant efforts have been made to optimize screen printing processes, including fine-line printing, narrowing finger widths, and improving screen designs, which reduce Ag consumption while maintaining electrical performance. Additionally, the development of Ag pastes with reduced Ag content or alternative conductive materials is essential.

Copper (Cu) has emerged as the most promising alternative due to its abundance, high conductivity, and cost-effectiveness. However, Cu faces significant challenges, including rapid oxidation and its tendency to diffuse into silicon can lead to the formation of detrimental Cu-related defects, necessitating robust barrier layers such as nickel (Ni) or titanium (Ti) or complete barrier layers underneath the contacts.

Aluminum (Al) and Ni also offer potential as alternative metallization materials, but their lower electrical conductivity and higher contact resistance pose limitations for front-side contacts. Recent advancements in hybrid and core-shell structures such as Cu-core/Ag-shell and Ni-core/Cu-shell configurations seek to leverage the favorable properties of each material while mitigating their individual limitations. These novel approaches aim to enhance performance and durability, although fully functional and industrially scalable implementations remain in development. These innovative approaches aim to balance the cost, performance, and reliability while reducing Ag dependency.

This study critically examines the current state of alternative metallization strategies for silicon solar cells, providing a systematic evaluation of advanced materials (e.g., Cu, Al, Ni) and hybrid/core-shell architectures as sustainable substitutes for Ag.

2 STRATEGIES AND OUTCOMES FOR SILVER REDUCTION and SILVER-FREE SOLAR CELLS

2.1 Ag reduction through fine line printing

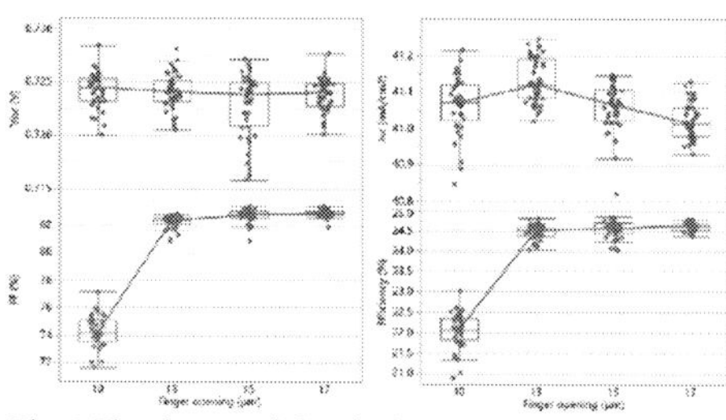

Fig. 1 The change of electrical parameters of a TOPCon solar cells with finger width

Fine-line printing has emerged as a critical strategy to reduce silver (Ag) consumption in silicon solar cells, addressing both cost and sustainability concerns. By narrowing Ag finger widths to 10–15 μm, significant reductions in Ag usage can be achieved without compromising cell efficiency [1]. Recent studies demonstrate that advanced grid designs, can reduce front-side Ag consumption by up to 20% while maintaining power conversion efficiency (PCE) [2], [3], [4]. Similarly, a dual-layer metallization approach, combining fine-line Ag dashes with non-silver fingers, reduced Ag consumption to 9 mg/W, a 25% improvement over standard designs [5]. However, challenges remain, including increased series resistance and printability issues with ultra-fine fingers (below 10µm) as shown in Fig. 1.

2.2 Hybrid and Core-Shell Pastes for Ag Reduction

Hybrid and core-shell structures offer a promising pathway to reduce Ag usage in metallization. These pastes combine the cost-effectiveness of abundant metals, such as Cu or Al, with the superior electrical and interfacial properties of thin Ag or Ni layers [6], [6]. By leveraging the strengths of multiple materials, these designs aim to achieve high performance while minimizing material costs.

In core-shell configurations, a conductive core (Cu) is encapsulated by a thin protective shell (Ag) to mitigate Cu's inherent drawbacks such as oxidation and diffusion into silicon while maintaining high conductivity. This strategy has proven effective for low-temperature applications, as shown in Fig. 2a. However, for solar cell architectures that require high-temperature firing processes (TOPCon and IBC), the protective shell tends to break down at temperatures exceeding 750 °C. When the shell is compromised, the Cu core becomes exposed, increasing the risk of diffusion into the silicon and oxidation, potentially leading to a declined in device performance.

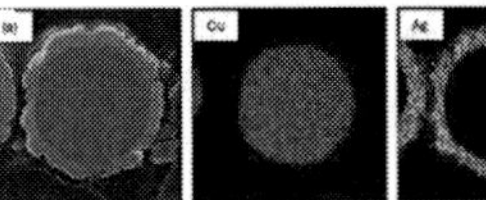
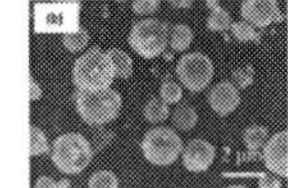

Fig. 2 (a) SEM images of Core (Cu) - Shell (Ag) structure and EDX analysis and (b) core-shell structure after high temperature annealing

One approach to mitigating high-temperature challenges is to incorporate Ag doping into alternative metals such as nickel [7], [8]. Doping Ni particles with a small percentage of Ag not only enhances conductivity but also lowers the metal work function, thereby ensuring optimal ohmic contact with silicon while reducing overall metallization costs (Fig. 3). For example, employing a 4% Ag-doped Ni paste in TOPCon silicon solar cells has demonstrated conversion efficiencies comparable to those of traditional silver contacts, while significantly reducing Ag consumption to below 0.5 mg/Wp [8].

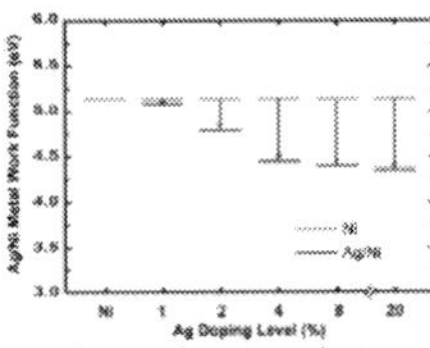
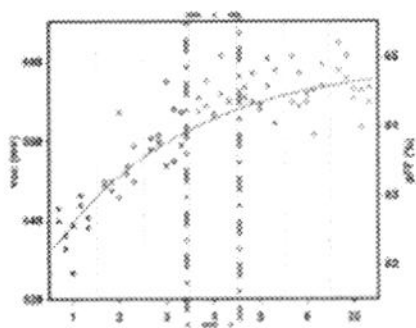

Fig. 3 Dependence of metal work function of Ni on Ag doping levels and the Suns-V_{OC} measurements of iV_{OC} values based on the doping level

2.3 Alternative Conductive Materials

The adoption of Cu metallization requires tailored approaches for low-temperature (SHJ) and high-temperature (e.g., TOPCon) cell architectures, addressing distinct challenges in diffusion control and interfacial engineering. SHJ cells, limited to processing temperatures < 250°C, benefit from Cu pastes cured at 180–220°C. Nanoparticle-based Cu inks with organic stabilizers

achieve line resistivities of 0.8–1.2 Ω/cm at 30 µm widths, comparable to Ag references, while maintaining adhesion forces >1 N/mm after lamination [6]. However, resistivity remains ~2× higher than Ag due to oxide formation, necessitating Ag-doped hybrid pastes (4–6 wt% Ag) to reduce contact resistivity to <3 mΩ·cm² [7]. For TOPCon cells requiring firing at 750–850°C, Cu diffusion into n+ poly-Si poses critical risks. Advanced glass frits in screen-printable pastes act as in-situ barriers, limiting Cu mobility while etching SiN$_x$. However, excessive glass frit content increases recombination ($J_{0,metal}$) to 500 fA/cm² and degrades passivation indicated by 45mV drop in open circuit voltage. Incorporating TiN or Al$_2$O$_3$ diffusion barriers beneath contacts reduces Cu ingress by 90%,

Aluminum-based pastes, while already common for rear-side metallization, face hurdles on the front side due to their higher resistivity and tendency to form insulating oxides. Recent hybrid approaches, including the incorporation of trace amounts of silver or integrating boron-doped silicon nanoparticles, have improved the performance of aluminum. However, challenges such as thermal expansion mismatch persists and require further investigation. Overall, advancing hybrid architectures and optimizing paste chemistries are crucial steps toward achieving reliable, cost-effective, silver-free metallization in next-generation photovoltaic manufacturing.

Acknowledgment
This conference paper is supported by TÜBITAK BİDEB.

References
[1] Y. Zhang *et al.*, "Ultra-Lean Silver Screen-Printing for Sustainable Terawatt-Scale Photovoltaic," *Solar RRL*, vol. 8, no. 17, p. 2400478, 2024, doi: 10.1002/solr.202400478.

[2] A. Ebong *et al.*, "Innovative front grid design, four-streets and five-busbars (4S-5BB), for high efficiency industrial Al-BSF silicon solar cell," *IEEE Electron Device Letters*, vol. 37, no. 4, pp. 459–462, 2016.

[3] V. Unsur *et al.*, "Rapid thermal processing of cost-effective contacts for silicon solar cells," *Progress in Photovoltaics*, vol. 27, no. 5, pp. 453–459, May 2019, doi: 10.1002/pip.3119.

[4] V. Unsur, "Implementation of nickel and copper as cost-effective alternative contacts in silicon solar cells," *Progress in Photovoltaics*, vol. 32, no. 4, pp. 267–275, Apr. 2024, doi: 10.1002/pip.3792.

[5] T. Schweigstill *et al.*, "Advanced Fine Line Printing With Glass Stencils: Achieving Metal Contact Fingers Below 10 µm," *Progress in Photovoltaics: Research and Applications*, vol. n/a, no. n/a, doi: 10.1002/pip.3885.

[6] D. Du *et al.*, "Low-Cost Metallization Based on Ag/Cu Fingers for Exceeding 25% Efficiency in Industrial Silicon Heterojunction Solar Cells," *Solar RRL*, vol. 8, no. 12, p. 2400052, 2024, doi: 10.1002/solr.202400052.

[7] B. Akgayev *et al.*, "Screen printable fire through nickel contacts for silicon solar cells," *Solar Energy Materials and Solar Cells*, vol. 261, p. 112528, Oct. 2023, doi: 10.1016/j.solmat.2023.112528.

[8] V. Unsur *et al.*, "Screen printed Ag-doped nickel metallization for industrial n-TOPCon silicon solar cells," *Solar Energy Materials and Solar Cells*, vol. 287, p. 113602, 2025.

Impact of doped polysilicon process for mass production TOPCon solar cell

Cheng-Wen Kuo, Ta-Ming Kuan, Yung-Chih Li, Chun-Wei Lee, Wei-Lo Chueh, Li-Guo Wu, Shih-Chieh Lin and Cheng-Yeh Yu
TSEC Corporation, No.85, Gaungfu N. Rd., Hsin-Chu 30351, Taiwan.

ABSTRACT: Tunnel oxide passivated contact solar cells have gradually become a mass-producible solar cell technology due to their excellent performance with cost-effectiveness, and further superimposing other technologies to improve conversion efficiency has become the focus of subsequent research. Heavy doping is usually required to achieve excellent field effect passivation and low contact resistivity in doped polysilicon (poly-Si). In order to increase the throughput, the poly-Si process improvements are needed. During this process, it could be found that as the temperature increases, more nanocrystalline structures will form on the surface of the polysilicon layer. In this study, the electrical properties and reliability of different doped polysilicon films were studied. Finally, industrial-sized (G10-L) TOPCon solar cells were fabricated on a production line with an average efficiency of 25.95%, 0.15% higher than the Baseline solar cells of 25.8%. The above results suggest that nano crystallization may be helpful for passivation, thereby obtaining efficient solar cells.
Keywords: TOPCon, mass production, Poly-Si

1 INTRODUCTION

With the world's growing demand for energy, while coping with human-caused global warming, has become one of the undisputed challenges facing humanity in the near future. This requires the use of clean and environmentally friendly resources to achieve sustainable energy production. Solar photovoltaic (PV) technology is gaining increasing attention, as clearly reflected in the statistics of the total installed capacity of global solar photovoltaic modules. Crystalline silicon (c-Si) has become the market-leading technology since its birth, accounting for nearly 95% of the market share due to its unique characteristics such as non-toxicity, abundant reserves and long-term stability [1]. On the other hand, as the number of solar photovoltaic installations increases and the land available for construction becomes less and less, the demand for high-efficiency solar energy becomes more important.

Using the passivated emitter rear cell (PERC) structure, the mass production efficiency has exceeded 23%, which is close to reaching its theoretical performance [2]. When the efficiency of PERC solar cells approaches 24%, most of the recombination losses are caused by metal contacts [3], making further improvement difficult, especially in the field of industrial manufacturing. Therefore, contact passivation has been a hot research topic in the field of photovoltaics for many years. Among the various materials and compositions studied, TOPCon remains the most interesting in the industry [4]. In the TOPCon design, the metal does not make direct contact with the wafer. Instead, a thin layer of tunnel oxide is applied first, followed by a layer of highly doped n-type or p-type polysilicon, which contacts the metal at the end. The back of the tunnel oxide does not affect the operation of the device because the tunnel oxide blocks one type of carrier. Therefore, these structures are often called passivated contacts. Fraunhofer ISE reported TOPCon cell efficiencies of 25.8% and POLO-IBC cell efficiencies of 26.1% with a specific surface area of 4 cm^2 [5-7]. Inspired by these outstanding research advances, attempts to introduce passive contacts into industrial solar cell manufacturing are fascinating. As a result, TOPCon has gradually gained industry recognition and is considered the next generation cell technology after PERC [8]. The key to achieving high performance of TOPCon lies in the preparation of high-quality nano-SiO$_x$ (T$_{ox}$) and heavily doped polysilicon. There are many reports

on Tox preparation methods, including thermal oxidation [9-12], wet chemical oxidation [12-14], ozone oxidation [12, 13], plasma-assisted oxidation [15-16] and plasma-assisted atomic layer deposition (PEALD) [17], with a composite current density (J$_0$) of less than 10 fA/cm^2 [18]. However, except for ozone oxidation and plasma-assisted oxidation, most of the above methods cannot be industrialized, which correspond to the following industrial preparation methods of amorphous silicon (α-Si) low-pressure chemical vapor deposition (LPCVD) and plasma-enhanced chemical vapor deposition (PECVD). Compared with ozone oxidation, plasma-assisted oxidation can be integrated with in-situ doping of polycrystalline silicon (n$^+$poly-Si) in the same tube, thereby reducing process steps and reducing process costs. In addition, PECVD is superior to LPCVD in terms of film deposition rate, wrap-around deposition and equipment-related consumables [30, 31].

In this study, our primary goal was to improve productivity while maintaining a certain level of performance. We modified the doping temperature and time for poly-Si. The results showed that as the temperature increased, the nanostructures became larger and more numerous, which improved the final performance, but the reliability remained similar. This new parameter not only improved productivity but also improved efficiency.

2 EXPERIMENTAL

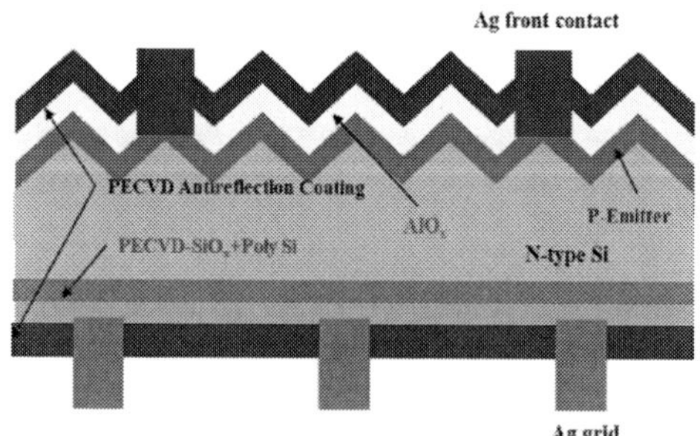

Figure 1: TOPCon structure as investigated in this work.

Figure 1 showed the TOPCon structure in this work. The G10-L size (182.0 mm x 183.75 mm) bifacial TOPCon solar cells were fabricated on 130 µm thick n-type Cz-silicon wafers with a resistivity of 0.4~1.6 Ω-cm..

The process sequence in this work was shown in Figure 2. Chemical wet etching methods were used for saw damage removal and surface texturing, which include alkaline etching for mono-crystalline silicon wafers. The solution composition of alkaline etching was potassium hydroxide (KOH) : deionized water (DI) = 1 : 50 and additives. The diffusion process of this work also improves the temperature curve and its uniformity.

The front side of the solar cells features an alkaline textured (random-pyramids) surface with a boron-doped p+emitter. The emitter was formed by BBr₃ tube furnace diffusion followed by drive-in oxidation, resulting in an emitter with a sheet resistance of R_{sheet} between 400~500 Ω/sq. The borosilicate glass (BSG) was then removed by HF-contained solutions, formed edge isolation in the meantime. Then, the rear surface is polished which removes 5-10 μm silicon in this work, in order to reduce the roughness and its impact on the effective charge carrier lifetime. The emitter was passivated with a 5~10 nm thick Al_2O_3 layer deposited with atomic layer deposition. In order to decrease PID effect and increase efficiency, we optimized the CVD process parameter to improve. An antireflection coating (ARC) layer of silicon nitride $(SiN_x:H)$ and/or $SiO_x/SiO_xN_y/SiN_x$ multi ARC was deposited by plasma enhanced chemical vapor deposition (PECVD) with thickness of 80-120 nm, as shown in Fig 3.

The rear side tunnel oxide layer and doped polysilicon (poly-si) were also deposited using PECVD technology. In order to improve the PECVD equipment's productivity, the polysilicon process parameters was adjusted in our experimental group by increasing the temperature and reducing the time. Figures 4 and 5 show that the back-side thickness was approximately 120-140 nm. The back-side laser aperture ratio was then optimized. The front side and rear side silver metallization layers were formed by screen printing technique and followed by co-firing process. Finally, the current-voltage characteristics of the solar cells were measured under AM 1.5 illumination.

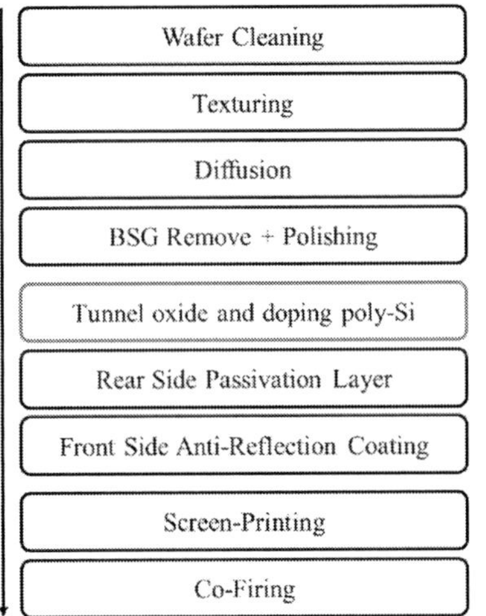

Figure 2: Process flow for the fabrication of PERC solar cell as developed in this work

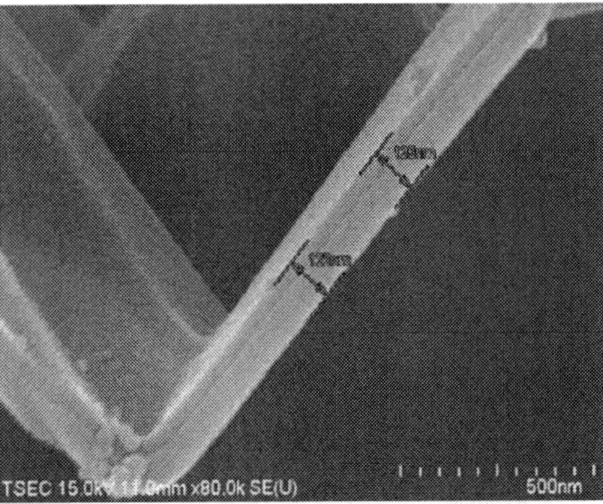

Figure 3: The scanning electron microscope (SEM) image of front side passivation layer for this work.

Figure 4: The scanning electron microscope (SEM) image of rear side layer for ref sample.

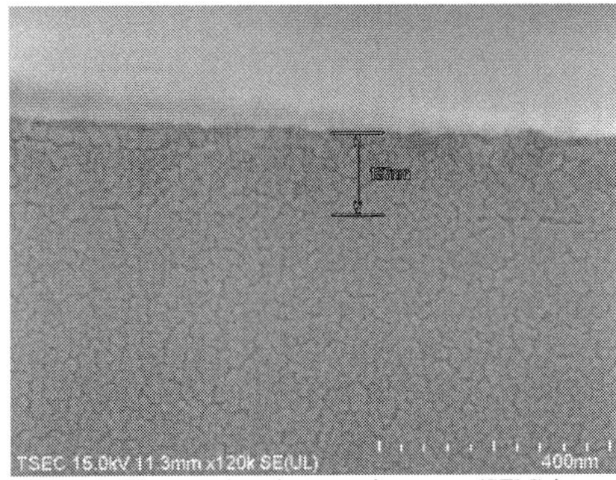

Figure 5: The scanning electron microscope (SEM) image of rear side layer for experiment sample.

3 EXPERIMENTAL RESULTS AND DISCUSSION

The goal of the mass production is to increase production capacity by adjusting the temperature of the PECVD equipment's doping poly-Si process without sacrificing efficiency. Reference 21 explains that as the temperature increases, the thickness of the amorphous silicon deposition increases, indicating that the doping poly-Si thickness can also increase. It implies that this condition can be adjusted to increase production capacity. Table 1 shows that the electrical properties are also better, which is consistent with the iVOC description in reference 21. In addition to the electrical properties, we also conducted top-view SEM analysis on doping poly-Si. From the top-view SEM images (Figs. 6 and 7), it could be observed that the number of poly-Si grains in the polycrystalline silicon layer of the experimental group is significantly larger and the size is larger. The formation of these nanocrystals may be a key factor in enhancing passivation, ultimately improving electrical performance and increasing solar cell efficiency. Besides, we tested the TOPCon tandem process with the research center and found that performance varied with the number of poly grain number.

Table 1: The average electrical results of the TOPCon cells.

	EFF (%)	FF (%)	V_{OC} (V)	I_{SC} (A)
REF TOPCon	25.80	84.64	0.7319	13.940
Experiment	25.95	84.94	0.7347	13.921

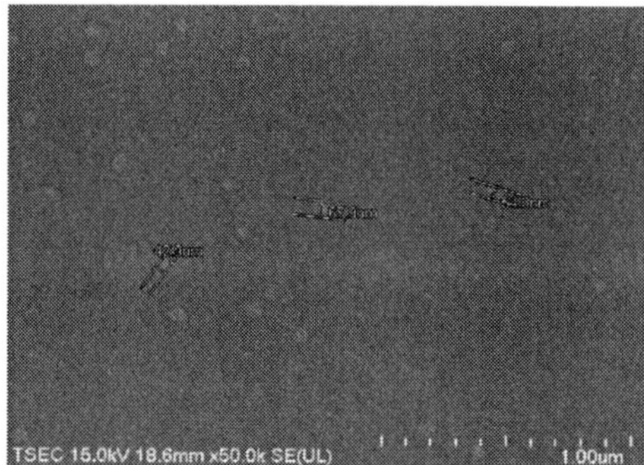

Figure 6: The top view SEM of poly Si layer for REF sample.

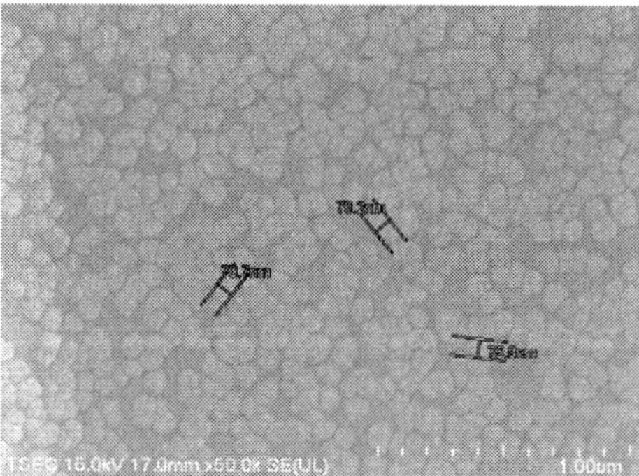

Figure 7: The top view SEM of poly Si layer for experiment sample.

Potential-induced degradation (PID) testing of solar cells also complies with IEC TS 62804-1 and was used in this experiment. Both the REF and experimental solar cells passed PID testing at 85°C and 85% RH, applying -1500 V for 96 hours in a climate chamber, as shown in Figure 7. After PID testing, both the REF and experimental ARC PERC solar cells showed less than 5% power loss and no

EL dark regions, demonstrating the effectiveness of the experimental results.

Sample	Pre-Test		Post-Test		EL		Decay Rate(%) (Spec<5%)
Sample	Rsh	Pmpp	Rsh	Pmpp	Pre-PID	Post-PID	∆Pmpp
REF-1	489.7	7.7587	554.3	7.6882			0.91%
REF-2	14685.5	7.6565	2426.2	7.5887			0.89%
REF-3	389.1	7.6360	3349.2	7.6301			0.08%
EXP-1	5759.2	7.5293	546.3	7.5004			0.39%
EXP-2	1527.9	7.5367	3915.8	7.4796			0.76%
EXP-3	2421.7	7.6887	496.2	7.5963			1.20%

Figure 8: Summary of power loss and EL images of pre-PID and post-PID of REF and experiment TOPCon solar cells. PID test condition is 85 degree Celsius / 85% RH biased -1500V for 96 hours.

4 CONCLUSIONS

In this work, we demonstrate the fabrication of industrial-scale TOPCon solar cells, achieving an average conversion efficiency of 25.95%, a 0.15% improvement over the benchmark efficiency of 25.8%. This achievement is due to optimization of the polycrystalline silicon (poly-Si) process, which is critical for achieving excellent field-effect passivation and low contact resistivity. These findings demonstrate that targeted process improvements can significantly advance the mass production of solar cells. The successful industrialization of this technology provides further improve the efficiency and yield of TOPCon solar cells.

5 REFERENCES

[1] H. Ullah, S. Czapp, S. Szultka, H. Tariq, U. B. Qasim, H. Imran., "Crystalline Silicon (c-Si)-Based Tunnel Oxide Passivated Contact (TOPCon) Solar Cells: A Review," Energies, vol. 16, pp. 715, 2023.

[2] J. Schmidt, R. Peibst, R. Brendel., "Surface passivation of crystalline silicon solar cells: present and future," Sol. Energy Mater. Sol. Cells vol.187, pp.39, 2018.

[3] M. Müller, G. Fischer, B. Bitnar, S. Steckemetz, R. Schiepe, M. Mühlbauer, R. Köhler, P. Richter, C. Kusterer, A. Oehlke, E. Schneiderlöchner, H. Sträter, F. Wolny, M. Wagner, P. Palinginis, and D. H. Neuhaus, "Loss analysis of 22% efficient industrial PERC solar cells," Energy Procedia, vol. 124, pp.131,2017.

[4] H. Yousuf, M. Q. Khokhar, S. Chowdhury, D. P. Pham, Y. Kim, M. Ju, Y. Cho, E. C. Cho, J. Yi, "A Review on TOPCon Solar Cell Technology," Current Photovoltaic Research, vol. 9, pp.9, 2021

[5] A. Richter, J. Benick, F. Feldmann, A. Fell, M. Hermle, S. W. Glunz, "n-Type Si solar cells with passivating electron contact: Identifying sources for efficiency limitations by wafer thickness and resistivity variation," Solar Energy Materials and Solar Cells, Vol. 173, pp. 96-105, 2017.

[6] M. A. Green, Y. Hishikawa, E. D. Dunlop, D. H. Levi, J. HohlEbinger, and A. W. Ho-Baillie, "Solar cell

efficiency tables (version 51)," Progress in Photovoltaics: Research and Applications, vol. 26, pp. 3, 2018.

[7] F. Haase, C. Hollemann, S. Schäfer, A. Merkle, M. Rienäcker, J. Krügener, R. Brendel, and R. Peibst, "Laser contact openings for local poly-Si-metal contacts enabling 26.1%-efficient POLOIBC solar cells," Solar Energy Materials and Solar Cells, vol.186, pp. 184, 2018.

[8] S. Ma, B. Liao,F.Y. Qiao,D. Ding, C. Gao,Z. P. Li, R. Tong, X.Y. Kong, and W.Z. Shen, "24.7% industrial tunnel oxide passivated contact solar cells prepared through tube PECVD integrating with plasma-assisted oxygen oxidation and in-situ doped polysilicon," Solar Energy Materials and Solar Cells, vol, 257, pp.112396, 2023.

[9] U. Römer, R. Peibst, T. Ohrdes, B. Lim, J. Krügener, T. Wietler, and R. Brendel, "Ion Implantation for Poly-Si Passivated Back-Junction Back-Contacted Solar Cells," IEEE Journal of Photovoltaics, vol.5, pp. 507, 2015

[10] D. Yan, A. Cuevas, J. Bullock, Y. Wan, and C. Samundsett, "Phosphorus-diffused polysilicon contacts for solar cells," Sol. Energy Mater. Sol. Cells, vol.142, pp.75, 2015.

[11] M.K. Stodolny, M. Lenes, Y. Wu, G.J.M. Janssen, I.G. Romijn, J.R.M. Luchies, and L.J. Geerligs,"n-Type polysilicon passivating contact for industrial bifacial n-type solar cells," Sol. Energy Mater. Sol. Cells, vol. 158, pp. 24, 2016.

[12] R. Peibst, Y. Larionova, S. Reiter, M. Turcu, R. Brendel, D. Tetzlaff, J. Krügener,T. Wietler, U. Höhne, J.D. Kähler, H. Mehlich, S. Frigge, "Implementation of n+ andp+ POLO junctions on front and rear side of double-side contacted industrial silicon solar cells," 32nd Europ. Photovolt. Sol. Energy Conference, Munich,Germany, pp.323, 2016.

[13]A. Moldovan, F. Feldmann, M. Zimmer, J. Rentsch, J. Benick, and M. Hermle, "Tunnel oxide passivated carrier-selective contacts based on ultra-thin SiO2 layers,"Sol. Energy Mater. Sol. Cells, vol.142, pp.123, 2015.

[14]A. Richter, J. Benick, R. Müller, F. Feldmann, C. Reichel, M. Hermle, S.W. Glunz, "Tunnel oxide passivating electron contacts as full-area rear emitter of high-efficiency p-type silicon solar cells," Prog. Photovolt Res. Appl., vol.26, pp. 579, 2018.

[15]M. Jeon, J. Kang, G. Shim, S. Ahn, N. Balaji, C. Park, Y. Lee, J. Yi, "Passivation effect of tunnel oxide grown by N2O plasma for c-Si solar cell applications," Vacuum, vol.141, pp152, 2017.

[16]Y.Q. Huang, M.D. Liao, Z.X. Wang, X.Q. Guo, C.S. Jiang, Q.Yang, Z.Z. Yuan, D.D. Huang, J. Yan, X.Y. Zhang, Q. Wang, H. Jin, M. Al-Jassim, C.H.Shou, Y.H. Zeng, B.J. Yan, J.C. Ye, "Ultrathin silicon oxide prepared by in-line plasma-assisted N2O oxidation (PANO) and the application for n-type polysilicon passivated contact,"Sol. Energy Mater. Sol. Cells, vol. 208, pp.110389, 2020.

[17] B.C. Liao, W.L. Wu, R.J. Yeo, X.Y. Wu, S. Ma, Q. Wang, Y.M. Wan, X.D. Su, W.Z. Shen, X. Li, W.M. Li, G.Q. Xing, B. Hoex, Atomic scale controlled tunnel oxide enabled by a novel industrial tube-based PEALD technology with demonstrated commercial TOPCon cell efficiencies > 24%, Prog. Photovolt Res. Appl., vol.31, pp.220, 2022.

[18] J. Schmidt, R. Peibst, R. Brendel, Surface passivation of crystalline silicon solar cells: present and future, Sol. Energy Mater. Sol. Cells, vol. 187, pp. 39, 2018.

[19] B. Steinhauser, J.I. Polzin, F. Feldmann, M. Hermle, S.W. Glunz, "Excellent Surface Passivation Quality on Crystalline Silicon Using Industrial-Scale Direct-Plasma TOPCon Deposition Technology," Solar RRL, vol. 2, pp.1800068, 2018.

[20] F. Frank, T. Fellmeth, B. Steinhauser, H. Nagel, D. Ourinson, M. Sebastian, E. Lohmuller, J. Polzin, J. Benick, A. Richter, A. Moldovan, M. Bivour, F. Clement, J. Rentsch, H. Martin, S.W. Glunz, "Large area TOPCon cells realized by a PECVD process," 36th European PV Solar Energy Conference and Exhibition, pp.304, 2019.

[21] W. Chen, T.N. Truong, H.T. Nguyen, C. Samundsett, S.P. Phang, D. MacDonald, A. Cuevas, L. Zhou, Y. Wan, D. Yan, "Influence of PECVD deposition temperature on phosphorus doped poly-silicon passivating contacts," Sol. Energy Mater Sol. Cells, vol. 206, pp.110348, 2020.

Impact of doped polysilicon process for mass production TOPCon solar cell

Speaker : Cheng-Wen Kuo

1BV.5.32

Outline

- **Introduction**
- **Experiment and Result**
- **Summary**

1BV.5.32

020022-002

Introduction

- To increase the throughput of TOPCon solar cells, we attempted to improve process parameters at key point.

- In the polysilicon process, It could be found that increasing the temperature leads to the formation of more nanocrystalline structures on the surface of the polysilicon layer.

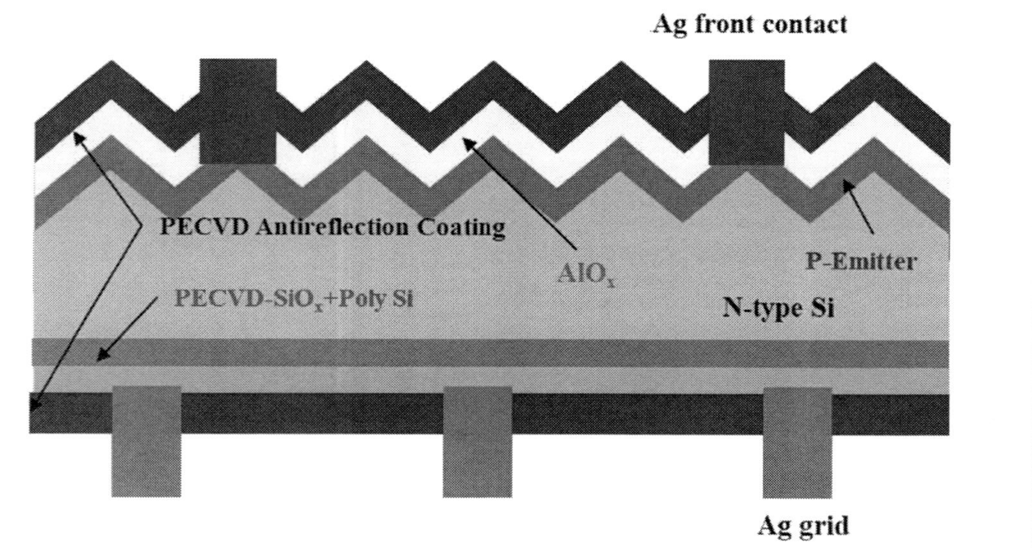

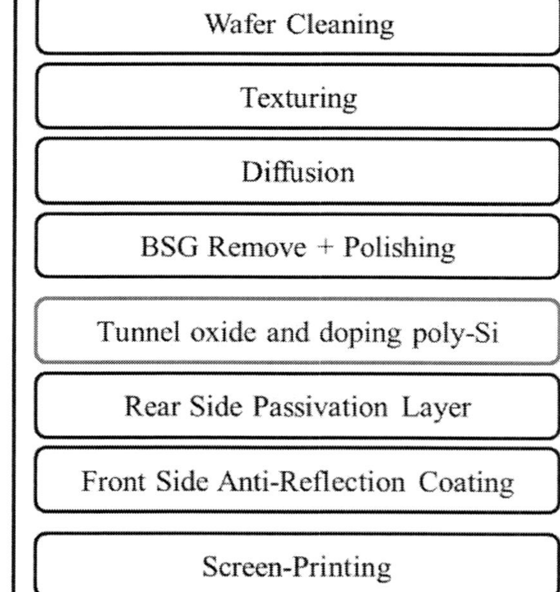

Experiment and Result

	poly grain size (nm)
REF	42 – 67
Experiment	70 – 76

	EFF (%)	FF (%)	V_{OC} (V)	I_{SC} (A)
REF TOPCon	25.80	84.64	0.7319	13.940
Experiment	25.95	84.94	0.7347	13.921

Summary

- We present a process method that improved yield and achieved better performance.

- For the both solar cells, the degradation in PID test is less than 5%.

- Finally, we tested the TOPCon tandem process with the research center and found that performance varied with the number of nanocrystal structures.

1BV.5.32

ANALYSIS OF TEXTURE ETCHING TO REDUCE LASER-INDUCED DAMAGE IN BORON-DOPED SELECTIVE EMITTERS

Bruno Krever Lopes, Adriano Moehlecke, Moussa Ly, Izete Zanesco, Felipe Chini de Freitas
Solar Energy Technology Nucleus, School of Technology, Pontifical Catholic University of Rio Grande do Sul - PUCRS
Av. Ipiranga, 6681, P.96A, 90619-900, Porto Alegre, RS, Brazil
e-mails: Lopes.bruno@edu.pucrs.br, moehleck@pucrs.br, moussa.ly@pucrs.br, izete@pucrs.br,
felipe.freitas@edu.pucrs.br

ABSTRACT: The photovoltaic industry is undergoing a transition from p-type to n-type silicon substrates, with most solar cells incorporating boron-doped emitters. Boron laser-assisted selective emitter is a key area of research in the mass production of high-efficiency devices. However, laser processing can damage silicon wafers and reduce the minority carrier lifetime. This paper presents an analysis of a process developed to obtain boron-doped emitters using laser-assisted doping, combined with texture etching to reduce surface damage. Boron-doped regions exhibit resistance to KOH-based etching, thereby enabling selective material removal and making this approach suitable for the fabrication of selective emitters. Boron was deposited by spin-coating, and diffusion was performed with a Nd-YAG laser. The samples were analysed by SEM images and minority carrier lifetime and sheet resistance measurements. SEM images revealed that, despite the presence of boron in the laser-processed areas, the anisotropic etching produced textured surfaces. The decrease in minority carrier lifetime was smaller in the samples processed using the proposed method compared to those subjected to the reference process. In conclusion, texture etching can be performed after boron diffusion to minimize silicon damage caused by laser processing and to increase the sheet resistance of the doped regions.
Keywords: silicon solar cell, laser processing, texture etching, selective emitter.

1 INTRODUCTION

In the past decade, the passivated emitter and rear solar cell (PERC) has emerged as the industry standard, replacing Al-BSF (aluminum-back surface field) devices. This technology transition occurred because the PERC structure minimizes minority charge carrier recombination on the surfaces and enhances the internal reflectance on the rear face of the device. To further reduce recombination, the tunnel-oxide passivated contact (TOPCon) structure has been introduced in industrial production lines in recent years. The combination of tunnel oxide and polysilicon films reduces recombination at the rear metal contact interface, enabling the fabrication of high-efficiency devices. However, approximately 50% of the recombination occurs at the front side of the devices, in the boron-doped emitter and contacts [1].

In manufacturing lines, PERC and TOPCon devices are typically fabricated using screen-printing to form electrical contacts. The screen-printing has led to significant electrical losses in the emitter, which is a limiting factor for the efficiency of industrial solar cells [2], [3]. These losses stem from the high contact resistance (ρ_c) between the homogeneous emitter and the metal contacts. One solution to this issue is the use of selective emitters, which involves creating a thick and highly doped region beneath the metal finger area, whereas the illuminated region between the fingers maintains a lower dopant concentration and a shallower p-n junction. The selective emitter can reduce ρ_c and Auger and Shockley-Read-Hall (SRH) recombination [4], enhancing solar cell efficiency.

Among the various techniques for selective emitter fabrication, laser-assisted doping is particularly advantageous due to its processing speed, cost-effectiveness, compatibility with industrial production lines, and minimal requirement for additional process steps in solar cell manufacturing [4], [5]. According to the International Technology Roadmap for Photovoltaics (ITRPV) [6], the laser diffusion technique will constitute the mainstream process for obtaining selective emitters in the coming decade. However, notably, the laser diffusion technique introduces defects in the silicon lattice, which are associated primarily with surface melting induced during processing. The recombination centers for minority charge carriers significantly decrease the solar cell efficiency, as evidenced in previous research [7-12]. For example, Gu et al. [12] analyzed the impact of laser pulses on recombination in boron-doped emitters. They reported that the laser irradiation partially destroyed the surface pyramid structure, leading to an increase in surface defects and dangling bonds. A post-oxidation process was proposed to repair laser-induced damage [12].

Moehlecke and Luque [13] proposed an anisotropic surface etching process in a KOH solution to create selective emitters, exploiting the resistance of boron-doped silicon surfaces to anisotropic etching. The strong B-Si bond increases the rigidity of the lattice, increasing the energy required to remove a silicon atom, high enough to stop etching altogether [14]. In the case of KOH solutions, the rate of anisotropic etching can be reduced by approximately twenty times on the surface of silicon with boron concentrations higher than 10^{20} cm^{-3} [14]. In recent years, this concept has been applied to TOPCon and interdigitated back contact (IBC) solar cells [15], [16]. For instance, Hoβ et al. [16] developed TOPCon devices with patterned p-type fingers to obtain local passivating contacts on the front side.

This paper presents an analysis of a process developed to obtain boron-doped emitters using laser-assisted doping, combined with texture etching to reduce surface damage. In the proposed approach, texture etching was performed subsequent to boron diffusion. The results obtained were compared to those from reference processes to evaluate the effectiveness of the method. The use of boron to reduce the etching of selective emitters and laser-induced degradation represents an innovation in solar cell processing. Samples with boron-doped regions were processed and characterized by scanning electron microscopy (SEM) images, the sheet resistance of the boron-doped emitters, and the minority charge carrier lifetime of the silicon wafers.

2 MATERIALS AND METHODS

2.1 Processes

Fig. 1 illustrates the main steps of the proposed process, as well as two reference processes. In the proposed process (A), boron diffusion was performed before texture etching. The reference process B involved anisotropic etching before laser processing, the standard sequence used in industries and labs. The reference process C focused on laser processing of textured silicon wafers without boron doping, aiming to evaluate only the effect of laser on minority carrier lifetime.

Proposed process - A

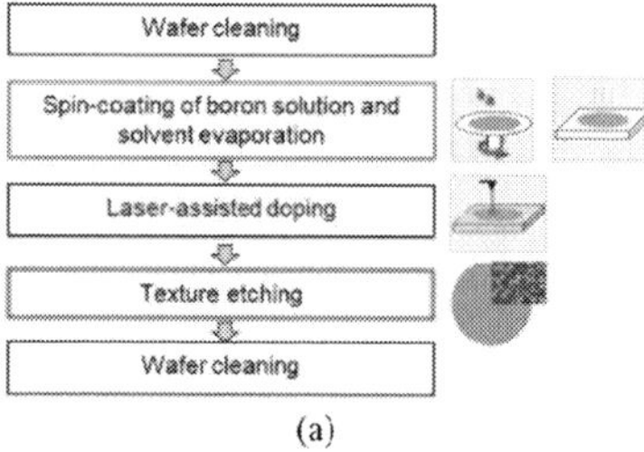

(a)

Reference process - B

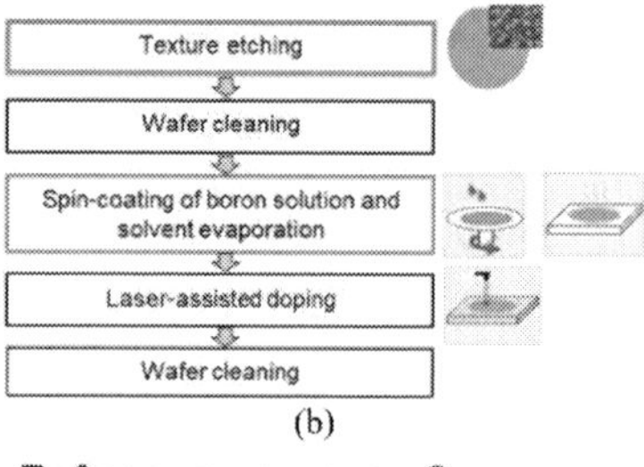

(b)

Reference process - C

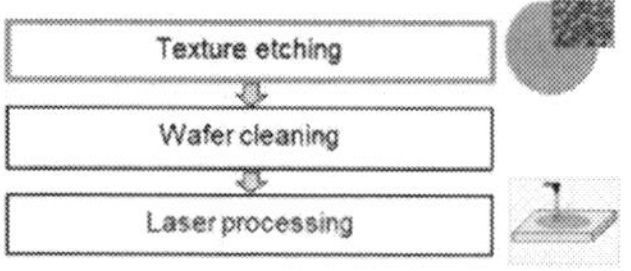

(c)

Figure 1: (a) Process A – boron diffusion performed before the texture etching; (b) Process B – standard sequence for boron-doped emitter formation, with texture etching as the initial step; (c) Process C – laser processing of silicon wafers without prior boron deposition by spin-coating.

In the proposed processing sequence (process A), the silicon wafers were cleaned in a CP4 solution, which consists of nitric acid, hydrofluoric acid, and acetic acid. The wafers were subsequently cleaned in a standard RCA2 solution composed of hydrogen peroxide, hydrochloric acid, and deionized water. The boron dopant was PBF20 solution (Filmtronics), which was deposited onto the wafer surface using the spin-coating method. The laser-assisted doping processes were carried out with a Nd:YAG laser

equipment (wavelength of 1064 nm), with a nominal power of 18 W. After laser processing, the texture etching was performed in a solution containing potassium hydroxide, isopropyl alcohol, and deionized water at a temperature of approximately 90 °C. The etching times ranged from 20 min to 60 min.

The texture etching was carried out in the first steps in reference processes B and C. The immersion time of the silicon wafers was 60 min, which is a standard time to produce lower reflectance and pyramid heights ranging from 5 μm to 8 μm. After texture etching, the wafers were cleaned in low concentration hydrofluoric acid followed by RCA2 solution. Boron was deposited by spin-coating and diffused by laser irradiation in process B. To assess the damage caused by laser irradiation, no boron-diffused regions were formed in Process C.

2.2 Sample processing

N-type monocrystalline float-zone (FZ) silicon wafers, doped with phosphorus and with resistivity of 1 Ω.cm - 20 Ω.cm, were processed. Six square samples of 4.18 cm² with laser diffusion in the "finger areas" and three samples of 4.18 cm² with homogeneous laser diffusion were developed in each silicon wafer, as depicted in Fig. 2. The "finger areas" are those that receive the metal contact in solar cells; thus, with boron diffusion only in the finger regions, a selective emitter can be formed.

Three different laser processing configurations were applied, based on processes developed previously [8], [9], namely: 1) Configuration 1, laser produced circular regions (spots) in the "finger areas", without superposition of the spots [8]: laser intensity of 95%, beam scanning speed of 3000 mm/s, and pulse rate frequency of 30 kHz.
2) Configuration 2, circular regions (spots) produced by laser processing were superposed to obtain lines ("fingers") [9]: laser intensity of 95%, beam scanning speed of 500 mm/s, and pulse rate frequency of 60 kHz.
3) Configuration 3: the laser parameters were identical to those of the config. 2, but boron diffusion was performed uniformly over the entire 4.18 cm² area. This configuration was used to measure the sheet resistance of the boron doped emitter.

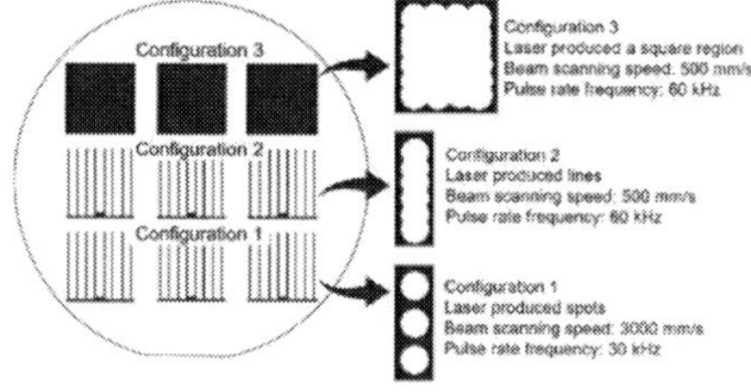

Figure 2: Structure of the samples produced via laser processing. In Configurations 1 and 2, laser processing created "fingers" to form selective emitters, whereas in Configuration 3, the entire surface was laser-processed to enable R_{SH} measurements.

2.3 Characterization techniques

The surface of the silicon wafers was examined by scanning electron microscopy to compare the selective emitters formed in Processes A and B, as well as Laser Configurations 1 and 2.

The minority charge carrier lifetime (τ) was measured using the microwave-photoconductivity decay (μPCD) technique [17]. In this method, the recombination rate of minority charge carriers is measured based on the decay of conductivity, detected by the reflected microwave power [18]. The equipment used was the WT-2000PV, Semilab and the wafers were immersed in an iodine-ethanol solution [19] to reduce surface recombination.

The sheet resistance (R_{SH}) of the boron-doped regions was measured using the four-probe technique [20] in the square areas of the samples (Laser Configuration 3).

3   RESULTS AND ANALYSIS

In Fig. 3, the SEM images of the boron-doped regions formed in process A after four different texture etching times are compared with results obtained in reference process B, both for laser configuration 1. The SEM image of a sample obtained with process B1 (process B and configuration 1) shows an untextured region formed by the laser radiation. In this process, laser radiation melts the silicon wafer near the surface, and in the subsequent re-solidification, the texture is removed. In contrast, the images related to the A1 sample (process A and configuration 1) show the formation of micropyramids in the boron selective emitter region, particularly in the central area of the spot formed by the laser beam. In this process, the hole was shallower than that formed in the process B, independently of etching time. For samples etched during 45 min, the boron doped selective emitter displays a complete texture, with only the edge region of the spot of the laser beam remaining without micropyramids.

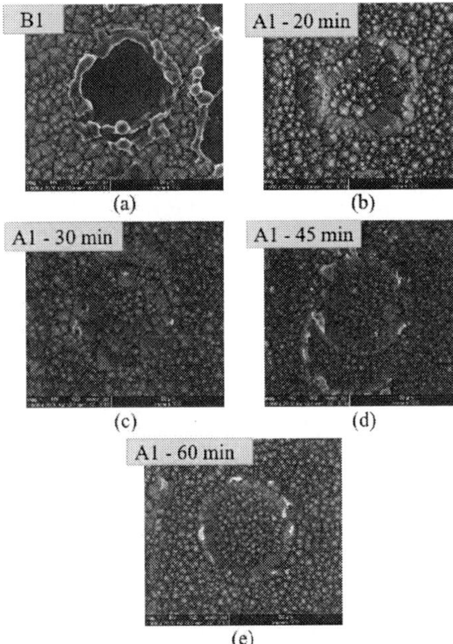

Figure 3: SEM images of silicon wafers submitted to (a) process B – Config. 1, (b) Process A – Config. 1 – texture etching of 20 min, (c) Process A1: texture etching of 30 min, (d) process A1 – 45 min, and (e) process A1 – 60 min. Letter indicates the process and number the laser configuration.

Fig. 4 shows the SEM images of the boron-doped selective emitters formed in process A compared with those produced in process B, for laser configuration 2. The image B2 shows that the texture was removed with laser processing. However, in process A2, the selective emitter region was textured after 20 minutes of etching. According to Garcia [7], the surface boron concentration is approximately of 4×10^{18} cm^{-3} after laser processing. As shown in Fig. 3 and Fig. 4, this boron concentration was not sufficient to prevent the formation of micropyramids.

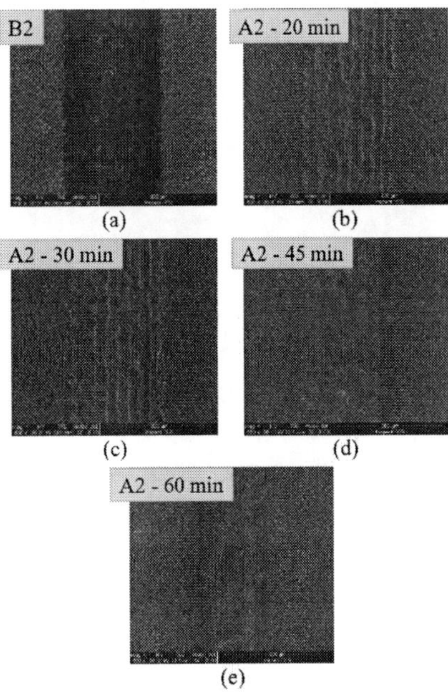

Figure 4: SEM images of silicon wafers submitted to (a) Process B - Config. 2, (b) Process A – Config. 2 – texture etching of 20 min, (c) Process A – Config. 2 – 30 min, (d) Process A – Config. 2 – 45 min, and (e) Process A – Config. 2 – 60 min.

Fig. 5 illustrates the two-dimensional distribution of minority charge carrier lifetime (τ) of samples produced with processes A, B, and C. In the three samples the same behavior was observed: a low minority carrier lifetime in the laser-processed regions. Considering the different initial τ values in the silicon wafers, an analysis of relative data was performed to compare the effect of texture etching on the minority carrier lifetime. Using the software of the WT-2000PV equipment, a pixel line was drawn in the central region of the 4.18 cm^2 sample, as shown in Fig. 6. The τ values from all the pixels in the line were subsequently extracted, and the minority carrier lifetime values as a function of the pixel position was generated. The results are presented in Fig. 7.

The higher values of τ in Fig. 7 were observed in the central regions between the finger areas, where no laser processing occurred. The lower values in Fig. 7 correspond to the central regions of the fingers formed by laser processing. Using these minority carrier lifetime values, the average values τ_{p+} of the regions with laser processing and the average values $\tau_{without\ diffusion}$ for each region between the fingers were calculated. Thus, the percentage difference ($\Delta\tau$) between $\tau_{\text{without diffusion}}$ and τ_{p+} was determined. This figure of merit was employed to evaluate the degradation of the laser-processed region and the potential improvements introduced by subsequent texturing. Although the reference Process C did not include a p^+ (boron-doped) region, the same methodology was applied to compare minority carrier lifetime results. Table I presents the results obtained, and Fig. 8 shows the $\Delta\tau$ of the samples concerning the texture etching times after boron diffusion, for laser configurations 1 and 2. Results from samples of Process B and C (without texture etch after boron diffusion and without boron, respectively) are also depicted.

(a)   (b)

(c)

Figure 5: Two-dimensional distribution of τ measured using the µPCD technique: (a) sample from the proposed process (A), with 45 min of texturing, (b) sample from reference process B and (c) sample from reference process C.

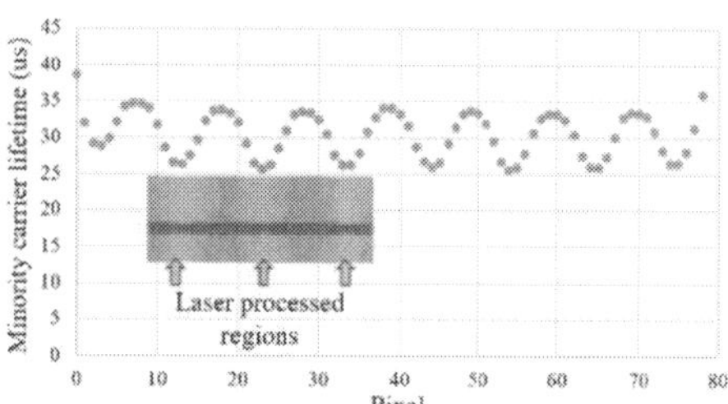

Figure 6: Two-dimensional distribution of τ measured using the µPCD technique for a 4.18 cm² sample, with a selected pixel line (red line). The image was extracted from Fig. 5 (a) (square marked with a red dashed line).

Figure 7: Minority carrier lifetime along the highlighted pixel red line in Fig. 6.

Table I: Average τ_{p+}, $\tau_{\text{without diffusion}}$, and $\Delta\tau$ (%) of the samples with laser processed regions. The texture time is presented in the first column for samples processed with proposed process (A) and both laser configurations.

Process-Laser configuration	Average τ_{p+} (µs)	Average $\tau_{\text{without diffusion}}$ (µs)	$\Delta\tau$ (%)
B1	175 ± 18	235 ± 9	34 ± 11
B2	157 ± 5	200 ± 8	28 ± 5
C1	26 ± 1	33 ± 1	29 ± 5
C2	24 ± 2	32 ± 2	33 ± 11
A1 20 min	85 ± 4	100 ± 6	18 ± 7
A2 20 min	78 ± 5	93 ± 7	20 ± 10
A1 30 min	112 ± 7	135 ± 9	24 ± 8
A2 30 min	99 ± 4	117 ± 4	18 ± 5
A1 45 min	91 ± 3	103 ± 4	13 ± 5
A2 45 min	76 ± 5	86 ± 7	13 ± 11
A1 60 min	91 ± 2	100 ± 2	11 ± 3
A2 60 min	80 ± 3	91 ± 3	13 ± 5

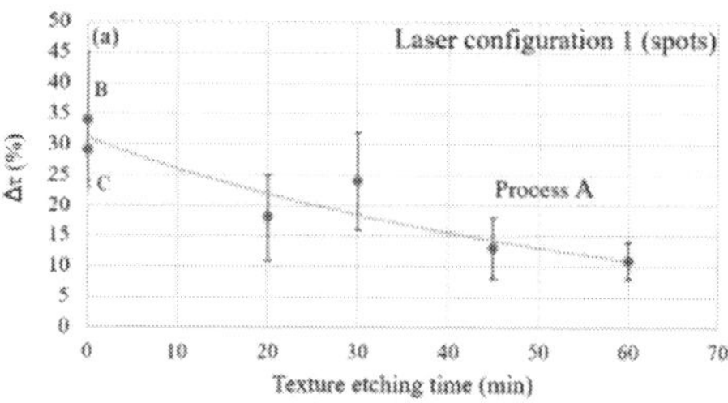

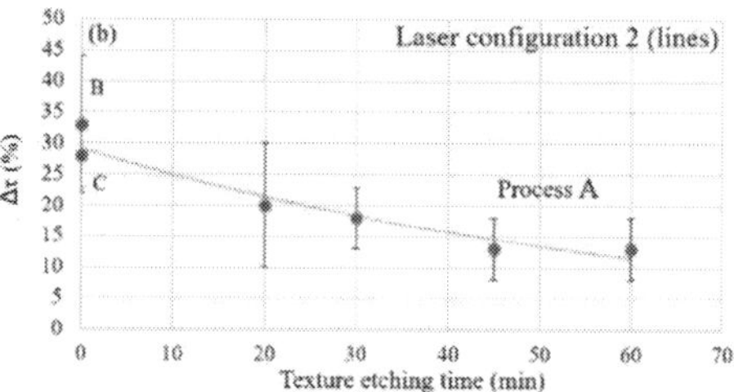

Figure 8: $\Delta\tau$ (%) of samples produced via processes A, B, and C, with laser configurations 1 (a) and 2 (b). The dashed line represents the trend line.

Analysis of the data presented in Table I revealed no significant difference in $\Delta\tau$ (%) between samples processed with laser configuration 1 and those processed with configuration 2. This indicates that, regardless of whether the laser beam overlapped, the damage caused to the wafers during processing was equivalent. When comparing the results from reference processes B and C and laser configurations 1 and 2, the $\Delta\tau$ (%) values are similar. Therefore, the recombination in boron doped regions is not the key factor in reducing minority carrier lifetime in laser processed regions.

A reduction in $\Delta\tau$ is observed in the samples processed with the proposed process (A) compared with those subjected to reference processes B and C. The longer the texture etching period is, the smaller the difference in $\Delta\tau$, as shown in Fig. 8. Therefore, texture etching reduced the damage caused by laser processing, and the minority carrier lifetime values were closer to those in regions without laser processing.

Table II presents the average values and standard deviations of the R_{SH} for the boron-doped emitter obtained using processes A and B. For all samples processed using the proposed method (A), regardless of texturing time, R_{SH} values ranged from 53 to 60 Ω/sq, which are higher than those of the reference process (B), where values ranged from 26 to 28 Ω/sq. The increase in R_{SH} indicated that texture etching reduced the boron concentration and the depth of the p-n junction. However, these values are consistent with the sheet resistances reported in other studies about selective or homogeneous boron emitters [21], [22], [23]. Additionally, according to the ITRPV roadmap [6], the sheet resistance of boron emitters used in industrial solar cells is expected to increase over the next decade, reaching values above 185 Ω/sq. In the proposed method, the increasing of texture etching time can produced high R_{SH}.

Table II: Average sheet resistance of boron-doped samples produced by Processes A and B. The texture time is presented in first column for samples processed with proposed process and both laser configurations.

Process – Laser configuration	Sheet Resistance (Ω/sq)
B-1	28.2 ± 1.5
B-2	26.5 ± 1.4
A-1 - 20 min	60.0 ± 5.6
A-2 - 20 min	60.0 ± 1.9
A-1 - 30 min	55.1 ± 2.5
A-2 - 30 min	53.4 ± 2.9
A-1 - 45 min	60.7 ± 3.9
A-2 - 45 min	60.4 ± 0.8
A-1 - 60 min	59.5 ± 1.8
A-2 - 60 min	60.6 ± 1.6

4 CONCLUSIONS

Boron laser-assisted doping of selective emitters was investigated, with a focus on reducing surface degradation by performing texture etching after boron diffusion.

SEM images of the laser-diffused regions revealed that boron did not inhibit the texture etching. The standard process, which involves laser-assisted boron diffusion after texture etching, produces boron-doped regions with sheet resistances of approximately 27 Ω/sq. However, performing texture etching after boron diffusion increased the sheet resistance, which ranged from 53 to 60 Ω/sq. This result demonstrates that the boron-doped regions were partially etched during the process. Therefore, the boron surface concentration resulting from laser-assisted doping was insufficient to inhibit anisotropic etching.

Regarding the analysis of minority carrier lifetime, no significant difference was observed in the $\Delta\tau$ values of samples processed with laser configurations 1 (spots) and 2 (lines). Furthermore, when comparing processes with pre-laser etching (process B) and those without the presence of the dopant during laser processing (process C), no difference in the $\Delta\tau$ values of the samples was identified. Thereby, the damage caused by laser processing might have a more pronounced effect on the degradation of the minority carrier lifetime than the recombination provided by boron doping.

The proposed process, involving texture etching after boron diffusion via laser, resulted in less damage than the samples from reference process B, which involved pre-laser texture etching. Moreover, the longer the texture etching period is, the smaller the difference in minority carrier lifetime between regions with and without laser processing. Thus, applying an anisotropic KOH-based etch after laser-assisted doping can be an approach to reduce the surface damage induced by the laser process.

5 ACKNOWLEDGMENTS

The authors acknowledge the financial support of the Brazilian funding agencies CNPq (National Council for Scientific and Technological Development), grant numbers 440044/2019-7 and 306916/2017-7, and FINEP (Funding Authority for Studies and Projects), grant number n° 01.22.0194.00 (Ref. 0130/21). BKL is grateful for the grant provided by CAPES (Coordination for the Improvement of Higher Education Personnel) and Hewlett-Packard Brasil Ltda. (with resources from the IT Law Lei n° 8.248, de 1991).

REFERENCES

[1] S. Glunz, F. Feldmann, A. Richter, M. Bivour, C. Reichel, H. Steinkemper, J. Benick, M. Hermle. The irresistible charm of a simple current flow pattern – 25% with a solar cell featuring a full-area back contact, *31st European Photovoltaic Solar Energy Conference and Exhibition (EU PVSEC)*, (2015) 259 - 263. https://doi.org/10.4229/EUPVSEC20152015-2BP.1.1

[2] S. Tepner and A. Lorenz, Printing technologies for silicon solar cell metallization: a comprehensive review, *Progress in Photovoltaics: Research and Applications*, 31 (2023) 557-590. https://doi.org/10.1002/pip.3674

[3] H. Haverkamp, A. Dastgheib-Shirazi, B. Raabe, F. Book, and G. Hahn, Minimizing the electrical losses on the front side: Development of a selective emitter process from a single diffusion, *33rd IEEE Photovoltaic Specialists Conference*, IEEE, (2008) 1–4. https://doi.org/10.1109/PVSC.2008.4922443.

[4] C.W. Kuo, T.-M. Kuan, W.-L. Chueh, L.-G. Wu, C.-C. Huang, and C.-Y. Yu, Impact of laser-doped selective emitters parameter for industrial mono PERC solar cells, *2018 IEEE 7th World Conference on Photovoltaic Energy Conversion (WCPEC)* (A Joint Conference of 45th IEEE PVSC, 28th PVSEC & 34th EU PVSEC), (2018) 1029–1032. https://doi.org/: 10.1109/PVSC.2018.8547466.

[5] U. Jäger, S. Mack, C. Wufka, A. Wolf, D. Biro, and R. Preu, Benefit of selective emitters for p-type silicon solar cells with passivated surfaces, *IEEE Journal of Photovoltaics*, 3(2) (2013) 621–627. https://doi.org/10.1109/JPHOTOV.2012.2230685.

[6] VDMA, *International Technology Roadmap for Photovoltaic (ITRPV) - 2024 Results, 16th Edition*, 2025.

[7] S. Wang, Laser technology in the fabrication of high efficiency solar cells, Doctor Thesis. Sydney, Australia: University of New South Wales (2018). https://doi.org/10.26190/unsworks/20572

[8] V. F. Salvador, Development and analysis of n-base solar cells with selective emitter formed by laser radiation, MSc Dissertation. Porto Alegre, Brazil: Pontifícia Universidade Católica do Rio Grande do Sul, (2019).

https://primo-pmtna01.hosted.exlibrisgroup. com/ permalink/f/164fi7o/puc01000 496600

[9] S. B. Garcia, Development and comparison of p⁺nn⁺ solar cells with homogeneous and selective emitter. Dr. Thesis. Porto Alegre, Brazil: Pontifícia Universidade Católica do Rio Grande do Sul, (2016). http://tede2.pucrs.br/ tede2/handle/tede/6707

[10] Z. Sun, M.C. Gupta, A study of laser-induced surface defects in silicon and impact on electrical properties, *Journal of Applied Physics*, 124 (2018) 223103. https://doi.org/10.1063/1.5058143

[11] G. Poulain, D. Blanc, A. Focsa, M. De Vita, K. Fraser, Y. Sayad, M. Lemiti, Characterization of laser-induced damage in silicon solar cells during selective ablation processes, *Materials Science and Engineering B*, 178 (2013) 682-685. https://doi.org/ 10.1016/j.mseb. 2012.11.015

[12] S. Gu, L. Yuan, K. Guo, W. Huang, L. Li, Y. Yang, X. Jiang, N. Yuan, Q. Wang, J. Ding, Laser damage and post oxidation repair performance of n-TOPCon solar cells with laser assisted doping boron selective emitter, *Solar Energy Materials and Solar Cells*, 274 (2024) 112988. https://doi.org/10.1016/j.solmat.2024.112988.

[13] A. Moehlecke and A. Luque, New approach to obtain boron selective emitters for Si solar cells, *Proceedings of 1994 IEEE 1st World Conference on Photovoltaic Energy Conversion - WCPEC (A Joint Conference of PVSC, PVSEC and PSEC)*, IEEE, (1994) 1492–1495. https://doi.org/10.1109/WCPEC.1994.520233.

[14] K. E. Petersen, Silicon as a mechanical material, *Proceedings of the IEEE*, 70(5) (1982) 420–457. https://doi.org/10.1109/PROC.1982.12331.

[15] J. Linke, F. Buchholz, C. Peter, J. Hoß, J. Lossen, V.D. Mihailetchi, R. Kopecek, Fully passivating contact IBC solar cells using laser processing, *8th World Conference on Photovoltaic Energy Conversion* (2022). https://doi.org/ 10.4229/WCPEC-82022-1CV.2.11

[16] J. Hoß, S. S. Kalaghichi, M. Comak, P. Preis, J. Lossen, J. Linke, L. J. Koduvelikulathu, F. Buchholz, Advanced TOPCon solar cells with patterned p-type poly-Si fingers on the front side and vanishing metal induced recombination losses, *EPJ Photovoltaics*, 15, 43 (2024). https://doi.org/10.1051/epjpv/2024040

[17] T. Asada, Y. Ichikawa, and M. Kato, Carrier lifetime measurements in semiconductors through the microwave photoconductivity decay method, *Journal of Visualized Experiments*, 146 (2019). https://doi.org/ 10.3791/59007.

[18] D. K. Schroder, *Semiconductor Material and Device Characterization*. Wiley (2005). https://doi.org/10.1002/ 0471749095.

[19] T. S. Horányi, T. Pavelka, and P. Tüttö, In situ bulk lifetime measurement on silicon with a chemically passivated surface, *Applied Surface Science*, 63(1–4) (1983) 306–311. https://doi.org/10.1016/0169-4332(93)90112-O.

[20] D.K. Schroder. *Semiconductor Material and Device Characterization*. Wiley, 2005.

[21] Y. Tomizawa, Y. Ikeda, and T. Shiro, Development of n-type selective emitter silicon solar cells by laser doping using boron doped silicon paste, *Energy Procedia*, 92 (2016) 419–426. https://doi.org/10.1016/ j.egypro.2016.07.122.

[22] W. Lin *et al.*, Green-laser-doped selective emitters with separate BBr₃ diffusion processes for high-efficiency n-type silicon solar cells, *Solar Energy Materials and Solar Cells*, 210 (2020) 110462. https://doi.org/10.1016/j.solmat.2020.110462.

[23] M. Peng, Q. Wang, M. Zhang, X. Xi, G. Liu, L. Wang, L. Chen, Optimization of boron depletion for boron-doped emitter of n-type TOPCon solar cells, *Materials Science in Semiconductor Processing*, 178 (2024) 108424. https://doi.org/ 10.1016/j.mssp.2024.108424

PONTIFICAL CATHOLIC UNIVERSITY OF RIO GRANDE DO SUL – PUCRS
SCHOOL OF TECHNOLOGY
SOLAR ENERGY TECHNOLOGY NUCLEUS – NT SOLAR

ANALYSIS OF TEXTURE ETCHING TO REDUCE LASER-INDUCED DAMAGE IN BORON-DOPED SELECTIVE EMITTERS

Bruno Krever Lopes, Adriano Moehlecke, Moussa Ly, Izete Zanesco and Felipe Chini de Freitas

AIM

Analysis of a process to produce boron-doped emitters using laser-assisted doping, combined with texture etching to reduce the surface damage.

Boron-doped regions may reduce or inhibit the silicon etch rate during KOH-based etching, making it a suitable approach for producing selective emitters.

METHODOLOGY

NT-SOLAR / PUCRS / BRAZIL

LASER CONFIGURATIONS

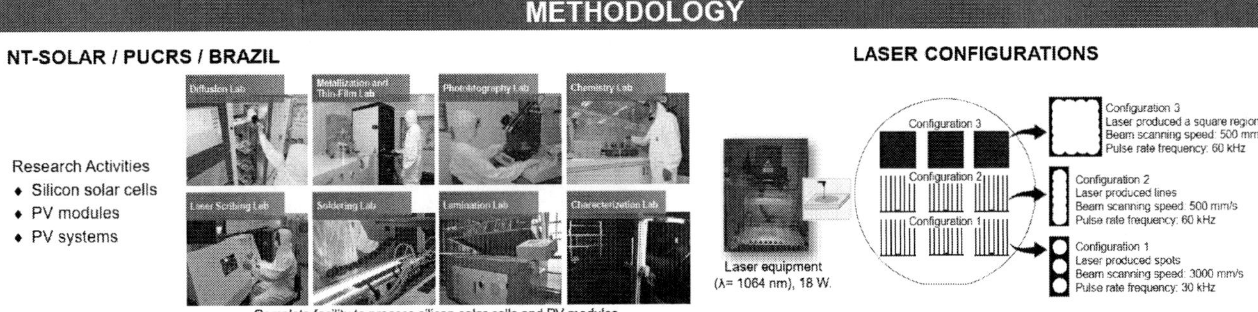

PROCESSES

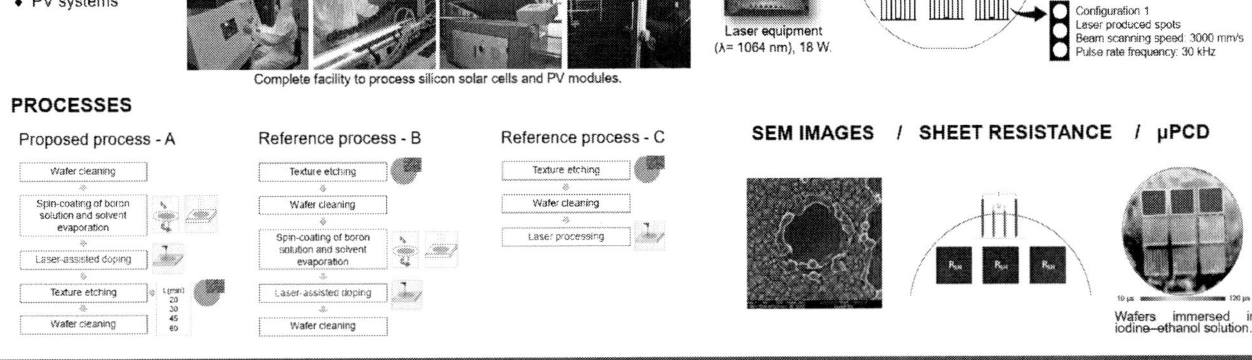

RESULTS AND ANALYSIS

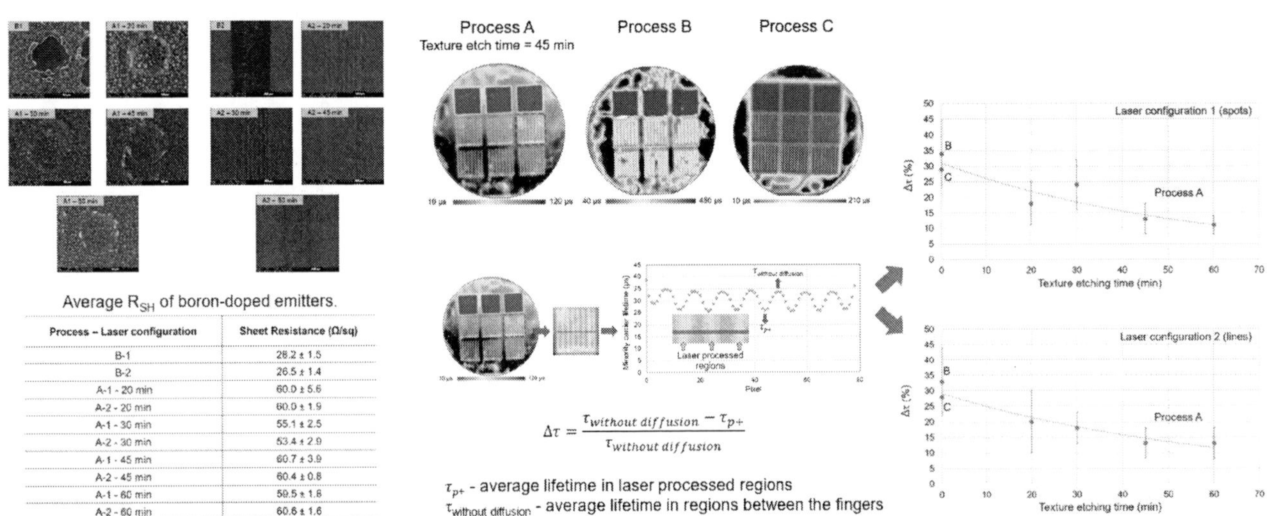

Average R_{SH} of boron-doped emitters.

Process – Laser configuration	Sheet Resistance (Ω/sq)
B-1	28.2 ± 1.5
B-2	26.5 ± 1.4
A-1 - 20 min	60.0 ± 5.6
A-2 - 20 min	60.0 ± 1.9
A-1 - 30 min	55.1 ± 2.5
A-2 - 30 min	53.4 ± 2.9
A-1 - 45 min	60.7 ± 3.9
A-2 - 45 min	60.4 ± 0.8
A-1 - 60 min	59.5 ± 1.6
A-2 - 60 min	60.6 ± 1.6

$$\Delta\tau = \frac{\tau_{without\ diffusion} - \tau_{p+}}{\tau_{without\ diffusion}}$$

τ_{p+} - average lifetime in laser processed regions

$\tau_{without\ diffusion}$ - average lifetime in regions between the fingers

CONCLUSIONS

- SEM images of laser-diffused regions showed that boron did not inhibit texture etching.

- Laser doping after texture etching yielded R_{SH} ~27 Ω/sq; texture etching after doping increased R_{SH} to 53–60 Ω/sq.

- Laser configurations 1 (spots) and 2 (lines) showed no significant difference in Δτ.

- Proposed process A caused less laser damage than process B (pre-laser texture), with longer etching times reducing minority carrier lifetime differences between processed and unprocessed regions.

Acknowledgments: Brazilian financing agencies FINEP, CNPq and CAPES; HP Brasil Ltda.

INFLUENCE OF REDUCED GAS FLOW RATES ON THE SHEET RESISTANCE OF BORON-DOPED LAYERS PERFORMED IN A COMPACT FURNACE

Izete Zanesco, Lucas Teixeira Caçapietra Pires da Silva, Adriano Moehlecke, Moussa Ly,
João Victor Zanatta Britto and Vitor Gomes de Venuto
Pontifical Catholic University of Rio Grande do Sul, School of Technology, Solar Energy Technology Nucleus
Av. Ipiranga, 6681, Porto Alegre, RS, Brazil - Corresponding author: izete@pucrs.br

ABSTRACT: Manufacturing processes for bifacial TOPCon and PERC solar cells have been investigated to increase efficiency and reduce costs. Considering that quartz tube furnaces are usually employed to produce doped layers, in this work, we analyse the influence of reduced gas flow rates on the sheet resistance of boron-doped layers formed in a new compact furnace to produce the emitter of TOPCon and the BSF of bifacial PERT solar cells. A compact furnace prototype was developed according to the granted patent BR102012030601-8. The spin-coating method was used to deposit a boron solution on one face of the Si wafer, and diffusion was carried out with reduced and baseline gas flow rates. The average sheet resistance (R_{sh}) of B-BSF produced with oxygen and nitrogen flow rates reduced, respectively, by 50% and 90% ranged from 43.3 to 48.6 Ω/sq, and the standard deviation (SD) was lower than 3.2%. Although the average R_{sh} from 103 to 158 Ω/sq produced with baseline gas flow rates was higher, the SD was 2% - 11%. The emitter formed with reduced gas flow rates presented a R_{sh} from 88 to 118 Ω/sq with a SD between 4% and 7%. Additionally, the boron concentration in the emitter increased slightly at depths greater than 0.45 µm.
Keywords: Boron diffusion, compact furnace, emitter sheet resistance, BSF sheet resistance.

1 INTRODUCTION

Bifacial high efficiency solar cell structures, such as n-type tunnel oxide passivated contact (TOPCon) and p-type passivated emitter and rear (PERC) solar cells, represented 55% and 35%, respectively, of the market share in 2024 [1]. Considering this trend, the dominant technologies in the next decade will remain bifacial high efficiency architectures manufactured with reduced production costs.

TOPCon and PERC solar cells are manufactured using thermal processes for dopant diffusion and silicon oxide growth. Boron is the dopant used to form the p$^+$ emitter of n-type TOPCon (n-TOPCon) solar cells and the back surface field (BSF) of the p-type passivated emitter and rear totally diffused (p-PERT) solar cells [2], a structure of the PERC family.

Currently, BCl$_3$ in the vapour phase introduced into a quartz tube furnace is the usual approach to produce a boron-doped layer in homojunction silicon solar cells, although BBr$_3$ has been the main dopant source used in the last decade [3]. Nevertheless, alternative methods have been investigated to produce boron-doped layers, such as ion implantation, epitaxial growth, deposition of dopant solution by spin coating followed by diffusion using laser or a conventional quartz tube furnace. These alternative methods are usually carried out with nontoxic sources [4].

In p-type TOPCon solar cells, a boron-doped poly-Si/SiO$_2$ stack is deposited on the rear side to form passivated contacts. Low-pressure chemical vapour deposition (LPCVD) is commonly used to deposit a layer of doped amorphous silicon (a-Si) or polysilicon. However, the deposition of intrinsic a-Si/µ-polysilicon by LPCVD or plasma enhanced chemical vapour deposition (PECVD) and a subsequent doping process has also been investigated [5], [6].

Quartz tube furnaces are widely used for dopant diffusion to manufacture silicon solar cells, and they are often referred to as conventional furnaces. Nevertheless, diffusion methods carried out in different technology furnaces, such as rapid thermal processing furnaces and belt furnaces, have been employed.

With respect to boron diffusion to form a selective emitter of n-type TOPCon solar cells, Wang *et al.* [7] developed p^{++} and p$^+$ layers formed by 3D printing mask technology and a secondary diffusion using BCl$_3$ as the dopant source in a quartz tube furnace. The results showed that the drive-in and oxidation processes had more impact than the BCl$_3$ gas flow rate on the emitter dark saturation current density. The sheet resistance of the boron selective emitter was 75 Ω/sq (p^{++}) and 230 Ω/sq (p$^+$), and the achieved solar cell efficiency was 24.2%.

To develop n-type TOPCon solar cells, Liu *et al.* [8] presented an alternative method to perform the selective emitter in one step with BCl$_3$ as the dopant source and a boron-doped silicon paste deposited by screen printing. A diffusion temperature of 950 °C for 20 min was selected based on simulations and experimental results. Boron concentrations of 8.68x10^{18} atoms/cm^3 and 2.35x10^{19} atoms/cm^3 were obtained in the p$^+$ and p^{++} layers, respectively, with junction depths of 0.53 (p$^+$) µm and 0.82 µm (p^{++}). The efficiency of TOPCon solar cells achieved in a production line was 25.17%.

An energy-efficient and low-cost approach for boron diffusion was developed by Meßmer *et al.* [9]. A borosilicate glass layer was formed by atmospheric pressure chemical vapour deposition (APCVD) as the boron source, and diffusion was performed in a subsequent thermal step in a quartz tube furnace. With a vertically stacked configuration of silicon wafers, the sheet resistance demonstrated uniform boron diffusion, similar to the results obtained with BBr$_3$ as the dopant source. The average sheet resistance was (111 ± 4) Ω/sq, and the efficiency of the TOPCon solar cell was 23.1%.

Considering that boron diffusion requires more time than phosphorus diffusion, Lohmüller *et al.* [10] optimized boron diffusion using BBr$_3$ as the dopant source to form a high-quality emitter with a sheet resistance of approximately 150 Ω/sq and a standard deviation lower than 5%. A reduction in the diffusion process time from 3.5 h to 2 h was achieved by increasing the temperature. The boron profile presented a maximum boron concentration of 1.5x10^{19} atoms/cm^3 and a junction depth of 0.8 µm.

Chu *et al.* [11] optimized the boron doping profile and specific contact resistivity for n-TOPCon solar cells. For a sheet resistance of 150 Ω/sq, a surface dopant

10.4229/EUPVSEC2025/1BV.5.35

concentration of 3.0×10^{19} atoms/cm³ resulted in a minimum saturation current density. Moreover, the authors concluded that the specific contact resistivity was influenced by the ramp-up and cool-down rates during the firing process.

The influence of the boron back surface field (B-BSF) sheet resistance on the electrical parameters of bifacial p-PERT solar cells was investigated [2]. B-BSF and phosphorus-doped emitter were produced in the same thermal step. The average sheet resistance of the B-BSF obtained at a diffusion temperature of 950 °C was 54 Ω/sq. with a standard deviation of 6%. After the diffusion of phosphorus, the B-BSF depth was approximately 1.0 μm, and the boron concentration on the surface of a silicon wafer was 6.4×10^{19} atoms/cm³, with a slight increase in the boron concentration up to a depth of 0.3 μm. The short-circuit current density obtained with incident irradiance on the boron-doped side of bifacial PERT solar cells was the electrical parameter most affected by the B-BSF sheet resistance, influencing both the efficiency and the maximum power bifaciality coefficient.

Considering that boron diffusion is an essential step for producing the emitter of n-TOPCon solar cells and the BSF of bifacial PERT solar cells and that new approaches are being investigated, in this work, we analyse the influence of reduced gas flow rates on the sheet resistance of boron-doped layers formed in a new compact quartz tube furnace to produce the emitter of n-TOPCon solar cells and the BSF of the bifacial p-PERT structure. To reduce production costs, a compact quartz tube furnace prototype to form doped layers in silicon wafers was developed, and the gas flow rates were decreased in relation to a baseline process. The main feature of the developed furnace is that the quartz tube volume is reduced compared with that of a conventional furnace.

2 EXPERIMENTAL METHODS

Fig. 1 shows a prototype of the compact quartz tube furnace developed according to the granted patent BR102012030601-8. The quartz tube length is smaller than that of a conventional furnace to reduce the gas volume used in the processing of silicon wafers. The furnace consists of 1) a thermal heating system with electrical resistance, 2) a compact quartz tube and 3) inlet and outlet gas cabinets. The quartz tube diameter is 300 mm, and the flat zone length is 400 mm. The dimensions of the prototype are depicted in Fig. 1.

Figure 1: Prototype of the compact quartz tube furnace developed to diffuse dopants in silicon wafers according to the granted patent BR102012030601-8.

The methodology adopted is summarized in Fig. 2.

The B-BSF of the bifacial PERT solar cell and the boron-doped emitter of the TOPCon device were performed in p-type and n-type Si-Cz wafers, respectively. In the first stage of the investigation, B-BSF was produced with 1) reduced and 2) baseline gas flow rates in the compact furnace and 3) baseline gas flow rates in a conventional quartz tube furnace. In the second stage, the boron-doped emitter was produced in the compact furnace with reduced gas flow rates. The oxygen and nitrogen flow rates were reduced by 50% and 90%, respectively, compared with the gas flow rates used in the baseline process of a conventional furnace. To assess the effect of gas flow reduction in the doped regions, the sheet resistance was measured in all samples, and the boron doping profiles of the emitter and BSF produced with reduced gas flow rates were evaluated.

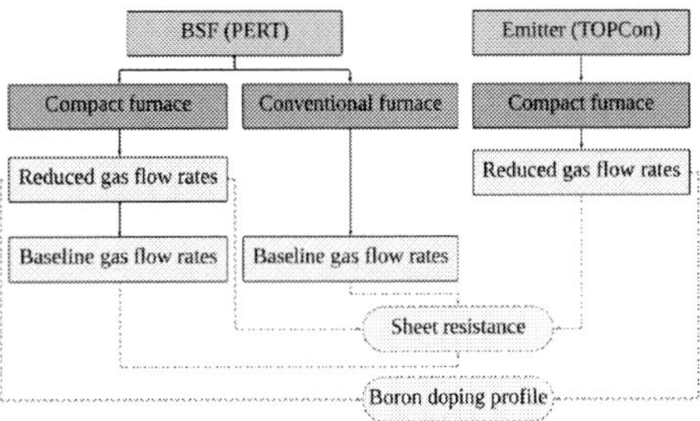

Figure 2: Flow chart of the methodology adopted.

Fig. 3 shows the process sequence for producing samples with a boron-doped emitter and B-BSF in n-type and p-type Si-Cz wafers, respectively, which had a thickness of around 200 μm and resistivity ranging from 1 Ω.cm to 20 Ω.cm. The processing sequence used to produce the samples was as follows: alkaline texture etching in a KOH solution, RCA cleaning, boron diffusion under different conditions and borosilicate glass removal.

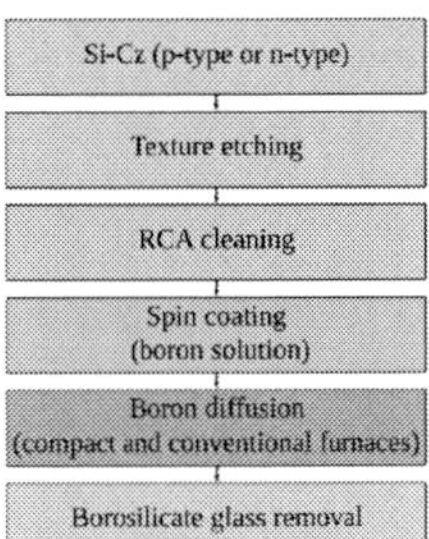

Figure 3: Process sequence to produce samples with the emitter of TOPCon solar cells (n-type Si-Cz wafers) and B-BSF of bifacial PERT solar cells (p-type Si-Cz wafers).

The boron-doped layers were produced using the spin-coating method to deposit a uniform thin layer of boron solution (PBF20, Filmtronics) on one face of the Si wafers. In sequence, the solvents were evaporated, and boron diffusion was performed at a temperature of 950 °C with reduced and baseline gas flow rates. Two samples were introduced at different positions in the flat zone of the compact furnace, as shown in Fig. 4. Position A is located close to the gas flow inlet.

The sheet resistance (R_{sh}) of the boron-doped layers and boron doping profiles were measured to investigate the uniformity of boron diffusion in each silicon wafer and in different positions in the flat zone. The R_{sh} after boron diffusion was measured in 13 regions of each sample.

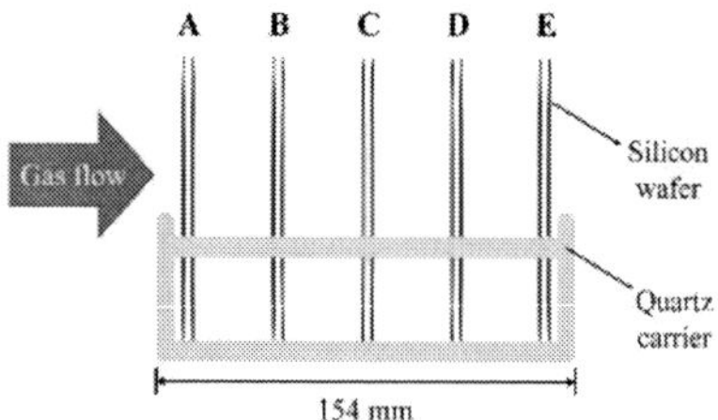

Figure 4: Distribution of samples in the carrier and their respective positions. Position A is located close to the gas flow inlet, and position E is near the gas flow outlet.

3 RESULTS AND DISCUSSION

3.1 Analysis of the boron-doped back surface field of bifacial PERT solar cells

Fig. 5 shows the sheet resistance (R_{sh}) of the B-BSF in samples, which were placed in different positions in the flat zone of the compact furnace and produced with reduced gas flow rates. Excluding a wafer located close to the gas flow outlet (position E – sample Cp15), a typical uniformity in R_{sh} was observed. The results obtained with this sample were not considered in the analysis. To overcome this problem, a Si wafer may be placed in this position as a part of the processing chamber. Table I shows that the standard deviation of the sheet resistance of each silicon wafer was lower than 3.2%, demonstrating the uniformity of boron diffusion in a specific silicon wafer. Considering all the samples and excluding a wafer located close to the gas flow outlet, R_{sh} ranged from 39.0 to 49.8 Ω/sq.

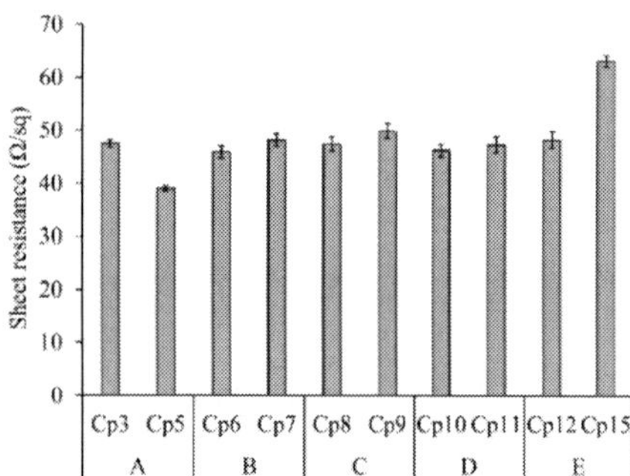

Figure 5: Sheet resistance of the B-BSF produced with reduced gas flow rates in samples located at different positions in the flat zone of the compact furnace. A, B, C, D and E represent five different locations, and Cp# represents a p-type Si wafer.

The average R_{sh} of the B-BSF produced in the compact furnace with reduced gas flow rates, presented in Table II, allows us to analyse the uniformity of boron diffusion in the flat zone. Considering positions A (close to the gas flow inlet) to E, the average sheet resistance at each position ranged from (43.3 ± 0.6) to (48.6 ± 1.4) Ω/sq, with a maximum standard deviation of 3.2%. This standard deviation is lower than that reported in the literature with boron diffusion using BBr$_3$ as the dopant source [10].

Considering all the Si wafers distributed in the carrier, the average sheet resistance of B-BSF was (46.8 ± 1.2) Ω/sq. Therefore, the sheet resistance of B-BSF of bifacial PERT solar cells can be produced with high uniformity in the compact furnace using reduced gas flow rates.

Table I: Sheet resistance of the B-BSF produced with reduced gas flow rates in samples located at positions A, B, C, D and E in the flat zone of the compact furnace.

Position	Sample	Sheet resistance (Ω/sq)	
A	Cp3	47.5 ± 0.7	47.5 ± 1.4%
	Cp5	39.0 ± 0.5	39.0 ± 1.2%
B	Cp6	45.9 ± 1.1	45.9 ± 2.4%
	Cp7	48.1 ± 1.2	48.1 ± 2.5%
C	Cp8	47.4 ± 1.3	47.4 ± 2.8%
	Cp9	49.8 ± 1.4	49.8 ± 2.8%
D	Cp10	46.2 ± 1.2	46.2 ± 2.5%
	Cp11	47.3 ± 1.5	47.3 ± 3.2%
E	Cp12	48.2 ± 1.5	48.2 ± 3.2%
	Cp15	63.2 ± 1.0	63.2 ± 1.6%

Table II: Average sheet resistance of the B-BSF produced in the flat zone of the compact furnace with reduced gas flow rates.

Position	Sheet resistance (Ω/sq)	
A	43.3 ± 0.6	43.3 ± 1.3%
B	47.0 ± 1.1	47.0 ± 2.4%
C	48.6 ± 1.4	48.6 ± 2.8%
D	46.8 ± 1.4	46.8 ± 2.9%
E	48.2 ± 1.5	48.2 ± 3.2%
Average	46.8 ± 1.2	46.8 ± 2.7%

The dopant concentration profiles of the B-BSF are presented in Fig. 6. In all samples, typical boron depletion is observed near the surface, caused by the borosilicate glass (BSG) formed in the Si wafers in the presence of oxygen in the quartz tube [12], [13]. Boron segregated to the BSG layer, and consequently, the dopant concentration slightly decreased from a depth of approximately 0.1 µm to the surface.

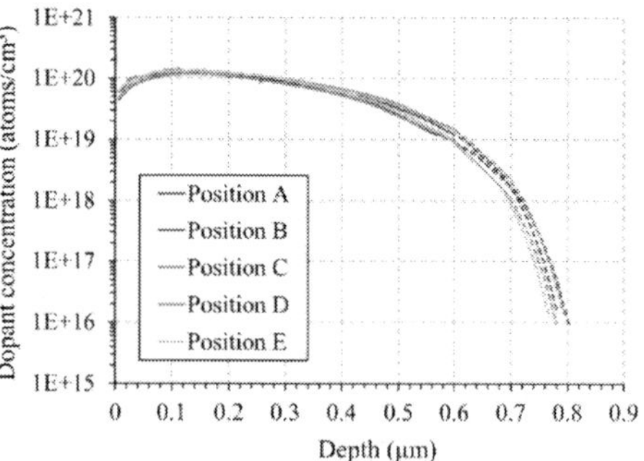

Figure 6: Boron concentration as a function of depth (doping profile) of the B-BSF processed with reduced gas flow rates in the compact furnace and diffusion temperature of 950 °C. The solid lines show the measured doping profiles, whereas the dashed lines indicate the values obtained from fitting the experimental results reported in [14].

The doping concentration on the silicon wafer surface of the BSF produced in the compact furnace with reduced gas flow rates ranged from 4.5×10^{19} to 6.0×10^{19} atoms/cm^3, and the estimated BSF depth was less than 0.8 μm.

In Fig. 7, the average R_{sh} of the B-BSF processed with reduced gas flow rates in the compact furnace (FR-red) is compared with the results obtained with baseline gas flow rates in the compact (FR-bas) and conventional (FRC-bas) furnaces. A comparison of the results obtained with the reduced gas flow rates to those obtained with the baseline gas flow rates in the compact furnace revealed that the sheet resistance increased with increasing gas volume in the baseline process.

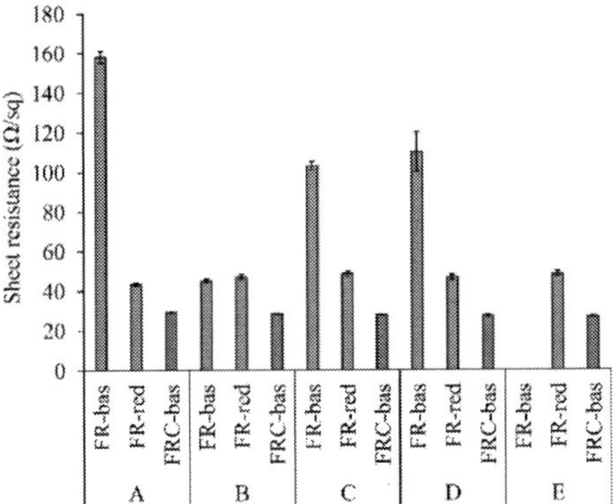

Figure 7: Comparison of the average sheet resistance of B-BSF produced in the 1) compact furnace with baseline gas flow rates (FR-bas), 2) compact furnace with reduced gas flow rates (FR-red), and 3) conventional quartz tube furnace with baseline gas flow rates (FRC-bas).

Table III shows that the sheet resistance obtained with FR-bas ranged from 103 to 158 Ω/sq, with a high value close to the gas flow inlet (position A). The average R_{sh} of the B-BSF was (122 ± 7) Ω/sq, with a standard deviation of 6%, which was higher than the result obtained with reduced gas flow rates.

Table III: Comparison of the average sheet resistance of B-BSF produced in the flat zone of the compact furnace with reduced ($R_{sh\text{-}FR\text{-}red}$) and baseline ($R_{sh\text{-}FR\text{-}bas}$) gas flow rates and in a conventional furnace with baseline gas flow rates ($R_{sh\text{-}FRC\text{-}bas}$).

Position	Compact		Conventional
	$R_{sh\text{-}FR\text{-}red}$ (Ω/sq)	$R_{sh\text{-}FR\text{-}bas}$ (Ω/sq)	$R_{sh\text{-}FRC\text{-}bas}$ (Ω/sq)
A	43.3 ± 0.6	158 ± 3	29.2 ± 0.3
B	47.0 ± 1.1	116 ± 8	28.4 ± 0.3
C	48.6 ± 1.4	103 ± 2	27.8 ± 0.2
D	46.8 ± 1.4	110 ± 12	27.4 ± 0.4
E	48.2 ± 1.5	–	26.7 ± 0.4
Average	46.8 ± 1.2	122 ± 7	27.9 ± 0.3

However, the R_{sh} of B-BSF produced in a conventional furnace was low, ranging from 26.7 to 29.2 Ω/sq. These results indicate high uniformity of boron diffusion in the flat zone of a conventional furnace. The average R_{sh} was (27.9 ± 0.3) Ω/sq, with a standard deviation lower than 1.5%.

3.2 Analysis of the boron-doped emitter of TOPCon solar cell

Fig. 8 shows the R_{sh} of the boron emitter of TOPCon solar cells produced with reduced gas flow rates in the flat zone of the compact furnace. Considering all the samples, the sheet resistance of the emitter, presented in Table IV, ranged from 87 to 120 Ω/sq, and the standard deviation was lower than 8%. These results lead to the conclusion that the sheet resistance and standard deviation of the emitter were higher than those of the B-BSF, as shown in Fig. 9.

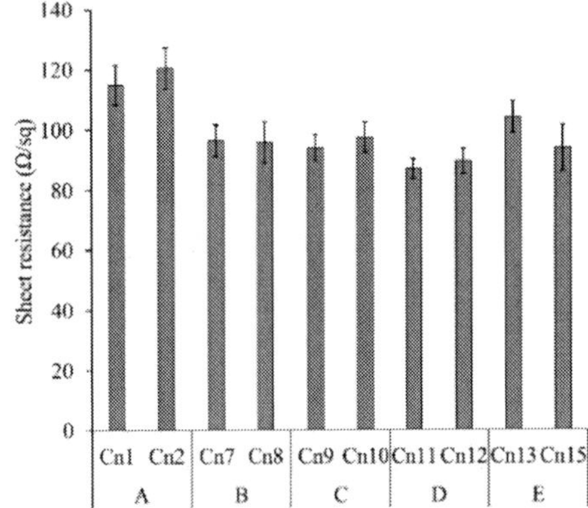

Figure 8: Sheet resistance of the boron-doped emitter of TOPCon solar cells produced with reduced gas flow rates at different positions in the flat zone of the compact furnace. Cn# represents a n-type silicon wafer.

Table IV: Sheet resistance of the boron-doped emitter of TOPCon solar cells formed with reduced gas flow rates in samples located at positions A, B, C, D and E in the compact furnace.

Position	Sample	Sheet resistance (Ω/sq)	
A	Cn1	115 ± 7	$115 \pm 6\%$
	Cn2	120 ± 7	$120 \pm 6\%$
B	Cn7	96 ± 5	$96 \pm 5\%$
	Cn8	96 ± 7	$96 \pm 7\%$
C	Cn9	94 ± 4	$94 \pm 5\%$
	Cn10	98 ± 5	$98 \pm 5\%$
D	Cn11	87 ± 3	$87 \pm 4\%$
	Cn12	89 ± 4	$89 \pm 5\%$
E	Cn13	104 ± 5	$104 \pm 5\%$
	Cn15	94 ± 8	$94 \pm 8\%$

Table V shows that the average R_{sh} of the emitter of TOPCon solar cell was (99 ± 6) Ω/sq. The standard deviation of 6% was higher than the value of 2.7% found for R_{sh} of the B-BSF. However, Tables I and IV indicate that samples close to the gas flow inlet or outlet exhibited higher sheet resistance, independent of B-BSF or emitter formation.

The boron doping profiles of the emitter are presented

in Fig. 10. As expected, in the doping profile of a sample at position A, in which the sheet resistance was higher, the boron concentration was lower for depths greater than 0.2 μm. Consequently, in this sample, the estimated depth of the emitter region was slightly lower than the results found in silicon wafers located at other positions.

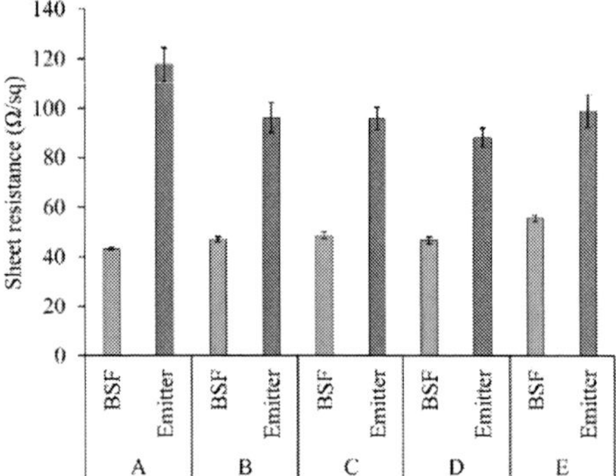

Figure 9: Comparison of the average sheet resistance of the boron-doped emitter with that of B-BSF produced with reduced gas flow rates in the compact furnace.

Table V: Average sheet resistance of the boron-doped emitter produced in the flat zone of the compact furnace with reduced gas flow rates.

Position	Sheet resistance (Ω/sq)	
A	118 ± 7	$118 \pm 6\%$
B	96 ± 6	$96 \pm 6\%$
C	96 ± 5	$96 \pm 5\%$
D	88 ± 4	$88 \pm 4\%$
E	99 ± 7	$99 \pm 7\%$
Average	99 ± 6	$99 \pm 6\%$

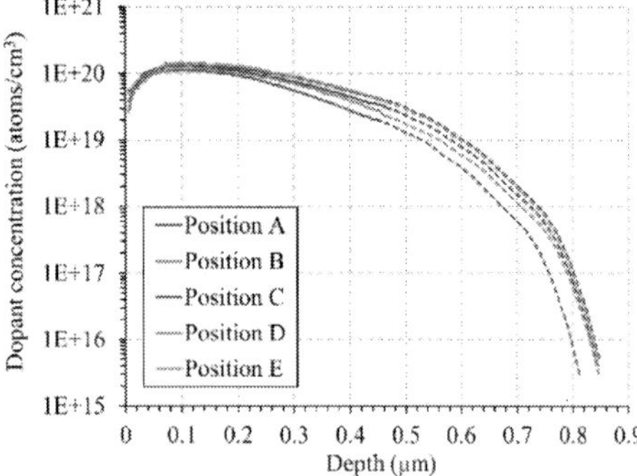

Figure 10: Boron doping profile of the emitter processed with reduced gas flow rates in the compact furnace and diffusion temperature of 950 °C. The solid lines show the measured doping profiles, whereas the dashed lines indicate the values obtained from fitting the experimental results reported in [14].

The boron doping profiles obtained for the samples located at positions B, C, D and E were similar, resulting

in an estimated emitter depth of approximately 0.85 μm. However, the surface doping concentration ranged from 2.7×10^{19} to 6.3×10^{19} atoms/cm^3, representing a range slightly greater than the results found for B-BSF.

Fig. 11 compares the boron doping profiles of the emitter and BSF, processed with reduced gas flow rates and placed in the center of the flat zone of the compact furnace. The doping profiles were similar up to a depth of approximately 0.45 μm. However, at depths greater than 0.45 μm, the boron concentration of the emitter was slightly higher than that of the BSF. As a result, the boron-doped emitter was deeper than the B-BSF. The estimated junction depth was 0.85 μm, and the BSF depth was 0.78 μm. In the emitter, the surface boron concentration of 5.5×10^{19} atoms/cm^3 was slightly higher than the doping concentration of BSF, which was 4.8×10^{19} atoms/cm^3.

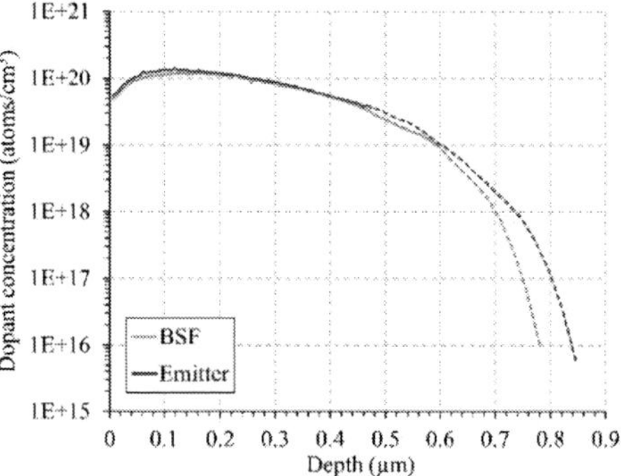

Figure 11. Boron doping profile of emitter and BSF processed with reduced gas flow rates in the compact furnace.

4 CONCLUSIONS

The average R_{sh} of the B-BSF produced with reduced gas flow rates in p-type Cz-Si wafers located at different positions in the flat zone of the compact furnace ranged from 43.3 to 48.6 Ω/sq, and the standard deviation of R_{sh} in each sample was lower than 3.2%. The results obtained with the baseline gas flow rates were higher, ranging from 103 to 158 Ω/sq. In this case, the standard deviation of each sample was greater, from 2% to 11%, demonstrating a lower uniformity of boron diffusion. The average R_{sh} produced in a conventional furnace was (27.9 ± 0.3) Ω/sq, with a low standard deviation of the sheet resistance. The average R_{sh} of the emitter produced with reduced gas flow rates in the compact furnace ranged from 88 to 118 Ω/sq, with a standard deviation of 4 - 7%. This result demonstrates that boron diffusion in n-type Si-Cz wafers was less uniform than that in p-type Si-Cz wafers under the same processing conditions.

The boron doping profile of the emitter, produced with reduced gas flow rates in the compact furnace, was slightly higher than that of B-BSF for depths greater than 0.45 μm. Additionally, the boron-doped emitter was slightly deeper than the B-BSF.

The use of reduced gas flow rates produced an average sheet resistance of (46.8 ± 1.2) Ω/sq and (99 ± 6) Ω/sq for the B-BSF and the boron-doped emitter, respectively. The standard deviation indicated that the boron diffusion was uniform in each Si wafer and in samples located at different positions in the flat zone of the compact furnace, similar to the results reported in the literature. These sheet resistances are compatible with the current technology used to produce the BSF of bifacial p-PERT solar cells and the emitter of the TOPCon structure.

ACKNOLEDGEMENTS

The authors acknowledge the financial support of the Funding Authority for Studies and Projects (FINEP), grant number 01.22.0194.00; Research Support Foundation of Rio Grande do Sul (FAPERGS), grant number 21/2551-0002152-7; and the National Council for Scientific and Technological Development (CNPq), grant numbers 305554/2021-2 and 306916/2017-7.

REFERENCES

[1] VDMA, International Technology Roadmap for Photovoltaic (ITRPV) 2024 Results, Frankfurt am Main, Germany, May 2025.

[2] T. Crestani, I. Zanesco, A. Moehlecke, L. T. C. P. da Silva, and J. V. Z. Britto, Optimization of the boron back surface field produced with reduced thermal steps in bifacial PERT solar cell, *Energies (Basel)*, vol. 18, no. 9, p. 2347, May 2025, doi: 10.3390/en18092347.

[3] Y. Hasnain *et al.*, A Review on TOPCon solar cell technology, *Current Photovoltaic Research*, vol. 9, no. 3, pp. 75–85, 2021, doi: 10.21218/CPR.2021.9.3.075.

[4] A. El Amrani, A. Boucheham, A. Guendouzi, B. Labdelli, C. Nasraoui, and R. Si-Kaddour, Co-diffusion processing of $p^+/n/n^+$ structure for n-type silicon solar cells using boron doped paper sheets, *Silicon*, vol. 14, no. 1, pp. 223–228, Jan. 2022, doi: 10.1007/s12633-020-00809-3.

[5] W. J. Choi *et al.*, Development of 22.5% p-type tunnel oxide passivated contact solar cells through efficiency enhancement by replacing local Al-BSF in PERC cells with (p^+) poly-Si/SiO₂ carrier selective contact, *Solar Energy Materials and Solar Cells*, vol. 283, May 2025, doi: 10.1016/j.solmat.2025.113436.

[6] H. Tong *et al.*, Total-area world-record efficiency of 27.03% for 350.0 cm² commercial-sized single-junction silicon solar cells, *Nature Communications*, vol. 16, no. 1, Dec. 2025, doi: 10.1038/s41467-025-61128-y.

[7] Q. Wang *et al.*, Boron tube diffusion process parameters for high-efficiency n-TOPCon solar cells with selective boron emitters, *Solar Energy Materials and Solar Cells*, vol. 253, p. 112231, May 2023, doi: 10.1016/j.solmat.2023.112231.

[8] X. Liu *et al.*, High-efficiency TOPCon solar cell with superior p^+ and p^{++} layer via one-step processing, *Solar Energy*, vol. 271, p. 112448, Mar. 2024, doi: 10.1016/j.solener.2024.112448.

[9] M. Meßmer *et al.*, Stack diffusion process for cost- and energy-efficient boron emitter formation, *IEEE J Photovolt*, vol. 12, no. 6, pp. 1393–1399, 2022, doi: 10.1109/JPHOTOV.2022.3214437.

[10] E. Lohmüller *et al.*, BBr₃ diffusion: Process optimization for high-quality emitters with industrial cycle times, *37th European Photovoltaic Solar Energy Conference and Exhibition*, no. September, pp. 7–11, 2020.

[11] M. Chu *et al.*, Boron doping and specific contact resistivity optimization strategies for high performance n-type TOPCon solar cells, *Inorg Chem Commun*, vol. 180, Oct. 2025, doi: 10.1016/j.inoche.2025.115004.

[12] M. Peng *et al.*, Optimization of boron depletion for boron-doped emitter of n-type TOPCon solar cells, *Mater Sci Semicond Process*, vol. 178, Aug. 2024, doi: 10.1016/j.mssp.2024.108424.

[13] Y. Zhou *et al.*, Study of boron diffusion for p^+ emitter of large area n-type TOPCon silicon solar cells, *Applied Physics A*, vol. 126, no. 9, p. 671, Sep. 2020, doi: 10.1007/s00339-020-03851-5.

[14] A. Moehlecke, I. Zanesco, and A. Luque, Practical high efficiency bifacial solar cells, *1st World Conference on Photovoltaic Energy Conversion*, 1994, pp. 1663–1666. doi: 10.1109/WCPEC.1994.520538.

PONTIFICAL CATHOLIC UNIVERSITY OF RIO GRANDE DO SUL – PUCRS
SCHOOL OF TECHNOLOGY
SOLAR ENERGY TECHNOLOGY NUCLEUS – NT SOLAR

INFLUENCE OF REDUCED GAS FLOW RATES ON THE SHEET RESISTANCE OF BORON-DOPED LAYERS PERFORMED IN A COMPACT FURNACE

Izete Zanesco, Lucas Teixeira Caçapietra Pires da Silva, Adriano Moehlecke, Moussa Ly, João Victor Zanatta Britto and Vitor Gomes de Venuto

AIM

Analysis of the influence of reduced gas flow rates on the sheet resistance of boron-doped layers formed in a new compact quartz tube furnace to produce the emitter of n-TOPCon solar cells and the BSF of the bifacial p-PERT structure.

EXPERIMENTAL METHODS

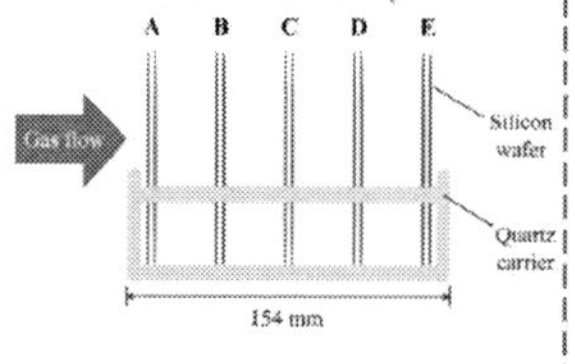

RESULTS AND DISCUSSION

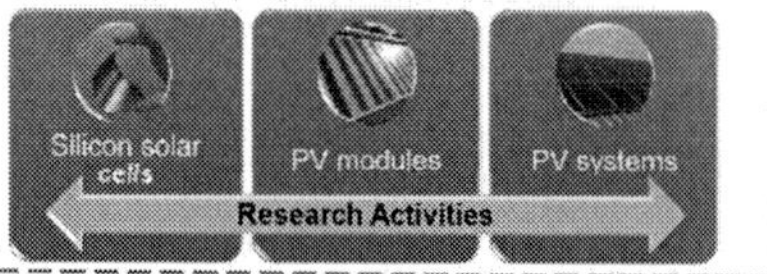

Boron-BSF:
- Compact furnace: reduced gas flow rates (FR-red)
- Compact furnace: baseline gas flow rates (FR-bas)
- Conventional furnace: baseline gas flow rates (FRC-bas)

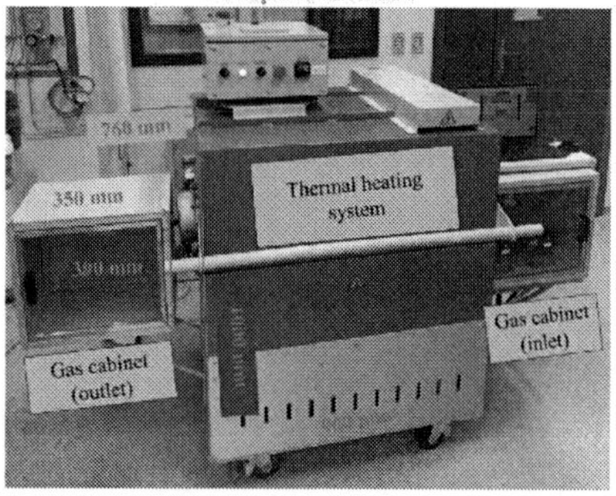

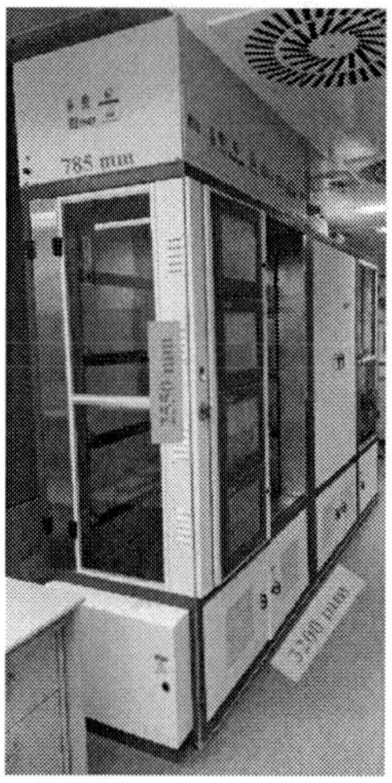

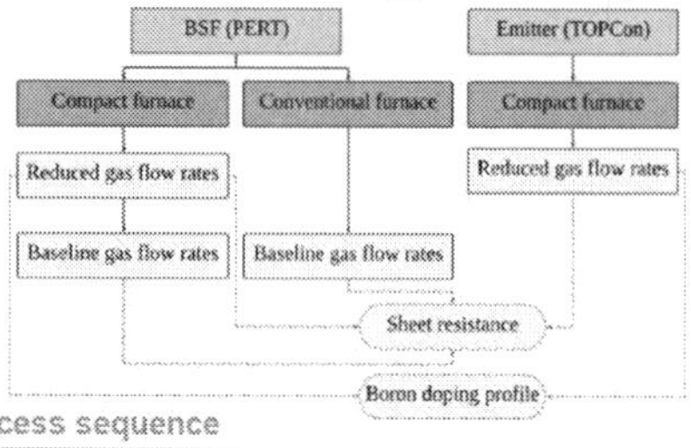

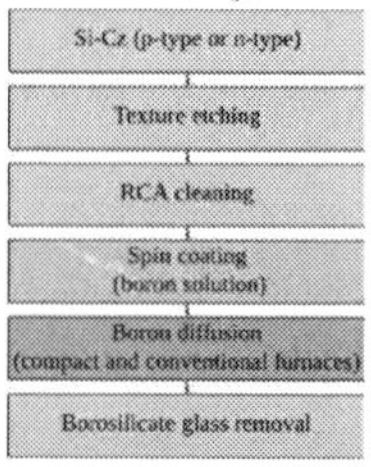

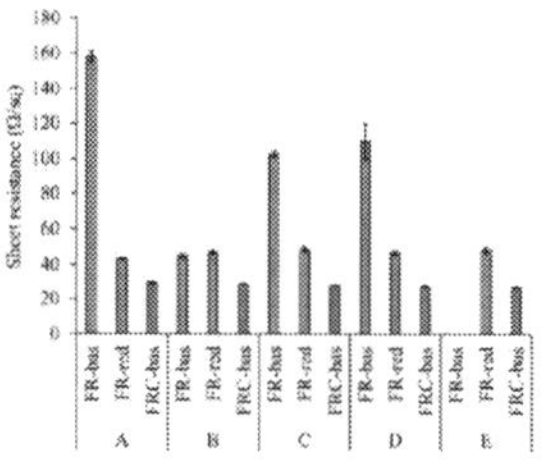

| | Compact | Compact | Conventional |
Position	$R_{sh\text{-FR-red}}$ (Ω/sq)	$R_{sh\text{-FR-bas}}$ (Ω/sq)	$R_{sh\text{-FRC-bas}}$ (Ω/sq)
A	43.3 ± 0.6	158 ± 3	29.2 ± 0.3
B	47.0 ± 1.1	116 ± 8	28.4 ± 0.3
C	48.6 ± 1.4	103 ± 2	27.8 ± 0.2
D	46.8 ± 1.4	110 ± 12	27.4 ± 0.4
E	48.2 ± 1.5	–	26.7 ± 0.4
Average	46.8 ± 1.2	122 ± 7	27.9 ± 0.3

Boron-BSF (p-type Si-Cz)

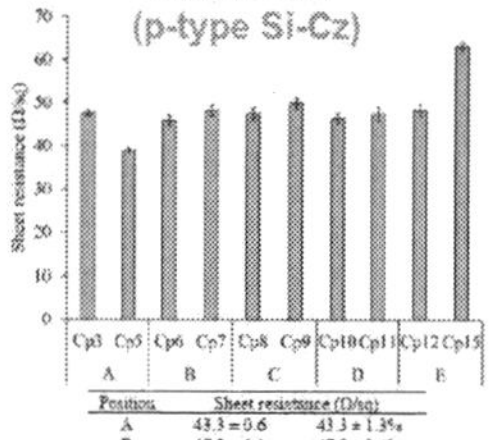

Position	Sheet resistance (Ω/sq)	
A	43.3 ± 0.6	43.3 ± 1.3%
B	47.0 ± 1.1	47.0 ± 2.4%
C	48.6 ± 1.4	48.6 ± 2.8%
D	46.8 ± 1.4	46.8 ± 2.9%
E	48.2 ± 1.5	48.2 ± 3.2%
Average	46.8 ± 1.2	46.8 ± 2.7%

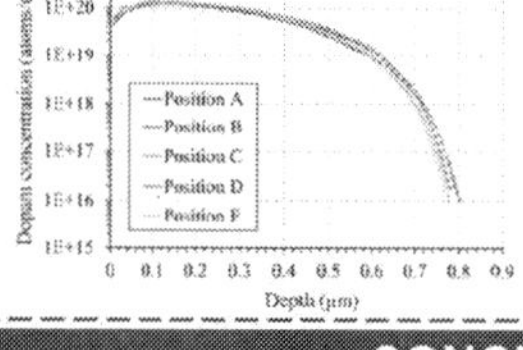

Boron-doped emitter (n-type Si-Cz)

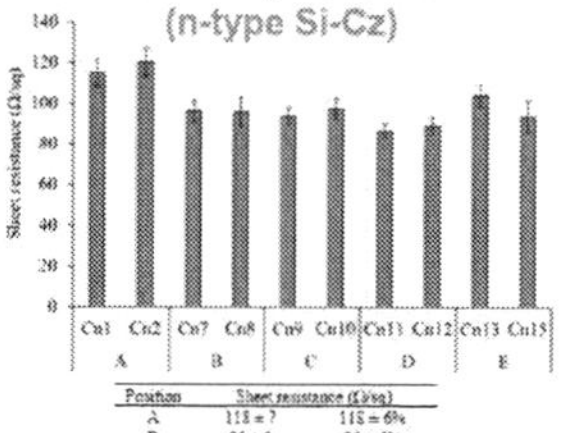

Position	Sheet resistance (Ω/sq)	
A	118 ± 7	118 ± 6%
B	96 ± 6	96 ± 6%
C	96 ± 5	96 ± 5%
D	88 ± 4	88 ± 4%
E	99 ± 7	99 ± 7%
Average	99 ± 6	99 ± 6%

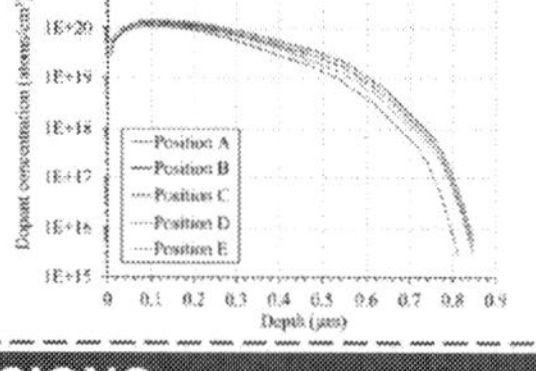

Boron-BSF x Emitter

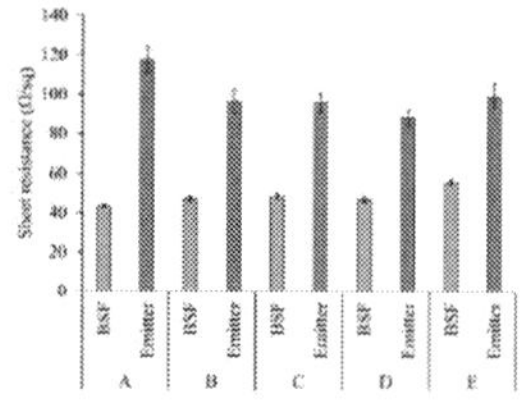

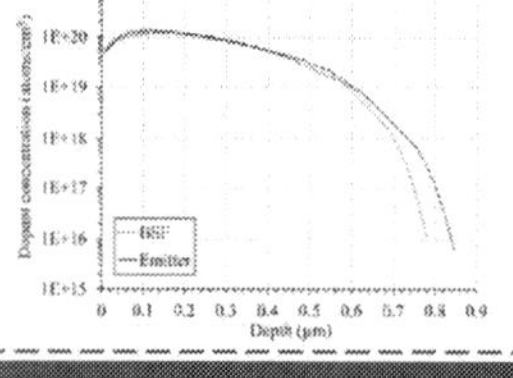

CONCLUSIONS

- B-BSF of p-PERT solar cells (p-type Si-Cz):
  - Compact furnace:
    - reduced gas flow rates $\rightarrow R_{sh} \rightarrow$ 43.3 to 48.6 Ω/sq with a standard deviation lower than 3.2%
    - baseline gas flow rates $\rightarrow R_{sh} \rightarrow$ 103 to 158 Ω/sq with a standard deviation from 2% to 11%
  - Conventional furnace: ◆ baseline gas flow rates $\rightarrow R_{sh} \rightarrow$ 26.7 to 29.2 Ω/sq with a standard deviation lower than 1.5%
  - The uniformity of boron diffusion in the compact furnace improved under reduced gas flow rates
- Boron-doped emitter of TOPCon solar cells (n-type Si-Cz):
  - Compact furnace: ◆ reduced gas flow rates $\rightarrow R_{sh} \rightarrow$ 88 to 118 Ω/sq with a standard deviation from 4% to 7%
  - Average R_{sh} of the emitter of (99 ± 6) Ω/sq was higher than the R_{sh} of the B-BSF of (46.8 ± 1.2) Ω/sq and boron diffusion was less uniform in n-type than in p-type Si-Cz wafers
- Boron concentration profile of the emitter was slightly higher than that of B-BSF for depths greater than 0.45 µm and emitter region was slightly deeper

Acknowledgments: Brazilian financing agencies FINEP, FAPERGS and CNPq

kalyon·PV
R&D

1BV.5.36

INNOVATIONS IN PERC AND TOPCON SOLAR CELL METALLIZATION: REDUCTION OF PROCESS STEPS AND EFFICIENCY IMPROVEMENT

Mert KAHRAMAN[1], Özlem COŞKUN[1], Burcu GÜMÜŞ ÇİFTCİ[1], T.Meriç Yanar[1]

[1] Kalyon PV Research and Development Center, Kalyon Güneş Teknolojileri Üretim A.Ş., 06909 Ankara, Turkey
Email: mkahraman@kalyonpv.com

INTRODUCTION & MOTIVATION

- While PERC used to be the most widely adopted mass production technology, it has now been largely replaced by TOPCon. This study covers both technologies.
- According to the NREL best cell efficiency chart, single crystal Si cell highest efficiency is 27.8% and commercial products efficiency values are between 23.0%-26.3% for crystal Si cell technologies[1]. This shows that there is a significant efficiency improvement potential and metallization design is one of the parameter which significantly influences the solar cell efficiency.
- This study aims to reduce the rising screen costs in mass production lines by integrating different screen types into printing equipment, thereby enabling the printing process with a single screen model. Furthermore, potential printing defects occurring during mass production in the metallization process will be monitored and controlled within a single printing step.

EXPERIMENTAL METHODS

- The front busbar and front finger screens used in M10-size PERC and TOPCon technologies have each been combined into a single screen model. The properties of these screens are shown in the table on the side.
- In PERC technology, due to the use of aluminum paste on the rear side during metallization, this project can only be applied to front-side printing. In contrast, in TOPCon technology, it can be implemented for both front and rear-side printing.
- PERC cells were produced on this screen using silver pastes with 92% Ag content.
- Temperatures in the drying and fast-firing furnaces were fine-tuned for optimal performance.
- Trial production of more than 30,000 pieces with trial and baseline groups was carried out.

Table. Specifications of busbar and finger screens.

Screen Specs	Busbar + Finger
Type	Knotless
Mesh	640
Wire Diameter(μm)	5
Tension(N)	14.5±1
Angle	90°
Yarn Thickness	12±1
EOM	5±1
Finger Count	166
Busbar Witdh(μm)	20
Finger Witdh(μm)	12
Mesh Material	Tungsten Steel

Figure. Microscope images of screen.

RESULTS

PRODUCTION LINE SCHEMATIC

- Tests were performed on the PERC metallization line shown below.

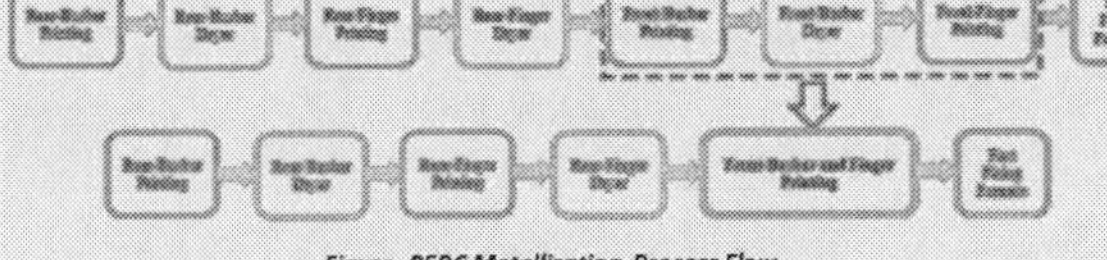

Figure. PERC Metallization Process Flow.

- The metallization production scheme for cell production in TOPCon technology is shown below.

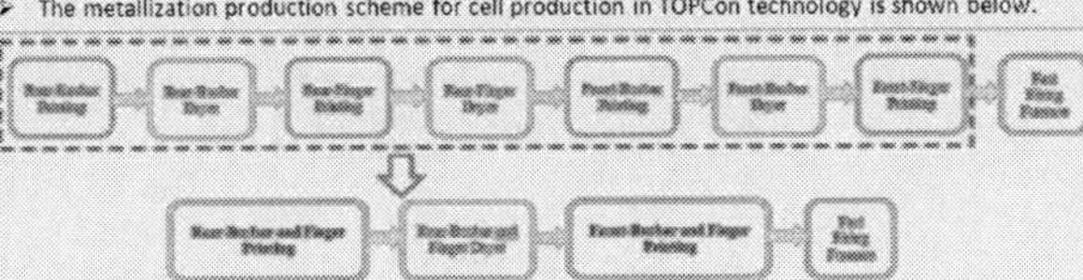

Figure. TOPCon Metallization Process Flow.

- In PERC technology, one dryer and one printing equipment were optimized, while in TOPCon, two dryers and two printing units were optimized, simplifying operations and enabling energy savings.

PASTE COMPARISON

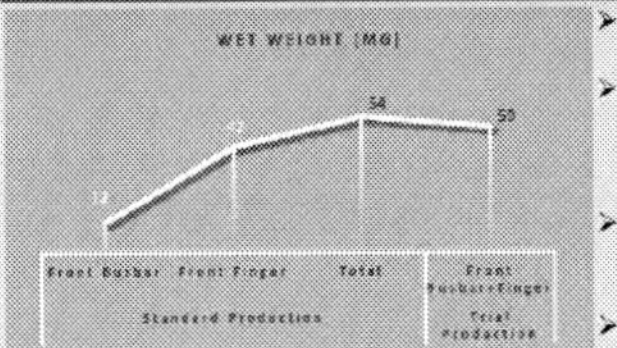

Figure. Silver Paste Wet Weight Comparison

- Comparison of Average Wet Weight of Standard and Trial Cells (shown beside).
- In standard production, 12 mg of silver paste is used for the front busbar and 42 mg for the front fingers, resulting in a total consumption of 54 mg.
- Electrical parameters of A+ class cells from test and standard production are shown in the table below.
- The new screen uses a total of 50 mg silver paste, yielding a paste saving compared to standard production.

EFFICIENCY IMPROVEMENT

- The EL image of the cell produced with the new screen shows increased brightness compared to the standard cell. EL and SEM images of the standard and new-screen cells are shown.

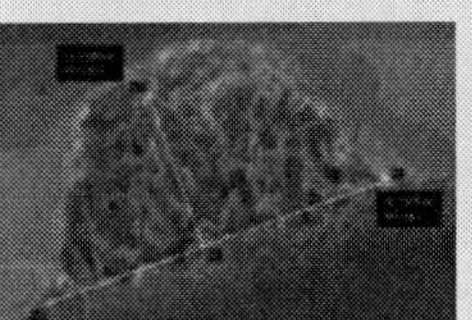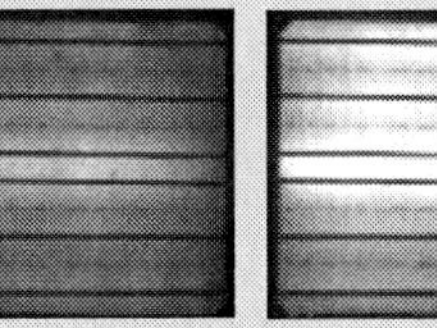

Figure. SEM images of front finger for PERC cell with efficiency of 23,44%.

Figure. EL images of standard PERC production cell (L) and cell with PERC new metallization screens (R).

- Comparison of the I-V parameters of both groups is shown in the figure below.
- Comparison of trial and standard Uoc, Fill Factor, and Efficiency is shown below. The new screen design increased the Fill Factor by 0.13, while Rser increased by 0.003 Ω.
- Optimization of the emitter sheet resistance and fast firing in the trial group led to a gain of 3,1 mV compared to the baseline production group.

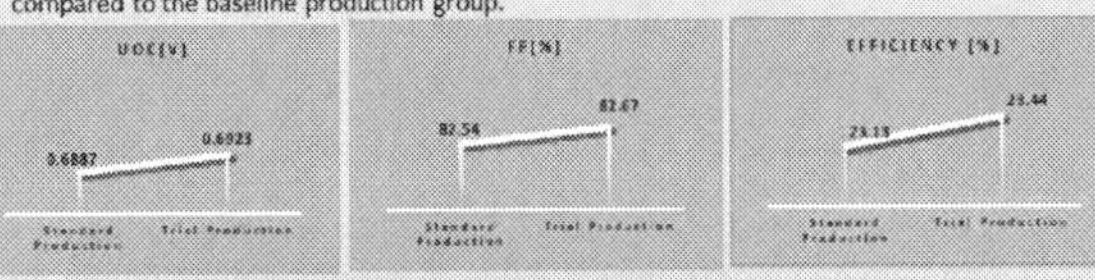

Figure. Comparison of I-V parameters for the standard and trial production groups.

- Comparison of the I-V parameters for the two groups is shown in the table below.
- An absolute gain of 0.31% was observed in the trial group with the newly designed finger and busbar screens combined into a single screen.
- Electrical parameters of A+ class cells from test and standard production are shown in the table below.

Table. Comparison of I-V parameters for the standard and trial production group.

A+ Grade PERC Cell I-V Results						
Groups	Efficiency[%]	Isc[A]	Uoc[V]	FF[%]	Rser[ohm]	Rshunt[ohm]
Standard Production	23,13	13,43	0,6887	82,54	0,0031	374
Trial Production	23,44	13,53	0,6923	82,67	0,0028	298

CONCLUSIONS

- In this study, efficiency improvement studies on PERC solar cell with M10 sizes have been completed carried out.
- In this scope, combining screen designs in PERC cell technology improved FF (%) and Voc (V), leading to higher efficiency. This study serves as a reference for TOPCon cell production, with future trials planned for TOPCon.
- Mass production average efficiency of 23.13% have been achieved with a maximum efficiency of 23.44%.

REFERENCES

[1] NREL Best Research Cell Efficiencies Chart, 2025.]

WET ETCHING PATHWAYS FOR TOPCON SOLAR CELL PLATING PREPARATION: ETCHANT EFFECTIVENESS AND PINHOLES FORMATION

Roberto Boccardi[1*], Clara B. Brendstrup Møller[1], Io Mizushima[2], Torben Tang[2], Rasmus S. Davidsen[3], Peter B. Poulsen[1], Gisele A. dos Reis Benatto[1], Sune Thorsteinsson[1]

[1]Technical University of Denmark, Department of Electrical and Photonics Engineering, 4000 Roskilde, Denmark;
[2]IPU P/S, 2830 Virum, Denmark;
[3]Aarhus University, Department of Electrical and Computer Engineering, 8200 Aarhus N, Denmark.
*Corresponding author: robbo@dtu.dk

ABSTRACT: Due to material scarcity, studies are focusing on replacing the Ag metallization of TOPCon with Cu deposited via electroplating, with the outer passivation layers selectively removed to obtain conductive surfaces. Wet etching is being studied as an alternative to the usual laser contact opening (LCO), to reduce the thermal stress on the precursors, and avoid laser damage introduction. Previous tests of photolithography and wet etching with buffered hydrofluoric acid (BHF) showed slower etch rate than expected and formation of pinholes in the poly-Si layer, negatively affecting the cell performance. This work evaluates 10% HF as alternative etchant and aims to determine the mechanism of the pinhole formation. Optical microscope investigation and cross-section SEM images show that 10% HF reduces the etching time for complete passivation removal from 36 to 12 min, when compared to BHF. Moreover, the pinholes originate from pre-existing trenches in the poly-Si, where the passivation is thinner and is completely removed earlier than in the rest of the sample. Additionally, BHF locally over-etches the poly-Si around the exposed trenches, likely due to grain boundary reactivity, while 10% HF leaves the surface intact.
Keywords: Wet etching, Pinholes, TOPCon, Cu plating, Metallization

1 INTRODUCTION

With solar photovoltaic (PV) installations around the world growing significantly (more than 30% total installed capacity increase in 2023 [1]), the silver (Ag) scarcity is an important sustainability bottleneck for solar cells: with the current rate, 85-98% of the currently known Ag reserve will be consumed by the PV industry by 2050, with n-type cells' rapid growth unveiling worse scenarios [2]. Cheaper and more abundant Cu is then being studied as alternative metallization, mainly deposited via electroplating and with Ni as barrier layer to avoid diffusion of copper into the silicon in the metalized areas [3], where it creates recombination traps in the middle of the bandgap.

Electroplating happens on conductive areas, while most of the high efficiency PV cells like the tunnel oxide passivated contact (TOPCon) one present strong surface passivation on both sides. The latter needs then to be selectively removed, and most of the previous studies involved laser contact opening (LCO), exposing the underlying p-doped c-Si and n-doped poly-Si. However, particularly on the front side, laser-induced thermal damage impacts the iVoc, indicating need for further improvement [4].

A valuable alternative to LCO is wet etching: the passivation layers are opened via photolithographic patterning of a mask with busbar and fingers, followed by submersion into etchant chemicals. Compared to LCO, wet etching is expected to cause less or no damage to the PV stack when used for passivation opening of p-type Cz-Si cells [5] or seed layer removal in HJT metallization [6], but previous tests for TOPCon passivation opening in buffered hydrofluoric acid (BHF) showed high etching times and formation of pinholes in the poly-Si [7].

Buffering is the process of mixing an acid with its conjugate base, in this case HF with ammonium fluoride (NH₄F), so that it maintains a constant pH value throughout its use. When buffered, HF provides a stable etch rate, and when used in conjunction with photoresists it doesn't penetrate it through microscopic holes and

cracks as much as HF [8].

This work investigates the effectiveness of 10% HF as alternative etchant to BHF and aims to determine the pinholes formation mechanisms to ultimately avoid it, combining optical microscope analysis and Scanning Electron Microscope (SEM) cross-section imaging.

2 EXPERIMENTAL

2.1 TOPCon precursors

The precursors are 135 µm thick M10 industrial TOPCon cells without metallization, with the emitter (or front) side textured as pyramids and the TOPCon (or rear) side chemically polished. The cell stack is shown in Fig. 1, together with some approximate thicknesses.

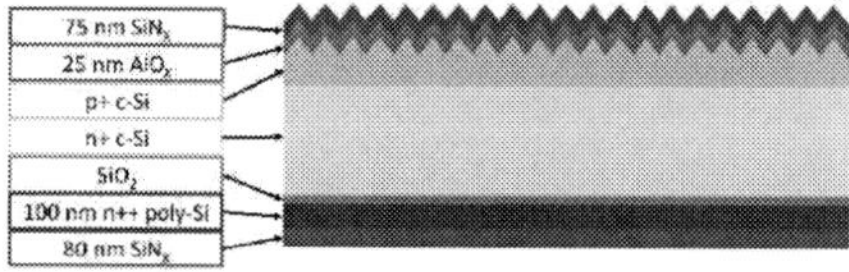

Figure 1: Materials stack of the TOPCon precursors, with approximate thicknesses of the outmost layers.

The cells are scribed with a 1064 nm laser and cleaved into 25x50 mm samples.

2.2 Wet etching

The samples are etched in beaker into two different etchants, Buffered HF (BHF) and 10% HF, which details can be found in Table I.

The samples are etched until the passivation layers are completely removed from both sides, respectively SiNx and AlOx from the front and SiNx from the rear. Intermediate steps are also analysed to compare the etchants effectiveness and study the mechanism of pinholes formation.

Table I: Chemicals used for wet etching with relative details. The chemical compositions are taken from the manufacturer labels, while the pH is measured with pH test strips.

Etchant	Chemical composition	pH
BHF	10-30% HF 30-50% NH₄F	5
HF	10% HF	2

2.2 Characterization

Samples with different etching times are characterized by optical microscope and Scanning Electron Microscopy (SEM) imaging, with two different goals on front and rear sides.

On the front side, SEM cross-section imaging focuses on studying the etchants effectiveness, determining how and where the residual passivation is located when not completely removed.

On the rear side, SEM cross-section images are backed up by top-view optical microscope analyses, to spot the pinholes and study their development with increasing etching time.

3 RESULTS AND DISCUSSION

3.1 Front side – etchant effectiveness

From cross-section SEM imaging of the front side, the SiNx and AlOx layers can't be distinguished but are visible as a single brighter layer on top of the c-Si, as in Fig. 2. Moreover, the pyramids' tips appear rounded, getting sharper when the c-Si is completely exposed (Fig. 3a-b).

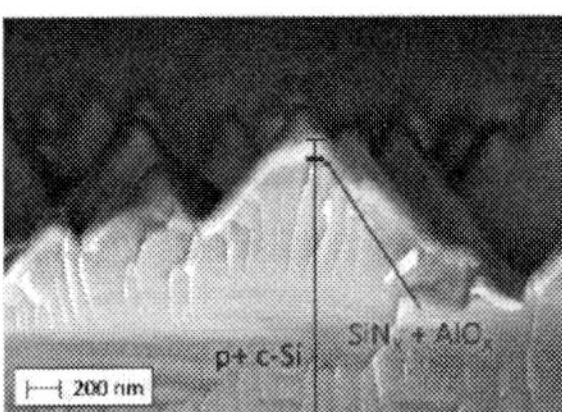

Figure 2: Front side cross-section SEM image of an unetched (Reference) sample. The SiNx and AlOx layers can be seen as a single layer above the c-Si, as observed in previous work [7]

Different behavior can be observed for the two etchants when not completely removing the outer layers. After 27 min etching in BHF, the residual passivation can be seen only at the base of the pyramids, suggesting a wetting limitation of the etchant due to the surface texture (Fig. 3a). After 7 min etching in 10% HF, instead, the residual passivation is more uniformly distributed along the sides of the pyramids, suggesting a more isotropic etching and no wetting issues (Fig. 3b).

Etching times necessary to completely remove the passivation are respectively 36 min for BHF and 12 min for 10% HF.

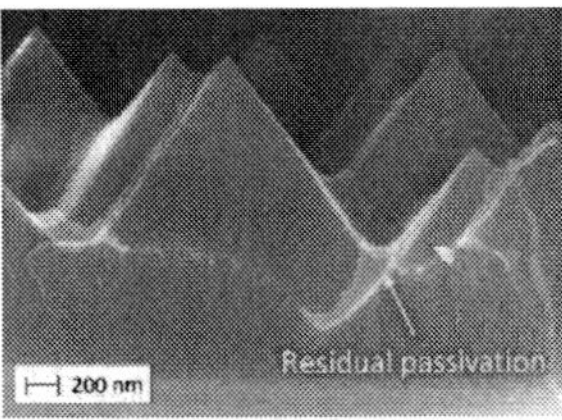

(a)

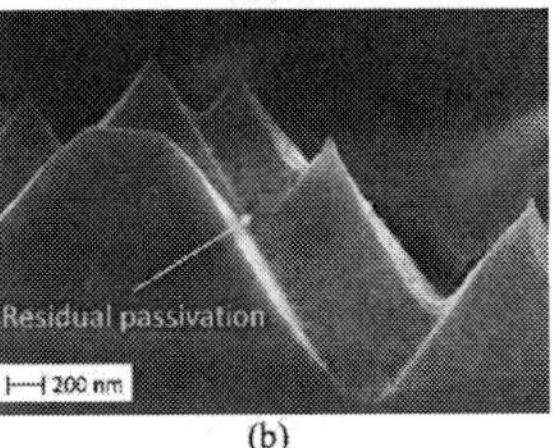

(b)

Figure 3: Front side cross-section SEM images after wet etching in BHF for 27 min (b) and 10% HF for 7 min (c). Both cases present residual passivation, concentrated at the base of the pyramids for BHF (likely due to wetting issues) and more uniformly distributed along the pyramids' sides for 10% HF.

3.2 Rear side – pinholes formation

From cross-section SEM imaging of the rear side, the SiNx layer is clearly visible on top of the poly-Si, the latter being of easy distinction thanks to the typical multi-crystalline aspect [9], as in Fig. 4. Moreover, with the polished texture not perfectly flat, part of the bottom surface is also visible.

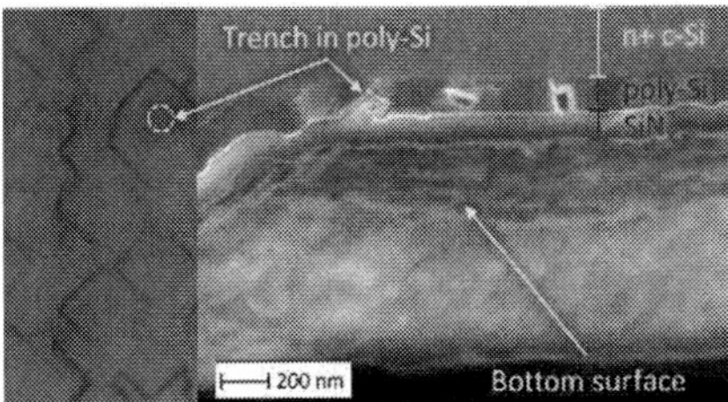

Figure 4: Rear side top-view with optical microscope (left) and cross-section SEM image (right) of an unetched (Reference) sample. Due to the texture not being completely flat, part of the bottom surface is also visible. A trench-defect in the poly-Si is visible in both images, appearing as brownish spots in the optical microscope image.

Fig. 4 contains an important feature for this study: a trench-defect in the poly-Si, filled with air and SiNx of overall lower thickness and therefore different colour appearance (brownish instead of blue) in the optical microscope view compared to the rest of the passivation. In fact, a visual analysis of the rear side showed that the colour appearance changes significantly with the thickness of SiNx, as in Fig. 5, ranging from blue for full thickness, through brownish and becoming grey when completely removed.

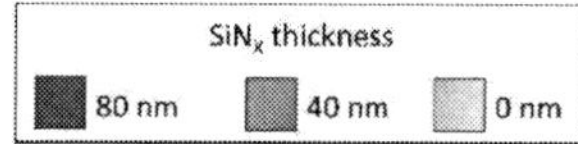

Figure 5: Rear side colour appearance with different thicknesses of SiNx

While etching the samples in BHF and in 10% HF, we observed that the poly-Si in proximity of the trench defects is exposed sooner to the etchant, compared to the rest of the surface, being covered by thinner SiN$_X$. The latter becomes more exposed as well and is etched more quickly. Therefore, when having residual passivation, the SiN$_X$ appears thinner in the proximity of the trenches, as visible in Fig. 6a-b. This effect is clearly visible both from optical microscope analysis and SEM cross-section imaging, when etching with 10% HF, as in Fig. 6b where the trench-influenced area is visible. When using BHF an additional effect happens, as previous work demonstrated, where the grain boundary reactivity of the poly-Si causes over-etching, expanding the trench to a bigger hole as the exposure to the buffered etchant increases [10], reaching a point where the underlying SiOx is exposed and the TOPCon layer damaged significantly.

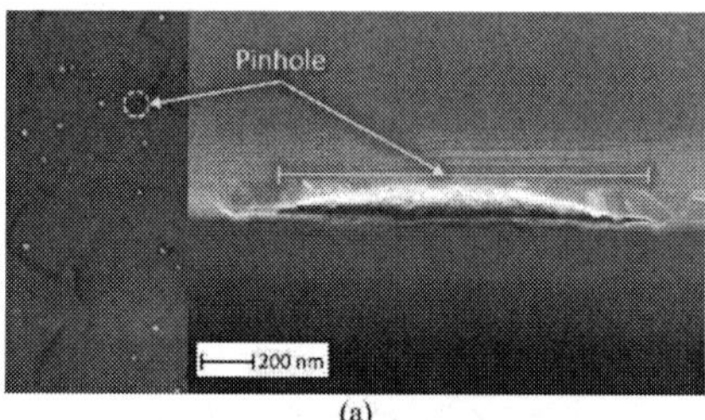

(a)

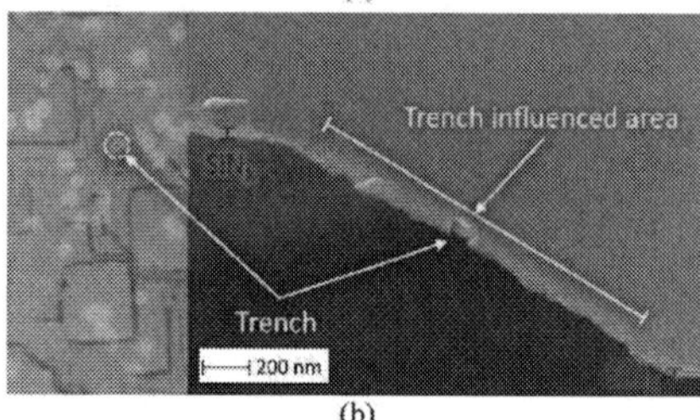

(b)

Figure 6: Rear side top-view with optical microscope (left) and cross-section SEM images (right) after wet etching in BHF for 27 min (a) and in 10% HF for 9 min (b). When etching with 10% HF a trench-influenced area becomes visible (b), with SiNx getting thinner in the proximity of the trench, while with BHF the poly-Si over-etching makes the area look like a crater (a) that we identify as pinhole.

Etching times necessary to completely remove the passivation are respectively 36 min for BHF and 12 min for 10% HF. At this stage, as shown in Fig. 7a, the trench-induced pinholes during BHF etching present dimensions in the order of the micrometers. Much different situation is observed for 10% HF, Fig. 7b, where only the pre-existing trenches are visible, and the rest of the surface is unaffected.

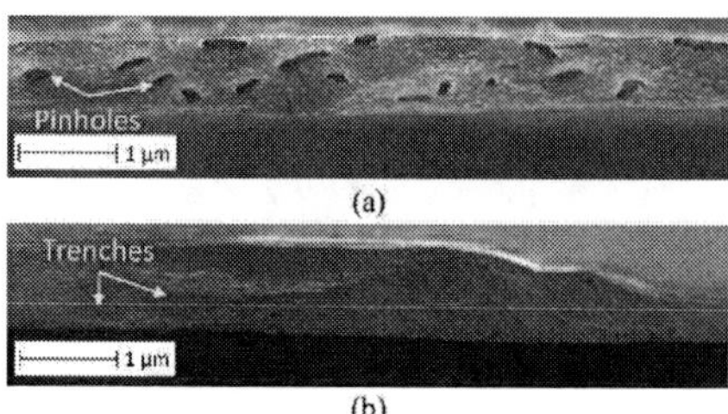

(a)

(b)

Figure 7: Rear side cross-section SEM images after complete passivation removal in BHF for 36 min (a) and 10% HF for 12 min (b), with focus on the samples bottom surface. Big pinholes are visible after BHF etching, while only the pre-existing trenches appear as defects after 10% HF passivation removal.

4 CONCLUSIONS AND FUTURE WORK

As concluded in previous work and confirmed in the current one, buffered HF (BHF) damages the poly-Si, due to the combination of pre-existing trench-defects, grain boundary reactivity and long etching time. The cause of the trenches in the poly-Si is yet to be verified, but a valuable hypothesis could be the formation phosphorus silicate glass (PSG) and relative post-crystallization cleaning [11], which might be unavoidable and hardly controllable.

The use of a pure acid like 10% HF seems a promising alternative, as it proved to be faster and not inducing pinholes from the trenches, but a strong photolithography masking is required due to the low pH. In fact, initial tests on a photo-resist masked sample showed critical photoresist durability.

Future tests will include testing hot H_3PO_4 as alternative etchant, where a strong masking is required due to the temperature involved, as well as a combination of BHF and 10%HF in sequential steps.

5 ACKNOWLEDGEMENTS

This research has been funded by Innovation Fund Denmark as part of the "ACES - Advanced Contact Engineering and Surface Passivation for Solar Cells" project under grant 3148-00044B.

6 REFERENCES

[1] G. Masson, E. Bosch, A. Van Rechem and M. de l'Epine, "Task 1 strategic PV analysis and outreach – 2024 snapshot of global PV markets", *Report IEA-PVPS T1-42:2024*, 2024, p.11.

[2] B. Hallam, M. Kim, Y. Zhang, L. Wang, A. Lennon, P. Verlinden, P.P. Altermatt and P.R. Dias, "The silver learning curve for photovoltaics and projected silver demand for net-zero emissions by 2050", in *Progress in Photovoltaics: Research and Applications*, vol. 31, i. 6, pp. 598-606, 2023.

[3] R. Sakakibara, A. Lachowicz, J. Hurni, C. Allebé, B. Paviet-Salomon, F.-J. Haug, C. Ballif, A. Hessler-Wyser and A. Morisset, "Investigating interfacial phenomena in copper-covered, n-type polysilicon-

based contacts by electron microscopy", *EU PVSEC 2024*, 2024.

[4] B. Grübel, G. Cimiotti, C. Schmiga, S. Schellinger, B. Steinhauser, A. A. Brand, M. Kamp, M. Sieber, D. Brunner, S. Fox and S. Kluska, "Progress of plated metallization for industrial bifacial TOPCon silicon solar cells", in *Progress in Photovoltaics: Research and Applications*, vol. 30, i. 6, pp. 615-621, 2022.

[5] M. Aleman, N. Bay, D. Barucha, A. Knorz, D. Biro, R. Preu, S. W. Glunz, "Advances in electroless nickel plating for the metallization of silicon solar cells using different structuring techniques for the ARC", *EU PVSEC 2009*, 2009.

[6] A. Letize, B. Lee and D. Cullen, "Wet chemical metallization of silicon solar cells: status and perspective of industrial application", *EU PVSEC 2016*, 2016.

[7] R. Boccardi, C. B. B. Møller, I. Mizushima, T. Tang, R. S. Davidsen, P. B. Poulsen, G. A. Dos Reis Benatto and S. Thorsteinsson, "Towards simultaneous double-side Ni/Cu plated contacts on wet etch opened TOPCon solar cells", in *Proceedings of 2025 IEEE 53rd Photovoltaic Specialists Conference*, pp. 734-737, 2025.

[8] A. Sarangan, "Nanofabrication: Principles to Laboratory Practice – Chapter 6: Lithography", *CRC Press*, p. 140, 2016.

[9] F. Edelman, A Chack, R. Weil, R Beserman, Yu.L. Khait, P. Werner, B. Rech, T. Roschek, R. Carius, H. Wagner and W. Beyer, "Structure of PECVD Si:H films for solar cell applications", in *Solar Energy Materials and Solar Cells*, vol. 77, i. 2, pp. 125-143, 2003.

[10] S. Tseng, W.-T. Kary Chien and B.-C. Cai, "Improvement of poly-silicon hole induced gate oxide failure by silicon rich oxidation", in *Microelectronics Reliability*, vol. 43, i.5, pp. 713-724, 2003.

[11] Q. Wang, M. Zhang, M. Peng, L. Yu, C. Lin, L. Wang, T. Yan, G. Liu and X. Xi, "Effect of annealing conditions on phosphorus inward diffusion from N+ Poly-Si layer in N-type TOPCon solar cells", in *Materials Science in Semiconductor Processing*, vol. 176, 2024.

Wet Etching Pathways for TOPCon Solar Cell Plating Preparation: Etchant Effectiveness and Pinholes Formation

Roberto Boccardi[1*], Clara B. Brendstrup Møller[1], Io Mizushima[2], Torben Tang[2], Rasmus S. Davidsen[3], Peter B. Poulsen[1], Gisele A. dos Reis Benatto[1], Sune Thorsteinsson[1]

[1]Technical University of Denmark, Department of Electrical and Photonics Engineering, 4000 Roskilde, Denmark;

[2]IPU P/S, 2830 Virum, Denmark; [3]Aarhus University, Department of Electrical and Computer Engineering, 8200 Aarhus N, Denmark.

*robbo@dtu.dk

Introduction

- Due to material scarcity, Ag metallization of TOPCon is being replaced by Cu via electroplating. Outer **passivation layers** are selectively **removed** to obtain conductive surfaces.
- **Wet etching** is being studied as an alternative to the usual Laser Contact Opening (LCO), to reduce the thermal stress on the precursors, and avoid laser damage introduction.
- Previous tests [1] of photolithography + wet etching with Buffered HF (BHF) showed **slower etch rate** than expected and **formation of pinholes** in the poly-Si layer, negatively affecting the cell performance.
- This work focuses on the effectiveness of **10% HF as alternative etchant** and on the **mechanism of pinholes formation**.

Methodology

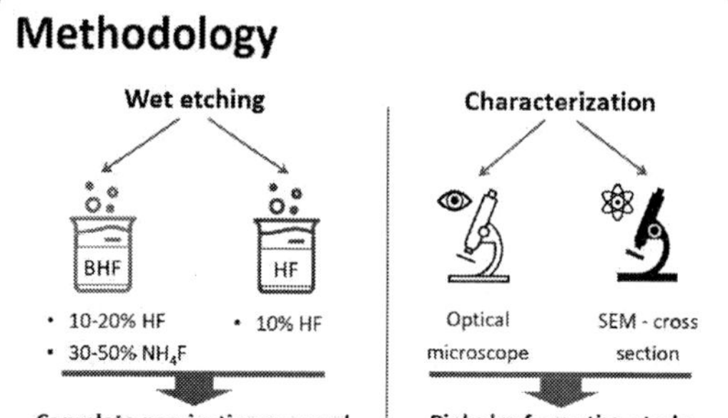

Results and Discussion

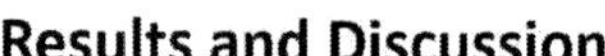

------------ Etching in BHF ------------   ------------------ Reference ------------------   ------------ Etching in 10% HF ------------

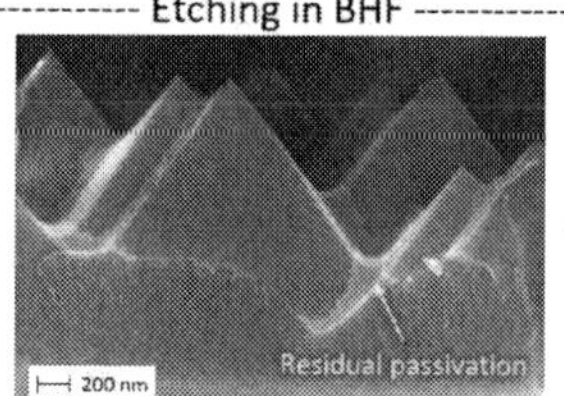

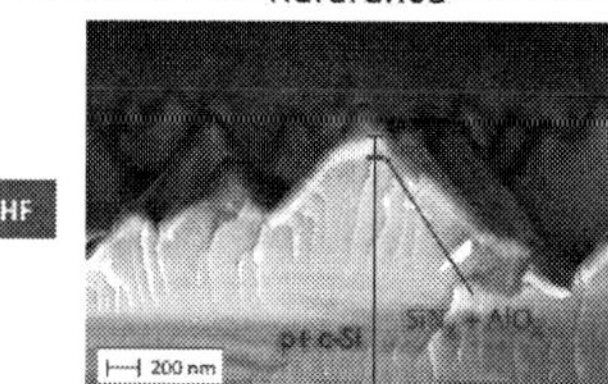

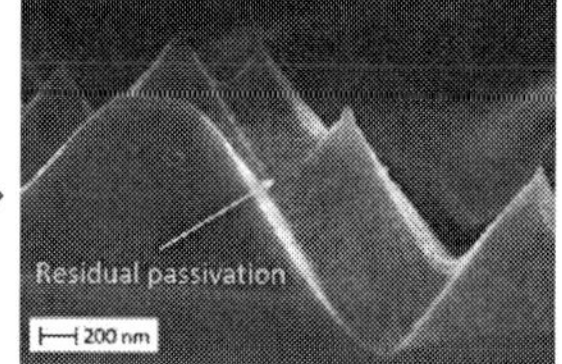

- Residual passivation at the base of the pyramids
- Complete removal after 36 min

↑ **Front side** ↑

↓ **Rear side** ↓

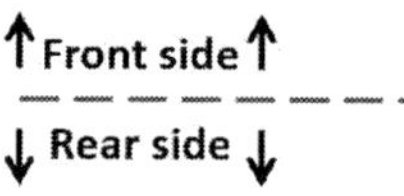

- Residual passivation distributed along the pyramids walls
- Complete removal after 11 min

↑ **Front side** ↑

↓ **Rear side** ↓

------------ Etching in BHF ------------   ------------------ Reference ------------------   ------------ Etching in 10% HF ------------

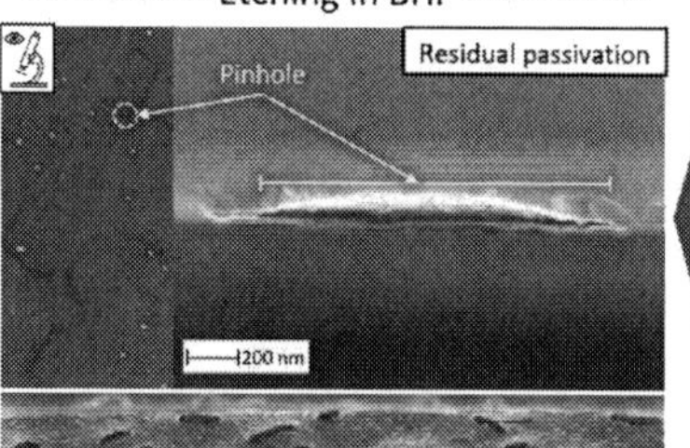

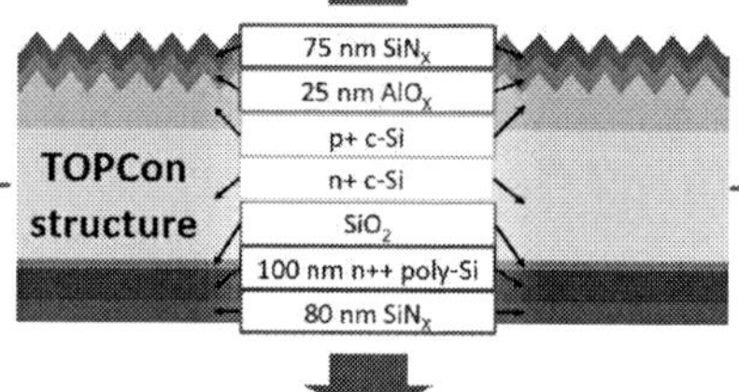

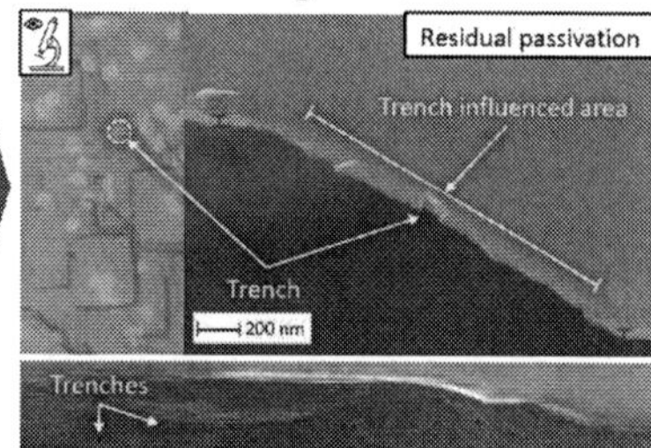

- SiNx changes colour around the trenches, due to different thickness

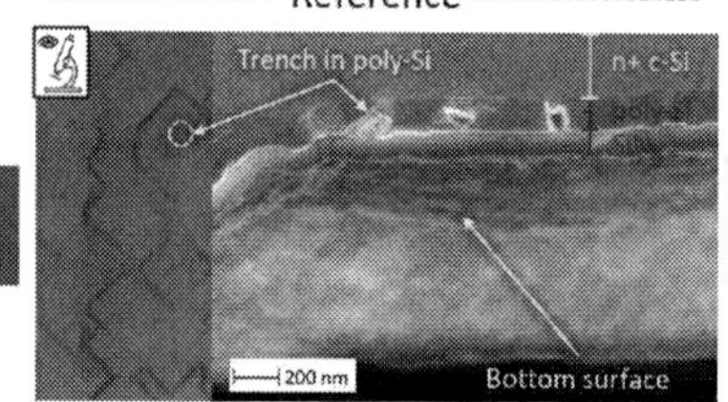

Conclusions and Future work

- Buffered HF damages the poly-Si, due to **long etching time** and **grain boundary reactivity** [2]. Trenches in poly-Si could be caused by post-crystallization cleaning and might be unavoidable.
- Pure acid like **10% HF** seems a promising alternative, being **faster** and **not inducing pinholes**, but a strong photolithography masking is required due to the **low pH**.
- Etching in hot H$_3$PO$_4$ will be tested, or a combination of steps with BHF and 10% HF, to evaluate the best etchant.

Etchant	Time
BHF	36 min
10% HF	12 min

Etching time required for complete passivation removal

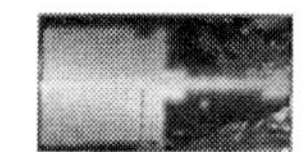

Photoresist delamination after etching in 10% HF – rear side

020029-001

References

[1] R. Boccardi et al., "Towards simultaneous double-side Ni/Cu plated contacts on wet etch opened TOPCon solar cells", DOI: 10.1109/PVSC59419.2025.11133113

[2] S. Tseng et al., "Improvement of poly-silicon hole induced gate oxide failure by silicon rich oxidation", DOI: 10.1016/S0026-2714(03)00059-3

Acknowledgement

This research has been funded by Innovation Fund Denmark as part of the "ACES - Advanced Contact Engineering and Surface Passivation for Solar Cells" project under grant 3148-00044B.

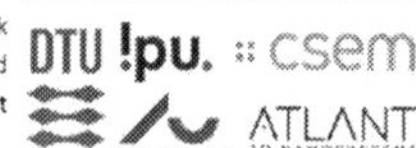

Optimization of Cu metallization in HJT solar cell manufacturing and investigation of possible Cu diffusion

42nd European Photovoltaic Solar Energy Conference and Exhibition

Y. Wu, L.A.G. Okel, E. J. Kossen, E. B. Kucuk, A. Gutjahr, V. Rosca, L. J. Geerligs
Solar Energy Group, Unit of Energy Material Transition, TNO, The Netherlands

Motivation

- To achieve a stable, *silver-free* metallization process for silicon heterojunction (HJT) solar cell manufacturing.
- Reduction of power loss in Cu compared to Ag metallized HJT solar cells.
- Interconnection technology for Cu metallized HJT solar cell

Why screen-printed Cu metallization

Pros:

- Screen printing for drop-in replacement of Ag in the HJT solar cell manufacturing
- Complying to the mainstream metallization process and equipment of PV industry
- Lean process without extra equipment investment

Cons:

- Risk of oxidation during the process
- Risk of Cu diffusion to impact the cell and module performance

Improvement of Cu metallization stability

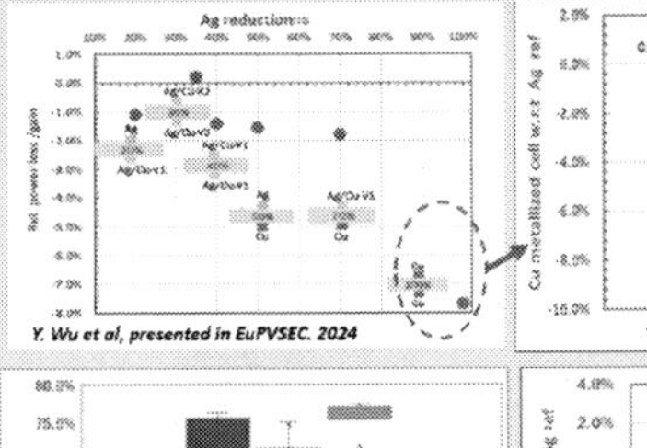
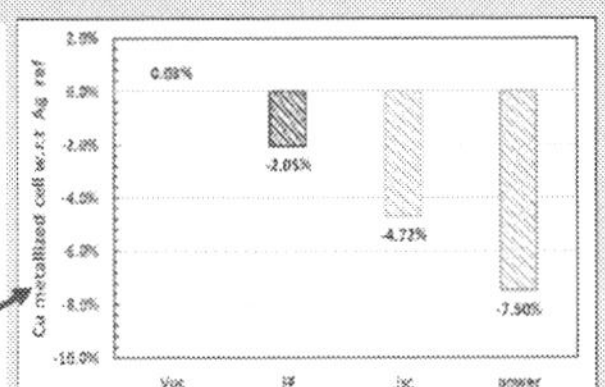

Y. Wu et al, presented in EuPVSEC. 2024

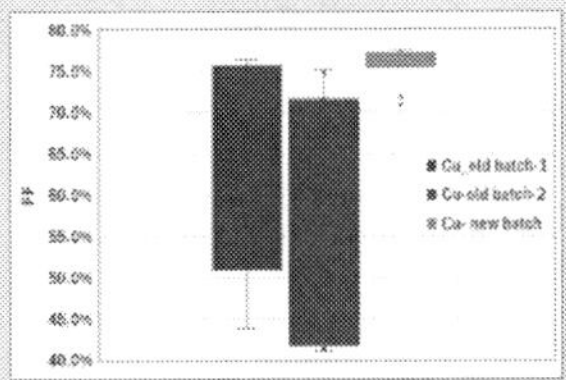
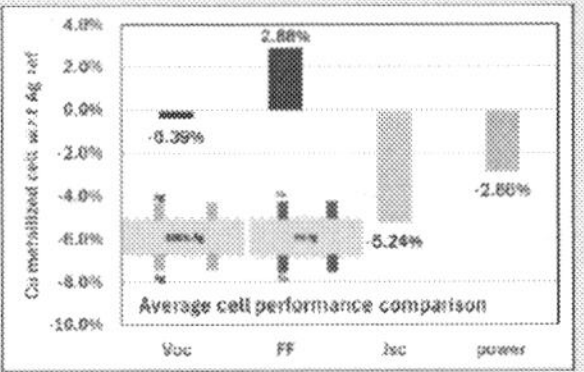

- Optimization of Cu paste printability to improve line definition.
- Refining post-print thermal treatment to enhance metal bulk conductivity and uniformity and prevent oxidation in the process.
- The variation previously noted (e.g., FF) due to unstable Cu metallization has been greatly reduced. However, current loss persists relative to the Ag reference and remains a primary factor in power loss.

Cu fine line printing

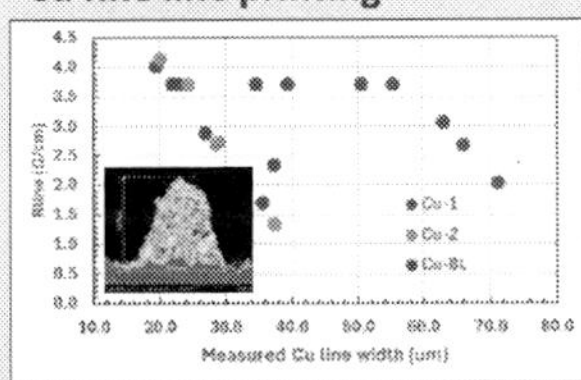
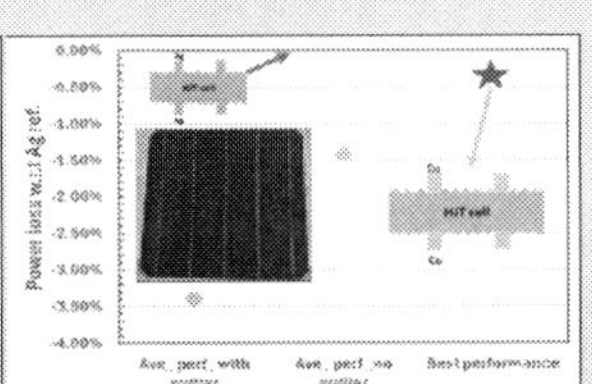

- Cu fine-line printing aims to address current loss issues.
- Cu fine-line printing with finger widths < 20µm has been achieved.
- Pastes 1&2 show lower R_{line} than Cu BL-paste at narrow finger width.
- I_{sc} loss is < 2%. Power loss *w.r.t* Ag reference is down to rel. 0.4% for the best Cu-metallized cell.

Results of interconnection for Cu metallized HJT solar cell

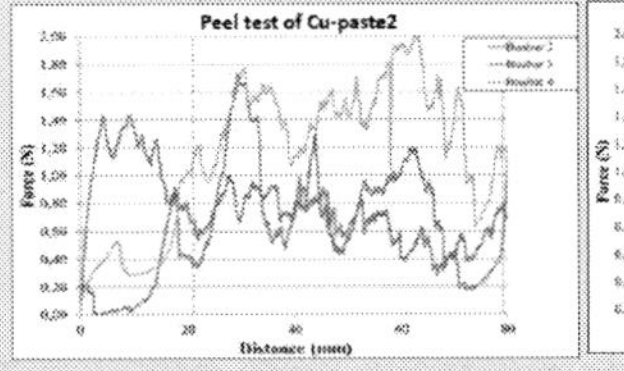
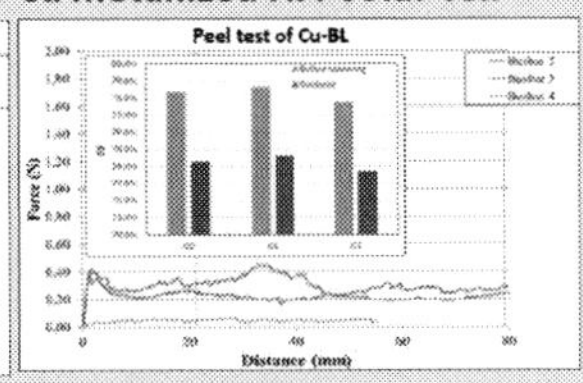

- Low-temperature manual Cu soldering achieves adequate peel force with the new Cu paste (left) but is weaker with the baseline Cu paste (right).
- Soldered Cu metallized HJT cell shows a ~4% FF loss (inset), likely due to a suboptimal manual soldering process that will require further detailed investigation.

Investigation of performance degradation at elevated temperature and damp heat (DH)

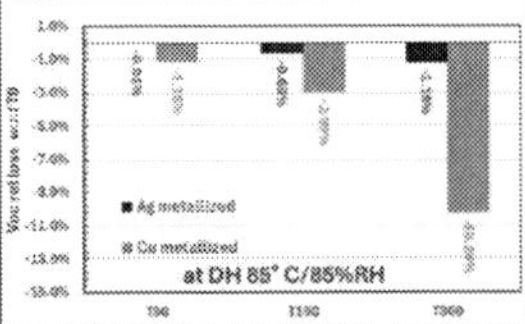
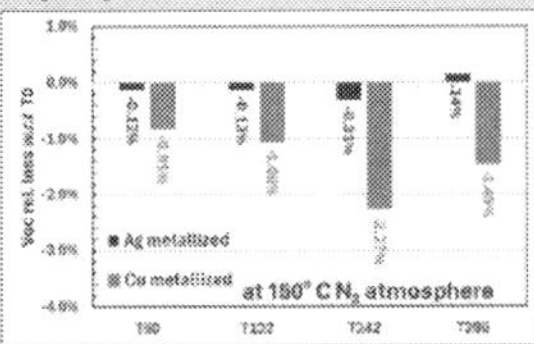

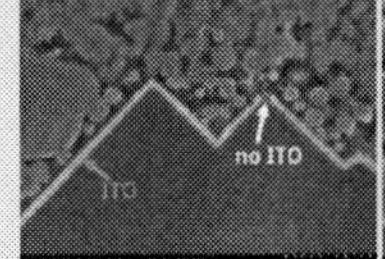
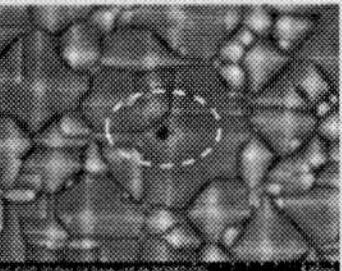
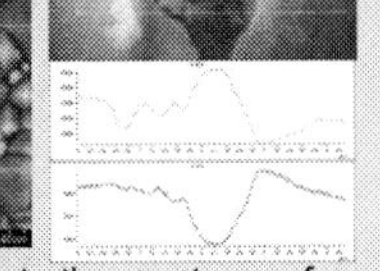

- Ag- and Cu-metallized HJT solar cells with similar starting performance were used.
- The pronounced V_{oc} degradation observed in the Cu-metallized cell during DH testing is likely attributable to Cu diffusion into the silicon bulk via ITO defects (such as pinholes), potentially induced by processing damage. While V_{oc} loss at 150°C in the Cu-metallized cell is less significant, definitive evidence of Cu diffusion has not been identified. Further investigations are currently underway.

Summary & outlook

- ❖ A robust screen-printed Cu metallization process now enables Ag-free HJT solar cells with only ~0.1% lower efficiency than Ag reference, and fine lines under 20µm wide.
- ❖ Cell performance degradation presumably due to Cu diffusion highlights the importance of ITO layers quality.
- ❖ Initial results for Cu contact interconnection are promising, further optimization is necessary to ensure stable, high quality device performance.
- ❖ Efforts to develop compatible cell lamination processes, as well as ongoing module reliability assessment and optimization, are currently underway.

Acknowledgment

Fundings:

This work was supported by SolarNL, a national research, innovation and industrial development program funded by the Netherlands National Growth Fund

This work was supported by TKI-Energie from the Toeslag voor Topconsortia voor Kennis en innovatie (TKI's) of the ministry of Economic Affairs and Climate, project SusCon, project number 2221203.

Dr. M. Bruggeman for sample preparation and SEM measurement

Dutch industrial partner:

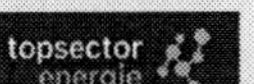

SELECTIVE ETCHING OF DOPED POLYSILICON LAYERS

Sebastian Mack[1], Viola Neuber [1], Marius Meßmer[1], Fabian Geml[2], Joshua Kamphues[2], Barbara Terheiden[2],
Laurent Clochard[3], Andreas Wolf[1]
[1]Fraunhofer Institute for Solar Energy Systems, Heidenhofstr. 2, 79110 Freiburg, Germany
[2]University of Konstanz, Universitätsstraße 10, 78464 Konstanz, Germany
[3]Nines Photovoltaics, Synergy Centre, TU Dublin - Tallaght, D24 A386, Dublin, Ireland
sebastian.mack@ise.fraunhofer.de

ABSTRACT: The implementation of p-type passivating contacts is a promising approach to reduce overall recombination in tunnel oxide passivating contact (TOPCon) or back-contact solar cells. Due to the high absorption coefficient in highly doped silicon layers, the polysilicon layer should be confined to the regions near the contact, which requires a structuring process of full area deposited layers. We report on a co-diffusion process using doped phosphosilicate glass layers from APCVD, with a drive-in during BBr_3 diffusion to generate differently doped polysilicon layers in a single thermal process. By exploiting the lower etching rate of highly boron-doped polysilicon layers, we demonstrate the ability to selectively remove n-type polysilicon while only marginally affecting the p-type polysilicon layer, using either alkaline texturing or atmospheric dry etching (ADE) with F_2 gas. This doping-type selective etching is more pronounced in the ADE process. Symmetric samples show a very low level of surface recombination of 5fA/cm² for boron-doped polysilicon layers after passivation.

Keywords: TOPCon, Polysilicon, Structuring, Etching, Mask

1 INTRODUCTION

Over the last decade, tunnel oxide passivating contact (TOPCon) solar cells have evolved from initial publications at research institutes to becoming the dominating solar cell technology in the market [1]. One advantage over its predecessor passivated emitter and rear cell (PERC) is the reduced minority carrier recombination at the rear side, achieved through the introduction of a passivating contact. However, the front side still features a direct contact between metal and the boron-diffused emitter, characterized by a high recombination current density $j_{0,met}$. This value has decreased significantly due to the implementation of current assisted contact formation approaches such as laser-enhanced contact optimization (LECO) [2] in combination with screen-printed Ag pastes that contain low or no Al. Nevertheless, to reduce $j_{0,met}$ below 10 fA/cm², the introduction of a passivating front contact is required, as proposed in this work.

Etching processes play a crucial role in the fabrication of silicon solar cells. Prominent examples of exploiting material-dependent etching rates include diluted HF solutions, which etch silicon oxide (SiO_x) layers while only marginally affecting crystalline silicon. Also, alkaline solutions are used in TOPCon solar cell processing to remove the parasitic Si rear emitter, while the borosilicate glass on the front side acts as an etch stop due to a lower etching rate. Structuring of (sacrificial) dielectric layers such as SiO_x or silicon nitrides (SiN_x) by processes such as laser ablation or mask and etch allows for producing local passivating contacts, which otherwise are difficult to realize. Prominent exceptions are masked deposition of passivating contacts, e.g. by shadow masks made out of thin glass [3] or additive local printing of passivating contacts [4]. Alternatively, local etching of full area polysilicon (poly-Si) layers is being investigated [5] by means of doping type-selective etching. This concept exploits the significantly different etching rates for p- and n-type poly-Si layers, potentially circumventing costly structuring processes. Additionally, the impact of dopant concentration on etching rates is well documented in the literature [6]. This approach has already been successfully used for the fabrication of solar cells with local p-type passivating front contacts (poly-Si fingers), as demonstrated by Hoß et al. [7].

In this work, we present our results for co-diffusion of poly-Si layers with p- and n-dopants in one single thermal process and subsequent doping type-selective etching of poly-Si layers using either wet-chemical etching or atmospheric dry etching (ADE). The results presented here form the basis for the later integration into device fabrication processes, such as local passivating contacts on the front side or interdigitated back contact solar (IBC) cells. However, this technological implementation is beyond the scope of this paper.

2 SAMPLE PREPARATION

Gallium doped and phosphorus doped Cz-Si wafers serve as starting materials. Initially, wet-chemical etching removes the saw damage. Following a wet-chemical cleaning step in ozonized water, a 1.3 nm thick tunnel oxide is grown by thermal oxidation, upon which an intrinsic poly-Si layer with a thickness of 80 nm or 160 nm is deposited by means of low-pressure chemical vapor deposition (LPCVD). Subsequent surface doping is achieved by exposing the samples to either $POCl_3$ or BBr_3 diffusion, resulting in n-type or p-type doping, respectively. As an alternative method for n-type doping, phosphosilicate glass (PSG)/SiO_x layer stacks are deposited using atmospheric pressure chemical vapor deposition (APCVD) at University of Konstanz [8,9], which includes a short HF dip prior deposition. All other processes are performed at Fraunhofer ISE. For the APCVD samples, the drive-in from the PSG dopant source takes place in a BBr_3 diffusion processes, with the PSG/SiO_x layer stack acting as a diffusion source and as a barrier, which prevents boron form the process atmosphere from diffusion into the silicon wafer. Using a single-sided dopant source, this co-diffusion approach enables simultaneous n- and p-type doping of intrinsic poly-Si layers in a single cost-effective high temperature step.

To determine the etch selectivity between n- and p-doped surfaces, two approaches are employed. The first approach uses wet-chemical etching in alkaline solution, while the second one applies atmospheric dry etching in F_2 gas at moderate temperatures of around 200°C. Figure 1 shows a sketch of the experiment process flow for the different sample groups.

10.4229/EUPVSEC2025/1CV.2.3

To evaluate recombination properties, the surfaces are passivated using an Al_2O_3 layer deposited by atomic layer deposition (ALD), an outgassing step in N_2 ambient, and hydrogenated SiN_x layers formed by plasma-enhanced chemical vapor deposition (PECVD). A contact firing process releases hydrogen for effective surface passivation. Photoconductance decay measurements (PCD) performed with a Sinton WCT-120 provide insights into the recombination current densities at the surfaces.

Additional characterization includes weighing of samples before and after etching, sheet resistance measurements, dopant profiling by electrochemical capacitance voltage (ECV) measurement, and transmission measurements at the corresponding stages of processing.

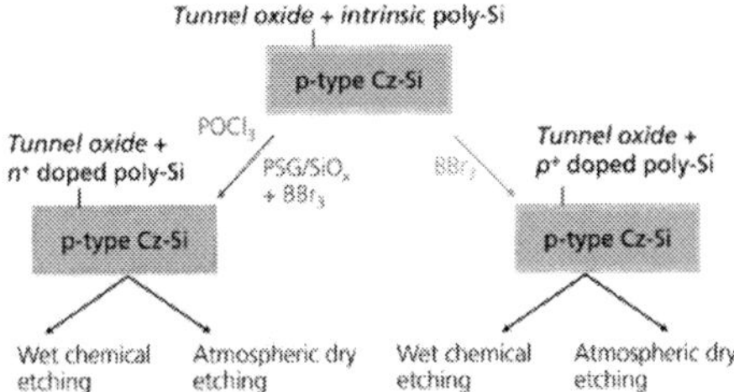

Figure 1: Sketch of the experiment process flow

3 EXPERIMENTAL RESULTS

3.1 Co-diffusion of intrinsic poly-Si layers

Figure 2 shows dopant profiles of p- and n-type poly-Si layers. The black profile represents an 80 nm thick intrinsic poly-Si layer that has been doped in a BBr₃ diffusion process. The diffusion process has been specifically designed to result in a boron dopant profile with a high active dopant concentration, which could show beneficial with respect to contacting and also with respect to etch selectivity, which is a function of dopant concentration [5]. Also shown are n-type poly-Si layers with thicknesses of either 80 nm or 160 nm, doped via a PSG/SiOₓ stack containing approximately 4 wt.% or 8 wt.% phosphorus. The P content was calculated from the gas flow rates based on an empirical calibration, and the doping was performed in the same BBr₃ diffusion process as described above. The use of 4 wt.% PSG layers results in a phosphorus dopant concentration of only 10^{19}cm⁻³. However, for the 8 wt.% PSG layer, both the BBr₃ diffusion and the 8 wt.% PSG layer allow for final dopant concentrations around 10^{20}cm⁻³, which proofs the successful implementation of a co-diffusion process doping of poly-Si layers. The results show that a wide variety of dopant profiles can be achieved for poly-Si layers of different thickness in one single high temperature step, due to the flexibility in controlling the P content in the PSG layer. PSG layers with phosphorus concentrations higher than 8 wt.% result in even higher dopant concentrations, as has been shown in other results with the same BBr₃ diffusion.

Apart from the local active dopant profiles, also the homogeneity of doped layers is of utmost importance, as it is not only relevant to cell parameters such as contact resistivity and carrier recombination but also might affect the homogeneous etching of those layers for advanced solar cell structures, which require a structuring of those layers.

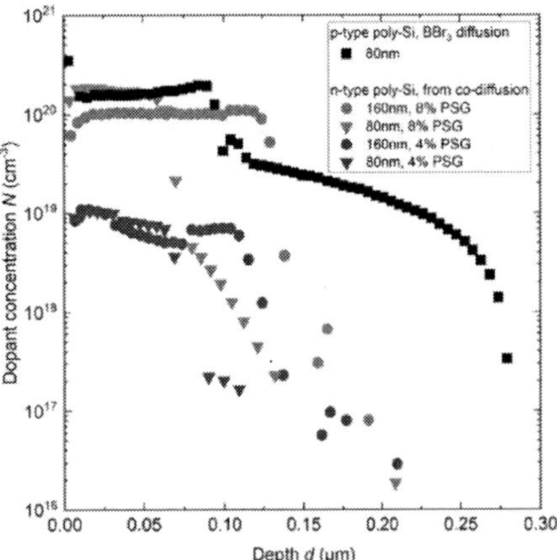

Figure 2: Doping profiles for poly-Si:B and poly-Si:P layers, achieved in one single high temperature step, measured by ECV on planar surface

Figure 3 depicts the 4pp mapping (100 measurement points) of an 80 nm thick poly-Si:P layer, formed on top of a planar p-type Cz-Si wafer. A 4pp measurement on this structure yields the sheet resistance R_{sheet} of the n-doped surface layer, that includes both the poly-Si:P layer as well as the tail of the dopant profile in the c-Si wafer. Here, the poly-Si(i) layer has been doped by an 8 wt.% PSG/SiOₓ stack in a BBr₃ diffusion. The ECV profile measured in the center of the wafer has been shown in Figure 2. The low relative standard deviation $\sigma = 6\%$ over the wafer indicates a homogeneous dopant source deposition by APCVD and a homogeneous temperature distribution during BBr₃ diffusion.

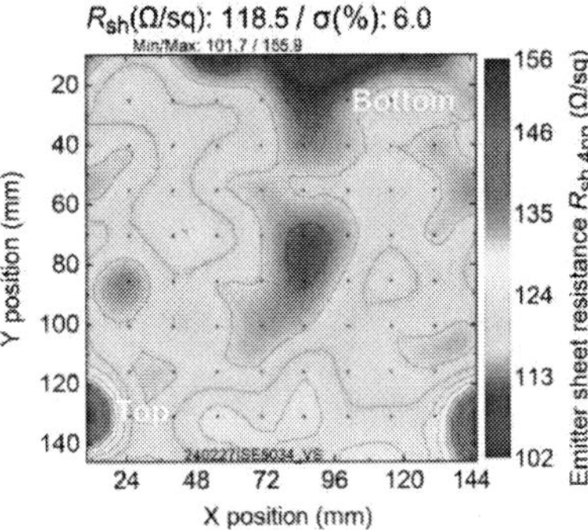

Figure 3: 4pp mapping of a poly-Si:P layer, on top of a p-type Si wafer with planar surface. Also shown are mean sheet resistance R_{sh} and relative standard deviation σ

Figure 4 shows the passivation results of poly-Si:B layers, doped via three different BBr₃ diffusions, after Al_2O_3/SiN_x surface passivation and subsequent contact firing. The three diffusions result in a profile very similar to that shown in Figure 2, but with a shallower dopant tail in c-Si, with B5 having the deepest of the three and B1 the shallowest. The results, which have been achieved on planar surfaces, indicate a high level of surface passivation for the passivating front contact with up to 734 mV implied open circuit voltage iV_{oc}, corresponding to a recombination parameter of 5 fA/cm².

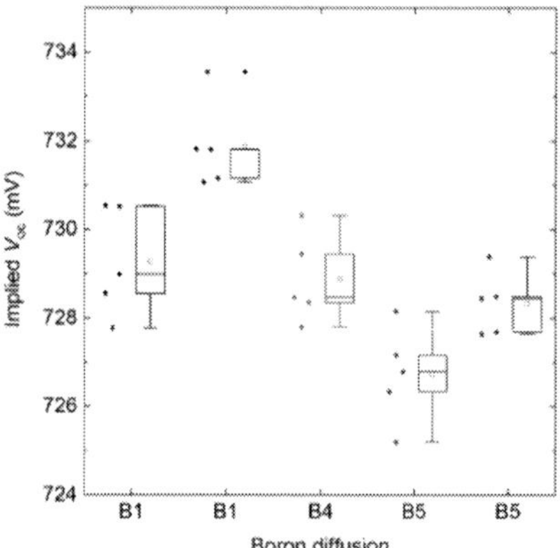

Figure 4: Implied V_{oc} results of symmetric n-type test structures with planar surface and boron doped poly-silicon layers on both sides, measured by PCD after Al_2O_3/SiN_x surface passivation and subsequent contact firing

3.2 Doping type-selective etching of poly-silicon layers

As described above, local passivating contact structures can be formed through doping-type selective etching. To investigate the feasibility of this approach, we conducted an experiment to test the etching rates of p- and n-type poly-Si layers formed by the co-diffusion processes described in section 3.1. For this, we used a wafer with saw damage etched surface, capped with a tunnel oxide and 160 nm thick intrinsic poly-Si. The sample featured a 4 wt.% PSG/SiO$_x$ stack only on the rear side and was doped in a BBr$_3$ diffusion, leading to poly-Si layers of different polarity on front and rear side of the wafer. Figure 5 shows the results after additional alkaline texturing. The fact that the front side still exhibits a saw-damage etched surface demonstrates that the boron-doped poly-Si layer prevents texturing of the surface, indicating its significantly lower etch rate compared to the phosphorus-doped counterpart. However, a look on the rear side clearly indicates the presence of textured surface with upright random pyramids, thus, the n-doped poly-Si layer has been removed completely, as planned.

Figure 5: Photographs of front and rear side of a M10 wafer after doping type-selective alkaline texturing step. The initial surface before etching was saw-damage etched and capped with a doped poly-Si layer. (left) boron doped poly-Si, still featuring a saw damaged etch surface, indicating a low etching rate. (right) textured surface, indicating the complete removal of n-doped poly-Si in the texturing process

To further investigate the doping type selective etching process, symmetric samples with both sides p- or n-doped poly-silicon layers have been weighed before and after texturing, and from the weight difference, the silicon removal has been calculated, assuming a density of 2.33 g/cm^3 for the poly-silicon layer. Table 1 lists the findings. In case of the poly-Si:P sample, characterized by a doping surface concentration of $5*10^{20}cm^{-3}$, as extracted from ECV data, the alkaline texturing step leads to a Si removal of 2.68 μm, averaged over several samples. This is well above the deposited poly-Si layer thickness of 80 nm and further supports the finding of a complete poly-Si layer removal during texturing. In case of the poly-Si:B samples, Table 1 lists results of two diffusion processes, which result in dopant profiles with $7*10^{19}cm^{-3}$ (lightly doped) and $1.3*10^{20}cm^{-3}$. Both surface concentrations are lower than that of the poly-Si:P layer. For the more lightly doped poly-Si:B layer, a Si removal of 0.88 μm is determined after alkaline texturing, whereas only 0.08 μm removal is obtained for the more heavily doped sample. As 0.08 μm corresponds to the thickness of the poly-Si layer before etching it might well be that the poly-Si layer has been removed completely by alkaline etching, but nevertheless the Si removal was too low to lead to the formation of upright pyramids.

Table 1 further depicts the Si removal, when samples of the same groups are subject to ADE instead of alkaline texturing. Here, ADE leads to significantly lower Si removal, which in case of poly-Si:P still exceeds the poly-Si thickness. This changes when going to poly-Si:B layers, where the corresponding Si removals are 0.04 μm and 0.02 μm for the more highly doped layer, respectively. This is below the thickness of the deposited poly-Si layer, and thus, a selective etching of poly-Si:P layers becomes possible by ADE in F$_2$ gas, even if both polarities are located on the same side of the wafer, which makes the process specifically suited for other advanced cell structures such as back contact cells. The results indicate that selective removal of poly-Si:P layers compared to poly-Si:B is possible.

Table 1: Poly-Si layer and Si removal during alkaline etching or ADE for samples doped with gas phase diffusion. Dopant surface concentration as determined by ECV

Type	Dopant surface conc. (cm^{-3})	Si removal (μm)	
Etching method	-	Alkaline	ADE
Poly-Si:P	$5*10^{20}$	2.68	0.25
Poly-Si:B	$7*10^{19}$	0.88	0.04
Poly-Si:B	$1.3*10^{20}$	0.08	0.02

To further investigate the impact of the etching processes on the poly-Si:B layers, we also perform ECV measurements. The results are shown in Figure 6. Shown are dopant profiles in the states "initial after diffusion", "after ADE" and, alternatively, "after alkaline texturing". The comparison of the respective profiles after diffusion and after ADE shows a slight shift in the profile along the x-axis, corresponding to very low removal of poly-Si in that process. In contrast to this, the wet-chemical process leads to a complete removal of the poly-Si:B layer, however, the doping-tail in the c-Si wafer is still visible.

This might be explained by the tunnel oxide layer sandwiched between c-Si and poly-Si:B acting as an etch stop during wet-chemical etching. If a complete removal of the dopant profile is needed, a longer etching time is needed to break up the thin interface oxide layer. In both etching cases, a poly-Si:P (n-doped) layer has been removed completely.

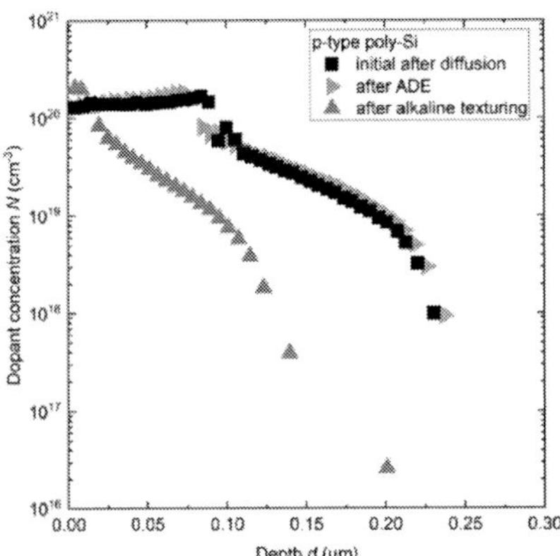

Figure 6: ECV data of poly-Si:B layers after diffusion, as well as after either alkaline etching or ADE

Figure 7 shows results of light transmission measurements before etching and after either alkaline texture or ADE, measured on symmetric samples. The initial thickness of the poly-Si layer before etching is 80 nm. BBr₃ diffusion leads to the formation of boron doped poly-Si, POCl₃ diffusion to phosphorous doped poly-Si. As ADE is a single sided process, the corresponding samples are etched once per side, to also yield symmetric samples. An increased transmission within the 1000 to 1200 nm range corresponds to a removal of poly-Si layers. In the first plot in Figure 7 before etching, the transmission T of the sample with n-poly-Si is measured to 23%, in between that of the more highly doped p-poly-Si layer with 22% and the more lightly doped p-poly-Si layer with 29%, all measured at a wavelength $\lambda = 1200$ nm. Wet-chemical etching of the samples in an alkaline texture bath leads to a strong increase of T to over 48% in case of the n-poly-Si layer, which represents the case of full removal of that layer, as explained above. Subjecting samples with p-poly-Si layers in the same texturing step also leads to an increase of T to values between 34 and 45%, indicating a reduce in poly-Si layer thickness, but not yet a complete removal. Here, the more highly doped p-poly-Si layers feature the values in the lower part of that range, slightly differing from sample to sample.

Looking at samples after ADE, the difference in selectivity becomes easily visible. Here, the n-poly-Si layer also gets removed completely, indicated by $T = 44\%$, and slightly less than for the sample after alkaline texturing, which is expected to be mainly a result of the different surface morphology of the sample. However, there are quite large differences with respect to etching of p-poly-Si layers. The more highly doped samples show only a minor increase in T, from $T = 22\%$ before etching to 23-24%, while the lightly doped p-poly-Si layer exhibits a slightly higher increase from $T = 29\%$ before etching to values between 31% and 33% after etching. These results are in accordance with the weighing results in Table 1.

The observed changes in IR transmission strongly support the findings from above, that wet-chemical etching removes both n- and p-poly-Si layers, whereas ADE only leads to a very small removal of Poly-Si:B, while still removing the Poly-Si:P layer completely.

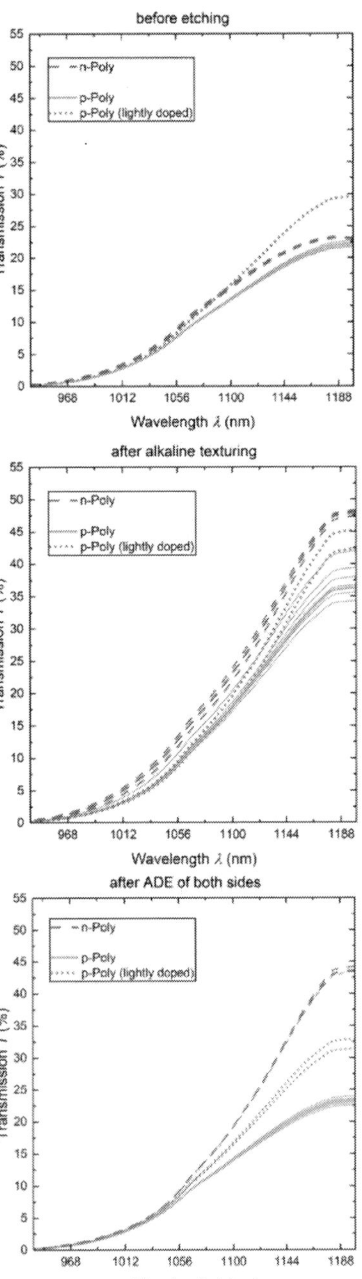

Figure 7: Transmission measurement results of symmetric samples with either n- or p-poly-Si, in different stages of processing: before etching, after wet-chemical etching, after both sides ADE

4   SUMMARY

This paper has focused on the formation of p- and n-type poly-Si layers by either gas-phase diffusion or the combination of APCVD dopant source and drive-in. Further work has been done to selectively etch poly-Si:P layers, thereby exploiting a lower etching rate for poly-Si:B layers in both alkaline texturing solutions and F_2 gas. The results indicate that doping type-selective removal of poly-Si layers is possible.

It has been shown that boron doped poly-Si layers with higher surface concentration feature a lower etching rate than more lightly doped layers. Still, a very high level of surface passivation is achieved for p-type poly-Si layers on planar surface.

The results could help to pave the way for a cost-effective formation of TOPCon solar cells with poly-Si fingers on the front side.

Acknowledgements
The authors want to thank all colleagues at Fraunhofer ISE for the excellent atmosphere and the support of TOPCon activities in general, by means of processing, simulation, discussions or financing.
This work was funded by the German Federal Ministry for Economic Affairs and Energy within the research project "WamTec", Grant Number: Fkz 03EE1193; Funding via the Clean Energy Transition Partnership CETP.

REFERENCES
[1] ITRPV, International Technology Roadmap for Photovoltaics (ITRPV): Results 2024. [Online] Available: https://www.vdma.org/international-technology-roadmap-photovoltaic.
[2] T. Fellmeth, H. Höffler, S. Mack, E. Krassowski, K. Krieg, B. Kafle, and J. Greulich, Prog Photovolt Res Appl., vol. 30, (2022), 1393.
[3] T. Dullweber, V. Mertens, M. Stöhr, J. Langlois, L. Mettner, U. Baumann, F. Haase, R. Brendel, J. Libal, A. Hähnel, A. Müller, V. Naumann, A. Vogt, N. Ambrosius, T. Pernau, H. Haverkamp, Proceedings 8th World Conference on Photovoltaics, 2022, 35.
[4] Z. Kiaee, A. Lösel, C. Reichel, R. Müller, M. Nazarzadeh, M. Jahn, R. Singh, I. Uecker, A. Qazzazie, T. Hanf, A. Terfort, M. C. Holthausen, T. Hanemann, and R. Keding, Proceedings 11th International Conference on Crystalline Silicon Photovoltaics, 2022, 110002.
[5] Clochard L., M. Yu, R. S. Bonilla, P. Tierney, J. Wright, F. Rougieux, and Y. Cai, Proceedings 41st EU-PVSEC, 2024, 020022.
[6] R. Charavel, J.-P. Raskin, Proceedings 16th International Conference on Ion Implantation Technology, 2006, 325.
[7] J. Hoß, S. S. Kalaghichi, M. Comak, P. Preis, J. Lossen, J. Linke, L. J. Koduvelikulathu, and F. Buchholz, EPJ Photovoltaics, 15, 2024, 43.
[8] F. Geml, S. Sanz, D. Wurmbrand, G. Micard, H. Plagwitz, G. Hahn, and B. Terheiden, AIP Conf. Proc. 2826, 2023, 050002.
[9] F. Geml, Dissertation, Universität Konstanz (2024)

Selective Etching of Doped Polysilicon Layers

Sebastian Mack[1], Viola Neuber[1], Marius Meßmer[1], Fabian Geml[2], Joshua Kamphues[2], Barbara Terheiden[2], Laurent Clochard[3], Andreas Wolf[1]

[1]Fraunhofer Institute for Solar Energy Systems ISE, Heidenhofstr. 2, 79110 Freiburg, Germany
[2]University of Konstanz, Universitätsstraße 10, 78464 Konstanz, Germany
[3]Nines Photovoltaics, Synergy Centre, TU Dublin - Tallaght, D24 A386, Dublin, Ireland
Phone +49 761/4588-5048, sebastian.mack@ise.fraunhofer.de

Introduction

- Local poly-Si structures highly relevant for advanced cell processing such as iTOPCon with p-type poly-Si fingers or interdigitated back contact (IBC)
- Doping-type selective etching exploits doping-type [1] and concentration dependent [2] etching rates for selective etching of n-type poly-Si

Sample Preparation

- Symmetric samples
- Tunnel oxide + intrinsic polysilicon by low-pressure chemical vapour deposition (LPCVD)
- Co-diffusion using stack of phosphosilicate glass (PSG) and silicon oxide (SiO_x) from atmospheric pressure chemical vapour deposition (APCVD)
- Alkaline texturing or atmospheric dry etching (ADE) using F_2 gas

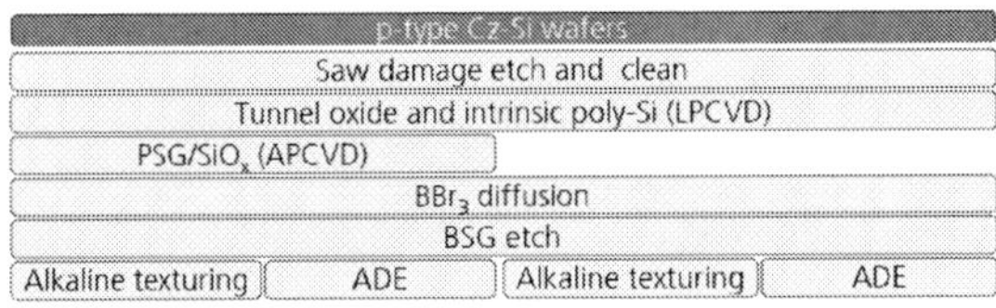

Figure 1: Sketch of the experiment process flow

Dopant Profiles

- Dopant profiles before and after etching
- Wide range of phosphorous dopant profiles realizable in one high temperature step, depending on dopant concentration
- n-type poly-Si and dopant tail removed completely by both etching process, Si removal of 2.7 µm (alk. texturing) and 0.25 µm (ADE)
- p-type poly-Si
  - removed completely by alk. texturing (80 nm removed), but tail in c-Si still present
  - marginally effected by ADE (20 nm removed)
- → Selective removal of n-type poly-Si possible

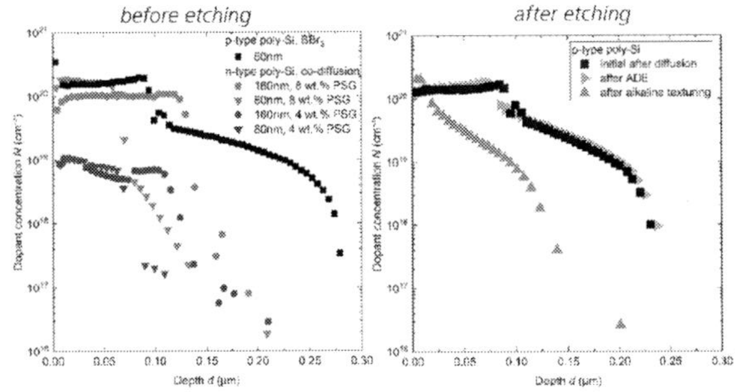

Figure 2: ECV data of before and after etching

Passivation of p-type Poly-Si

- BBr_3 diffused poly-Si samples
- Three diffusions, dopant profiles as above
- Symmetric samples with planar surfaces
- Passivation by Al_2O_3/SiN_x
- Up to 734 mV, average 5 fA/cm²
- → High level or surface passivation

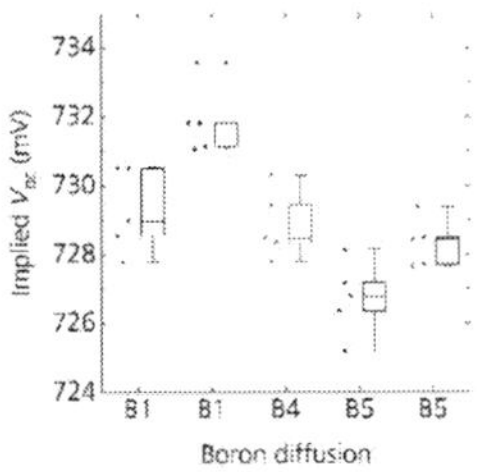

Figure 3: Passivation results after contact firing

Alkaline Texturing of Asymmetric Samples

- Samples with planar surfaces
- p-type poly-Si on front side, n-type poly-Si on rear side
- Planar surface still visible for p-type poly-Si (left) after texturing
- Textured surface for n-type poly-Si (right) indicates full poly-Si removal
- → p-type poly-Si lower etch rate

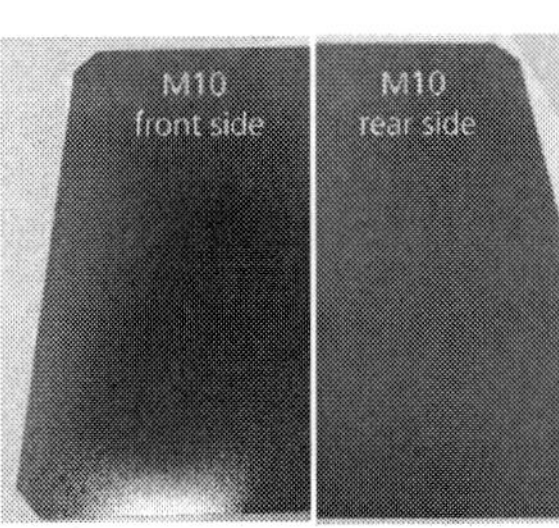

Figure 4: Photographs of front and rear after alkaline texturing process

Transmission

- Alkaline texturing leads to large increase in transmission → poly-Si removed
- ADE removes n-poly, p-poly ($7*10^{19}$ cm⁻³) partly, p-poly ($1.3*10^{20}$ cm⁻³) not
- → Increased transmission further proof of selective removal of n-type poly-Si

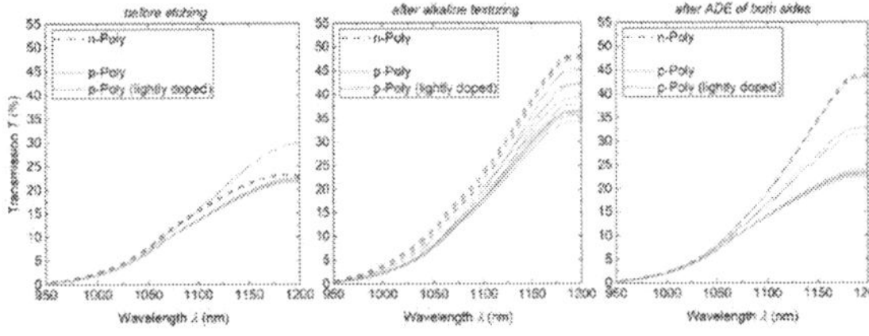

Figure 5: Transmission data for symmetric samples

Summary

- Co-diffusion process with APCVD PSG/SiOx in BBr_3 diffusion developed for simultaneous p- and n-doping of poly-Si layers in one process
- Doping type selective etching for selective removal of n-type poly-Si demonstrated using ADE and wet chemical texturing
- Selectivity of ADE much higher compared to wet chemical texturing

[1] Clochard L., M. Yu, R. S. Bonilla, P. Tierney, J. Wright, F. Rougieux, and Y. Cai, Proceedings 41st EU-PVSEC, 2024, 020022.
[2] R. Charavel, J.-P. Raskin, Proceedings 16th International Conference on Ion Implantation Technology, 2006, 325.

Supported by:
Federal Ministry for Economic Affairs and Energy

Funding via the Clean Energy Transition Partnership (CETP) project "WaMTec" (Fkz 03EE1193) from German Federal Ministry for Economic Affairs and Energy (BMWE) is gratefully acknowledged.

A TOPCon IBC Solar Cell Architecture with Sputtered Tunnel Oxide and Polysilicon Doped Regions: Design and Process Optimization

ISC research for a sunny future

Valentin D. Mihailetchi[1], Vaibhav V. Kuruganti[1], Thomas Buck[1], Volker Linß[2], Eric Schneiderlöchner[2]

1. ISC Konstanz e.V., Rudolf-Diesel-Str. 15, 78467 Konstanz, Germany
2. VON ARDENNE GmbH, Am Hahnweg 8, 01328 Dresden, Germany

Background & Aim

- **c-Si solar cells & modules** dominate PV market with record efficiencies:
    - *n*-type bifacial **i-TOPCon cells**[1]: 27.03%
    - **TOPCon IBC modules (TBC)**[2]: 25.2%
    - **Si heterojunction IBC cells (HIBC)**[3]: 27.8%
- **Current challenge:** reduce LCOE with simpler, more cost-effective processes
- **Our approach:** Develop a **novel PVD-sputtered route** to fabricate **TBC cells**
    - Inline high-throughput **DC sputtering** of a multilayer stack: TO/a-Si/doped & undoped SiOx
    - **Masking + laser patterning** for selective removal
    - **Ex-situ annealing & doping** for interdigitated regions
- **Advantages of PVD sputter process:**
    - Single-side deposition (no wrap-around)
    - No hazardous gases
    - Precise thickness and doping control
- **Target:** Demonstrate high efficiency with a simplified PVD-based TBC solar cell process

VON ARDENNE inline PVD sputter tool for our pilot line cell development

Fabrication and Characterization Methods

Main process steps[4]

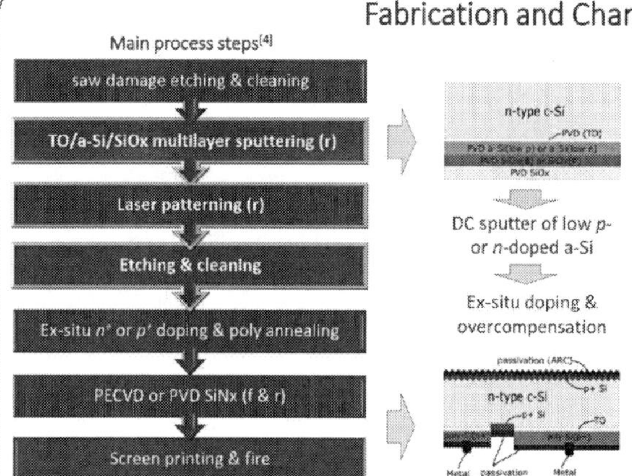

PVD-sputtered low-doped a-Si – overcompensation & passivation:

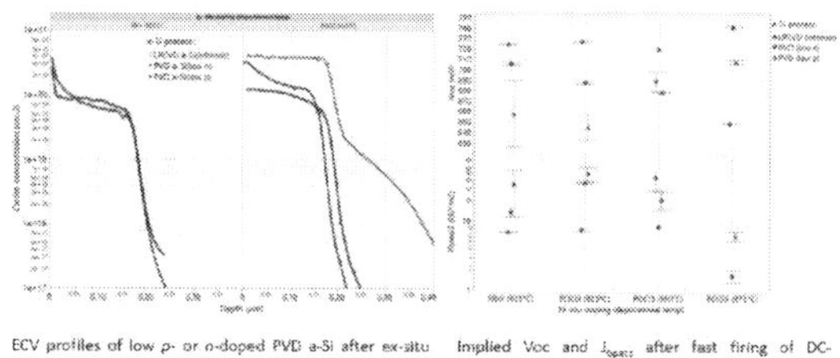

ECV profiles of low p- or n-doped PVD a-Si after ex-situ doping and 925°C annealing in BBr3 or POCl3; LPCVD intrinsic poly-Si shown as reference.

Implied Voc and J_{0pass} after fast firing of DC-sputtered low p- or n-doped a-Si, as function of ex-situ doping and annealing (925–975°C). A thermally grown TO with a thickness of ≈1.4 nm was used in this study for all samples.

- Both low *p*- and *n*-doped PVD a-Si layers can be ex-situ overcompensated by B or P diffusion, but doping concentration is below LPCVD poly-Si layer.
- n+ PVD poly-Si achieved iVoc ≈ 740 mV and J_{0pass} ≈ 1.6 fA/cm².

Individual Process Steps Optimization

PVD-sputtered TO layer – preliminary results:

iVoc and J_{0pass} of lifetime test structures with different TO/poly-Si combinations: p+ poly-Si from PVD (low p) or LPCVD (intrinsic) a-Si, B-doped and annealed (TO: 1.4 nm @875°C, 2.2 nm @1025°C).

Estimated bulk lifetime from QSSPC for different TO / poly-Si combinations.

- PVD TO + LPCVD poly-Si → highest iVoc (730 mV).
- PVD TO comparable to or better than thermal TO.

Conclusions

- Both low *p*- and *n*-doped PVD a-Si layers are suitable for **ex-situ doping** in TBC processes.
- **PVD-based poly-Si layers** can reach **high passivation quality** and compete with **LPCVD benchmarks**.
- Demonstrates strong potential for a **simplified, cost-effective, scalable PVD route** to high-efficiency (>25%) TBC solar cells.

Ongoing work

- Further optimize **PVD-deposited TO layer**.
- Optimize **laser patterning** for process integration.
- Full **TBC solar cells** fabrication.

References

[1] Tong, H., Tan, S., Zhang, Y. et al., Nat. Commun. 16, 5920 (2025)
[2] Aiko, PV Magazine 2024 (https://www.pv-magazine.com/2024/06/19)
[3] Longi, PV Magazine 2025 (https://www.pv-magazine.com/2025/04/14)
[4] ISC-Konstanz patent pending 2024

Acknowledgements

This work is under development within the framework of the BMWE research project "ParIS" (contract No. 020E-100636800).

Supported by:
Federal Ministry for Economic Affairs and Energy

020033-001

isc-konstanz.de

COMPARISON OF PASSIVATION PROPERTIES OF PHOSPHORUS AND BORON EX-SITU DOPED POLY-SILICON ON OXIDE LAYERS

Raphaël Cabal[1], Clarisse Laurens-Berge[1], Baptiste Marteau[2], Anis Jouini[2], Sebastien Dubois[1]
[1]Univ. Grenoble Alpes, CEA, LITEN, Campus INES, 73375 Le Bourget du Lac, France
[2]ECM Technologies, Grenoble, France
raphael.cabal@cea.fr

ABSTRACT: Passivating the contacts of crystalline silicon (c-Si) solar cells with a polycrystalline silicon layer (poly-Si) on a thin oxide (SiO_x) film is an effective approach to minimize the recombination current at the metal/c-Si interface. Combined with an ex-situ doping step ($POCl_3$ diffusion), this approach has become mainstream in PV market for TOPCon solar cells rear side passivation by poly-Si (P) / SiO_x stacks. Beyond the optimization of n-type poly-Si / SiO_x stacks, this study investigates the use of a BCl_3 diffusion to form poly-Si (B) / SiO_x stacks. Those p-type TOPCon stacks are of high interest both at short term to improve industrial TOPCon front surface passivation and for the development of double side passivated TOPCon bottom-cells for tandem applications. Thereafter are presented the doping profiles and passivation properties of both p and n-type ex-situ doped poly-Si / SiO_x stacks deposited on polished and textured surfaces, as well as their stability toward firing.

1 INTRODUCTION

Current TOPCon industrial structure involves already a poly-Si based passivating contact (n-type) on the rear polished side of the cell. In the future, one probable evolution of this structure should introduce a second poly-Si based passivating contact (p-type) on the front side of the cell, at least locally [1]. Considering that single junction devices feature a textured front surface, the introduction of a boron-doped poly-Si passivating contact remains a challenge: beyond light absorption issues, the passivation properties of p-type poly on textured surface does not reach at the moment the excellent passivation level offered by its phosphorus-doped counterpart [2]. From this sole perspective, there is still a need for improving the poly-Si (B) layers. On the other hand, one key parameter for a successful integration of poly-Si (B) on next generation TOPCon devices is the fact that it should be easy to implement on industrial lines. For this reason, the choice of BCl_3 diffusion (already in use in standard TOPCon lines for diffused emitter formation) seems of great relevance.

2 EXPERIMENTAL

In this work, a first batch of samples was made from Cz n-type wafers with a 3.6 Ohm.cm resistivity (M2 format). The wafers underwent a conventional texturing process (3µm-size pyramids) followed by a SC1/SC2/HF-HCl cleaning sequence, before being submitted to LPCVD growth of an interfacial SiO_x film (~2nm thick) followed by the deposition of an intrinsic poly-Si layer with a thickness of 80nm. Part of these samples were submitted to $POCl_3$ diffusion at temperatures ranging between 830°C and 860°C, while the other part was submitted to BCl_3 diffusion process carried out in the 900-990°C range. Diffused emitter resulting from the 990°C recipe applied directly onto the textured surface (without poly-Si/SiO_x stack) was considered as a reference. 4PP / ECV, and IC-PCD measurements were carried out onto these samples respectively before / after the BSG was removed in HF-HCl, in order to estimate poly-Si / SiO_x stacks sheet resistance (R_{sheet}), active doping profile and implied V_{oc}. Additional hydrogenation (using single SiN_x layer or an AlO_x / SiN_x passivation stack on poly-Si top surface) and firing (using a peak temperature of 790°C) were applied to

the samples in order to assess poly-Si (B) structures performance along TOPCon processing sequence (i-V_{oc} was re-measured after the most relevant step).

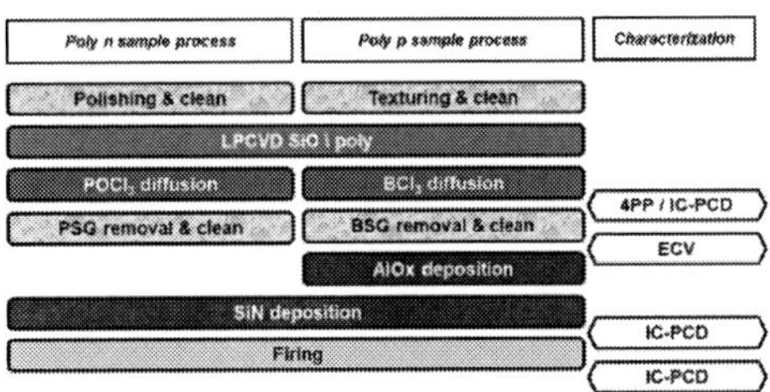

Figure 1: Symmetrical structures process-flow considered in this work.

3 RESULTS

3.1 Poly-Si (P)

Poly-Si (P) doping profiles feature a plateau above $3\times10^{20}\text{cm}^{-3}$ and a sharp diffusion tail in the c-Si (depth inferior to 60nm). Figure 2 presents the poly-Si (P) sheet resistances (measured on p-type wafers) for the different $POCl_3$ diffusion processes conducted on poly-Si layers. In this figure are also reported the corresponding active doping profiles measured by ECV. Diffusion temperatures of 830°C, 840°C, 850°C and 860°C were investigated. $POCl_3$ was injected during either 10min (Figure 2b) or 20min (Figure 2c). Similar doping profiles can be obtained for different diffusion temperature conditions, evidencing the robustness of tunnel oxide toward phosphorus dopant migration. Only a combination of high temperature (860°C) and prolonged $POCl_3$ injection permits to slightly increase the final diffusion tail. One can notice the thickness of poly-Si tends to shrink through the doping process leading to a final thickness around 60nm (confirmed by ellipsometry).

The i-V_{oc} measured on SiN_x coated poly-Si (P) structures before firing are also reported in Figure 2, showing values above 740mV for any diffusion temperature (here the $POCl_3$ injection was set to 20min). Passivation properties obtained with the poly-Si (P) reference structures are in good agreement with state-of-the art high levels. Nonetheless, in the present case, the poly-Si (P) samples exhibited poor passivation stability towards firing, significant blistering appearing concomitantly to huge i-V$_{oc}$ losses. For this reason, another batch of devices was fabricated on sister wafers, aiming at investigating different firing conditions (T$_{peak}$ of 750°C, 780°C, 810°C) but also other passivation schemes than SiN$_x$ alone: a stack of AlO$_x$ \ SiN$_x$ including a 8nm-thick layer of alumina was considered.

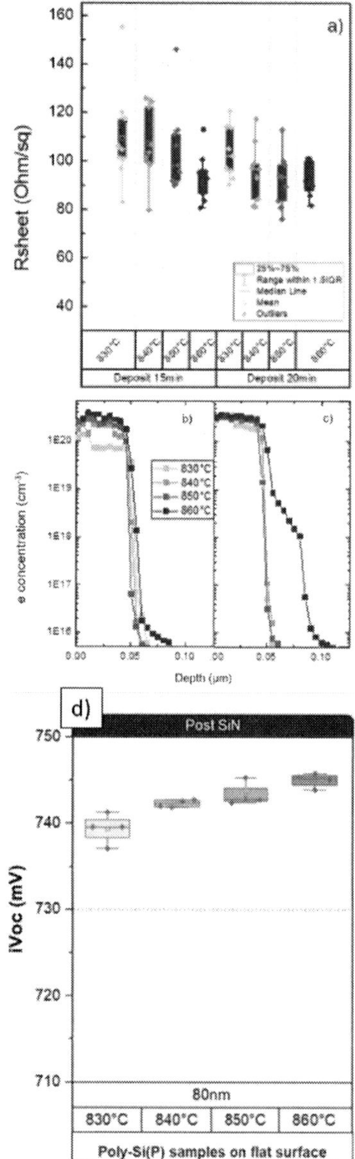

Figure 2: Doping and passivation features of poly-Si (P) structures: (a) R$_{sheet}$ values; and doping profiles (b) for 15min and (c) 20min POCl$_3$ deposit; with (d) i-V$_{oc}$ after SiN$_x$ coating (20min deposit)

As can be noticed from Figure 3, the higher the firing peak temperature, the larger the i-V$_{oc}$ degradation (for both SiN$_x$ and AlO$_x$\SiN$_x$ passivation schemes). In this context,

one can notice that a firing done at low temperature (here 750°C) does not alter passivation, while SiN$_x$ coated samples fired at 810°C features an i-V$_{oc}$ loss of ~70mV, concomitant with a noticeable blistering of SiN$_x$ layer. In addition, i-V$_{oc}$ further drops in time (as observed by measuring the samples after 2 days of storage). This additional passivation degradation is assumed to be caused by an exposition of poly-Si and/or c-Si wafer surface to air, consequently to the aforementioned blistering.

The introduction of the 8nm-thick under layer of AlO$_x$ improves greatly i-V$_{oc}$ stability toward both firing and ageing. When fired at 810°C, AlO$_x$\SiN$_x$-coated structures exhibit an i-V$_{oc}$ loss reduced from 70mV to 15mV. Blistering is also visibly mitigated, and time stability is improved accordingly (see Figure 3). Another approach for stabilizing passivation was investigated, focusing on poly-Si layer rather than upper dielectric stacks. A third batch of SiN$_x$ coated poly-Si (P) / c-Si (n) / poly-Si (P) samples was processed integrating thicker poly-Si layer (110nm). This batch exhibits i-V$_{oc}$ drops limited to 15mV after firing, and also a degradation in time reduced to 5mV. The combination of such 110nm-thick poly layer with AlO$_x$ \ SiN$_x$ appears as a good way to completely stabilize passivation properties of this n-type passivating contact.

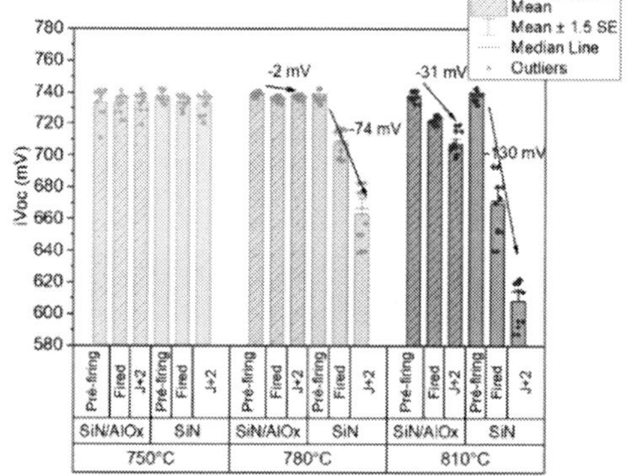

Figure 3: Variation of i-V$_{oc}$ of SiN$_x$ and AlO$_x$\SiN$_x$ coated poly-Si (P) / c-Si (n) / poly-Si (P) structures through firing temperature and storage (2 days).

3.2 Poly-Si (B) results

We fabricated first reference p$^+$/n/p$^+$ samples (i.e. without poly-Si) integrating on both sides a 100 Ohm/sq boron emitter with a 2×10^{19}.cm^{-3} surface boron concentration and a 0.8µm depth. Once passivated by AlO$_x$ \ SiN$_x$ and fired at 790°C, these p$^+$/n/p$^+$ samples reach iV$_{oc}$ of 680mV.

Poly-Si (B) doping profiles obtained from BCl$_3$ diffusions at 850°C, 900°C, 950°C and 990°C are reported in Figure 4, along with reference (i.e. without poly) 100 Ohm/sq emitter profile. BCl$_3$ drive-in temperature has a strong effect on the diffusion depth of boron dopants into c-Si underlying substrate, but hardly affects the active doping in the poly layer itself, that stays at approximately 5×10^{19}cm^{-3} whatever the conditions. As expected, lowering the BCl$_3$ drive-in temperature helps reducing boron diffusion in the c-Si, and sharp optimal diffusion tails are obtained for temperature below 900°C. However, this combination of low active doping in poly-Si layer and sharp diffusion tails in c-Si leads to high sheet resistance values (from ≈400 Ohm/sq to ≈1000 Ohm/sq for respectively 950°C and 850°C boron diffusion) and could potentially cause losses at cell level. A first solution to tackle the issue is the development of specific print technologies for those high sheet resistance structures. A second one would be the use of c-Si (p) bulk materials, as widely published by Fraunhofer ISE with the TOPCoRE solar cells [3].

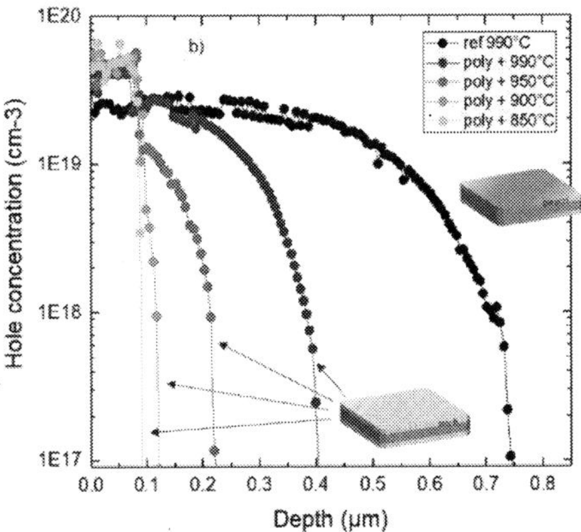

Figure 4: Doping profiles of ex-situ doped poly-Si (B) and reference 100 Ohm/sq diffused emitter (black symbols).

Some good passivation results (not shown here) could be obtained with poly-Si (B) on textured samples (up to 695mV) however reproducibility still need to be improved, some of the samples featuring a peripheral pattern defectivity activated by firing and imaged through PL. By investigating the origin of this pattern, we could evidence that the defect at play was not affecting the wafer bulk since the pattern disappears once poly-Si (B) was chemically etched (after a subsequent re-passivation). Neither the LPCVD nor the BCl₃ diffusion was found to introduce the aforementioned pattern, the latter being more likely the result of an undesired interaction of boron diffusion with the poly-Si / SiO$_x$ stack, presumably causing a disruption / degradation of the underlying tunnel oxide, as evoked in the literature for PECVD poly-Si (B) layers [4]. To check this assumption, and discretize which among boron dopant migration or sole thermal budget is responsible for the supposed SiO$_x$ degradation, another batch of textured samples was fabricated integrating undoped poly-Si / SiO$_x$ on both sides. These samples were either exposed to conventional BCl₃ diffusion (950°C) or exposed to a boron-deprived process featuring the very same thermal budget. The unwanted PL pattern was shown to appear on samples exposed to the boron deprived diffusion cycle, evidencing that temperature alone is already greatly responsible for the tunnel oxide degradation. Two approaches were used with the aim of making tunnel oxide more resistant toward high temperature cycles: the first being an extended oxidation step of 20min-long (against 10min so far); the second consisting in a pre-oxidizing chemistry based on SC2 cleaning. Both approaches provided promising results when applied onto flat surfaces (KOH polished): baseline poly-Si (B) / c-Si (n) / poly-Si (B) structures (with 10min-long oxidation) exhibit i-V$_{oc}$ around 685mV after firing, despite the presence of the PL imaged pattern. Prolonging LPCVD oxidation to 20min did not improve the average i-V$_{oc}$ value but almost suppressed the PL pattern.

Eventually, the combination of chemical oxide with 20min-long LPCVD oxidation permits to suppress the pattern too, but also to improve significantly i-V$_{oc}$ values up to 710mV. When applied to textured samples, this best condition still permits to suppress the PL pattern; nonetheless the best resulting i-V$_{oc}$ (660mV, i.e. a +30mV gain compared to baseline 10min long LPCVD oxidized samples) remains too low for a cell integration.

4 CONCLUSION

The combination of ex-situ doping via low pressure diffusion with LPCVD poly-Si is investigated here for both poly-Si (P) and poly-Si (B) structures, using respectively POCl₃ and BCl₃ diffusion processes. The passivation levels (740mV or more) reached with poly-Si (P) structures on flat surface evidence the good quality of poly-Si deposition and doping processes. The passivation stability to firing required nonetheless further optimizations: SiN$_x$-coated samples exhibited important blistering and i-V$_{oc}$ drop (70mV). Thickening poly-Si to 110nm and replacing SiN$_x$ passivation by an AlO$_x$ \ SiN$_x$ stack were found to stabilize passivation properties of the n-type passivating contact through both firing and time.

The evaluation of poly-Si (B) passivation properties on textured surface resulted in i-V$_{oc}$ values up to 695mV, when BCl₃ diffusion was carried out at a temperature of 900°C onto 80 nm-thick poly-Si layers. Nonetheless we found difficulties reproducing this result, due to the appearance of a defectivity pattern activated through firing, and limiting i-V$_{oc}$ to 630-640mV. This pattern is attributed to a degradation of SiO$_x$ tunnel oxide during BCl₃ diffusion process. Strengthening the oxide by prolonging LPCVD oxidation step permitted to suppress the pattern; and combining it with a chemical pre-oxidation, improved i-V$_{oc}$ on both polished and textured samples. While the i-V$_{oc}$ obtained on flat surface are quite good (710mV), the values measured on textured surfaces (660mV) still need to be improved.

References

[1] J. Hoß, S.S. Kalaghichi, M. Comak, P. Preis, J. Lossen, J.Linke, L. Koduvelikulathu, F. Buchholz, Advanced TOPCon solar cells with vanishing metal induced recombination losses, EPJ Photovolt. 15, 43 (2024). https://doi.org/10.1051/epjpv/2024040

[2] F. Feldmann, M. Simon, M. Bivour, C. Reichel, M. Hermle, S.W. Glunz, Efficient carrier-selective p- and n-contacts for Si solar cells, Sol. Energy Mater. Sol. Cells 131 (2014) 100–104, https://doi.org/10.1016/j.solmat.2014.05.039.

[3] A. Richter, R. Müller, J. Benick, et al. Design rules for high-efficiency both-sides-contacted silicon solar cells with balanced charge carrier transport and recombination losses. Nat Energy 6, 429–438 (2021). https://doi.org/10.1038/s41560-021-00805-w

[4] A. Morisset, R. Cabal, V. Giglia, A. Boulineau, E. De Vito, A. Chabli, S. Dubois, J. Alvarez, J-P. Kleider, Evolution of the surface passivation mechanism during the fabrication of ex-situ doped poly-Si(B)/SiOx passivating contacts for high-efficiency c-Si solar cells, Solar Energy

Materials and Solar Cells, Volume 221, 2021, 110899,
ISSN 0927-0248,
https://doi.org/10.1016/j.solmat.2020.110899.

OVERCOMING PROCESS RELATED LIMITATIONS IN THE CONTEXT OF THE BACK CONTACTED POLYZEBRA SOLAR CELL TECHNOLOGY

Jonathan Linke, Lazhar Rachdi, Sebastian Veerman,
Jan Hoß, Jan Lossen, Lejo Joseph Koduvelikulathu, Florian Buchholz
ISC Konstanz e.V., Rudolf-Diesel-Str. 15, 78467 Konstanz, Germany
Corresponding author: jonathan.linke@isc-konstanz.de

ABSTRACT: TOPCon-based back-contacted silicon solar cells are a bridging technology between current TOPCon industrial standard and future fabrication of high efficient tandem technology. The polyZEBRA concept is such a back-contacted solar cell and promises a lean and cost-effective fabrication. In this contribution, the recent progress in technology optimization is reported, namely the influence of the base resistivity, of an improved screen-printing paste and of the AlO_x deposition technique. The results indicate the usage of high ohmic base material, improved screen-printing paste and of atomic layer deposition for AlO_x passivation. The combined learnings of those aspects lead to a 24.3% efficient champion cell.

Keywords: TBC, polyZEBRA, poly-Si, copper metallization

1 INTRODUCTION

The TOPCon technology is the current mainstream in silicon solar cell production, while many research activities are now focusing on tandem solar cells, which have a significant higher conversion efficiency potential. In the meantime, TOPCon-based back-contacted (TBC) solar cells are an important bridging technology. It has an inherently higher efficiency potential from a higher current due to the absence of optical shading on the front side of the solar cell. However, patterning of the rear side requires advanced technologies and has stronger requirements on process stability.

Successful industrial implementation of TBC solar cells and modules was already achieved by Maxeon SunPower, Aiko and Longi. Naturally, details about their fabrication processes are not available to the public and so the estimation of the actual production costs is difficult. In contrast, the polyZEBRA TBC solar cell production process was published before [1]. It promises a lean and cost-effective process flow that relies on equipment that is already used for industrial mass production such as laser-based patterning of the rear side [2,3] and standard screen-printing technology. Furthermore, it is compatible with screen-printed Cu pastes, which is able to reduce the Ag consumption to <5 mg/W_p [4]. Minimizing the Ag consumption is of high importance as the Ag price is expected to increase in the future as the demand steadily increases with increasing world-wide solar cell production capacity.

This contribution reports about recent progress in optimization of polyZEBRA TBC solar cells since the last publication [5]. In particular, the influence of the base resistivity, of an improved screen-printing paste and of the AlO_x deposition technique is discussed.

2 EXPERIMENTAL

2.1 Cell fabrication and characterization

polyZEBRA solar cells were fabricated according to the process flow reported in [1] and are shown in Figure 1. Cz-grown phosphorous-doped n-type M6 wafers with an initial thickness of 150µm were used. After tunnel oxide growth and LP-CVD poly-Si depositions (Fig. 1, step 1,6), the rear side was patterned by laser ablation of a previously deposited SiN_x mask for the base region (Fig. 1, step 3,4) and laser activation [2,3] of

boron-doped poly-Si for the emitter region (Fig. 1, step 8). After texturing of the front side and the gap region, which separates both polarities (Fig. 1, Step 9), a boron diffusion was applied to form a front-floating emitter (Fig. 1, step 10). For surface passivation of both sides, an AlO_x/SiN_y stack was deposited in a conventional PE-CVD tube furnace (Fig. 1, step 11). The solar cells were contacted by simultaneous screen-printing of Ag-based paste on both polarities and a subsequent fast firing step. The busbars were screen-printed either by Ag or Cu paste (Fig. 1, step 12a/b).

The cells were characterized in a conventional cell flasher (Halm elektronik GmbH), simultaneously recording electroluminescence (EL) images. The properties of the individual regions (base, emitter, gap) were monitored on test structures with squares of several centimeters dimensions to enable standard characterization methods like QSSPC.

3 RESULTS

In the following sections 3.1 - 3.3, the three improvements, namely the optimized base resistivity, screen-printing paste and AlO_x deposition technique, are described in detail. In section 3.4 it is described, how the combination of these improvements lead to the best performing polyZEBRA cell batch so far.

3.1 Base Resistivity

The base resistivity of the wafers used for fabrication of back-contacted solar cells has two contradicting effects [6]: First, with higher base resistivity the bulk lifetime and in turn the J_{sc} increases. And second, with higher base resistivity the internal resistivity increases, which in turn decreases the FF. The optimum of this trade-off has to be determined experimentally and depends among others on the cell concept, patterning layout and wafer quality.

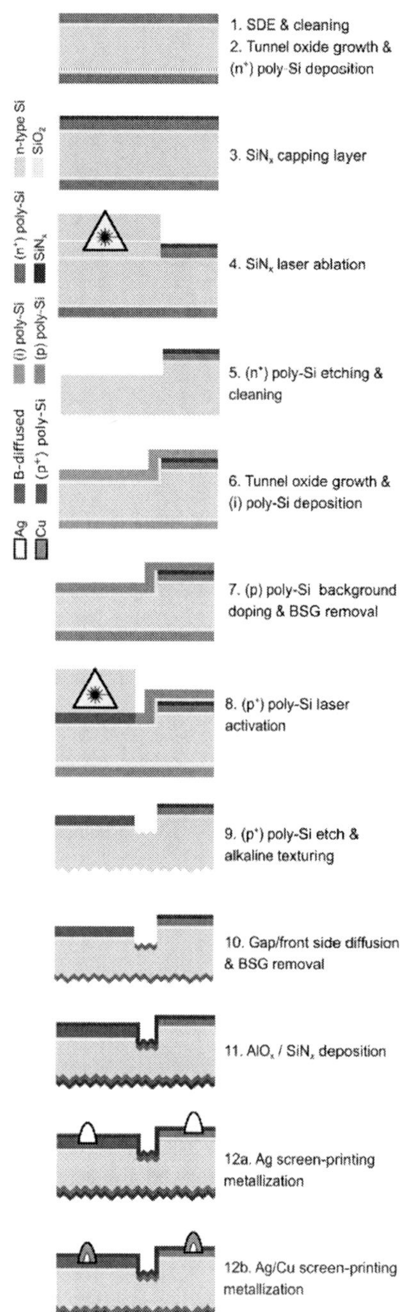

Figure 1: polyZEBRA solar cell fabrication process flow taken from [1].

Figure 2 shows the IV data of polyZEBRA solar cells that were fabricated in the same batch, but on phosphorous-doped Cz wafers with different base resistivities of either 1.25 Ωcm or 5.2 Ωcm. The expected increase in J_{sc} of ~0.5 mA/cm² is clearly visible. However, the FF drops only marginally and so the gain in J_{sc} dominates, which is reflected in the +0.3%abs gain in cell efficiency. It seems that the usage of ~5 Ωcm material is mandatory for high efficiencies.

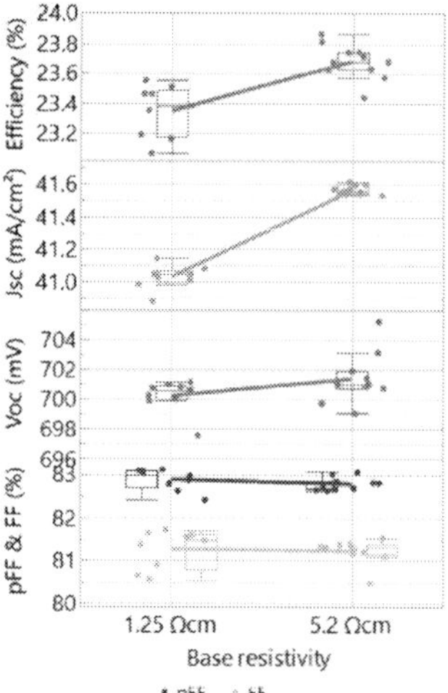

Figure 2: IV measurement data of polyZEBRA solar cells fabricated in the same production batch but on phosphorus-doped n-type M6 wafers with different base resistivity.

3.2 Improved screen-printing paste

For screen-printing of the Ag contacts to the silicon, "paste A" was used for a long time. However, it induced a quite significant metal recombination, visible in the high iV_{oc}-to-V_{oc} loss of 7 mV (Table I, "passivation"). Typical values for TOPCon structures are 1-2 mV. To solve this issue, an improved "paste B" was tested. After optimization of the firing conditions, the iV_{oc}-to-V_{oc} loss was reduced significantly to ~2 mV (Table I, "passivation"), which is a strong indication of vanishing metal recombination. This conclusion of less spiking of the metal through the tunnel oxide is further supported by a higher shunt resistance and +0.4%abs pFF (Table I, "contact").

Table I: Passivation and contact properties of polyZEBRA solar cells fabricated in the same production batch but with different Ag screen-printing pastes for the first layer, which forms the contact to the silicon. Fast-firing conditions were optimized for each paste respectively. The iV_{oc}-to-V_{oc} loss serves as a measure for the metal recombination and the pFF-to-FF loss as a measure for the series resistance.

		Paste A	Paste B
Passivation	PL2V_{oc} cell precursor	716mV	708mV
	V_{oc} cell	709mV	706mV
	iV_{oc}-to-V_{oc} loss	7mV	2mV
Contact	pFF	82.7%	83.1%
	FF	80.3%	81.2%
	pFF-to-FF loss	2.4%	1.9%

At the same time, also the series resistance was reduced, which is reflected in a lower pFF-to-FF loss of 1.9% compared to 2.4% of "paste B" (Table I, "contact"). Since the parameters of all remaining metallization steps were kept the same and these following steps define the grid resistance, the lower series resistance is attributed to a lower contact resistivity. This conclusion is supported by the much smoother EL image of paste B over the whole cell surface (Figure 3).

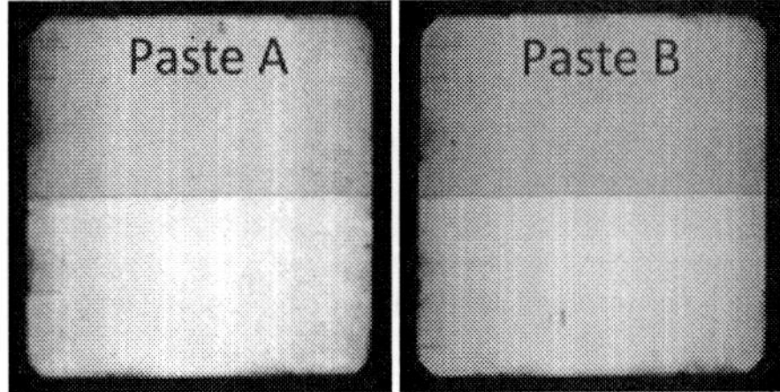

Figure 3: EL images of polyZEBRA solar cells fabricated in the same production batch but with different Ag screen-printing pastes for the first layer, which forms the contact to the silicon. Fast-firing conditions were optimized for each paste respectively.

In this sense, "paste B" is a significant improvement as it decreased the metal recombination and contact resistivity at the same time. However, the potential of this improvement is not fully transferred to the cell efficiency. The firing parameters that were optimized for good electrical performance of paste B, are not optimal for the gap and front side passivation. This is reflected in -8 mV iV_{oc} of not metallized cell precursors compared to precursors that were fired with the parameters optimized for "paste A" (Table I, "passivation"). This effect is even more detrimental than the gain from the lower metal recombination, so that the final V_{oc} of the solar cells is even reduced. However, the +0.9%abs higher FF from lower contact resistivity and higher pFF, overcompensates the loss in V_{oc} and results in an efficiency gain of +0.1%abs (Fig. 4).

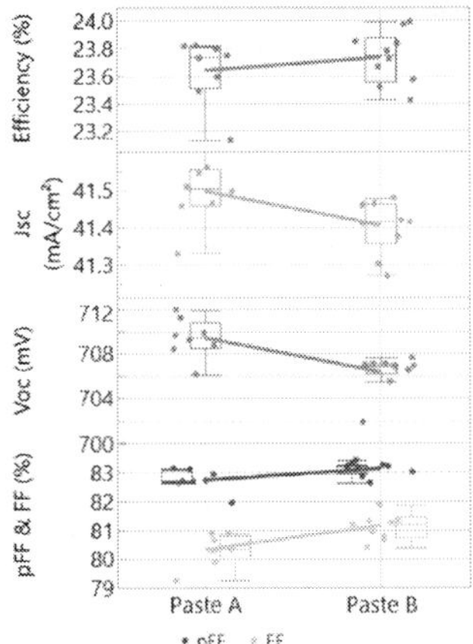

Figure 4: IV measurement data of polyZEBRA solar cells fabricated in the same production batch but with different Ag screen-printing pastes for the first layer, which forms the contact to the silicon. Fast-firing conditions were optimized for each paste respectively.

3.3 AlO$_x$ deposition technique

On the front side of the polyZEBRA solar cells a front floating emitter was formed in a boron diffusion (Fig. 1, step 10), which does also dope the gap region on the rear side. For proper surface passivation, an AlO$_x$/SiN$_y$ stack was deposited on both sides (Fig. 1, step 11). The properties of the AlO$_x$ layers are key for good cell performance for two reasons. First, excellent surface passivation of the front side is mandatory for high cell voltages [6]. And second, since efficient hydrogenation is important for high quality passivation on the rear side, the AlO$_x$ layer must not hinder hydrogen diffusion towards the poly-Si/SiO$_x$ stacks.

Two AlO$_x$ deposition techniques were compared, namely plasma-enhanced chemical vapor deposition (PE-CVD), which was standard method for polyZEBRA cells in the past, and plasema-enhanced atomic layer deposition (PE-ALD). The recipes of each deposition were previously optimized towards high passivation quality. The IV results are shown in Fig. 5. The cells with PE-ALD deposited AlO$_x$ have a 2 mV higher V_{oc}. Test structures with squares of each region showed that this gain originates from a lower J_0 of the (n) poly-Si region. Considering that the AlO$_x$ properties are influencing the penetration of hydrogen [7], this finding points into the direction of a more efficient hydrogen supply from the SiN$_x$ through the AlO$_x$ layer towards the tunnel oxide. Since also the pFF increases by +0.2%abs, it is assumed that the more efficient hydrogen supply through the PE-ALD deposited AlO$_x$ does also improve the bulk lifetime of the wafer.

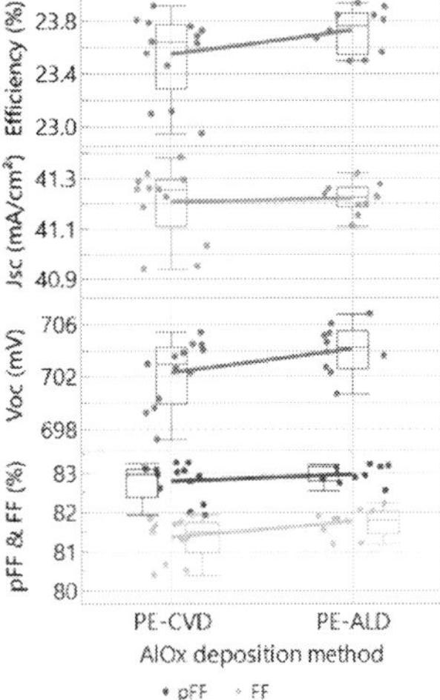

Figure 5: IV measurement data of polyZEBRA solar cells fabricated in the same production batch but with different AlO$_x$ deposition techniques from the same tube furnace.

A second improvement from the PE-ALD deposition compared to the PE-CVD technique is a lower series resistance, which is reflected in a lower pFF-to-FF loss of 1.2%abs compared to 1.4%abs for the PE-CVD deposited AlO$_x$. One explanation for this behavior could be that the screen-printed Ag paste does solve and penetrate the PE-ALD deposited AlO$_x$ more efficient than the PE-CVD deposited AlO$_x$. At least for SiO$_x$ layers it is known, that it has a strong influence on paste penetration and can even block it totally [8].

In sum, the increase in V_{oc} as well as FF from lower series resistance and higher pFF leads to an increase of the cell efficiency of +0.2%abs. This improvement highlights the limitation of the current toolset in our labs. In particular, AlO_x deposition by thermal ALD is expected to further increase the cell efficiency.

3.4 Combination of all improvements

In Section 3.1 the importance of ~5 Ωcm base resistivity was highlighted as optimum of the trade-off between high J_{sc} and FF. In Section 3.2 and 3.3 significant improvements by an improved screen-printing paste and PE-ALD AlO_x deposition, respectively, were shown. Table I shows the IV results of a cell batch that combined all these learnings. In addition, the cells feature Cu busbars, which were screen-printed and afterwards snap-cured in an industrial tool. Replacing the Ag busbars by Cu busbars saved 44% of the total Ag usage.

Table II: Solar cell parameters of a polyZEBRA production batch, that combined all improvements presented in section 3.1–3.3.

	η	J_{sc} (mA/cm²)	V_{oc} (mV)	FF	pFF
Champion cell	24.3%	41.6	711	82.1%	83.7%
Mean	24.0%	41.5	708	81.6%	83.1%
Stdev	0.3%	0.1	3	0.4%	0.4%

The mean cell efficiency was 24.0% with a champion efficiency of 24.3%. This is an improvement of +0.2%abs efficiency compared to the previously published results [1], [5]. The main improvement is a significant increase of the pFF from vanishing metal recombination, thus spiking through the tunnel oxides, and PE-ALD AlO_x deposition. The highest potential remaining for improvement is the V_{oc} of 708 mV, which is quite low considering that both polarities are passivated with poly-Si/SiO_x stacks. As stated in Section 3.2, this low V_{oc} originates mostly from the firing conditions of the improved paste, which are not aligned with the surface passivation of the front side and gap region. This issue is the current focus of further investigations.

4 CONCLUSION

The polyZEBRA TBC solar cell concept has the potential for a lean and cost-effective production. The importance of high ohmic base material was emphasized. Vanishing metal recombination, which is the main advantage of passivating poly-Si/SiO_x contacts, was achieved with an improved paste and adjusted firing settings. However, the front side and gap surface passivation is not yet aligned with this adjusted firing step. Changing from PE-CVD to PE-ALD boosted the cell efficiency and a combination of those improvements yielded a champion cell efficiency of 24.3% on a cell with Cu busbars, wich saved 44% of the total Ag usage. These results are very promising considering the limitations of our labs in comparison to a future production line that is built from scratch.

5 ACKNOWLEDGEMENTS

This work was partly funded by EU's Horizon Europe programme under the grant agreement No. 101084259 (IBC4EU).

6 REFERENCES

[1] J. Linke et al., ">24% Efficient Tunnel Back Contacted polyZEBRA Solar Cells," in *Proc. of 41th European Photovoltaic Solar Energy Conference and Exhibition EUPVSEC*, 020006, 2024, 10.4229/EUPVSEC2024/1AO.6.5.

[2] F. Buchholz et al., "Local Passivating Contacts from Laser Doped p+ Polysilicon," in *Proc. of 38th European Photovoltaic Solar Energy Conference and Exhibition EUPVSEC*, Online, 140–143, 2021, 10.4229/EUPVSEC20212021-2BO.11.3.

[3] S. Sharbaf Kalaghichi, J. Hoß, R. Zapf-Gottwick, and J. H. Werner, "Laser Activation for Highly Boron-Doped Passivated Contacts," *Solar* 3, 362–381, 2023, 10.3390/solar3030021.

[4] N. Chen et al., "Thermal Stable High-Efficiency Copper Screen Printed Back Contact Solar Cells," *Solar RRL* 7 (2), 2200874, 2022, 10.1002/solr.202200874.

[5] J. Linke et al., "24% Efficient TOPCon-Based Back Contacted polyZEBRA Solar Cells," *EPJ Photovoltaics* 16 (8), 2025, 10.1051/epjpv/2024051

[6] P. Verlinden, "Interdigitated Back Contact Solar Cells," in *Photovoltaic Solar Energy*, A. Reinders, P. Verlinden, W. van Sark, and A. Freundlich, Eds., Chichester, UK: John Wiley & Sons, Ltd, 2017, 92–103, 10.1002/9781118927496.ch10.

[7] A. Schmid et al., "On the Role of AlOx Thickness in AlOx/SiNy:H Layer Stacks Regarding Light- and Elevated Temperature-Induced Degradation and Hydrogen Diffusion in c-Si," *IEEE J. Photovolt.* 11 (4), 967–973, 2021, 10.1109/JPHOTOV.2021.3075850.

[8] R. Glatthaar et al., "Silver Metallization with Controlled Etch Stop Using SiO_x Layers in Passivating Contacts for Improved Silicon Solar Cell Performance," *Solar RRL* 7 (21), 2300491, 2023, 10.1002/solr.202300491.

Overcoming Process Related Limitations of the BC polyZEBRA Solar Cell Technology

Jonathan Linke, Lazhar Rachdi, Sebastian Veerman, Jan Hoß, Jan Lossen, Lejo Joseph Koduvelikulathu, Florian Buchholz

ISC Konstanz e.V., Rudolf-Diesel-Str. 15, 78467 Konstanz, Germany
jonathan.linke@isc-konstanz.de / +49-7531-36183-362

Overview

- Integration of TOPCon technology in IBC cells
- polyZEBRA concept with both polarities TOPCon-structures, patterned by laser processes[1,2]
- Previously reported champion cell efficiency 24.1% and simulated efficiency potential >25%[3]
- Recent improvements presented here

Takeaways

- Vanishing metal recombination with improved paste
- Integration of PE-ALD AlO_x improves V_{oc}/pFF/FF
- High base resistivity ~5Ωcm mandatory for high efficiency
- Combination of all learnings enables 24.3% champion cell efficiency
- Champion cell with screen-printed Cu-BBs
  → Ag consumption reduced by 44%

polyZEBRA fabrication process[3]

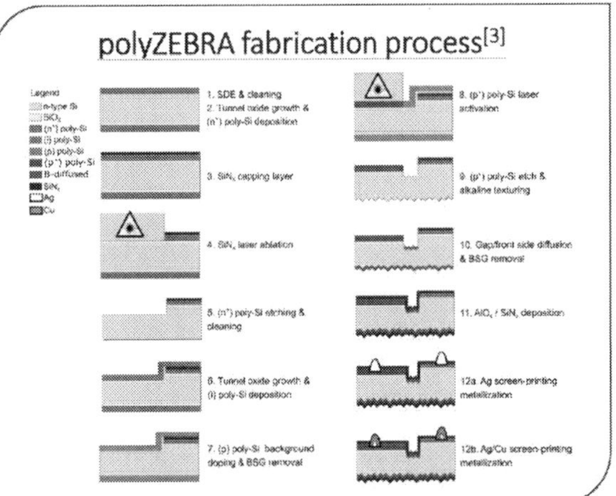

Improved screen-printing paste

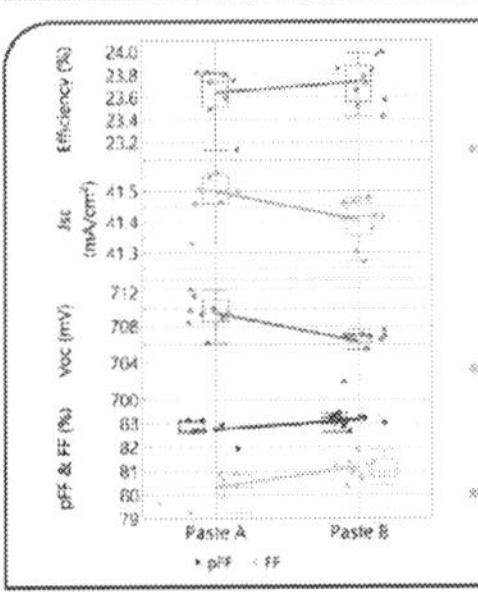

- Vanishing metal recombination with paste B:
  - Barely measurable iV_{oc}-to-V_{oc} loss
  - Higher R_{shunt}, pFF
    (→ less spiking through tunnel oxide)
- Better contact of paste B (lower pFF-to-FF loss)
  → EL image smoother
- Poor precursors from paste B firing parameters, which degrade front side passivation

		Paste A	Paste B
Passivation	PL2V_{oc} cell precursor	716mV	708mV
Passivation	V_{oc} cell	709mV	706mV
Passivation	iV_{oc}-to-V_{oc} loss	7mV	2mV
Contact	pFF	82.7%	83.1%
Contact	FF	80.3%	81.2%
Contact	pFF-to-FF loss	2.4%	1.9%

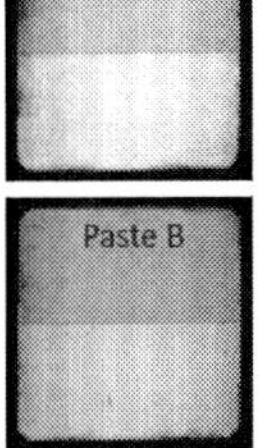

AlO_x deposition technique

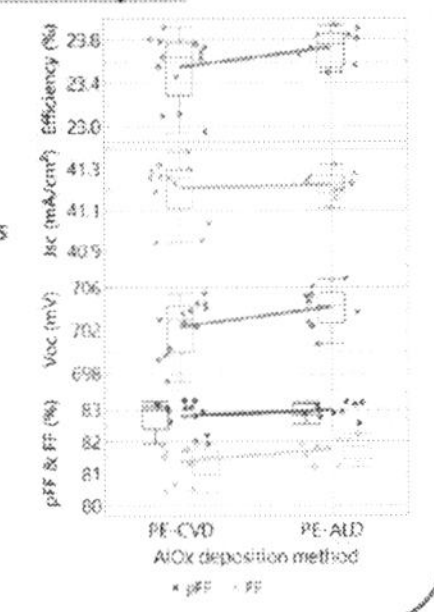

- AlO_x deposition techniques from same tube furnace: PE-CVD, PE-ALD
- PE-ALD AlO_x with superior ...
  - ... hydrogenation of (n) poly-Si/SiO_x structures → +2mV V_{oc}
  - ... series resistance, pFF → +0.4% FF
  - ... efficiency +0.2%
- → PE-ALD AlO_x more penetrable for hydrogen and paste

Base resistivity

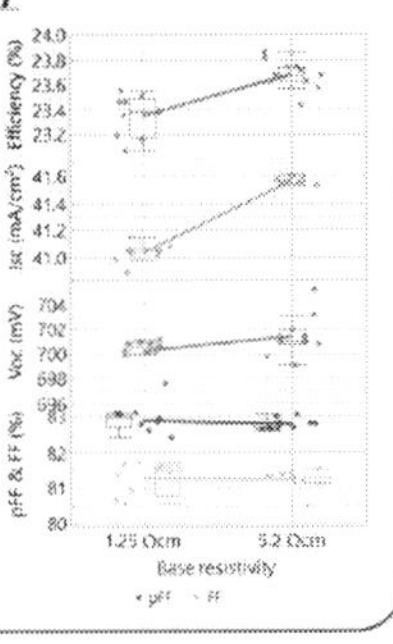

- Theory:
  Towards higher base resistivity, increasing J_{sc} (higher bulk lifetime), but decreasing FF (higher internal resistivity)[4]
- Experiment:
  Base resistivity 1.25 → 5.2Ωcm
  - J_{sc} +0.5mA/cm²
  - FF only slight decrease
  - → +0.3% efficiency

Combination of improvements

	η	J_{sc} (mA/cm²)	V_{oc} (mV)	FF	pFF
Champion cell	24.3%	41.6	711	82.1%	83.7%
Mean ± stdev	24.0 ± 0.3%	41.5 ± 0.1	708 ± 3	81.6 ± 0.4%	83.1 ± 0.4%

- Best polyZEBRA cell batch so far
- Champion cell efficiency +0.2% compared to previous reported data[3]
- Main gain in pFF (thus FF) from improved paste and PE-ALD AlO_x
- With screen-printed Cu-BB, cured on industrial laminator tool
  → Ag consumption reduced by 44%

References

[1] F. Buchholz et al., Proc. EUPVSEC 2021, 140-143
[2] J. Linke et al., Proc. WCPEC 2022, 102-106
[3] J. Linke et al., Proc. EUPVSEC 2024, 020006
[4] P. Verlinden, in Photovoltaic Solar Energy, John Wiley & Sons, Ltd, 2017, pp. 92–103.

Acknowledgements

This work was partly funded by EU's Horizon Europe programme under the grant agreement No. 101084259

020036-001

ADVANCING TOPCON SILICON SOLAR CELLS WITH LASER-GROOVED BURIED CONTACT TECHNOLOGY

Mohammad Hossein Mohammadi [*a], Roberto Boccardi [b], Io Mizushima [c], Irene Tosi [c], Gisele Alves dos Reis Benatto [b],
Peter Behrensdorff Poulsen [b], Torben Tang [c], Sune Thorsteinsson [b], Rasmus Schmidt Davidsen [a]
[a] Department of Electrical and Computer Engineering, Aarhus University, 8200, Denmark
[b] DTU Electro, Technical University of Denmark, 2800 Kgs. Lyngby, Denmark
[c] IPU P/S, Virum, Denmark

ABSTRACT: The integration of the TOPCon structure with Cu-plated metallization and laser-grooved BC technology is a new and untested combination in crystalline silicon solar cell design. This approach will likely leverage the excellent passivation and carrier selectivity of TOPCon to minimize recombination losses and enhance power conversion efficiency (PCE). Cu plating, known for its high conductivity and low cost, reduces resistive losses while supporting sustainability due to the well-known Ag scarcity. Laser ablation enables precise and repeatable groove formation, creating a highly efficient top surface with minimal losses. The narrow metal lines of buried contacts potentially reduce shading losses and finger resistance. This innovation addresses key challenges like shading, parasitic resistance, and cost, while being suitable for advanced applications.
Keywords: TOPCon, Cu-plated metallization, buried contact (BC), laser-grooved BC technology

1 INTRODUCTION

Global solar PV installations are expanding rapidly, with total installed capacity rising by over 30% in 2023 [1]. A key sustainability challenge for solar cells lies in the limited availability of silver (Ag): at the current consumption rate, the PV sector could deplete 85–98% of existing Ag reserves by 2050, with even higher demand expected under scenarios of accelerated n-type cell adoption [2]. As a result, copper (Cu), which is more affordable and abundant, is being explored as an alternative for metallization. This is typically achieved through electroplating, with a nickel (Ni) barrier layer applied to prevent Cu diffusion into silicon in the metallized regions [3], since copper can form recombination centers within the bandgap [1-4].

Among high-efficiency PV technologies, tunnel oxide passivated contact (TOPCon) cells have been extensively investigated for copper plating metallization. In most reported approaches, the passivation layers are selectively opened on both sides using laser contact opening (LCO), exposing the underlying p-type crystalline silicon and n-type polycrystalline silicon. Electroplating of Ni/Cu is then carried out on each side sequentially, followed by immersion plating of a silver capping layer [4].

The integration of buried contact (BC) technology, where grooves are precisely formed using laser ablation, further optimizes the solar cell design [5]. Laser processing ensures high precision and repeatability, enabling the creation of well-defined grooves that serve as pathways for plated metal contacts [6, 7]. This technology drastically reduces shading losses and enhances light absorption by confining metal contacts to the grooves [8, 9]. Unlike conventional screen-printed contacts, the BC structure achieves a high metal aspect ratio, allowing for densely spaced fingers with minimal shading loss [10]. This innovation reduces emitter and grid resistance while leveraging Cu low resistivity to improve overall conductivity. Furthermore, the inclusion of a self-aligned, selective emitter in the BC design minimizes contact recombination and supports higher open-circuit voltages. Together, these features enable efficiency improvements compared to traditional screen-printed solar cells, while also reducing parasitic resistance and enabling low-cost electricity generation.

The synergy of the TOPCon structure, Cu-plated metallization, and laser-formed BC technology presents a robust pathway toward high-efficiency and cost-effective solar cells. This integration not only addresses current performance limitations but also offers scalable solutions for advanced photovoltaic systems, paving the way for more sustainable and economical solar energy production.

2 EXPERIMENTAL

Standard TOPCon precurses were received comprising of the standard TOPCon structure as outlined in Fig. 1. The precursors will further be laser processed using a 'microSTRUCT' laser micromachining tool from 3D-Micromac AG. The aim is to produce laser grooves with maximum depth and minimum width for buried contacts. The tool is equipped with a 50 W picosecond laser capable of emitting light at three wavelengths: 355 nm, 532 nm, and 1064 nm, with a pulse repetition rate ranging from 200 kHz to 8000 kHz. Initially, the green laser (λ=532 nm) with a picosecond pulse duration was utilized. The laser source emitted pulses with a duration of 10 ps in TEM00 mode. The scanning speed was set to 300 mm/min, and the laser pulse repetition rate ranged from a single shot to 200 kHz. Additionally, both the laser power and the number of scanning passes were adjustable. To reduce the width of each groove, the laser source was switched from green (532 nm) to red (355 nm) while keeping all other parameters unchanged. The samples are electrically connected to a non-submerged contacting pin at the "electroplating spot" and vertically immersed in the Cu electrolyte solution to approximately 75% of their length for 5–10 minutes. The finalized cells are subsequently characterized using scanning electron microscopy (SEM), optical microscopy, and profilometry.

3 RESULTS AND DISSCUSIONS

First, we examine how the power and repetition in laser can affect the surface properties and groove quality as well as depth during the laser grooving process on TOPCon. The experiments utilized a 532 nm green laser and a 355 nm UV laser on a TOPCon under varying repetition rates. A SEM, optical profilometer, and optical microscopy are employed to assess surface features,

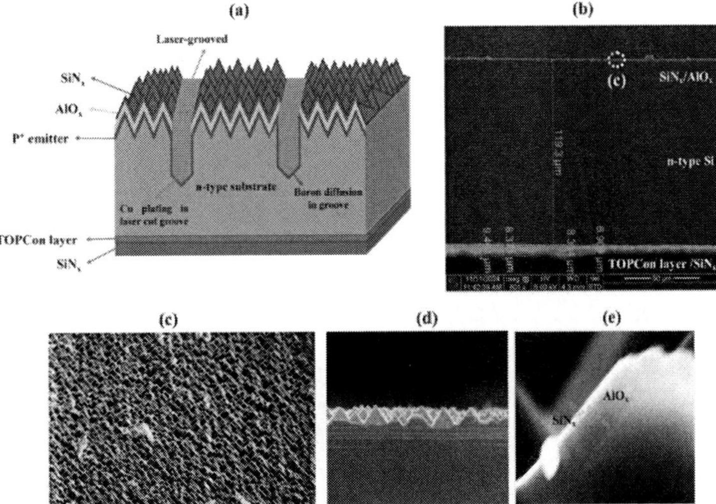

Fig.1. (a) schematic of BC structure with the laser grooved filled out plated Cu. (b), (c), (d) and (e) SEM images of TOPCon surface solar cell before laser scribing.

groove quality, groove profile, and the groove's width and depth. results in more refined and deeper grooves, which is beneficial for improving metallization quality, electrical contact, and ultimately the efficiency of the solar cell. Fig. 2 presents the SEM images of the laser-formed grooves, highlighting the ablation area and visible laser-induced damage. The extent of surface modifications and defects caused by the laser process can be clearly observed. The effect of the number of laser passes on the groove morphology is shown in Fig. 2. With 30 passes, the grooves remain shallow and insufficient to fully penetrate the passivation layer, resulting in incomplete contact opening. At 50 passes, the grooves reach greater depth, but localized damage in the underlying silicon becomes visible, which could negatively affect the electrical performance by introducing defect sites. Increasing the number of passes to 70 and 80 produces grooves with larger depth and width, creating well-defined openings that are more suitable for subsequent metallization steps. However, when the number of passes is further increased to 100, excessive ablation occurs, leading to over-etching and significant structural damage at the groove edges. These observations suggest that while higher numbers of passes improve groove definition, excessive laser exposure compromises surface quality, emphasizing the need to optimize the number of passes to balance sufficient contact opening with minimal substrate damage. Optical microscopy images of the grooves formed with different

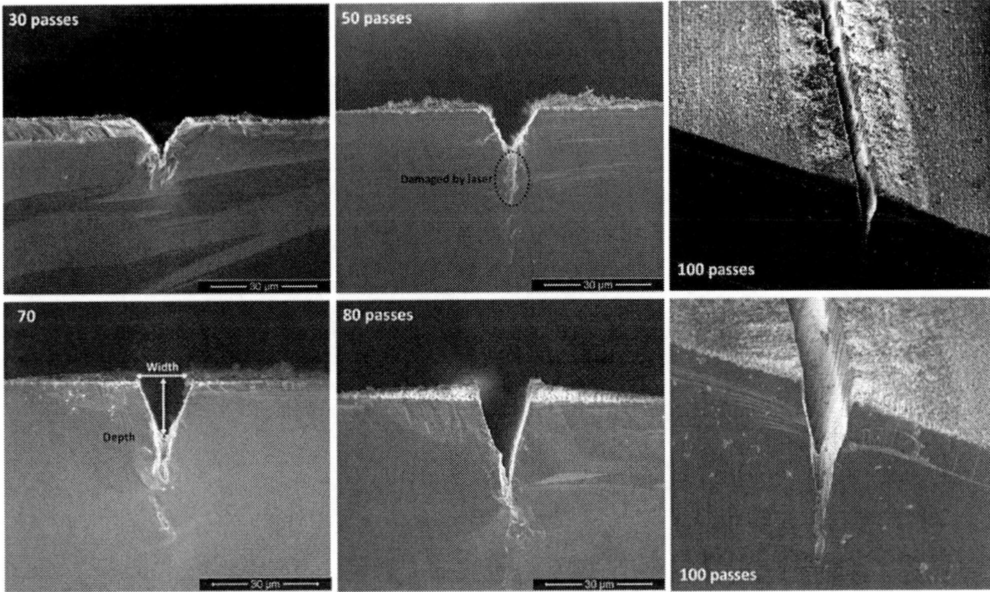

Fig.2. SEM images of the groove profiles resulting from different number of passes (30, 50, 70, 80 and 100).

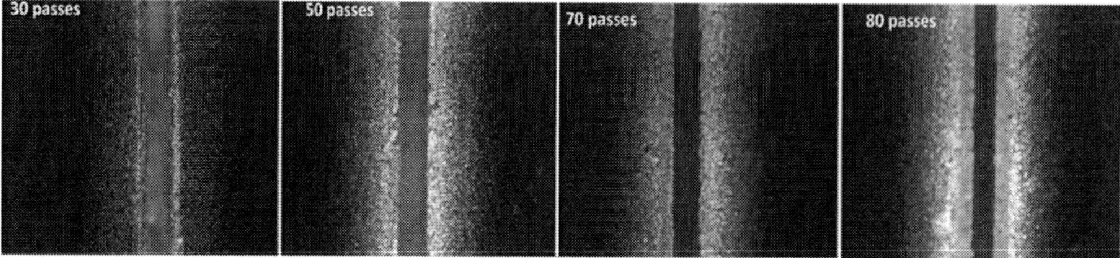

Fig.3. Optical microscope images (top view) of laser-formed grooves on a TOPCon solar cell with varying laser passes (30, 50, 70, 80 and 100 passes).

numbers of laser passes are shown in Fig. 3. At 30 passes, the groove appears narrow and irregular, with incomplete removal of the passivation layer. Increasing to 50 passes results in a more continuous and defined groove, though some surface roughness remains visible along the edges. At 70 passes, the groove becomes wider and cleaner, with more uniform sidewalls compared to lower pass counts. With 80 passes, the groove shows the best definition, exhibiting a well-opened channel with reduced debris accumulation at the edges. These results are consistent with the SEM observations, confirming that higher numbers of passes improve groove opening; however, excessive passes, as previously noted, may also introduce damage. Thus, an intermediate range between 70 and 80 passes appears optimal for achieving clean and well-defined contact openings. Fig. 4 presents the groove depth profiles obtained under different laser conditions. For the 533 nm wavelength at 2.6 W and 200 kHz (left), the groove depth increases with the number of repetitions, ranging from ~3 µm at a single pass to ~8.3 µm at eight repetitions. The profiles also reveal a progressive broadening of the groove with higher repetition numbers, indicating cumulative material removal but also the onset of thermal effects that may degrade edge sharpness. In contrast, for the 355 nm wavelength at 1.3 W and 200 kHz (right), the groove depth is more strongly dependent on the number of passes. Depth increases from ~10 µm at 30 passes to ~35 µm at 100 passes, showing a nearly linear trend up to higher pass counts. Compared to the 533 nm case, the 355 nm laser provides deeper and narrower grooves, reflecting more efficient material ablation at the shorter wavelength. These results suggest that while both

laser parameters can achieve selective passivation opening, UV wavelengths offer higher precision and deeper penetration, whereas visible wavelengths provide shallower and wider grooves, potentially more prone to surface damage. The morphology of the grooves after Cu electroplating is presented in Fig. 5. SEM cross-sections reveal that copper successfully deposits along the vertical walls of the laser-etched grooves, forming a relatively uniform layer with thickness values in the range of ~1.18–1.57 µm (Fig. 5c). This indicates effective nucleation and growth of copper within the recessed regions, ensuring electrical continuity along the contact opening. However, in addition to sidewall coverage, significant copper accumulation is observed at the top edges of the grooves (Fig. 5d), with lateral overgrowth reaching thicknesses of ~6–7 µm. Such overplanting may increase series resistance due to uneven current distribution and could interfere with subsequent capping or passivation steps. These results suggest that while electroplating enables conformal filling of grooves, optimization of plating parameters is required to minimize excessive deposition at the groove edges while ensuring sufficient coverage inside the contact region.

4   SUMMERY AND FUTURE WORK

This study investigated the combination of TOPCon structures with BC technology through laser grooving and Cu-based metallization. The results confirmed that groove morphology is highly sensitive to laser wavelength, power, and number of passes. Optical, SEM, and profilometry analyses showed that increasing passes

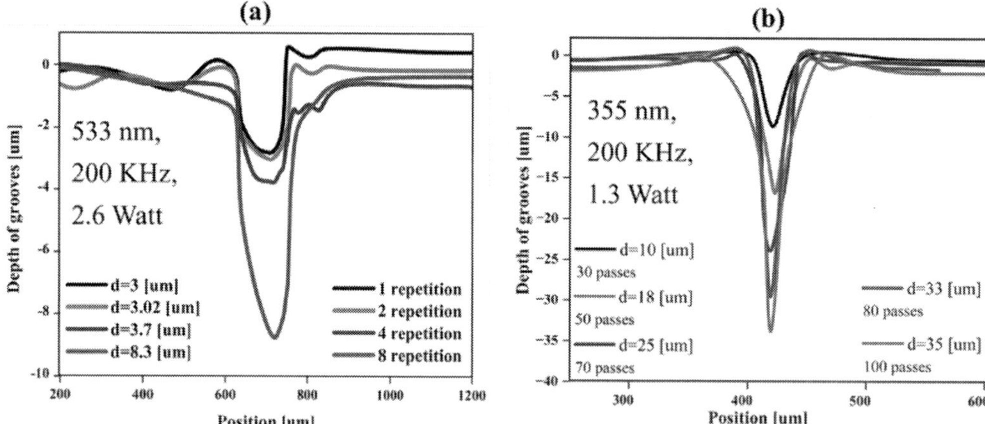

Fig.4. Optical profilometer measurements of laser-formed grooves on a TOPCon solar cell with varying laser passes (30, 50, 70, 80 and 100 passes) for two different wavelengths (a) 533 nm and (b) 355 nm, respectively.

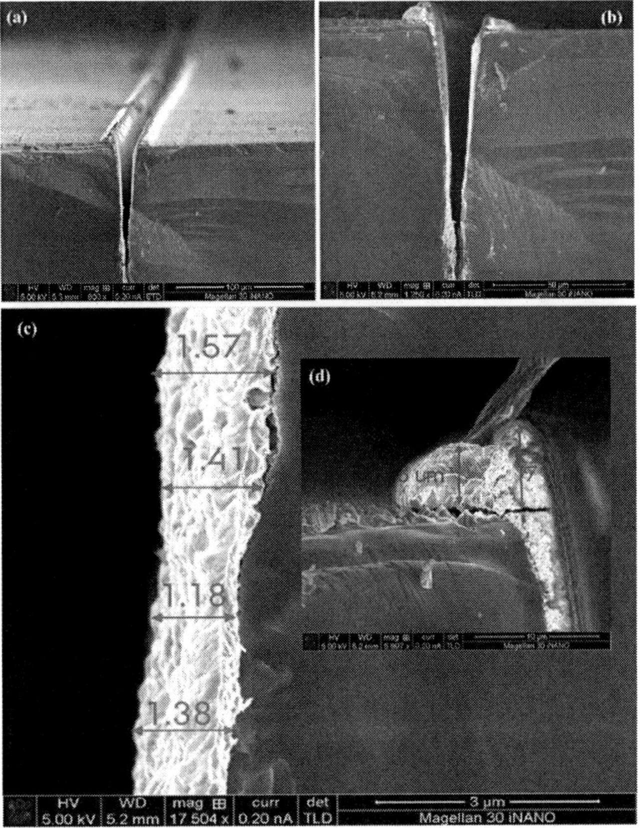

Fig. 5. (a) SEM images of laser-opened grooves after Cu electroplating. (b) Cross-sectional views of the groove showing copper deposition along the walls. (c) Magnified SEM image highlighting Cu coverage inside the groove, with deposited layer thickness ranging from ~1.18 to 1.57 μm. (d) SEM image of copper accumulation on top of the groove, indicating lateral overgrowth with thicknesses of ~6–7 μm.

improves depth and definition, though excessive ablation can introduce surface damage. The 355 nm wavelength produced narrower, deeper grooves than 532 nm, offering better prospects for fine-line contacts. Ni/Cu plating effectively filled the grooves, but challenges such as copper overgrowth at groove edges and uniformity along sidewalls remain.

Future work will concentrate on optimizing laser parameters to balance groove quality with minimal damage, improving plating chemistry to enhance adhesion and conformity, and assessing the electrical performance of complete devices. Long-term stability studies will also be undertaken to evaluate copper diffusion and durability. With these refinements, the BC–TOPCon approach has strong potential to deliver scalable, high-efficiency, and cost-effective crystalline silicon solar cells.

5 SCIENTIFIC INNOVATION AND RELEVANCE

Ni/Cu electroplated metallization, when integrated with laser-grooved buried contacts in TOPCon structures, offers a strong alternative to conventional screen-printed Ag. The laser process enables precise and repeatable formation of narrow, deep grooves that act as conductive pathways for the plated metals. This approach not only minimizes the front metalized area, thereby reducing shading and enhancing light absorption, but also ensures low series resistance due to the high conductivity of Cu. Conducting metallization on both sides further streamlines the process, while maintaining the integrity of the TOPCon stack. Together, the synergy of laser structuring and Ni/Cu plating provides a scalable route toward improving device performance and addressing sustainability challenges linked to silver scarcity.

6 ACKNOLOWDGNENT

This research is financially supported by the CuSun project, funded by the Energy Technology Development and Demonstration Program (EUDP) in Denmark, under grant number 640231-510356.

7 COMPETING INTREST

The authors declare no competing interests.

8 REFERENCES

[1] G. Masson, E. Bosch, A. Van Rechem and M. de l'Epine, "Task 1 strategic PV analysis and outreach– 2024 snapshot of global PV markets ", Report IEA-PVPS T1-42:2024, 2024, p. 11.

[2] B. Hallam, M. Kim, Y. Zhang, L. Wang, A. Lennon, P. Verlinden, P.P. Altermatt and P.R. Dias, "The silver learning curve for photovoltaics and projected silver demand for net-zero emissions by 2050 ", in Progress in Photovoltaics: Research and Applications, vol. 31, i. 6, pp. 598–606, 2023.

[3] R. Sakakibara, A. Lachowicz, J. Hurni, C. Allebé, B. Paviet-Salomon, F.-J. Haug, C. Ballif, A. Hessler-Wyser and Y. Xiang, "Investigating interfacial phenomena in copper-covered, n-type polysilicon-based contacts by electron microscopy ", EU PVSEC 2024, 2024.

[4] B. Grübel, S. Kluska, G. Cimiotti, C. Schmiga, V. Arya, B. Steinhauser, B. S. Goraya, S. Nold, M. Hermle, M. Kamp, M. Passig, M. Sieber and D. Brunner, "Plating metallization for bifacial i-TOPCon silicon solar cells ", SiliconPV 2021, 2022.

[5] B. Richards, "Comparison of TiO2 and other dielectric coatings for buried-contact solar cells: a review," Progress in photovoltaics: research and applications, vol. 12, no. 4, pp. 253-281, 2004.

[6] T. Crawford, A. Borowiec, and H. Haugen, "Femtosecond laser micromachining of grooves in silicon with 800 nm pulses," Applied Physics A, vol. 80, pp. 1717-1724, 2005.

[7] T. Ner, P. Rana, and D. Marla, "Pulsed laser grooving of silicon under different ambient media," Lasers in Manufacturing and Materials Processing, vol. 10, no. 4, pp. 626-644, 2023.

[8] Y. H. Cho, A. Ebong, E. Cho, D. Kim, and S. Lee, "Advanced buried contact solar cell structure," Solar energy materials and solar cells, vol. 48, no. 1-4, pp. 173-177, 1997.

[9] J. H. Guo, P. J. Cousins, and J. E. Cotter, "Investigations of parasitic shunt resistance in n-type buried contact solar cells," Progress in Photovoltaics: Research and Applications, vol. 14, no. 2, pp. 95-105, 2006.

[10] S. Wenham, "Buried-contact silicon solar cells," Progress in photovoltaics: research and applications, vol. 1, no. 1, pp. 3-10, 1993.

Advancing TOPCon Silicon Solar Cells with Laser-Grooved Buried Contact Technology

Mohammad Hossein Mohammadi [*a], Roberto Boccardi [b], Io Mizushima [c], Irene Tosi [c], Gisele Alves dos Reis Benatto [b], Peter Behrensdorff Poulsen [b], Torben Tang [c], Sune Thorsteinsson [b], Rasmus Schmidt Davidsen [a]

[1]Department of Electrical and Computer Engineering, Aarhus University, 8200, Denmark
[2]DTU Electro, Technical University of Denmark, 2800 Kgs. Lyngby, Denmark
[c] IPU P/S, Virum, Denmark

Department of Electrical and Computer Engineering

1CV.2.10-291

Introduction

- ❖ TOPCon's thin SiO_x between Si and poly-Si provides strong passivation and carrier selectivity, reducing recombination and raising V_{oc} and efficiency.
- ❖ Cu/Ni plated metallization forms fine, low-resistance grids at low temperatures, preserving TOPCon layers while providing high conductivity and enabling scalable, cost-effective manufacturing.
- ❖ Laser-grooved buried contacts confine plated metal, reducing shading and boosting absorption, while high-aspect-ratio fingers and a self-aligned selective emitter minimize contact and grid resistance.
- ❖ Integrating TOPCon, Cu-plated metallization, and laser-grooved BC reduces recombination, resistive, and optical losses, offering a robust, cost-effective route to next-generation high-efficiency c-Si solar cells.

AIM AND APPROACH

- ❖ Advance the efficiency and scalability of crystalline silicon solar cells by integrating the TOPCon, Cu plated metallization, and laser-grooved buried contacts; burying the metal reduces resistive and optical losses.
- ❖ Develop and optimize a UV laser scribing process for form narrow, deep grooves for buried front contacts on TOPCon.
- ❖ Define robust process grooves (laser power, pulse repetition rate, scan speed, and pass count) that produce groove geometries compatible with Cu plated for metallization, enabling low series resistance and low contact recombination.
- ❖ Key challenges are laser-scribing high-aspect-ratio, low-roughness grooves for buried contacts without harming the crystalline silicon and then achieving uniform, void-free Cu plating with a reliable Ni seed/barrier.

Experimental Setup

- ❖ Sample Preparation
- ➤ For front-side preparation, silicon wafers were textured in KOH and the boron emitter was formed by high-temperature BBr_3 diffusion.
- ➤ For rear stack formation, the rear surface was polished; 85 nm boron-doped poly-Si was deposited; a silicon oxide film was grown at 1000 °C in ozone; AlO_x was deposited by ALD and activated by a 450 °C anneal.
- ➤ For final coatings, SiNx was deposited on both sides by PECVD.

- ❖ Laser Parameters
- ➤ Tool / type: 3D-Micromac microSTRUCT picosecond laser micromachining system.
- ➤ Output power: 50 W.
- ➤ Wavelengths available: 355 nm, 532 nm, 1064 nm (initially used 532 nm; later switched to 355 nm to narrow groove width).
- ➤ Pulse duration: 10 ps, pulse repetition rate: 200 kHz and scanning speed: 300 mm/min.
- ➤ Adjustable parameters: laser power and number of scanning passes (kept unchanged when switching to 355 nm).

- ❖ Characterization Tools
- ➤ Optical microscopic: Surface morphology
- ➤ SEM: cross section morphology, line widths
- ➤ Profilometric: measure the roughness and depth

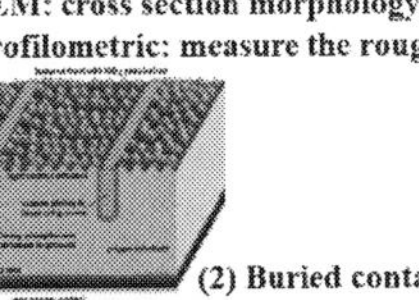

(1) TOPCon sample

(3) Laser device

(2) Buried contact structure

Results

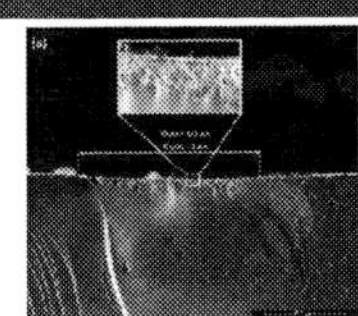

(4) Laser parameters: 532 nm, 200 KHz, 2.6 Watt
(a) 1 repetition and (b) 8 repetition

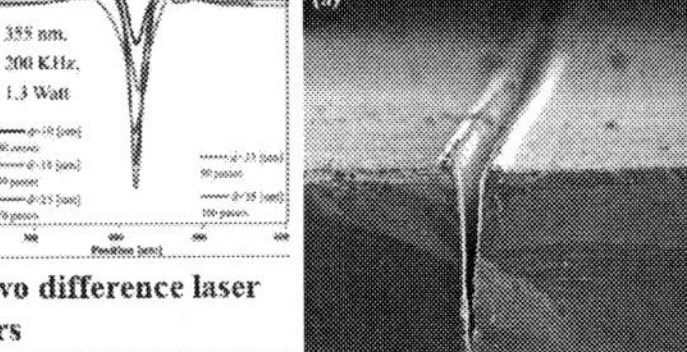

(7) Depth of groove with two difference laser parameters

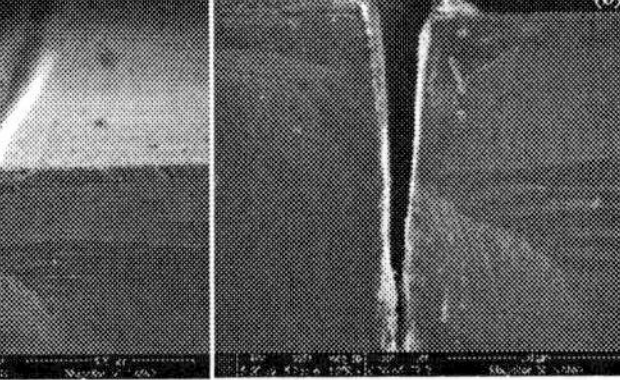

(10) SEM of groove after Cu plating

(5) SEM of groove with laser parameters : 355 nm, 200 KHz, 1.3 Watt, (a) 30, 50, 70, 80, 100 repetition

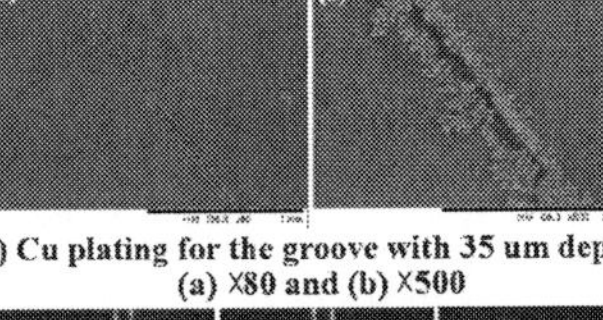

(8) Cu plating for the groove with 35 um depth
(a) X80 and (b) X500

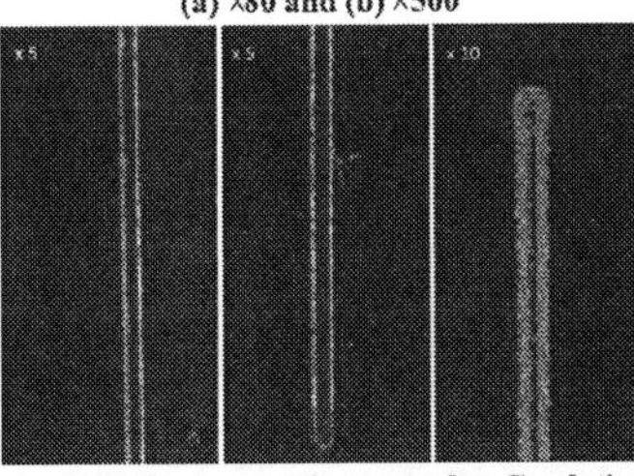

(9) Optical microscopy of groove after Cu plating

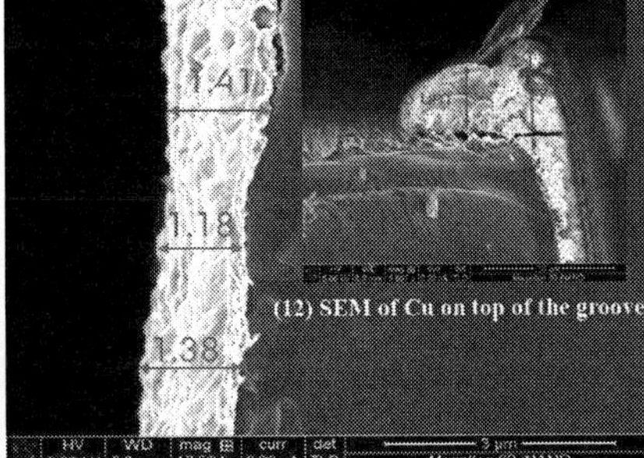

(12) SEM of Cu on top of the groove

(6) Optical microscopy, x50 magnification

(11) SEM of Cu inside groove plated on the wall of groove

Conclusions

- ❖ Combining TOPCon, laser-grooved buried contacts (BC), and Ni/Cu-plated metallization shows promising efficiency gains over conventional c-Si cells.
- ❖ TOPCon passivation and carrier selectivity suppress recombination at critical interfaces.
- ❖ Ni/Cu-plated metallization delivers high conductivity, lowering series resistance and supporting higher fill factor.
- ❖ Power, repetition rate, and wavelength set groove depth/width parameters that strongly govern BC performance.
- ❖ Narrow buried metal lines minimize front contact area, boosting light absorption and reducing shading losses enabling higher PCE.

Scientific Innovation

- ➤ Innovative Integration of TOPCon with Cu-Plated, Laser-Grooved Buried
- ➤ Silver-Saving Cu Metallization with TOPCon: Low-Loss, High-PCE c-Si Cells
- ➤ Reducing Recombination, Shading, and Resistance via TOPCon & Cu Buried Contacts

Acknowledgements

➤ Energy Technology Development and Demonstration Program (EUDP) in Denmark (CuSun , No. 640231-510356)

Collaborators:

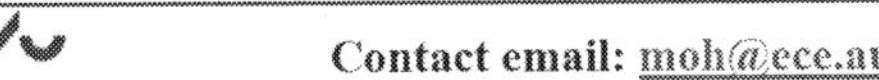

Funding:

Contact email: moh@ece.au.dk

AARHUS UNIVERSITY

Local Edge Passivation of Laser Scribed Shingle Cells for Compensating Cut Losses

Dheeraj Sah[1*], Karolis Parfeniukas[2], Roberto Boccardi[3], Narendra Bandaru[1], Agata Lachowicz[4]
Benjamin Borie[2], Mira Baraket[2], Maksym Plakhotnyuk[2], Gisele Benatto[3], Sune Thorsteinsson[3],
Peter B. Poulsen[3], Rasmus Schmidt Davidsen[1]

[1]Department of Electrical and Computer Engineering (ECE), Aarhus University, Denmark
[2]ATLANT 3D, Maarkaervej 2B, 2630 Taastrup, Denmark
[3]Technical University of Denmark (DTU), Department of Electrical and Photonics Engineering, Denmark
[4]CSEM, Switzerland
*dsah@ece.au.dk

Introduction

- Cutting full cell into half or small bits results in lower resistive losses, however, during cutting new defects and recombination centers generated at fresh edges results in lower lifetime and cell parameters[1]

- Covering the defected edges with dielectric layers helps to lower the losses by minimizing the dangling bond density at these edges[2,3]

- Combining high efficiency silicon cell architectures like tunnel oxide passivated contact (TOPCon), heterojunction thin film (HJT) with novel edge passivation techniques may help to achieve high module efficiencies with shingling concept

Objectives

- Key objective of the present work is **"Local Edge Passivation"**
Local edge passivation i.e. depositing passivation layer in and around the edges only. Here, it is achieved by innovative **"Direct Atomic Layer Processing (DALP)®"** using NANOFABRICATOR® Lite tool developed by ATLANT 3D[4]

- Testing of TiO_2 as edge passivating material for TOPCon solar cells

Schematic of TOPCon cell   Conventional edge passivation approach   Local edge passivation Approach

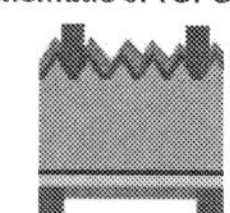

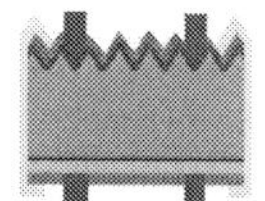

Experiment

- Non metallized industrial size (182 mm × 184 mm) TOPCon cells cut into small pieces of size 25 mm × 50 mm using laser scribing and mechanical cleaving

- 50 nm TiO_2 passivating layer at 150℃ is deposited using DALP® around the edges only, with TTIP and water as the precursor

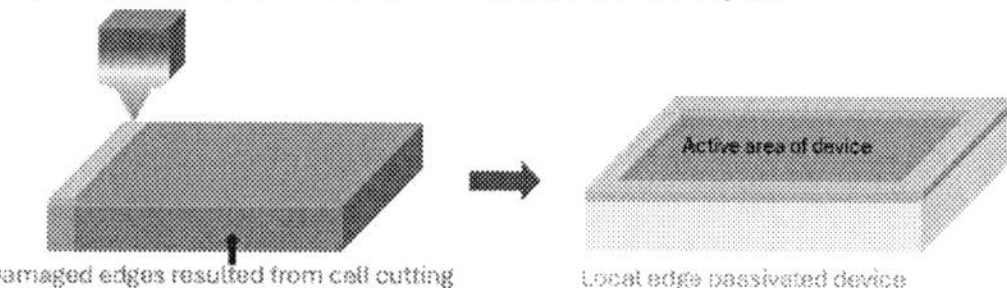

- Edge passivated samples are then annealed at 180℃, 200 ℃,215℃ for 10 minutes each

- 6 non passivated samples are also annealed at various temperature conditions to understand the impact of passivation layer on device lifetime

- MDP mapping and Sinton lifetime tester WCT-120PL are used to verify the effectiveness of edge passivation on the device lifetime

Results

Optical and SEM-EDS images of the passivation layer

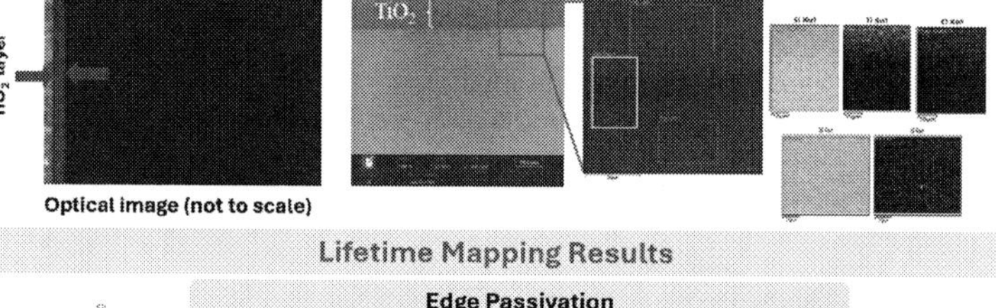

Lifetime Mapping Results

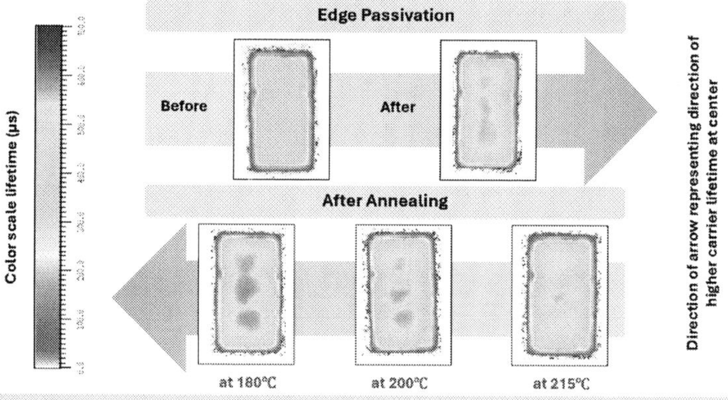

Lifetime results

Edge passivated sample

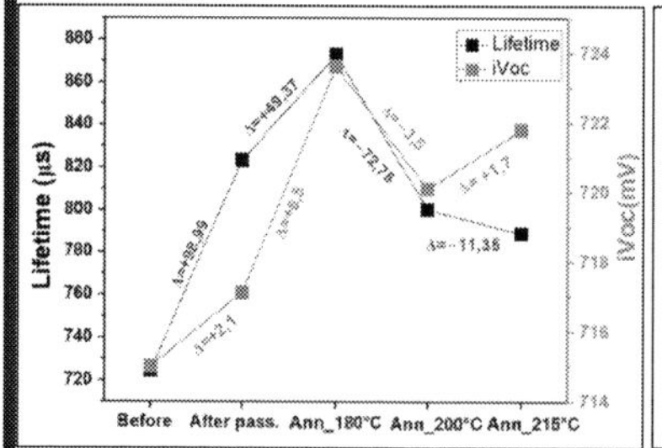

Non-passivated sample

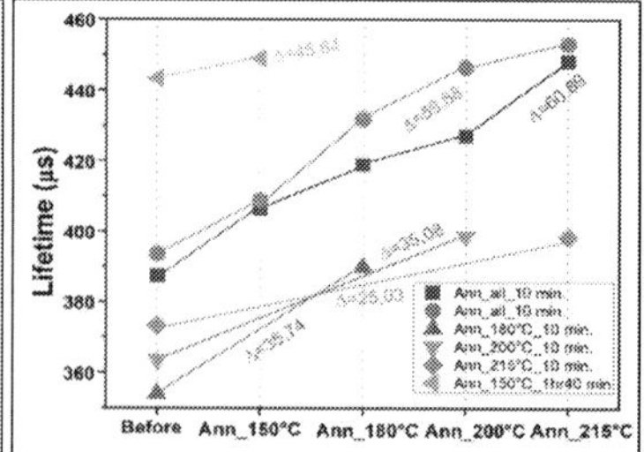

Variation in lifetime (at 1×10^{15}) and iVoc for an edge passivated sample

Variation in lifetime (at 1×10^{15}) for only annealed non-passivated samples

Conclusion

- Successful deposition of TiO_2 as edge passivating layer using DALP®

- Optical and SEM images confirmed the localized nature of passivating layer with an approximated width of 230-240 µm around the edges

- Layer deposition followed by annealing at 180℃ lead to an improvement of 148.36 µs in lifetime and 8.6 mV in iVoc

- Further annealing at 200℃, 215℃ degraded the device lifetime which may be due to transition from amorphous to crystalline phase of deposited film

- The lifetime results are further supported by MDP mapper where clear changes in the topogram were observed during the experiment

- Compared to passivated samples, only annealed non-passivated samples has shown much lower improvements in lifetime effectively highlighting the good passivation offered by TiO_2 film

- Obtained results suggest that local edge passivation with dielectric films like TiO_2 (tested here), Al_2O_3 (future work) can be a good choice to compensate for the cut losses in shingle cell architectures

References

1. B. Martel et al. (2023). *Solar Energy Materials and Solar Cells, 250*, 112095
2. A. Münzer et al. (2021) *IEEE Journal of Photovoltaics, 11(6)*, 1343-1349
3. E. Lohmüller et al. (2023). Solar Energy Materials and Solar Cells, 258, 112419.
4. I. Kundrata et al. (2022) *Small Methods, 6(5)*, 2101546.

Acknowledgement

This work is supported by Innovation Fund Denmark under the "ACES- Advanced Contact Engineering and Surface Passivation for Solar Cells with grant number 3148-00044B.

BORON DOPED NANOCRYSTALLINE SILICON AS A REAR-EMITTER IN SILICON HETEROJUNCTION SOLAR CELLS

Amanda Merino[1,2], Tristan Gageot[1], José Alvarez[2], Jean-Paul Kleider[2], Delfina Muñoz[1]
[1]Université Grenoble Alpes CEA, Liten, Campus Ines, Le Bourget du Lac, 73375, France
[2]Laboratoire de Génie Electrique et Electronique de Paris (GeePs), CNRS, CentraleSupélec, Université Paris-Saclay,
Sorbonne Université, F- 91190 Gif sur Yvette, France / Institute(s)
Corresponding author: amanda.merinoleiva@cea.fr / +33666394298
tristan.gageot@cea.fr ; jose.alvarez@centralesupelec.fr ; jean-paul.kleider@centralesupelec.fr ; delfina.munoz@cea.fr

ABSTRACT: The best silicon heterojunction (SHJ) solar cells show the potential of hydrogenated nanocrystalline silicon (nc-Si:H) to improve their performance on both the emitter and back surface field (BSF) sides. However, in production, nc-Si:H presents several challenges, particularly in terms of deposition rate, reproducibility and stability of layers and interfaces, as well as substrate selectivity and the amorphising nature of boron for p-type layers. A seed layer, such as (p) a-SiOx:H, can be introduced to promote nucleation of crystals and protect the passivation layers. In this work, a seed layer was optimized for SHJ integration using (p) nc-Si:H of different thicknesses and doping concentrations. Solar cell integration of (p) nc-Si:H deposited on the doped seed layer shows V_{oc} and FF gains of +2.4 mV and +6.5%abs, respectively, compared to those with undoped seed layer. The best solar cells with (p) nc-Si:H as rear-emitter reached 22.2% of power conversion efficiency (PCE), only 0.7%abs lower than the (p) a-Si:H based reference, showing the potential of this material.
Keywords: nanocrystalline silicon, silicon heterojunction, PECVD.

1 INTRODUCTION

Among single-junction photovoltaic technologies, silicon heterojunction (SHJ) solar cells stand out for their ability to achieve high power conversion efficiencies (PCE). In this technology, the buffer and carrier collector layers are typically based on amorphous silicon (a-Si:H) due to its optoelectrical and passivation properties. However, the solar cell performance is limited by the low doping efficiency of a-Si:H, which results in high series resistance and poor contact with the adjacent TCO [1]. Several works [2]-[4] have shown that nanocrystalline silicon (nc-Si:H) is a promising alternative due to its superior electronic and optical properties which are enhanced by crystallinity, allowing higher PCE, with the world record using this type of layers being at 27.3% [5]. However, the deposition of nc-Si:H layers presents several challenges, particularly in terms of deposition rate, reproducibility and layer stability. The properties of nc-Si:H are highly dependent on its crystallinity and evolve during its growth, and its deposition on amorphous substrates results on a thicker incubation layer [6], making its integration in SHJ cells challenging with a relatively thin layer (10-30 nm) [7]. In addition, the growth of boron-doped nc-Si:H films presents an additional challenge, due to the amorphising nature of boron [8]. In order to optimize the properties of (p) nc-Si:H it is important to promote a rapid nucleation, and a suitable seed layer is required. Several optimizations of the seed layers have been reported in the literature, such as oxygen treatment [3], [9] or a thin intrinsic or n-type nc-Si:H film [10]-[12]. More recently, a high performance SHJ with 25.15% of PCE was reported by using a boron-doped a-SiOx:H buffer layer to promote nucleation on the (p) nc-Si:H emitter [13]. In order to achieve higher SHJ cell performances, it is necessary to evaluate the growth and properties of (p) nc-Si:H both as a material and as a solar cell precursor, and to develop a suitable seed layer.

In this work, we present the characterization of (p) nc-Si:H films grown on a 1 nm boron-doped a-SiOx:H seed layer with different doping concentrations, in order to subsequently integrate the optimized layer as a rear-emitter for SHJ solar cells grown in an industrial scale equipment.

2 METHODS

For film characterization purposes, seed and (p) nc-Si:H layers were deposited on n-type crystalline silicon (c-Si) and Corning glass using an industrial size plasma enhanced chemical vapour deposition (PECVD) system from Meyerburger Helia. All nc-Si:H films were grown on top of a 9 nm (i) a-Si:H buffer layer to replicate the backside SHJ conditions. Deposition was performed with an RF generator at 13.56 MHz, 200 °C and 175 °C and chamber pressures of 2.5 mbar and 9.5 mbar for amorphous and nanocrystalline layers, respectively. Film precursors and average mass flow are presented in Table I. The diborane mass flow was varied between 1 and 2000 sccm and between 20 and 500 sccm for seed layer ($[B_2H_6]_{seed\ layer}$) and (p) nc-Si:H ($[B_2H_6]_{nc}$) deposition, respectively. The thickness of the films was obtained from spectroscopic ellipsometry (SE) measurements. Crystallinity fraction (φ_c) was obtained from SE and Raman spectra [14]. Conductivity (σ) was measured using the 4-point probe (4PP) technique.

Table I: Average mass flow of film precursors during PECVD deposition

Layer	H_2 (sccm)	SiH_4 (sccm)	CO_2 (sccm)	B_2H_6 (sccm)
(p) a-SiOx:H	3015	400	500	1-2000
(p) nc-Si:H	10000	30	-	20-500

For SHJ cell integration, (i/n) a-Si:H stacks were deposited on the front side of double-sided textured (n) c-Si wafers. An (i/p) a-Si:H stack was deposited on the rear-side of the wafer for the reference cell (Fig. 1a). To understand the effect of adding a doped seed layer, we integrated (p) nc-Si:H films deposited either directly on the 9 nm thick (i) a-Si:H buffer layer (Fig. 1b) or by adding a 1 nm thick (p) a-SiO$_x$:H film as doped seed layer with [B$_2$H$_6$]$_{seed\ layer}$=100 sccm (Fig. 1c). The thickness of the nc-Si:H film was varied from 15 to 45 nm and [B$_2$H$_6$]$_{nc}$=30-80 sccm. Indium tin oxide (ITO) layers were subsequently deposited on both sides of the cells by physical vapour deposition (PVD). Silver electrodes were screen-printed and cured at 200 °C for 20 minutes. Minority carrier lifetime of the cell precursors before and after PVD were obtained from photoconductance decay measurements using a Sinton WCT-120, while solar cell parameters were obtained from I-V measurements measured right after screen-printing in the Tempo Preto Line. The I-V measurements were repeated after the cells underwent light-soaking treatment.

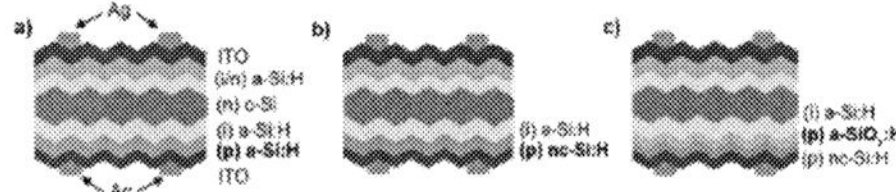

Figure 1: SHJ structures with **a)** (p) a-Si:H (reference) **b)** (p) nc-Si:H and **c)** (p) nc-Si:H deposited on a doped seed layer as rear-emitter used in this work.

3 RESULTS

3.1 Layer characterization

Figure 2 shows the Raman crystallinity and conductivity of 12-120 nm thick (p) nc-Si:H films with [B$_2$H$_6$]$_{nc}$=45 sccm grown directly on (i) a-Si:H. By increasing the thickness from 12 to 120 nm the crystallinity increases from 14±2% to 50±2% and conductivity increases from 0.22±0.02 S/cm to 6.7±0.6 S/cm.

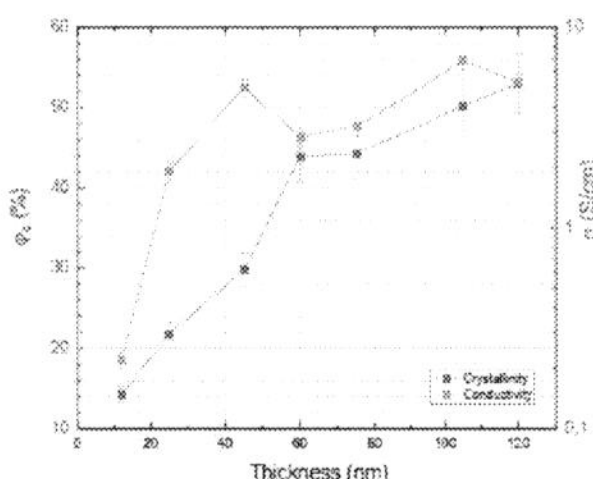

Figure 2: Raman crystallinity and conductivity versus Thickness for (p) nc-Si:H films with no seed layer ([B$_2$H$_6$]$_{nc}$=45 sccm).

Fig. 3 shows the SE crystallinity and conductivity of 13 nm thick (p) nc-Si:H films with [B$_2$H$_6$]$_{nc}$=45 sccm grown on a doped seed layer with increasing [B$_2$H$_6$]$_{seed\ layer}$. Films grown on the undoped seed layer have a crystallinity of 37±2%. The crystallinity of the nc films grown on seed layers with low [B$_2$H$_6$]$_{seed\ layer}$ sharply drops when adding 1 sccm of B$_2$H$_6$ to the seed layer deposition. When increasing [B$_2$H$_6$]$_{seed\ layer}$ from 1 to 30 sccm the crystallinity quickly increases, reaching the level of the nc films grown on undoped seed layer. The crystallinity continues to increase up to [B$_2$H$_6$]$_{seed\ layer}$=80 sccm, where it stabilizes around 42%. Similarly, with increasing [B$_2$H$_6$]$_{seed\ layer}$, there is an increase in σ of up to three orders of magnitude.

SE crystallinity and conductivity of 13 nm thick (p) nc-Si:H films with [B$_2$H$_6$]$_{nc}$=0-100 sccm are shown on Figure 4. At 0 sccm, the SE crystallinity is maximum with

58±2% and it decreases to 35±5% by 100 sccm. Films with 0 and 20 sccm are too resistive. Films with [B$_2$H$_6$]=30 sccm have a conductivity of 1.5±0.1 mS/cm and it quickly increases two orders of magnitude by 60 sccm. After this point, the conductivity stabilizes around 0.6±0.1 S/cm.

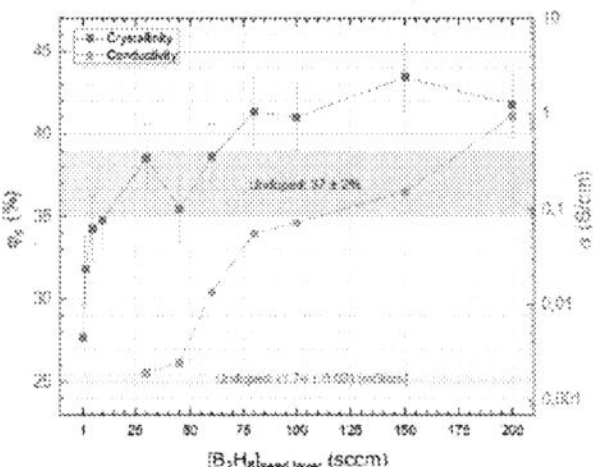

Figure 3: SE crystallinity and conductivity versus B$_2$H$_6$ flow during seed layer deposition ([B$_2$H$_6$]$_{seed\ layer}$) for 13 nm thick (p) nc-Si:H films ([B$_2$H$_6$]$_{nc}$=45 sccm)

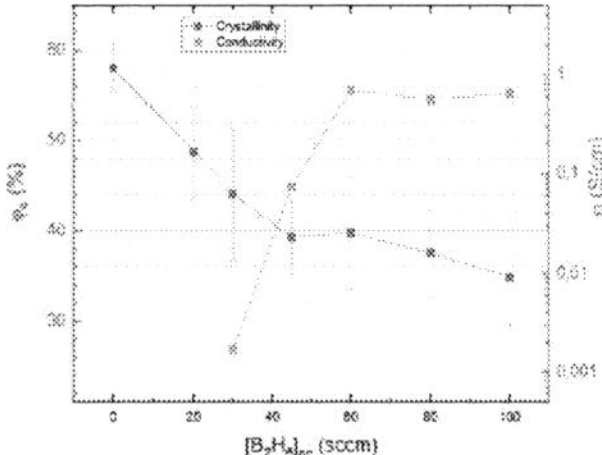

Figure 4: SE crystallinity and conductivity versus B$_2$H$_6$ flow on nc layer ([B$_2$H$_6$]$_{nc}$) for 13 nm thick (p) nc-Si:H films deposited on doped seed layer ([B$_2$H$_6$]$_{seed\ layer}$=100 sccm)

3.2 Solar cell integration

Figure 6 shows the PCE, short-circuit current (J$_{sc}$), open circuit voltage (V$_{oc}$) and fill factor (FF) of the integrated solar cells with 15-45 nm thick (p) nc-Si:H films ([B$_2$H$_6$]$_{nc}$=45 sccm) grown directly onto the (i) a-Si:H layer and a 20 nm thick (p) nc-Si:H film deposited onto the seed layer ([B$_2$H$_6$]$_{seed\ layer}$=100 sccm). There is high dispersion on the performance of the cells in each configuration. Electroluminescence (EL) measurements (Fig. 5) show a clear inhomogeneity of the PECVD deposition on the tray, demonstrating the variability of nc-Si:H growth depending on the substrate position on the chamber. The results shown in the graph are based only on the best 15 cells for each configuration.

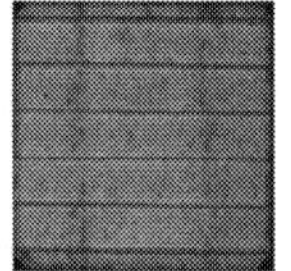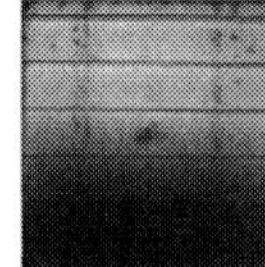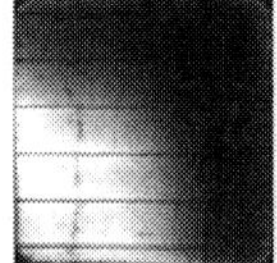

Figure 5: EL images of SHJ devices with (p) nc-Si:H as rear-emitter showing inhomogeneous deposition.

The J$_{sc}$ (Fig. 6b) of all splits is similar to that of the reference (around 38.6 mA/cm^2). By comparing the cells with 15-45 nm thick (p) nc-Si:H films deposited directly on (i) a-Si:H, we can see an increase in FF and V$_{oc}$ by increasing the thickness of the (p) nc-Si:H film to 30 nm, which is a result of a higher crystallinity and conductivity of the film. However, by further increasing the thickness, V_{oc} and FF decrease due to higher recombination losses and high series resistance. As shown in Fig. 6a, cells with a doped seed layer have a higher V_{oc}, especially when comparing the 20 nm thickness (+2.4 mV), and are comparable to that of the reference (<1 mV difference). Figures 6c,d show that the limiting factor for the PCE is the FF of the cells. This is due to the high series resistance and low shunt resistance (not shown here). Integration with the seed layer give the best performance among cells with (p) nc-Si:H as emitter, with a mean PCE at 22.22%, only 0.70%abs lower than the a-Si:H reference.

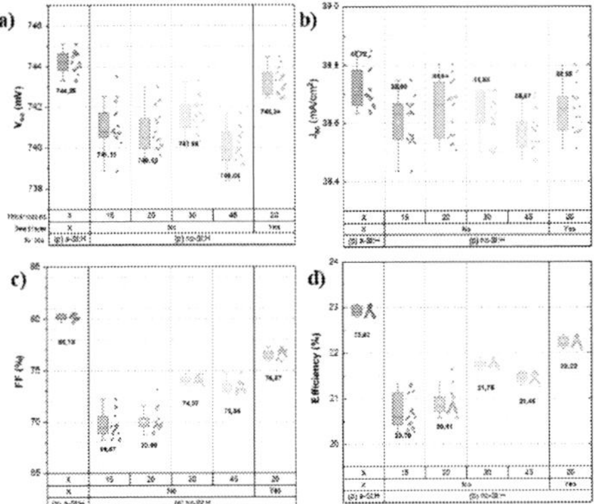

Figure 6. a) V_{oc}, **b)** J_{sc}, **c)** FF and **d)** efficiency of SHJ using (p) nc-Si:H films with different thicknesses with and without seed layer as rear-emitter compared to (p) a-Si:H reference ($[B_2H_6]_{seed\ layer}$=100 sccm, $[B_2H_6]_{nc}$=45 sccm)

Figure 7 shows the V_{oc} and FF before and after light soaking (LS) of the integrated solar cells with 20 and 30 nm thick (p) nc-Si:H films ($[B_2H_6]_{nc}$=30-60 sccm) deposited onto the seed layer ($[B_2H_6]_{seed\ layer}$=100 sccm). Integration with $[B_2H_6]_{nc}$=80 sccm resulted in unmeasurable devices. Both V_{oc} and FF drop when increasing the thickness of the (p) nc-Si:H film with $[B_2H_6]_{nc}$=45 sccm from 20 to 30 nm. Before LS, the best V_{oc} is achieved by the 30 sccm device, reaching 1 mV higher than the reference, due to less dispersion. The V_{oc} (Fig. 7a) of the nc-Si:H devices slightly drops when increasing the doping to 45 and 60 sccm. After LS, the reference V_{oc} is strongly improved (+6.2 mV) while the 20 nm nanocrystalline devices only obtain a slight improvement of around 1 mV. The FF (Fig. 7b) seems to be slightly better (+1%abs) when doping with 45 sccm among the 20 nm devices. The LS improves the FF of all devices in at least 2%abs. The 20 nm thick (p) nc-Si:H films with 45 sccm devices resulted in the highest PCE among the nanocrystalline configurations, with 21.48% and 22.24% before and after LS, respectively, around 1.3%abs lower than the reference. The FF remains as the limiting factor for the performance of the nanocrystalline devices due to their high series resistance (double than reference) and low shunt resistance (>200 Ω on nc-Si:H devices; 1500 Ω for reference device) (not shown here).

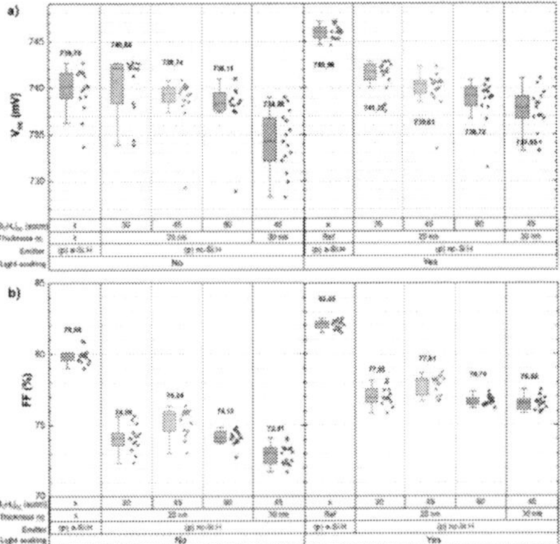

Fig. 7. a) V_{oc} and **b)** FF before and after LS of SHJ using 20 and 30 nm thick (p) nc-Si:H films with different B_2H_6 flow ($[B_2H_6]_{nc}$) deposited on seed layer as rear-emitter compared to (p) a-Si:H reference ($[B_2H_6]_{seed\ layer}$=100 sccm).

4 CONCLUSIONS

Boron-doped nc-Si:H films were deposited in an industrial-scale PECVD equipment for layer optimization as a rear-emitter in SHJ solar cells. Thickness and doping for both the (p) nc-Si:H and the (p) a-SiO$_x$:H seed layer were assessed from the crystallinity and conductivity of the resulting layers. The layers were later integrated in SHJ solar cells.

The addition of a doped seed layer resulted in a performance improvement with a 2.4 mV and 6.5%abs gain in V_{oc} and FF, respectively, leading to a 1.3%abs PCE gain. The optimum thickness of the (p) nc-Si:H film on devices without seed layer results in 30 nm, while by adding a doped seed layer it shifts to 20 nm. This shows that, due to the substrate selectivity of the layer, parameter optimization cannot be directly translated to films grown on different interfaces. Light soaking on reference cell strongly improves V_{oc} while it remains at the same level on nc-Si:H devices. Light soaking resulted in a 2-4%abs FF gain on nc-Si:H devices.

The FF is the limiting factor for the PCE of the nc-Si:H devices, due to high series resistances and extremely low shunt resistances (>200 Ω). The resistance issues could be caused either by a high contact resistance between the nc-Si:H layers and the TCO or to improper TCO masking. Further studies are ongoing.

5 ACKNOWLEDGEMENTS

Funded by the European Union. Views and opinions expressed are however those of the author(s) only and do not necessarily reflect those of the European Union or RIA. Neither the European Union nor the granting authority can be held responsible for them. NEXUS project has received funding from the European Union's Horizon Europe research and innovation program under grant agreement No. 101075330.

6   REFERENCES

[1] M. Bivour, C. Reichel, M. Hermle, et S. W. Glunz, « Improving the a-Si:H(p) rear emitter contact of n-type silicon solar cells », *Solar Energy Materials and Solar Cells*, vol. 106, p. 11-16, nov. 2012, doi: 10.1016/j.solmat.2012.06.036.

[2] H. Lin *et al.*, « Silicon heterojunction solar cells with up to 26.81% efficiency achieved by electrically optimized nanocrystalline-silicon hole contact layers », *Nat Energy*, vol. 8, n° 8, p. 789-799, 2023, doi: 10.1038/s41560-023-01255-2.

[3] L. Mazzarella, A. Morales-Vilches, L. Korte, R. Schlatmann, et B. Stannowski, « Versatility of Nanocrystalline Silicon Films: from Thin-Film to Perovskite/c-Si Tandem Solar Cell Applications », *Coatings*, vol. 10, n° 8, p. 759, 2020, doi: 10.3390/coatings10080759.

[4] Y. Li *et al.*, « Flexible silicon solar cells with high power-to-weight ratios », *Nature*, vol. 626, n° 7997, Art. n° 7997, 2024, doi: 10.1038/s41586-023-06948-y.

[5] J. Casey, « LONGi unveils heterojunction back-contact cell with record 27.3% conversion efficiency ». visited: 24 june 2024. [Online]. Available on: https://www.pv-tech.org/longi-heterojunction-back-contact-cell-27-3-conversion-efficiency/

[6] P. Roca i Cabarrocas, N. Layadi, T. Heitz, B. Drévillon, et I. Solomon, « Substrate selectivity in the formation of microcrystalline silicon: Mechanisms and technological consequences », *Applied Physics Letters*, vol. 66, n° 26, p. 3609-3611, 1995, doi: 10.1063/1.113803.

[7] L. Mazzarella, S. Kirner, B. Stannowski, L. Korte, B. Rech, et R. Schlatmann, « p-type microcrystalline silicon oxide emitter for silicon heterojunction solar cells allowing current densities above 40 mA/cm2 », *Applied Physics Letters*, vol. 106, n° 2, p. 023902, 2015, doi: 10.1063/1.4905906.

[8] S. Juneja et S. Kumar, « Effect of Power on Crystallinity and Opto-Electronic Properties of Silicon Thin Films Grown Using VHF PECVD Process », *Silicon*, vol. 13, n° 11, p. 3927-3940, 2021, doi: 10.1007/s12633-020-00697-7.

[9] A. N. Fioretti, M. Boccard, R. Monnard, et C. Ballif, « Low-Temperature p-Type Microcrystalline Silicon as Carrier Selective Contact for Silicon Heterojunction Solar Cells », *IEEE J. Photovoltaics*, vol. 9, n° 5, p. 1158-1165, 2019, doi: 10.1109/JPHOTOV.2019.2917550.

[10] O. Vetterl, M. Hülsbeck, J. Wolff, R. Carius, et F. Finger, « Preparation of microcrystalline silicon seed-layers with defined structural properties », *Thin Solid Films*, vol. 427, n° 1-2, p. 46-50, 2003, doi: 10.1016/S0040-6090(02)01237-3.

[11] E. Fathi, Y. Vygranenko, M. Vieira, et A. Sazonov, « Boron-doped nanocrystalline silicon thin films for solar cells », *Applied Surface Science*, vol. 257, n° 21, p. 8901-8905, 2011, doi: 10.1016/j.apsusc.2011.05.052.

[12] G. Nogay *et al.*, « Nanocrystalline Silicon Carrier Collectors for Silicon Heterojunction Solar Cells and Impact on Low-Temperature Device Characteristics », *IEEE J. Photovoltaics*, vol. 6, n° 6, p. 1654-1662, 2016, doi: 10.1109/JPHOTOV.2016.2604574.

[13] L. Wen *et al.*, « Boron-doped amorphous buffer layer for p-type microcrystalline silicon emitter to prepare efficient silicon heterojunction solar cell », *Solar Energy Materials and Solar Cells*, vol. 278, p. 113216, 2024, doi: 10.1016/j.solmat.2024.113216.

[14] C. Droz, E. Vallat-Sauvain, J. Bailat, L. Feitknecht, J. Meier, and A. Shah, "Relationship between Raman crystallinity and open-circuit voltage in microcrystalline silicon solar cells," Solar Energy Materials and Solar Cells, vol. 81, no. 1, pp. 61–71, 2004, doi: 10.1016/j.solmat.2003.07.004.

BORON DOPED NANOCRYSTALLINE SILICON AS A REAR-EMITTER IN SILICON HETEROJUNCTION SOLAR CELLS

Context

The best silicon heterojunction (SHJ) solar cells show the potential of hydrogenated nanocrystalline silicon (nc-Si:H) to improve their performance on both the emitter and back surface field (BSF) sides. However, in production, nc-Si:H presents several challenges, particularly in terms of deposition rate, reproducibility and stability of layers and interfaces, as well as substrate selectivity [1] and the amorphising nature of boron for p-type layers. A seed layer, such as (p) a-SiO$_x$:H [2], can be introduced to promote nucleation of crystals and protect the passivation layers. In this work, a seed layer was optimized for SHJ integration using (p) nc-Si:H of different thicknesses and doping concentrations.

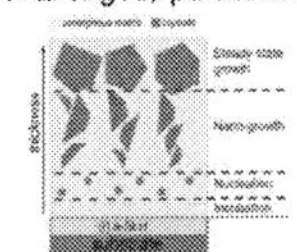

Fig. 1. Schematic representation of nc-Si:H growth on (i) a-Si:H

Methods

- Nanocrystalline silicon films were deposited on both n-type crystalline silicon (c-Si) and Corning glass using a plasma enhanced chemical vapour deposition (PECVD) system at 175 °C with hydrogen (H$_2$) and silane (SiH$_4$) as precursor gases. For p-type films, diborane (B$_2$H$_6$) was added to the mixture. All nc-Si:H films were grown on top of an (i) a-Si:H buffer layer to replicate the backside SHJ conditions.

- The crystallinity fraction (ϕ_c) was extracted from spectroscopic ellipsometry (SE) and Raman spectra [2] and conductivity was measured using the four-point probe (4PP) technique.

- For SHJ integration, ITO was sputtered by physical vapour deposition (PVD) and silver electrodes were screen-printed for 20 minutes.

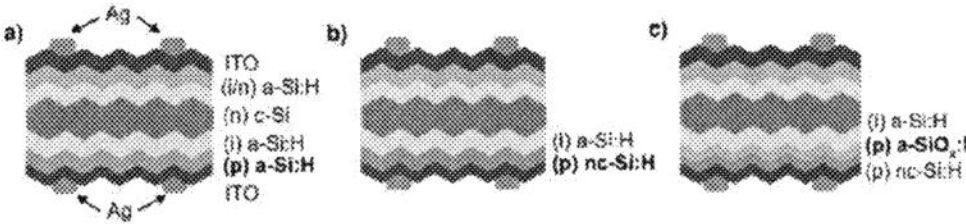

Fig. 2. SHJ structures with a) (p) a-Si:H (reference) b) (p) nc-Si:H and c) (p) nc-Si:H deposited on a doped seed layer as rear-emitter used in this work

Thickness

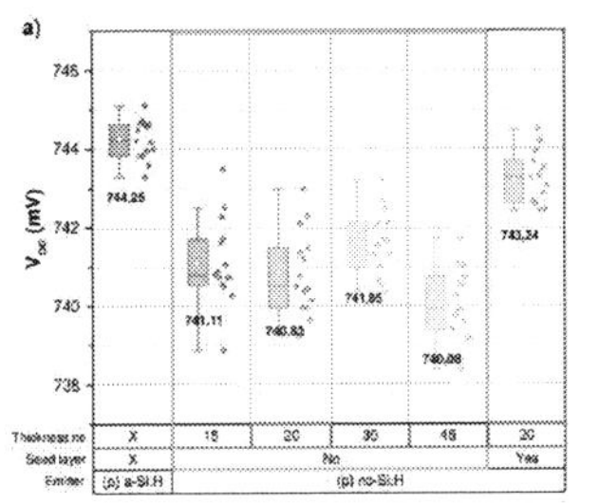

Fig. 3. Raman crystallinity and conductivity versus Thickness for (p) nc-Si:H films with no seed layer ([B$_2$H$_6$]$_{nc}$=45 sccm)

Seed Layer

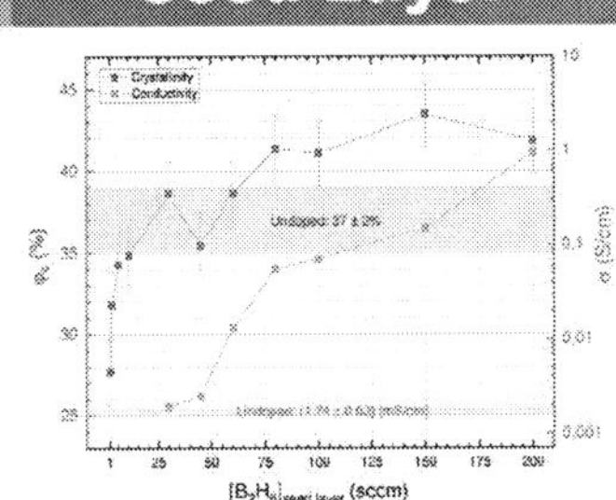

Fig. 4. SE crystallinity and conductivity versus B$_2$H$_6$ flow during seed layer deposition ([B$_2$H$_6$]$_{seed\ layer}$) for 13 nm thick (p) nc-Si:H films ([B$_2$H$_6$]$_{nc}$=45 sccm)

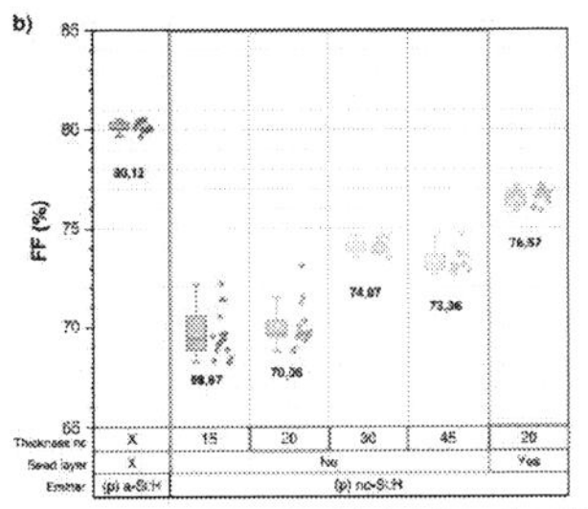

Fig. 5. a) Open-circuit voltage (V$_{oc}$) and b) Fill factor (FF) of SHJ using (p) nc-Si:H films with different thicknesses with and without seed layer as rear-emitter compared to (p) a-Si:H reference ([B$_2$H$_6$]$_{seed\ layer}$=100 sccm, [B$_2$H$_6$]$_{nc}$=45 sccm)

- **Optimum (p) nc-Si:H thickness: 30 nm**

- **Adding seed layer increases FF, V$_{oc}$ and PCE (Fig. 6)**

- Power conversion efficiency (PCE) of best cells with (p) nc-Si:H only 0.7%$_{abs}$ lower than amorphous reference

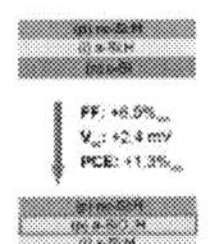

Fig. 6. Effects of adding seed layer

Doping

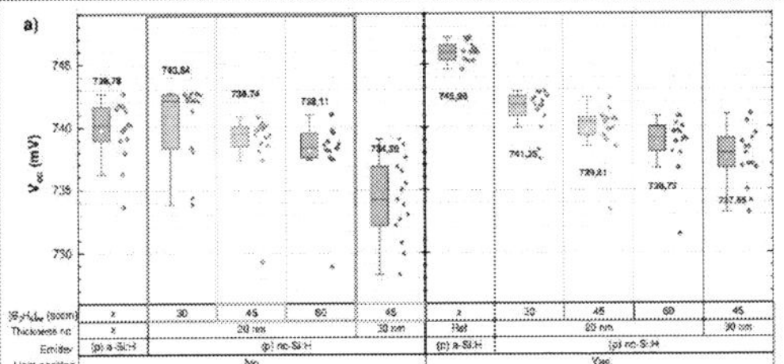

Fig. 8. a) Open-circuit voltage (V$_{oc}$) and b) Fill factor (FF) before and after light-soaking (LS) of SHJ using 20 and 30 nm thick (p) nc-Si:H films with different B$_2$H$_6$ flow ([B$_2$H$_6$]$_{nc}$) deposited on seed layer as rear-emitter compared to (p) a-Si:H reference ([B$_2$H$_6$]$_{seed\ layer}$=100 sccm)

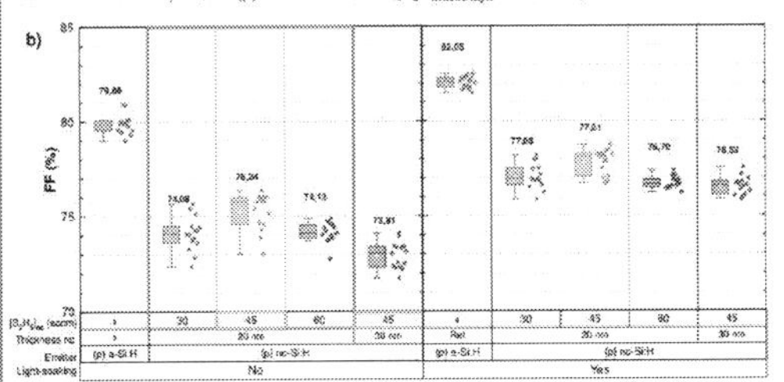

Fig. 7. SE crystallinity and conductivity versus B$_2$H$_6$ flow on nc layer ([B$_2$H$_6$]$_{nc}$) for 13 nm thick (p) nc-Si:H films deposited on doped seed layer ([B$_2$H$_6$]$_{seed\ layer}$=100 sccm)

- **V$_{oc}$ decreases with increasing [B$_2$H$_6$]$_{nc}$**

- **After LS:**
  V$_{oc}$ not improved on 20 nm cells
  FF improvement in all nc cells (≥2.5%$_{abs}$)

- **Optimum (p) nc-Si:H doping: 45 sccm**

- Optimum thickness for films deposited on seed layer: 20 nm

Perspectives

Efficiency is limited by FF

- TCO/(p) nc-Si:H contact resistance measurements required.
- SHJ integration with different TCOs.
- TCO/(p) nc-Si:H interface plasma treatment.
- Optimization of the nanocrystalline silicon deposition.

References

[1] P. Roca i Cabarrocas et al., *Applied Physics Letters*, **1995**, vol. 66, no 26, p. 3609-3611.
[2] L. Wen et al., *Solar Energy Materials and Solar Cells*, **2024** vol. 278, p. 113216.
[3] Droz, C et al., *Sol. Energy Mater. Sol. Cells* **2004**, *81*, 61–71.

Acknowledgements

Funded by the European Union. Views and opinions expressed are however those of the author(s) only and do not necessarily reflect those of the European Union or RIA. Neither the European Union nor the granting authority can be held responsible for them.NEXUS project has received funding from the European Union's Horizon Europe research and innovation program under grant agreement No. 101075330.

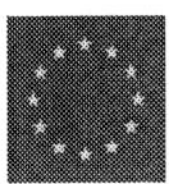

Commissariat à l'énergie atomique et aux énergies alternatives
INES | 50 avenue du lac Léman | 73375 Le Bourget-du-Lac
www.liten.cea.fr / www.ines-solaire.org

CONTACT :
Amanda Merino Leiva
amanda.merinoleiva@cea.fr
020041-001

ADVANCEMENTS IN AMORPHOUS SILICON HETEROJUNCTION (SHJ) SOLAR CELLS THROUGH THE USE OF PLASMONIC NANOPARTICLES

Brahim Aïssa*, M.I. Hossain and Alessandro Sinopoli
Qatar Environment and Energy Research Institute (QEERI), Hamad Bin Khalifa University (HBKU), Qatar Foundation,
Doha, 5825, Qatar
* baissa@hbku.edu.qa

ABSTRACT: This study investigates the incorporation of gold (Au) nanoparticles into indium tin oxide (ITO)/silicon heterojunction (SHJ) solar cells through a drop-casting method, with nanoparticle density finely tuned by varying the number of deposited drops from a 0.05 mg/mL solution. The systematic adjustment of Au-network densities enabled a detailed evaluation of their influence on the photovoltaic response of SHJ devices. The results revealed a maximum short-circuit current (Jsc) enhancement of 11.5% at an optimal nanoparticle density corresponding to six drops, confirming the beneficial role of localized surface plasmon resonance (LSPR) in boosting light absorption and photocurrent generation. However, this improvement in Jsc was accompanied by declines in other photovoltaic parameters, including open-circuit voltage (Voc), fill factor (FF), and overall power conversion efficiency (PCE), particularly at higher nanoparticle densities. These outcomes underscore the delicate balance between plasmonic optical enhancement and electrical performance, emphasizing the need to carefully optimize nanoparticle concentration and distribution depending on the specific requirements of the intended optoelectronic application. To further assess real-world viability, the performance of SHJ solar cells incorporating Au nanoparticles was also evaluated under varying temperature conditions, simulating the hot desert climate of Qatar. The temperature-dependent behavior revealed additional challenges, as elevated temperatures further influenced the photovoltaic parameters, reinforcing the importance of thermal stability in plasmonic device engineering. Overall, these findings provide initial yet valuable insights into the opportunities and trade-offs of integrating plasmonic nanostructures into SHJ solar cells. They highlight both the potential for photocurrent enhancement and the challenges posed by recombination, transport losses, and environmental conditions. This work thus underscores the need for continued research into advanced plasmonic designs, optimized nanoparticle configurations, and hybrid strategies that could fully harness the promise of plasmonics while ensuring robust, efficient, and climate-resilient solar cell performance.

1 INTRODUCTION

The integration of plasmonic nanostructures into solar cells has emerged as a powerful strategy for enhancing optical absorption within the active layer, thereby offering a pathway toward improved power conversion efficiencies [1–3]. Among the different plasmonic designs, ranging from metallic nanogratings and nanoholes to patterned metasurfaces, metallic nanoparticles (NPs) remain the most versatile due to their tunability, straightforward fabrication, and ability to be strategically positioned within the device architecture. Depending on the intended effect, nanoparticles can be deposited directly onto the solar cell surface, embedded at the transparent conductive oxide (TCO)/semiconductor interface, or incorporated into intermediate functional layers. Their presence introduces new optical functionalities into the device, primarily through two well-established mechanisms: near-field light concentration and light scattering. When metallic nanoparticles interact with incident electromagnetic radiation, their conduction electrons undergo collective oscillations. If the oscillation frequency coincides with that of the incoming photons, the condition of surface plasmon resonance (SPR) is satisfied. At resonance, intense localized electric fields are generated near the nanoparticle surface, amplifying optical absorption in the surrounding semiconductor material [4,5]. This effect is especially pronounced when nanoparticles are positioned within the optical near-field of the p–n junction, typically on the emitter or TCO layer. In such configurations, the enhanced electric fields increase the probability of photon absorption and subsequent electron–hole pair generation, directly contributing to higher photocurrent densities.

In addition to near-field enhancement, metallic nanoparticles play a second crucial role through plasmonic light scattering (PLS). At their SPR frequency, nanoparticles act as highly efficient scattering centers, redirecting incident photons into oblique trajectories that increase the optical path length within the absorber layer. This mechanism effectively "traps" light inside the solar cell, particularly benefiting thin-film devices that suffer from limited absorption thickness. The scattering efficiency strongly depends on nanoparticle size and geometry. Small nanoparticles (<20 nm) tend to absorb more strongly than they scatter, which can result in parasitic absorption losses within the metallic particles themselves. In contrast, larger nanoparticles (>50 nm) exhibit enhanced scattering cross-sections and more effectively redirect light into the absorbing medium. Thus, an optimized balance of nanoparticle size, density, and distribution is essential to maximize scattering benefits while minimizing detrimental absorption. [6,7]

A variety of metallic materials have been explored for plasmonic solar cells, including copper (Cu), aluminum (Al), gold (Au), silver (Ag), and palladium (Pd). Among these, Cu and Al are attractive for their low cost and natural abundance, yet their susceptibility to oxidation undermines the stability of their SPR response, limiting long-term applicability. Noble metals, particularly Au and Ag, have gained more traction due to their chemical inertness and strong, stable plasmon resonances in the visible range. Silver is often considered the most effective plasmonic material for photovoltaics, owing to its high scattering cross-section and relatively low absorption losses. [8,9] However, Ag is prone to forming thin oxide layers on its surface, which can dampen resonance effects and compromise device stability. Gold, by contrast, is resistant to oxidation and maintains

10.4229/EUPVSEC2025/1CV.2.24

long-term stability, but effective scattering requires larger Au nanoparticles compared to Ag [10,11]. Interestingly, larger Au nanoparticles not only enhance scattering efficiency but also preferentially scatter light forward into the active layer, making them particularly suitable for deposition on the top surface of the solar cell. [12-14]

Overall, the careful design of plasmonic nanoparticles, considering factors such as size, distribution, material choice, and placement within the solar architecture, is crucial for harnessing their full potential. By striking the right balance between near-field enhancement and light scattering, plasmonic nanoparticles offer a versatile platform for improving solar cell efficiency, particularly in thin-film and next-generation photovoltaic technologies.

2 METHODOLOGY

Indium tin oxide (ITO) thin films were prepared using a radio frequency (RF) magnetron sputtering technique, a well-established method for fabricating transparent conductive oxides (TCOs) with precise control over film composition and uniformity. A ceramic target composed of 90 wt.% In_2O_3 and 10 wt.% SnO_2 was employed, ensuring optimal stoichiometry for balancing high optical transparency with excellent electrical conductivity. The depositions were carried out at room temperature under an RF power density of 2.5 W/cm^2, conditions chosen to maintain a stable plasma environment while preventing substrate heating that could otherwise induce unwanted structural changes. To regulate film stoichiometry, the oxygen-to-total-gas flow ratio was maintained at 0.5%, a critical parameter for minimizing oxygen vacancies while preserving the degenerately doped, conductive nature of the ITO.

The film thickness was carefully controlled to 60 ± 3 nm, providing sufficient optical transparency in the visible spectrum while maintaining continuous conductivity across the substrate. Depositions were performed on multiple substrates, including cleaned borosilicate glass, (n)a-Si:H/(i)a-Si:H/glass, and (n)μc-Si:H/(i)a-Si:H/glass, in order to examine the influence of underlying layers on film growth, crystallinity, and interfacial properties. Substrates were pre-cleaned using standard ultrasonic treatment in acetone, isopropanol, and deionized (DI) water, followed by nitrogen drying to eliminate surface contaminants.

A comprehensive suite of characterization techniques was applied to probe the structural, electrical, optical, and surface properties of the deposited ITO thin films:

- Structural characterization was carried out using X-ray diffraction (XRD) in standard Bragg–Brentano geometry. This analysis provided insights into crystallinity, grain orientation, and phase composition, distinguishing between amorphous and polycrystalline states and identifying preferential orientations induced by different substrate types.

- Electrical properties, including electrical conductivity (σ), carrier concentration (N_e), and Hall mobility (μ_H), were measured using a four-point probe system integrated with Hall effect measurements at room temperature. These measurements elucidated the balance between doping level, charge carrier mobility, and scattering effects, all of which are central to optimizing the trade-off between transparency and conductivity.

- Optical characterization was performed using a UV–Vis spectrophotometer equipped with an integrating sphere, enabling accurate measurements of transmittance (T) and reflectance (R) over the wavelength range of 300–1100 nm. From these data, the absorptance (A) was calculated using the relation:

$$A(\%) = 100 - (T + R).$$

This comprehensive optical analysis enabled the assessment of ITO's suitability for photovoltaic applications, where maximizing visible transparency while minimizing parasitic absorption is essential.

- Surface morphology and topography were investigated using atomic force microscopy (AFM) in tapping mode, providing high-resolution three-dimensional images of surface features. Roughness parameters and grain structures were quantified to correlate morphology with optical scattering and charge transport behavior.

- Depth profiling and elemental composition were examined using X-ray photoelectron spectroscopy (XPS) with depth profiling capability. To probe subsurface chemistry, controlled argon ion sputtering at 500 eV was applied, ensuring sufficient resolution to distinguish between the ITO film and the underlying silicon or glass layers. This analysis revealed not only the elemental composition but also the oxidation states of indium and tin, which are closely tied to the electrical and optical functionality of the ITO films.

Finally, to simulate post-deposition thermal treatments commonly employed in device fabrication, all ITO thin films were subjected to thermal annealing at 250 °C for 30 minutes in a nitrogen atmosphere. This annealing step was designed to relax internal stresses, reduce defect densities, and improve grain connectivity, thereby optimizing the ITO's transparent conductive oxide properties. Enhanced conductivity, improved mobility, and reduced scattering following annealing confirmed its importance in tailoring the ITO films for subsequent integration into silicon heterojunction (SHJ) solar cells. Taken together, this deposition and characterization workflow established a detailed understanding of how sputtering conditions, substrate choice, and post-deposition annealing collectively influence the structure–property relationships of ITO thin films. These insights are crucial for engineering ITO layers that achieve the delicate balance between optical transparency and electrical conductivity required for next-generation photovoltaic and optoelectronic applications.

3 RESULTS AND DISCUSSION

In this study, gold (Au) nanoparticles were incorporated onto the surface of indium tin oxide (ITO)/silicon heterojunction (SHJ) solar cells through a carefully controlled drop-casting technique. The density of the plasmonic Au network was modulated by varying the number of deposited drops from a precursor solution with a concentration of 0.05 mg/mL. This systematic approach allowed for precise adjustment of the surface coverage and nanoparticle distribution, thereby enabling a direct assessment of how varying plasmonic densities influence device performance.

The introduction of Au nanoparticles had a pronounced impact on the photovoltaic characteristics of the SHJ devices. The most notable improvement was observed in the short-circuit current density (Jsc), which exhibited a maximum relative gain of 11.5% when six drops were applied. This enhancement is attributed to the localized surface plasmon resonance (LSPR) effect, whereby Au nanoparticles act as optical antennas, concentrating and scattering incident light into the active layers of the device. This process improves light harvesting efficiency and promotes stronger photocurrent generation, particularly in spectral regions where silicon absorption is weaker.

However, while Jsc improved with increasing nanoparticle density, other critical performance metrics displayed more complex trends. The open-circuit voltage (Voc) initially increased at low Au coverage, reflecting improved interface passivation and light–matter interaction, but subsequently declined at higher densities. This reduction is likely due to enhanced carrier recombination and perturbations in the heterojunction's electrical properties induced by excessive nanoparticle loading. Similarly, the fill factor (FF%) decreased with higher Au densities, suggesting that excessive nanoparticles may introduce resistive losses or act as recombination centers, thereby impeding efficient charge extraction. Consequently, the overall power conversion efficiency (PCE) demonstrated a non-linear response, peaking at intermediate densities before declining at higher coverage levels.

These observations highlight the need for careful optimization of plasmonic nanoparticle density to strike a delicate balance between enhanced optical absorption and the preservation of favorable electrical properties. For practical optoelectronic applications, the ideal nanoparticle concentration will depend on whether the emphasis is on maximizing photocurrent generation, maintaining high Voc and FF stability, or achieving the best compromise for overall PCE.

Beyond density optimization, the study also explored the temperature dependence of SHJ solar cell performance, simulating the harsh operating conditions typical of Qatar's desert climate. The results confirmed that elevated temperatures exacerbate performance degradation, particularly impacting Voc due to increased intrinsic carrier concentration and recombination losses. The interplay between nanoparticle-induced optical enhancement and thermally induced electrical degradation emphasizes the importance of tailoring plasmonic designs not only for spectral control but also for thermal resilience in real-world environments.

These findings are preliminary yet promising, offering a foundation for the development of plasmonically enhanced SHJ solar cells tailored for deployment in challenging climates. Ongoing research is directed toward refining nanoparticle deposition techniques, exploring alternative plasmonic materials, and integrating multilayer designs that combine infrared filtering, self-cleaning, and plasmonic functionalities into a single scalable architecture. Together, these advances aim to pave the way toward next-generation high-efficiency solar technologies capable of delivering reliable performance under the demanding environmental conditions characteristic of the MENA region.

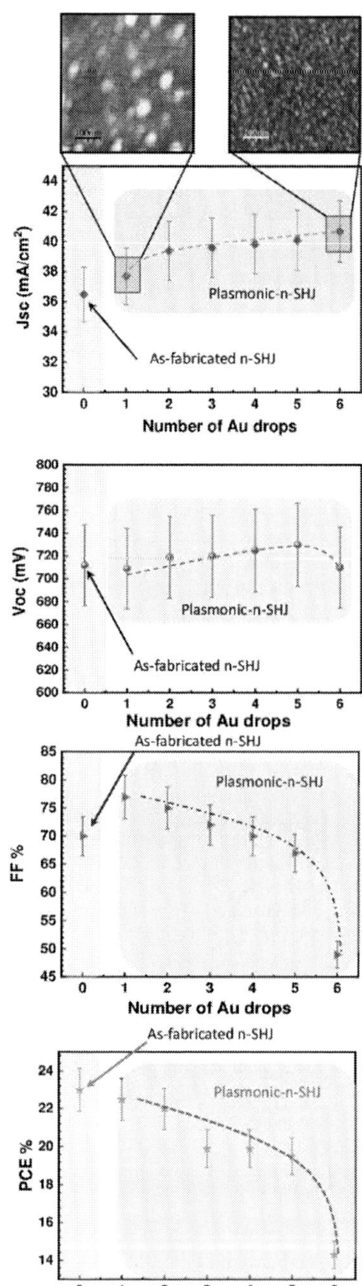

Figure 1: Photovoltaic performance parameters of n-type silicon heterojunction (n-SHJ) solar cells as a function of plasmonic Au nanoparticle network density, controlled by the number of applied drops. The plots illustrate the variation of short-circuit current density (Jsc), open-circuit voltage (Voc), fill factor (FF%), and overall power conversion efficiency (PCE). Increasing Au network density enhances Jsc through improved light absorption, while Voc initially rises before declining at higher densities, indicative of recombination effects.

The FF% decreases with increasing Au content, leading to a non-linear trend in PCE, underscoring the importance of optimizing nanoparticle density to balance plasmonic enhancement with favorable electrical performance.

(a)

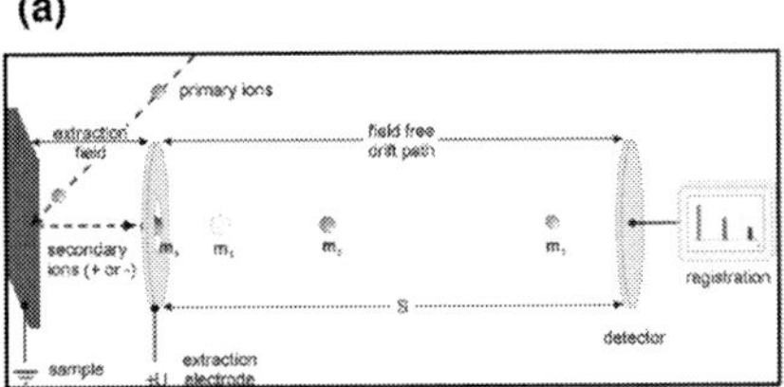

(b)

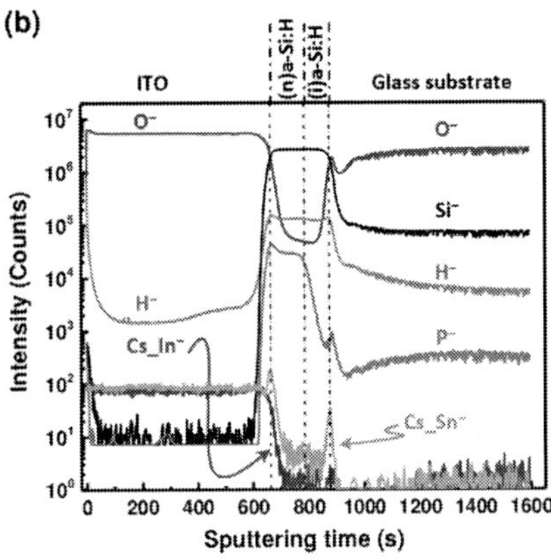

Figure 2: (a) Schematic illustration of the time-of-flight secondary ion mass spectrometry (TOF-SIMS) measurement principle, showing the sputtering of the film surface by a primary ion beam and the subsequent mass analysis of ejected secondary ions. This technique enables high-resolution depth profiling of multilayer thin-film structures. (b) Representative TOF-SIMS depth profile of ITO deposited onto the (n)a-Si:H/(i)a-Si:H/glass stack at an oxygen flow rate of $r(O_2) = 0.01$. The elemental distributions of indium (In) and tin (Sn) are probed using Cs_Sn and Cs_In fragments to avoid spectral overlap with other compounds, ensuring accurate identification. The profiles clearly demonstrate the transition from the ITO layer into the underlying silicon layers, with a decrease in In and Sn signals accompanied by the rise of Si- and H-related signals, thereby confirming distinct compositional gradients across the interfaces. Time-of-flight secondary ion mass spectrometry (TOF-SIMS) was employed to investigate the elemental composition and interfacial characteristics of the deposited thin films, as illustrated in Figure 2. This technique provided detailed depth profiles of the elemental distributions across the multilayer stacks, thereby offering valuable insights into the integrity and sharpness of the interfaces within the heterostructures.

The analysis focused on the detection of key elements, including indium, tin, and oxygen (associated with the ITO layer), and silicon, phosphorus, and hydrogen (associated with the silicon-based layers). Two representative device configurations were examined: ITO/(n)a-Si:H/(i)a-Si:H/glass and ITO/(n)μc-Si:H/(i)a-Si:H/glass.

For both structures, the depth profiles revealed consistent and well-defined trends. Signals corresponding to the ITO layer components (In, Sn, O) gradually diminished as the interface with the n-type silicon layers was approached, while the intensities of silicon, phosphorus, and hydrogen increased accordingly. Within the (n)a-Si:H/(i)a-Si:H and (n)μc-Si:H/(i)a-Si:H regions, a pronounced rise in H, P, and Si signals was observed, reflecting the elemental composition of the doped and intrinsic silicon layers. These signals then exhibited a sharp drop at the glass substrate interface, confirming clear layer termination. Conversely, oxygen, indium, and tin concentrations decreased substantially near the ITO/silicon boundary, in agreement with the expected compositional transition from the transparent conductive oxide to the semiconductor layers.

Although TOF-SIMS does not yield absolute quantitative data, the relative trends clearly demonstrate the existence of distinct compositional gradients at each interface. Such gradients are crucial for understanding the electrical, optical, and recombination properties of the ITO/silicon heterostructures, as even minor interfacial intermixing or diffusion can influence carrier transport, passivation quality, and overall device performance.

These results highlight the capability of TOF-SIMS to provide depth-resolved insights into interfacial chemistry, thereby serving as a powerful diagnostic tool for optimizing multilayer stacks in silicon-based photovoltaics and other thin-film optoelectronic devices.

4 CONCLUSIONS

In conclusion, the integration of Au nanoparticles into ITO/silicon heterojunction solar cells demonstrates a pronounced effect on the key photovoltaic parameters, revealing both the benefits and challenges of plasmonic enhancement. The most consistent improvement was observed in the short-circuit current density (Jsc), which steadily increased with the incorporation of Au nanoparticles. This enhancement can be attributed to localized surface plasmon resonance (LSPR), which promotes stronger light absorption and improved photocurrent generation within the active layer.

The open-circuit voltage (Voc), however, exhibited a more complex behavior. At lower nanoparticle densities, Voc increased, suggesting that moderate plasmonic incorporation can enhance junction properties and reduce recombination pathways. Yet, at higher densities, Voc declined, likely due to increased surface recombination, local field effects, or perturbations at the heterojunction interface caused by excessive nanoparticle loading. Similarly, the fill factor (FF) showed a decreasing trend as Au nanoparticle content increased. This reduction points to negative impacts on charge transport and extraction, possibly linked to increased series resistance or localized recombination centers introduced by the nanoparticles. The combined effects translated into a non-monotonic variation in power conversion efficiency (PCE), where moderate Au incorporation yielded performance gains, but excessive densities compromised device efficiency. These findings highlight the critical importance of optimizing nanoparticle density, size, and spatial distribution to strike a delicate balance between enhanced light harvesting and the preservation of favorable electronic properties. Properly engineered, Au nanoparticle integration offers a powerful route to improving solar cell performance through plasmonic effects. However, without careful control, the benefits of increased photocurrent may be offset by electrical losses. This underscores the necessity of a holistic design approach that couples plasmonic nanostructure engineering with device architecture optimization to achieve sustainable improvements in next-generation plasmonic-enhanced photovoltaic technologies.

5 REFERENCES

[1] B. K. Ghosh, C. N. J. Weoi, A. Islam, and S. K. Ghosh, "Recent progress in Si hetero-junction solar cell: A comprehensive review," Renewable and Sustainable Energy Reviews, vol. 82, pp. 1990–2004, 2018.

[2] Q. Gao, Z. Xu, Y. Yan, W. Li, Y. Song, J. Wang, M. Zhang, et al., "Efficient hole transport layers for silicon heterojunction solar cells by surface plasmonic modification in MoOx/Au NPs/MoOx stacks," Materials Today Energy, vol. 45, p. 101681, 2024.

[3] A. Sharma, D. Pathak, D. P. Sharma, and J. M. Nunzi, "Recent advances in bulk-heterojunction solar cells: a review," The European Physical Journal Applied Physics, vol. 97, p. 81, 2022.

[4] A. K. Dikshit, G. Das, N. Mukherjee, and P. Chakrabarti, "SHJ solar cells on an adequately thin c-Si wafer with dome-like front and double-layer ITO nanoparticles as rear light trapping arrangements," IEEE Transactions on Electron Devices, vol. 69, no. 1, pp. 216–224, 2021.

[5] B. Demaurex, J. P. Seif, S. Smit, B. Macco, W. M. M. Kessels, J. Geissbühler, S. De Wolf, and C. Ballif, "Atomic-layer-deposited transparent electrodes for silicon heterojunction solar cells," IEEE Journal of Photovoltaics, vol. 4, no. 6, pp. 1387–1396, 2014.

[6] L. L. Lebel, B. Aïssa, M. A. El Khakani, and D. Therriault, Composites Science and Technology, vol. 70, no. 3, pp. 518–524, 2010.

[7] W. Julia, C. Luis, R. Federico, et al., Advanced Functional Materials, vol. 23, pp. 5591–5598, 2013.

[8] D. T. H. Dalir, R. D. Farahani, V. Nhim, B. Aïssa, et al., Langmuir, vol. 28, no. 1, pp. 791–803, 2011.

[9] A. Ali, F. El-Mellouhi, A. Mitra, and B. Aïssa, Nanomaterials, vol. 12, no. 5, p. 788, 2022.

[10] R. D. Farahani, D. T. H. Dalir, V. Le Borgne, A. Loick, et al., Composites Science and Technology, vol. 72, no. 12, pp. 1387–1395, 2012.

[11] N. M. H. Gavi, B. D. Ngom, A. C. Beye, A. M. Strydom, B. Aïssa, V. V. Srinivasu, and M. Chaker, Journal of Magnetism and Magnetic Materials, vol. 324, no. 6, pp. 1172–1176, 2012.

[12] B. Aïssa and M. A. El Khakani, Nanotechnology, vol. 20, no. 17, p. 175203, 2009.

[13] M. A. Habib, M. Barkat, B. Aïssa, and T. Denidni, Progress in Electromagnetics Research, vol. 88, pp. 135–148, 2008.

[14] H. Zhao, H. Kimura, Z. Cheng, X. Wang, and T. Nishida, Applied Physics Letters, vol. 95, p. 232904, 2009. https://doi.org/10.1063/1.3271032.

PRECISION UV LASER SCRIBING FOR AMORPHOUS SILICON SOLAR CELLS: LAYER-SPECIFIC ANALYSIS AND OPTIMIZATION

Narendra Bandaru[1*], Asbjørn Moltke[2], Ole Bang[2], Rasmus Schmidt Davidsen[1]
[1]Department of Electrical and Computer Engineering, Aarhus University, 8200, Denmark
[2]DTU Electro, Technical University of Denmark, 2800 Kgs. Lyngby, Denmark
* Corresponding author: narendra.bandaru@ece.au.dk

ABSTRACT: The demand for efficient and scalable photovoltaic manufacturing necessitates advanced techniques for material processing. This study investigates the use of UV lasers for the scribing process on intrinsic and n-type amorphous silicon layers, focusing on optimizing parameters such as pulse energy (26–30 µJ), repetition rate (1–10 kHz), and environmental conditions. A commercial p-type silicon wafer with intrinsic and n-type layers of 27 nm and 82 nm thickness, respectively, was scribed under precise conditions to minimize thermal effects and material redeposition. The intrinsic layer showed line widths ranging from 16.29 µm to 17.30 µm in SEM analysis, while AFM data revealed widths of 20.27 µm to 24.37 µm, indicating smooth surface morphologies. For the n-type layer, depth values ranged from 13.87 nm to 266.56 nm, with consistent nano-crystalline features observed. Despite challenges such as edge irregularities and surface roughness, the process proved robust, achieving uniform scribing with minimal defects. These findings highlight the adaptability of the laser system for applications in optical and electronic devices and provide valuable insights into improving device efficiency, scalability, and cost-effectiveness. Future work will aim to optimize the scribing process by refining laser parameters to achieve greater precision, uniformity, and scalability in photovoltaic applications.
Keywords: UV laser scribing, amorphous silicon, photovoltaic manufacturing, surface morphology

1 INTRODUCTION

Solar energy continues gaining importance as a clean energy source. Pursuit of higher efficiency, lower cost, and reliable large-area fabrication drives innovation in device architecture and processing methods. Among thin-film solar technologies, hydrogenated amorphous silicon (a-Si:H) retains interest for its flexibility in tuning optical and electrical properties and its compatibility with low-temperature deposition on diverse substrates. To integrate such layers into advanced cell structures (e.g. heterojunction, tandem, or back-contact designs), precise patterning and interconnection become essential. In thin-film and hybrid cell stacks, monolithic series interconnection is typically realized by multi-step laser scribing to remove selected layers in narrow stripes, thereby isolating subcells and enabling current flow through contact zones. Laser scribing offers non-contact precision, minimal mechanical stress, and fine line widths compared to mechanical scribing techniques. The method largely dominates high-throughput manufacturing for thin film photovoltaics [1]. However, laser ablation must be finely controlled to avoid defects such as microcracks, redeposited debris, heat-affected zones, edge roughness, and damage to underlying layers. The quality of scribed grooves and the preservation of electrical continuity in adjacent regions critically influence module efficiency and reliability [1].

Because a-Si:H films (intrinsic or doped) differ in optical absorption, thermal diffusivity, thickness, and adhesion, selective removal (ablation) of these layers demands tailored laser parameters (pulse energy, repetition rate, wavelength, scanning speed). Several works have shown that UV lasers, especially at 355 nm or shorter, help in achieving selective ablation with sharper edges and lower collateral damage [2, 3]. Lauzurica et al. studied selective ablation of a-Si:H thin films using UV lasers (ns and ps pulses at 355 nm), demonstrating that tuning fluence can yield clean removal without significant damage to adjacent regions [2]. García-Ballesteros et al. investigated how laser scribing influences electrical

parameters of a-Si:H modules and found that optimized scribing minimally degrades module efficiency [4]. In more recent literature, broader reviews of laser scribing in photovoltaic thin films outline challenges in scaling, defect control, and throughput. Jamaatisomarin et al. provide a comprehensive assessment of laser parameter effects, scribe quality metrics, and guidelines for future improvements [1]. Ishteev et al. examine pulsed laser scribing of transparent conductive oxide / perovskite stacks, contributing to understanding of process limits in mixed-material stacks [3].

Additionally, comparisons between nanosecond and picosecond regimes highlight trade-offs: longer pulses may increase heat diffusion and defect formation, whereas ultrashort pulses reduce thermal damage though require higher peak powers [5, 6]. The formation of crystalline features or defect structures under UV irradiation of a-Si has also been observed, pointing out possible morphological changes even under moderate exposure intensities [7]. Beyond silicon-based systems, laser patterning is being extended to novel absorber stacks (e.g. perovskites) where scribing effects on performance mapping and module integration are actively studied. For example, Schultz et al. analyze P3 patterning in perovskite modules via hyperspectral photoluminescence imaging to correlate fluence to performance losses [8]. Morozov et al. use UV laser scribing to fabricate pixelated perovskite photodiodes, illustrating precision patterning capabilities in thin-film devices [9]. In the realm of advanced silicon architectures, laser-based patterning is also explored as a lithography-free alternative. For instance, Turan et al. propose laser-induced forward transfer (LIFT) for patterning heterojunction full back-contact solar cells without photolithographic steps [10].

This work demonstrates a UV-based scribing route for a-Si:H that is explicitly layer-specific for both intrinsic and n-type films on p-type c-Si. By mapping a robust process window (pulse energy, repetition rate, ambient pressure), we suppress debris, roughness, and depth non-uniformity while preserving underlying wafer quality [11, 12]. The resulting grooves exhibit stable widths and depths across wafers, enabling reliable interconnect formation without collateral damage. These advances translate ultrashort-pulse UV control into manufacturable scribing suitable for modern silicon PV stacks (e.g., SHJ/TOPCon, back-contact), improving scribe quality, reliability, and scalability for high-efficiency module fabrication. Despite extensive prior work, a gap remains in targeted studies of UV laser scribing of intrinsic and n-type a-Si:H layers deposited on p-type crystalline silicon wafers under controlled pulse-energy and repetition-rate regimes optimized for minimal defect formation and strong interconnect integrity. The present work addresses that gap. We systematically vary pulse energy (≈26–30 μJ), repetition frequency (1-10 kHz), and ambient conditions, and we characterize scribe morphology by scanning electron microscopy (SEM) and atomic force microscopy (AFM). The goal is a clearly defined processing window that enables clean, uniform, damage-free scribes suitable for sophisticated layered solar devices.

2   EXPERIMENTAL PROCEDURES

A commercial 4-inch p-type float zone (FZ) double-side polished silicon wafer, supplied by TOPSIL, with a diameter of 100 mm, bulk resistivity of 3 Ω cm, and thickness of 280 ± 25 μm (100 crystal orientation) was used. The wafer underwent cleanroom processing via multi-chamber plasma-enhanced chemical vapor deposition (PECVD) to fabricate intrinsic (a-Si:H:i) and n-type (a-Si:H:n) amorphous silicon layers. To prevent contamination, the i-layer and n-layer were deposited at 230 °C and 200 °C, respectively, in separate chambers, each with a deposition time of 5 minutes.

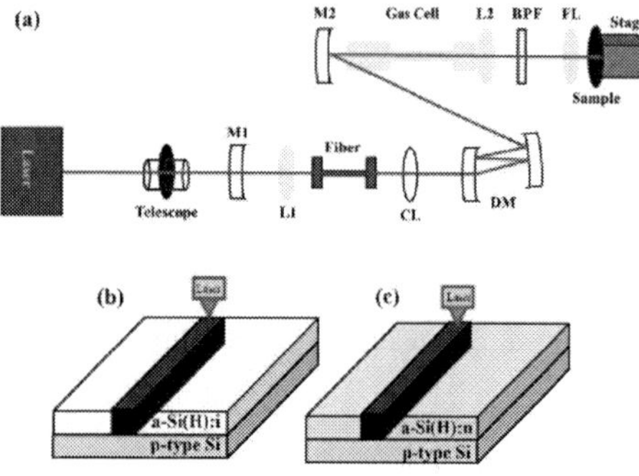

Figure 1. (a) Experimental setup of the UV laser scribing process; Laser Scribing Process Across Different Layers of Silicon: (b) Intrinsic a-Si:H (i-layer) and (c) n-type a-Si:H (n-layer).

The UV laser scribing process is depicted in Figure 1(a). A femto-second Yb-doped laser, operating at 1030 nm with a pulse duration of 300 fs, is initially coupled to a hollow core fiber and subsequently reflected off a set of dispersive mirrors (DM) to temporally compress the pulse to approximately 30 fs. The compressed pulse is then passed through a gas-filled hollow core fiber to generate a UV-supercontinuum. A band-pass filter (BPF) is used to isolate the desired UV wavelength [13]. This setup ensures high precision with minimal groove width and depth variation, critical for uniform scribing performance across samples. The laser scribing process utilized a UV laser operating at a wavelength of 343 nm, generated by 1030 nm pulses with pulse energies of 26–30 μJ applied at repetition rates of 1 kHz and 10 kHz, depending on the layer. For the intrinsic (i) layer, at 1 kHz, 6.9 bar argon pressure was used, while the n-type layer (82 nm thick) was processed with the same pulse energy at 10 kHz at 7.3 bar. Laser pulse energy used was 1.6 μJ for the intrinsic layer and 1.0 μJ for the n-type layer, as applied in this study. These parameters ensured precise material removal across the silicon wafer. Ellipsometry measured the intrinsic a-Si:H layer thickness at 27 nm and the n-type a-Si:H layer at approximately 82 nm. SEM analysis examined the laser-treated side morphologies and widths, while AFM measured topography, width, and depth of the laser-processed samples. Figure 1(b-c) illustrates a schematic of the laser scribing on the respective layers.

3   RESULTS AND DISCUSSION

This study examined laser scribing under two scenarios: (i) scribing on the intrinsic (i-layer) of a p-wafer and (ii) scribing on the n-layer of a p-wafer, focusing on the effects of laser parameters on structural integrity, line quality, and surface morphology. Laser scribing on the i-layer of the p-type wafer, analyzed using SEM and AFM, revealed variations in line morphology and measurements across three sets (i.e., 1, 2 and 3) despite consistent laser parameters (refer to Figure 2). SEM images showed differences in line widths and edge quality, while AFM data highlighted variations in surface roughness and depth uniformity. In Set 1, SEM-measured widths ranged from 16.29 μm (L1) to 17.30 μm (L2), with AFM-measured widths increasing from 20.27 μm to 24.37 μm, reflecting increased roughness and edge deformation. Depth measurements indicated symmetrical material removal in L1, with minor asymmetry emerging in L2 and L3, likely due to cumulative thermal effects and material redeposition, as seen in SEM images showing broader lines and debris in L3. Set 2 SEM widths remained relatively consistent for L1 and L2 but increased to 18.05 μm in L3, suggesting heightened thermal effects. AFM measurements showed smaller widths compared to SEM, indicating smoother surface regions while emphasizing laser interaction dynamics. The highest depth asymmetry was observed in L2, where uneven material removal was prominent. SEM images in Set 2 also revealed irregularities and debris accumulation, particularly in L3, attributed to thermal effects and redeposition. Set 3 showed the largest SEM-measured widths, increasing from 22.48 μm (L1) to 26.30 μm (L2), with AFM measurements reflecting similar trends. Pronounced edge deformation and debris were evident in SEM morphology, especially in L2, highlighting the thermal impact. Variations across sets, despite identical parameters, were likely caused by localized surface inhomogeneities, minor laser beam fluctuations, and cumulative thermal effects from repeated passes. AFM consistently indicated increasing roughness and depth variability in later lines, corroborated by SEM images showing edge deformation and material redeposition.

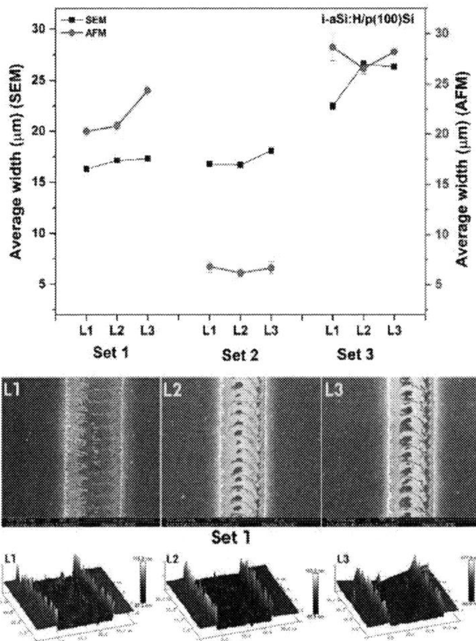

Figure 2: Comparison of SEM and AFM Measurements Across Sets 1, 2, and 3, with SEM and AFM images (L1, L2, L3) for Laser Scribing on Intrinsic a-Si:H Layers in Set 1.

The laser scribing process on the n-layer deposited p-type c-Si wafer was carried out using the same parameters. SEM and AFM analyses revealed distinct surface morphology and topography changes across Sets 1, 2, and 3 (see in figure 3). In Set 1, SEM images displayed smooth surfaces with minimal structural changes, while AFM indicated moderate roughness. Depth values were shallow at L2 (13.87 ± 2.72 nm) and deeper at L3 (266.56 ± 35.52 nm). AFM width measurements variations from 7.12 ± 0.45 μm (L2) to 10.40 ± 0.64 μm (L1), reflecting limited but uniform material modification. Set 2, SEM images showed granular features, indicating localized surface changes. AFM analysis recorded higher roughness at L2, where the depth reached its maximum at 1.86 ± 0.77 nm, while L3 showed a reduction to 1.06 ± 0.05 nm. Widths ranged from 5.55 ± 0.31 μm (L1) to 12.23 ± 0.40 μm (L3), indicating uneven material redistribution with greater interaction at L3. Set 3, SEM revealed well-defined nano-crystalline formations, particularly at L2 and L3, suggesting prominent structural changes due to localized melting and rapid cooling. AFM showed pronounced roughness, with L2 having the highest width (19.06 ± 0.80 μm) and L3 closely following (19.18 ± 1.11 μm). These findings confirm L2 as the region of most effective laser interaction, with enhanced scribing effects. A progression from smooth surfaces in Set 1 to granular structures in Set 2 and nano-crystalline formations in Set 3 was evident. The prominence of L2 across all sets highlights the effectiveness of the central laser zone for consistent material modification. Nano-crystalline formations in Set 3 suggest potential for optical and electronic applications, where precise surface features are critical. Microscopic observations showed localized stress patterns, but no significant degradation like ablation or melting was detected. Despite minor edge irregularities, line widths and continuity were consistent, indicating robust laser control. Further optimization of parameters could improve uniformity and functional properties. Laser scribing on the n-layer highlights the challenges of balancing precision and processing speed. The findings demonstrate that while scribing on the n-layer is feasible, minor edge effects need to be addressed to ensure uniformity and maintain the functional integrity of the n-layer, which plays a critical role in forming the p-n junction. The findings emphasize the importance of optimizing laser parameters to achieve precise, defect-free scribing, enhancing the quality and scalability of thin-film processing.

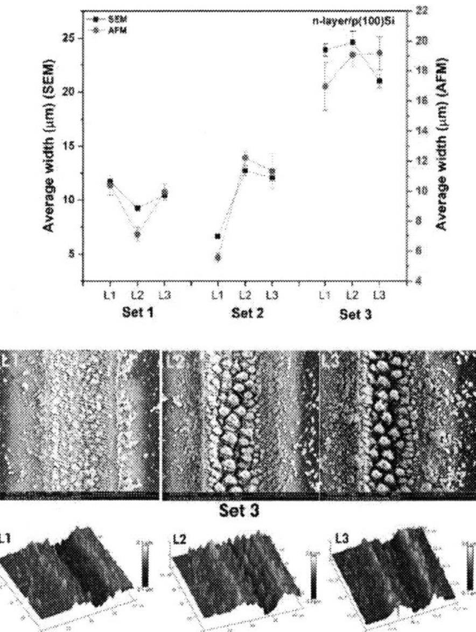

Figure 3: SEM and AFM Width Measurements Across Sets 1, 2, and 3, with SEM and AFM images (L1, L2, L3) for Laser Scribing on n-type a-Si:H Layers in Set 3.

4 CONCLUSIONS

This study establishes the feasibility of UV laser scribing for precise modifications to intrinsic and n-type amorphous silicon layers, demonstrating its potential for achieving smooth and nano-crystalline surface features. While challenges such as edge irregularities and surface roughness remain, the process showed robust and consistent performance. Further optimization of parameters like pulse energy and scan stage stability will enhance uniformity, scalability, and efficiency, paving the way for cost-effective advancements in thin-film manufacturing.

5 ACKNOWLEDGEMENTS

We acknowledge financial support from Innovation Fund Denmark through the project UVSOLAR (project No. 2081-00016A).

6 DECLARATIONS

Conflict of interest: There is no conflict of interest, according to authors.

7 REFERENCES

[1] M. Smith, A. Miller, Proceedings 17ᵗʰ European Photovoltaic Solar Energy Conference, Vol. I (2002) 903.Jamaatisomarin, F., Chen, R., Hosseini-Zavareh, S. and Lei, S., 2023. Laser scribing of photovoltaic solar thin films: A review. Journal of Manufacturing and Materials Processing, 7(3), p.94.

[2] Lauzurica, S., García-Ballesteros, J.J., Colina, M., Sánchez-Aniorte, I. and Molpeceres, C., 2011. Selective ablation with UV lasers of a-Si: H thin film solar cells in direct scribing configuration. Applied Surface Science, 257(12), pp.5230-5236.

[3] Ishteev, R., Gostishchev, P., Tiukhova, M., Sorokin, A., Ishteev, A. and Kondratenko, V., 2024. Technological parameters of thin-film pulsed laser scribing for perovskite photovoltaics. Clean Energy, 8(3), pp.127-135.

[4] Garcia-Ballesteros, J.J., Torres, I., Lauzurica, S., Canteli, D., Gandía, J.J. and Molpeceres, C., 2011. Influence of laser scribing in the electrical properties of a-Si: H thin film photovoltaic modules. Solar Energy Materials and Solar Cells, 95(3), pp.986-991.

[5] Schultz, C., Fenske, M., Dagar, J., Zeiser, A., Bartelt, A., Schlatmann, R., Unger, E. and Stegemann, B., 2020. Ablation mechanisms of nanosecond and picosecond laser scribing for metal halide perovskite module interconnection–An experimental and numerical analysis. Solar Energy, 198, pp.410-418.

[6] Abdul Fattah, T.O., Chen, J., McNab, S., Wilshaw, P.R. and Bonilla, R.S., 2025. Nanosecond vs picosecond: The potential for advanced solar cell processing via pulsed laser technology. Journal of Applied Physics, 138(8).

[7] Persheyev, S.K. and Cairns, J.A., 2016. The formation of well-defined crystalline structures by UV laser irradiation of amorphous silicon films. arXiv preprint arXiv:1606.00181.

[8] Schultz, C., Fenske, M., Otto, N., Dion-Bertrand, L.I., Gélinas, G., Marcet, S., Dagar, J., Schlatmann, R., Unger, E. and Stegemann, B., 2025, April. Loss Analysis of P3 Laser Patterning of Perovskite Solar Cells via Hyperspectral Photoluminescence Imaging. In Solar (Vol. 5, No. 2, p. 13). MDPI.

[9] Morozov, A.P., Gostishchev, P.A., Zharkova, A., Vasilev, A.A., Aleksandrov, A.E., Luchnikov, L.O., Tameev, A.R., Kiselev, D.A., Ilina, T.S., Ishteev, A.R. and Didenko, S.I., 2024. Micro-pixelated halide perovskite photodiodes fabricated with ultraviolet laser scribing. Applied Physics Letters, 124(22).

[10] Turan, B., Ding, K. and Haas, S., 2015. A concept for Lithography-free patterning of silicon heterojunction back-contacted solar cells by laser processing. arXiv preprint arXiv:1506.02879.

[11] Wang, P., Sridharan, R., Ng, X.R., Ho, J.W. and Stangl, R., 2021. Development of TOPCon tunnel-IBC solar cells with screen-printed fire-through contacts by laser patterning. Solar Energy Materials and Solar Cells, 220, p.110834.

[12] Harrison, S., Nos, O., D'Alonzo, G., Denis, C., Coll, A. and Munoz, D., 2016. Back contact heterojunction solar cells patterned by laser ablation. Energy Procedia, 92, pp.730-737.

[13] Smith, C.R., Moltke, A., Adamu, A.I., Michieletto, M., Bowen, P., Moselund, P.M., Markos, C. and Bang, O., 2020. Low-noise tunable deep-ultraviolet supercontinuum laser. Scientific Reports, 10(1), p.18447.

Precision UV Laser Scribing for Amorphous Silicon Solar Cells: Layer-Specific Analysis and Optimization

Narendra Bandaru[1*], Asbjørn Moltke[2], Ole Bang[2], Rasmus Schmidt Davidsen[1]

[1]Department of Electrical and Computer Engineering, Aarhus University, 8200, Denmark

[2]DTU Electro, Technical University of Denmark, 2800 Kgs. Lyngby, Denmark

Department of Electrical and Computer Engineering

1CV.2.25-326

Introduction

- ❖ The global shift toward renewable energy drives demand for efficient photovoltaic manufacturing methods.
- ❖ Ultraviolet (UV) lasers provide advanced capabilities for precise material processing in solar cells.
- ❖ Precision and scalability are critical factors to ensure high-performance and cost-effective device production.
- ❖ Laser-based processing paves the way for next-generation photovoltaic technologies.

Aim

- ❖ Develop and optimize a UV laser scribing process for intrinsic and n-type amorphous silicon layers.
- ❖ The aims is to improve structural integrity, surface precision, and scribing quality.
- ❖ Challenges such as edge irregularities, surface roughness, and material redeposition are specifically addressed.
- ❖ The ultimate goal is to enable scalable and reliable processing for improved photovoltaic device performance.

Experimental Setup

- ❖ **Sample Preparation**
- ➤ Substrate: 4-inch p-type float-zone (FZ) double-side polished silicon wafer
- ➤ Wafer properties: 100 mm diameter, 3 $\Omega \cdot$cm bulk resistivity, 280 ± 25 µm thickness, (100) orientation
- ➤ Layer deposition: Intrinsic (a-Si:H:i, 27 nm) at 230 °C and n-type (a-Si:H:n, 82 nm) at 200 °C via PECVD in separate chambers.

- ❖ **Laser Setup**
- ➤ Femtosecond Yb-doped laser, initial wavelength 1030 nm, pulse duration ~300 fs
- ➤ Compressed to ~30 fs through dispersive mirrors and hollow-core fiber
- ➤ UV supercontinuum generated, isolated with band-pass filter (λ = 343 nm)

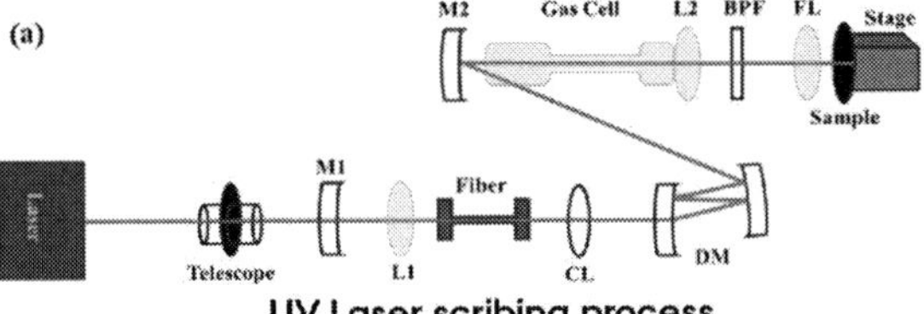

UV Laser scribing process

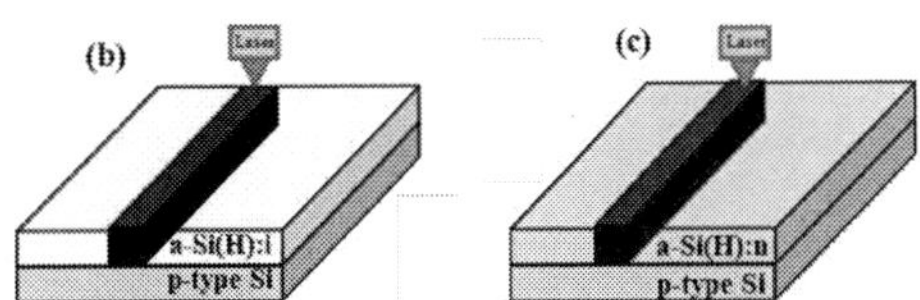

- ❖ **Scribing Parameters**
- ➤ Pulse energy: 26–30 µJ
- ➤ Repetition rates: 1 kHz (i-layer) and 10 kHz (n-layer)
- ➤ Processing gases: 6.9 bar argon (i-layer), 7.3 bar argon (n-layer)
- ➤ Applied energies: 1.6 µJ (i-layer) and 1.0 µJ (n-layer)

- ❖ **Characterization Tools**
- ➤ Ellipsometry: Measured layer thickness
- ➤ SEM: Surface morphology, line widths
- ➤ AFM: Topography, roughness, depth

Results

- ❖ **Intrinsic Layer (i-layer, 27 nm)**
- ➤ Line widths (SEM): ~16–26 µm across sets
- ➤ AFM widths: ~20–24 µm
- ➤ Surface roughness and edge deformation increased in later scans
- ➤ Thermal effects and redeposition observed

- ❖ **N-type Layer (n-layer, 82 nm)**
- ➤ Depth range: ~14–267 nm depending on line and set
- ➤ AFM widths: ~7–19 µm
- ➤ Progression from smooth → granular → nano-crystalline features
- ➤ Central laser zone (L2) showed most effective scribing
- ➤ Robust control with minor edge irregularities

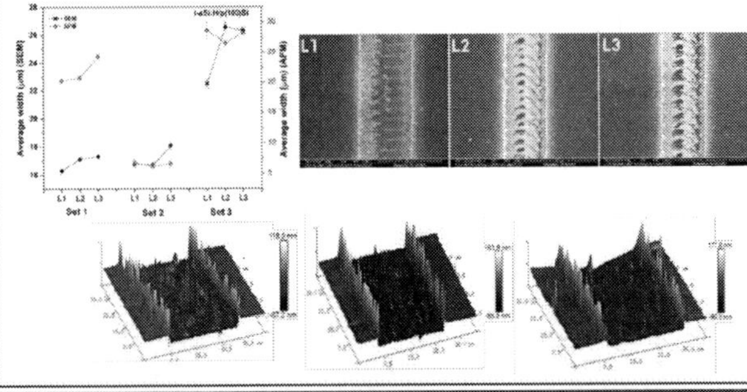

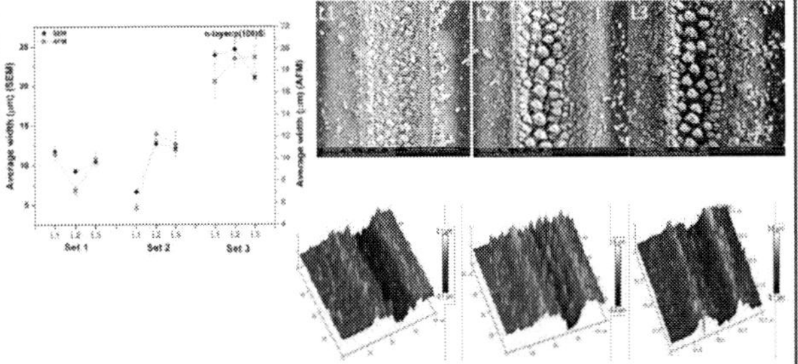

Conclusions

- ❖ UV laser scribing enables precise modifications of intrinsic and n-type amorphous silicon layers
- ❖ Achieved smooth and nano-crystalline surface features with minimal defects
- ❖ Some challenges remain: edge irregularities and surface roughness
- ❖ Process shows robust and consistent performance across layers
- ❖ Further optimization of pulse energy and scan stability will improve uniformity, scalability, and cost-effectiveness

Scientific Innovation

- ➤ First UV laser scribing study with this precision for i- and n-layers
- ➤ Improved control compared to conventional lasers
- ➤ Potential impact on thin-film solar manufacturing

Acknowledgements

- ➤ Innovation Fund Denmark (UVSOLAR, No. 2081-00016A)

Collaborators:

Funding:

AARHUS UNIVERSITY

Contact email: narendra.bandaru@ece.au.dk

Impact of Pre-Oxidation Treatment on Al₂O₃ Layers for High-Performance Silicon Solar Cells

Kyung Taek Jeong*, Minsoo Jeong, Sang Hee Lee, Yunae Cho, Hee-eun Song , Yong-Jin Kim **

Photovoltaics Research Department, Korea Institute of Energy Research

Motivation

A thermally grown SiO_2 interlayer was introduced between the Si substrate and Al_2O_3 to enhance surface passivation. Unlike conventional Al_2O_3 deposition relying on native SiO_2 formation, the deliberate SiO_2/Al_2O_3 stack yielded improved passivation quality. QSSPC and C–V analyses showed higher iV_{OC}, reduced interface defect density, and more uniform defect distribution compared to single Al_2O_3 layers. SEM and SIMS revealed that the SiO_2 interlayer suppressed hydrogen diffusion and mitigated blister formation during annealing, indicating improved interfacial stability.

Experimental

- Controlled oxide formation prior to Al_2O_3 deposition
  - Group A : Al_2O_3 deposited without an additional oxide layer
  - Group B : Thermally grown SiO_2(~2nm) introduced before Al_2O_3 deposition
- Annealing condition optimization for both groups (fig. 1)
  - Group A : optimum at 425℃
  - Group B : optimum at 500℃
  - Group A showed a larger decrease in iV_{OC} after firing
- Additional analysis performed to investigate the role of the SiO_2 interlayer at the interface (fig.3)

Fig. 1. Process for iV_{OC} optimization and SEM measurements

Fig. 2. IV_{OC} measurement results according to firing temperature

Fig. 3. Process for CV, SIMS, XPS measurements

Results & Analyses

- C–V measurement
- C–V measurements were carried out to analyze the fixed charge density (Q_f) and interface trap density (D_{it}), with D_{it} calculated by the conductance method.
- Both Q_f and D_{it} decreased when the SiO_2 growth was deliberately controlled, attributed to the positive fixed charges introduced by SiO_2 and the suppression of dangling bonds on the Si surface.

- SEM measurement
- SEM clearly revealed structural differences depending on the presence of the SiO_2 layer.
- Blistering is known to be strongly influenced by hydrogen content.
- Without SiO_2: blisters were observed, particularly around the valleys of the pyramid texture.
- With SiO_2: surface remained stable without blister formation.

- SIMS measurement
- SIMS analysis was performed to examine hydrogen and impurity distributions across the interface.
- Higher hydrogen concentration at the Al_2O_3/Si interface without SiO_2.
- Thermally grown SiO_2 effectively blocked hydrogen diffusion from Al_2O_3 into Si.
- This suppression reduced blister formation and improved interfacial stability.
- Depth profiles also confirmed more uniform elemental distribution in the stacked structure.

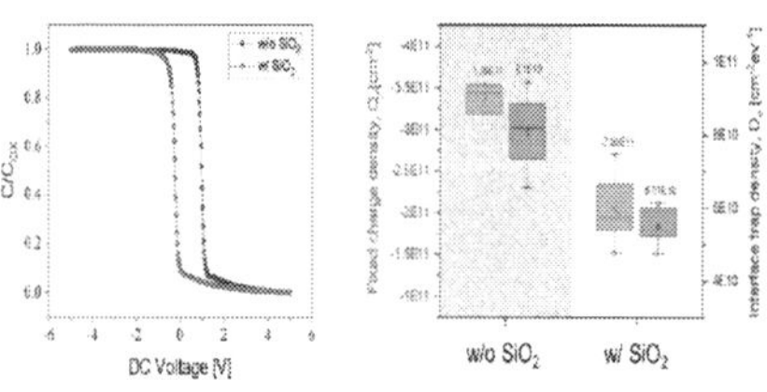

Fig. 4. C–V measurement results according to w/o and w/ SiO_2 layer and calculation results of Q_f and D_{it}

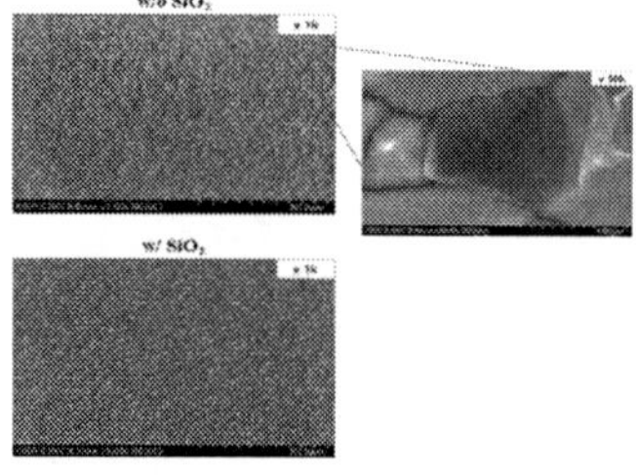

Fig. 5. SEM images according to w/o and w/ SiO_2 layer

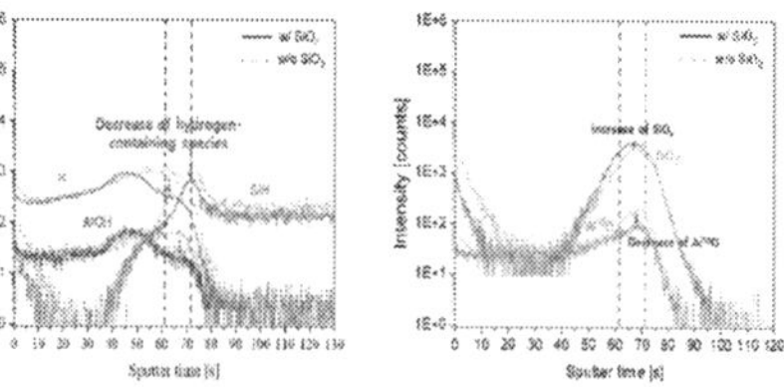

Fig. 6. SIMS profile of w/o and w/ SiO_2

Conclusion

- Introducing a thermally grown SiO_2 interlayer effectively improved interfacial passivation and stability.

- SIMS results indicated that SiO_2 growth reduced hydrogen-related bonding while enhancing oxygen bonding at the Si surface.

- This implies that SiO_2 passivated dangling bonds with oxygen and simultaneously blocked hydrogen incorporation and diffusion.

- Consequently, the SiO_2 interlayer suppressed blister formation during annealing and contributed to more reliable surface passivation.

HIGH EFFICIENCY SHJ SILICON BOTTOM CELL WITH IWO/SIO₂ STACK LAYER FOR III-V/SI TANDEM PHOTOVOLTAICS

Y. Ohshita[1], K. Nakamura[1], H. Lee[2], A. Ogura[2]

[1]Toyota Technological Institute, 2-12-1 Hisakata, Tempaku-ku, Nagoya 468-8511, Japan
[2]Meiji University, 1-1-1 Higashi-mita, Tama-ku, Kawasaki, Kanagawa 214-8571, Japan
Phone: +81-52-809-1876; e-mail: y_ohshita@toyota-ti.ac.jp

ABSTRACT: In this contribution, we demonstrated a route towards high-efficiency SHJ bottom subcells for the fabrication of high-efficiency and low-cost III−V/c-Si tandem solar cells. By optimizing the thickness of front IWO thin films, the reduced reflection loss in the near-infrared region and the contact resistance loss are achieved. This leads to a higher FF and Jsc of optimized SHJ solar cells. It is also shown that, by applying IWO/SiO₂ stack thin films for the fabrication of SHJ solar cells, we can obtain a high Jsc gain as well as high FF gain due to the reduced front reflection and enhanced rear reflection. Finally, we are able to improve the power conversion efficiency of SHJ solar cells from 22.80% to 24.88%, mainly driven by FF and Jsc improvement. Applying TCO/SiO₂ stack thin films for SHJ solar cells is a promising way to enhance both optical and electrical performance of SHJ solar cells for the fabrication of high-efficiency and low-cost III−V/c-Si tandem solar cells.
Keywords: transparent conducting oxide, IWO/SiO₂ stack, silicon heterojunction cell, III−V/c-Si tandem cell

1 INTRODUCTION

Vehicle integrate photovoltaics (VIPV)-powered electric vehicle (VIPV-EV) applications are very attractive for reducing CO_2 emission and creation of new market. In our previous study the Toyota Prius demonstration car powered by III−V three-junction solar cell modules with efficiency of more than 30% has shown actual driving distance of 29.1 km/day at 4.1 kWh/m²/day irradiation and 36.6 km/day at 6.2 kWh/m²/day irradiation conditions, respectively [1]. In addition, CO_2 emission reduction of 62 % has been demonstrated [2]. Despite this notable accomplishment, further efficiency improvements of solar cell modules more than 35% and cost reduction of solar cell modules are necessary in order to achieve longer driving distance of VIPV-EV with a daily driving distance of more than 30 km under average solar irradiation of 4 kWh/m²/day [3]. For the fabrication of such high-efficiency and cost-effective solar cells, III−V solar cells with the highest spectral efficiency among the high-bandgap materials appear as ideal tandem partners for low-cost crystalline silicon (c-Si) solar cells. Meanwhile, it has been reported that c-Si bottom subcells are a key limiting factor in the overall efficiency of III−V/c-Si tandem solar cells. Therefore, enhancing light absorption in the c-Si bottom subcell is crucial for enhancing the overall performance of III−V/c-Si tandem solar cells. In this contribution, we have studied to enhance near-infrared wavelength response of silicon heterojunction bottom subcells by optimizing the light management of silicon heterojunction bottom subcells.

2 EXPERIMENTAL PROCEDURES

Silicon heterojunction (SHJ) solar cells were prepared using n-type Czochralski (CZ) c-Si with 1-5 Ω·cm resistivity. The wafers were cleaned by RCA cleaning. Its surfaces were then textured with KOH and an additive to obtain random pyramids with heights in the range of 1-3 μm with <111> oriented facets and resulting in ~300 μm thick wafers. After RCA cleaning and a dip in a 2.5% diluted hydrofluoric acid solution, nominally 4 nm (i)a-Si:H plus 10 nm (p)a-Si:H layers were deposited at the rear side of the wafer to form the hole contact (rear junction). For the electron contact at the front side a 4 nm (i)a-Si:H and 12 nm (n)a-Si:H stack was deposited. The a-Si depositions were carried out by plasma-enhanced chemical vapor deposition (PECVD). Indium tungsten oxide (IWO) thin films were deposited by reactive plasma deposition (RPD) technique. Silver (Ag) electrodes were formed by photolithography and thermal evaporation of Ag. The fabricated SHJ solar cells were cured at 220 ∘C for 5 min on a hot-plate under an atmospheric condition. On top of the front and/or rear finished contacts a 110 nm SiO₂ thin film was deposited by sputtering. All SHJ solar cells were light-soaked under 1 sun illumination. To evaluate the SHJ solar cell performance, current–voltage (J-V) characteristics were measured under standard test conditions (AM1.5, 25 °C and 100 mW/cm²). External quantum efficiency (EQE) and reflectance were measured on a 20 × 20 mm² area on the cells with grids inside.

3 RESULTS AND DISCUSSION

3.1 Effects of front IWO thin film thicknesses on the performance of SHJ solar cells

For the investigation of the effects of front IWO thin film thicknesses on the optical and electrical properties of the fabricated SHJ solar cells, the SHJ solar cells with the front IWO thickness of 100, 120, 160, and 250 nm have been fabricated and the reflectance of these SHJ solar cells was measured. As shown in Fig. 1(a), when the IWO thickness increased from 100 nm to 250 nm, the wavelength at which the reflectance approaches zero was shifted to longer wavelength and the reflectance decreased in the near-infrared (NIR) spectral region. In Fig. 1(b), the measured EQE of the SHJ solar cells is shown. The measured EQE in the wavelength range of 300–550 nm decreased as the ITO thickness increased from 100 to 250 nm. However, the measured EQE in the wavelength range of 550–1100 nm increased as the IWO thickness increased. The wavelength range in which the EQE response increases is in line with the range in which the reflection is reduced. In Table 1, the J–V characteristics of the SHJ solar cells are shown. Due to the short-circuit current density (Jsc) and fill factor (FF) increased in the SHJ solar cells with thicker IWO thin films, the power conversion efficiency (PCE) of SHJ solar cells was significantly enhanced. The best SHJ solar cell with 120-nm-thick IWO thin films showed the PCE gain of 1%abs, the FF gain of

10.4229/EUPVSEC2025/1CV.2.42

0.021%abs, and Jsc gain of 0.74 mA/cm²abs compared to the SHJ solar cell with 100-nm-thick IWO thin films.

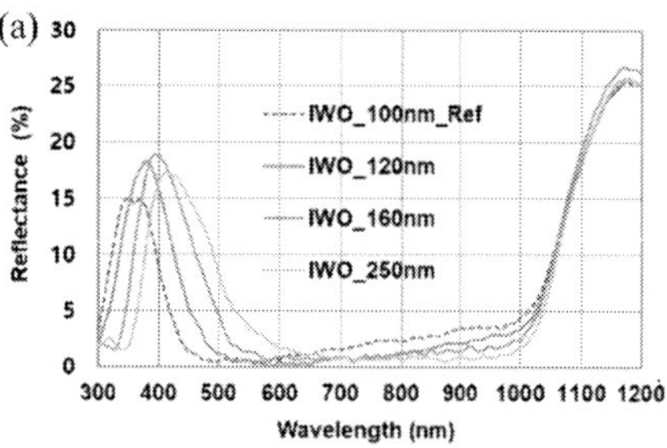

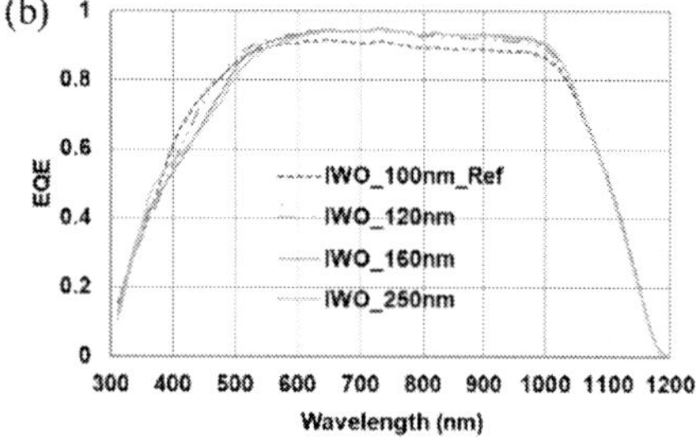

Figure 1: (a) Reflectance and (b) EQE of the SHJ solar cells with different thicknesses of front IWO thin films

Thickness of front IWO thin films	Sample	Isc [A]	Jsc [mA/cm²]	Voc [V]	FF [%]	η [%]
100nm	1-1	0.875	38.00	0.711	0.767	20.72
	1-2	0.896	38.90	0.721	0.804	22.53
	Avg.	0.886	38.45	0.718	0.786	21.63
120nm	2-1	0.903	39.20	0.718	0.802	22.59
	2-2	0.903	39.19	0.718	0.812	22.84
	Avg.	0.903	39.19	0.718	0.807	22.71
160nm	3-1	0.896	38.90	0.717	0.810	22.60
	3-2	0.896	38.90	0.717	0.803	22.40
	Avg.	0.896	38.90	0.717	0.807	22.50
250nm	4-1	0.890	38.61	0.718	0.803	22.27
	4-2	0.894	38.79	0.715	0.796	22.10
	Avg.	0.882	38.70	0.717	0.800	22.18

Table 1: J–V characteristics of the SHJ solar cells with different thicknesses of front IWO thin films

3.2 Effects of IWO/SiO₂ stack thin films on the performance of SHJ solar cells

For the investigation of the effects of IWO/SiO₂ stack thin films on the optical and electrical properties of the fabricated SHJ solar cells, the SHJ solar cells with the front-sided IWO/SiO₂ stack thin film, the rear-sided IWO/SiO₂ stack thin film, or the front/rear-sided IWO/SiO₂ stack thin films. As shown in Fig. 2(a), when the front-sided IWO/SiO₂ stack thin film and the front/rear-sided IWO/SiO₂ stack thin films were fabricated on the SHJ solar cells, the wavelength at which the reflectance approaches zero was shifted to longer wavelength and the reflectance decreased in the whole spectral region except the wavelength range of 420–530 nm. However, the rear-sided IWO/SiO₂ stack thin film demonstrated that the wavelength at which the reflectance approaches zero was shifted to shorter wavelength and the reflectance increased in the wavelength range of 450–1200 nm. In Fig. 2(b), the measured EQE of the SHJ cells is shown. The measured EQE in the whole spectral region increased when the IWO/SiO₂ stack thin films are applied on the SHJ solar cells. For the case of application of the front-sided IWO/SiO₂ stack thin film and the front/rear-sided IWO/SiO₂ stack thin films, the wavelength range in which the EQE response increases is in line with the range in which the reflection is reduced. However, for the case of application of the rear-sided IWO/SiO₂ stack thin film, the wavelength range in which the EQE response increases is in line with the range in which the reflection increases. This confirms the improved spectral response by the rear-sided IWO/SiO₂ stack thin film in the whole spectral region. In Table 2, the J–V characteristics of the SHJ solar cells are shown. Due to the increased Jsc and FF for the SHJ solar cells with IWO/SiO₂ stack thin films, the PCE of SHJ solar cells with IWO/SiO₂ stack thin films was significantly enhanced. The best SHJ solar cell with the front/rear IWO/SiO₂ stack thin films showed the PCE gain of 2.1%abs, the FF gain of 0.044%abs, and Jsc gain of 1.44 mA/cm²abs compared to the SHJ solar cell without IWO/SiO₂ stack thin films.

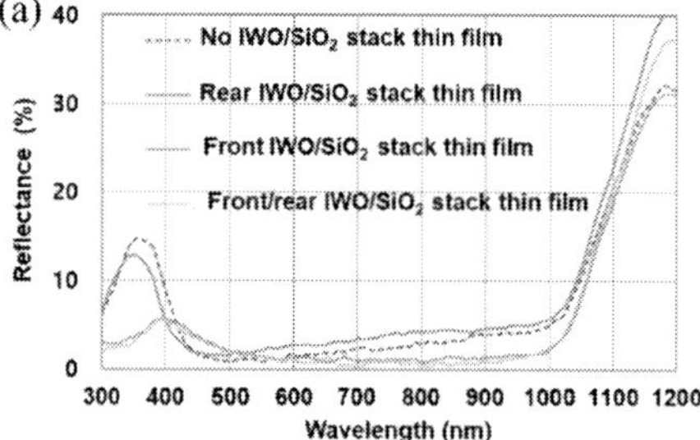

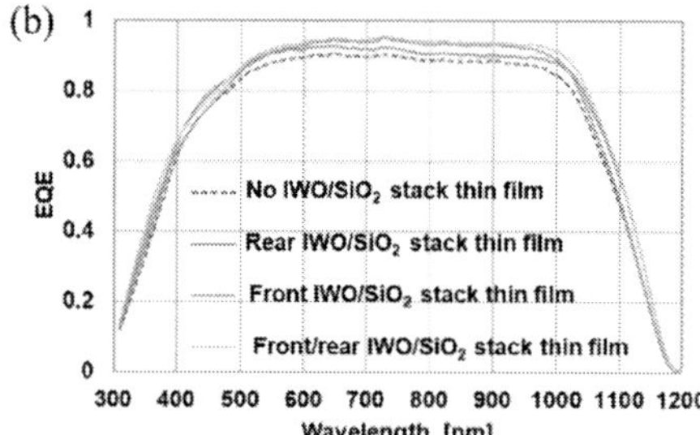

Figure 2: (a) Reflectance and (b) EQE of the SHJ solar cells with front-sided, rear-sided, and front/rear-sided IWO/SiO₂ stack thin films, and without an IWO/SiO₂ stack thin film.

Sample	Isc [A]	Jsc※ [mA/cm²]	Voc [V]	FF [%]	η [%]
No stack	0.919	39.88	0.722	0.792	22.80
Both side stack	0.950	41.22	0.722	0.836	24.88

Table 2: J–V characteristics of the SHJ solar cells with front/rear-sided IWO/SiO₂ stack thin films and without the IWO/SiO₂ stack thin film.

4 SUMMARY AND CONCLUSION

We demonstrated a route towards high-efficiency SHJ bottom subcells. By using an optimized front IWO thin film, reduced reflection and contact resistance losses were achieved. This led to a higher FF and Jsc of SHJ solar cells. It was also shown that, by applying IWO/SiO₂ stack thin films, we could obtain a higher Jsc gain in SHJ solar cells due to the reduced front reflection and enhanced rear reflection. Finally, we were able to improve the PCE of

SHJ solar cells from 22.80% to 24.88%, mainly driven by FF and Jsc improvement. Applying TCO/SiO$_2$ stack thin films on SHJ solar cells is a promising way to enhance both optical and electrical performance of SHJ solar cells for the fabrication of high-efficiency and cost-effective III−V/c-Si tandem solar cells.

ACKNOWLEDGEMENTS

This study was supported by a grant from the New Energy and Industrial Technology Development Organization (NEDO), Japan.

REFERENCES

[1] M. Yamaguchi, T. Masuda, K. Araki, et al. Prog. Photovolt. 29 (2021) 684-693.

[2] M. Yamaguchi, T. Masuda, T. Nakado, et al. IEEE J. Photovolt. 13 (2023) 343-348.

[3] T. Masuda, M. Yamaguchi, S. Iwasaki, et al. EPJ Photovolt. 16 (2025) 20.

Temperature Distribution in c-Si PV Modules Unraveled by Detailed Thermal Modeling

Špela Tomšič, Benjamin Lipovšek, Matevž Bokalič, Marko Topič
University of Ljubljana, Faculty of Electrical Engineering, Ljubljana, Slovenia

UNIVERSITY OF LJUBLJANA
Faculty of Electrical Engineering

Abstract

We first investigate the steady-state temperature profile of the entire frameless PV module installed in an open-rack configuration, operating at its maximum power point. We focus on studying the impact of various influencing parameters, such as the optical power density incident on a module, natural convection dependent on the module inclination angle, and forced convection induced by wind. After discerning the temperature distribution across the individual cells of the module, we finally analyze the power loss associated with this temperature inhomogeneity.

Modeling

The PV module studied in this work consists of 60 solar cells arranged in a 6 x 10 layout, with each cell having a surface area of $A_{sc} = 16.6\ \text{cm} \times 16.6\ \text{cm}$. The cells are spaced 2 mm apart at a distance of 43 mm and 10 mm from the short and long edge of the module, respectively. COMSOL Multiphysics simulation tool was used to obtain the temperature distribution within the complete PV module.

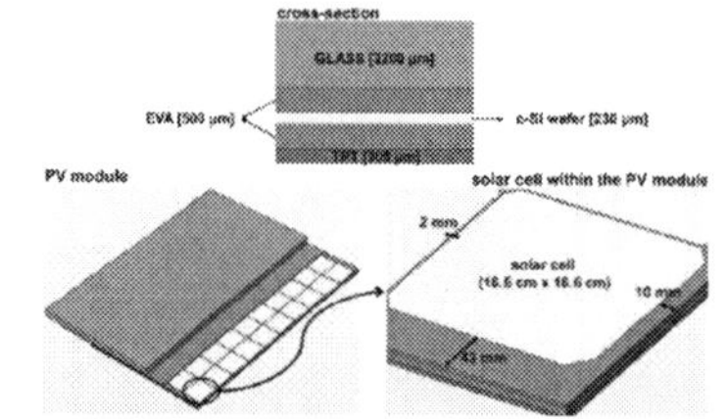

Natural convection vs. forced convection

The influence of natural convection and inclination angle

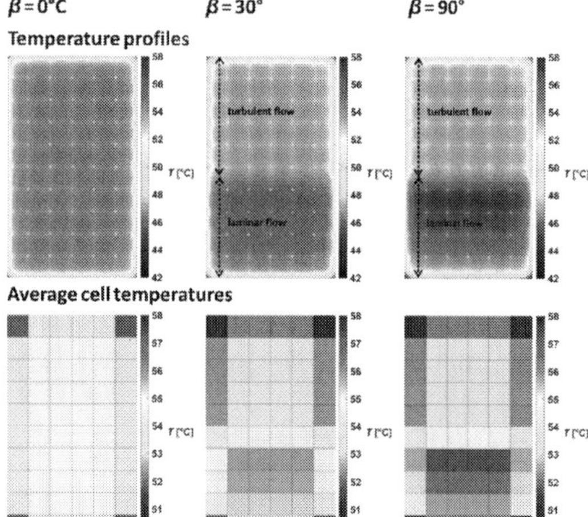

$\beta = 0°C$ $\beta = 30°$ $\beta = 90°$

Temperature profiles

Average cell temperatures

We first analyzed the influence of the inclination angle β on the convection of the PV module installed in portrait orientation. In the case of a horizontally positioned ($\beta = 0°$) PV module, we can notice a more homogenous temperature distribution compared to the profiles obtained at the other two β angles. This is because the heated air can travel more easily along the vertical ($\beta = 90°$) or tilted ($\beta = 30°$) rear surface of the module and may even transform from laminar flow to turbulent flow.

> **laminar flow can transform to turbulent flow at PV module surface**

Power loss analysis

Finally, we investigated to what extent the temperature inhomogeneity within the investigated PV module affects its output power. For this purpose we performed thermal modeling of the entire PV module, installed on the rooftop and calculated:

- the module power by considering the series connection of its cells,

- the power of the module by summing the power of the individual cells, as if they were operating independently from each other, and

- the power of the module as if all cells were operating at the same constant temperature.

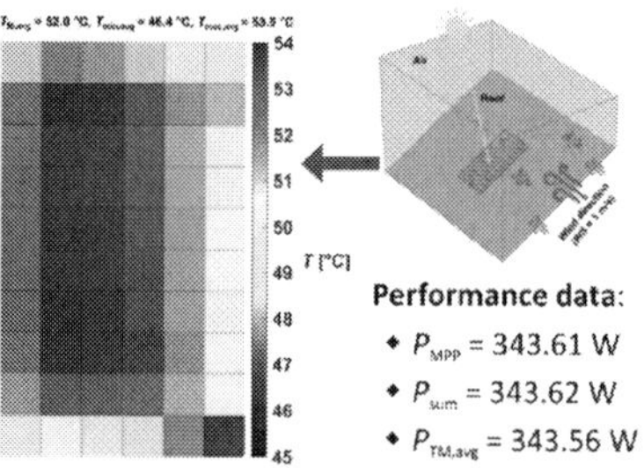

Performance data:
- $P_{MPP} = 343.61\ \text{W}$
- $P_{sum} = 343.62\ \text{W}$
- $P_{TM,avg} = 343.56\ \text{W}$

> **power loss of the PV module induced by operation of its solar cells at different temperatures is negligible**

The influence of forced convection and PV modue orientation

Next, we investigated the impact of the forced convection in the form of wind on the PV module temperature. In both module operation cases, the enhanced cooling effect begins once a sufficiently high wind speed is surpassed.

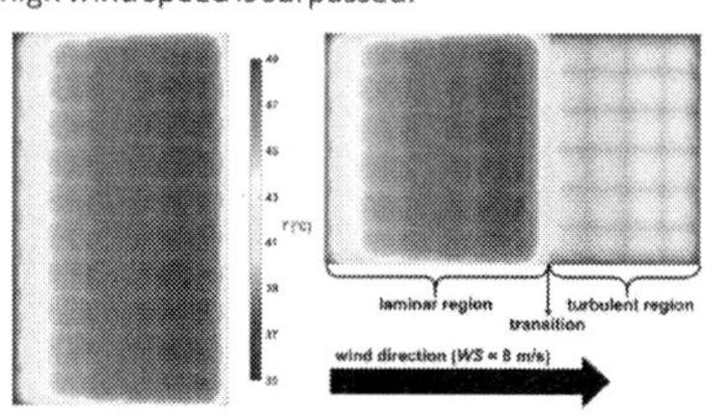

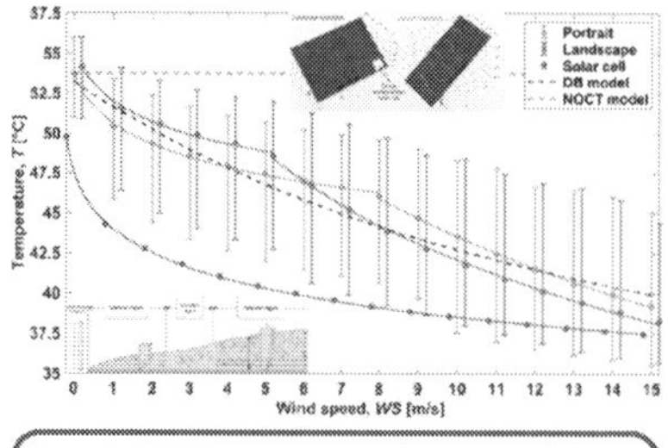

> **more than a 2 °C drop in average temperature at wind speed of 1 m/s**

Further details in ...

Š. Tomšič *et al.*, "Unraveling Temperature Distribution Within Crystalline Silicon PV Modules by Different Finite Element Method-Based Thermal Modeling Approaches," *Advanced Theory and Simulations*, p. 2401026, Mar 2025, doi: 10.1002/adts.202401026.

Acknowledgements

Slovenian Research and Innovation Agency: research program P2-0415

REVERSE ANALYSIS OF CONSTITUTIVE PROPERTIES OF SCREEN-PRINTED SILVER OF SILICON HETEROJUNCTION SOLAR CELLS FROM NANOINDENTATIONS

Pei-Chieh Hsiao[1], Jack Colwell[2], Daniel Chen[2], Chris Huang[2], Vince Allen[2], Alison Lennon[1] and Renate Egan[1]
[1] School of Photovoltaics and Renewable Energy Engineering, UNSW, Sydney, Australia, 2052
[2] Sundrive Solar Pty Ltd, Kurnell, NSW, Australia, 2231

ABSTRACT: The accuracy of long-term module reliability simulations requires the application of high-fidelity constitutive models of materials in the modules. Characterization of the constitutive model of screen-printed Ag contacts is not straightforward since tensile tests are not applicable for their thin-film structure. Although nanoindentation measurements are capable of measuring material hardness and the Young's modulus, the plastic response is not readily available. Reverse analysis through finite element analysis was applied to determine the power law constitutive model of screen-printed Ag contacts of silicon heterojunction solar cells (SHJ).

Keywords: Finite element analysis, screen-printed silver, constitutive model

1 INTRODUCTION

To ensure a 25-year warranty for silicon solar modules, the integrity and reliability of PV modules are routinely examined by a series of durability tests defined in the IEC 61215 standard. Nevertheless, the outdoor performance of PV modules operating in the field may appear differently due to various reasons. As such, reliability is an area of increasing interest and concern in the PV community and at academic institutes. Supplement to the deficiency of IEC tests, finite element modelling provides a systematic analysis in versatile approaches. Pivotal to the accuracy of simulations is applying high fidelity constitutive models of materials in the modules.

Screen printed metal contacts are the dominant method of metallization in silicon solar cells. Owing to their thin film morphologies, measuring the stress-strain curve from tensile tests is not possible, thereby their constitutive models are lacking in literature. The material properties of Ag paste of Al-BSF cells reported in [1] are likely unsuitable for TOPCon or SHJ cells due to the changes in the paste formulation for higher efficiency cells. In this report, the power law model of screen-printed Ag contacts was reverse analyzed using finite element modelling from nanoindentation measurements.

2 EXPERIMENTAL

A G12 screen-printed Ag SHJ cell was laser cleaved into small circles (diameter of 20 mm) and glued onto a hot-mount stub. The sample was ultrasonic cleaned for 1 min and sequentially polished using 1.0 and 0.5 μm abrasive disks to create a smooth surface suitable for nanoindentation performed using a Bruker Hysitron TI 900 TriboIndenter with a 3D Berkovich indenter. The load (P) displacement (h) curves were recorded with varying maximum loads beween 1 and 8 mN and a fixed strain rate of 0.1 s⁻¹. In total 25 measurements were performed with a spacing of 15 μm to avoid interference.

The stress (σ) strain (ε) relationship described in a power law constitutive model is,

$$\begin{cases} \sigma = E\varepsilon & \sigma < \sigma_y \\ \sigma = \sigma_y \left(1 + \frac{E}{\sigma_y}\varepsilon_p\right)^n & \sigma \geq \sigma_y \end{cases} \tag{1}$$

Where E is Young's modulus, σ_y is yield strength, ε_p is plastic strain and n is hardening exponent.

Nanoindentations typically report the hardness (H) and E of test materials. To describe the plastic response, a representative stress (σ_r) and a representative strain (ε_r) are used. The $\sigma - \varepsilon$ curves passing a specific point of (σ_r, ε_r) generally generate similar $P - h$ curves in nanoindentations. Therefore, the reverse analysis algorithm was developed in five steps:

- Step 1: use a reference $P - h$ curve of fused quartz to determine the indenter tip radius, r
- Step 2: determine σ_r by matching the loading phase of a $P - h$ curve
- Step 3: determine n by matching the slope of the unloading phase of a $P - h$ curve
- Step 4: determine ε_r by matching the complete $P - h$ curve
- Step 5: calculate σ_y

The finite element simulation applied 2D axisymmetric geometry. The nonideal bluntness of the indenter, which was modelled by a finite radius r, was estimated from the $P - h$ curve of fused quartz used for calibration with a known bilinear elastoplastic model from the literature [see Table 1]. Accurate tip radius is crucial as the tip geometry affects the required load for indentations. For the test material, σ_r was first determined by matching the loading phase of the $P - h$ curve using a bilinear elastic-perfect-plastic model. With an initial ε_r of 0.034 [2], the optimal n was decided by matching the stiffness (S), defined as the slope of the unloading phase of the $P - h$ curve near the maximum load (P_{max}). Subsequently, accurate ε_r was iteratively determined by coinciding the complete $P - h$ curve within a reasonable range around the initial ε_r. Once σ_r, ε_r and n were known, σ_y can be calculated according to Eq. (1).

The finite element simulation was conducted using ANSYS 2023R1 and the material properties listed in Table I. The Poisson ratio of screen-printed Ag is assumed to be 0.38 [2].

Table I: Material properties used in the reverse finite element analysis

Material	Young's modulus E (GPa)	Yield strength σ_y (MPa)	Poisson ratio ν	Isotropic tangent modulus E_T (GPa)
Indenter [3]	1014	-	0.07	-
Fused quartz [4]	71.4	6.0	0.17	13
Si [5]	170	-	0.28	-

3 RESULTS AND DISCUSSIONS

Figure 1 shows the fitted $P - h$ curve of reference fused quartz by varying the tip radius. An indenter tip with a radius of 200 nm resulted in a coinciding loading phase. Although the curves gradually deviated towards the end of the unloading phase due to the densification behavior of fused quartz, the plasticity model was sufficient to estimate the indenter tip radius

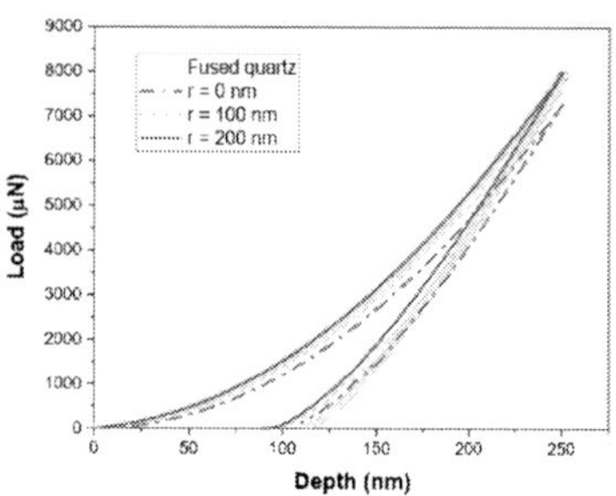

Figure 1: Fitted $P - h$ curves of fused quartz for the determination of indenter tip radius.

For nanoindentation of the test material, as indicated in Figure 2 (a), larger σ_r led to higher load at the same indent depth. The whole loading phase and P_{max} were simultaneously matched with an estimated σ_r of 229 MPa. Figure 2 (b) shows that S was primarily influenced by n. Via interpolation, the optimal n (≈ 0.49) was determined. By dichotomy, ε_r was lastly determined as shown in Figure 2 (c). The best fitted parameters accurately matched most of the loading phase and the unloading phase. The difference at the initial loading phase resulted from indentation size effect [6-8] due to higher density of dislocations generated within the reduced deformation zone when the indentation size decreased. The bottom unloading curve was inconsistent most likely due to the porosity of screen-printed Ag contacts.

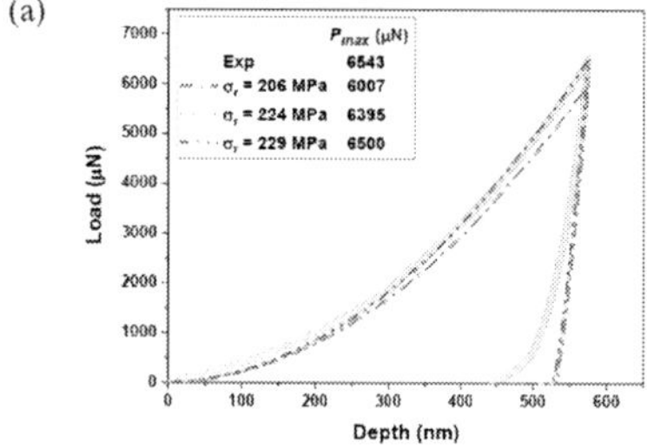

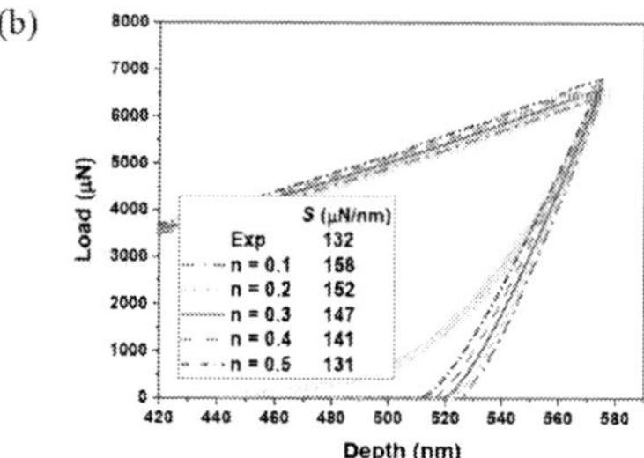

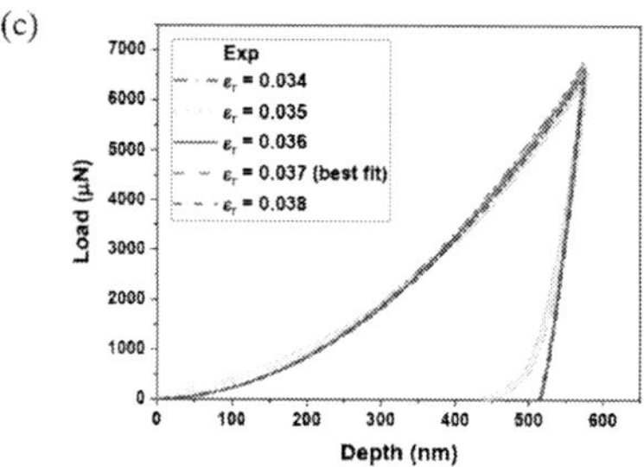

Figure 2: Fitted $P - h$ curves of screen-printed Ag of SHJ cells (a) Step 2 the determination of σ_r; (b) Step 3 the determination of n; and (c) Step 4 the determination of ε_r.

The estimated power law model is graphed in Figure 3. The developed model could assist in finite element simulation of cell and module reliability of emerging technologies, such as zero-busbar interconnection design, which aim to address demands to reduce Ag consumption. Direct bonding of wires to fingers has been demonstrated experimentally to show finger defects near the cell edges in wave-shaped wires soldering [9] and simulated higher stress in the outermost fingers interconnected by SWCT [10]. Consequently, zero-busbar interconnection requires thorough examination for its long-term mechanical stability.

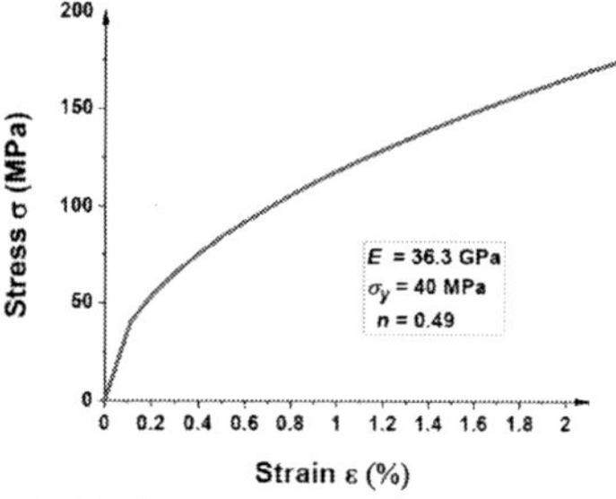

Figure 3: Fitted $P - h$ curves of screen-printed Ag of SHJ cells (a) Step 2 the determination of σ_r; (b) Step 3 the determination of n; and (c) Step 4 the determination of ε_r.

4 CONCLUSIONS

Estimation of power law constitutive model from nanoindentation load-displacement curves was investigated. The finite element reverse analysis consists of sequential determinations of indenter tip radius, representative stress, hardening exponent and representative strain. The extracted E, σ_y and n of screen-printed Ag of silicon heterojunction solar cells were 36.3 GPa, 40 MPa and 0.49, respectively. The developed model could assist in finite element simulation of cell and module reliability, for example direct bonding of wires to fingers in the zero-busbar interconnection.

ACKNOLOGEMENTS

This work has been supported by the Australian government through the Australian Renewable Energy Agency (ARENA), the Australian Centre for Advanced Photovoltaics (ACAP), and the NSW Government through its Environmental Trust. This research includes computations using the computational cluster Katana supported by Research Technology Services at UNSW Sydney. The authors also acknowledge the facilities and the scientific and technical assistance from School of Material Science.

REFERENCES

[1] C. Kohn *et al.*, "Analyses of warpage effects induced by passivation and electrode coatings in silicon solar cells," in *22nd European Photovoltaic Solar Energy Conference and Exhibition*, 2007.

[2] D. Paretkar, N. J. Glassmaker, K. R. Mikeska, G. Blackman, and A. Jagota, "Adhesion of screen-printed silver metallization to crystalline silicon solar cells," *IEEE Journal of Photovoltaics*, vol. 6, no. 5, pp. 1141-1151, 2016.

[3] Y. Li *et al.*, "Constitutive modelling of annealing behavior in through silicon vias-copper," *Materials Characterization*, vol. 179, p. 111359, 2021.

[4] D. Torres-Torres, J. Muñoz-Saldaña, L. Gutierrez-Ladron-de Guevara, A. Hurtado-Macías, and M. Swain, "Geometry and bluntness tip effects on elastic–plastic behaviour during nanoindentation of fused silica: experimental and FE simulation," *Modelling and Simulation in Materials Science and Engineering*, vol. 18, no. 7, p. 075006, 2010.

[5] M. Springer and N. Bosco, "On residual stresses and reference temperatures in thermomechanical simulations of photovoltaic modules using the finite element method," *IEEE Journal of Photovoltaics*, vol. 12, no. 3, pp. 853-859, 2022.

[6] M. S. De Guzman, G. Neubauer, P. Flinn, and W. D. Nix, "The role of indentation depth on the measured hardness of materials," *MRS online proceedings library (OPL)*, vol. 308, p. 613, 1993.

[7] N. Fleck, G. Muller, M. F. Ashby, and J. W. Hutchinson, "Strain gradient plasticity: theory and experiment," *Acta Metallurgica et materialia*, vol. 42, no. 2, pp. 475-487, 1994.

[8] W. D. Nix and H. Gao, "Indentation size effects in crystalline materials: a law for strain gradient plasticity," *Journal of the Mechanics and Physics of Solids*, vol. 46, no. 3, pp. 411-425, 1998.

[9] L. C. Rendler *et al.*, "Wave-shaped wires soldered on the finger grid of solar cells: Solder joint stability under thermal cycling," in *AIP Conference Proceedings*, 2018, vol. 1999, no. 1: AIP Publishing, p. 080001.

[10] P.-C. Hsiao *et al.*, "Comparative Models of Induced Thermomechanical Stress in Silicon Solar Cells Interconnected with Conventional Tabbing and Wire-Based Interconnection Methods," in *2019 IEEE 46th Photovoltaic Specialists Conference (PVSC)*, 2019: IEEE, pp. 0122-0125.

Reverse analysis of constitutive properties of screen-printed silver of silicon heterojunction solar cells from nanoindentations

Reverse analysis of constitutive properties of screen-printed silver of silicon heterojunction solar cells from nanoindentations

Pei-Chieh Hsiao[1], Jack Colwell[2], Daniel Chen[2], Chris Huang[2], Alison Lennon[1,2] and Renate Egan[1]

[1] School of Photovoltaics and Renewable Energy Engineering, UNSW, Sydney, Australia, 2052

[2] Sundrive Solar Pty Ltd, Kirrawee, NSW, Australia, 2232

Introduction

- Pivotal to the accuracy of finite element simulations is applying high fidelity constitutive models for a systematic analysis of Si solar cells and modules.
- Screen printed metal contacts are the dominant method of metallization in Si solar cells. Owing to their thin film morphologies, measuring the stress-strain curve by tensile tests is not possible.
- The power law model of screen-printed Ag contacts was reverse analyzed using finite element modelling from nanoindentation measurements.

Experimental

- Silicon heterojunction solar cell samples (2 mm in diameter) were ultrasonic cleaned and polished using 1.0 and 0.5 μm abrasive disks.
- Nanoindentation was performed using a Bruker Hysitron TI 900 TriboIndenter with a 3D Berkovich indenter.
- Load (P) - displacement (h) curves were recorded with varying maximum loads from 1 to 8 mN and a fixed strain rate of 0.1 s^{-1}.

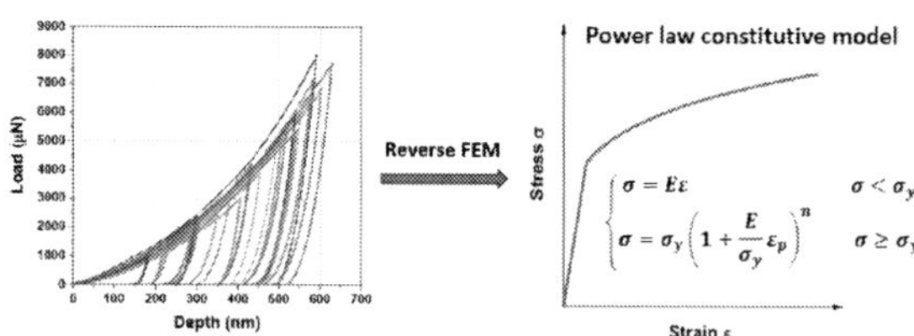

Reverse Finite Element Analysis

- **Material Properties**

Material	Young's modulus E (GPa)	Yield strength σ_y (MPa)	Poisson's ratio, v	Tangent modulus E_T (GPa)
Indenter [2]	1014	-	0.07	-
Fused quartz [3]	71.4	6.0	0.17	13
Si [4]	170	-	0.28	-
Screen-printed Ag	36.3	TBD	0.38	-

- **The algorithm consists of five steps**

Step 1 – use reference $P - h$ curve (fused quartz) to determine the tip radius of the indenter (r)
Step 2 – find representative stress (σ_r) using elastic-perfectly plastic model to match the loading phase
Step 3 – find stress hardening exponent (n) using power law model to match the slope of the unloading phase
Step 4 – find representative strain (ε_r) using power law model to match the complete $P - h$ curve
Step 5 – calculate σ_y

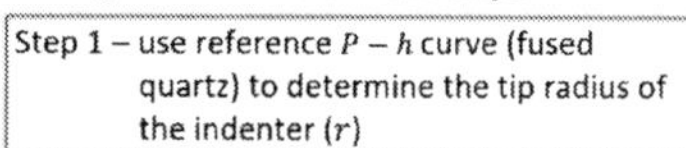

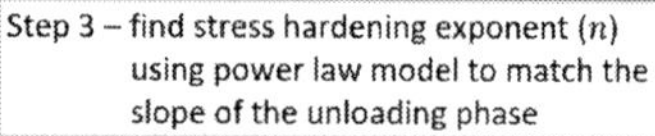

Results and Discussion

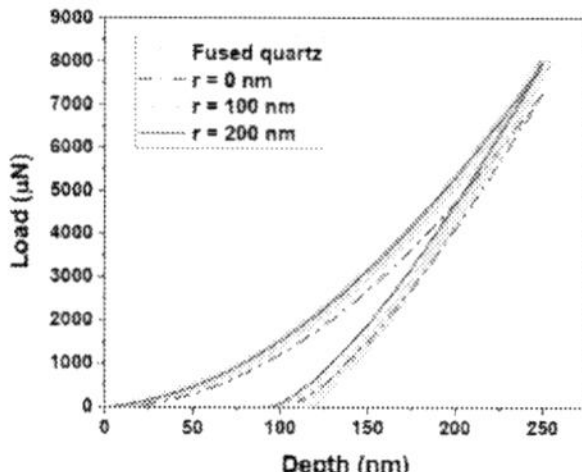

- Simple bilinear elastoplastic model can accurately simulate the loading phase but deviate at the unloading phase.
- The model is sufficient to determine the tip radius (r = 200 nm).

Step 2 - Find representative stress

- The initial σ_r is calculated by:

$$\frac{E_r}{H} = 0.231\frac{E_r}{\sigma_r} + 4.91$$

where H is hardness, E_r is reduced modulus.

- Subsequent σ_r is found by:

$$\sigma_r(i+1) = \sigma_r(i)\,\frac{P_{max}^{Exp}}{P_{max}^{FEM}}$$

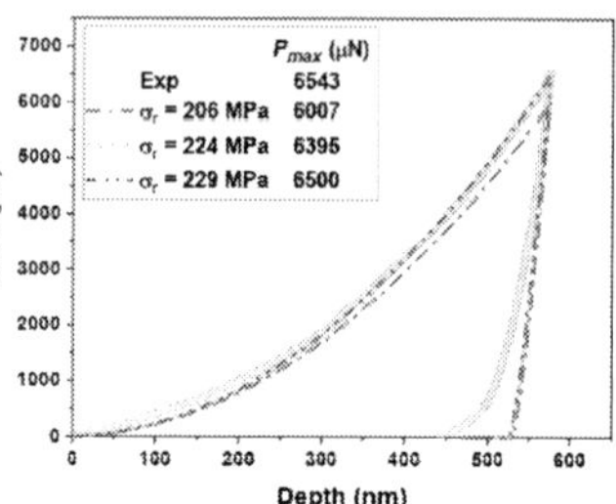

Step 3 - Find hardening exponent

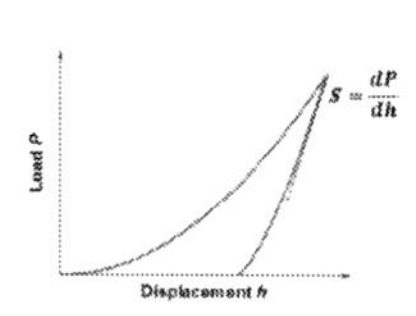

- Use an initial $\varepsilon_r = 0.034$ [1]

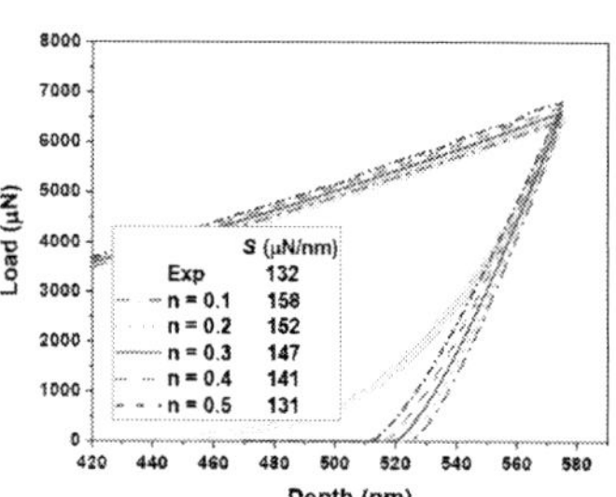

Step 4 - Find representative strain

- Vary ε_r around the initial ε_r.
- The difference at the initial loading phase resulted from indentation side effect.
- The bottom half of the unloading phase was not matched, possibly due to the porosity properties of screen-printed Ag.

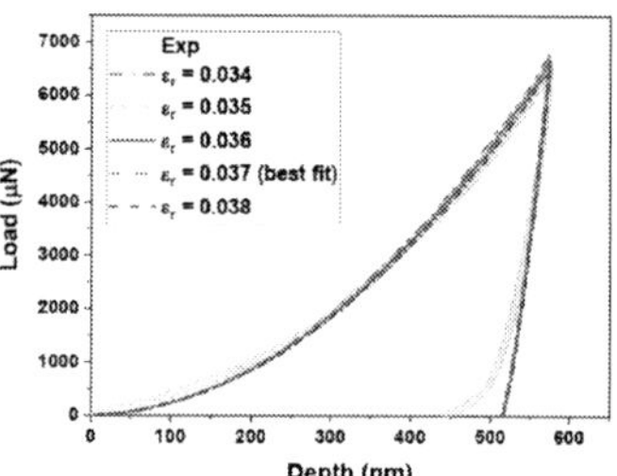

Step 5 – Apply to power law constitutive model

- The extracted E, σ_y and n of screen-printed Ag of silicon heterojunction solar cells were 36.3 GPa, 40 MPa and 0.49, respectively.

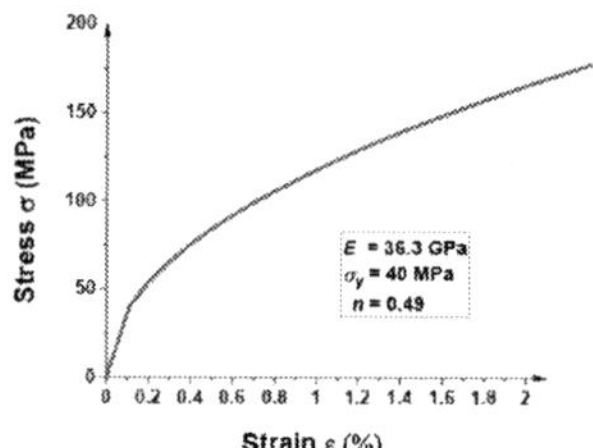

Conclusion

- Estimation of stress strain power law constitutive model from nanoindentation $P - h$ curves was investigated.
- The finite element reverse analysis consists of determining indenter tip radius, representative stress, hardening exponent and representative strain.
- The developed model could assist in finite element simulation in cell and module reliability, for example the zero-busbar interconnection design, which is an emerging technology in the pressing demand of reducing Ag consumption. Direct bonding of wires to fingers requires thorough examination for its long-term mechanical stability.

Acknowledgement

This project has been supported by the Australian government through the Australian Renewable Energy Agency (ARENA), the Australian Centre for Advanced Photovoltaics (ACAP) and the NSW Government through its Environmental Trust.

Reference

[1] J. Antunes, J. Fernandes, L. Menezes, and B. Chaparro, "A new approach for reverse analyses in depth-sensing indentation using numerical simulation," *Acta Materialia*, vol. 55, no. 1, pp. 69-81, 2007.

[2] Y. Li et al., "Constitutive modelling of annealing behavior in through silicon vias-copper," *Materials Characterization*, vol. 179, p. 111359, 2021.

[3] D. Torres-Torres, J. Muñoz-Saldaña, L. Gutierrez-Ladron-de Guevara, A. Hurtado-Macías, and M. Swain, "Geometry and bluntness tip effects on elastic-plastic behaviour during nanoindentation of fused silica: experimental and FE simulation," *Modelling and Simulation in Materials Science and Engineering*, vol. 18, no. 7, p. 075006, 2010.

[4] M. Springer and N. Bosco, "On residual stresses and reference temperatures in thermomechanical simulations of photovoltaic modules using the finite element method," *IEEE Journal of Photovoltaics*, vol. 12, no. 3, pp. 853-859, 2022.

STATUS AND PROSPECTS OF SOLAR CELL CHARACTERIZATION

K. Ramspeck, I. Djeukeu, J. Horn and M. Meixner
halm elektronik gmbh
Friesstraße 20, 60388 Frankfurt

ABSTRACT: This review presents an overview of state-of-the-art solar cell characterization techniques employed in end-of-line testing within high-throughput manufacturing environments. The technologies currently in use are introduced and their relevance to meeting industrial timing constraints is discussed. The effectiveness of established characterization methods is evaluated in the context of quality classification, price determination, and process optimization. Expanding beyond conventional approaches, the review addresses emerging requirements for advanced solar cell architectures - specifically tandem solar cells - and highlights novel techniques such as contactless IV measurements. The new requirements and challenges posed by tandem solar cell architectures are described, along with initial strategies developed to address these issues. Finally, a comparative assessment is provided of contactless and traditional contacting IV techniques based on their capability to satisfy the comprehensive requirements for solar cell characterization.
Keywords: Characterization, IV testing, production

1 INTRODUCTION

Solar cell characterization at the end of the production process is an important step in order to quantify the results of the foregoing process flow. Ever since, it has to serve certain goals. First of all, by measuring the power conversion efficiency solar cell characterization tests effectiveness of production output and determines its value. Furthermore, solar cell characterization shall determine, whether cell quality is good, or whether constraints in usability of the cells in modules are present. This adresses especially questions of security in usage of the cells. Finally, characterization of solar cells serves to understand cell technology. Potential for optimization and origins of efficiency losses have to be found and assigned to process steps in order to find better process settings and to test and compare new process flows. This sums up to the three main tasks of solar cell characterization in modern high speed production, quality sorting, price assignment and process/yield optimization. In order to deliver on these tasks, different approaches are required. Quality sorting requires a binary decision, whether or not a cell can be used in a solar module. Price assignment requires precise, quantitative information on efficiency, to group cells of identical power output and sell them accordingly. Process- and yield optimization opens up the widest field for characterization. Quantitative, spatially resolved and qualitative information is collected and used to identify and quantify defects and potentials, assign them to machines and processes and quickly detect occurrence of defects in order to remove the root cause creating them.

How these manifold and complex tasks are accomplished within the timing constraints of high throughput manufacturing by modern measurement equipment is the topic of our contribution.

2 INSTRUMENTATION

LED-based and Xenon-based flasher systems as the cetisPV-IUCT-LF3.1 or the cetisPV-IUCT-3600BF together with add-on options are capable of providing complete cell analysis within a total measurement time of 350 ms only. A number of versatile characterization techniques are combined in these systems with a typical timing for Si-solar cell characterization shown in Figure 1.

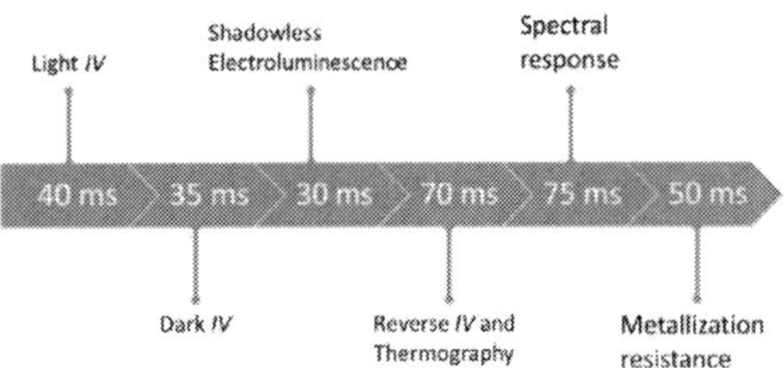

Figure 1: Timing overview for a complete Si-solar cell characterization.

In a first step, the light-IV curve is recorded within 40 ms, followed by 35 ms for acquisition of the dark-IV. Another 30 ms is reserved for electroluminescence (EL) imaging. Reverse-IV and thermography require a stake of approximately 70 ms. About 50 ms need to be reserved for thorough determination of metallization resistances and 75 ms is left over for spectral response (SR) measurements. It is worth noting, that different constraints on timing are set by different sorting machines and other options such as bifacial IV-measurements or Suns-V_{OC} may alter the total timing. Therefore, the sequence in Figure 1 gives just one possible example for illustration. Figure 2 displays a cetisPV-celltest5 laboratory setup, which utilizes the same components as the cetisPV-IUCT-LF3.1 production system and is capable of performing the above mentioned measurements within the required timing restrictions. A 28 wavelength LED light engine, cameras for shadowless EL, a pyrometer for temperature measurements, a thermography camera and versatile measurement electronics combined with a channel switching matrix for metallization resistance measurement make up the system.

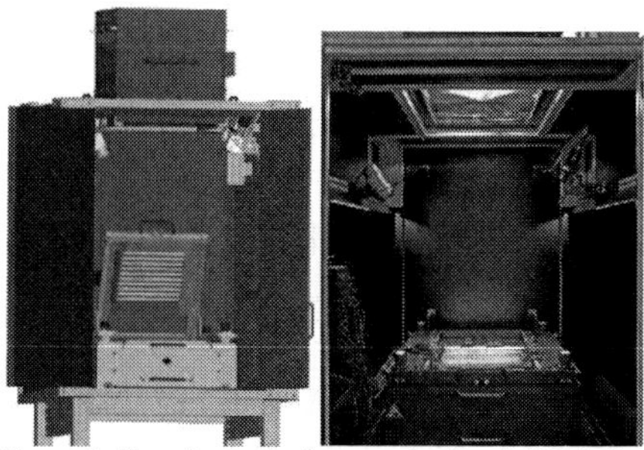

Figure 2: Drawing and photograph of cetisPV-Celltest5 for complete solar cell characterization.

The cell is mounted in a contacting station, positioned in the center of the dark room, which can be equipped with different contacting elements depending on the cell structure to be measured. Figure 3 features its spectrum and intensity map. A close match to AM1.5G and homogeneity of better than +/-1% over a 240 x 240 mm² illumination area are reached.

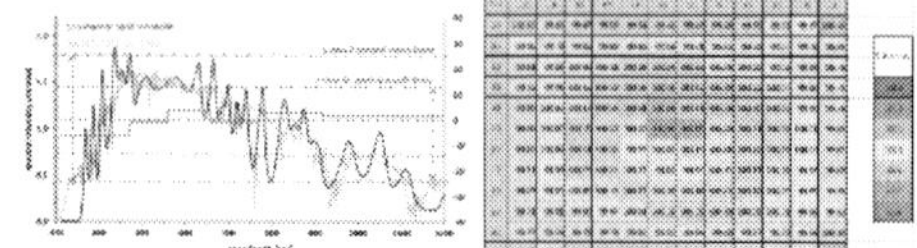

Figure 3: Spectrum compared to AM1.5G spectrum (left) and irradiance map (right) of LF3.1 light source.

3 STATE OF THE ART CHARACTERIZATION OF SI-SOLAR CELLS

The timing diagram in Figure 1 displays an exemplary measurement recipe performed for a complete characterization of solar cells in high throughput production. It comprises the measurement of light- and dark-*IV*, reverse characteristics and thermography, electroluminescence, spectral response and metallization resistances. In order to deliver precise results, the raw data as measured by the system requires sophisticated analysis and refinement. *IV*-curves need to be corrected for cell temperature, light intensity measured synchronized with the *IV*-data points [1], and transient effects caused by high charge carrier lifetimes in the Si-bulk which, for modern high efficiency cells are unavoidable within the timing constraints of production measurements [2]. While these transient effects are an obstacle in the determination of steady-state power output of the solar cell on the one hand, they provide additional information on the solar cell on the other hand and can be used i.e. to determine the cells base doping concentration [3]. Figure 4 gives an example of measured *IV*-curves on a modern high efficiency solar cell (upper left) together with the steady-state *IV*-curves derived from the raw-curves (upper right), the base doping concentration results (lower left) and the series resistance as a function of solar cell voltage (lower right). Notably, this parameter combines important resistive losses on the solar cell in one parameter of the diode model commonly used to describe the cells. As current flow patterns on the cell are altered when changing the operational state of the cell, the value for this so called „lumped series resistance" is not one fixed value for a solar cell, but changes as a function of the changes in current flow patterns [4].

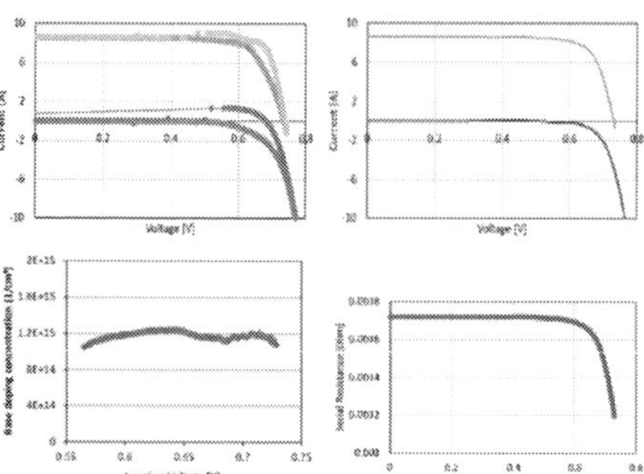

Figure 4: As measured *IV* data, derived steady-state *IV* curves, base doping concentration and series resistance as a function of voltage.

Being one of the main loss mechanisms in solar cells, the series resistance gains a lot of attention and separating origins of increased resistance is important for process and yield optimization. Two additional techniques are mainly utilized to gain further insight into this parameter. Measurements of metallization resistance between the contacts are used to determine the finger resistances and their contribution to the total series resistance and related losses. Making use of cell geometry and current, power losses, series resistance contribution and effect on fill-factor (FF) are calculated from the resistance values as shown in Table 1. One further information gained from these measurements is the minimum required silver or paste consumption to achieve the measured metallization resistance values. This information can be used to judge the effectiveness of the metallization process especially when combined with the paste consumption of the production line.

Table 1: Results from metallization resistance measurements and the derived impact on output power and silver consumption.

Parameter	Front Grid	Rear Grid
Measured Grid Resistance	41.5 – 45 mOhm	17.25 to 23.1 mOhm
Impact on FF	1.17 % – 1.27 %	0.49 % – 0.65 %
Rser contribution	0.82 – 0.89 mOhm	0.34 – 0.46 mOhm
Pmpp loss	96 – 104 mW	40 – 53 mW
Min Silver laydown	17 – 18.4 mg	33 – 44 mg
Min cost contribution	0.019 €/cell	0.042 €/cell

Besides the contribution of metallization resistance, sheet resistances, base resistance and contact resistance on both sides of the solar cell contribute to the total series resistance. As sheet resistance is often known with good accuracy, the effect of contact resistance is what remains and dominates series resistance variations not caused by the metallization directly. Thus, knowing the metallization resistance of each cell allows to discriminate the main causes for series resistance variation. Besides this global result, further spatial resolved information on series resistance is derived from electroluminescence imaging [5]. This widespread technique utilizes the intensity of radiative recombination which is suppressed in regions with competing increased nonradiative recombination. It reveals the geometrical distribution of all defects which act to reduce the charge carrier concentration in the solar cell under forward operating conditions in the dark. These defects comprise increased recombination by structural defects, impurities, surface passivation issues as well as series resistance related voltage variations. While commonly parts of the cell under test are shadowed by contacting structures, most recently shadowless EL-technique is introduced to the market, enabling to see the whole cell surface even in contacted state.

Figure 5: EL image, shadowless EL image and shadowless EL-image with marked defects of a Si-solar cell.

Figure 5 displays a standard EL and a shadowless EL-image of a modern multi-busbar cell, together with results from AI-based defect recognition. Due to different geometrical finger-prints, many different defects and root-causes for their appearance are discriminated from EL images, allowing intense feed-back into the process to optimize yield and cell quality. Given such a wealth of information, EL imaging has become one of the most important characterization techniques for Si-solar cell production and is used to sort out cells with severe local defects, to assign defective cells with less severe defects a quality grade B and to assess root causes for defects in order to optimize and monitor production [6].

One of the most important parameters of Si-solar cells is the short circuit current. It is influenced by the charge carrier diffusion length, metallization shading, reflective properties and light trapping. In order to assign root causes to fluctuations of this parameter, spectral response measurements are used. Spectral response variations show which of the parameters acting on the short circuit current has changed – which in turn can be related to certain process steps in production. Utilizing a large number of LEDs with different wavelengths, LED based flasher systems can directly be used to perform spectral response measurements of every solar cell produced [7]. Figure 6 displays results of an SR-measurement performed using the LED light engine of a cetis-PV Celltest5 system (blue dots).

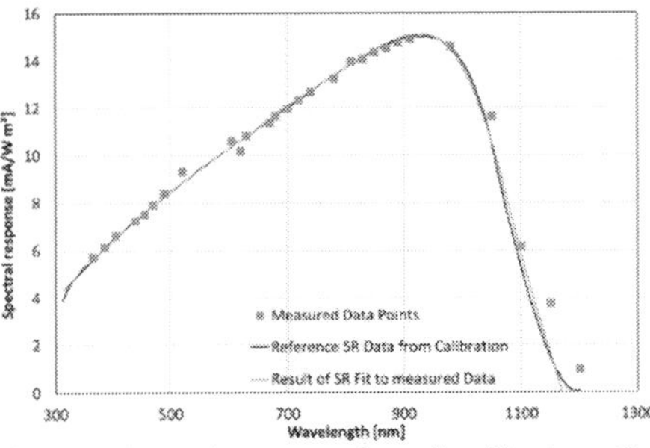

Figure 6: Spectral response data of a Si-solar cell as measured (blue dots) and spectral response curve derived from this data (orange curve) compared to the reference curve measured by an external certification institute (black curve).

The data requires further correction to account for the spectral distribution of each individual LED. The result of this correction is displayed as orange curve. As reference, measurement data from an external certification institute

is displayed as black curve. As shown in Figure 1, measurement time available in production is strongly limited and only about 75 ms are available for spectral response measurements. Therefore, not all LED channels can be measured under production conditions. Near neighbours and channels which do not provide additonal information can be omitted to increase the time available per channel for the other channels and still obtain the total SR information of the cell.

Finally, the reverse behaviour of solar cells is important to avoid hot-spots in the field. Reverse IV together with thermography measurements are used to cover this topic. As voltages under reverse biasing are much higher then forward operating voltages, power dissipation in local spots can be critical under these conditions while in operating conditions, these spots are completely inconspicuous. Therefore, a separate measurement under reverse bias is necessary. Either, a global reverse current criterium is used to sort out critical cells, or, using thermographic imaging, the distribution of reverse currents can be recorded and their impact on module temperature be calculated using a thermal model of the module [8,9]. This characterization technique is required for quality sorting of solar cells, to avoid unwanted hot spots which could cause module degradation and possibly failure under field operating conditions.

All this information on Si-solar cells is gathered and evaluated in about 350 ms time and thus made available in high-throughput manufacturing. It allows effective quality sorting, pricing and process tuning to optimize output and maintain quality of solar cell manufacturing. New solar cell concepts currently being developed add new requirements to characterization.

4 INCORPORATING TANDEMS

With perovskite-silicon tandem solar cells gaining more and more attention and constantly approaching maturity, characterization of such cells is required in laboratory environments as well as in production. However, the additional junction adds additional requirements for the measurements that need to be addressed. Since similar information is generally required for tandem cells as for single junction solar cells, we examine changes in the individual measurements and their impact on required measurement time. Most easily, metallization resistance measurement on two-terminal perovskite-Si tandem cells is not going to experience significant changes.

For the spectral response measurement a larger subsection of the total amount of available wavelengths will be required, as the spectral response curve form for two junctions is much more complex. Moreover, for a spectral response measurement on one subcell, the other subcell must be flooded with charge carriers to keep the cell under test limiting [10]. This means, that several wavelengths in the overlap region will have to be measured for both junctions, further increasing the required measurement time. Assuming a meaningful single junction measurement to be performed in 75 ms, we assume that about 125 ms might be required for a tandem measurement.

A similar consideration holds for reverse IV and hot-spot determination. As both junctions are connected in series, hot-spots need to be determined indivdually if spectral non-neutral shadowing is to be taken into consideration for outdoor conditions. This would directly double the required measurement time for reverse characterization from approximately 70 ms to 140 ms. Furthermore, evidence needs to be provided that such quick measurements with the reverse biased junction not being illuminated deliver meaningful results for judging the stability of the perovskite topcell.

For EL imaging, using two differently filtered cameras is a solution to measure the luminescence of both subcells synchronously [11]. Thereby, measurement time is not affected. Figure 7 shows EL images of a perovskite topcell and a silicon bottom cell, recorded with an image integration time of 100 ms each. For further reduction to 30 ms in production, binning of pixels is a commonly utilized technique.

Figure 7: Electroluminescence images of perovskite topcell (left) and silicon bottom cell (right)

Finally, the most basic and relevant characterization technique, measurement of IV curve and output power of the solar cells is what is most affected by the evolution from single junction Si solar cells to perovskite-Si tandem cells. Several requirements need to be adressed. First of all, spectral match must be taken into account for both junctions to obtain the correct current generation in both subcells. Even more important, however, are two effects acting on the form of the IV curve. The perovskite topcell tends to show metastability and change their recombination behavior depending on the operation condition. This effect may take place on different time scales causing hysteresis in quick IV measurements as shown in Figure 8, but as well causing slower effects like wake – up behavior of the cells upon illumination or degradation during the day and recovery over night [12, 13].

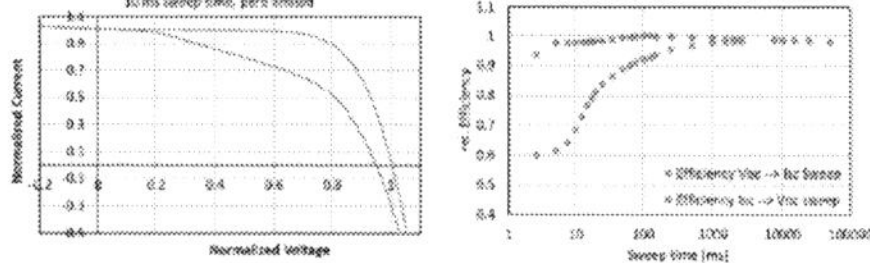

Figure 8: IV curves of a tandem solar cell in perovskite limiting illumination showing pronounced hysteresis and hysteresis behavior as a function of sweep time.

Figure 8 displays IV curves taken using 10 ms sweep time with a spectrum causing the cell to be limited by the perovskite topcell in current. The hysteresis observed shows a strongly different appearance compared to a standard single junction silicon hysteresis. Observing this behavior as a function of sweep time, pronounced hysteresis is observed even for relatively high sweep times up to about 1 sek in the case displayed in Figure 8.

For measurements with short sweep times, the hysteresis behavior of both subcells interact with each other. As the subcells are connected in series, current flow has to be

identical in both cells and hysteresis effects which alter the current flow of one cell shift the voltage of the other cell [14]. This hysteresis interplay complicates evaluation of the curves, which therefore need to be disentangled prior to applying hysteresis compensation methods. Finding suitable procedures for quick and precise IV characterization is currently still an active field and standard measurements of tandem cells still employ very slow IV sweeps and MPP tracking – often in the range of 5 min [15].

5 COMPARISON OF CONTACTLESS AND CONTACTED IV MEASUREMENTS

Recently, contactless IV measurements have been proposed [16, 17] as an alternative for standard IV measurements aiming to mitigate the need to develop contacting technologies for solar cell metallizations which are becoming more and more diverse. Such a technique could eventually replace the current IV testing systems, potentially reducing costs for production testing. In order to analyze the status of this technology we examine which information of the aforementioned characterization is gained by which measurement in contactless IV. Most importantly, the light IV parameters need to be measured precisely, i.e. power output, V_{OC}, I_{SC} and FF. V_{OC} can be derived from a calibrated PL measurement. Varying the light intensity, Suns-PL can be used to obtain a Suns-V_{OC} curve of the cell [18]. Parallel and series resistance require contactless EL-measurements effectively realized by two partially shaded PL measurements [19]. From the luminescence spectrum, the external quantum efficiency can be calculated [20] and a measurement of the spectral reflectance is used to complement this in order to determine the I_{SC} value. Aiming at a reduction of these measurements, AI has been proposed to derive IV data from Suns-PL and contactless EL alone in [16]. However, this approach requires contacted training data to be used and thus a development of contacting methods for the cell layouts it shall be applied to.

The proposed measurements require many aspects of standard measurement setups (luminescence cameras, sun simulator) and several measurements which might involve more than one light source or very high speed shutters. Moreover, while these approaches should allow to determine the light IV parameters no solution was presented for the measurement of reverse characteristics so far. As well, adaptability to new cell concepts and precision of contactless measurements remain to be proven, especially under production conditions. Moreover traceability and measurement uncertainty determination remain unclear especially in the case of the AI based application with reduced measurement effort. Furthermore, the treatment of transient effects that should be present e.g. in Suns-PL measurements as well was not adressed in literature so far. Finally, no operation of the cell at the operating point is possible, as all measurements are performed at open circuit conditions and only the partially shaded measurements allow a lateral current flow on the cell.

5 CONCLUSION

Characterization of single junction Si-solar cells in IV testers delivers a wealth of information in a very short period of time out of one single machine. Precise IV data, camera based luminescence measurements, reverse-characteristic, spectral response and metallization resistances allow to break-down loss mechanisms, detect and classify defects, sort out cells of minor quality or prone to hot-spots and finally assign a price to the finished device. Work is being done to expand this to tandem cell concepts where similar measurements deliver even more information to be evaluated. Finding solutions to reduce measurement times for methods which need to be applied to both junctions individually and mitigating metastable effects in *IV* measurement still need to be solved. Contactless *IV*, as a newly proposed method for analysis, still falls short in many aspects but provides valuable information and its concepts could be combined with state-of-the-art techniques to deliver even better inside into cell physics for each cell produced in volume manufacturing.

References

[1] IEC 60891:2021, VDE Verlag (2021)

[2] C. Monokroussos, M. Yoshita, K. Yamagoe, H. Müllejans, D. Pavanello, K. Ramspeck, D. Hinken, K. Bothe, Y. Fujita, G. Arnoux, F. Pinto, R. Ambigapathy, Q. Shi, H. Wilterdink, Y. F. Chen and Q. Gao, *Proc. of the 38th EU-PVSEC*, WIP, pp. 594 – 601 (2021)

[3] K. Ramspeck, L. Komp, S. Dauwe, K. Bothe, D. Hinken, M. Wolf and M. Meixner, *AIP Conf. Proc.* 2487, 030008 (2022)

[4] B. Fischer, P. Fath and E. Bucher, *Proc. of the 16th EU-PVSEC*, Glasgow, pp. 1365 – 1368 (2000)

[5] D. Hinken, K. Ramspeck, K. Bothe, B. Fischer and R.Brendel, *Appl. Phys. Lett.* 91, 182104 (2007)

[6] M. Alt, S. Fischer, S. Schenk, S. Zimmermann, K. Ramspeck and M. Meixner, *Proc. of the IEEE 7th WCPEC*, pp. 3298–3304, (2018)

[7] D. Chojniak, A. Schmid, J. Hohl-Ebinger, S. K. Reichmuth, G. Siefer, D. Kirk, C. Case and S. W. Glunz, *Solar RRL*, 9, 2400517 (2025)

[8] I. Geisemeyer, F. Fertig, W. Warta, S. Rein and M.C. Schubert, *Sol. En. Mat. & Sol. Cells*, 120, pp. 259 – 269 (2014)

[9] K. Ramspeck, S. Schenk, D. Duphorn, A. Metz and M. Meixner, *En. Proc.* 55, pp. 133 – 140 (2014)

[10] Y. Wang, X. Liu, Z. Zhou, P. Ru, H. Chen, X. Yang and L. Han, *Adv. Mater.*, 1803231 (2019)

[11] I. J. Djeukeu, J. Horn, M. Meixner, E. Wagner, S. W. Glunz and K. Ramspeck, *Solar RRL*, 8, 2400469 (2024)

[12] M. De Bastiani, E. Van Kerschaver, Q. Jeangros, A. U. Rehman, E. Aydin, F. H. Isikgor, A. J. Mirabelli, M. Babics, J. Liu, S. Zhumagali, E. Ugur, G. T. Harrison, T. G. Allen, B. Chen, Y. Hou, S. Shikin, E. H. Sargent, C. Ballif, M. Salvador and S. De Wolf, *ACS En. Lett.*, 6, pp. 2944 – 2951 (2021)

[13] M. Remec, Š. Tomšič, M. Khenkin, Q. Emery, J. Li, F. Scheler, B. Glažar, M. Jankovec, M. Jošt, E. Unger, S. Albrecht, R. Schlatmann, B. Lipovšek,C. Ulbrich and M. Topič, *Adv. En. Mat.*, 14, 2304452 (2024)

[14] J. Horn, F. Haas, K. Ramspeck, and M. Meixner, *Tandem PV Workshop*, Amsterdam (2024)

[15] M. Jošt, L. Kegelmann, L. Korte and S. Albrecht, *Adv. En. Mat.* 10, 1904102 (2020)

[16] J. M. Greulich, W. Wirtz, H. Hoeffler, N. Woehrle, M. K. Juhl, O. Kunz S. Rein and A. W. Bett, *Sol. En. Mat. & Sol. Cells*, 248, 111931 (2022)

[17] P. Kunze, J. M. Greulich, A. Tummalieh, W. Wirtz, H. Hoeffler, N. Woehrle, S. Glunz, S. Rein and M. Demant, *Solar RRL*, 2200599, 2022

[18] T. Trupke, R. Bardos, M. Abott and J. Cotter, *Appl. Phys. Lett.*, 87, 093503 (2005)

[19] H. Höffler, W. Wirtz, J.M. Greulich and S. Rein, *Proc. of the 38th EU-PVSEC*, WIP, pp. 233 – 236 (2021)

[20] U. Rau, *Phys. Rev. B*, 76, 085303 (2007)

Status and prospects of solar cell characterization

K. Ramspeck, I. Djeukeu, J. Horn and M. Meixner

halm elektronik gmbh, Friesstraße 20, 60388 Frankfurt am Main, Germany,

halm.

halm.

Motivation

- Solar cell characterization needs to deliver on three goals – quality control and sorting, value/price assignment, process control and optimization
- In reaching these goals no compromises on throughput are allowed
- We review state of the art characterization for all cell concepts in production and examine new requirement for future cell concepts

End of line characterization methods – state of the art

- cetisPV-IUCT-LF3.1 and cetisPV-IUCT3600-BF: LED and Xenon based sun simulators with add-on options provide complete analysis within 350 ms

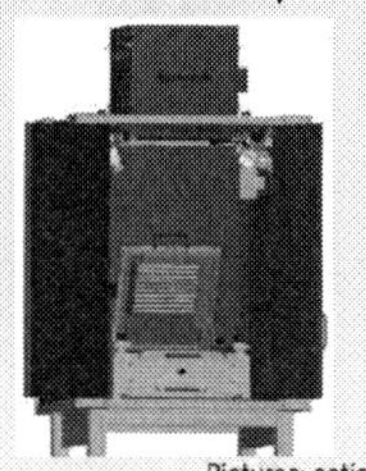

Pictures: cetisPV-celltest5 including light source LF3.1

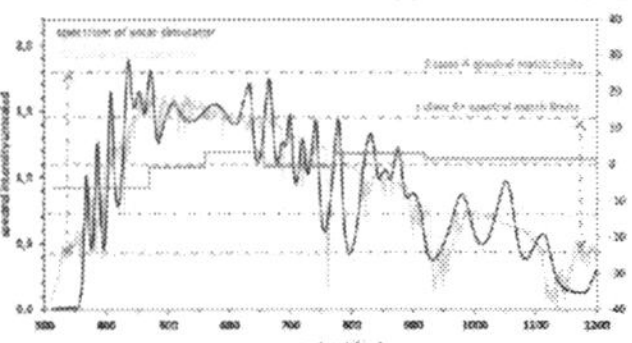
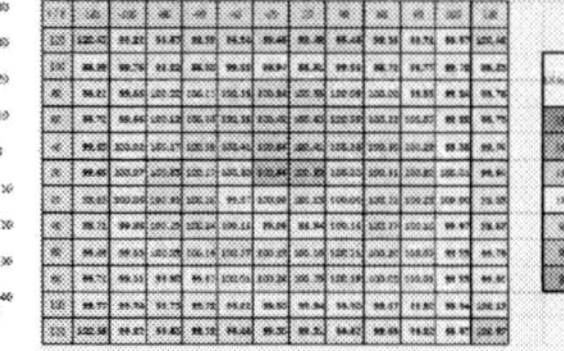

Spectrum and Irradiance map of light-source LF3.1

Typical timing of measurements done by the system for inline application – sub selections may alter the time available for individual measurements

Light IV 40 ms	Dark IV 35 ms	Shadowless Electroluminescence 30 ms	Reverse IV and Thermography – 70 ms	Spectral response – 75 ms	Metallization resistance – 50 ms

Data output of measurements and further evaluation

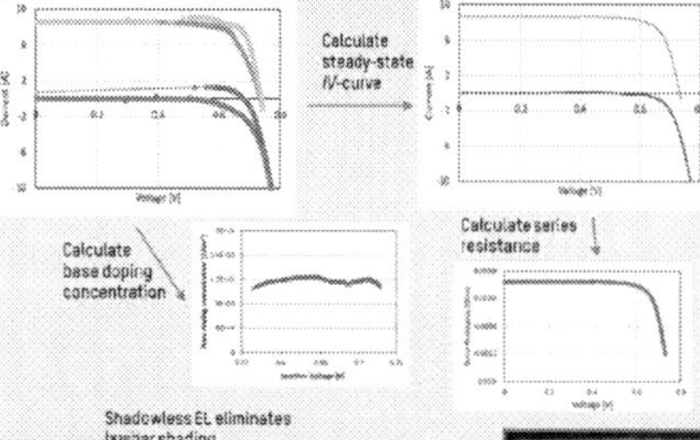

<u>Light and Dark IV:</u>
Hysteresis evaluation [1] yields Steady-State power output, series resistance, diode-model description, base doping and standard IV-parameters

Calculate steady-state IV-curve

Calculate base doping concentration

Calculate series resistance

<u>Shadowless EL:</u>
Discriminate numerous defects by lateral appearance [2], learn new defect classes, perform cell wide quality decision and process control/optimization

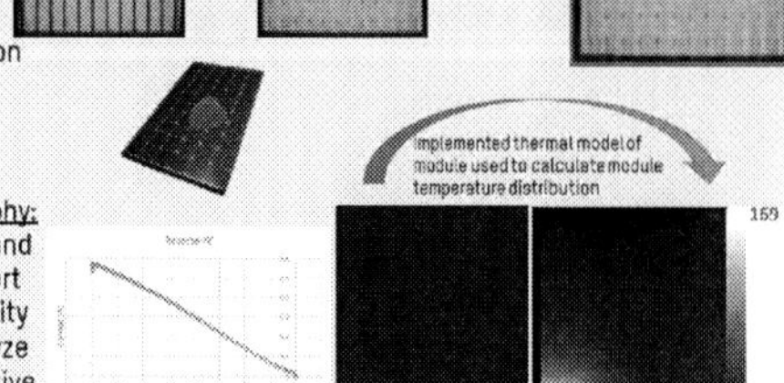

Shadowless EL eliminates busbar shading

AI evaluation to determine cell quality and discriminate defects

<u>Reverse IV and Thermography:</u>
Analyze shunt resistance and breakdown behavior [?], sort out cells that pose a security thread in operation – analyze root causes for reverse active defects

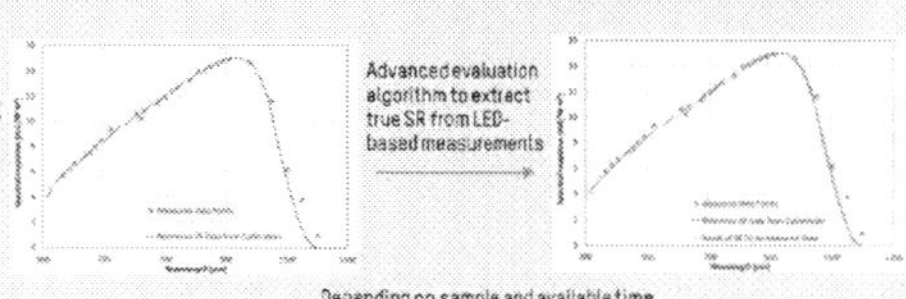

Implemented thermal model of module used to calculate module temperature distribution

<u>Spectral response:</u>
Gain insight into current losses and their origin, correlate with different layers in the cell

Advanced evaluation algorithm to extract true SR from LED-based measurements

Depending on sample and available time, reduction of measured channels required

Metallization resistance:

Examine series resistance contribution of contact grid, calculate minimum silver consumption for resistance

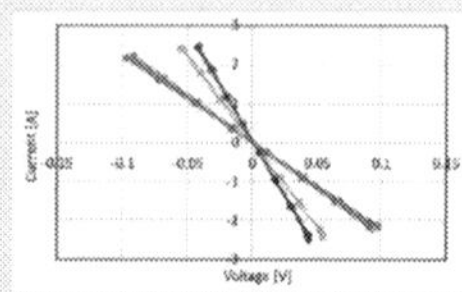

Parameter	Front Grid	Rear Grid
Measured Grid Resistance	41.5 – 45 mOhm	17.25 to 23.1 mOhm
Impact on FF	1.17 % – 1.27 %	0.49 % – 0.65%
Rser contribution	0.82 – 0.89 mOhm	0.34 – 0.46 mOhm
Pmpp loss	96 – 104 mW	40 – 53 mW
Min Silver laydown	17 – 18.4 mg	33 – 44 mg
Min cost contribution	0.019 €/cell	0.042 €/cell

Incorporating Tandems

Another junction adds new requirements – and measurements provide more information

Tandems add requirements for
- Light IV evaluation due to metastability [3] and interplay of Si and Pero hysteresis
- EL – due to defect coupling and two wavelength imaging
- Reverse characterization due to series interconnection
- SR – due to requirement to keep one cell limiting [4]
- Metallization resistance and dark IV measurement are mainly unchanged
- Pre-Conditioning

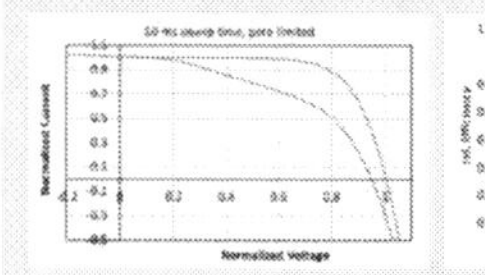
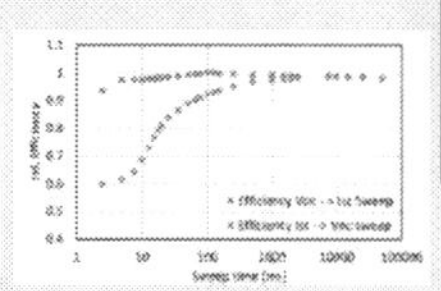

What happens with timing in production?

Light IV and Dark IV Currently – 5min	Shadowless Electroluminescence 30 ms	Reverse IV and Thermography – 140 ms	Spectral response – 125 ms	Metallization resistance – 50 ms

Contactless IV as a new solution?

Contactless IV – recently [5] proposed to mitigate contacting in solar cell characterization

Required measurements:
- Half shaded PL imaging (twice) for series resistance
- Spectral reflection for Shading and front side reflection → models used to get light trapping
- Luminescence Spectrum
- PL for V_{OC}, Suns-PL for Suns-V_{OC} → recombination behavior

I_{SC}:
- Shading by metallization
- Front side reflection
- Light trapping
- IQE
- Parasitic absorption

FF:
- Series Resistance
- SRH recombination
- Higher ideality recombination
- Shunt resistance

Pro Contactless IV	Contra Contactless IV
Remove contacting	Several PL measurements required
Remove IV-measurement and sun simulator	Yet no solution for reverse IV
Add-on measurements required anyway	I_{SC} definition from several different measurement methods
	Traceability and measurement uncertainty
	No operation at operating point
	Adaptability for new layouts and cell concepts
	Several additional equipment required
	Transient effects and their mitigation unclear

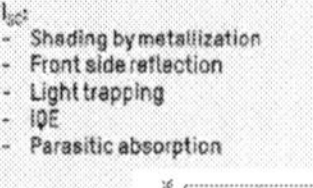
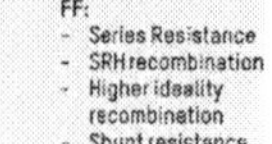
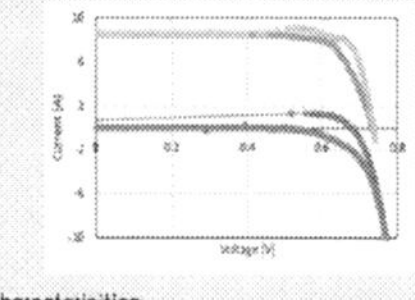
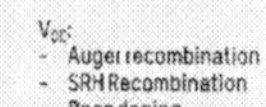

Reverse Characterisitics:
- Required to judge on hot-spot risks

V_{OC}:
- Auger recombination
- SRH Recombination
- Base doping
- Radiative recombination

Conclusion

Characterization of single junction Si-solar cells in IV-testers delivers a wealth of information in a very short period of time out of one single machine. Work is being done to expand this to tandem cell concepts where similar measurements deliver even more information to be evaluated. Contactless IV as a newly proposed method for analysis still falls short in many aspects but its concepts could be combined with state-of-the art techniques to deliver even better inside into cell physics for each cell produced in volume manufacturing.

References

[1] C. Monokroussos et al., Proc. of the 38th EU-PVSEC, 2021, p. 594 - 601

[2] M. Alt et al., Proc. of the 7th WCPEC, 2018, pp. 3298–330

[3] I. Geisemeyer et al., Sol. En. Mat. & Sol. Cells 120 (2014) 259 - 269

[4] Y. Wang et al., Adv. Mater. 2019, 1803231

[5] T. Song et al., Sol. RRL 2022, 6, 2200800

[6] P. Kunze et al., Sol. RRL 2022, 2200599

Email: k.ramspeck@halm.de

Applicability of Non-Contact Quantum Efficiency Measurements to Various Solar Cell Architectures

Hedayatullah Karimy, Manuel Meusel, Marko Turek

Motivation and Scope

1. LED sun simulators allow for innovative and fast measurement applications, e.g. rapid-EQE and rapid reflection [1]
2. Non-contact approaches have been developed, e.g. for I-V-measurements [2] and rapid-EQE measurements [3]
3. Industrial implementation of non-contact, non-STC measurements still open

→ Assessment of non-contact EQE (nc-EQE) approach using LED sun simulator

Experimental Approach Contactless rapid-EQE

- **LED sun simulator** SINUS360 with 27 LED-channels
- **Sensor** detecting local electro-luminescence
- **7 cell types** with variations in:
    - **Technology**: HJT vs. PERC / TOPCon
    - **Design**: busbars 9BB…3BB, sizes M6-M2
    - **Material**: mono-Si vs. multi-Si

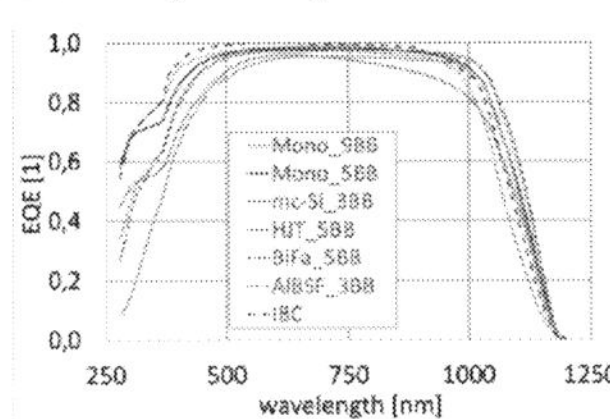

- **Reference EQE** data:
  LOANA tool → short and long wavelengths with clear variations

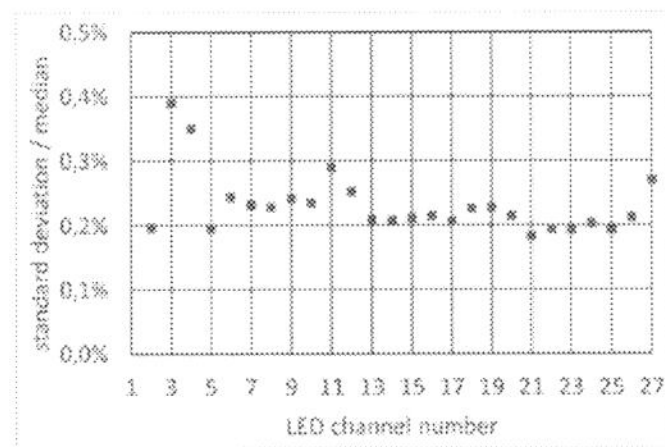

Assessment of measurement setup

- Repeatability for each LED-channel:

Result:

- LED-channel impacts overall signal → calibration by reference cells
- Low repeatability error of measurement chain »Light-source – EL-sensor«

Result: Example hetero-junction solar cell

- High agreement of nc-EQE with reference data
- Minor deviations at some specific wavelengths observed

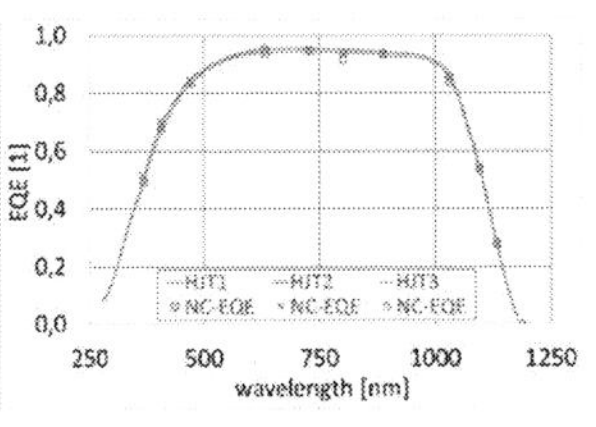

Result: Example mono-crystalline PERC cell

- High agreement of nc-EQE with reference data for some cells
- Few cells show clear deviations at several wavelengths

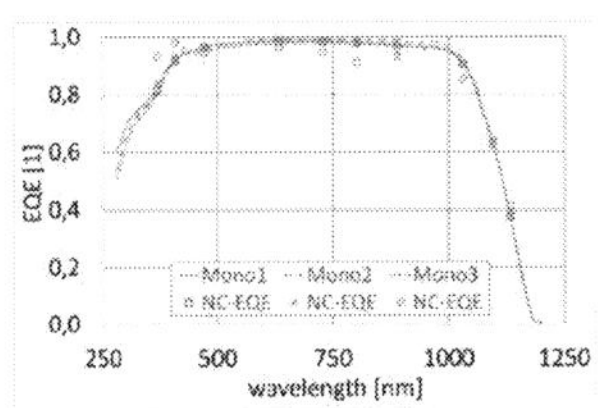

Result: Overview of all investigated cell types

- Overall relative integral errors below 1 % can be achieved
- A large spread can be observed for some cells
- Calibration cell of similar technology as test cell required

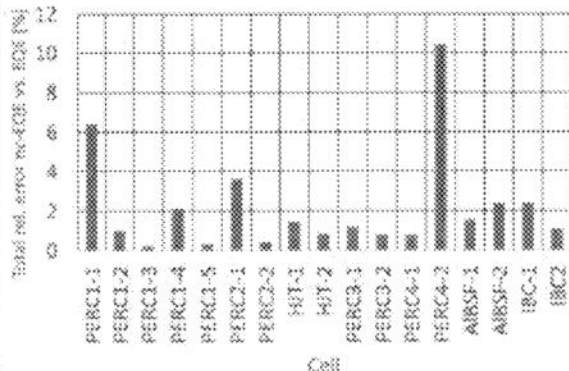

Summary

- Non-contact rapid-EQE using LED sun simulator implemented
- Measurement setup (light-source & sensor cell) with high repeatability
- Selection of suitable reference cell and correction algorithm essential
- Low relative errors <1 % can be achieved
- Large spread in nc-EQE data for individual cells due to local non-uniformities

Supported by the BMWK within the »OptiLearn«- project (FKZ 03EE1108A)

Supported by:
Federal Ministry for Economic Affairs and Energy
on the basis of a decision by the German Bundestag

Contact

Marko Turek
marko.turek@csp.fraunhofer.de
www.csp.fraunhofer.de

[1] M. Turek, K. Sporleder, T. Luka. Sol. Ener. Mat. & Sol. Cells 194, p 142 (2019).
[2] J. M. Greulich et. al. Sol. Ener. Mat. & Sol. Cells 248, p111931 (2022).
[3] K. S. Chan et al. Solar Energy Vol. 233, p 494 (2022)

STUDY FOR DECAY TREND OF THE SOLAR CELL UNDER VARIED RADIATION DOSE

Yean-San Long[1]*, Cheng-Wen Kuo[2], Yung-Tsung Liu[1], Min-An Tsai[1], Ta-Ming Kuan[2], Cheng-Yeh Yu[2]
[1]Center for Measurement Standards, Industrial Technology and Research Institute, Hsinchu 300, Taiwan.
[2]TSEC Corporation, No.85, Gaungfu N. Rd., Hsin-Chu 30351, Taiwan.
Contact information*: mickeylong88@itri.org.tw

ABSTRACT: Any parts and equipment used on satellites, including solar products, need to pass more stringent certification and testing standards than those on the surface. The low temperature and high radiation environment in space are very likely to have an adverse effect on electronic components, so testing the reliability of electronic components under low temperature conditions and their resistance to radiation is an important issue. In addition, the sources of space radiation include cosmic rays, solar flares and radiation belts. These sources contain various high-energy particles such as protons, electrons and heavy ions, which can cause degradation of satellite electronic components and temporary or permanent functional abnormalities. Therefore, before electronic components perform space missions, the impact of radiation needs to be evaluated on the ground. Damage to satellites from space radiation is inevitable, but it can be reduced through mitigation measures. The simplest method is shielding, but this will increase the satellite's payload weight and will not be effective in generating electricity for solar panels. Therefore, in this study, we use different ARC coating materials and consider the design of multi-layer anti-reflection layers to reduce the net charge accumulation at the interface so that it can be used in space environments. In addition, considering the subsequent module packaging method, it is also necessary to design the electrode pattern and the parameters that optimize the resistance to different radiation doses.
Keywords: Space, Solar cell, Dose

1 AIM AND APPROACH

The concept of Passivated Emitter and Rear Cells (PERC) was first proposed by Blakers et al. at the University of New South Wales (UNSW) in Australia in 1989. The main focus is on passivating the back surface of the silicon crystal cell and using local metal electrode contact to reduce the surface carrier recombination rate, increase the reflectivity of light on the back of the cell and the absorption of infrared light. The laboratory prototype cell is a small cell with a size of 2 cm × 2 cm and a P-type FZ silicon wafer. The photoelectric conversion efficiency can reach up to 22.8 %. Its structure is shown in the figure below. A few years later, UNSW developed a high-efficiency cell structure called Passivated Emitter and RearLocally Diffused (PERL) based on the PERC cell concept. Its conversion efficiency can reach 25 %, which remained the world record for quite a long time. The PERC cells in today's solar industry are still based on the PERC and PERL concepts proposed by UNSW. After more than 25 years of technical research and development by international research institutions and cell manufacturers, a low-cost, high-efficiency process has finally been developed, and the PERC prototype concept has been successfully introduced into industrial production. PERC has become the current silicon-based solar cell structure. Any parts and equipment used on satellites, including solar products, need to pass more stringent certification and testing standards than those on the surface. The low temperature and high radiation environment in space are very likely to have an adverse effect on electronic components, so testing the reliability of electronic components under low temperature conditions and their resistance to radiation is an important issue.

In addition, the sources of space radiation include cosmic rays, solar flares and radiation belts. These sources contain various high-energy particles such as protons, electrons and heavy ions, which can cause degradation of satellite electronic components and temporary or permanent functional abnormalities. Therefore, before electronic components perform space missions, the impact

of radiation needs to be evaluated on the ground. Damage to satellites from space radiation is inevitable, but it can be reduced through mitigation measures. The simplest method is shielding, but this will increase the satellite's payload weight and will not be effective in generating electricity for solar panels. Therefore, in this study, we use different ARC coating materials and consider the design of multi-layer anti-reflection layers to reduce the net charge accumulation at the interface so that it can be used in space environments. In addition, considering the subsequent module packaging method, it is also necessary to design the electrode pattern and the parameters that optimize the resistance to different radiation doses.

2 SCIENTIFIC INNOVATION AND RELEVANCE

The samples are PERC and TOPCon. All sample size are 1 cm2. In this study, we use different ARC coating materials and consider the design of multi-layer anti-reflection layers to reduce the net charge accumulation at the interface so that it can be used in space environments. In addition, considering the subsequent module packaging method, it is also necessary to design the electrode pattern and the parameters that optimize the resistance to different radiation doses. These I-V curves were carried out by Keithley Source Meter (Model 2651), and 3A solar simulator, meet IEC 60904 requirements. During the I-V measurement under solar simulator, the scan direction was forward and backward, the sample temperature should be stablized at 25 ℃ with a fluctuation of less than 1 ℃ and the irradiance intensity were determined using a reference cell (WPVS), respectively.The bias voltage we applied in the I – V measurement is changed stepwise from Isc to Voc (forward) or in the reverse direction (backward, Voc to Isc). Total Radiation flux：1×10^{13}、2×10^{13}、5×10^{13}、1×10^{14}、2×10^{14}、5×10^{14}、1×10^{15}, Testing Process shown in Fig 1

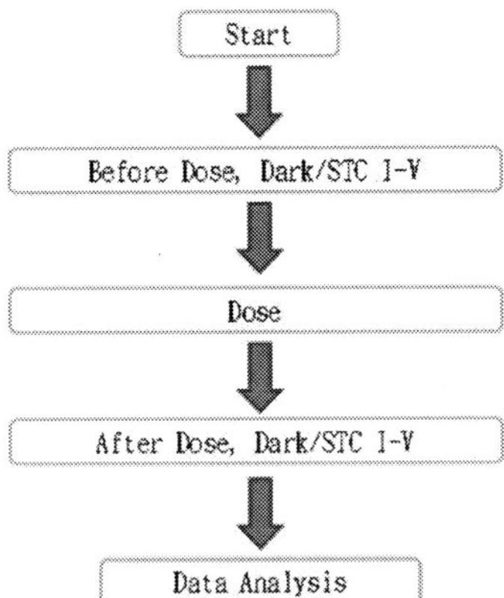

Fig. 1. Test process flow chart

3 RESULTS (OR PRELIMINARY RESULTS) AND CONCLUSIONS

In this work, we use different ARC coating materials and consider the design of multi-layer anti-reflection layers to reduce the net charge accumulation at the interface so that it can be used in space environments. In addition, considering the subsequent module packaging method, it is also necessary to design the electrode pattern and the parameters that optimize the resistance to different radiation doses. there is an irradiated part, and as the amount of irradiation increases, the back glass becomes darker. The Total dose under the irradiation flux is shown Fig. 2

In this work, from the electrical property difference before and after the test, we can get that the Pmax of Ref, S1 and S2 and TOPCon increases with the irradiation dose, ranging from 3 % to 28 % and has a certain balanced radiation resistance level at 1×10^{14} to 1×10^{15}. Therefore, the S2 cell designed this time has certain advantages in 1x1015.

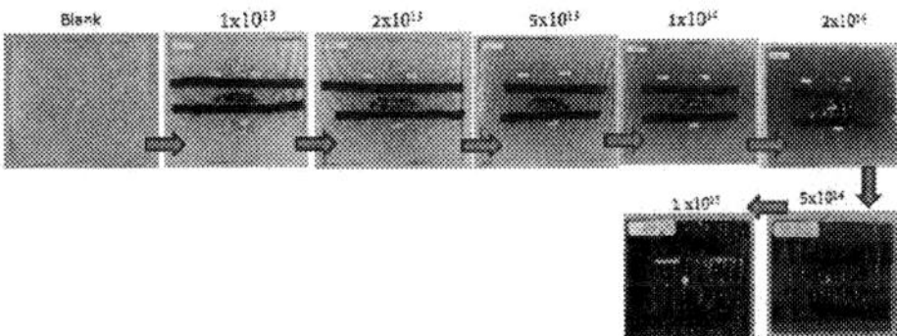

Fig. 2. Pictures for Visual Sample irradiation trend.

4 References

[1] Cory D. Cress et al.,"Radiation Effects in Carbon Nanoelectronics", Electronics, Vol. 1, pp. 23, 2012.
[2] A. W. Blakers, A. Wang, A. M. Milne, J. Zhao and M. A.Green, "22.8% efficient silicon solar cell", Appl. Phys. Lett., vol. 55, pp. 1363-1365, 1989.

Study for decay trend of the solar cell under varied Radiation dose

Yean-San Long[1*], Cheng-Wen Kuo[2], Yung-Tsung Liu[1], **Min-An Tsai**[1], Ta-Ming Kuan[2], Cheng-Yeh Yu[2]
Industrial Technology Research Institute (ITRI)[1] and TSEC Corporation[2]
*mickeylong88@itri.org.tw

ABSTRACT

Any parts and equipment used on satellites, including solar products, need to pass more stringent certification and testing standards than those on the surface. The low temperature and high radiation environment in space are very likely to have an adverse effect on electronic components, so testing the reliability of electronic components under low temperature conditions and their resistance to radiation is an important issue. In addition, the sources of space radiation include cosmic rays, solar flares and radiation belts. These sources contain various high-energy particles such as protons, electrons and heavy ions, which can cause degradation of satellite electronic components and temporary or permanent functional abnormalities. Therefore, before electronic components perform space missions, the impact of radiation needs to be evaluated on the ground. Damage to satellites from space radiation is inevitable, but it can be reduced through mitigation measures. The simplest method is shielding, but this will increase the satellite's payload weight and will not be effective in generating electricity for solar panels. Therefore, in this study, we use different ARC coating materials and consider the design of multi-layer anti-reflection layers to reduce the net charge accumulation at the interface so that it can be used in space environments. In addition, considering the subsequent module packaging method, it is also necessary to design the electrode pattern and the parameters that optimize the resistance to different radiation doses.

The samples are PERC and TOPCon. All sample size are 1 cm². In this study, we use different ARC coating materials and consider the design of multi-layer anti-reflection layers to reduce the net charge accumulation at the interface so that it can be used in space environments. In addition, considering the subsequent module packaging method, it is also necessary to design the electrode pattern and the parameters that optimize the resistance to different radiation doses. These I-V curves were carried out by Keithley Source Meter (Model 2651), and 3A solar simulator, meet IEC 60904 requirements. During the I-V measurement under solar simulator, the scan direction was forward and backward, the sample temperature should be stablized at 25 °C with a fluctuation of less than 1 °C and the irradiance intensity were determined using a reference cell (WPVS), respectively. The bias voltage we applied in the I–V measurement is changed stepwise from Isc to Voc (forward) or in the reverse direction (backward, Voc to Isc). Total Radiation flux： 1×10^{13}、2×10^{13}、5×10^{13}、1×10^{14}、2×10^{14}、5×10^{14}、1×10^{15}, Testing Process shown in Fig 1

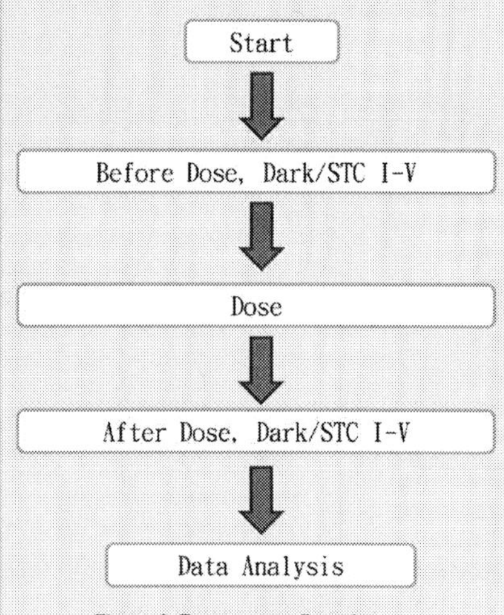

Figure 1: Test process flow chart

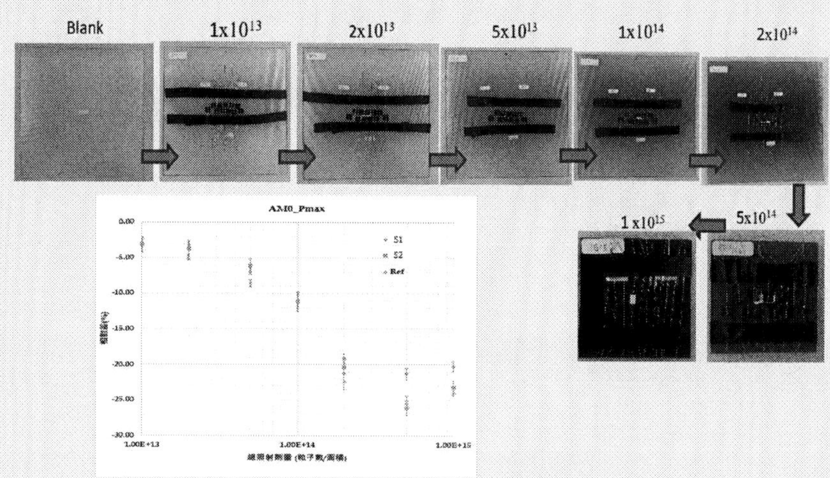

Figure 2: Pictures for Visual Sample irradiation trend

Conclusions

In this work, we use different ARC coating materials and consider the design of multi-layer anti-reflection layers to reduce the net charge accumulation at the interface so that it can be used in space environments. In addition, considering the subsequent module packaging method, it is also necessary to design the electrode pattern and the parameters that optimize the resistance to different radiation doses. there is an irradiated part, and as the amount of irradiation increases, the back glass becomes darker. The Total dose under the irradiation flux is shown Fig. 2

In this work, from the electrical property difference before and after the test, we can get that the Pmax of Ref, S1 and S2 and TOPCon increases with the irradiation dose, ranging from 3 % to 28 % and has a certain balanced radiation resistance level at 1×10^{14} to 1×10^{15}. Therefore, the S2 cell designed this time has certain advantages in 1×10^{15}.

ANALYSIS OF SERIES RESISTANCE EFFECTS IN CURRENT SOLAR CELL TECHNOLOGIES

Yeray Mateos, Aloña Otaegi, Eneko Cereceda, Vanesa Fano, Nekane Azkona, Eneko Ortega,
José Rubén Gutiérrez and Juan Carlos Jimeno
Institute of Microelectronic Technology, University of the Basque Country, UPV/EHU, Bilbao, Spain
Torres Quevedo ingeniaria plaza 1. 48013, Bilbao, Spain

ABSTRACT: Sunpower's IBC MAXEON III solar cells, composed of three subcells connected in parallel, are studied using a custom-designed PCB prototype adapted for back-contact measurement. The PCB includes metal strips inspired by old 3R12 batteries to ensure solid contact. In addition, the prototype consists of six jumpers, connected just before the cell connection pads allowing selective disconnection to simulate contact faults. EL images are obtained, when injecting 4 A to the cells and two scenarios were tested: in Scenario A, pad 3 (input of subcell) was disconnected, resulting in partially disconnection of subcell; in Scenario B, pads 3 and 4 were disconnected, complete disconnection of one of the subcells leading to minimal leakage current.
Keywords: PCB, IBC, contact-failure

1. INTRODUCTION

The evolution towards back-contact solar cells represents a significant advance in the efficiency of the cell since the incident effective area corresponds to the total geometric area of the front. This happens because, as the name suggests, the front contacts are moved to the back [1-3]. However, characterisation equipments are used to measure Al-BSF or PERC-type solar cells, and if front contacts are moved to the back, basic characterization measurements such as light or dark IV-curves or luminescent measurements become complicated. Furthermore, each manufacturer develops its back contact solar cells based on its own design, and multi-bus or pad-based back contact solar cells can be found in the market [3-4]. Therefore, to summarise this paragraph, it could be said that it is difficult to characterise IBC cells because it is not easy to find equipment adapted to every single design case.

On the other hand, if a prototype for measuring the back contact cells can be manufactured, it is possible to experiment with this prototype and adapt it in turn to characterise certain effects in the cells. If jumpers are added that disconnect certain connections of the solar cell, it would be possible, to go beyond basic characterization and study other effects, i. e. ribbon layer soldering failures, in order to analyse contact failures. Series resistance is the sum of different resistance contributions, including contact resistance. This contact resistance depends on certain factors, one of which is the metal pressure on temporary contacts (in measurements). The effect of a high series resistance is also detected if there is a contact fault or poor soldering, or cracking in the ribbon layer and the effect is a decrease in efficiency [5, 6].

The aim of this work is, on the one hand, to develop a prototype that allows a direct adaptation of characterisation equipment, previously used to measure conventional Al-BSF or PERC cells, in order to be able to measure back contact solar cells such as MAXEON III. On the other hand, it would be interesting to be able to induce contact faults in this prototype in order to detect poor soldering effects and study contact resistance series resistance increase.

2. PROTOTYPE IMPLEMENTATION

Sunpower's IBC MAXEON III are under study. These IBC cells consist of three subcells parallel connected by a thin metallic line in the borders. Fig. 1 shows the rear side of the cell; in this cell the pads have been numbered as if they were pins on an integrated circuit, counterclockwise from the first pad counting from the upper left corner, from 1 to 6. The detail show that pads 1 and 2 are connected by the thin metalic line, as well as pad 5 and 6. The three subcells are then defined by pads 1-6, pads 2-5 and pads 3-4.

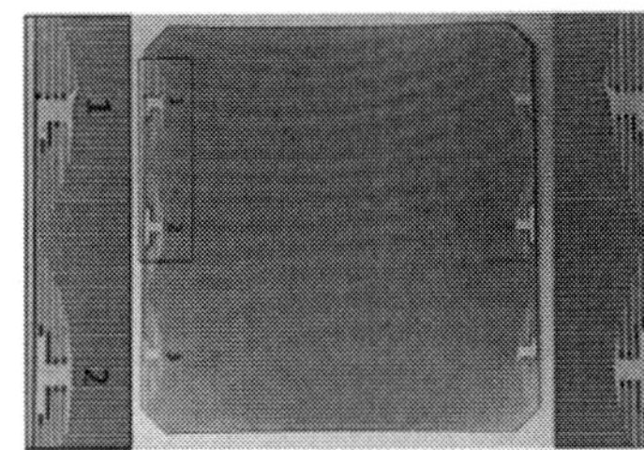

Figure 1: Rear side of the cell under study

Our measurement systems must be adapted to measure back contact cells, since until now it measured cells with contacts on both sides. For that, a prototype has been designed and fabricated, based on a printed circuit board (PCB) on which the footprints of the six contact pads of the solar cell have been engraved. A 0,22 ohm resistor has been added to the pad in order to equalize the current and ensure that each cell receives the same amount. The first measurements of IV curves showed high series resistance, indicating that there were contact problems between the pads of the solar cell and the pads of the PCB: our vacuum system caused the cell to bow, lifting it slightly at its perimeter, making poor contact. To ensure good contact, we were inspired by the metal contacting bars in old 3R12 flat 4,5 V batteries, such as shown in Fig. 2 (left). That is why we have soldered metal strips to the engraved pads on the PCB; that will help to make contact when the vacuum in our measuring equipment pulls the solar cell towards the PCB and the pads make contact with the metal strips. This is the detail that is shown in Fig. 2 with the green arrows. In addition, after ensuring good contact, some jumpers have been added to the prototype: by placing jumpers next to each pad we can force one pad to be disconnected from the measurement system by removing the jumper; thereby poor solding contacts, can be induced and the behaviour of the solar cell can be analysed in such condition. Jumpers are also shown in Fig. 2 (right).

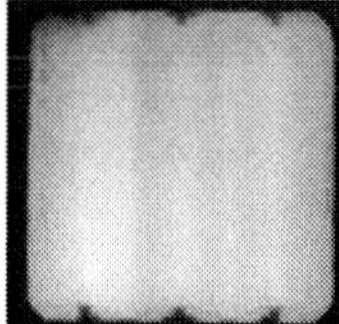

Figure 2: Old flat 4,5-volt battery (left); metal tabs plates to ensure electrical connection (right)

This prototype can be used both in luminescence measurement equipment and in IV curve measurement equipment. Fig. 3 (left) shows a luminescence image in which the brightness is fairly uniform, demonstrating that there are no contact problems. Fig. 3 (right) shows an illuminated IBC cell, ready for measuring its IV curves (which is beyond the scope of this manuscript).

Figure 3: Uniform EL image (left) and solar cell under illumination, ready for IV curves measurement (right)

From here, we would like to see what happens if a cell-contact fails. To do this, the jumpers of the prototype can be disconnected and the cell will react as it is under a bad soldering connection. We can partially disconnect one subcell, or disconnect the subcell completely, depending on which pads are loosened. The cell will behave as if one of its terminals were poorly connected, or as if the contact resistance were very high. According to technical data, the I_{sc} of these cells is around 6 amperes, which means that their operating point (at maximum power) is around 5,8 amperes [7]. Instead, the electroluminescence images to be taken are those corresponding to an injection of 4 amperes. Perhaps the measurements taken were too conservative, and it would be interesting to take measurements closer to 5,8 amperes.

3. PROCEDURE AND MEASUREMENTS

To see what happens if the cell is poorly connected, different disconnections are forced on the measurement platform. This is what the jumpers are for. If one of the current-input jumpers to the circuit is disconnected, the total injected current will enter through the two connected pads, and it will be redistributed throughout the cell and collected at the three output pads. It could also be decided to disconnect an entire subcell by opening the input and output jumpers, all the injected current will also be distributed as much as possible throughout the cell, but it will be collected in the output circuit again through the two output jumpers. In this setup, current will be injected by pads 1, 2 and 3 and the circuit will be closed by recollecting that current through pads 4, 5 and 6 respectively. As said before, in Fig. 1 it was observed that the solar cell consists of three subcells, being pad 1 and 6

the electrical connections for subcell 1, pads 2 and 5 the electrical connections for subcell 2 and pads 3 and 4 for subcell 3.

Again, this study has been quite conservative, as 4 amperes are injected instead of the 5,8 amperes that would replicate the current they would produce on a sunny day under one sun condition and at maximum power point. However, the results obtained are quite representative.

In order to analyse contacting failures, EL-measurements are performed according to two different scenarios, described bellow.

Scenario A: pad 3 is disconnected (corresponding jumper is removed). Subcell 3 is partially disconnected from the circuit by disconnecting its input terminal. However, since pad 4 is connected, the output terminal of the subcell is connected to the rest of the subcells.

Scenario B: pad 3 and pad 4 are disconnected (corresponding jumpers are removed). Subcell 3 is *entirely* disconnected from the circuit by disconnecting its input and output terminals.

In the case of contact failure analysis, the most common scenario would be for one of the soldering pads to fail, in which case simply removing a jumper would suffice, however, the case in which one of the subcells is completely disconnected (i.e. both of its respective solder joints fail) has also been analysed.

Fig. 4 shows the EL-images obtained (left), as well as a 3D representation of the image (right), corresponding to scenario A. If the jumper is not connected to pad 3, the current is injected into the cell only through pads 1 and 2. However, the current reaches the disconnected subcell either through the thin line between pads or through the base. There is a voltage drop in the disconnected area, as can be seen in the 3D representation, but it is not a drastic drop, since the current diverted to the disconnected subcell is collected in the output pad of that subcell. In this scenario, current leakage trough subcell 3 is significant, resulting in a greyish colour.

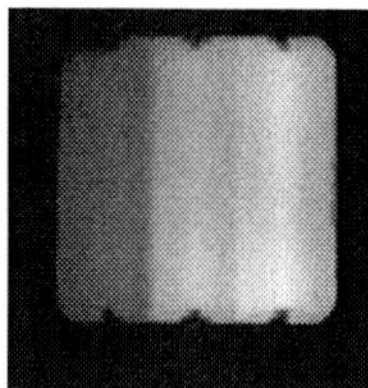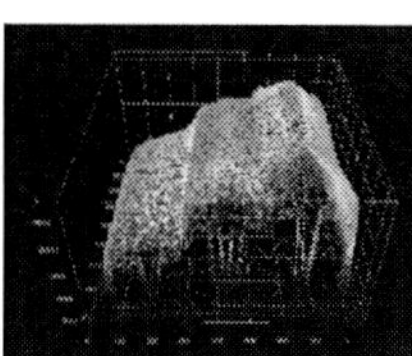

Figure 4: EL images (left) and 3D representation (right) from the solar cell with pad 3 disconneted.

Fig. 5 shows the EL-image obtained (left), as well as a 3D representation of the image (right), corresponding to scenario B. If the jumper is not connected to pad 3, the current is injected into the cell through pads 1 and 2. In this case the current does not reach the disconnected subcell, a little maybe from the thin line between pads or through the base. This is why the voltage drop in the disconnected area, is a drastic drop, which indicates that the subcell is disconnected from the rest. In this scenario, current leakages trough subcell 3 are not significant, resulting in a blackish colour that is considerably darker than in the previous scenario.

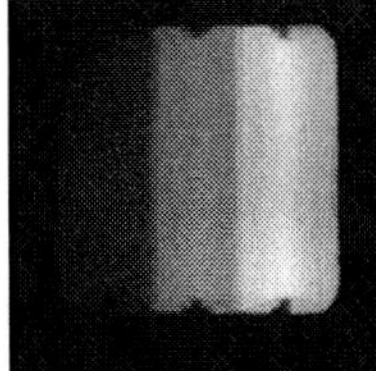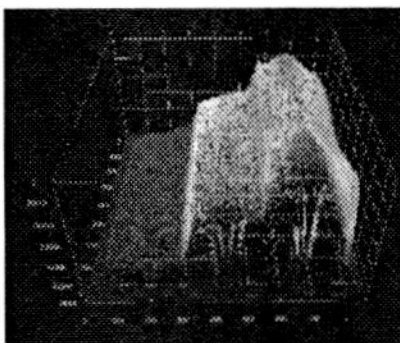

Figure 5: EL images (left) and 3D representation (right) from the solar cell with pads 3 and 4 disconneted.

If the jumper is not connected to pad 3 (Scenario A), the entire 4 A-s are injected into the cell through the two connected pads (1 & 2) and that current is collected up from pads 4, 5 and 6 to close the circuit around the measurement load. However, since there is a thin metal line connecting the three subcells, the current reaches the disconnected subcell either through that thin line between pads or through the base. As a result, the disconnected subcell is partially gray, indicating that photon emission is lower than in the other areas, but not zero, and suggesting that some current is indeed reaching that subcell.

However, it is interesting to observe that in both scenarios, photon emission the three subcells shine differently, indicating that their voltage distribution changes. In both scenarios, the subcell furthest from the failed contacts is the subcell that shines the most, as it is the least affected by current shunting towards the disconnected subcell. The voltage reference has been taken at the central subcell (pads 2 and 5), and the voltage measurements correspond to the values on Table I.

Table I: Voltage measurements in central subcell for the different scenarios

	Current	Voltage
Scenario A	4 A	1003 mV
Scenario B	4 A	1253 mV

The subcells are set to different voltages although the current is injected through two of them in both scenarios. Part of the current injected into the central subcell is diverted to the partially connected subcell in Scenario A. The subcell on the right does not suffer such marked current diversions, i.e., all the injected current is subject to recombination and emits a photon.

In scenario A, the voltage measured in the subcell corresponds to 1003 mV and the voltage map better observed in the 3D distribution, is not so abrupt. In Scenario B, on the one hand, the voltage measurement is higher than that obtained in Scenario A, 1253 mV vs. 1003 mV. It could be said that the effective area of the cell in Scenario B is smaller than in Scenario A, since the subcell 3 is almost disconnected from the rest of the solar cell. This is why the cell is turns to higher voltage, as it is being polarised slightly further away from the conduction knee.

4. CONCLUSIONS

A prototype has been built in which good contact has been achieved thanks to thin metal tabs solded to the pad footprint in the PCB. That prototype allows us to measure Sunpower's back contact cells MAXEON III, both EL-images and IV curves. By means of jumpers strategically placed in the prototype and near the pad connections, failed contacts can be induced and their consequences analysed. Several EL measurements are obtained under two different scenarios by removing jumpers and inducing undesirable situations that could arise if the connection pads are not soldered properly.

A simple PCB made using very basic methods serves as an interface to be added to cell measurement equipments with front and rear contacts, allowing rear contact cells to be measured. We are concerned that each manufacturer has its own IBC design, but the truth is that costs nothing to make a PCB that fits the design in question. However, we believe that to ensure good contact between the cell and the PCB, metal contactin bars such as those we have included are necessary.

2D/3D simulations of the structure to understand current distribution through the base with disconnected pads would be interesting. The metal line connecting the three subcells in parallel should also be characterized to determine the maximum current that can flow through it and to see at what current level it could have conduction problems.

Instead of being conservative, EL tests at around 5,8 A should be performed (better than at 4 A). IV-curves could also be measured at 1 sun condition and forcing contact failures. In that case, temperature measurements could also be taken to detect hotspots in such unexpected situations.

5. ACKNOLEDGEMENTS

This work was funded by the Ministerio de Ciencia, Innovación y Universidades of Spain within the project MCIU-O23/P45 (reference: PID2023-148369OB-C42) under the scheme Proyectos de Generación de Conocimiento 2023.

6. REFERENCES

[1] D.M. DeCeuster et al, Proceedings of 22nd EU PVSEC, 816-819, 2007.

[2] M.A. Green, K. Emery, Y. Hishikawa, W. Warta and E.D. Dunlop, "Solar cell efficiency tables", Prog. Photovolt.: Res. Appl. Vol. 24-1, pp. 3-11, 2016. https://doi.org/10.1002/pip.2728

[3] R. Kopecek et al. "Interdigitated back contact technology as final evolution for industrial crystallinesingle-junction silicon solar cell", Solar, vol. 3, pp. 1-14, 2023. https://doi.org/10.3390/solar3010001

[4] Jonas D et al, "Influence of interconnection concepts for IBC solar cell performance by simulation", AIP Conf. Proc. 1999, 020011. https://doi.org/10.1063/1.5049250 (2018).

[5] J-S. Jeong, N. Park, C. Han, "Field failure mechanism study of solder interconnection for crystalline silicon photovoltaic module", Microelectronics Reliability, vol. 52, pp. 2326-2330, 2012. https://doi.org/10.1016/j.microrel.2012.06.027

[6] S. Kumar, R. Gupta. Thermo-mechanical degradation at finger-solder interface in a crystalline silicon photovoltaic module under thermal fatigue conditions. IEEE 46th PVSC Conf. Proc., pp. 0118–0121, 2019. 10.1109/PVSC40753.2019.8980538

[7] D. D. Smith, P. J. Cousins et al. SunPower's Maxeon Gen III solar cell: High Efficiency and Energy Yield. IEEE 39th PVSC Conf. Proc., pp. 908-913, 2013. 10.1109/PVSC.2013.6744291

This presentation was selected by the Sc. Committee of the EU PVSEC 2025 for submission of a full paper to one of the EU PVSEC's collaborating peer-reviewed journals.

UNDERSTANDING REVERSE I–V CHARACTERISTICS OF SOLAR CELLS USING AN IRRADIANCE-DEPENDENT BISHOP MODEL

Ahmad Hashem[1,2], Hugo Sanchez[1,2], Leila Mortazavifar[1], Bengt Jaeckel[1,2] and Ralph Gottschalg[1,2]
[1]Hochschule Anhalt - Anhalt University of Applied Sciences, Bernburger Str. 55, 06366, Köthen, Germany
[2]Fraunhofer Center for Silicon Photovoltaics CSP, Otto-Eissfeldt-Str. 12, 06120 Halle (Saale), Germany
Email: ahmad.hashem@hs-anhalt.de

ABSTRACT: Mismatch in photovoltaic (PV) modules—arising from shading, soiling, or latent defects—forces individual cells into reverse bias, where their characteristics govern module power loss, hotspot formation, and long-term reliability. Despite substantial changes in cell technology, most system models still adopt Bishop's 1988 reverse-characteristic formulation, originally calibrated for Al-BSF cells. This work reassesses the adequacy of the Bishop model for modern architectures (PERC, TOPCon, HJT) and introduces an adapted formulation that captures the distinct irradiance dependencies observed in modern cells. The model's avalanche and shunt terms are extended with physics-motivated, irradiance-dependent multipliers and provide a stable parameter-extraction framework tailored to reverse-bias data. Model parameters are estimated via particle swarm optimization (PSO). Validation against measured I–V curves under controlled irradiance demonstrates materially improved fits in the reverse quadrant and more accurate prediction of module-level stress indicators, including hotspot onset and severity. The proposed approach supports more reliable system-level simulations under mismatch, enabling better thermal-risk assessment, bypass-diode coordination, and design margins for modern PV modules. Results indicate that updating reverse-bias models is critical to accurately forecasting field performance and mitigating reliability hazards in current and emerging PV technologies.

Keywords: Reverse Bias, Hotspot, Mismatch, Bishop Model, Irradiance Dependency

1 INTRODUCTIION

Reverse bias behavior in crystalline-silicon (c-Si) solar cells governs both reliability and safety at module and array scale. Local reverse conduction can concentrate power dissipation in small regions, triggering hot-spots that degrade encapsulants, activate solder fatigue, and in extreme cases cause thermal runaway. The risk escalates under mismatch—e.g., partial shading or cell defects—where bypass diode turn-on thresholds and the reverse I–V characteristics of shaded cells determine how much heat is localized in a single device versus diverted around it. Accurate reverse-bias models are therefore essential for predicting hot-spot severity and for designing string- and module-level mitigations [1]. Among compact models, the Bishop model [2] has become a practical standard because it augments forward-bias diode physics with an empirical reverse conduction branch that captures avalanche-like breakdown and the characteristic curvature of the reverse I–V. It balances fidelity and parsimony, enabling parameter extraction from laboratory I–V data and integration in circuit-level simulators used for module/array studies. Comparative reviews highlight Bishop's advantages relative to alternatives, while also noting open issues such as parameter identifiability and the sensitivity of hot-spot predictions to the chosen reverse branch [3].

Most prior Bishop-model studies extract the reverse-branch parameters at a single operating condition—typically dark I–V or one sun/STC—and then reuse those parameters across simulations, despite known non-stationarity of the reverse I–V with illumination. Meta-heuristic fits [4-5] likewise target one irradiance snapshot for numerical tractability, reinforcing the "single-G" calibration norm. Yet measurements show that photogeneration and carrier injection under light shift both reverse leakage and breakdown, with a stronger dependence in p-type/PERC than in n-type/TOPCon; using single-irradiance parameters therefore biases hot-spot predictions at real operating conditions [6].

For validation purposes the bishop model was fitted to reverse I–V data from three mainstream c-Si technologies Al-BSF, PERC, and TOPCon measured at 500 W/m²as shown in Figure 1.

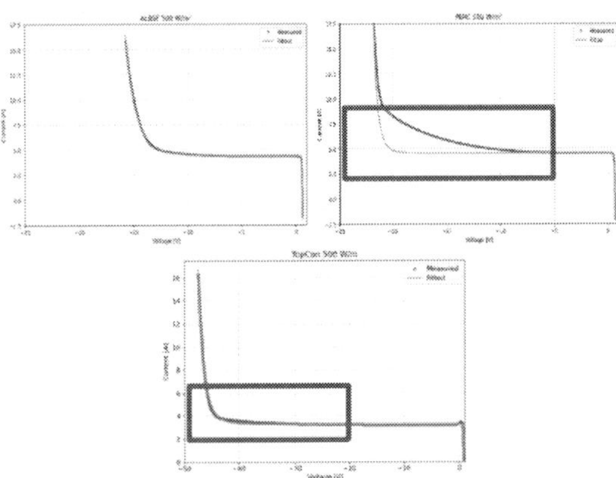

Figure 1: Comparison of Bishop Modelling for Different Cell Technologies

The Bishop model reproduces the Al-BSF reverse I–V very well, capturing both the breakdown knee and the far-tail with low residuals For TOPCon, the fit is serviceable but shows systematic deviations around the knee and in the high-field tail, For PERC, the mismatch is pronounced—the model underestimates leakage at moderate reverse bias and fails to capture the illumination-dependent curvature near breakdown yielding a poor overall fit.

2 METHODOLOGY

The aim of this study is to modify the Bishop reverse branch in equation 1 so it can capture the irradiance-dependent slope observed in modern cells—most notably the stronger light sensitivity of PERC compared with TOPCon and Al-BSF.

An irradiance gain was introduced based on equation 2 that multiplies the Bishop multiplication/curvature term, so the post-knee slope and far-tail increase with G. This form is monotonic, zero-anchored, and saturating: it reverts to the classical Bishop model in the dark ($k(0)=0$), grows approximately as $\propto G^{\gamma}$ at low light (capturing the super-linear onset seen in PERC), and remains bounded at high irradiance (k→k0) to avoid non-physical divergence.

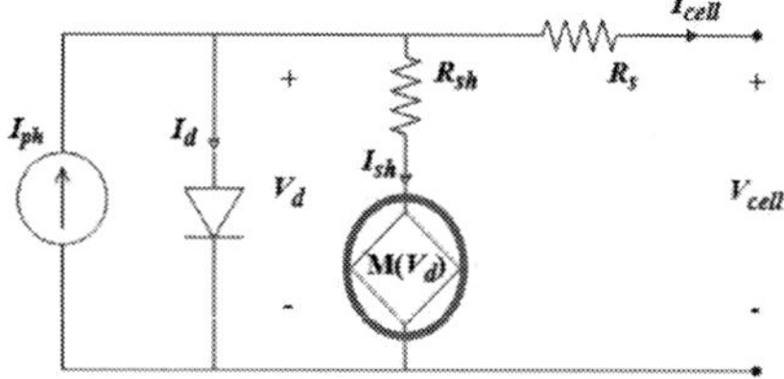

Figure 2 Bishop Model Circuit for PV Cell

$$I_{cell} = I_{ph} - I_0(e^{\frac{V_d}{A*Vt}} - 1) - \frac{V_d}{R_{sh}}(1 + a\frac{1 - V_d}{V_{br}})^{-m} \quad (1)$$

$$K(G) = K_0\left(1 - e^{-K_1\left(\frac{G}{1000}\right)^{\gamma}}\right) \quad (2)$$

PSO is used for the validation of the modified model against PERC & TopCon cells measured at Fraunhofer CSP using Halm A+A+A+ solar simulator with controlled temperature of 25°C and irradiances range between 100 to 1300 W/m2. Here the parameters are extracted with PSO under the hard, physics-based box constraints listed in Table 1.

Table 1: Parameters Boundary Conditions for PSO fitting

Parameter	Lower Bound	Upper Bound
I_{ph}	0	2* Isc
I_0	1e-12	1e-4
R_s	1e-4	0.1
R_s	10	10e6
n	0	3
V_{br}	-60	-5
K_0	1e-3	100
K_1	0	3
m	0	6
γ	0.5	2

3 RESULTS

The modified Bishop model is evaluated by fitting all measured reverse I–V curves across all irradiance range for each technology with a single parameter set per curve representing it. Fits are assessed both by RMSE and by residual maps plotted beneath each I–V curve, which emphasize the knee region and the post-knee tail that dominate hot-spot heating. For clarity, we first discuss PERC and then contrast with TOPCon in the following subsection.

Four irradiance levels are shown in Figure 3 to illustrate the behavior of the modified Bishop model. Relative to the standard Bishop formulation, the new term markedly improves the irradiance-dependent slope in the reverse region: the fits track both the knee and the post-knee tail across G. The residual plots beneath each I–V confirm this—errors are essentially zero in the forward quadrant and along the initial linear segment of reverse bias. At

1300 W m², where the slope enhancement is strongest, residuals remain minimal; at lower irradiance the residuals increase slightly but stay small and largely structure-free, indicating that the model still reproduces the measured curves well with an average root mean square error (RMSE) of 0.26.

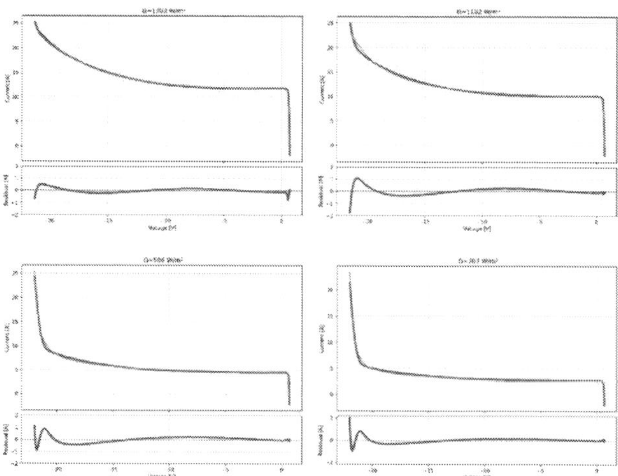

Figure 3: Actual vs Fitted I-V Curves for PERC Cell at varying Irradiances

Unlike PERC, the TOPCon cell exhibits mild hysteresis that appears as a small peak at the onset of reverse bias. To avoid biasing the fit, we used a two-phase procedure: (i) fit the forward quadrant only; (ii) skip a few samples around the peak and fit the reverse branch independently. Figure 4 shows two representative irradiance levels with the two-phase fit, residuals remain close to zero across the long reverse plateau and the knee is reproduced well; only a small, localized error persists near the hysteresis peak we excluded from the fit. Over all TOPCon curves, output an average RMSE of ≈ 0.10

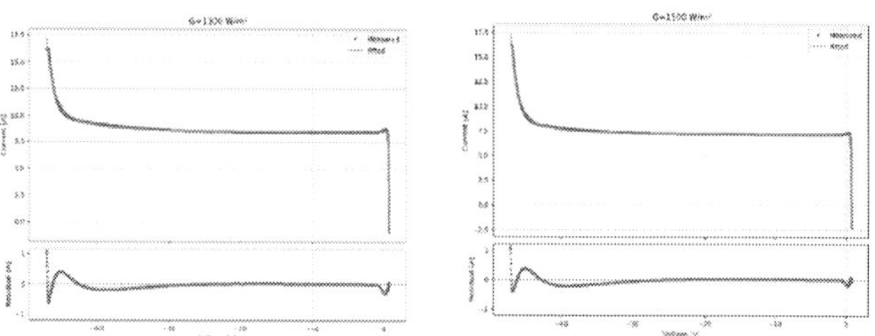

Figure 4: Actual vs Fitted I-V Curves for TopCon Cell at varying Irradiances

The onset of slope change occurs at much higher reverse voltages in TOPCon (≈ −40 V) than in PERC (≈ −10 V), indicating different breakdown initiation mechanisms and field profiles. Moreover, PERC exhibits a markedly steeper irradiance-dependent slope in the reverse region, whereas TOPCon's slope varies only weakly with G; this underscores PERC's higher sensitivity of breakdown behavior to illumination and motivates technology-aware, irradiance-dependent modeling in hot-spot assessments.

4 CONCLUSION

This work is a first-stage formulation. The classical Bishop reverse branch, while convenient, does not capture the illumination-dependent reverse behavior of modern cells. By augmenting Bishop with a bounded, irradiance-dependent multiplier and extracting parameters under physics-based constraints, we achieve stable fits across 100–1300 W m² and materially reduce reverse-quadrant errors (avg. RMSE $\approx$ 0.26 for PERC and $\approx$ 0.10 for TOPCon after hysteresis-peak exclusion), while reproducing the technology-specific knee and plateau (onset near −10 V for PERC and ~−40 V for TOPCon).

In the next stage, enhancement to the reverse branch will be done to better capture knee curvature and leakage dispersion, incorporate temperature-coupled breakdown, model minor hysteresis explicitly, and introduce cross-irradiance parameter tying/regularization. These upgrades are aimed at further lowering RMSE and improving prediction fidelity for hot-spot onset and severity in module- and array-level simulations.

5 REFERENCES

[1] Kim, K. A., & Krein, P. T. (2013, June). Photovoltaic hot spot analysis for cells with various reverse-bias characteristics through electrical and thermal simulation. *In 2013 IEEE 14th Workshop on Control and Modeling for Power Electronics (COMPEL)* (pp. 1-8). IEEE.

[2] Bishop, J. W. (1988). Computer simulation of the effects of electrical mismatches in photovoltaic cell interconnection circuits. *Solar cells, 25*(1), 73-89.

[3] Alonso-García, M. C., & Ruiz, J. M. (2006). Analysis and modelling the characteristic reverse of photovoltaic cells. *Solar Energy Materials and Solar Cells, 90*(7-8), 1105-1120.

[4] Restrepo-Cuestas, B. J., Montano, J., Ramos-Paja, C. A., Trejos-Grisales, L. A., & Orozco-Gutierrez, M. L. (2022). Parameters estimation of the bishop photovoltaic model using a genetic algorithm. *Applied Sciences, 12*(6), 2927.

[5] Restrepo-Cuestas, B. J., Durango-Flórez, M., Trejos-Grisales, L. A., & Ramos-Paja, C. A. (2022). Analysis of Electrical Models for Photovoltaic Cells under Uniform and Partial Shading Conditions. *Computation, 10*(7), 111.

[6] Clement, C. E., Singh, J. P., Birgersson, E., Wang, Y., & Khoo, Y. S. (2021). Illumination dependence of reverse leakage current in silicon solar cells. *IEEE Journal of Photovoltaics, 11*(5), 1285-1290.

A new method for Sb-doped CdSeTe/CdTe devices with superior stability

Elisa Artegiani, Mariyam Mukhtar and Alessandro Romeo

Laboratory for Photovoltaics and Solid State Physics, Department of Computer Science, University of Verona, Ca Vignal 1, Strada le Grazie 15, Verona, Italy.

Abstract - Currently, one of the primary activities in CdTe solar cell research is to identify an alternative to copper doping. Copper has limited solubility in the CdTe matrix, which restricts the achievement of higher open circuit voltages (Voc). It is also a fast diffuser, making it a major contributor to device degradation. Finding a suitable alternative doping element could enhance Voc, improve cell efficiency, and increase stability. This study introduces a new approach for inserting Sb in CdSeTe/CdTe matrix as a dopant, which will be explained in detail during the conference. This simple and easy method proves to be effective, as Sb-doped cells achieve efficiencies comparable to those of Cu-doped cells. Furthermore, in accelerated stress tests without encapsulation, Sb-doped samples demonstrate much greater stability than Cu-doped cells, comparable to undoped devices.

I. INTRODUCTION

While research into thin-film technologies continues to expand across various materials, cadmium telluride (CdTe) photovoltaic (PV) modules remain the dominant thin-film product in the global market. The efficiency of CdTe devices has consistently improved over time; in the last two decades, the record efficiency for research-scale cells has increased from 16.5 % to 23.1 %, as recently reported by the U.S. company First Solar. Additionally, module efficiencies have surpassed 19 %, and growing production volumes have enabled CdTe technology to go well below the 1 \$/Wp barrier [1].

To further advance the commercial viability of CdTe, it is essential to continue enhancing its efficiency while maintaining low production costs. To date, the primary driver of efficiency improvements has been the introduction of selenium (Se) into the absorber layer, forming a CdSeTe compound near the junction [2], [3]. Current efforts should focus on increasing the open-circuit voltage and improving device stability. Both objectives could potentially be achieved by replacing copper doping with group V elements. Achieving higher voltage requires higher doping levels, which Cu struggles to deliver. Moreover, Cu's high diffusivity in CdTe is widely

regarded as the primary contributor to device degradation [4].

Group V elements (N, P, As, Sb, and Bi) present a promising alternative, as they can form acceptor states by substituting tellurium (Te) sites [1].

Although Sb forms deeper acceptor levels than As, it can achieve substantial hole density due to the lower formation energy of Sb_{Te}, attributed to the small atomic radius difference between Te and Sb [5].

We have developed a new approach to dope CdTe with antimony, which will be presented in detail at the conference. This method also reduces the Schottky barrier at the back contact without needing additional etching processes or the introduction of hole transport layers.

II. DEVICES FABRICATION AND ANALYSIS

Our laboratory produces CdSeTe/CdTe devices in a superstrate configuration using a low-temperature substrate deposition process based on thermal evaporation (TE). The substrate and front contact comprise a commercial glass/SnO_2:F (FTO)/SnO_2 (TO) stack, referred to as TEC 12D, provided by NSG Pilkington. A 300 nm-thick CdSe layer is then deposited on TEC 12D, followed by a 300 nm-thick CdTe layer, both at a substrate temperature of 340 °C. This initial stack undergoes vacuum annealing at 450 °C for 30 minutes. Subsequently, an additional 1.4 μm-thick CdTe layer is deposited to complete the absorber, achieving a total thickness of 2 μm. The optimisation of the absorber's growth has been detailed in prior work [6].

Following this, the stack is subjected to a $CdCl_2$ activation treatment using a wet deposition method, followed by air annealing at 400 °C. Afterwards, the stack is immersed in boiling water to remove any $CdCl_2$ residues and to clean the surface.

For copper doping, a 1 nm-thick Cu layer is deposited on the sample by TE. Before this deposition, the sample undergoes a Br-MeOH etching process, which cleans the surface and enriches the absorber surface with Te. This promotes the formation of Cu_xTe compounds at the back contact, enhancing its ohmic properties and long-term stability [7], [8]. The back contact consists of a 30 nm-thick gold layer. Finally, the sample is annealed in air at 200 °C to enable Cu diffusion into the absorber.

For Sb doping, a novel approach is used without the application of the Br-MeOH etching step, the details of which we prefer to disclose directly at the conference.

The current density-voltage (JV) characteristics were recorded using a Keithley Source Meter 2420 under an AM 1.5 spectrum at 100 mW/cm², with a LOT Quantum Design Europe solar simulator (model LS0306). Drive Level Capacitance Profiling (DLCP) and Capacitance-Voltage (CV) measurements were performed using an HP4284A LCR meter.

III. RESULTS

CV-DLCP profiles have been collected for our Cu and Sb-doped samples and our undoped samples (as reference) to prove Sb doping.

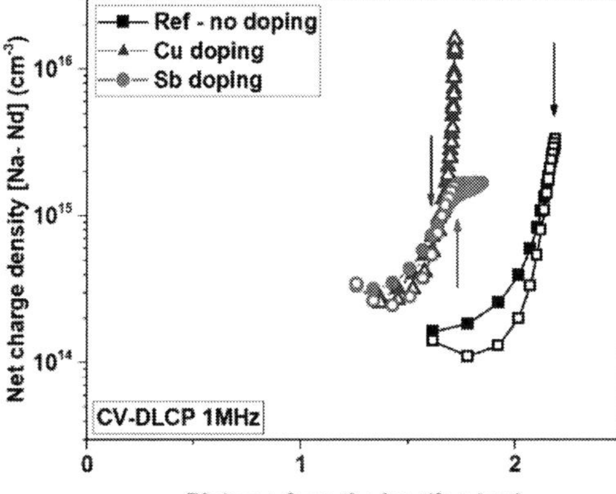

Fig. 1. CV-DLCP profiles of undoped, Cu and Sb-doped cells.

CV profiles reveal contributions from deep and shallow defects, with the deeper states having minimal impact on the DLCP curves [9]. Consequently, the net charge density of the samples is typically derived from the lowest segment of the DLCP curve. The arrows in the graphs indicate measurements at 0 V, which estimate the depletion region width. Fig. 1 shows that Cu and Sb doped cells have similar net charge density, higher than the undoped samples, as expected, demonstrating the successful doping of the devices with antimony.

Table I: efficiency parameters of Cu and Sb-doped cells.

Devices	Voc (mV)	Jsc (mA/cm²)	FF (%)	η (%)
Cu-doped	790	28.7	69	15.7
Sb-doped	797	28.4	68	15.4

Table I compares the Cu- and Sb-doped record devices, which exhibit nearly identical peak efficiencies, with values of 15.7% and 15.4%, respectively. Their efficiency parameters are also comparable, highlighting the potential of our method for doping CdTe.

Figure 2 shows the current-voltage characteristics of these record devices. As indicated by their efficiency parameters, the curves are almost identical. The main difference appears in the first quadrant of the graph: the Cu-doped device exhibits a slight rollover effect, whereas the Sb-doped device shows a more ohmic back contact. This is unexpected, as the Cu-doping process involves a Br-MeOH etching step that enriches the CdTe surface with Te, facilitating the formation of Cu_xTe compounds [7]. These compounds are intentionally formed to enhance the back contact's ohmic behaviour and improve the cells' stability [8], [10].

In contrast, the Sb-doping process does not include any etching process. Further analysis will be presented during the conference to clarify how this can happen.

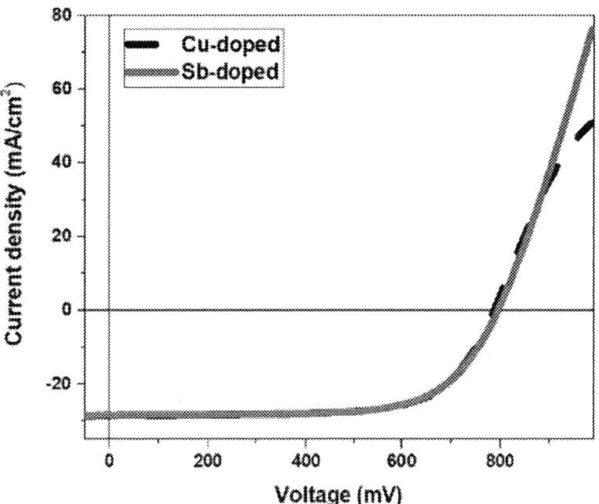

Fig. 2. JV characteristic of Cu and Sb-doped cells.

As previously highlighted, another key objective in exploring alternative doping methods for CdTe devices is to enhance their stability. To evaluate the long-term degradation of the samples, accelerated stress tests (AST) were conducted on both Cu- and Sb-doped devices. For comparison, undoped samples were also included in the tests. Precisely, the cells were placed inside a metal chamber, which provided exposure to 1 sun illumination at a constant temperature of 80 °C. Figure 3 presents the normalized efficiency of the devices relative to their initial values over the course of the AST.

The results of the copper-doped devices align with previous observations of our Cu-doped CdS/CdTe devices [4], [7]. Specifically, their stability is suboptimal, with average efficiency dropping to approximately 80 % of the initial value after about 75 hours and continuing to decline to below 65 % within 250 hours. This degradation is attributed to the diffusion of Cu from the back contact towards the junction and the instability of CuCd acceptor defects [4]. This explanation is supported by the significantly higher stability observed in the undoped samples, which retained about 90 % of their initial efficiency after 250 hours of aging. In these undoped devices, degradation is primarily due to the absence of encapsulation, leaving them vulnerable to moisture and oxygen exposure.

Remarkably, the Sb-doped devices demonstrate exceptional stability. After over 250 hours, they retain, on average, 90 % of their initial efficiency, comparable to the performance of the undoped samples. This indicates no evidence of degradation beyond what is expected from exposure to moisture and oxygen. The results suggest that the acceptor defects introduced [7] by Sb are stable, unlike those associated with Cu, further supporting Sb as a viable alternative dopant for improving device reliability and that our innovative Sb doping method is successful.

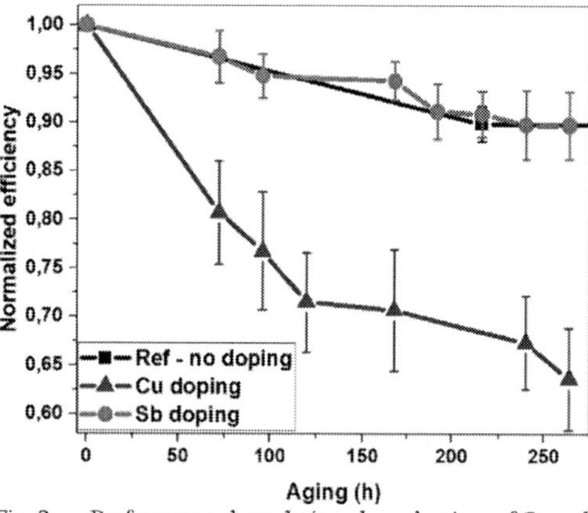

Fig. 3.   Performance degradation along the time of Cu and Sb-doped samples and the undoped cells, at different time steps of AST.

IV. CONCLUSIONS

A new method to dope CdSeTe/CdTe devices with Sb has been developed and will be presented in all detail during the conference. This approach effectively dopes CdTe with Sb, as evidenced by CV DLCP measurements, achieving peak efficiencies nearly matching those of Cu doping through the same low-temperature deposition method (15.4 % vs. 15.7 %).

In addition, Sb-doped cells exhibit improved back-contact ohmicity compared to Cu-doped cells, even without the use of etching or a hole transport layer. Accelerated stability tests highlight the superior stability of Sb-doped cells compared to their Cu-doped counterparts. The Sb-doped devices are so stable that their performance matches that of undoped cells, indicating that any observed degradation results solely from the absence of encapsulation in the experiment.

This novel doping technique has demonstrated its effectiveness in producing Sb-doped CdTe devices with efficiencies comparable to Cu-doped cells while offering remarkable stability. However, as this doping method is still in its early stages compared to the well-established Cu doping processes, there remains significant potential for enhancing cell efficiency.

REFERENCES

[1]   M. A. Scarpulla *et al.*, "CdTe-based thin film photovoltaics: Recent advances, current challenges and future prospects," 2023. doi: 10.1016/j.solmat.2023.112289.

[2]   N. R. Paudel and Y. Yan, "Enhancing the photo-currents of CdTe thin-film solar cells in both short and long wavelength regions," *Appl Phys Lett*, vol. 105, no. 18, pp. 1–6, 2014, doi: 10.1063/1.4901532.

[3]   J. Guo *et al.*, "Effect of selenium and chlorine co-passivation in polycrystalline CdSeTe devices," *Appl Phys Lett*, vol. 115, no. 15, 2019, doi: 10.1063/1.5123169.

[4]   E. Artegiani, J. D. Major, H. Shiel, V. Dhanak, C. Ferrari, and A. Romeo, "How the amount of copper influences the formation and stability of defects in CdTe solar cells," *Solar Energy Materials and Solar Cells*, vol. 204, p. 110228, Jan. 2020, doi: 10.1016/j.solmat.2019.110228.

[5]   B. Dou, Q. Sun, and S. H. Wei, "Optimization of Doping CdTe with Group-V Elements: A First-Principles Study," *Phys Rev Appl*, vol. 15, no. 5, 2021, doi: 10.1103/PhysRevApplied.15.054045.

[6]   E. Artegiani, A. Gasparotto, M. Meneghini, G. Meneghesso, and A. Romeo, "How the selenium distribution in CdTe affects the carrier properties of CdSeTe/CdTe solar cells," *Solar Energy*, vol. 260, 2023, doi: 10.1016/j.solener.2023.05.058.

[7]   E. Artegiani *et al.*, "Analysis of a novel CuCl2 back contact process for improved stability in CdTe solar cells," *Progress in Photovoltaics: Research and Applications*, vol. 27, no. 8, pp. 706–715, 2019, doi: 10.1002/pip.3148.

[8]   X. Wu *et al.*, "Phase control of CuxTe film and its effects on CdS/CdTe solar cell," *Thin Solid Films*, vol. 515, no. 15 SPEC. ISS., pp. 5798–5803, 2007, doi: 10.1016/j.tsf.2006.12.151.

[9]   J. T. Heath, J. D. Cohen, and W. N. Shafarman, "Bulk and metastable defects in CuIn1-xGaxSe2 thin films using drive-level capacitance profiling," *J Appl Phys*, vol. 95, no. 3, pp. 1000–1010, 2004, doi: 10.1063/1.1633982.

[10]   I. Rimmaudo *et al.*, "Improved stability of CdTe solar cells by absorber surface etching," *Solar Energy Materials and Solar Cells*, vol. 162, 2017, doi: 10.1016/j.solmat.2016.12.044.

MICRO-CRYSTAL GAAS ARRAY SUB-CELLS FOR SI TANDEM SOLAR CELLS

J.P. Connolly[1*], A. Nejim[3], A. Jaffré[1], J. Alvarez[1], J.P. Kleider[1], D. Mencaraglia[1], Laurie Dentz[2], G. Hallais[2], F. Hamouda[2], L. Vincent[2], D. Bouchier[2], C. Renard[2]

[1]GeePs, Group of Electrical Engineering Paris, CNRS, CentraleSupelec, Université Paris-Saclay, Sorbonne Université, 3&11 rue Joliot-Curie, Plateau de Moulon, 91192 Gif-sur-Yvette CEDEX, France

[2]C2N, Centre de Nanosciences et de Nanotechnologies, CNRS, Université Paris-Saclay, 10 Bd Thomas Gobert, 91120, Palaiseau, France

[3]SILVACO Technology Centre, Compass Point, St. Ives, Cambridgeshire PE27 5JL, UK

ABSTRACT: This work reports optical and electronic numerical modelling of a novel emerging structure which is the GaAs nanocrystal on Si tandem solar cell by epitaxial lateral overgrowth, a technique which allows defect free material growth. The techniqueconsists of creating nucleation sites in a silicon surface SiO_2 layer and initiating growth of nanoscalescale seeds, whereby strain energy remains below the Matthews-Blakeslee strain relaxation limit. This leads to Al_xGaAs growth in micro-crystals without generation of material defects. The focus of this presentation is optical and electrical modelling of nanocrystals for applications in the very active field of silicon based multijunction solar cells, and design of a Al_xGaAs/Si two terminal tandem, for compositions ranging from x=0 to x=30% in absorber layers. We present a model of the complete structure in two dimensions, consisting of a Al_xGaAs high bandgap subcell connected with a tunnel junction to the low bandgap Si junction. The elaboration of models is described, with an emphasis on the Al_xGaAs crystal featuring a non-planar pn-junction, and a focus on the optical properties of this lattice of micrometric AlGaAs crystals and in particular their light trapping properties from the resulting surface texture. The question of Al_xGaAs surface coverage is addressed, given that neighbouring Al_xGaAs crystals have different crystal orientations on a (111) Si surface, such that any coalescence of neighbour Al_xGaAs crystals leads to crippling defects at their interface. The result is that some high energy incident light above the Al_xGaAs bandgap is nevertheless transmitted directly to the Si cell, such that the resulting photogenerated carriers thermalise to the Silicon bandgap, and result in a loss of efficiency. The interface between Al_xGaAs and Si subcells is addressed, with an emphasis on current transport efficiency through the nanoseeds and tunnelling currents through appropriately designed SiO_2 buffer layers. This work therefore presents a theoretical framework for evaluating the potential of Al_xGaAs nanocrystal growth on Si for light trapping, for GaAs silicon two terminal tandem cell performance including tunnel junctions, and provides models and design rules for efficient Al_xGaAs microcrystal arrays as high bandgap subcells for tandem solar cells on silicon.

Keywords: III-V, silicon, texturing, epitaxial lateral overgrowth.
Corresponding author : james.connolly@centralesupelec.fr

1 Introduction

The multijunction solar cell is the most successful high efficiency concept. This has led to much work on on this topic based around silicon, for economic and industrial reasons [1].

As part of these efforts, there has been significant effort in integration of III-V semiconductors on Si substrates for photovoltaics and more broadly in opto-electronics. Avenues followed involve a range of techniques [2] which generally need to manage defect densities to lead to usable devices. One technique suggested some decades ago [3] which avoids these issues is the epitaxial lateral overgrowth (ELO) method which presents significant practical growth and fabrication challenges in obtaining high quality III-V films.

We explore the application of these micro-crystal arrays as the high band-gap subcell of III-V / Si two terminal series connected tandem solar cells. We evaluate strategies for optimum tandem designs in light of limiting efficiencies.

We focus on two topics of interest, which are the increased light-matter interaction resulting from light scattering by the micro-crystal array, and the monolithic integration and efficient current transport in the resulting III-V / Si multilayer photovoltaic device. The result is an innovative design which benefits from built-in texturing and light trapping, while developing a promising technological route for III-V integration on Si for wider applications.

2 Experimental context

This paper builds on the recent work [3] which has demonstrated technologically attractive and high quality arrays of single crystal GaAs micro-crystal arrays on Si by epitaxial lateral overgrowth (ELO). As illustrated in figure 1, ELO growth starts with a Si surface on which a 2nm surface SiO_2 layer is fabricated. Nucleation sites of diameter ≈50nm are etched in this oxide. Growth is initiated by epitaxial methods in these nucleation sites.

This technique has allowed the growth of defect free Al_xGaAs crystals on Si despite the mismatched Al_xGaAs/Si atomic lattices because the small contact area and 3D growth mode ensures strain energy never exceeds the Matthews-Blakeslee limit [4], and that no strain relaxation and formation of lattice defects occurs. Current growth methods yield two crystal types. The first is flat rectangular crystals with height to width ratios of 1/4, and of dimensions from 1μm to 2μm wide shown in figure 2(a). The second consists of the same rectangular base with a hexagonal "cap" with facets fixed at 30° from the horizontal, as shown in figure 2(b), which we call "textured".

The materials available are Al_xGaAs with x=0-40% for absorbers and higher x=75 for thin layers including windows or the front emitter.

We note that Al_xGaAs is a complex material. The Al content leads to instabilities in particular with respect to

reaction with oxygen such that Al_xGaAs layers need to be isolated from the atmosphere. This isolation is provided here by contact transparent conducting oxide layers, and anti-reflection coatings.

We note also intrinsic materials problems, in particular the well known DX centre [5] which is associated with Al compositions greater than $\approx$22% and high doping, which is nevertheless not a critical issue in the Al fractions available, and given the low doping we use in the absorber layer as detailed below.

Finally, GaAs at the lower x=0 composition has long been a nearly ideal solar cell material achieving to date AM1.5G efficiencies of 29% [6], close to the radiative limit of 31% [7].

This concludes the definition of available materials, for which we next present simulations evaluating potential device performance.

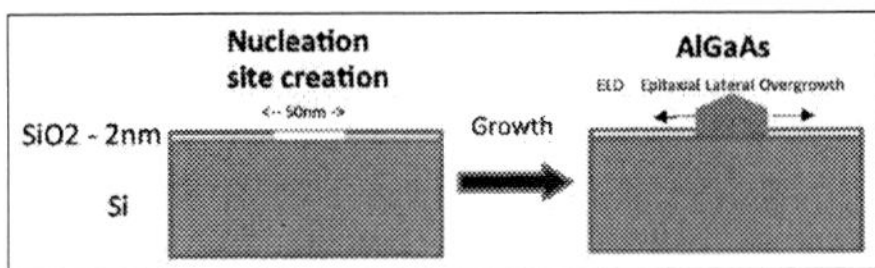

Figure 1 : the epitaxial lateral overgrowth technique, whereby AlGaAs nucleations sites are created by opening holes of some tens of nanometres in a two nanometre thick surface oxide.

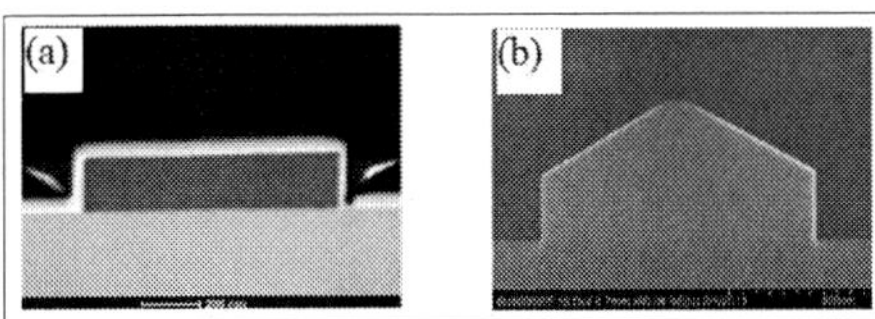

Figure 2 examples of 1μm wide (a) flat and (b) faceted ELO crystals

3 Theoretical limits and device design

It is worth reminding the well-known radiative efficiency limits with familiar efficiency – bandgap contour plots [1] which give an appreciation of potential efficiencies of proposed designs. The fundamental efficiency limit for a silicon based tandem is 41.9% under standard test conditions (STC), for of 1.74eV (top) and and 1.12 (bottom Si).

3.1 Optimum efficiency higher gap top cell

The optimum Si-based tandem upper gap of 1.74eVcorresponds to $Al_{25}Ga_{75}As$. This is a material with sufficienty materials properties for solar cells, as we have seen just above. The material is just above the range where materials issues start to become significant at x$\approx$22% but for highly doped materials. Since we are considering low-doped materials for the absorber region with a large depletion region with field driven transport, this composition is well within the tolerances for efficient photogenerated carrier diffusion and collection.

We can in addition retain higher composition Al_xGaAs for the frontmost emitter layer. This is because the role of this layer is to set up the *pn* junction and internal field. For this role, poor minority carrier transport is not an obstacle and indirect absorption is an advantage since light mainly absorbed in the more efficient absorber region.

We will therefore in further sections evaluate the potential performance of $Al_{25}GaAs$ microcrystals.

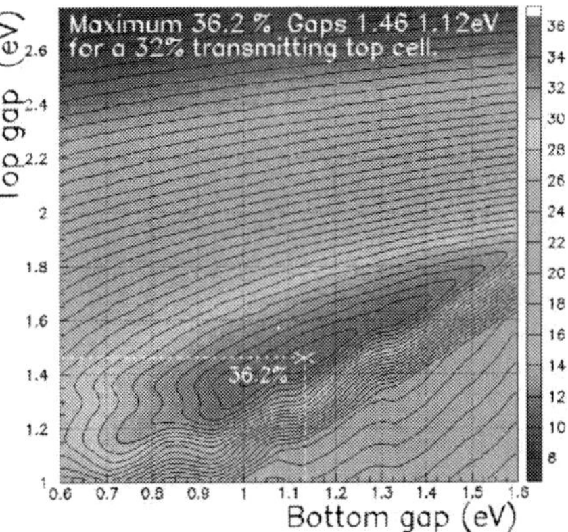

Figure 3 Radiative efficiency limit (STC) of a tandem cell where the top cell is optically thinned across the wavelength range such as to achieve an ideal tandem cell which features Si as the bottom cell at 1.12eV. The efficiency maximum is found a touch above GaAs for $Al_2Ga_{98}As$. This can be simplified by substituting GaAs which barely changes the achievable efficiency which for GaAs is 36%.

3.1 Optimum transport lower gap top cell

While the gap of GaAs is too low for a current-matched tandem cell on Si, with the GaAs cell over-producing, one can optically thin the top cell to achieve current matching.

This is non-ideal and reduces potential efficiency because photons with energies above the GaAs gap are absorbed in the Si. The resulting minority carriers are generated with higher energies than necessary, and lose this energy in thermalising to the Si band-edge. This may however be advantageous for a tandem if the thermalisation loss is small enough to allow high efficiency, and if tandem design is otherwise facilitated, as it is here as we shall see.

The potential efficiency can be evaluated by evaluating limiting radiative efficiency of an non-opaque or optically transmitting top cell which does not absorb all the light above its bandgap.

We tune the transmission of such a top cell such that the optimum bottom bandgap corresponds to Si. This procedure yields an optimum for a non-opaque top cell which transmits 32% of light above its bandgap. This has an achievable efficiency of 36.2% for al $Al_2Ga_{98}As$ cell on Si, which is essentially indistinguishable from a thinned GaAs/Si tandem.

We conclude with an important point which is that this "optical thinning" can be achieved by physically thinning the top cell material, or by depositing the top cell with partial coverage, leaving sections of the bottom Si cell directly exposed to the incident spectrum.

This solution is ideally suited to the ELO Al$_x$GaAs cell growth, since growth proceeds by nucleation of independent crystals. Complete coalescence is in fact a challenge, and while it may be in principle achieved, independent crystals are technologically far easier to fabricate.

For completeness, we mention here work towards complete coverage in similar work by Strömberg *et al.* [8]. This investigates ELO fabrication of GaAsP on Si.

4 Simulations

The simulations first aim to analyse the fabricated devices described in section 2 in order to establish the potential performance of available materials. We start by briefly summarising the modelling strategy, before presenting the properties of the structure assumed in the modelling, before presenting results of electrical and optical modelling.

3.1 Model specification

The simulation in this work is carried out with Silvaco finite element numerical software in the Victory suite, in particular the process, meshing, and device simulation modules which we will not describe and instead refer the reader to manuals and publications which provide these details [9].

The complexity of the multilayer textured structure consisting of two different cells and a range of materials, and the dimensions of the smallest elements in principle require a precise finite difference time domain model (FDTD). This is however computationally expensive. Furthermore the optically relevant layers range from 1μm to hundreds of microns, and the refractive index contrast with the thin Al$_x$GaAs emitter layer at the front remains small. For these reasons, these studies rely on ray tracing which is sufficient for preliminary investigations, subject to FDTD studies in future work if necessary.

	Dimension (μm)	Material	doping
Transparent conducting oxide	0.1	ITO	-
Top cell			
Crystal facet angle	30° and 0°	-	-
Emitter	0.1	Al$_x$GaAs, x=0.4-0.7	p 1E18
Base	1 - 2	Al$_x$GaAs, x=0.3-0.4	n 1E15
Interface oxide			
Oxide	2E-3	SiO$_2$	-
Seed	0.1	Al$_x$GaAs, x=0.3-0.4	n 1E15
Silicon bottom cell			
Tunnel 1	0.1	Si	n 1E19
Tunnel 2 / base	0.1	Si	p 1E19
Wafer	2 - 250	Si	n 1E15
Emitter/back contact	0.1	Si	n 1E20

Table 1 model device specification range of materials parameters consistent with current fabrication techniques.

3.2 Device specification

Since we are interested in evaluating the current materials, modelled devices are not optimised from the perspective of layer dimensions, doping, and light interaction (anti-reflection (AR) coatings) in order to match the current experimental achievements.

The modelled device specifications are detailed in table 1. They include both flat and textured geometries with the doping, dimensions indicated, the nucleation site. The chosen compositional parameters are an Al$_{40}$Ga$_{60}$As emitter and Al$_{30}$Ga$_{70}$As absorber.

Also indicated are preliminary definitions of the tunnel layers and the silicon bottom cell which are however not simulated in this work, again in line with prioritising the experimental status.

Figure 4 shows succinctly the modelled structures, flat and textured, which are analogies to the experimental structures in figure 2. The model structures differ in the presence of a contact transparent conducting oxide and a front surface emitter layer which are in development experimentally.

Figure 5 completes the numerical description of the full cell ranging from the nanometre scale nucleation site to the hundred micron scale silicon substrate. This study concentrates on the top cell and does not consider the tunnel layers and Si performance which are to be implemented experimentally once top cell devices are operational.

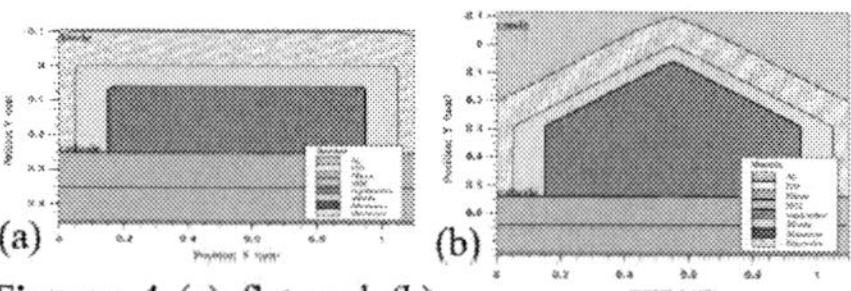

Figures 4 (a) flat and (b) textured GaAs crystals as defined by the process model for the lower 1μm dimension and inter-crystal separatin of 100nm. Also show are the tunnel junction layers for completeness which are not implemented in this study.

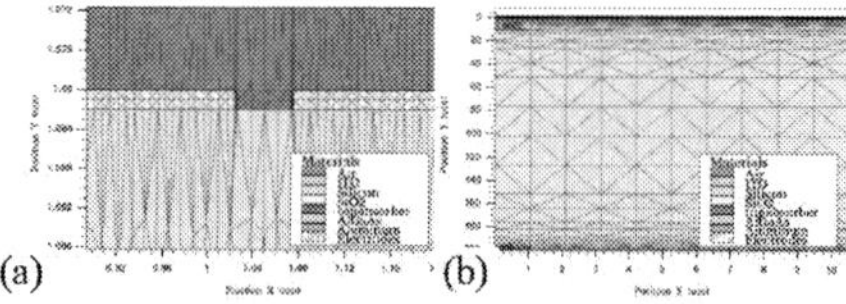

Figure 5 Schematics of the device and numerical Delaunay mesh over the range of scales from (a) the nanometre scale nucleation site to (b) the full device scale which is dominated by the Si substrate at the hundred micron scale.

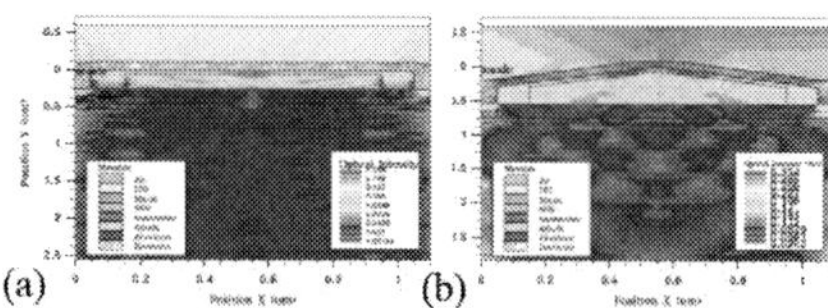

Figure 6 Light intensity map in cross section of (a) a flat 1μm crystal and (b) the textured analogue

3.3 Light management

Figure 6(a) shows light intensity maps in cross section of the flat device model. We note some light diffration at the edges due to the crystal separation. The centre shows an minor artefact corresponding to the nucleation site which however should not be considered reliable given the ray tracing model applied, and the size of this feature well below the incident photon wavelengths. Figure 6(b) shows the analogue for the textured sample.

We note first the difference in light intensity above the cell, with the flat structure reflecting significantly more light than the textured. This confirms the role of texturing as improving light interaction by reducing surface reflectivity, a well known phenomenon used in textured Si cells as pioneered by Green [10].

Quantification and optimisation of this reduction of reflectivity is at this stage preliminary since we are not considering AR coats at this stage as mentioned previously.

The second effect demonstrated at this state is light refraction within the cell by the surface texture provided by the micro-crystal array. This is evident in the light refraction visible in firure 6b compared to 6a. In the flat case, features in light distribution are visible laterally but as mentioned just above but are due to the presence of spacers.

In the textured case we see enhanced light intensity below the microcrystal which leads to enhanced photogeneration at shorter depths in the Si cell.

This reproduces the same light refraction and light trapping phenomena which are now standard in high efficiency textured Si solar cells[10].

We conclude that the Al_xGaAs ELO crystal array provides the same light management design features which allow a thinning of Si substrates and a higher efficiency due to shorted diffusion scales for carrier collection in the Si. They also provide similar advantages in the Al_xGaAs higher gap subcell.

Both these phenomena will be quantified in future work, including optical coupling between the two. On that point, we note that Al_xGaAs and Si have very similar real refractice indices in the wavelength region below the Al_xGaAs absorber bandgap range [11].

Design	J_{SC} (mA/cm^2)	V_{OC} (V)	FF (%)	Efficency (%)
Flat	61.9	1.38	88	7.58
Textured	91.5	1.39	90	11.5

Table 2 Simulated device performances for material geometries fabricated to date which lacking optimisation feature low efficiencies, but with textured devices close to twice the flat device performance.

3.4 Device performance

We first present in table 2 the performance of current materials with, as noted above, an $Al_{40}Ga_{60}As$ emitter and $Al_{30}Ga_{70}As$ absorber. Lacking optimisation of structure and materials, these are projected to achieve low efficiencies as might be expected.

More important is to note the significant efficiency enhancement in the textured device which at 11.5% is close to twice the efficiency of the flat at 7.6%. This is due for a number of contributing factors.

The difference in absorbing volume is the first. The thin cell, 1μm across and only 0.25μm high, is too thin to absorb the incident spectrum efficiently. In addition, surface reflection is particularly high in the absence of an AR coat. Finally, carrier diffusion lengths are maximised by the 1/4 hight to width geometry and the imposition of current transport through the centred nucleation site.

The textured device, in contrast, benefits first from a greater thickness from the hexagonal cap which raises the maximum thickness by about a third, and increases absorption. This is amplified by the surface refraction by the facets which adds light trapping in the top cell,

increasing the absorption of the greater absorbing thickness compared to the flat case. Finally, of course, the surface reflection is reduced by the texturing as we have seen earlier in the light management analysis.

We do not include here the quantum efficiencies and light current characteristics for succinctness but note they are shown in the EUPVSEC2025 presentation available on the conference website.

We conclude by evaluating routes to improvement for the top cell. The first is the modification of the emitter by increasing the Al composition to $Al_{70}Ga_{30}As$, close to the maximum, and reducing the absorber Al composition zero, that is, GaAs.

We also eliminate the spacer which is currently not feasible but which is under investigation by other workers in similar studies [7].

The third and final modification is to increase crystal width to the current achieved of 3μm. This gives a base height of 0.75μm and a cap height of approximately 1.3μm, as shown in figure which is sufficient for complete light absorption above its bandgap of 1.42eV. if slightly above the largest size achieved to date which is 2μm.

The quantum efficiency and power/voltage curve for this device are shown in figures 8a and 8b. This device achieved efficiency f 22%, for a JSC of 216mA/cm2, VOC of 1.15V, and fill factor of 89%.

Extrapolating this to our target 32% transmitting top cell yields a final top cell efficiency in this simple first case of 15.0%.

The achievable tandem efficiency remains low with a Si bottom cell efficiency of just 9.2% based on an optically coupled model for which we show the EQE only for brevity in figure 9. This uses a 200μm Si cell optically coupled to a GaAs surface microcrystal array with 32% transmission. The combined tandem efficiency is of 24.2%, which remains low since as we have already mentioned the intention of this presentation is a preliminary evaluation of potential performance rather than a full optimisation which will follow.

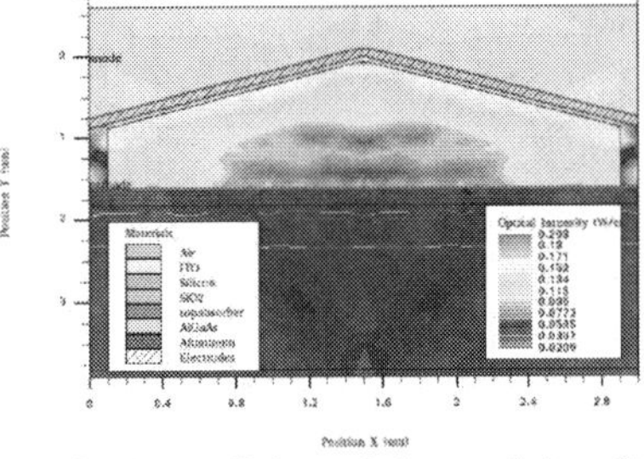

Figure 7 Higher efficiency design consisting of GaAs cell with no spacer, and 3μm width leading to a crystal base height 0.75μm and cap height 1.55μm sufficient for total absorption in the GaAs.

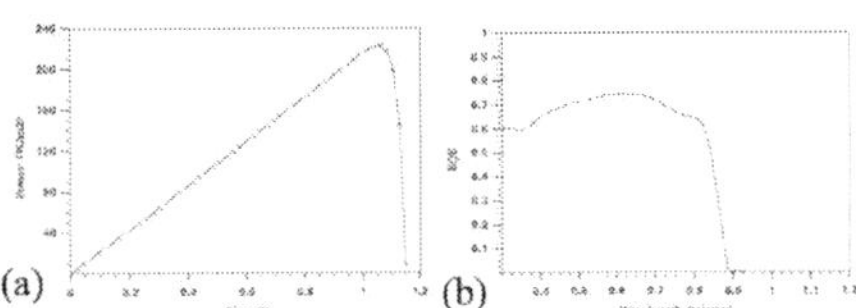
(a) (b)

Figure 8 power-voltage (a) and quantum efficiency (b)

of idealised device with no spacer and a GaAs top composition

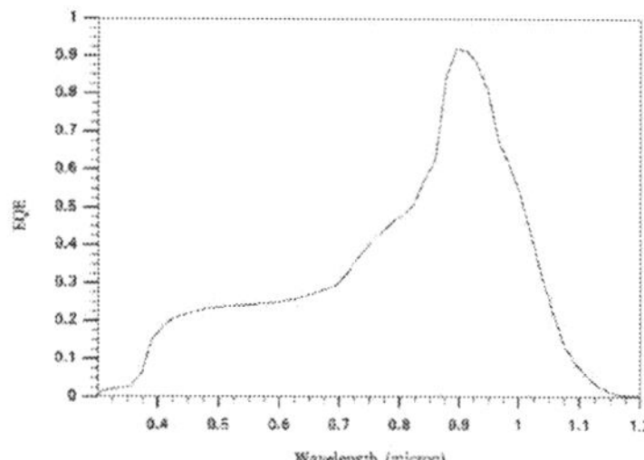

Figure 9 Quantum efficiency of a 200μm think Si bottom cell under 32% optically transmitting GaAs microcrystal array for current matching.

5 Conclusions

We have presented modelling of textured ELO AlGaAs crystals on Si. We find first that these structures allow light scattering of the same type as used in high efficiency standard silicon solar cells. An array of AlGaAs microcrystals is therefore very well suited to provide an effective texturing on a tandem III-V/Si solar cell, with the Si cell consisting of a thinner Si substrate as in high effiicency Si solar cells.

We have evaluated the potential efficiency of the current state of the art ELO crystals. Efficiencies remain low because of a lack of optimisation of optical and structural properties.

We have shown that based on current materials a 32% transmitting top GaAs cell with an efficiency of 15% is achievable, consistent with current matching to a lower gap Si cell.

This is projected to reach efficiencies in tandem structures which reach 24%, which while not impressive for a complex tandem device is nevertheless consistent current materials status and where identified routes to significantly higher performance is clear, and consists of standard solar cell optimisation.

We also note that a higher bandgap design has been identified as   an $Al_{20}Ga_{80}As$ providing current matching. While this is currently not achievable since it requires complete coverage, work in the field towards complete top cell coverage makes this an even higher efficiency design to consider in future.

The next steps will be to simulate the top and bottom cell structures and combined tandem performance with experimental developments in the direction of top cell, bottom cell, and complete tandem devices, and thereby evaluate the light management and tandem potential of ELO AlGaAs for photovoltaic and broader applications.

Acknowledgments

The authors acknowledge the support of the French National Research Agency (ANR) financing the project HELLO-PV (ANR22-CE050-0011) which has made this work possible.

References

[1] Connolly J.P., Mencaraglia D., Renard C., Bouchier D., Designing III–V multijunction solar cells on silicon, Prog. in Photovoltaics, vol. 22 (07), p. 810-820, 2014; https://doi.org/10.1002/pip.2463

[2] Masafumi Yamaguchi, Kan-Hua Lee, Kenji Araki and Nobuaki Kojima, 2018 A review of re- cent progress in heterogeneous silicon tandem solar cells J. Phys. D: Appl. Phys. 51 133002; https://doi.org/10.1088/1361-6463/aaaf08

[3] Yoshinori Ujiie and Tatau Nishinaga 198, Epitaxial Lateral Overgrowth of GaAs on a Si Substrate Jpn. J. Appl. Phys. 28 L337; · https://doi.org/10.1143/JJAP.28.L337

[3] Charles Renard et al.; High current density GaAs/Si rectifying heterojunction by defect free Epitaxial Lateral overgrowth on Tunnel Oxide from nano-seed; Scientific Reports (Nature) 6, 25328, 2016; doi: 10.1038/srep25328, www.nature.com/articles/srep25328

[4] J.W. Matthews, A.E. Blakeslee, Defects in epitaxial multilayers: I. Misfit dislocations, Journal of Crystal Growth, Volume 27, 1974, Pages 118-125, https://doi.org/10.1016/S0022-0248(74)80055-2.

[5] H. Mizuta, K. Yamaguchi, M. Yamane, T. Tanoue and S. Takahashi, "Two-dimensional numerical simulation of Fermi-level pinning phenomena due to DX centers in AlGaAs/GaAs HEMTs," in IEEE Transactions on Electron Devices, vol. 36, no. 10, pp. 2 3 0 7 - 2 3 1 4,   O c t.   1 9 8 9, https://doi.org/10.1109/16.40915

[6] Martin A. Green, Ewan D. Dunlop, Masahiro Yoshita, Nikos Kopidakis, Karsten Bothe, Gerald Siefer, Xiaojing Hao, Jessica Yajie Jiang Solar Cell Efficiency Tables (Version 66) Prog Photovolt Res Appl. 33, 7, https://doi.org/10.1002/pip.3919

[7] Henry CH. Limiting efficiencies of single and multiple energy gap terrestrial solar cells. Journal of Applied Physics 1980; 51(8): 4494. https://doi.org/10.1063/1.328272

[8] Axel Strömberg, Balaji Manavaimaran, Lakshman Srinivasan, Sebastian Lourdudoss, Yan-Ting Sun, (2023). Epitaxial Lateral Overgrowth of GaAsP for III-V/Si-Based Photovoltaics. Physica Status So- lidi (a) Applications and Materials Science, 220(8); https://doi.org/10.1002/pssa.202200623

[9] Silvaco Victory TCAD website contining manuals and webinars websit https://silvaco.com/tcad/interactive-tools/

[10] Green, Martin A, Forty years of photovoltaic research at UNSW., Journal and proceedings of the Royal Society of New South Wales, 148, 1, pp 2-14, https://doi.org/10.5962/p.361724

[11] Refractive index database https://refractiveindex.info/

EUPVSEC 2025

Micro-crystal GaAs array sub-cells for Si tandem solar cells

J.P. Connolly[1], A. Nejim[3], A. Jaffré[1], J. Alvarez[1], J P. Kleider[1], D. Mencaraglia[1], Laurie Dentz[2], G. Hallais[2], F. Hamouda[2], L. Vincent[2], D. Bouchier[2], C. Renard[2]

[1]GeePs, Group of Electrical Engineering Paris, CNRS, CentraleSupelec, Université Paris-Saclay, Sorbonne Université, 3&11 rue Joliot-Curie, Plateau de Moulon, 91192 Gif-sur-Yvette CEDEX, France

[2]C2N, Centre de Nanosciences et de Nanotechnologies, CNRS, Université Paris-Saclay, 10 Bd Thomas Gobert, 91120, Palaiseau, France

[3]SILVACO Technology Centre, Compass Point, St. Ives, Cambridgeshire PE27 5JL, UK

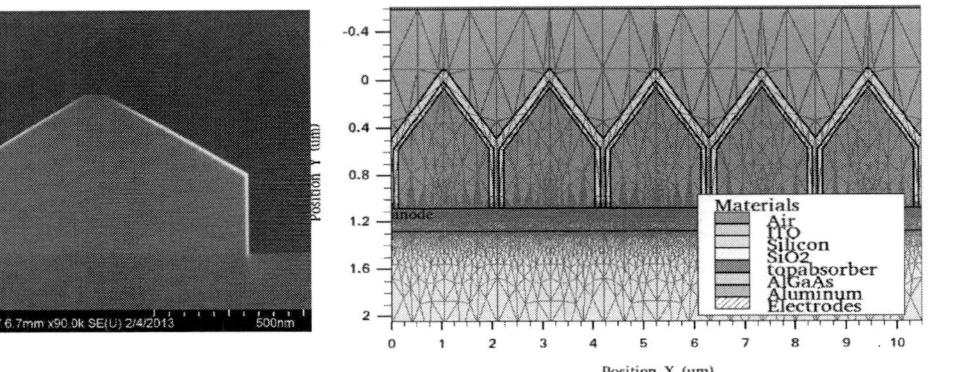

Overview

- Fabrication : Epitaxial lateral overgrowth (ELO)
- Tandems on silicon : ideal bandgaps
- AlGaAs for high gap tandem subcells
- Current top cell device structure
- Model
- Light management
- Device performance
- Higher efficiency
- Next priorities

Epitaxial lateral overgrowth[1]

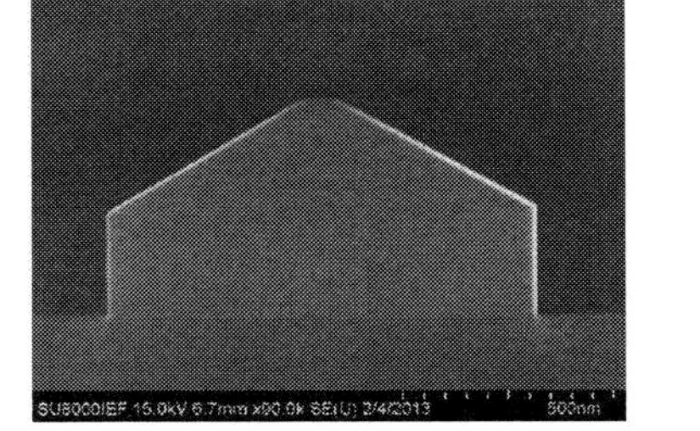

ELO : Epitaxial lateral overgrowth

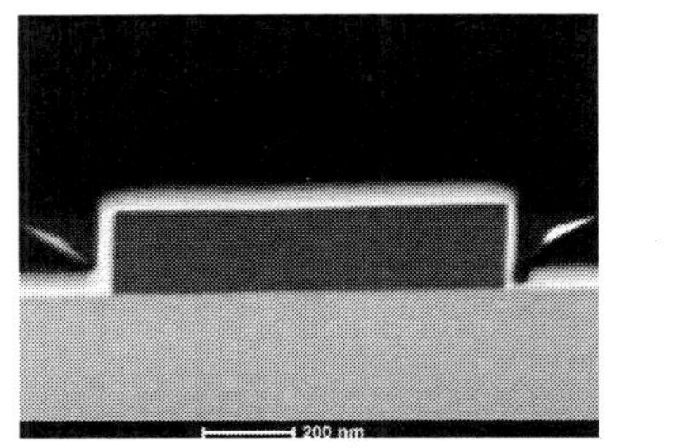

Fabrication : Flat and faceted / "textured" crystals micron scale

Available materials :
GaAs -> Al_{30}GaAs (gaps 1.424eV/870nm to 1.8eV/690nm) for absorbers
-> Al_{75}GaAs (to gap 2.3eV/535nm) for thin layers : emitter.

Available geometries:
Flat and faceted ("textured") materials
Base aspect fixed : height to width ration 1/4
Cap aspect ratio fixed : 30° angle to the horizontal.

(1) Charles Renard, Timoth´e Moli`ere, Nikolay Cherkashin, Jos´e Alvarez, Laetitia Vincent, Alexandre Jaffr´e, G´eraldine Hallais, James Patrick Connolly, Denis Mencaraglia & Daniel Bouchier , High cur- rent density GaAs/Si rectifying heterojunction by defect free Epitaxial Lateral overgrowth on Tunnel Oxide from nano-seed. Sci. Rep. 6, 25328; https://doi.org/10.1038/srep25328 (2016)

4

III-V silicon tandem efficiencies[2]

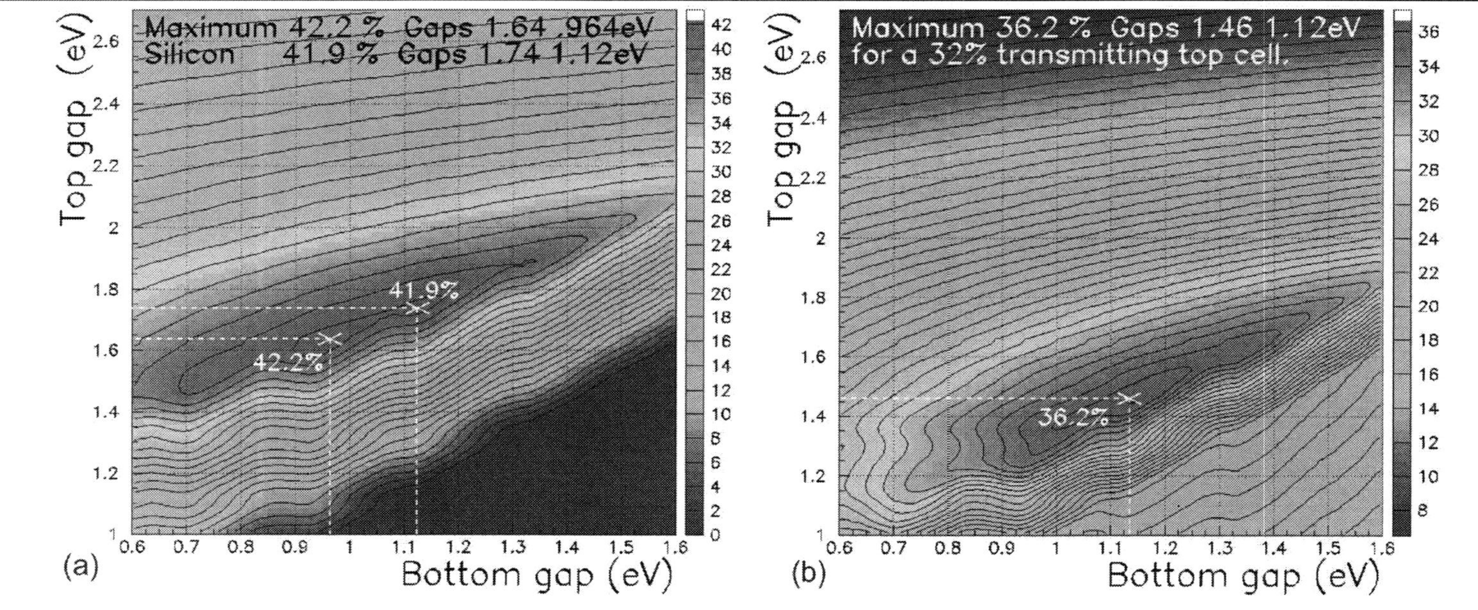

- Al_xGaAs bandgap range : 1.424 -> 2.7eV (1.424+1.247*x)
- GaAs gap too low for tandem application

=> Two solutions :
- Increase gap, add aluminium *but* : material problems
- "Optically thin" the top (AlGaAs) cell : Less ideal, but current matched

=>

Highest AlGaAs on Si efficiency :	41.9%	Gap 1.74eV is $Al_{25}Ga_{75}As$	
Highest GaAs on Si efficiency:	36.2%	Gap 1.46eV is $Al_2Ga_{98}As$	

Conclusion : Desirable absorber materials 0% - 40% are within fabrication range

[2] J.P. Connolly, D. Mencaraglia, C. Renard, D. Bouchier, Designing III–V multijunction solar cells on silicon, Progress in Photovoltaics, vol. 22 (07), p. 810-820, 2014; https://doi.org//10.1002/pip.2463

Al$_x$GaAs material notes

Note : AlGaAs material issues for solar cells :

- Close to lattice matched across the range GaAs to AlAs

- Direct / Indirect transition above x≈45%

- Reactive material : oxidation especially ; transport problems

- Doping challenge : tendency to unindentional p doping (Carbon)

- Materials issues at high Al compositions : DX centres, defective – transport problems

- GaAs : Excellent material quality (record cells 29%[3])

Conclusions :

Available compositions absorber 0 -30% well suited in principle
High Al composition suitable for window and emitter layers.
Transport issues with increasing Al content a potential problem

Next : Evaluate efficiency of current III-V crystals by ELO

(3) Martin A. Green, Ewan D. Dunlop, Masahiro Yoshita, Nikos Kopidakis, Karsten Bothe, Gerald Siefer, Xiaojing Hao, Jessica Yajie Jiang Solar Cell Efficiency Tables (Version 66) Prog Photovolt Res Appl. 33, 7, https://doi.org/10.1002/pip.3919

Model essentials

Numerical finite element model Silvaco Victory :

- V-Process : composition and deposition of materials (1D - 3D)

- V-mesh : non-linear mesh definition algorithms (Delaunay)

- V-device : Device performance

Note : latest update replacing previous "Atlas", "Athena", "Devedit" models.

Applied here to fabricated devices rather than optimised

Device structure

	Dimension (μm)	Material	doping
Transparent conducting oxide	0.1	ITO	-
Top cell			
Crystal facet angle	30° and 0°	-	-
Emitter	0.1	Al_xGaAs, x=0.4-0.7	p 1E18
Base	1 - 2	Al_xGaAs, x=0.3-0.4	n 1E15
Interface oxide			
Oxide	2E-3	SiO_2	-
Seed	0.1	Al_xGaAs, x=0.3-0.4	n 1E15
Silicon bottom cell			
Tunnel 1	0.1	Si	n 1E19
Tunnel 2 / base	0.1	Si	p 1E19
Wafer	2 - 250	Si	n 1E15
Emitter/back contact	0.1	Si	n 1E20

- Top cell : AlGaAs cell : flat or faceted

- Tunnel junction : Standard Si design (not implemented here)

- Bottom cell : Standard untextured Si cell (not shown in this work).

We focus on the AlGaAs textured cell following fabrication achievements.

Process and mesh steps

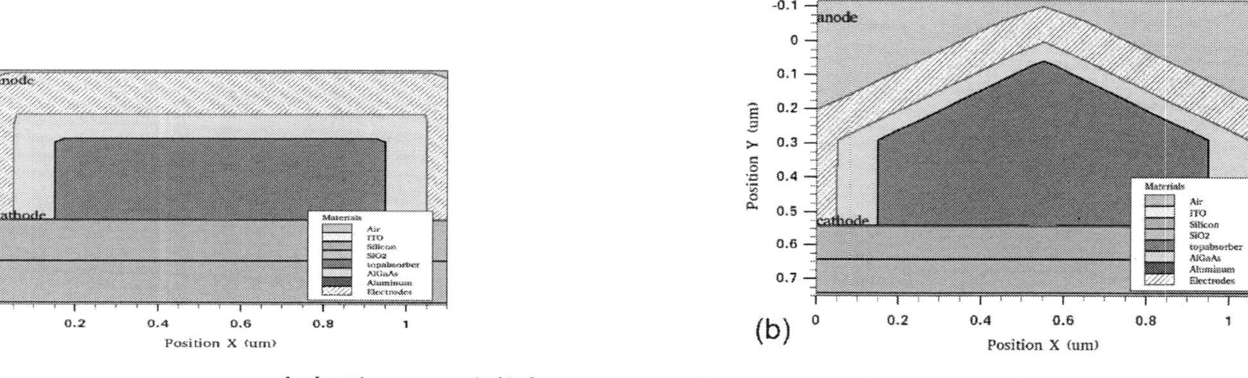

(a)

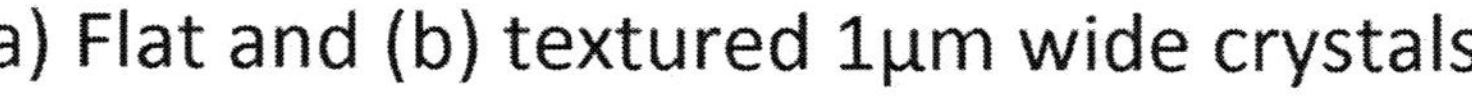

(b)

(a) Flat and (b) textured 1μm wide crystals

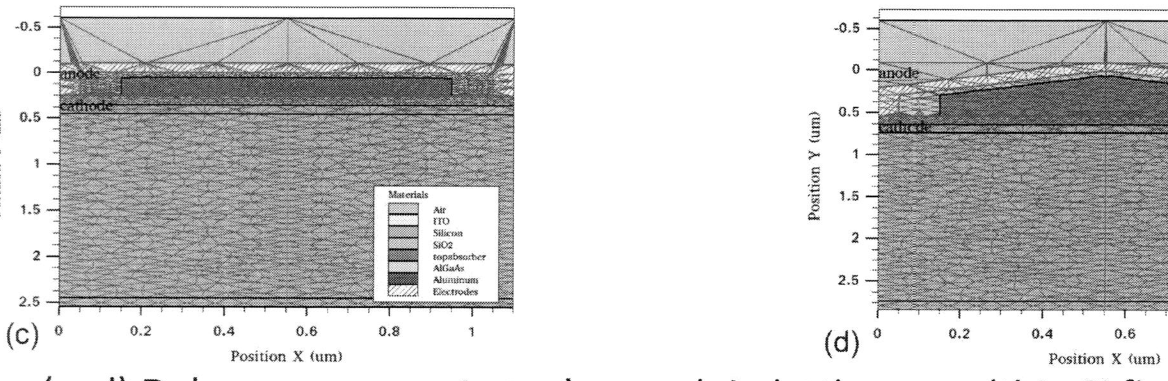

(c)

(d)

(c, d) Delaunay non-rectangular mesh in both cases, (thin Si fine mesh)

Flat and single crystal textured structures (with a thin 2μm Si cell for illustrative purposes)

Full structure, five period array

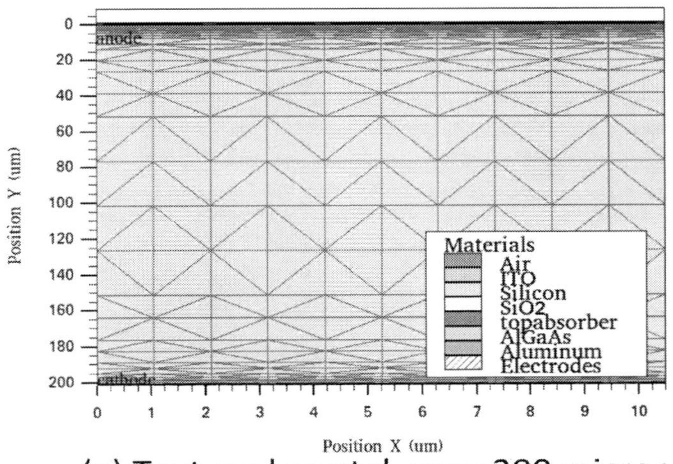

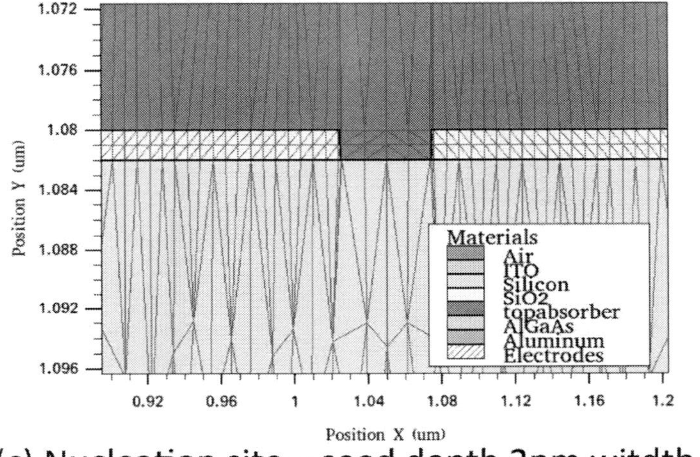

(a) Textured crystal array 200 micron Si cell loose mesh in Si bulk

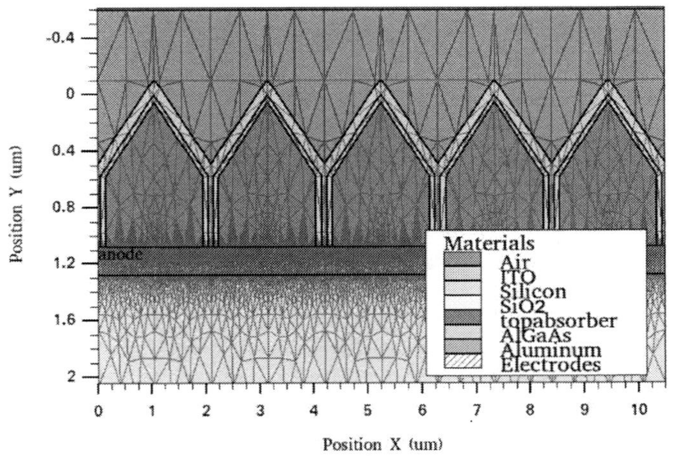

(b) Surface crystal array separation 50nm

(c) Nucleation site – seed depth 2nm witdth 50nm

Textured five crystal period structure with a thin 200μm Si cell and showing nucleation site

Light management one period

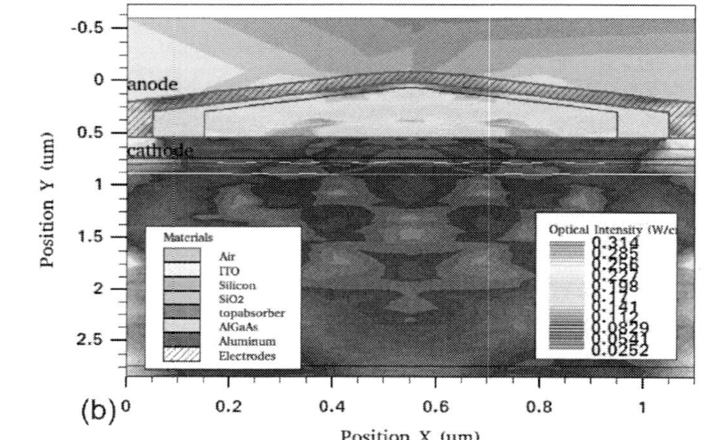

(a)

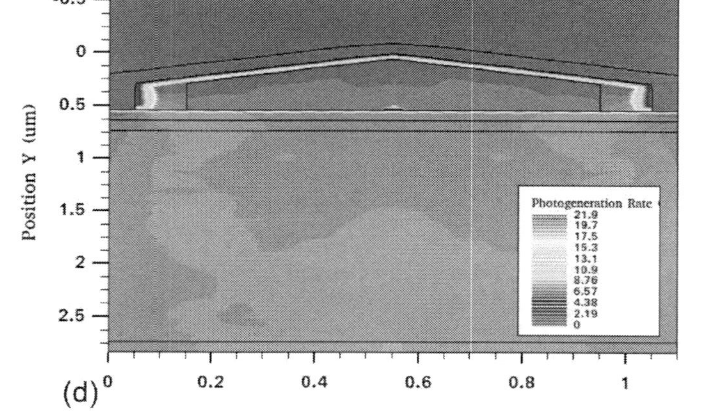

(b)

- Intensity maps of (a) flat (b) textured crystals

- Texture reduces reflection
- Texture refracts and traps light : increased absorption

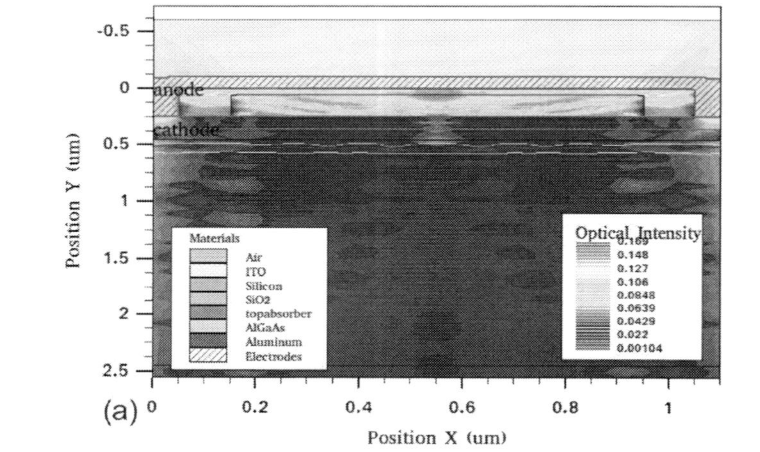

(c)

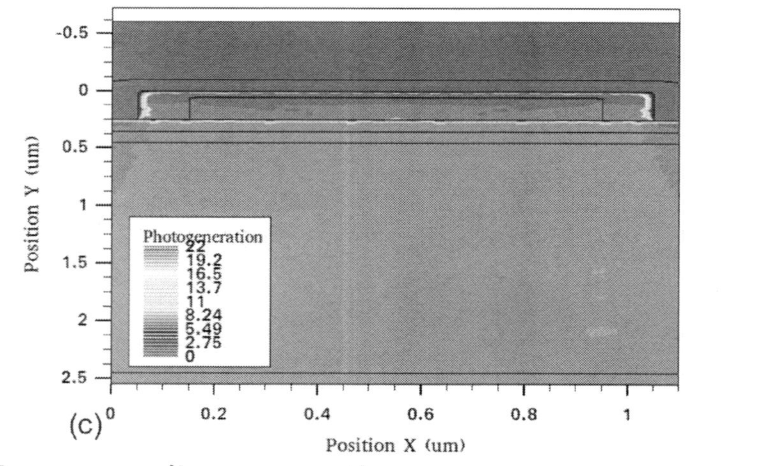

(d)

- Corresponding generation maps

Conclusion : Faceted crystal arrays performing the same role as Si cell texturing[4]

(4) Green, Martin A, Forty years of photovoltaic research at UNSW., Journal and proceedings of the Royal Society of New South Wales, 148, 1, pp 2-14, https://doi.org/10.5962/p.361724

Five periods

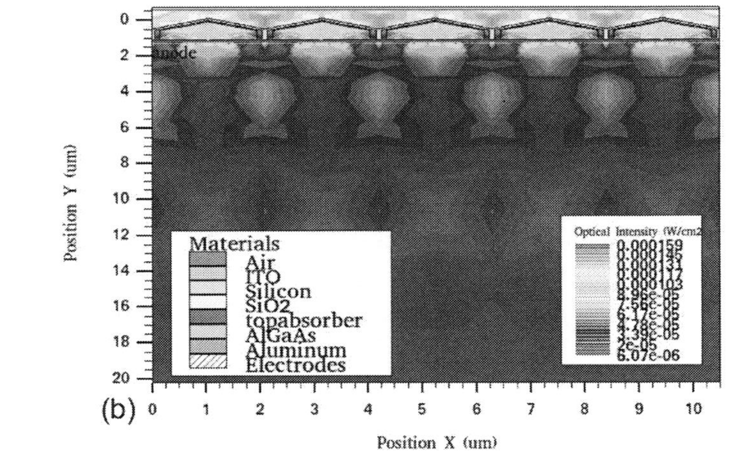

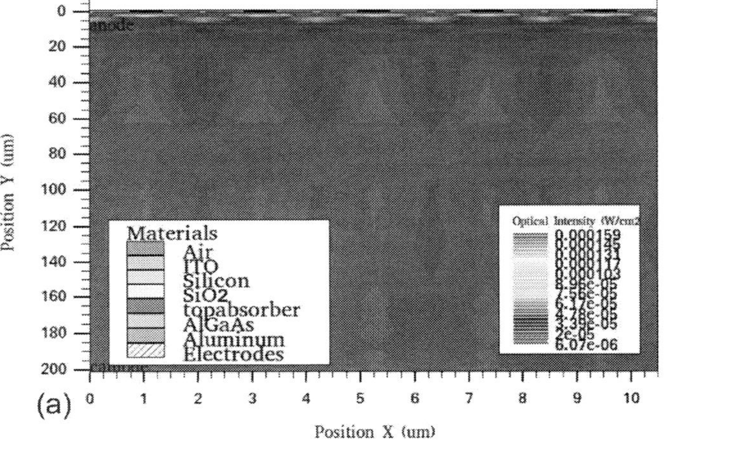

For completeness : Light intensity over (a) whole structure and (b) a zoom over the first 20µm

Device performance

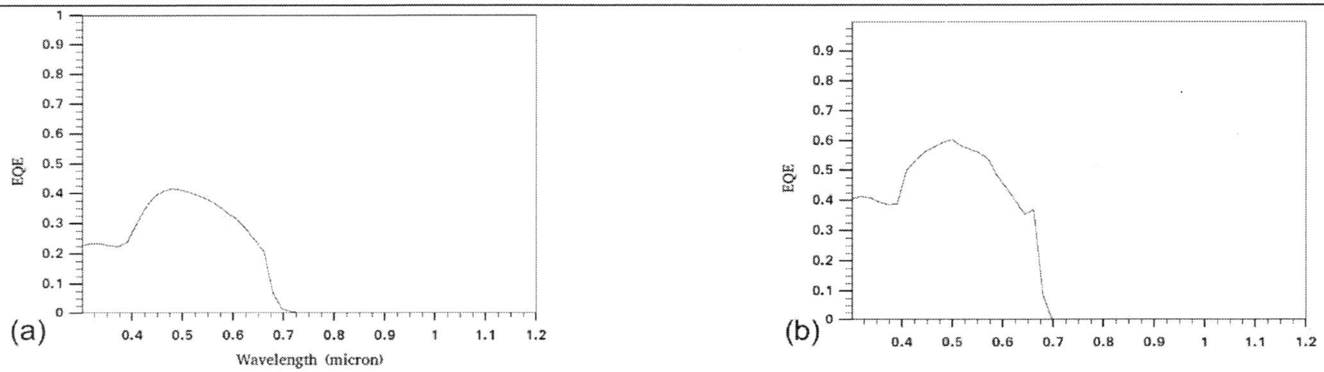

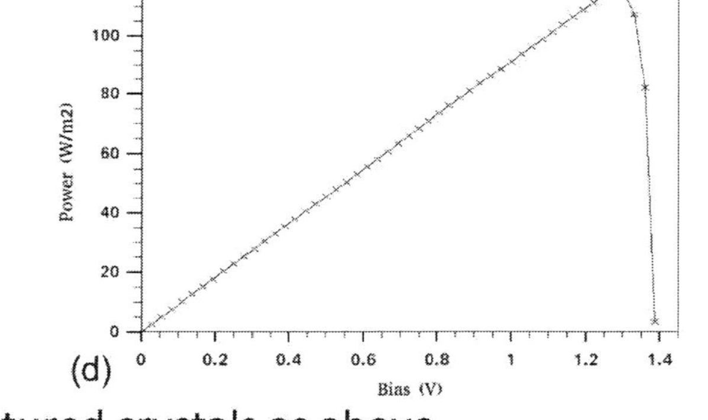

- Plain EQE of (a) flat and (b) textured crystals : no optimisation (AR coat, doping, dimensions0

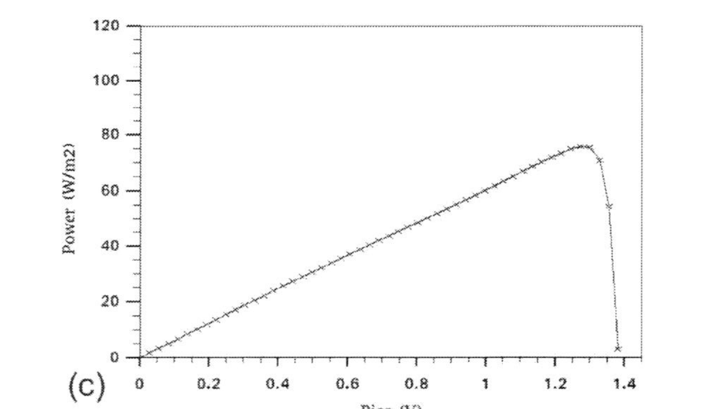

- Power output under STC AM1.5G (a) flat and (b) textured crystals as above

Design	J_{SC} (mA/cm^2)	V_{OC} (V)	FF (%)	Efficency (%)
Flat	61.9	1.38	88	7.58
Textured	91.5	1.39	90	11.5

Performance : Faceted (textured) much better – Efficiencies low, first devices yet to be made
(*nb. Performance independent of number of periods*)

Dimension studies

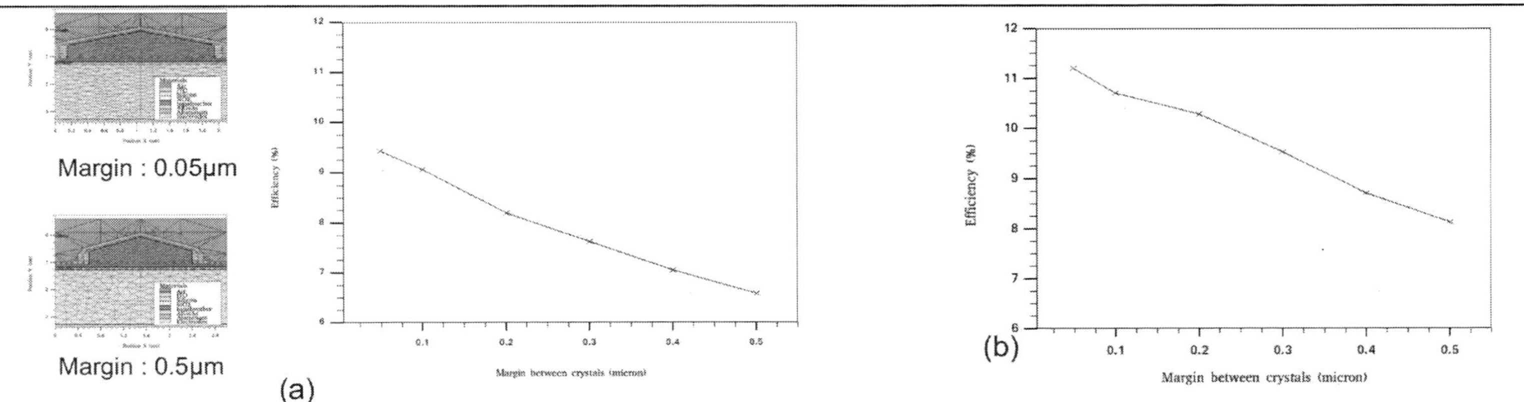

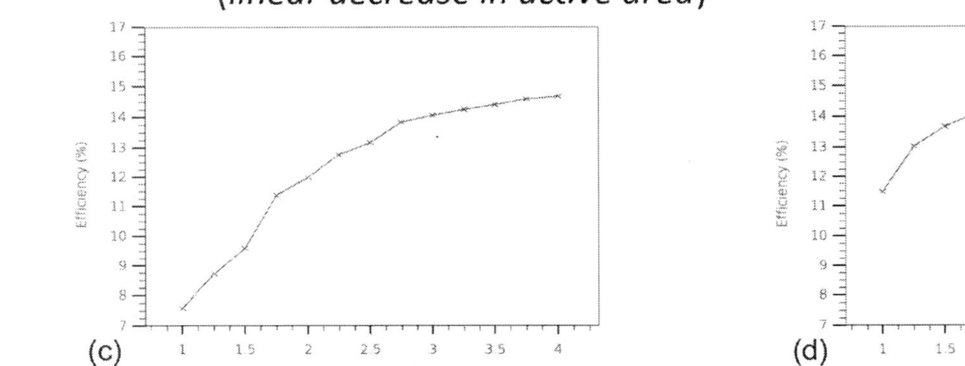

Impact of crystal spacing : (a) flat (b) textured decrease inter-crystal margin gives linear efficiency decrease
(*linear decrease in active area*)

Impact of crystal size : Log. increase in efficiency – textured (d) higher than flat (c)

Conclusions :   Faceted textured crystals are better
Zero crystal separation for highest efficiencies : complete coverage.
Crystal size to be large enough for complete absorption above AlGaAs gap
Proviso : Partly transmitting non-optimal but high efficiency concepts

Higher efficiency GaAs device example

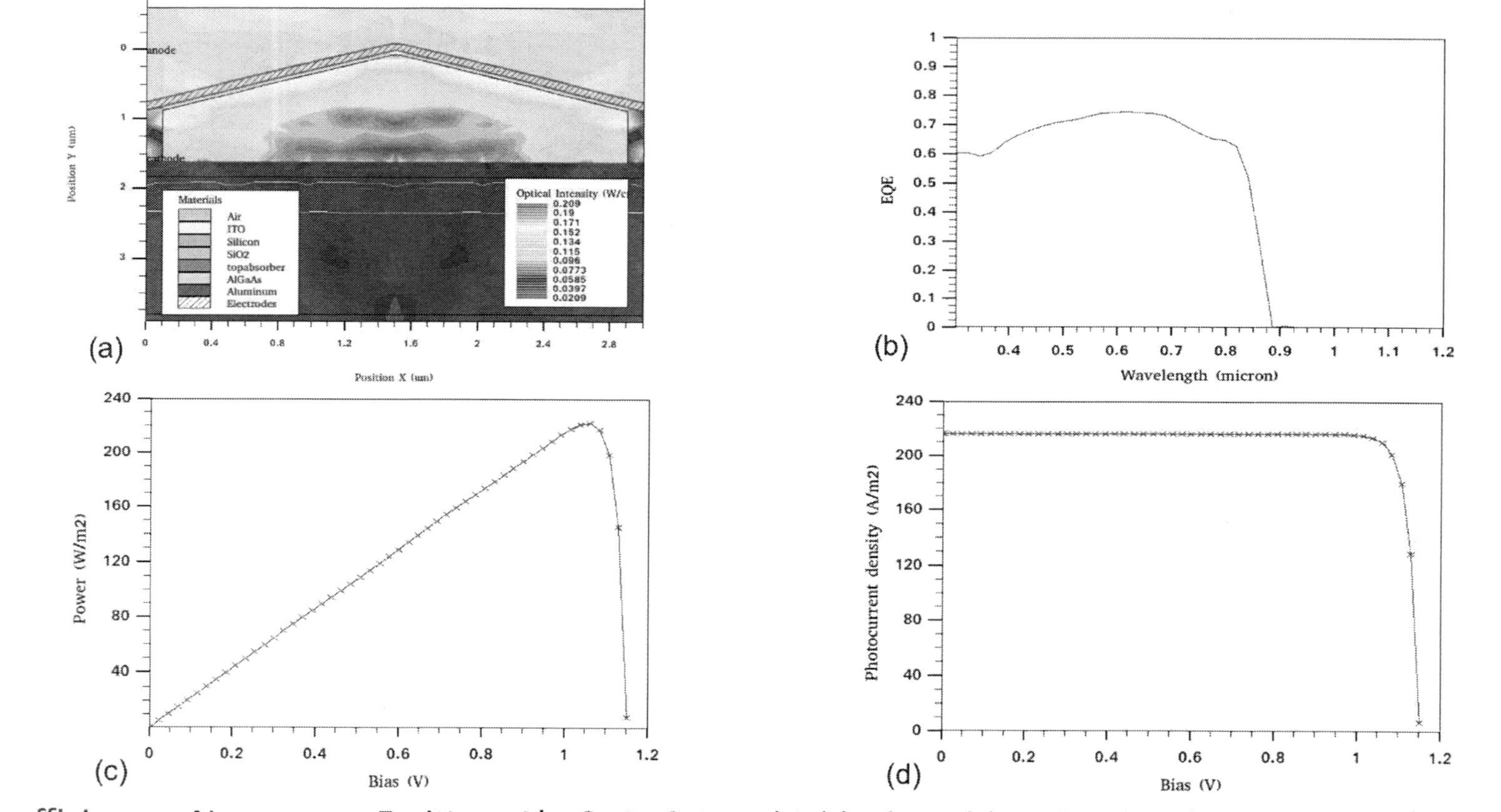

Higher efficiency : No spacer ; Emitters $Al_{0.7}$GaAs 0.1μm highly doped (1E18emitter) ; GaAs absorber

=> STC Efficiency 22% (Jsc=216mA/cm2, Voc=1.15V, FF=89%)

Notes : Far from 29% GaAs record, and not optimised, but an indication of routes to investigate
Not the main route to high efficiency : That is Al_{25}GaAs top array 32% tranmitting to Si.

020059-014

Conclusions

- Preliminary model : low efficiencies for first devices projected : not optimised

- Light trapping potential demonstrated : equivalent of Si texturing

- We have only touched on incomplete absorption mentioned at the start :
  Spaced and thinned $Al_{25}Ga_{75}As$ crystals the most promising route

- Optimisation : both light and current transport
  (AR coats, light transmission ; Doping, material, and structure)

- Much broader III-V on Si applications we have not touched on

=> Next photovoltaic priorities :

- $Al_{25}Ga_{75}As$ surface crystal arrays transmitting 32%
- Si cell optimisation with nanocrystal light trapping

MULTISCALE MODELS FOR PEROVSKITE OPTIMISATION

Philippe. Baranek[1,2,*], James P. Connolly[3], Antoine Gissler[1,2,4], Philip Schulz[4], Michel Rérat[5] and Roberto Dovesi[6]

[1] EDF R&D, EDF Lab Paris-Saclay, Department SYSTEME, 7 boulevard Gaspard Monge, F-91120 Palaiseau, France
[2] IPVF, Institut Photovoltaïque d'Ile-de-France, 18 boulevard Thomas Gobert, F-91120 Palaiseau, France
[3] 1GeePs, Group of Electrical Engineering Paris, CNRS, CentraleSupelec, Université Paris-Saclay, Sorbonne Université, 3&11 rue Joliot-Curie, Plateau de Moulon, 91192 Gif-sur-Yvette CEDEX, France
[4] École Polytechnique, IPVF, UMR 9006, CNRS, 18 boulevard Thomas Gobert, F-91120 Palaiseau, France
[5] Université de Pau et des Pays de l'Adour, E2S UPPA, CNRS, IPREM, 2 avenue du Président Pierre Angot, F-64053 Pau, France
[6] Accademia Delle Science di Torino, via Accademia delle Science 6, I-10123 Torino, Italy

ABSTRACT: This paper presents a multiscale approach to evaluate perovskite solar cell performance which determines material properties at the atomistic scale with first-principles calculations, and applies them in macro-scale device models. This work focuses on the MAPbI$_3$ (MA = CH$_3$NH$_3$) perovskite and how its phase transitions impact on its optical, electronic, and structural properties which are investigated at the first-principles level. The obtained data are coupled to a numerical drift-diffusion device model enabling evaluation of the performance of corresponding single junction devices. The first-principles simulation applies a hybrid exchange-correlation functional adapted to the studied family of compounds. Validation by available experimental data is presented from materials properties to device performance, justifying the use of the approach for predictive evaluation of existing and novel perovskites. The coupling between atomistic and device models is described in terms of a framework for exchange of optical, vibrational, and electronic parameters between the two scales. The result of this theoretical investigation is a methodology for designing and optimising perovskite materials for both cell performance and stability, the key obstacle in the societal implementation of these record-breaking new materials.

Keywords: Perovskites, optoelectronic properties, cell efficiency, first-principles, drift-diffusion.

1 INTRODUCTION

Perovskite solar cells have progressed extremely rapidly from 3.8% in 2009 to 27.3% in September 2024. Tandem efficiencies have furthermore breached the single-junction Shockley-Queisser efficiency limit, reaching 34.6% in June 2024 (LONGI, certified) [1, 2]. While this rapid efficiency increase is unmatched by any other technology, it remains crippled by stability issues, obstacle for the industrial and societal application of these materials. State of the art perovskite absorber materials still suffer stability issues linked to temperature, to volatile organic cations for the organic case and its reactivity to the air moisture among other issues. Both air moisture and temperature induce phase transitions which degrade the performance and durability of perovskite solar cells (PSCs): the moisture leads to the appearance of a non-perovskite phase (the so-called δ black phase) which is optically inactive, while the temperature can lead to a rich sequence of phase transitions. Their impact concerns mainly the electronic properties and the domains and surface stabilities of the different compounds. A key element is stability implications of the effect of phase transitions on the nonlocal lattice distribution of organic moieties through the lattice

In this work, we focus on the phase transitions impacts on the cell efficiency. They are associated in particular to the existence of soft phonon modes which can locally generate phase instabilities. For both organic and inorganic perovskites, they are linked to the lattice and halide octahedra deformations. However, for the organic case, another factor has to be taken into account which is the nonlocal ordering of the organic moieties inside the lattice through the different phase transitions.

Li and co-workers [3, 4] showed that the inorganic-framework deformation depends on the orientation of the organic cation which directly influences the stability of the hybrid perovskites and deserves a multiscale approach to obtain a good description of their properties.

If we consider CH$_3$NH$_3$PbI$_3$ as a paradigmatic case from an experimental point of view, the difficulty in obtaining an accurate characterization of its phase transitions comes from the determination of the methalominium (CH$_3$NH$_3^+$, MA) atomic positions inside the PbX$_3$ lattice: since the measurements are mainly performed with X-Ray diffraction, the positions of the MA moiety are ill or not defined. Therefore, for the $Pm3m$ cubic phase the commonly used assumption is to consider MA as an intrinsic chemical entity which lies in the center of the cubic cell. However, this is not consistent from a crystallographic point of view: For instance, since the MA point group is C_{3v}, the corresponding space groups is C_{3v} ($R3m$) if the C–N bond is along the [1,1,1] direction of the cubic cell. Moreover, with this description MAPbI$_3$ is necessarily in a ferroelectric phase which might lead to a wrong characterization of its optoelectronic properties.

In this paper, using a theoretical multiscale approach, we illustrate how phase transitions can impact the performance of solar cells. This modelling couples atomistic scale first-principles calculations to device scale numerical models. The coupling between atomistic and device models is described in detail by presenting a framework for exchange of optical, and electronic parameters between the two scales.

This approach is based on a crystallographic description of MAPbI$_3$ which allows to take the MA ordering into account. We first describe this crystallographic model. At the first principles level, it is used to determine a

---

*Corresponding author: philippe.baranek@edf.fr

hybrid exchange-correlation functional adapted to the MAPbX$_3$ (x = Cl, Br and I) family of perovskites. The evolution induced by the phase transitions on the electronic and dielectric properties of MAPbI$_3$ is then systematically investigated. The corresponding band gaps, electron affinities and dielectric responses serve as input data to the device model which integrates these data in the absorber of a standard perovskite solar cell design [5] which we will not detail here. This device model yields the corresponding solar cell performance allowing evaluation of the impact of materials configurations at the atomistic scale on device performance and stability.

2 METHODOLOGICAL ASPECTS

2.1 First-principles approach

We define a crystallographic structure allowing evaluation of the ordering of the MA moities inside the lattice through the different phase transitions (see figure 1).

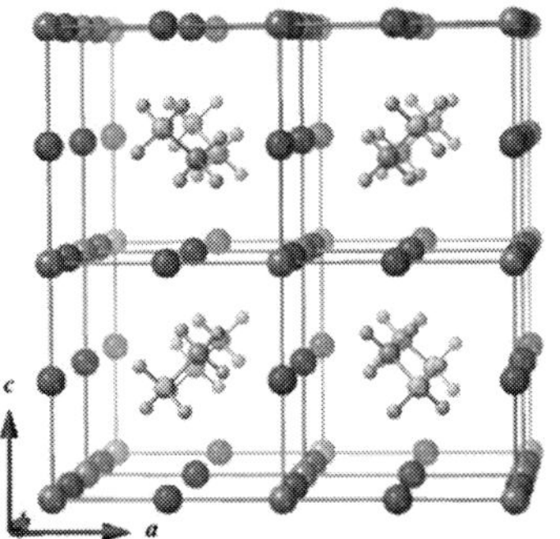

Figure 1: Used crystallographic structure of the *Pm3m* cubic phase of MAPbI$_3$.

First-principles calculations have been performed with the use of the CRYSTAL code [6, 7]. This program enables solution of both the Hartree–Fock (HF) and the Kohn–Sham (KS) systems of equations, combining them within a hybrid scheme. This work uses a hybrid exchange-correlation functional optimized to yield description of the structural, electronic, and dynamic properties of MAPbX$_3$ (X = Cl, Br and I) in good agreement with experiment, and has recently been used efficiently to study the influence of alkali metals on the properties of chalcopyrites, perovskites surface properties and the humidity-induced degradation products of halide perovskites [8-10]. In this work, the Hamiltonian (denoted as **PBEx**) combines 19% of HF exact exchange with the PBE exchange correlation functional [11]. It provides results consistent with a more homogeneous quantitive description of their properties than the most commonly used screened hybrid functional HSE [12] consistent with the most sophisticated methods based on the GW approximation: the obtained mean absolute average errors on the lattice parameters and band gaps of their different phases are 2 and 5 %, respectively, with respect to the available experimental data (as illustrated by the Table II for the cubic phase).

At the first-principles level, the changes induced by the phase transitions of the electronic, vibrational, and

dielectric properties of each perovskite is systematically investigated. The resulting band gaps, work functions and dielectric responses serve as input data to the device model which yields the performance of solar cells.

2.2 Device model

The device scale numerical modelling is performed by on SILVACO's ATLAS simulator [13]. This uses the drift diffusion model, solving the current, continuity, and Poisson equations on a one to three dimension mesh. The full list of parameters identified are summarised in table I. The multiscale coupling consists of identifying device level parameters which can be provided by atomistic scale density functional theory materials models.

Table I: Full set of device scale drift-diffusion (DD) model inputs from atomistic scale density functional theory (DFT) level. This study uses a subset which are band parameters and optical functions.

Parameter	Definition
τ_{SRH}	Electron and hole charge neutral and depletion layers Shockley-Read-Hall lifetimes
μ	Carrier mobility, majority and minority, electron and hole
D_N, D_P	Hole and electron diffusion coefficients
C_A	Auger coefficient
ε	Permittivity related to complex refractive index
n, k	Real and imaginary refractive indices
m_e^*	Electron and hole effective masses
χ	Electron affinity
N_C, N_V	Band parameters - conduction and valence band effective densities of states
E_C, E_V, E_g	Band parameters - Conduction and valence band edges and bandgap

In this study, we limit the interaction to optical and band structure parameters since the device model is only weakly dependent on the other parameters listed. The model structure is a simple inverted structure consisting of electron transport layer, perovskite, and hole transport layer with contacts on a glass substrate, simulated with a transfer matrix methodology and diffusive optics to simulate imperfectly planar surfaces of typical structures. The model outputs include all the usual performance figures of merit as presented in the results section.

3 RESULTS AND DISCUSSION

Figure 1 depicts the *Pm3m* cubic unit cell used to perform the calculations and table II gives the results obtained for lattice parameter, band gap and electron affinity, for the cubic MAPbI$_3$: This 96-atoms primitive cell enables us to begin to consider the influence of the distribution of the molecular entity across the lattice on the structural, vibrational and optoelectronic properties of MAPbI$_3$. As noted previously, this unit combined with the optimized Hamiltonian to reproduce the properties of the MAPbX$_3$ perovskites allows the estimation of the lattice parameters and band gaps with an average error of 2. and 5 %, respectively, with respect to the available experimental data. As indicated in the section 2.1, the **PBEx** functional allows us to obtain data of interest in better agreement with experiment than the most commonly used PBE functional (which strongly underestimates the band gap, for instance).

Table II: Calculated lattice parameters (a in Å), band gap (E_g in eV) and electron affinity (χ in eV) for the cubic phase of MAPbI₃ at the **PBEx** level. The data obtained at the PBE level (between parenthese) and experimental data are given for comparison.

	Calc.	Exp.
a	6.368	6.329[a], 6.308[b]
	(6.383)	
E_g	1.68	1.62 (1.50 – 1.69)[c]
	(0.92)	
χ	3.79	3.45[d], 3.90[e], 4.10[f]
	(4.06)	

[a]Ref [14]; [b]Ref. [15]; [c]average value of experimental data from Table 2 and between parentheses range of variation of the band gap with different materials formings and measurement techniques cited in Table 1 of Ref. [16], respectively; [d]Ref. [17]; [e]Ref. [18]; [f]Ref. [19].

Table III gives the variation of the band gap and electron affinity for different phases of MAPbI₃. For each cell, the systems are fully optimized.

Table III: Calculated band gap (E_g in eV) and electron affinity (χ in eV) for different phases of MAPbI₃ at the **PBEx** level. The results on the single cell (12 atoms) are given for comparison.

Phase	E_g	χ.
Cubic	1.68	3.79
Pm3m		
Tetra.	2.17	3.49
I4/mcm		
Ortho.	2.25	3.46
P222₁		
Single cell	2.25	3.45

We note an increase of the band gap and a decrease of the electron affinity with the symmetries lowering of the different phases. As has been noted in the literature (see for instance references 3 and 4), this is due to the combined effects of the octahedra tilting, MA ordering and induced lattice deformations which yields a shift of the top of valence and of the bottom of the conduction bands.

Figure 2 shows the resulting optoelectronic responses for the cubic and tetragonal phase of MAPbI₃ compared with experimental data and other DFT calculations at the GW level realized on the single cell [20]. It clearly shows that the proposed method, which takes the MA ordering into account, improves the description of the dielectric responses (notably the peak at 3.5 eV) compared to the local approach based on the single cell or the one obtained at the PBE level. It also illustrates that the phase transitions will directly influence the optical response of the considered perovskites. The corresponding theoretical absorption spectra are in a qualitative agreement with experimental data.

We next evaluated device performance. As mentioned above, the device model simulates standard design consisting of a front ITO surface conductor, MoO_x buffer, PTAA hole transport layer, the perovskite absorber, followed by a SnO_2 electron transport layer, the whole on a glass substrate [5].

Table IV gives the performance of devices for different phases of MAPbI₃. We note here important advances, which are comparison of **PBEx** functional results and evaluation of the performance of perovskite phases and their stability, a major question in current PSC development.

a)

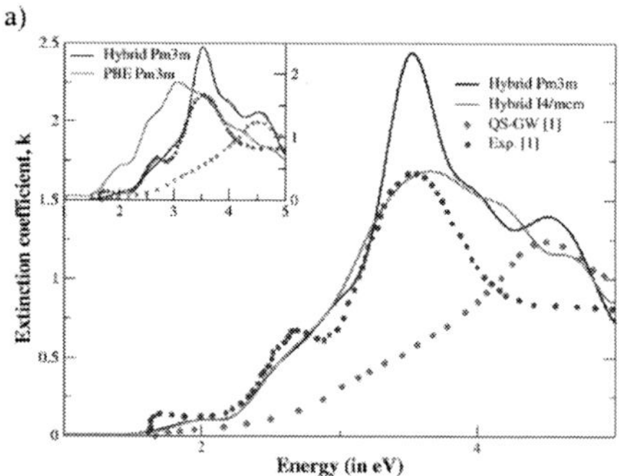

b)

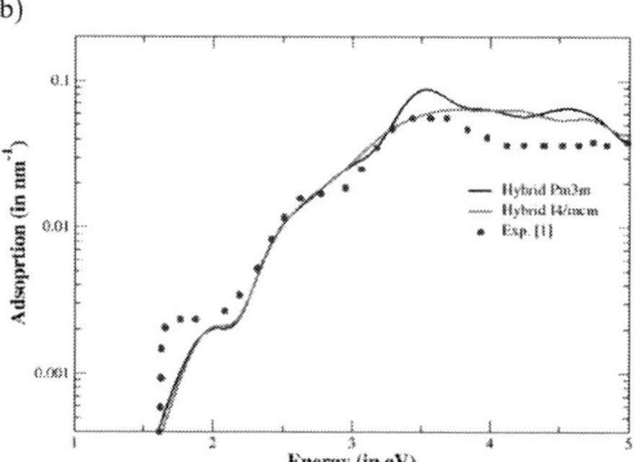

Figure 2: a) Obtained extinction coefficient k and b) absorption for the cubic (*Pm3m*, black) and tetragonal (*I4/mcm*, red) phases of MAPbI₃. The blue and green dots present the experimental data obtained via ellipsometry on monocrystal and the theoretical results obtained on the pristine cell at the GW level, respectively [20].

Table IV: Device performance modelling for parameters taken from the experimental data of literature [20], and from successive theoretical **PBEx** calculations ranging from the single cell (12 atoms cell) to tetragonal and cubic phases (96 atoms cell), showing a peak performance for the cubic phase.

Data source	Jsc (A/m²)	V_{oc} (V)	V_{mp} (V)	FF (%)	η (%)
Single cell	13.4	1.82	1.40	71.9	17.5
Ortho. *P222₁*	11.6	1.80	1.42	73.6	15.5
Tetra. *I4/mcm*	13.4	1.73	1.37	74.6	17.2
Cubic *Pm3m*	18.2	1.25	1.11	84.3	19.2
Exp. [20]	17.5	1.25	1.10	84.3	18.5

Following, the example of the dielectric properties, taking into account the MA ordering in MAPbI₃ improves the qualitative description of the device performances with respect to experiment. It shows that the best agreement is obtained for the cubic phase of MAPbI₃ which possess the highest efficiency. The efficiency of the device decreases with the increase of the bang gap the lowest one corresponding to the orthorhombic phase.

To explain this trend, figure 3 shows band alignments for **PBEx** data set values of affinities and band parameters of the cubic and orthorhombic phases. We note cliffs in absorber-transport layer band profiles (just below 1.2 μm) which translate as drops in charge carriers potential corresponding to drops in maximum power voltage. The significantly greater cliff in the ortho case leads to greater thermalisation losses for both electrons and holes as visible in the step in the electron quasi-Fermi level. This is in part responsible for the lower efficiency of the ortho material compared to the cubic.

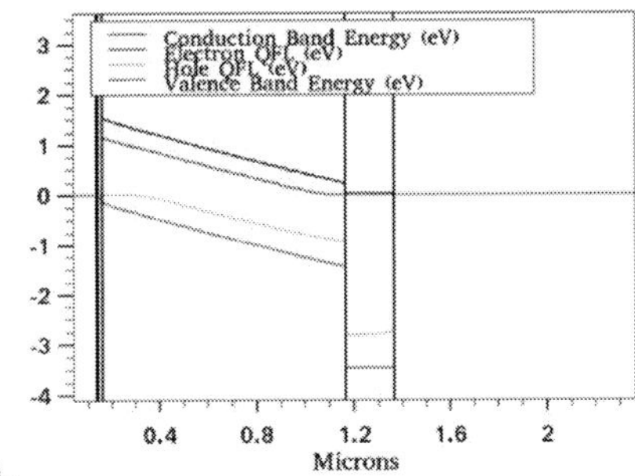

a)..

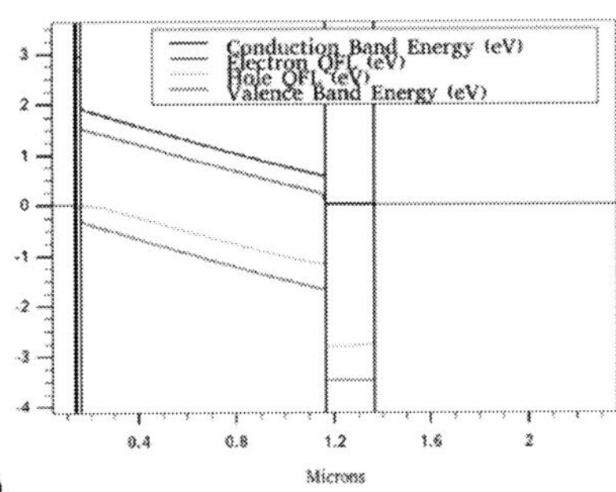

b).

Figure 3: Example of a perovskite cell calculated band profile under illumination at short circuit for experimental parameter input values to the device model for a) the cubic and b) the orthorhombic phases. The **PBEx** input to the device model in this case is the 19.2% efficient cubic dataset .

Figure 4 a) shows the corresponding light current curve for which the figures of merit are given in table III. We note here that the lack of steps and flat IV curve for much of the voltage range which corresponds to a high fill factor is evidence of good band alignments in the device. Figure 4 b) shows the (external) quantum efficiency. This shows a broad tail below the electronic gap which is 1.68eV (wavelength 0.74 μm). This requires further work since there is a significant contribution to the photocurrent which is not reflected in experimental data.

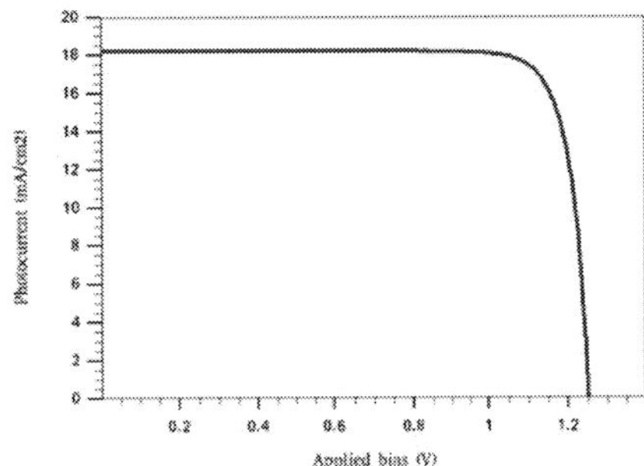

a)

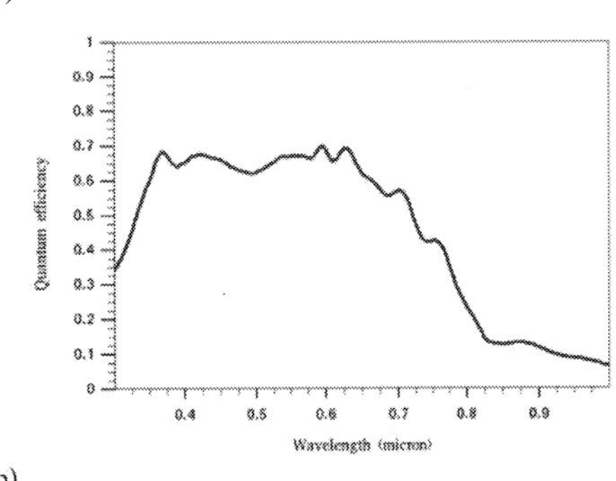

b)

Figure 4: Light current (a) and quantum efficiency (b) showing absorption below the gap at 0.74eV which needs further investigation.

4 CONCLUSIONS

In conclusion, we present the basis of a pragmatic multiscale approach using atomistic scale first-principles calculations coupled to device scale numerical models. At the first-principles level, a hybrid exchange-correlation functional optimized to yield description of their structural, electronic, and phonon properties in good agreement with experiment, has been used. The obtained band gaps, work functions and dielectric responses served as input data to the device model to estimate the performance of solar cells. The preliminary theoretical atomistic and device model results are both in qualitative agreement with experimental data. This methodology has to be proven on a more detailed sets of perovskites, but, if the trends are confirmed, it might allow to provide a set of criteria for optimizing the materials for different PV applications and for suggesting effective complex perovskites. While the main focus of this work is perovskite materials and therefore of single-junction perovskite solar cells, the extension to tandem solar cells is included given the importance of multijunction device exceeding single junction Shockley-Queisser efficiency limits.

Acknowlegments

The authors thank the ANRT (French National Association for Research and Technology) for its financial support within CIFRE agreement 2023/0728 (industrial convention for training through research), and support from the France 2030 programme PEPR-TASE ("Programme et Equipements Prioritaires de Recherche sur les Technologies Avancées des Systèmes Energétiques") specifically within the MINOTAURE project, Grant ANR-22-PETA-0015.

References

[1] M.A. Green *et al.* Prog. Photovolt. Res. Appl. 33 (2025) 795, https://doi.org/10.1002/pip.3919.

[2] https://www.nrel.gov/pv/cell-efficiency

[3] J. Li and P. Rinke, Phys. Rev. B 94 (2016) 045201, https://doi.org/10.1103/PhysRevB.94.045201.

[4] J. Li *et al.*, Phys. Rev. B 96 (2018) 045201, https://doi.org/10.1103/PhysRevB.98.045201.

[5] M.A. Green *et al.* Nature Photonics 8 (2014) 506, https://doi.org/10.1038/nphoton.2014.134.

[6] R. Dovesi *et al.* WIREs Comput. Mol. Sci. 8 (2018) e1360, https://doi.org/10.1002/wcms.1360.

[7] R. Dovesi *et al.* CRYSTAL17 User's Manual (University of Torino, Torino, 2017).

[8] F. Lafond *et al.*, J. Phys. Chem. 124 (2020) 10353, https://doi.org/10.1021/acs.jpcc.0c01767.

[9] A. Mishra *et al.*, Surfaces and Interfaces 25 (2021) 101264, https://doi.org/10.1016/j.surfin.2021.101264.

[10] S. Mejaouri *et al.* Small Methods 8 (2024) 230091, https://doi.org/10.1002/smtd.202300901.

[11] J.P. Perdew et al. Phys. Rev. Lett. 100 (2008) 136406, https://doi.org/10.1103/PhysRevLett.100.136406.

[12] A. Krukau *et al.* J. Chem. Phys. 125 (2006) 224106, https://doi.org/10.1063/1.2404663.

[13] https://silvaco.com.

[14] A. Poglitsch and D. Weber, J. Chem. Phys. 87 (1987) 6373, https://doi.org/10.1063/1.453467.

[15] S.S.H. Dintakurti *et al.* Phys. Chem. Chem. Phys. 24 (2024) 18004, https://doi.org/10.1039/D2CP02131E.

[16] T. Das *et al.* J. Phys. Chem. 126 (2022) 2184, https://doi.org/10.1021/acs.jpcc.1c09594.

[17] M. Caputo *et al.* Sci. Rep. 9 (2019) 15159, https://doi.org/10.1038/s41598-019-50108-0.

[18] J. Ji *et al.* Crystals 9 (2019) 539, https://doi.org/10.3390/cryst9100539.

[19] S. Olthof and K. Meerholz, Sci. Rep. 7 (2016) 40267, https://doi.org/10.1038/srep40267.

[20] A.M.A. Leguy *et al.*, Nanoscale 8 (2016) 6317, https://doi.org/10.1039/C5NR05435D.

Multiscale Models for Perovskites Optimization

Ph. Baranek[1,2], J.P. Connolly[3], A. Gissler[1,2], Ph. Schulz[2], M. Rérat[4] and R. Dovesi[5]

[1]EDF R&D, [2]IPVF, [3]GEEPS,

[4]UPPA, [5]Academia delle Scienze di Torino

EUPVSEC 2025, 21 – 26 September 2025

Introduction

Bottleneck : **Instability of certain perovskites with temperature and moisture.** IPVF

- Soft phonon modes which can locally generate phase instabilities [1].

- Moisture-induced degradation important in terms stability issues [2].

Considerable efforts devoted to the understanding of the underlying mechanisms.

Tandem solar cells

$\rightarrow$ **Impact of the chemical composition (phase transition and ordering in MAPbI$_3$) on their optoelectronic properties.**

Atomic modeling interesting alternative to understand their effects [3]

At the atomic level : Study of the influence of intrinsic/extrinsic defect or substitution on the electrical and optoelectronic properties

-> **Link to the microscopic properties of compounds and macrosopic data to evaluate performances of devices**

[1] G. Sophia *et al.*, Phys. Chem. Chem. Phys. **24**, 27064 (2022).
[2] S. Mejaouri *et al.*, Small Methods **8**, 2300901 (2024).
[3] Q. Li *et al.*, Applied Surfaces Sciences **538**, 148058 (2021).

eDF

020061-002

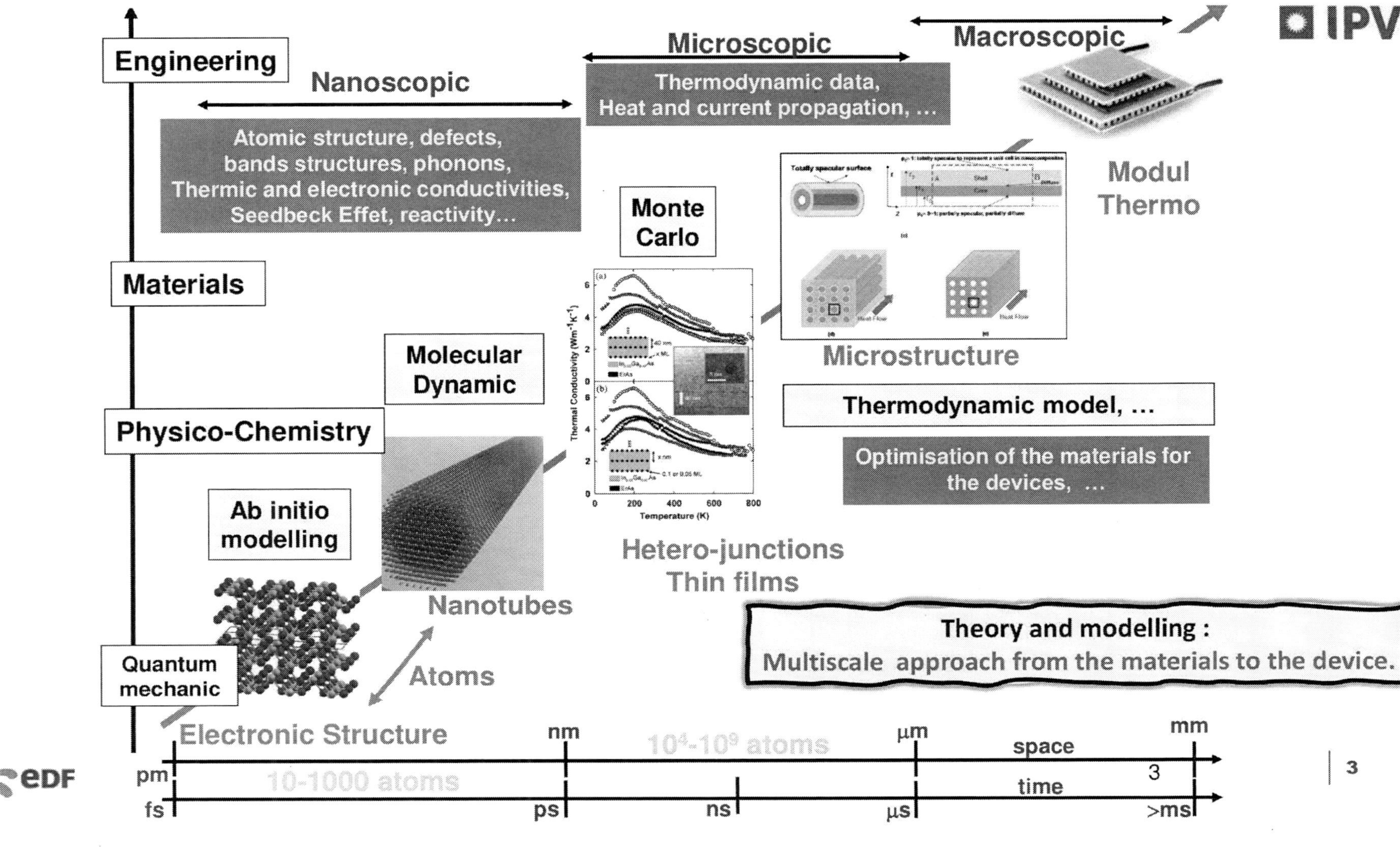
IPVF
Engineering
Nanoscopic
Microscopic
Macroscopic
Thermodynamic data,
Heat and current propagation, ...
Atomic structure, defects,
bands structures, phonons,
Thermic and electronic conductivities,
Seedbeck Effet, reactivity...
Modul
Thermo
Monte
Carlo
Materials
Microstructure
Molecular
Dynamic
Thermodynamic model, ...
Physico-Chemistry
Optimisation of the materials for
the devices, ...
Ab initio
modelling
Hetero-junctions
Thin films
Nanotubes
Atoms
Quantum
mechanic
Theory and modelling :
Multiscale approach from the materials to the device.
Electronic Structure
nm
10⁴-10⁹ atoms
µm
space
mm
pm
10-1000 atoms
3
fs
ps
ns
time
µs
>ms
eDF
3

Implement a pragmatic use of the first-principles approaches (DFT)

◫ IPVF

Development of simple models of complex materials

Study of the electronic and dynamical properties of bulk materials and interfaces

Determination of the properties of interest for photovoltaic

Perovskites

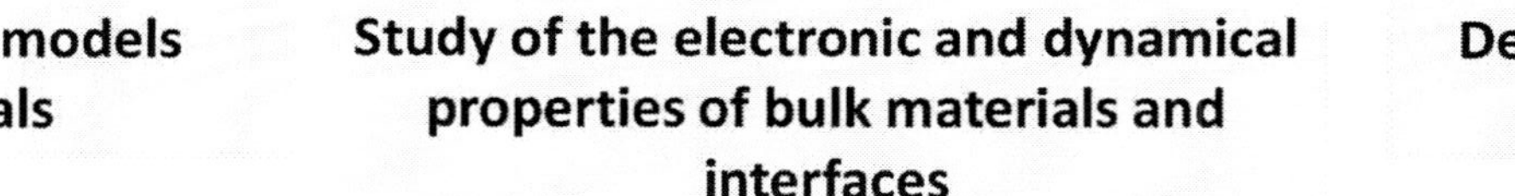

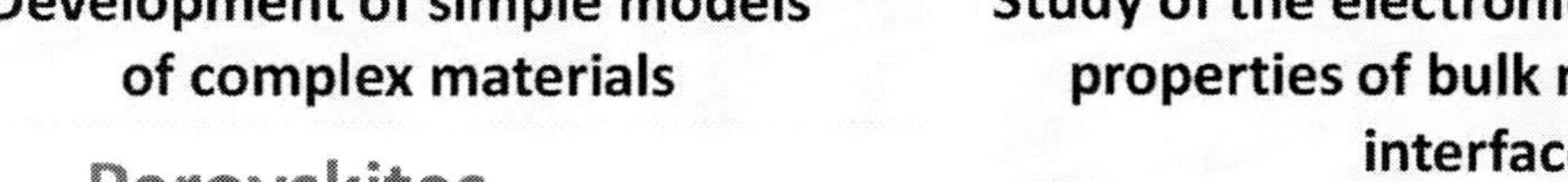

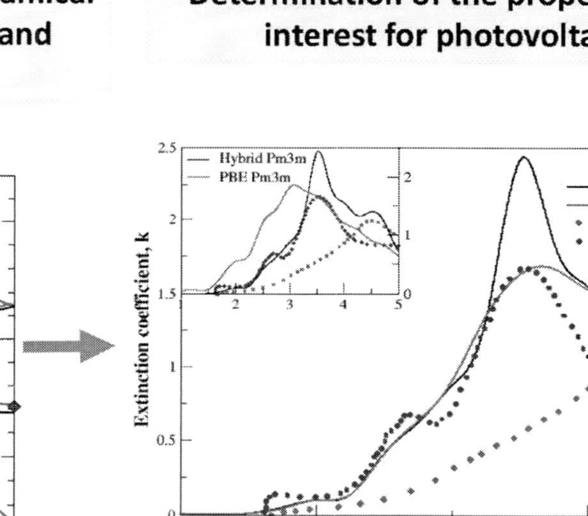

Application to:

- Band alignement at the interfaces
- Electronic affinity
- Surfaces and interfaces stability

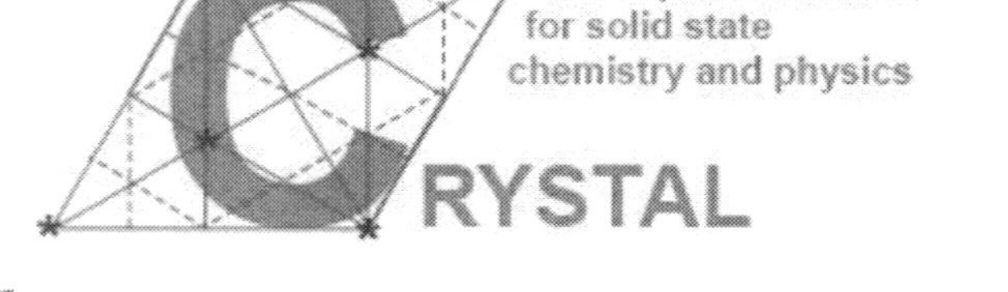

eDF [4] Malone et al., J. Phys. Cond. Matt. (2013)
[5] O. Madelung, The Landolt-Bornstein Database, Springer Material (2001).

Study of the ageing of the halide perovskites ABX_3

Ph. Baranek, A. Gissler, A. Mishra, P. Schulz and A. Postnikov

IPVF

Bottleneck : Instability of certain perovskites with temperature

Link : Intrinsic properties of materials
- Influence of the phase transitions on the band gap
-> Anharmonicity of the materials
-> Unstable phonon modes

A = Li, K, Na, Rb, Cs, CH_3NH_3
B = Ge, Sn, Pb
X = Cl, Br and I

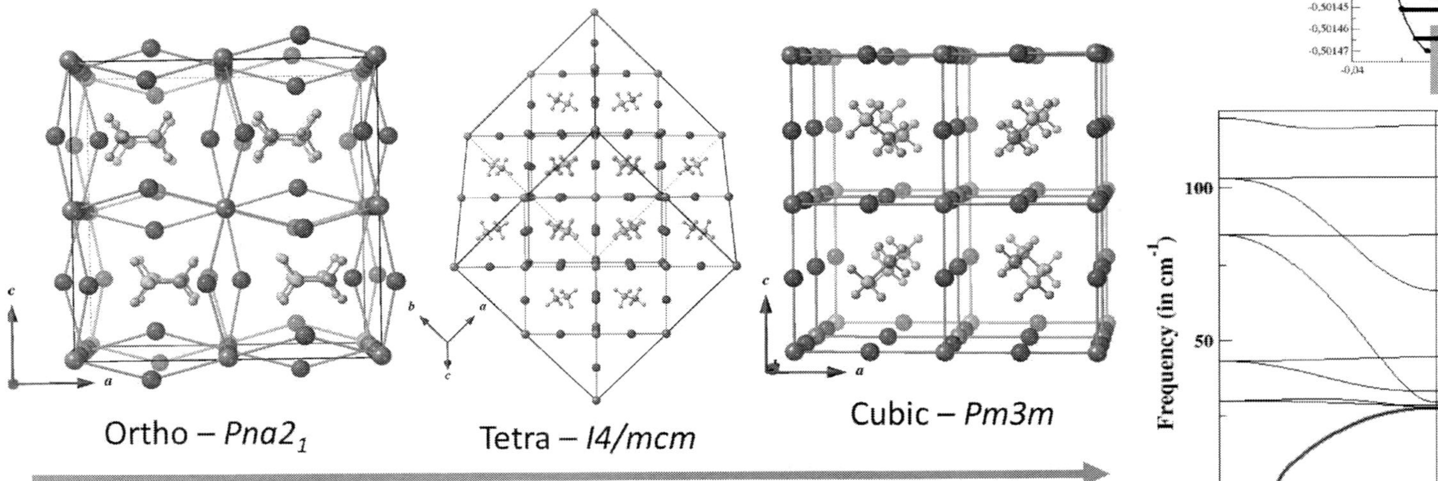

020061-005

Electronic structure of halides perovskites:

A. Gissler, Ph. Schulz and Ph. Baranek

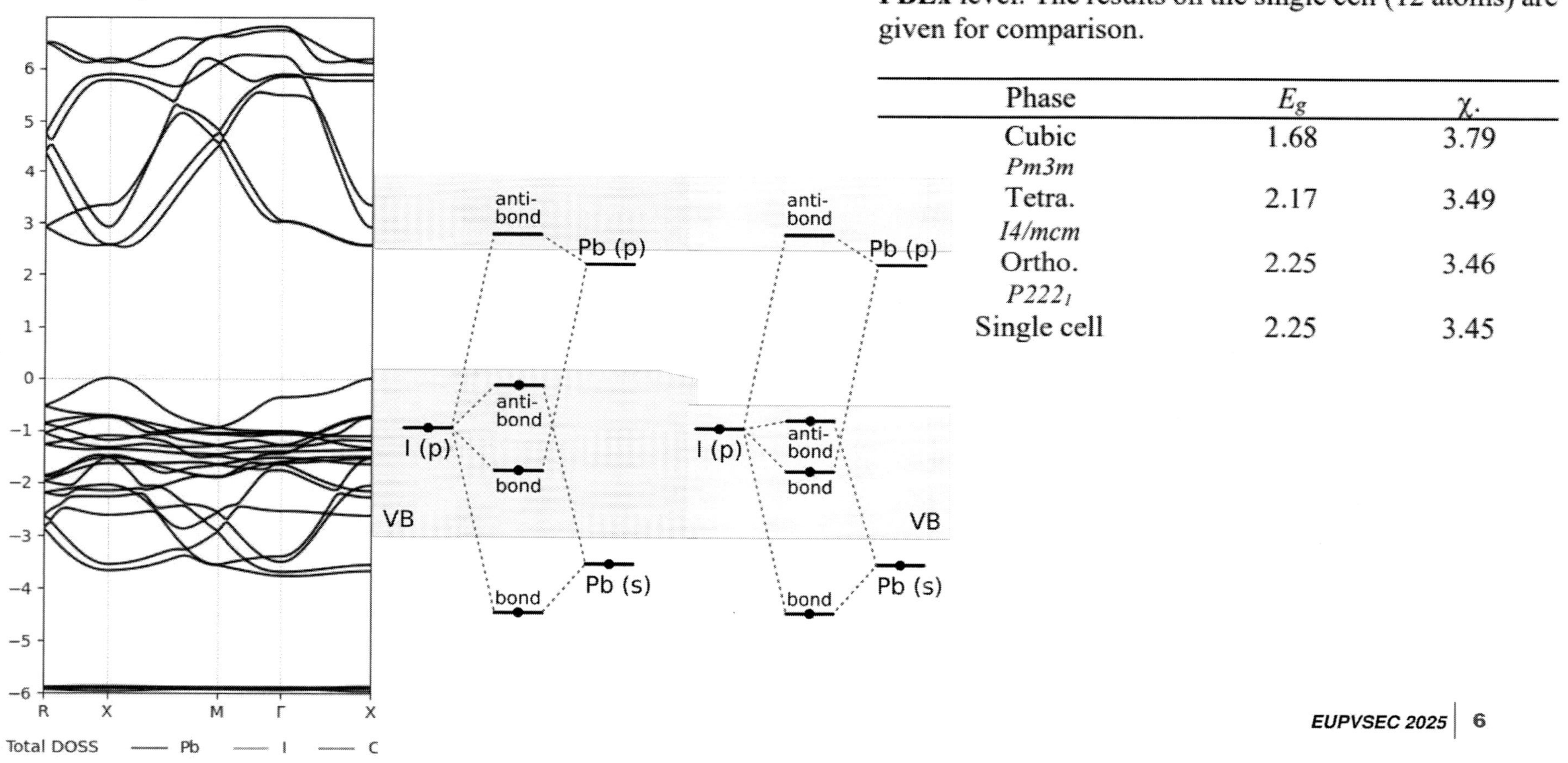

Table III: Calculated band gap (E_g in eV) and electron affinity (χ in eV) for different phases of MAPbI$_3$ at the **PBEx** level. The results on the single cell (12 atoms) are given for comparison.

Phase	E_g	$\chi.$
Cubic *Pm3m*	1.68	3.79
Tetra. *I4/mcm*	2.17	3.49
Ortho. *P222₁*	2.25	3.46
Single cell	2.25	3.45

Dielectric properties: The case of MAPbI$_3$

Ph. Baranek, M. Rérat and R. Dovesi

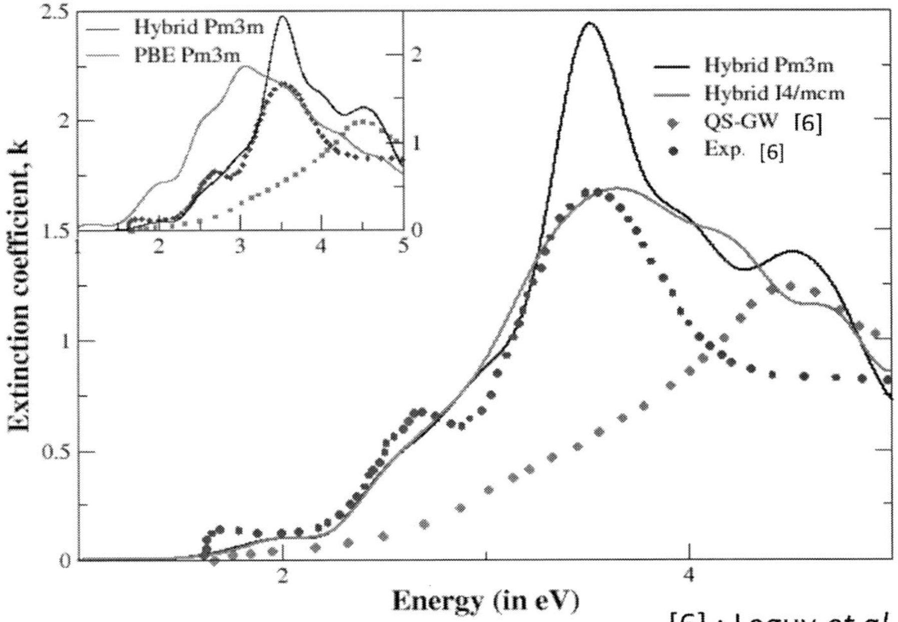

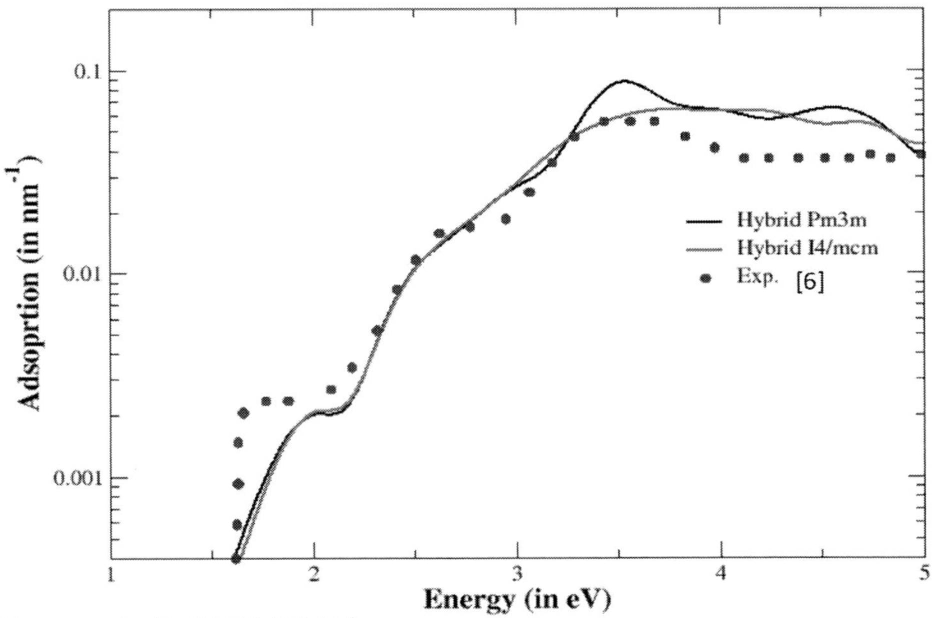

[6] : Leguy *et al.*, Nanoscale **8**, 6317 (2016)

Ph. Baranek, J.P. Connolly et al. to be submitted

Impact on the cells efficiency: via drift diffusion model

SILVACO   **IPVF**

J.P. Connolly, Ph. Baranek

Parameter	Definition
τ_{SRH}	Electron and hole charge neutral and depletion layers Shockley-Read-Hall lifetimes
μ	Carrier mobility, majority and minority, electron and hole
D_N, D_P	Hole and electron diffusion coefficients
C_A	Auger coefficient
ε	Permittivity related to complex refractive index
n, k	Real and imaginary refractive indices
m_e^*	Electron and hole effective masses
χ	Electron affinity
N_C, N_V	Band parameters - conduction and valence band effective densities of states
E_C, E_V, E_g	Band parameters - Conduction and valence band edges and bandgap

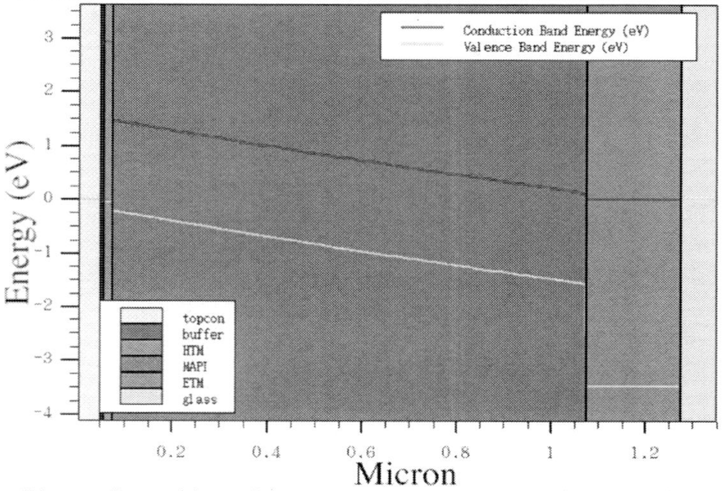

Figure: Perovskite cell layer structure and calculated band profile for experimental parameter input values to device model.

Table IV: Device performance modelling for parameters taken from the experimental data of literature [19], and from successive theoretical **PBEx** calculations ranging from the single cell (12 atoms cell) to tetragonal and cubic phases (96 atoms cell), showing a peak performance for the cubic phase.

Data source	Jsc (A/m^2)	V_{oc} (V)	V_{mp} (V)	FF (%)	η (%)
Single cell	13.4	1.82	1.40	71.9	17.5
Ortho. *P222$_1$*	11.6	1.80	1.42	73.6	15.5
Tetra. *I4/mcm*	13.4	1.73	1.37	74.6	17.2
Cubic *Pm3m*	18.2	1.25	1.11	84.3	19.2
Exp. [19]	17.5	1.25	1.10	84.3	18.5

Ph. Baranek, J.P. Connolly et al. to be submitted

Impact on the cells efficiency: via drift diffusion model

J.P. Connolly, Ph. Baranek

Cubic

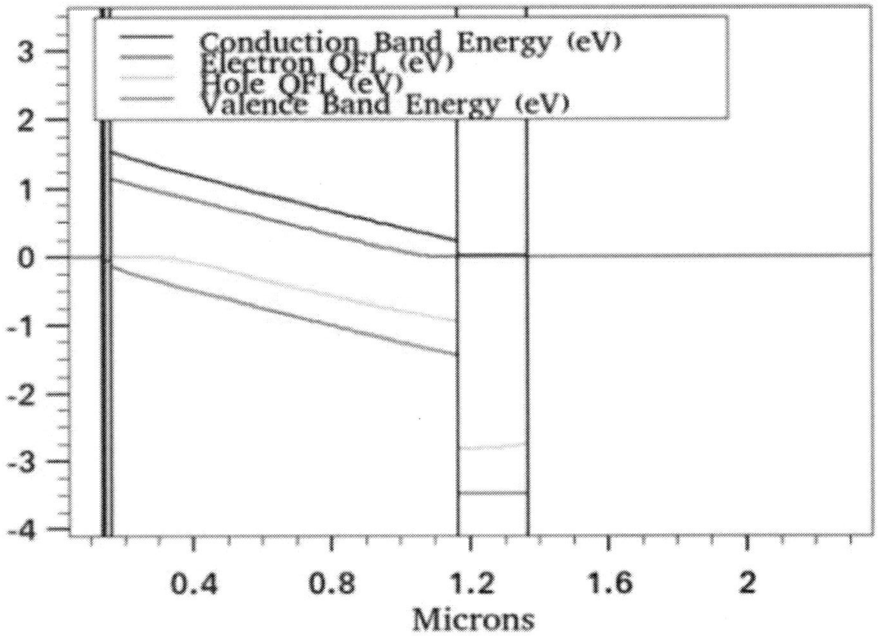

Ortho

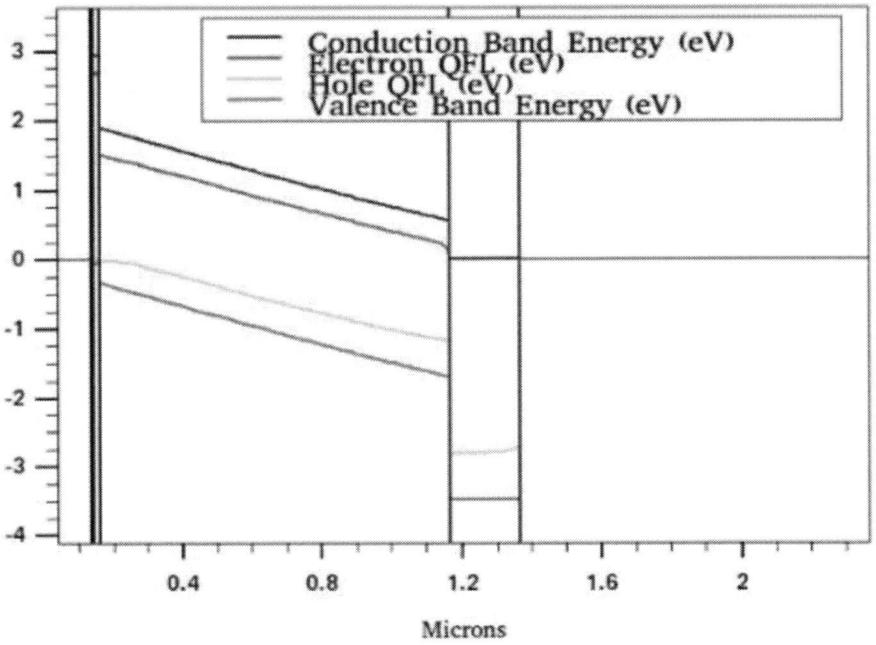

020061-009

Impact on the cells efficiency: via drift diffusion model

J.P. Connolly, Ph. Baranek

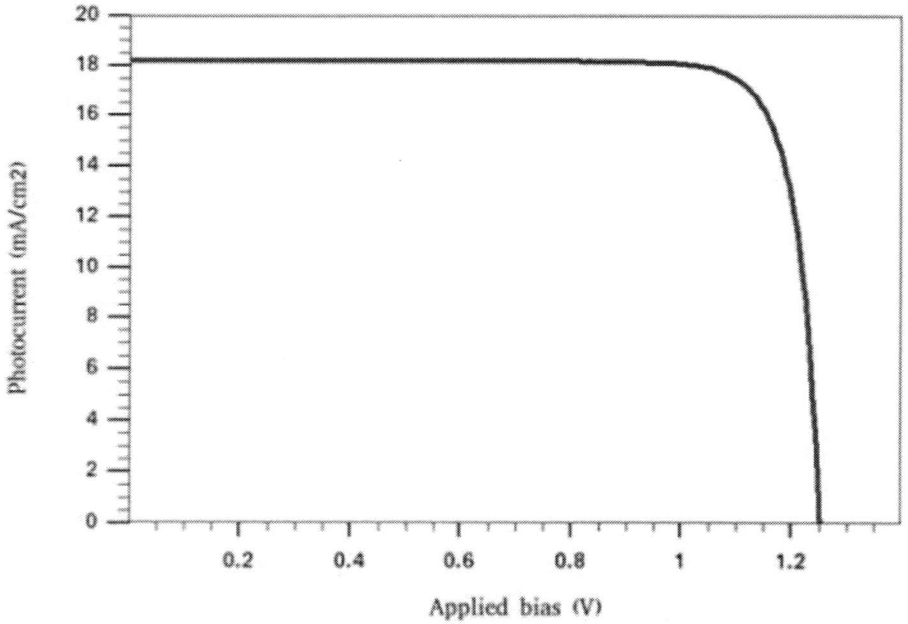

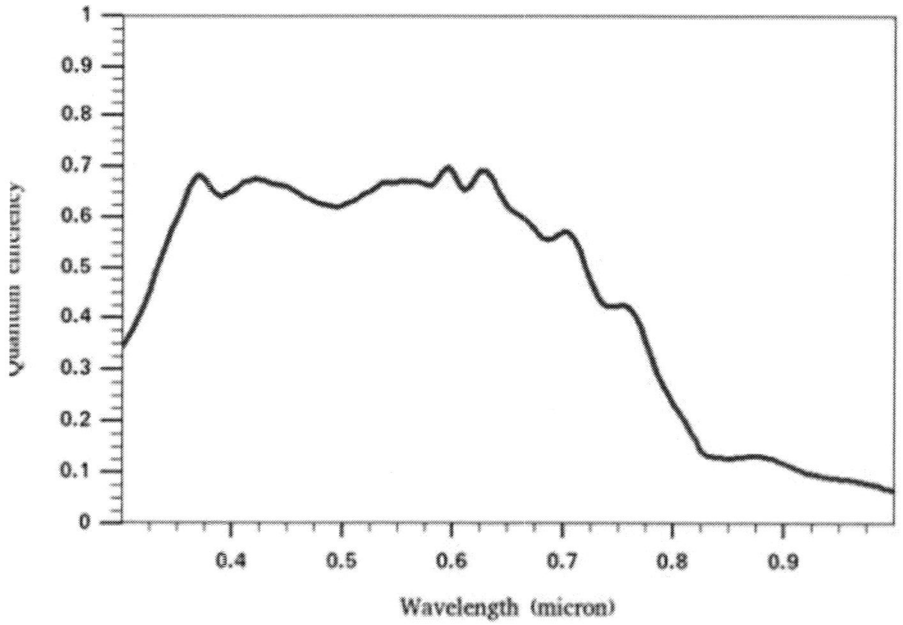

020061-010

Conclusions

- A pragmatic multiscale approach: atomistic first-principles methods coupled to device numerical model.

  - Based on DFT approaches optimized to obtain a good description of a given family of compound.
  - Definition of adapted hybrid functional for a given compound.

  -> Evaluation of the perovskites performances in good agreement with experimental data.

- Provide a set of criteria for optimizing the materials for different PV applications and for suggesting effective complex perovskites.

- Can be used on different materials and types of devices.

Example of optimisation of inorganic perovskites:

A. Gissler *et al.* "Ab-Initio Approach to Guide the Optimization of Inorganic Halide Perovskites"

Session 2.2 talk 2DO.8 – 25 Sept. 13:30

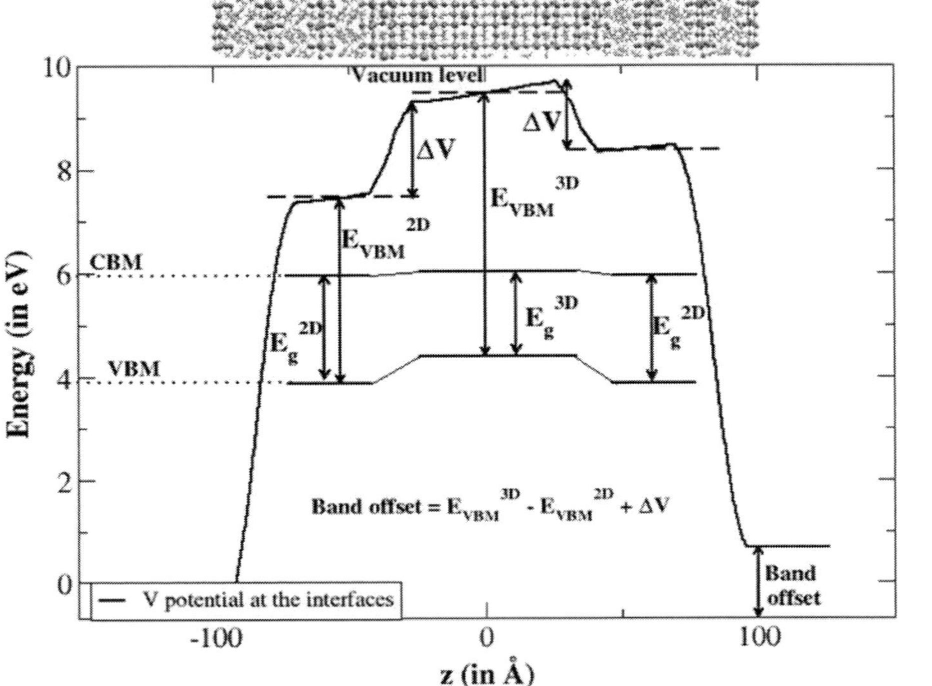

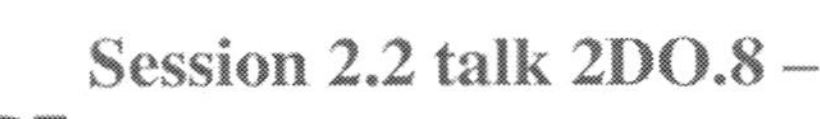

IPVF

THANK YOU
FOR
YOUR ATTENTION

eDF

020061-012

Modelling Recovery in Perovskite Solar Cells Under Light and Dark to Address Stability Challenges

Session 2AO.3.6
September 22nd, 2025
Bilbao, Spain

Guillem ÁLVAREZ PÉREZ[1,2], Jean Baptiste PUEL[1,3], and Jean François GUILLEMOLES[1,2]

[1] Institut Photovoltaïque d'Île-de-France (IPVF), Palaiseau, 91120, France
[2] InstitutPhotovoltaïque d'Île-de-France (IPVF), UMR 9006, CNRS, École Polytechnique, IP Paris, Chimie Paristech, PSL, Palaiseau, 91120, France
[3] EDF R&D, Palaiseau, 91120, France

020062-001

MOTIVATION

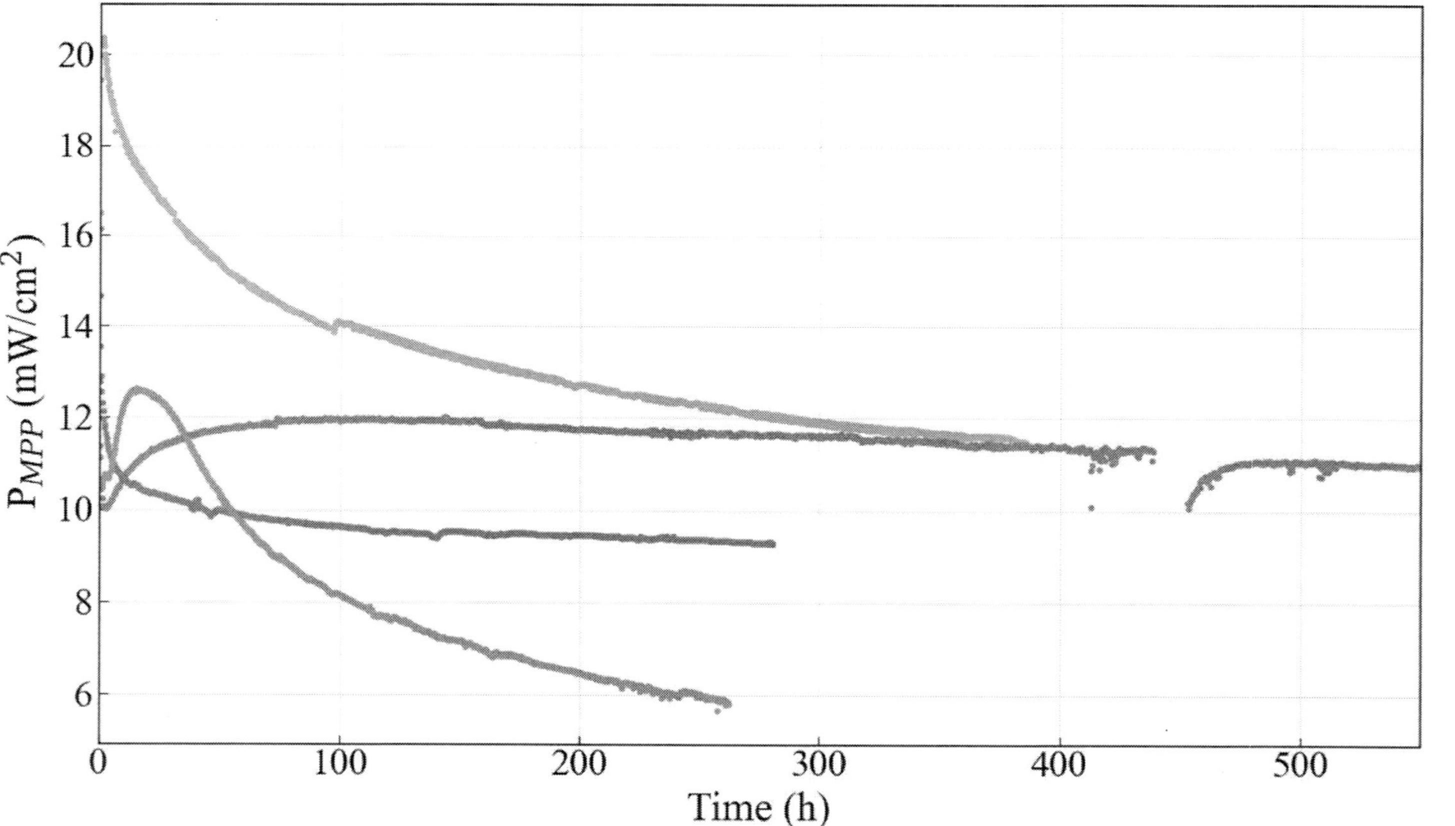

020062-002

STABILITY ISSUES

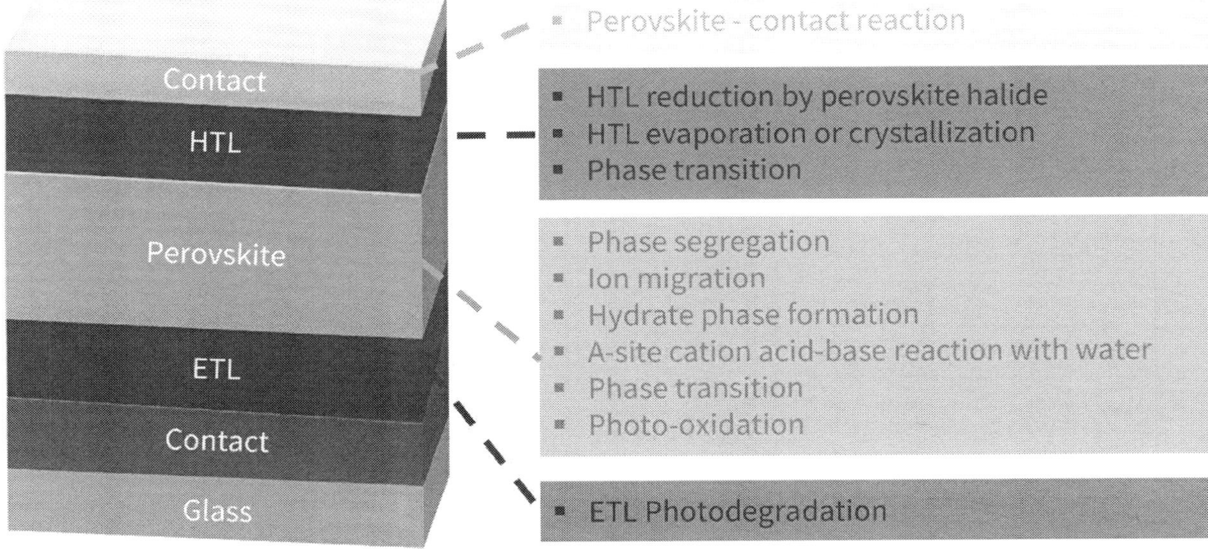

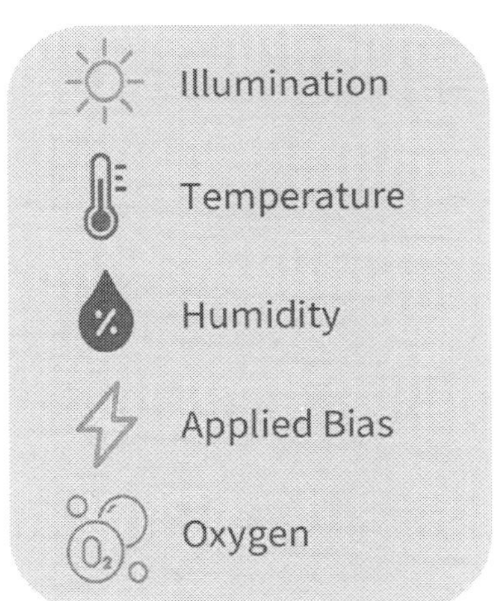

Boyd, C. et al (2019). Chemical Reviews, 119(5), 3418-3451. doi 10.1021/acs.chemrev.8b00336

nature energy

CONSENSUS STATEMENT
https://doi.org/10.1038/s41560-019-0529-5
OPEN

Consensus statement for stability assessment and reporting for perovskite photovoltaics based on ISOS procedures

IPVF

020062-003

OUR APPROACH

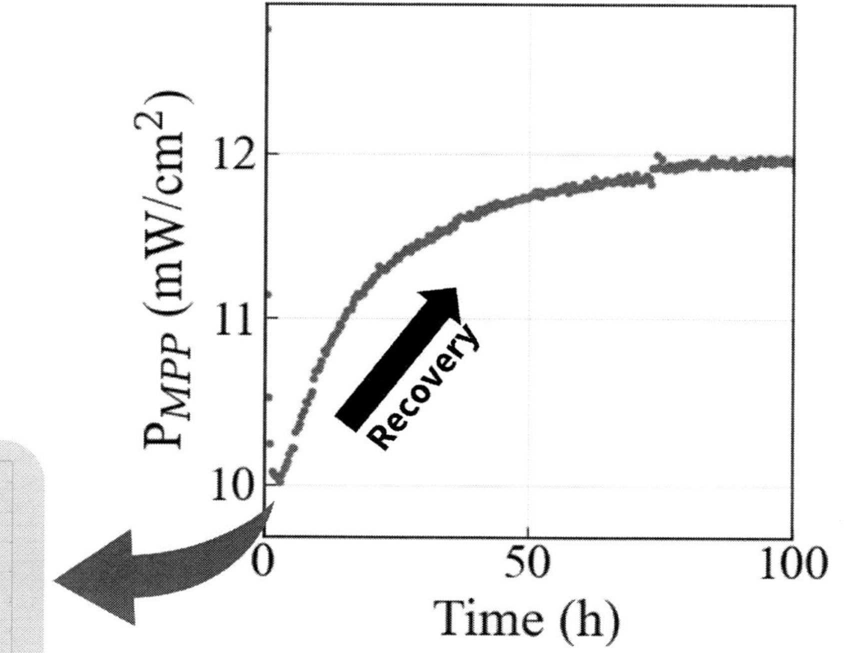

IPVF

OUR APPROACH

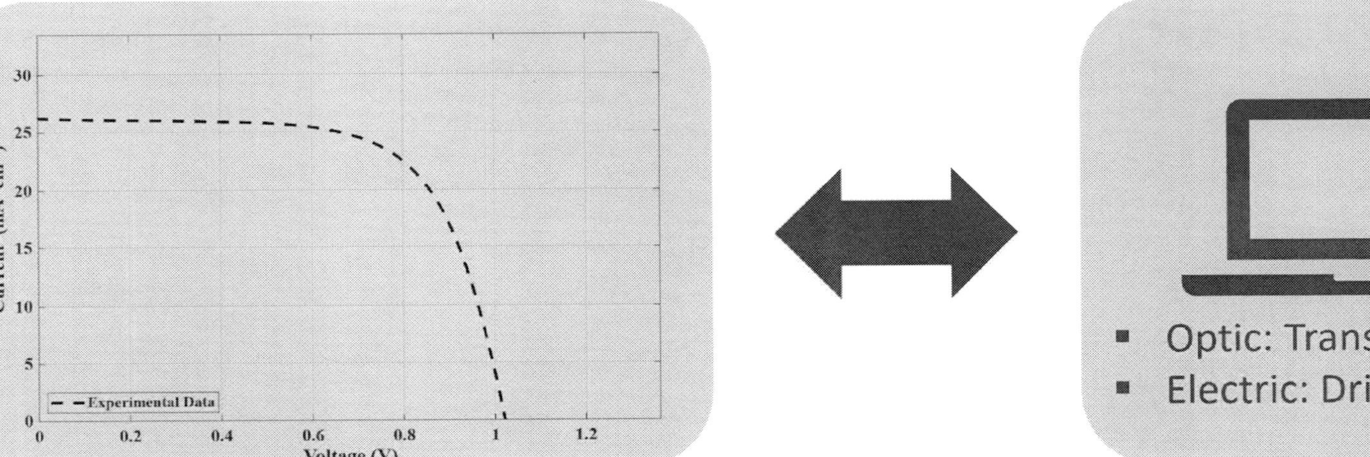

GENETIC ALGORITHM

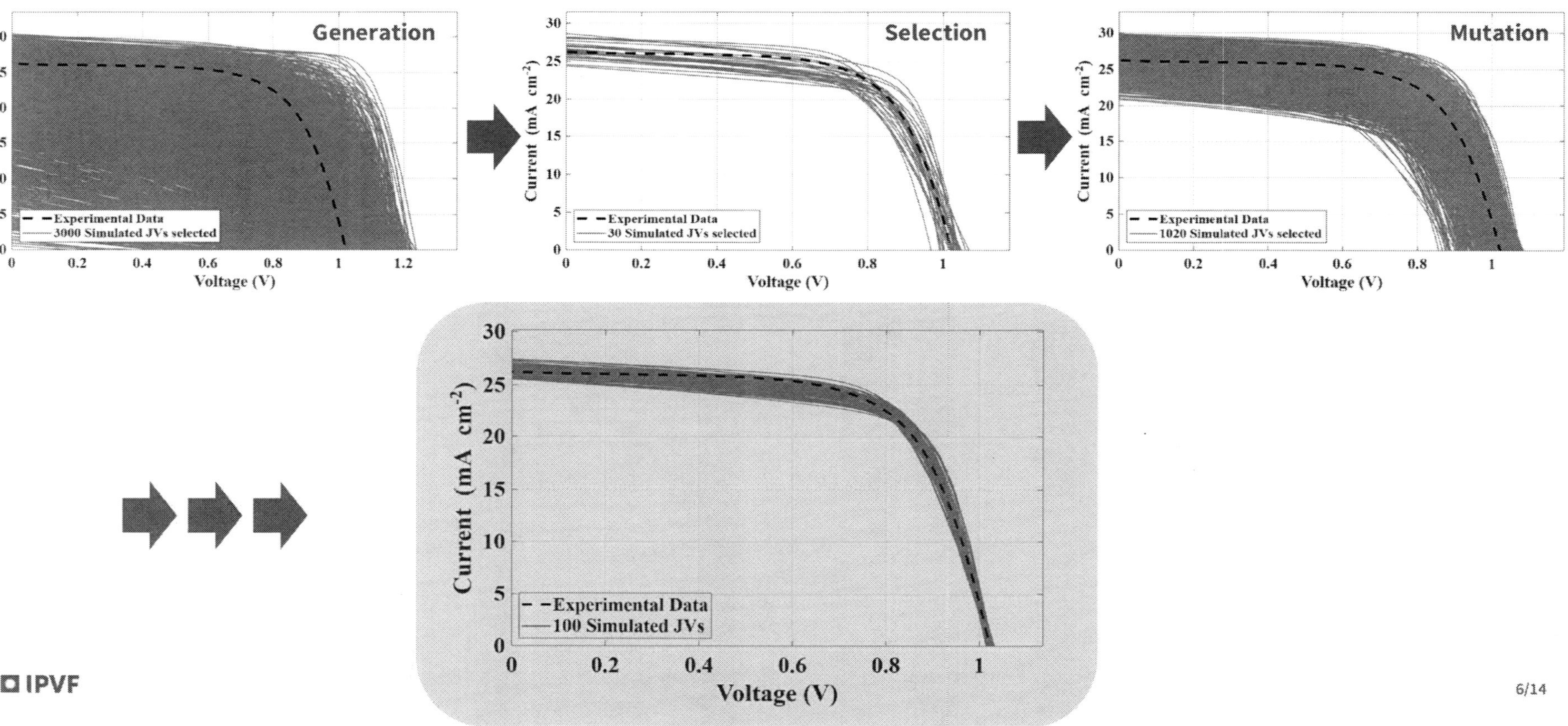

IPVF

GENETIC ALGORITHM

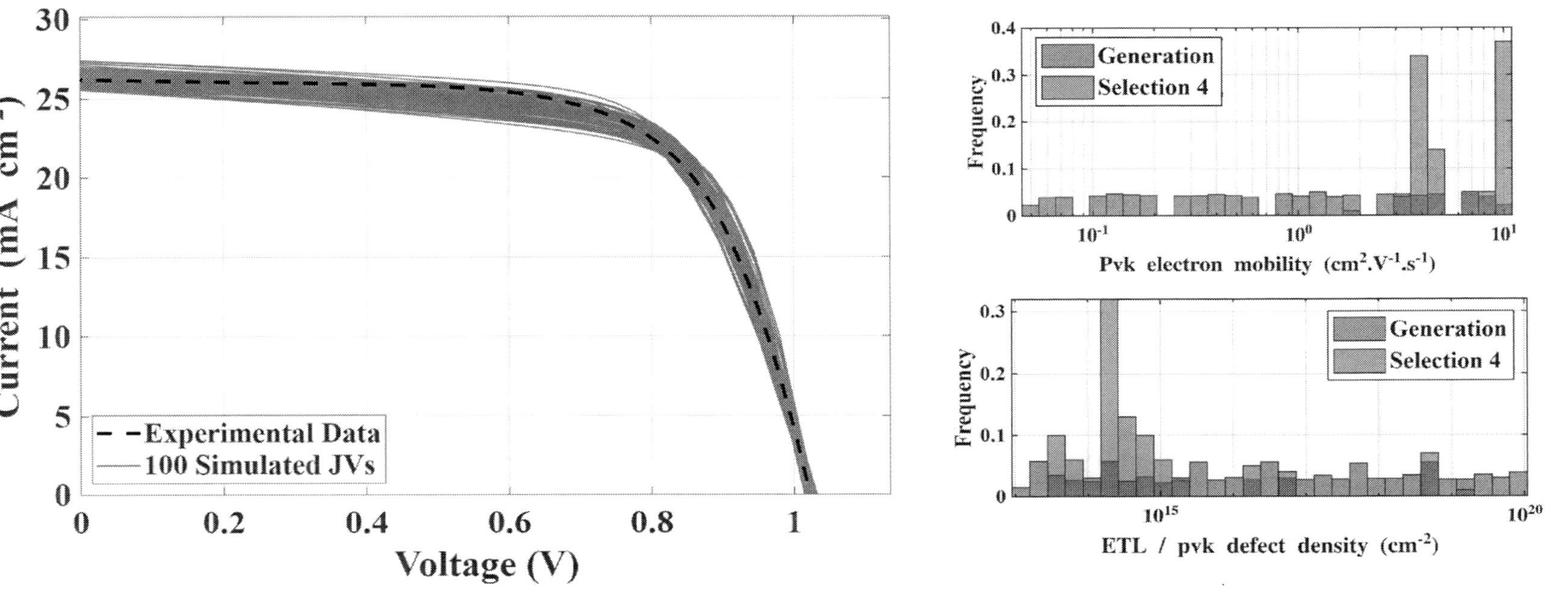

SIMULATING RECOVERY

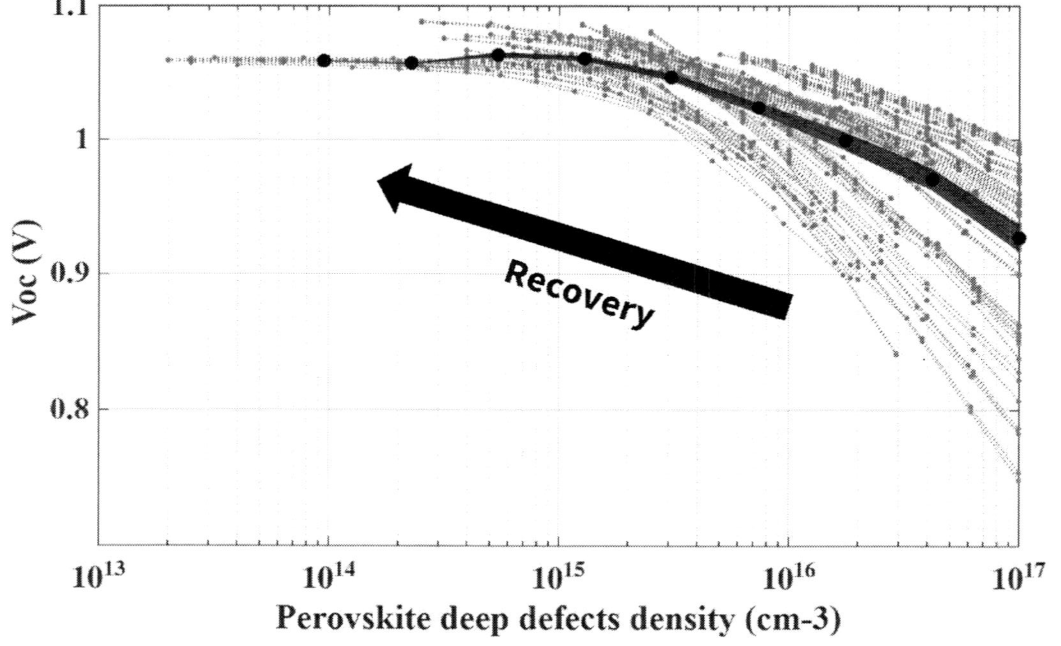

020062-008

CORRELATION PATHWAYS

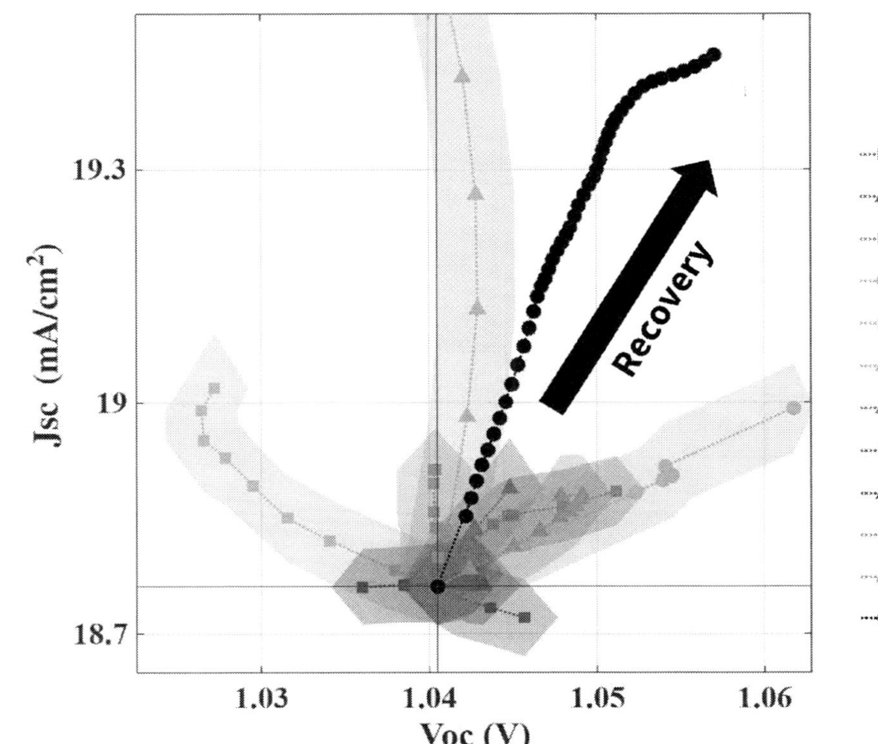

(Voc, Jsc, FF, Rs, Rsh)

RESULTS

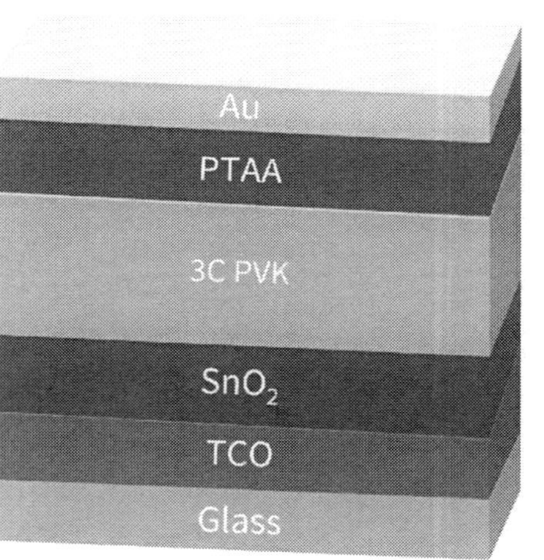

Perovskite Layer Synthesis Conditions	
Sample ID	**Condition**
Cells 1, 2	Solution prepared @ Day 0
Cells 3, 4	Solution prepared @ Day 0 + Heated 70 °C, 1h
Cells 5, 6	Solution prepared @ Day-1
Cells 7, 8	Solution prepared @ Day-1 + Heated 70 °C, 1h

IPVF

RESULTS

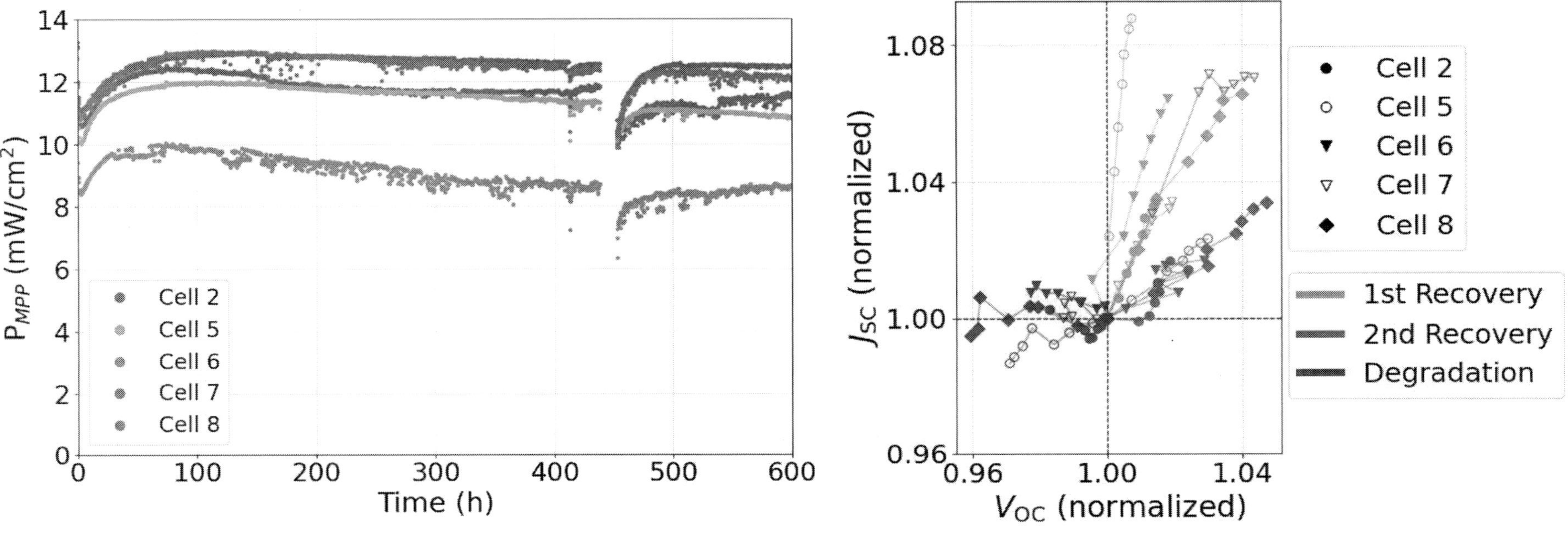

14
12
10
8
6
4
2
0
P_{MPP} (mW/cm^2)
Cell 2
Cell 5
Cell 6
Cell 7
Cell 8
0 100 200 300 400 500 600
Time (h)
1.08
1.04
1.00
0.96
J_{SC} (normalized)
0.96 1.00 1.04
V_{OC} (normalized)
Cell 2
Cell 5
Cell 6
Cell 7
Cell 8
1st Recovery
2nd Recovery
Degradation

RESULTS

Close to experimental pathways

Far from experimental pathways

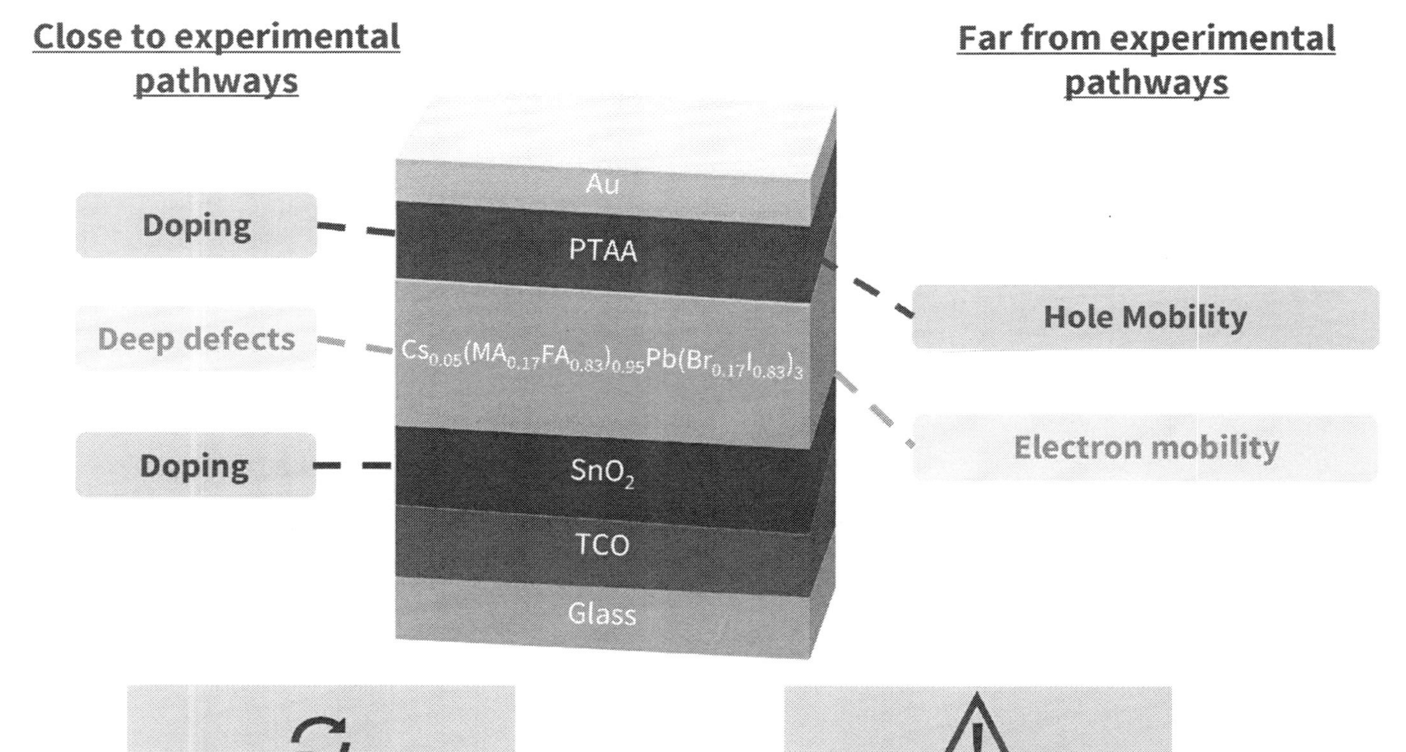

IPVF

020062-012

SUMMARY AND PERSPECTIVES

- Framework to link experiments $\leftrightarrow$ simulations in correlation space
- Insights into instabilities under light/dark

Modelling outcomes

Suggest mechanisms causing recovery and degradation

Discard mechanisms that are far from experimental data

Identify Reversible Mechanisms

- Extend number of devices studied
- Apply framework to different ISOS tests

020062-013

THANK YOU

Guillem ÁLVAREZ PÉREZ[1,2], Jean Baptiste PUEL[1,3], and Jean François GUILLEMOLES[1,2]

[1]Institut Photovoltaïque d'Île-de-France (IPVF), Palaiseau, 91120, France
[2]Institut Photovoltaïque d'Île-de-France (IPVF), UMR 9006, CNRS, École Polytechnique, IP Paris, Chimie Paristech, PSL, Palaiseau, 91120, France
[3]EDF R&D, Palaiseau, 91120, France

Contact: guillem.alvarez@ipvf.fr

- EUPVSEC 2025
- Session 2AO.3.6
- September 22nd, 2025
- Bilbao, Spain

020062-014

On perimeter losses in perovskite top- and poly-Si-passivated silicon bottom cells – do small area tandems reveal the full efficiency potential?

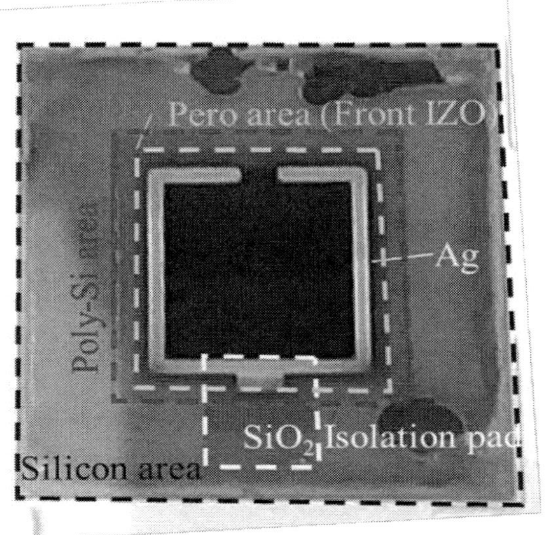

F. Haase[1], L. Brockmann[1], A. Raugewitz[1], V. Steckenreiter[1],
V. Barnscheidt[1], R. Clausing[1], S. Baumann[1], J. Vollbrecht[1],
W. Veurman[1], J. Löhr[1], D. Liu[1], M. Turcu[1], L. Nasebandt[1],
U. Römer[1], D. Sylla[1], J. Strey[1], M. Löhning[1], L. Mettner[1], R. Winter[1],
A. Christ[1], H. Kohlenberg[1], C. Marquardt[1], E. Brueckner[1],
H. Rabiei[1], M. Rienäcker[1], S. Kajari-Schröder[1], T. Wietler[1,2], R. Peibst[1,3]

[1]Institute for Solar Energy Research Hamelin (ISFH), Germany
[2]Institute of Solid-State Physics, Leibniz University Hannover, Germany
[3]Institute of Electronic Materials and Devices, Leibniz University Hannover, Germany

020063-001

Influence of shaded perimeter and edge on performance

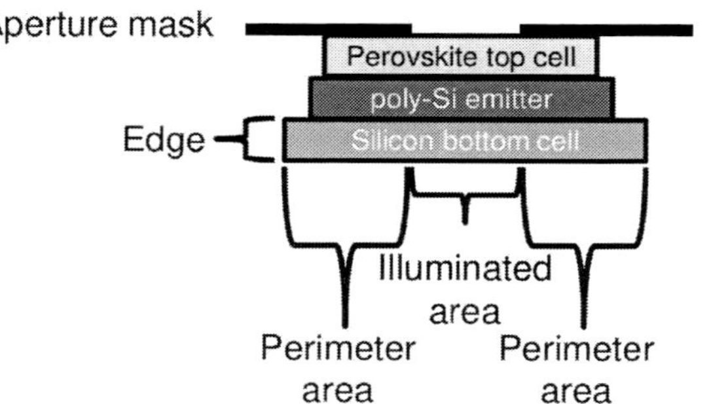

- Record efficiencies of perovskite-silicon tandem cells on 1 cm^2 aperture area

- Influence of different layer perimeter areas? Often not reported

- Reports on single junction cell perimeter losses [1-3]

- **This work: Perimeter losses of different layers in tandem device**

[1] P.P. Altermatt, et al., Prog. Photovolt: Res. Appl., 4 (1996). https://doi.org/10.1002/(SICI)1099-159X(199609/10)4:5<355::AID-PIP145>3.0.CO;2-X
[2] F. Haase et al., IEEE Journal of Photovoltaics, vol. 8, no. 1, (2018). https://doi.org/10.1109/JPHOTOV.2017.2762592
[3] D. Kiermasch et al., Joule 3, (2019). https://doi.org/10.1016/j.joule.2018.10.016

020063-002

Experimental results: poly-Si passivated c-Si bottom cell

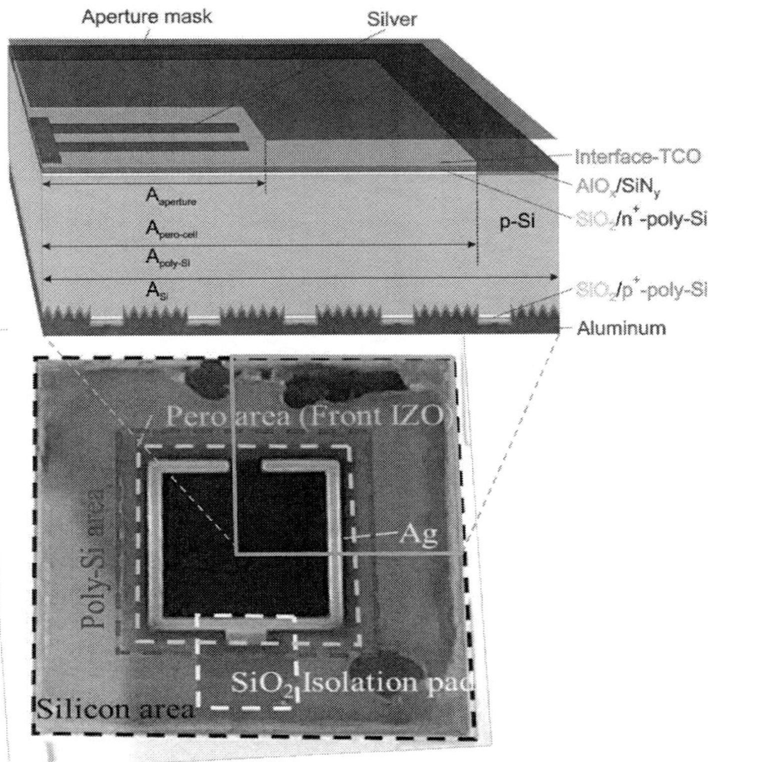

- 25×25 mm^2 bottom cell with metal front grid on 10×10 mm^2 area

020063-003

Experimental results: poly-Si passivated c-Si bottom cell

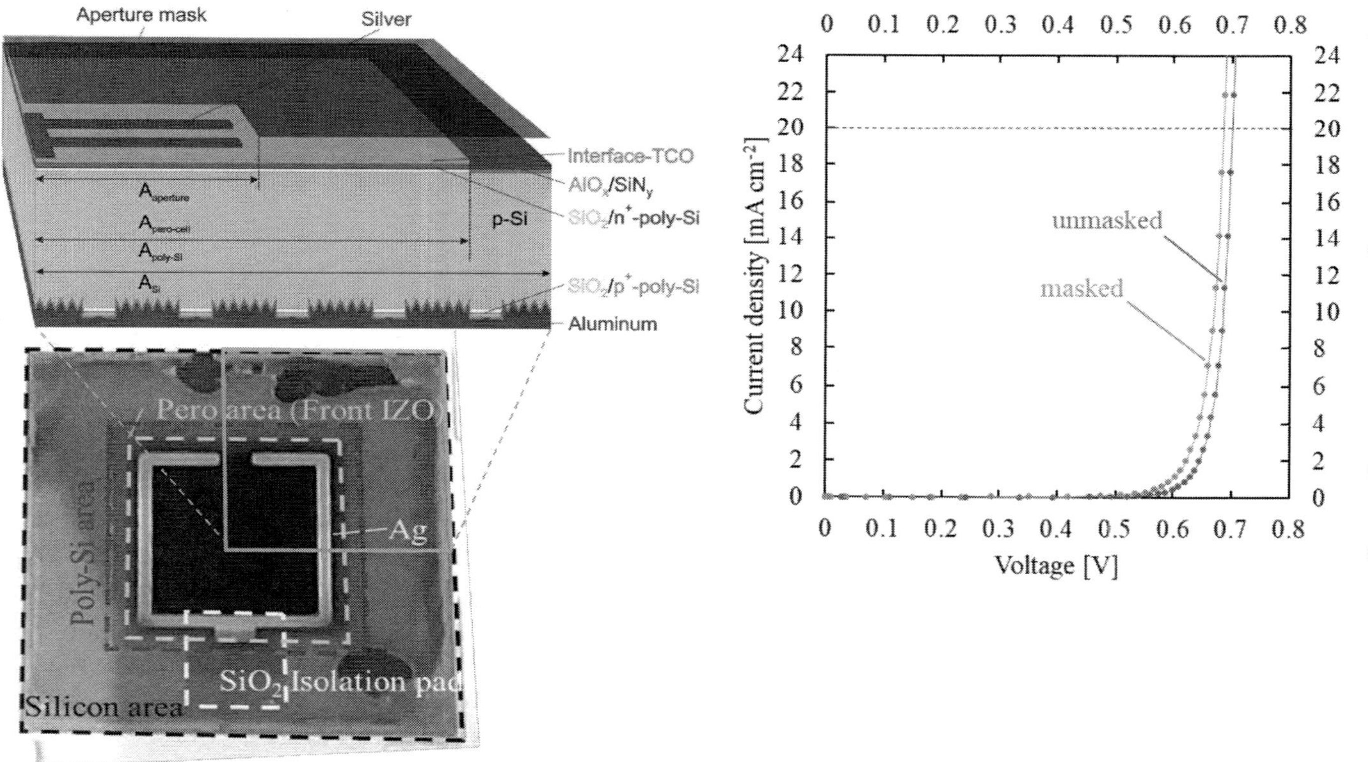

- 25×25 mm^2 bottom cell with metal front grid on 10×10 mm^2 area

- J_{SC}-V_{OC} measurement with and without 10×10 mm^2 aperture area mask

- 19 mV V_{OC} loss

- Best pseudo efficiency of 11.5%

Experimental results: perovskite top cell

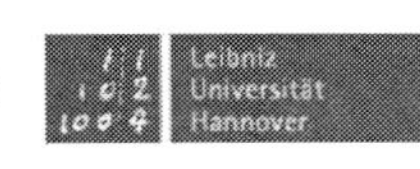

- Wet chemically processed HTL, perovskite and EDAI$_2$

- Evaporated ETL and electrode

- Improvement of EDAI$_2$ passivation layer increases efficiency from 21.4% to 23.3%

- Adding 11.5% from bottom cell gives 32.9% (34.8% with improved EDAI$_2$) tandem efficiency

020063-005

Experimental results: tandem cell

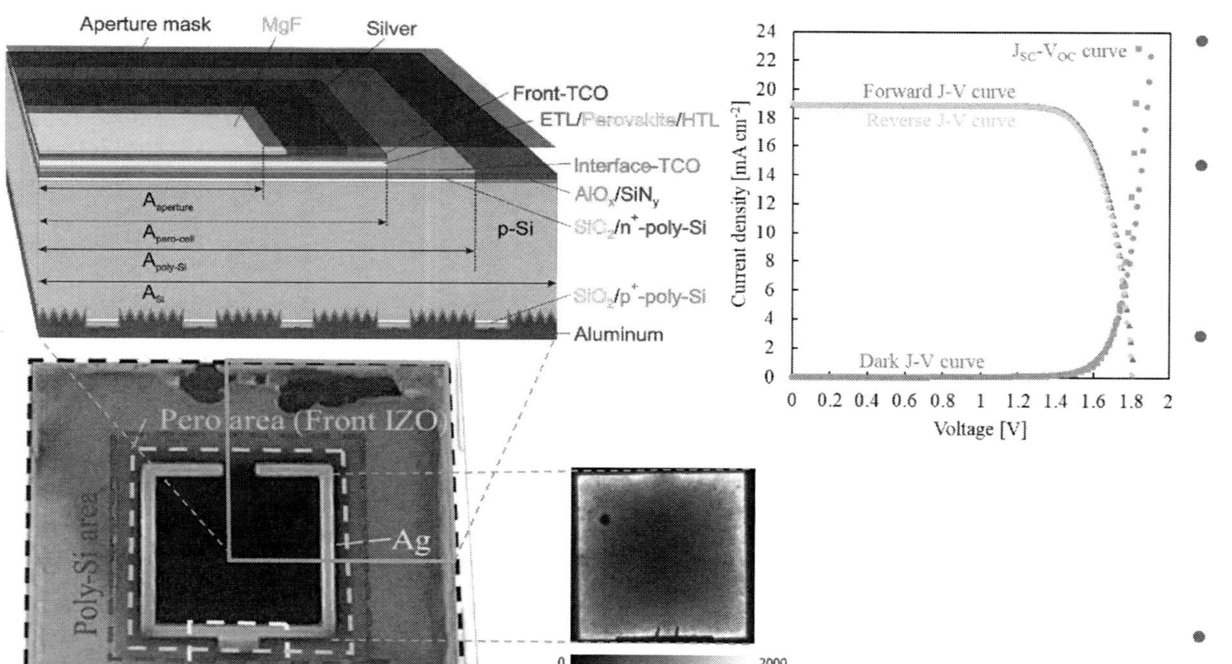

- Measured 26.7% falls behind the theoretical efficiency of 32.9%

- Large series resistance due to low conductive front TCO (4%$_{abs}$ fill factor loss)

- Current limited to 19 mA/cm^2 by parasitic absorption of

  - Unintended thick poly-Si layer of 115 nm

  - Front C60 layer

- Adapted limit 28%

- **Influence of perimeter region?**

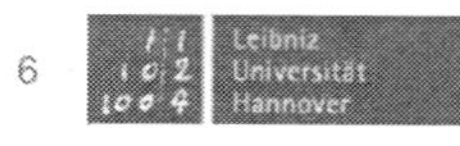

020063-006

Simulated tandem device

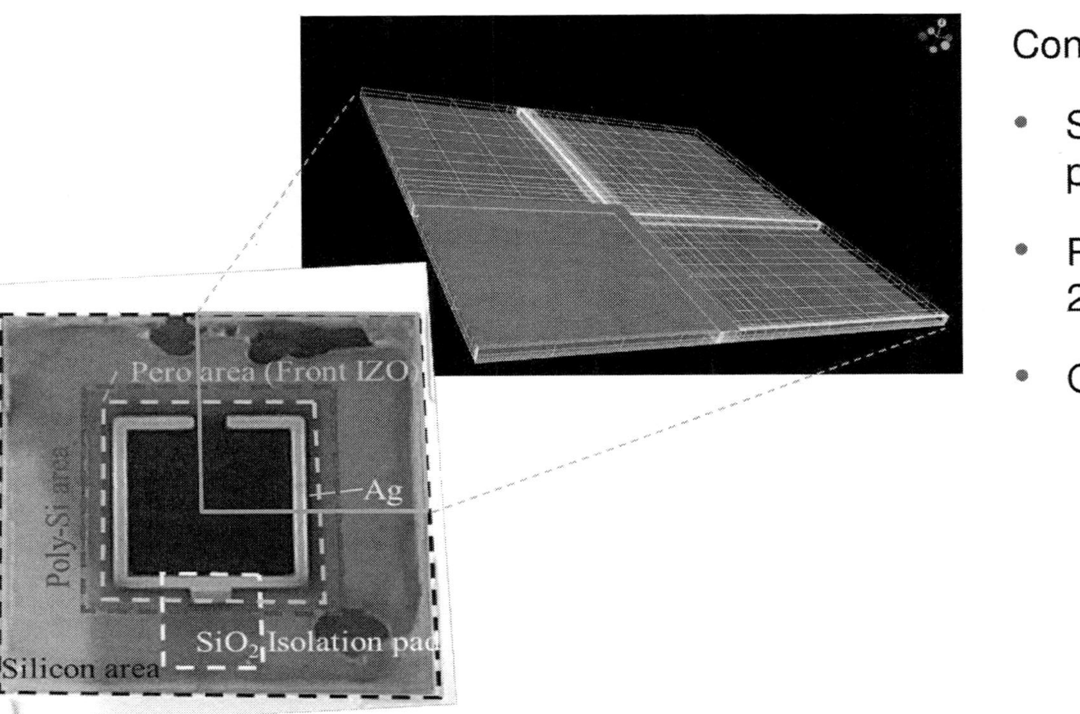

Conductive boundary model [4], Quokka3 [5]:

- Si bottom cell based on measured input parameters

- Perovskite top cell fit to the 1st generation 21.4% measured SJ J-V curve

- Quarter of the tandem cell simulated

[4] R. Brendel, Progress in Photovoltaics: Research and Applications 20 (1) (2012). https://doi.org/10.1002/pip.954
[5] Quokka3, https://www.quokka3.com/ accessed at 04.09.2025

Simulated variations

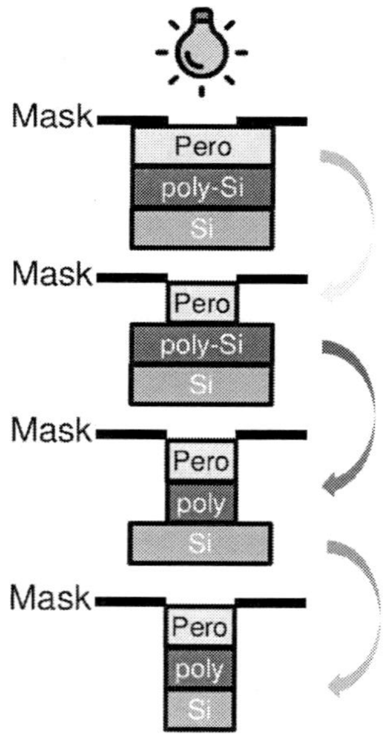

Conductive boundary model [4], Quokka3 [5]:

- Starting with full area of all layers

- Reducing one layer after the other

[4] R. Brendel, Progress in Photovoltaics: Research and Applications 20 (1) (2012). https://doi.org/10.1002/pip.954
[5] Quokka3, https://www.quokka3.com/ accessed at 04.09.2025

V_{OC} gain without perimeter region

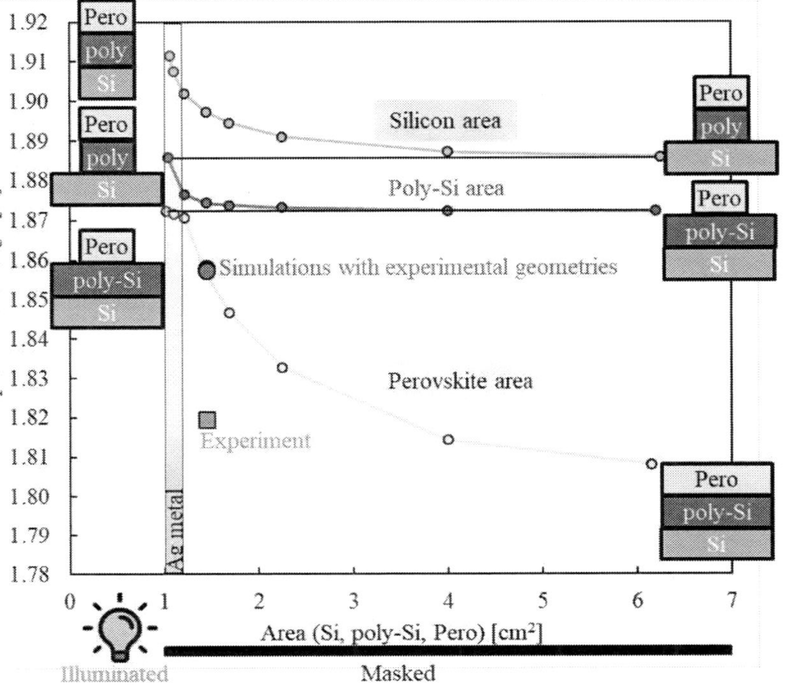

- Perovskite perimeter induces largest loss (ΔV_{OC} = 64 mV)

- 170 Ω-resistant poly-Si layer has minor influence

- Well passivated FZ silicon wafer has induces ΔV_{OC} = 26 mV

Leibniz Universität Hannover

020063-009

V_{OC} loss with high edge recombination

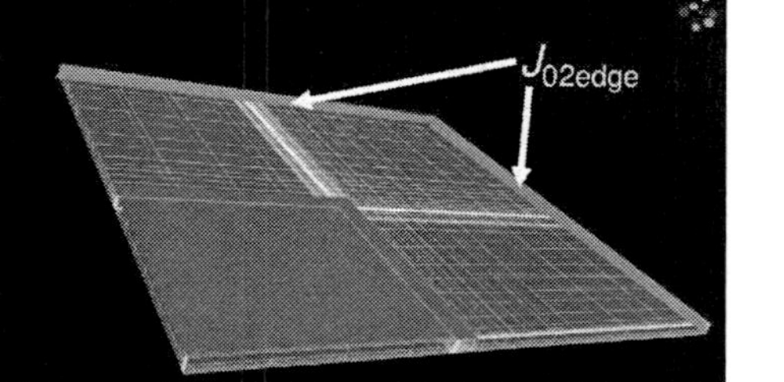

Adding diffusion limited recombination with ideality factor 2 J_{02edge} at silicon outer edge decreases V_{OC} when

- Perovskite area (front TCO) is increasing

- Poly-Si (emitter) extends to silicon edge

- Silicon edge gets closer to illuminated area (up to 52 mV when Si wafer is equal to illuminated area)

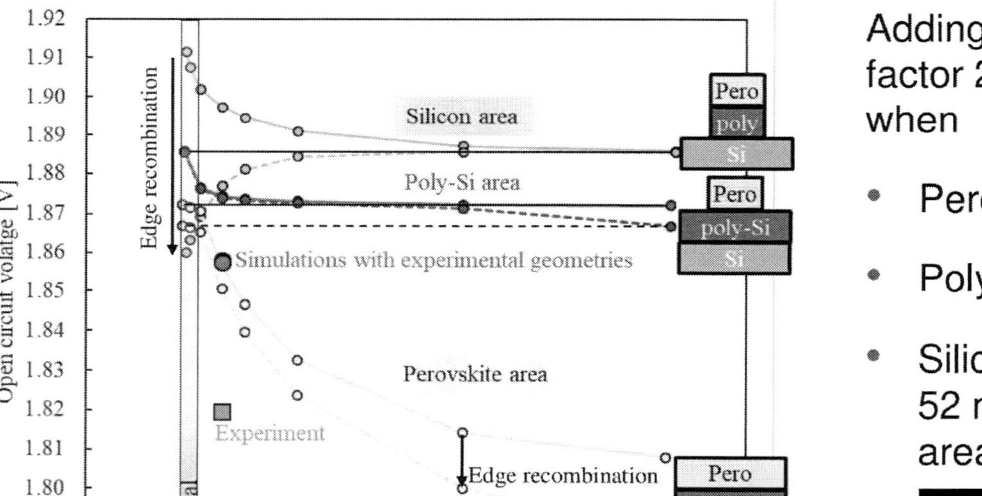

020063-010

Fill factor loss with high edge recombination

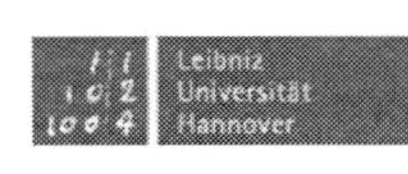

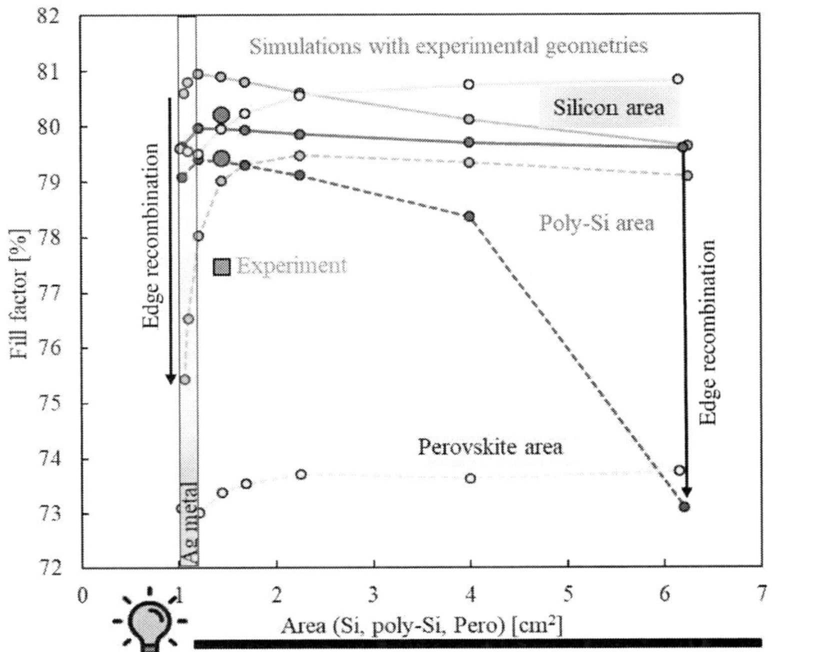

- Without edge recombination fill factor slightly dependent on shaded perimeter

- With edge recombination J_{02edge} the fill factor decreases by

  - $7\%_{abs}$ if poly-Si (emitter) extends to silicon edge

  - $5\%_{abs}$ if Si wafer is equal to illuminated area

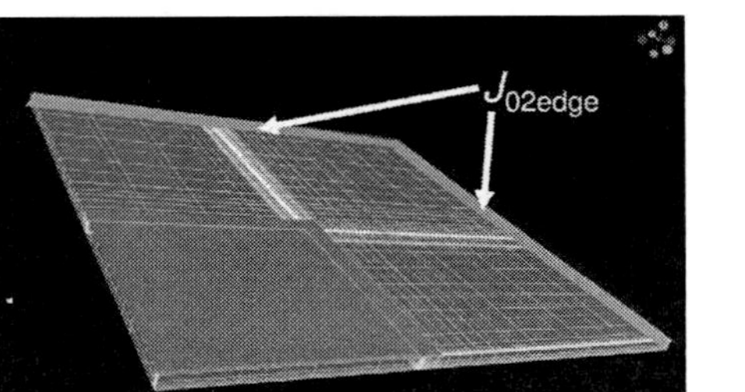

020063-011

Efficiency gains and losses

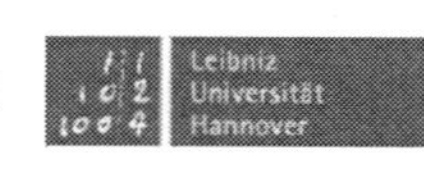

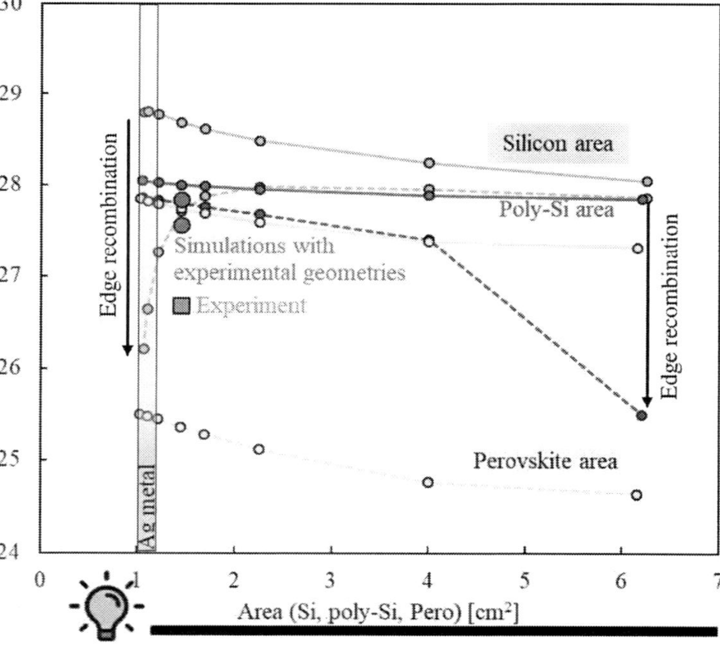

- Short circuit current independent on perimeter losses

- Without edge recombination
  - 28% simulated as sum of both SJ cells
  - Less perimeter increases efficiency by more than $1\%_{abs}$

- With edge recombination
  - $2.8\%_{abs}$ efficiency loss if poly-Si (emitter) extends to silicon edge
  - $2.6\%_{abs}$ efficiency loss if silicon edge gets close to illuminated area

020063-012

Efficiency gain by 2nd generation perovskite and front fingers

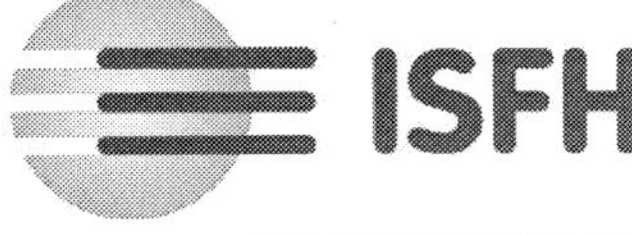

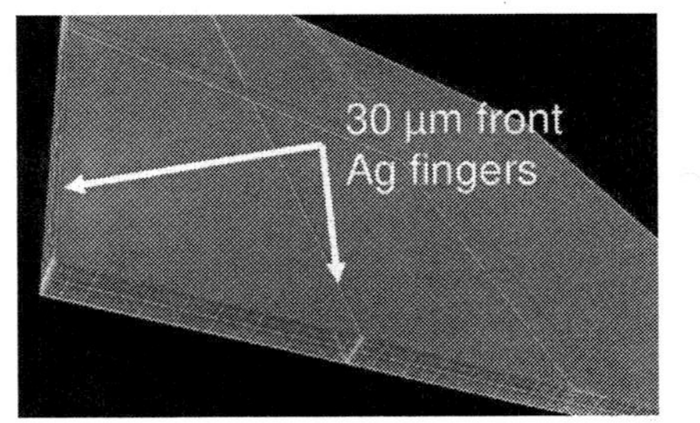

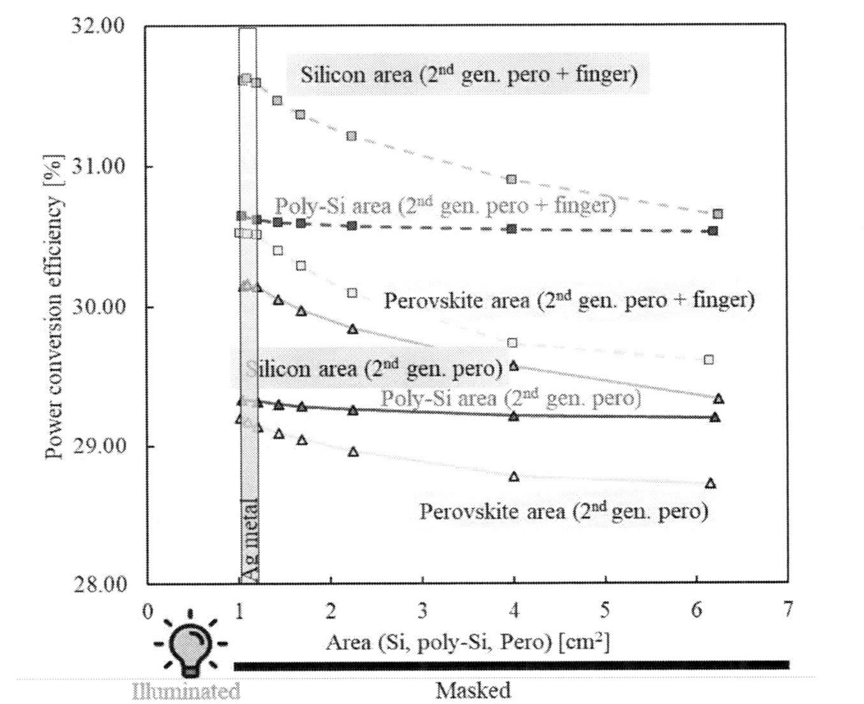

- 2nd generation perovskite cell shows higher fill factors and V_{OC} and thus higher efficiency

- Implementation of front fingers reduces front TCO resistance losses and increases fill factor and efficiency

- Reducing poly-Si and C60 thickness allows >33%

020063-013

Conclusion

Experimental:

- 11.5%-efficient poly-Si passivated bottom cells

- 23.3%-efficient 1.68 eV perovskite single junction cells

- 26.7%-efficient tandem cells

Simulations:

- Efficiency gain by reducing perovskite and poly-Si emitter perimeter area

- Efficiency loss by high edge recombination in combination with small Si area or large poly-Si emitter

020063-014

Acknowledgments

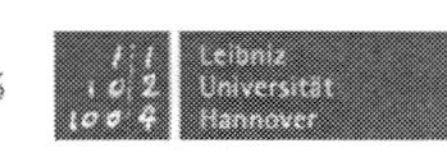

This work was funded by the state of Lower Saxony under grant number ZN4271 (NextGenPV) and the Federal Ministry for Economic Affairs and Energy (BMWE) under grant number 03EE1080C (TOP) and 03EE1113B (APERO).

We thank Ulrich Paetzold, Paul Faßl (both KIT) and Lars Korte (HZB) for fruitful discussions about the perovskite processing.

Supported by:

Federal Ministry
for Economic Affairs
and Energy

on the basis of a decision
by the German Bundestag

zukunft.
niedersachsen

020063-015

IN-DEPTH CHARACTERIZATION AND SIMULATION APPROACH FOR THE UNDERSTANDING OF IN- AND OUTDOOR DEGRADATION OF PEROVSKITE SOLAR CELLS

Jonathan Parion[1,2,3,4], Amit Kumar Harit[1,3,4], Elias Peraticos[5,6], Vasiliki Paraskeva[5,6], Maria Hadjipanayi[5,6], Aranzazu Aguirre[1,3,4], Filip Duerinckx[1,3,4], Hariharsudan Sivaramakrishnan Radhakrishnan[1,3,4], Jef Poortmans[1,3,4,7], Johan Lauwaert[2] and Bart Vermang[1,3,4].

[1] Hasselt University, imo-imomec, Martelarenlaan 42, 3500 Hasselt, Belgium; [2] Ghent University, Department of Electronics and Information Systems, Technology Park 126, 9052 Zwijnaarde, Belgium; [3] Imec, imo-imomec, Thor Park 8320, 3600 Genk, Belgium; [4] EnergyVille, imo-imomec, Thor Park 8320, 3600 Genk, Belgium; [5] PV Technology Laboratory, Department of Electrical and Computer Engineering, University of Cyprus, Nicosia 1678, Cyprus; [6] PHAETHON Centre of Excellence (CoE) for Intelligent, Efficient and Sustainable Energy Solutions, Nicosia 2109, Cyprus; [7] KU Leuven, Department of Electrical Engineering, Kasteelpark Arenberg 10, 3001 Leuven, Belgium

ABSTRACT: Perovskite solar cells (PSCs) have recently shown, on top of their very high power-conversion efficiency (PCE), a remarkable improvement in stability. Despite this, very few studies focus on the long-term testing of these devices. The exact mechanisms governing degradation are yet to be discovered and there is still a lack of a consensus on which accelerated tests can be used to accurately mimic stresses in real-life field deployment. To address these issues, this work uses several of the International Summit on Organic Photovoltaic Stability (ISOS) protocols, combined with an electrical characterization and simulation toolbox, to compare outdoor field testing of PSCs with indoor accelerated tests. The study reveals that long-term outdoor exposure mainly leads to the degradation of the perovskite absorber layer. On the contrary, the very popular dark thermal stress test affects the perovskite/electron transport layer (ETL) interface. It is also shown that testing thermal stability under light and under maximum power point tracking (MPPT) is the closest accelerated test to mimic outdoor exposure, with similar degradation features observed. Overall, this study highlights some of the key degradation modes occurring in PSCs, while showing the importance of diversified testing to better comprehend and improve the stability of these devices.
Keywords: Perovskite degradation, Perovskite outdoor, ISOS protocols, S-shape

1 INTRODUCTION

Perovskite solar cells (PSCs) have recently shown, on top of their very high power-conversion efficiency (PCE), a remarkable improvement in stability [1, 2]. They show the ability to succeed in several indoor accelerated degradation tests, defined by the International Summit on Organic Photovoltaic Stability (ISOS) protocols [3]. Even though this is an important step in the deployment of the perovskite technology, there is still a significant lack of validation of these results in real outdoor conditions. It is moreover unclear which indoor stability tests are the most suited to mimic degradation induced by real-life field exposure. Finally, despite the stability improvements, there is poor understanding as to the exact physical origin of the degradation.

This work aims at addressing these issues, by comparing in- and outdoor degradation of perovskite cells using electrical characterization combined with Devsim TCAD [4] simulations. More specifically, an ISOS-O2 test is performed in Nicosia, Cyprus for a duration of 5 months and compared with a 2000h-long ISOS-D2 test and an 85h-long ISOS-L2 test. The cells that are characterized in this work use a semi-transparent inverted p-i-n architecture and FAPbI$_3$-based perovskite deposited by blade coating. The cell stack is composed of ITO/NiO$_x$/perovskite/LiF/C$_{60}$/LiF/ITO/Ag. The NiO$_x$ acts as a p-doped hole transport layer (HTL), and the LiF/C$_{60}$/LiF stack acts as a n-doped electron transport layer (ETL).

2 OUTDOOR STABILITY TESTING

The outdoor stability of a PSC was tested on the island of Cyprus for a period of 5 months, in between April and August 2025. The evolution of performance is shown in Figure 1. During that period, the cell maintains

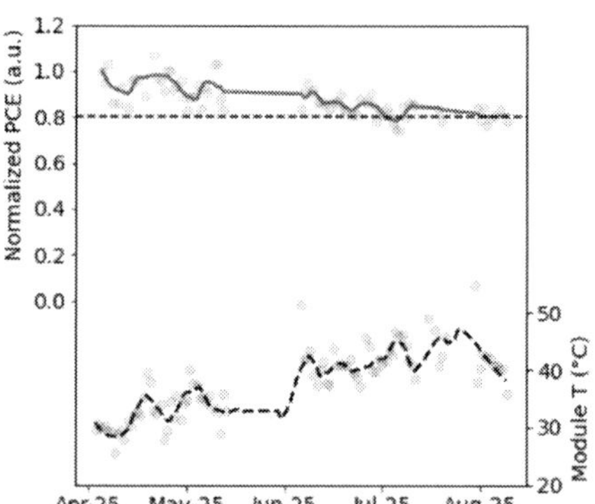

Figure 1: IV measurement of the reference and passivated PSCs, with the main figures of performance given in the table inset. The black arrow shows a slight kink in the reference curve.

approximately 80% of its initial performance. The measurements were interrupted for a period of approximately 1 month between May and June and the sample was kept in dark storage at room temperature during that period. Interestingly, this does not seem to have affected the cell performance. The average sample temperature varied between 30°C and 50°C for the entire testing period, getting hotter during the summer months compared to spring.

In Figure 2a, IV curves taken at different stages of outdoor exposure are depicted. They show that the performance loss was mainly caused by a reduction in short-circuit current density (J$_{sc}$) and in fill-factor (FF), while the open-circuit voltage (V$_{oc}$) remained stable

10.4229/EUPVSEC2025/2BO.10.5

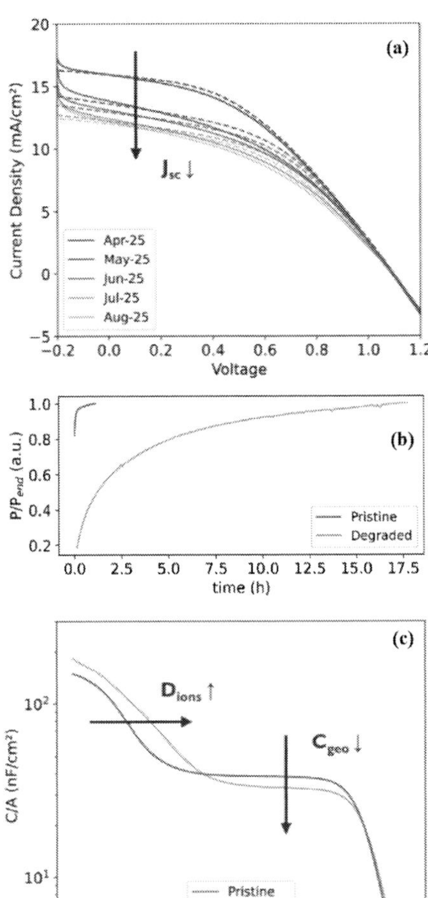

Figure 2: (a) IV curves taken at different dates during outdoor exposure with the solid and dashed curve respectively showing the forward and reverse scans, (b) maximum power point tracking of the device before and after outdoor exposure normalized by the end power value and (c) Capacitance versus frequency (Cf) measurements performed before and after outdoor exposure.

during the testing period. The J_{sc} loss is likely related to a deterioration of the absorber layer, as discussed further. The FF loss seems to be caused by an increased series resistance (R_s). This last one is initially already large, due to the interconnection method used in this specific sample. It is also worth mentioning that the hysteresis of the IV curve increases slightly as the cell degrades, which indicates a change in the behavior of mobile ionic charges. This is confirmed by the data shown in Figure 2(b), where the device MPP was measured for the pristine and degraded sample. Before this measurement, the device is stored in the dark for a few days in order to get to a resting state. Then, MPPT at room temperature and 1 sun irradiance is performed until a stabilized power output is reached. As observed on the Figure, the degraded device takes a significantly longer time to reach a steady-state,

while also starting at a much lower value. This highlights the role of degradation as an accelerator for perovskite transient effects: after degradation, the device takes a significantly longer time to reach its maximal power output than before. In Figure 2(c), the capacitance versus frequency (Cf) characteristic is represented before and after the ISOS-O2 test. In the $10^3 - 10^5$ Hz frequency region, where the geometric capacitance C_{geo} dominates, a clear reduction is observed after outdoor exposure. This is a sign of the perovskite layer degradation, in line with the J_{sc} drop and with results from previous works [5-7]. At frequencies below 10^2 Hz, the increase in capacitance is typically related to the movement of mobile ionic charges. These contribute to the total capacitance of the device only when the AC excitation is slow enough. In the present case, the low-frequency region is shifted to the right after outdoor exposure. Typically, such feature indicates an increase in the ionic diffusivity D_{ions}[6]. This is coherent with the larger hysteresis observed with time (Figure 2(a)) as well as with the increased transient effect (Figure 2(b)). Overall, these results indicate that the outdoor exposure of perovskite cells causes degradation of the absorbing layer, while increasing the transient behavior of the cell caused by mobile ions.

3 INDOOR STABILITY TESTING

Despite being fully representative of real-life operation of the cells and modules, outdoor tests are very long and therefore not practical for development and validation of new PSC architectures. For this reason, accelerated tests are often performed, the two most popular being ISOS-D2 (thermal stress in the dark) and ISOS-L2 (thermal stress under light and at MPPT). In this section, these tests are performed, analyzed and compared with the ISOS-O2 outdoor protocol to highlight the differences and similarities in the perovskite cell degradation.

3.1 ISOS-D2
In this test, samples are placed at 85°C and kept in the dark during 2000h. The IV curves taken before and after the test are represented in Figure 3(a). Two main contributors to the reduced performance are identified: a strong reduction of V_{oc} combined with a significant FF loss caused by the appearance of an "S-shape". This kind of feature is often attributed to the formation of an energy barrier at one of the perovskite/transport layer interfaces [8, 9]. To support the understanding of the S-shape origin, a Devsim TCAD [4] simulation model of the perovskite single-junction cell was created. The results obtained from this model are represented in solid lines in Figure 3(a). To obtain a good agreement with the experimental points, two parameters were varied between the pristine and degraded samples:

- The density N_t of the defect at the interface between the perovskite and the ETL layer was increased from $N_t = 10^9 \mathrm{cm}^{-2}$ to $N_t = 3 \cdot 10^{13} \mathrm{cm}^{-2}$
- The mobility of electrons in the ETL layer μ_{ETL} was changed from $\mu_{ETL} = 5 \cdot 10^{-4} \, cm^2 V^{-1} s^{-1}$ to $\mu_{ETL} = 4 \cdot 10^{-7} \, cm^2 V^{-1} s^{-1}$.

This confirms that the ISOS-D2 test mainly affects the perovskite/ETL interface, while leaving the perovskite bulk unchanged, at least for the blade-coated FAPbI₃-based absorber used in this work. It is worth mentioning

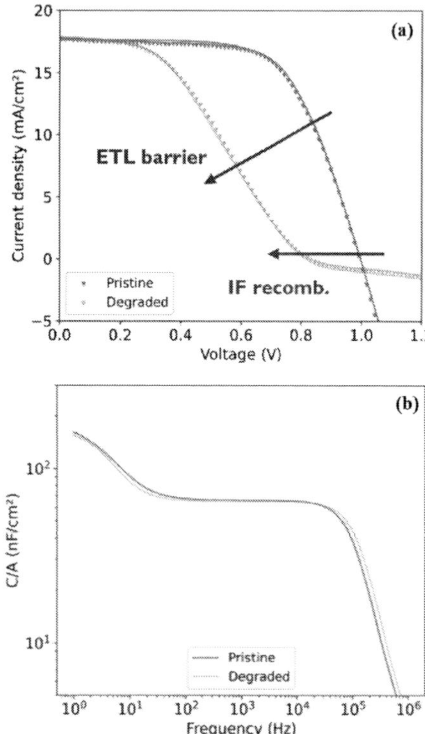

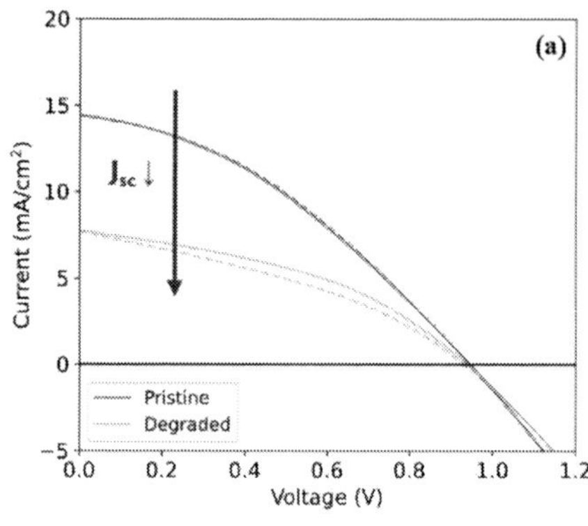

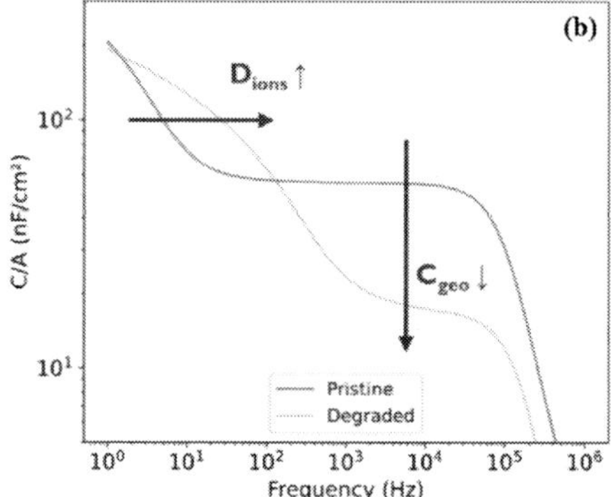

Figure 3: (a) Experimental (triangles) and simulated (solid lines) IV curves before and after ISOS-D2 test and (b) Capacitance versus frequency (Cf) measurements performed before and after ISOS-D2 test.

Figure 4: (a) Experimental IV curves before and after ISOS-L2 test. The solid and dashed lines represent respectively the forward and reverse scans. (b) Capacitance versus frequency (Cf) measurements performed before and after ISOS-L2 test.

that changing HTL parameters and inteface defect density instead of the ETL does not yield a similar result as in Figure 3(a). That layer is moreover less likely to deteriorate under thermal stress, as discussed in previous work [9-11]. Turning to Figure 3(b), this last hypothesis is further confirmed by the Cf measurements. They show no change in the intermediary capacitance region, contrarily to what was observed after outdoor exposure. There is also no change in the low frequency region of the capacitance, indicating no modification of the mobile ion transport properties. While the ISOS-D2 stress does not seem to be representative of the cell outdoor degradation for this specific case, it still enables to highlight the instabilities that can occur at the perovskite/ETL interface under thermal stress. Previous work on long-term outdoor exposure of perovskite cells and modules mentions the appearance of such S-shapes for some ETL compositions [9], which motivates the need for accelerated dark thermal stress tests such as ISOS-D2.

3.2 ISOS-L2

In this test, the sample is placed at 60°C under light and its maximum power point is tracked for a duration of 85h. The IV curves before and after the test are given in Figure 4(a). In this case, the effect of degradation on the IV curve is very similar to the ISOS-O2 test shown in Figure 1(a). There is a significant J_{sc} loss, related to the degradation of the perovskite absorber, as well as a FF loss

caused by an increased R_s. Increased hysteresis is furthermore also observed after degradation and attributed to an increased D_{ions} after analysis of Figure 4(b). There, the same reduction in the geometric capacitance and increase in the transition of the low frequency capacitance are observed in the degraded sample, similarly to the ISOS-O2 case. It indicates a degradation of the absorber layer as well as an increase in the perovskite transient behavior. From Figure 4, it is very clear that the ISOS-L2 test leads in this case to the same type of degradation as the ISOS-O2 outdoor exposure, while being significantly faster. This is a promising result to support the use of the ISOS-L2 protocol to test the stability of perovskite cells.

4 CONCLUSION

This work investigated the stability behavior of PSCs in different testing conditions, both in- and outdoors. Outdoor exposure (ISOS-O2) of the cells leads to a degradation of the perovskite absorber and to an increase of the perovskite transient behavior. The same degradation is observed during indoor MPP tracking under light and heat conditions (ISOS-L2), though on a much shorter time scale. This poses the ISOS-L2 protocol as a solid candidate to validate PSCs stability in lab conditions. Finally, dark thermal stress (ISOS-D2) leads to the deterioration of the perovskite/ETL interface, while leaving the absorber intact. Overall, this work clearly highlights the importance of diversified testing of PSCs. Indoor accelerated tests are useful for laboratory development and validation but need to be correctly tailored to mimic real outdoor deployment. In future steps, more emphasis should be placed on understanding the intrinsic causes of degradation. Moreover, recovery and seasonality effects are key topics to be investigated in order to further improve the stability of PSCs.

5 ACKNOWLEDGEMENTS

This work was financed by the Fonds voor Wetenschappelijk onderzoek (FWO) with grant number 1S01525N, by the European Union through the TESTARE project (Grant ID: 101079488) and the TRIUMPH project (Grant ID: 101075725) and by the European Regional Development Fund and the Republic of Cyprus through the DegradationLab project (Grant ID: INFRASTRUCTUR ES/1216/0043).

6 REFERENCES

[1] H. Zhu *et al.*, 'Long-term operating stability in perovskite photovoltaics', *Nat. Rev. Mater.*, vol. 8, no. 9, pp. 569–586, Sep. 2023, doi: 10.1038/s41578-023-00582-w.

[2] M. Helal Miah *et al.*, 'Key degradation mechanisms of perovskite solar cells and strategies for enhanced stability: issues and prospects', *RSC Adv.*, vol. 15, no. 1, pp. 628–654, 2025, doi: 10.1039/D4RA07942F.

[3] M. V. Khenkin *et al.*, 'Consensus statement for stability assessment and reporting for perovskite photovoltaics based on ISOS procedures', *Nat. Energy*, vol. 5, no. 1, pp. 35–49, Jan. 2020, doi: 10.1038/s41560-019-0529-5.

[4] J. E. Sanchez, 'DEVSIM: A TCAD Semiconductor Device Simulator', *J. Open Source Softw.*, vol. 7, no. 70, p. 3898, Feb. 2022, doi: 10.21105/joss.03898.

[5] J. Parion *et al.*, 'Multifaceted Characterization Methodology for Understanding Nonidealities in Perovskite Solar Cells: A Passivation Case Study', *Sol. RRL*, vol. 8, no. 21, p. 2400529, 2024, doi: 10.1002/solr.202400529.

[6] C. Messmer *et al.*, 'Understanding Ion-Related Performance Losses in Perovskite-Based Solar Cells by Capacitance Measurements and Simulation', *Sol. RRL*, vol. 8, no. 24, p. 2400630, 2024, doi: 10.1002/solr.202400630.

[7] J. Parion *et al.*, 'In-depth study of degradation in scalable wide bandgap perovskite cells', *Mater. Futur.*, vol. 4, no. 4, p. 045101, Sep. 2025, doi: 10.1088/2752-5724/ae01c1.

[8] R. Saive, 'S-Shaped Current-Voltage Characteristics in Solar Cells: A Review', *IEEE J. Photovolt.*, vol. 9, no. 6, pp. 1477–1484, Nov. 2019, doi: 10.1109/jphotov.2019.2930409.

[9] J. Parion *et al.*, 'A novel way of analyzing perovskite outdoor degradation: the S-Voc', *EES Sol.*, Aug. 2025, doi: 10.1039/D5EL00079C.

[10] U. Erdil *et al.*, 'Delamination of Perovskite Solar Cells in Thermal Cycling and Outdoor Tests', *Energy Technol.*, vol. 13, no. 1, p. 2401280, 2025, doi: 10.1002/ente.202401280.

[11] M. De Bastiani *et al.*, 'Mechanical Reliability of Fullerene/Tin Oxide Interfaces in Monolithic Perovskite/Silicon Tandem Cells', *ACS Energy Lett.*, vol. 7, no. 2, pp. 827–833, Feb. 2022, doi: 10.1021/acsenergylett.1c02148.

Faculty of Engineering
School of Photovoltaic and Renewable Energy Engineering

SINGLET FISSION ROUTE FOR >30% EFFICIENT SOLAR CELLS: Silicon Cell Requirements

EUPVSEC, Bilbao
23rd September 2025

Dr. Shona McNab

Shona McNab, Alex J. Baldacchino, Pheobe Pearce, Alvin Mo, Alison Ciesla, Bram Hoex, Nicholas J. Ekins-Daukes, Murad J. Y. Tayebjee, Michael P. Nielsen

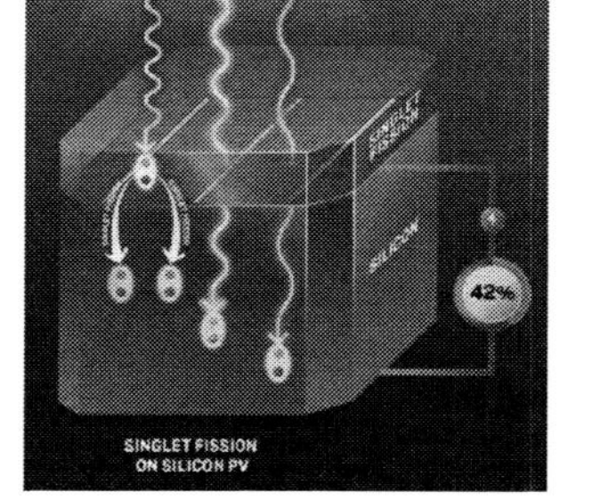

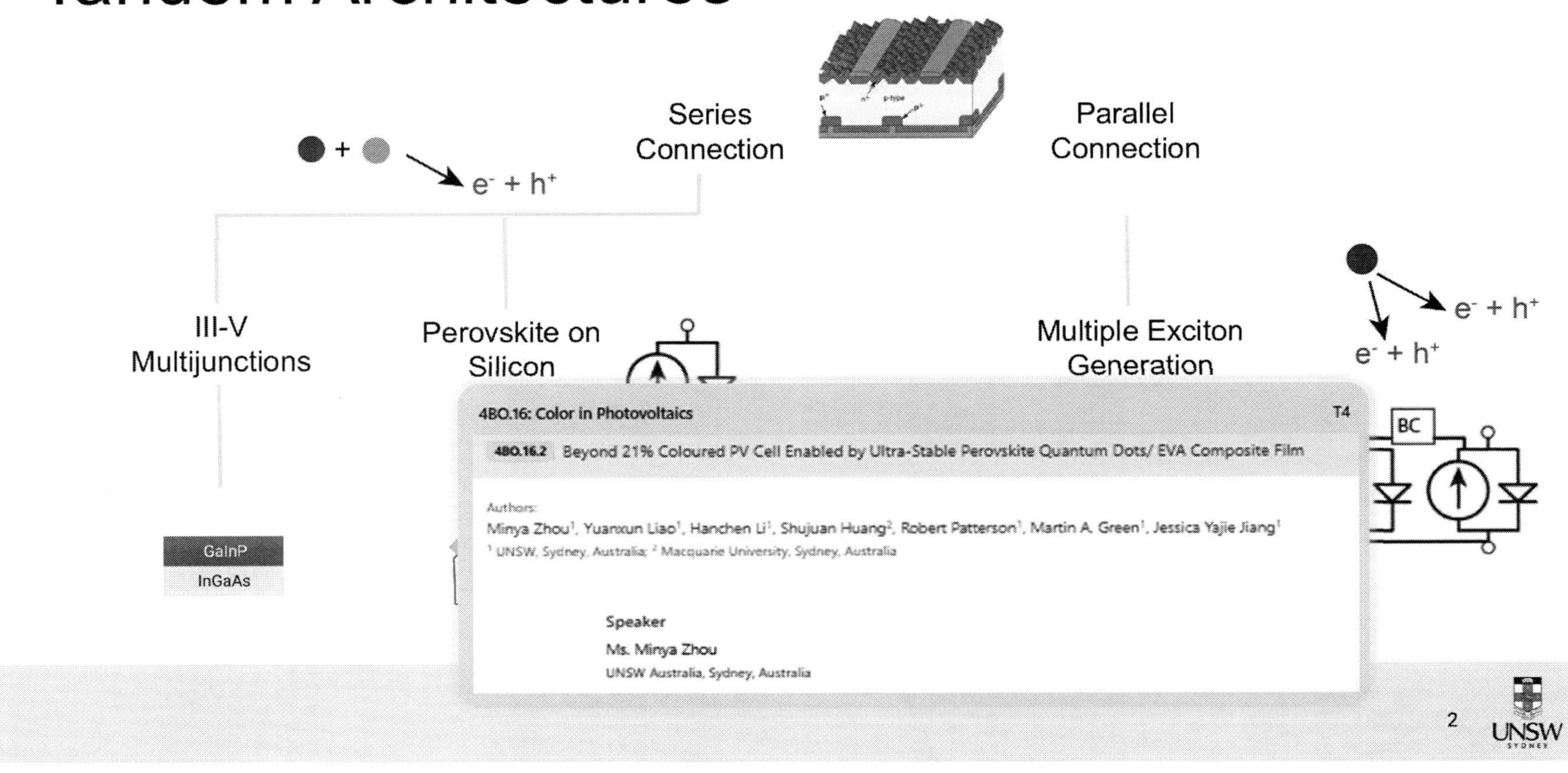

Tandem Architectures
III-V Multijunctions
GaInP
InGaAs
Series Connection
Perovskite on Silicon
Parallel Connection
Multiple Exciton Generation
e⁻ + h⁺
e⁻ + h⁺
e⁻ + h⁺
BC
4BO.16: Color in Photovoltaics
T4
4BO.16.2 Beyond 21% Coloured PV Cell Enabled by Ultra-Stable Perovskite Quantum Dots/ EVA Composite Film
Authors:
Minya Zhou¹, Yuanxun Liao¹, Hanchen Li¹, Shujuan Huang², Robert Patterson¹, Martin A. Green¹, Jessica Yajie Jiang¹
¹ UNSW, Sydney, Australia; ² Macquarie University, Sydney, Australia
Speaker
Ms. Minya Zhou
UNSW Australia, Sydney, Australia
2
UNSW
SYDNEY

Singlet Fission (SF) Down Conversion

- **One** photon yields **two** excitons
- 200% yield of **long-lived** triplet excitons

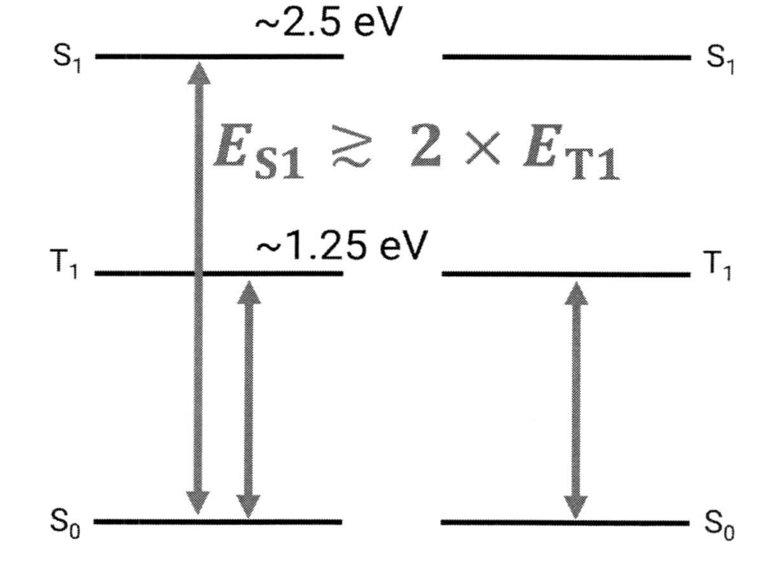

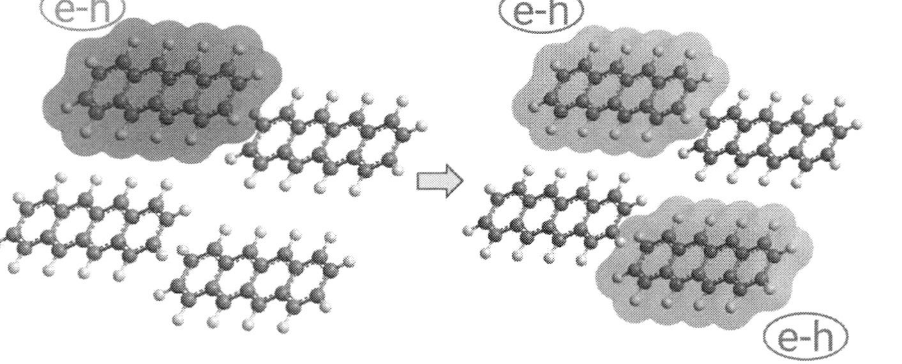

3

UNSW
SYDNEY

020065-003

Direct Energy vs Radiative Transfer

Direct Energy Transfer

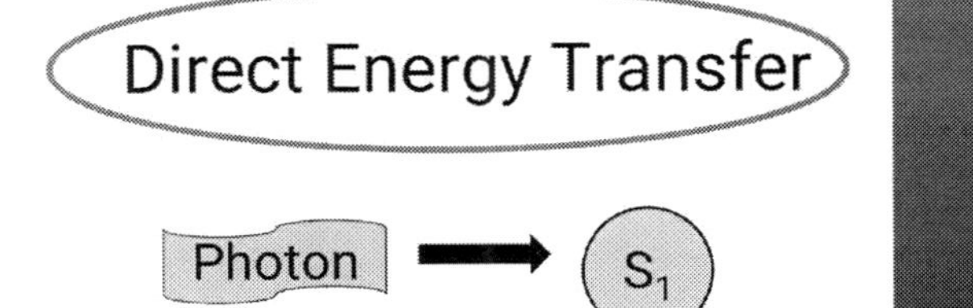

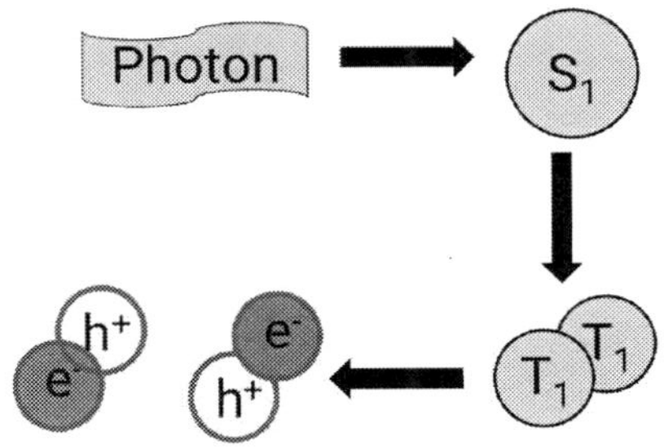

✓ Higher potential efficiency

! Modified Si front surface.

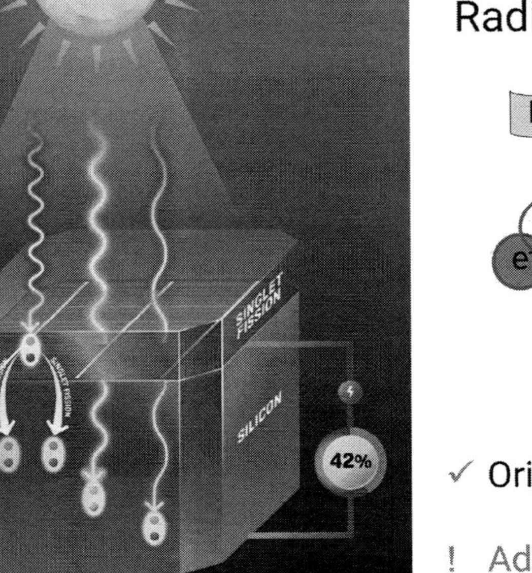

Radiative Transfer

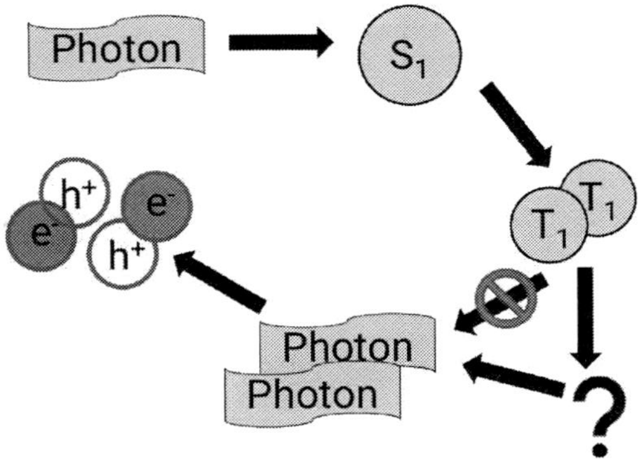

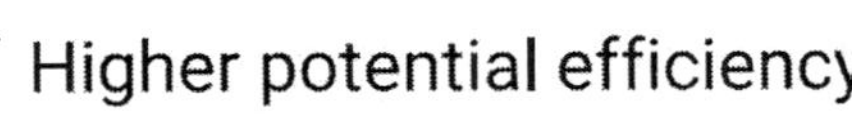

✓ Original silicon cell front surface

! Additional step results in energy loss

! How to get triplets to emit?

✓✓ - Simple device structure – no contact to organic material

UNSW SYDNEY

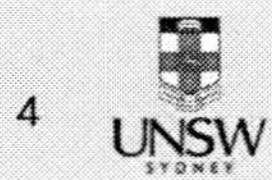

SF Adjusted Generation Profile

- How much additional current can we get?

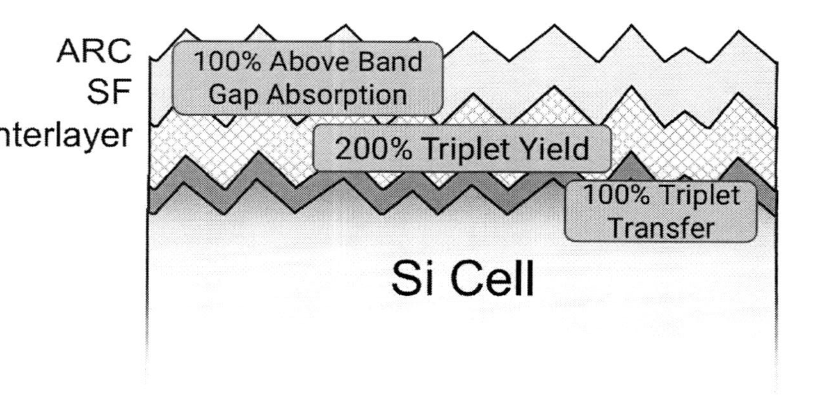

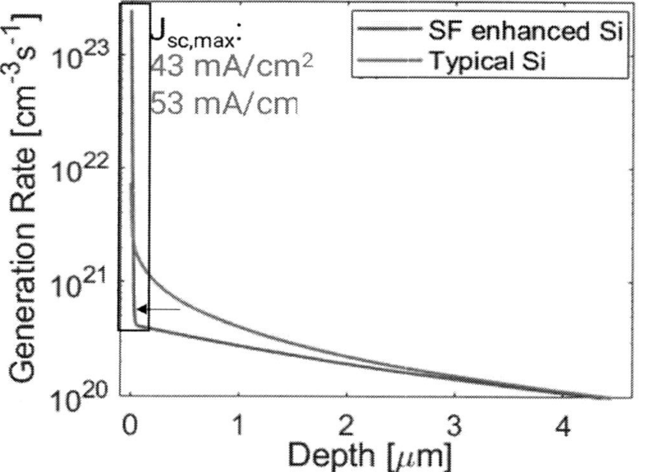

Triplet excitons transferred **very** close to the front surface

Efficiency of the silicon cell will depend on how effectively e-h pairs are collected from the front surface

Calculated using RayFlare: https://rayflare.readthedocs.io

5

Which Si Cell Architectures

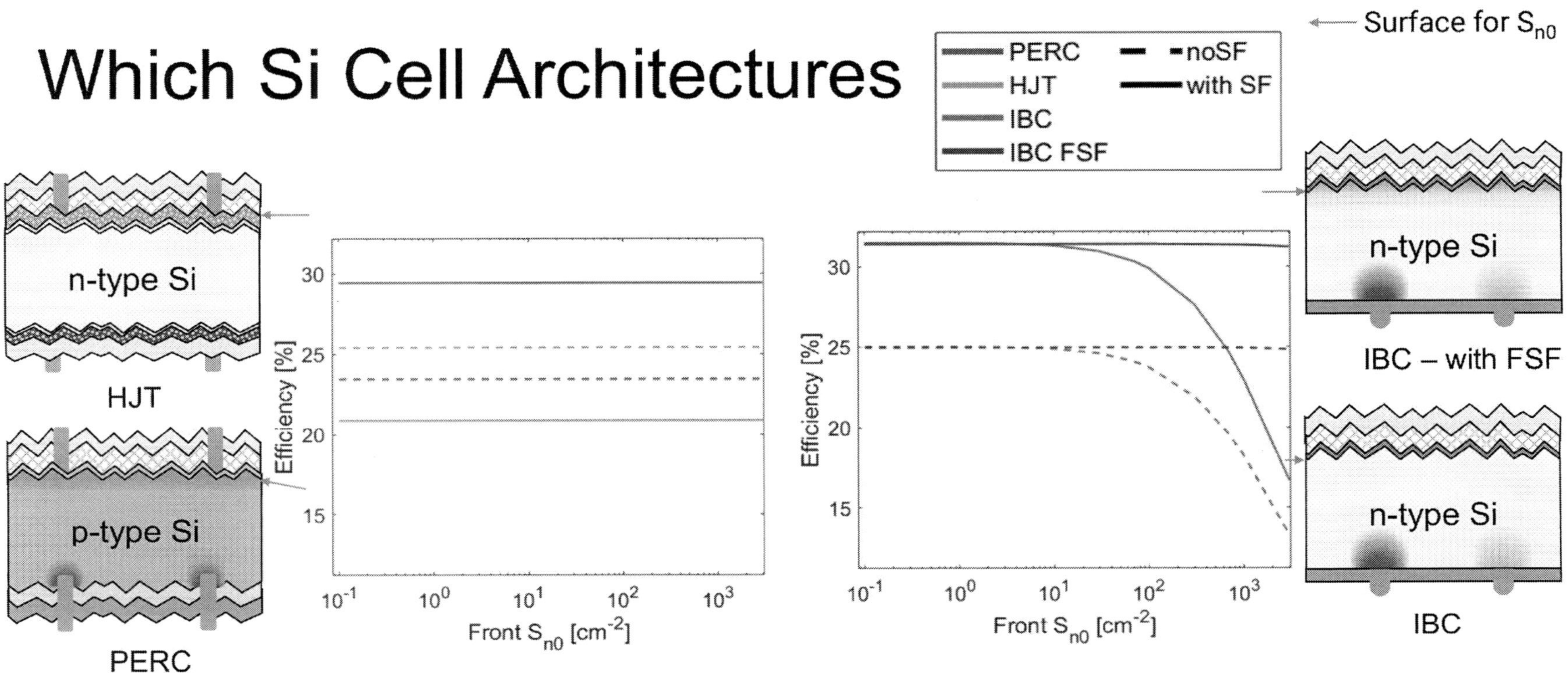

The Importance of Band Alignment for Triplet Transfer

- Both electron and hole must be transferred into silicon

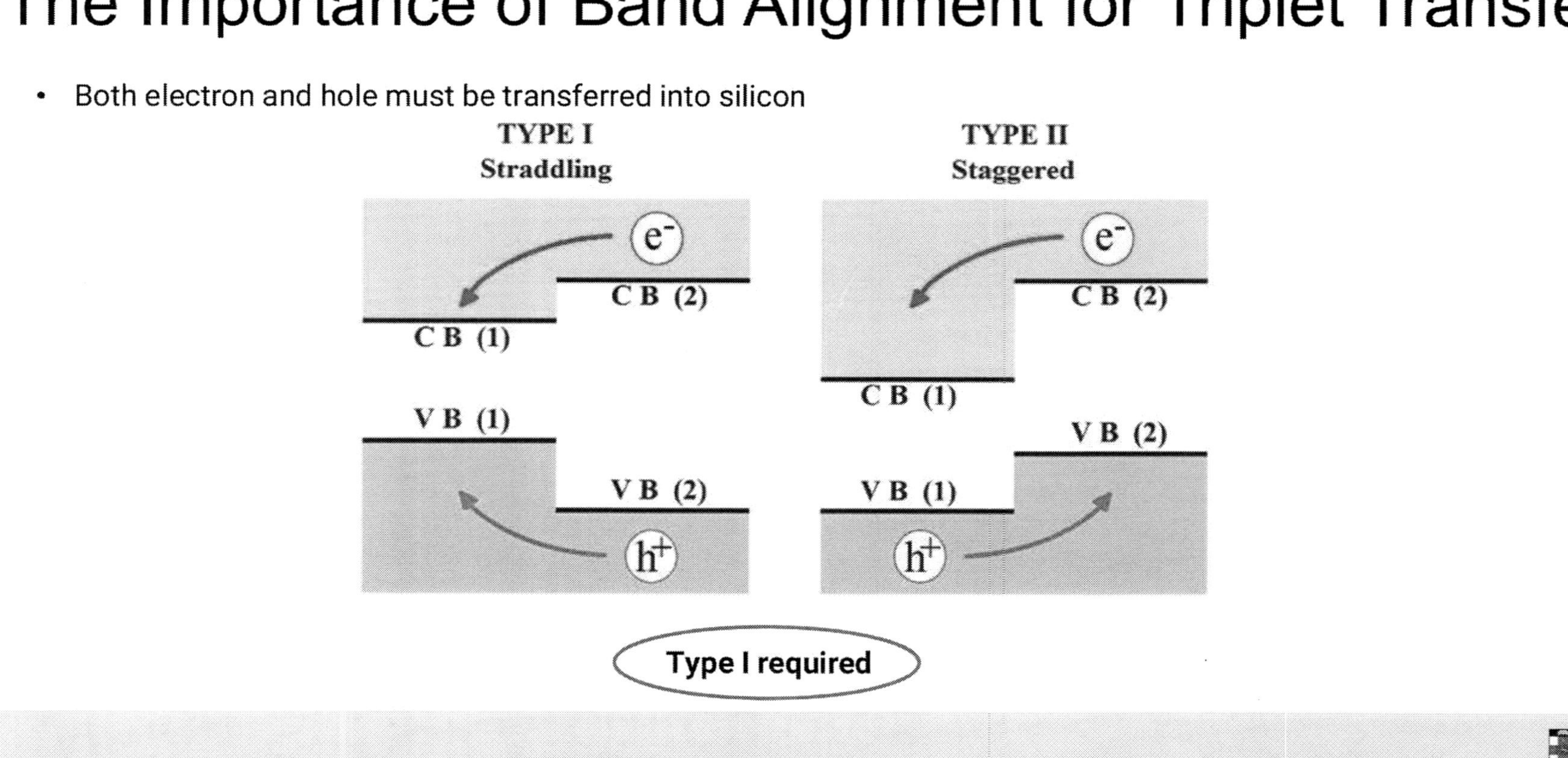

A. Giampietri, *Advanced Materials Interfaces*, vol. 4, no. 11, p. 1700144, Jun. 2017.

UNSW
SYDNEY

Mechanisms for Energy transfer

Dexter

- Exciton transfer directly into the silicon
- Limited band alignment required
  - Triplet state can 'float' anywhere in the Tc Singlet energy levels

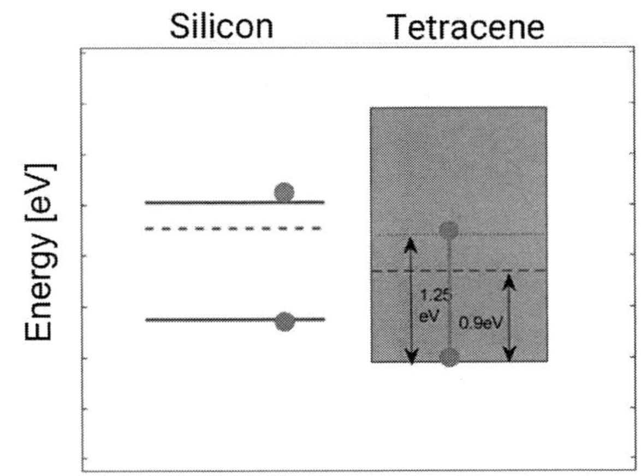

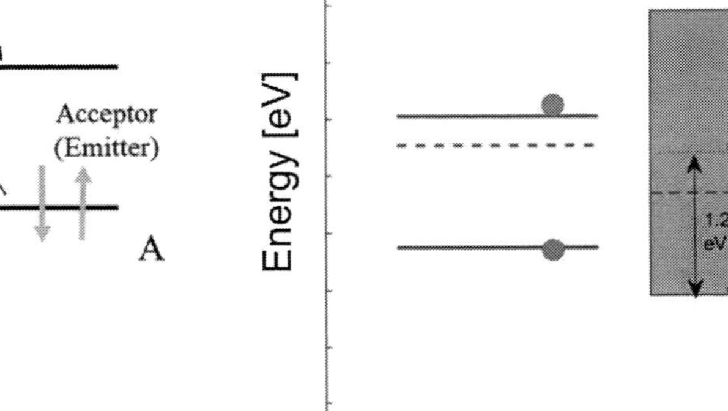

[1]M. Micheva, S. Baluschev; 2022. "Thermally activated delayed fluorescence in an optically accessed soft matter environment" *J. Mater. Chem. C*, 10, 4533-4545

020065-008

Mechanisms for Energy transfer

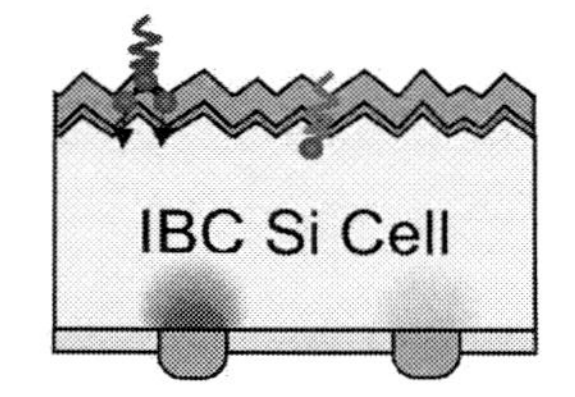

Charge Transfer

- 2 Step Process
- Charge Transfer state
- Band alignment matters to transfer **both** carriers

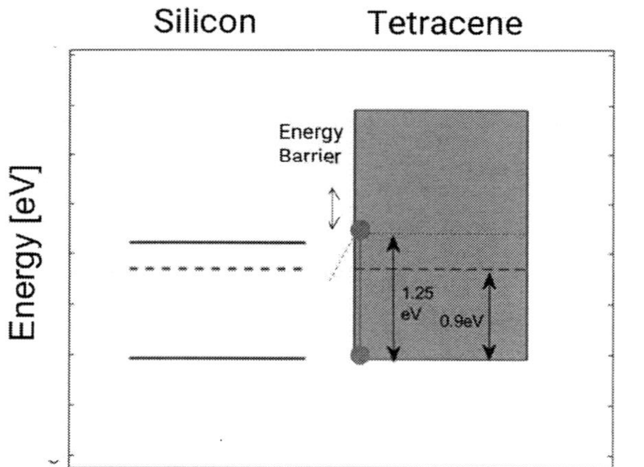

Mechanisms for Energy transfer

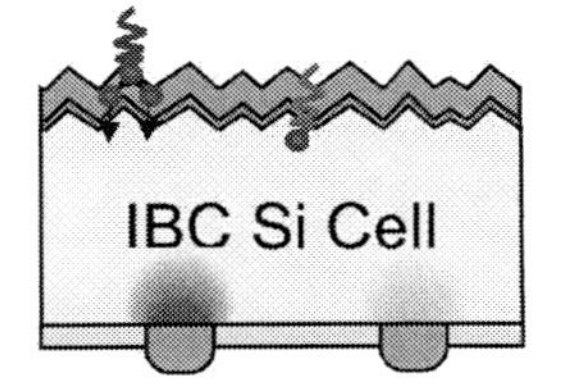

Charge Transfer

- 2 Step Process
- Charge Transfer state
- Band alignment matters to transfer **both** carriers

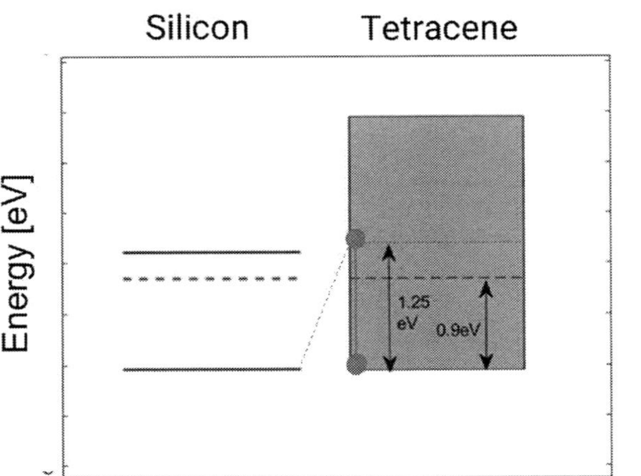

Band Alignment

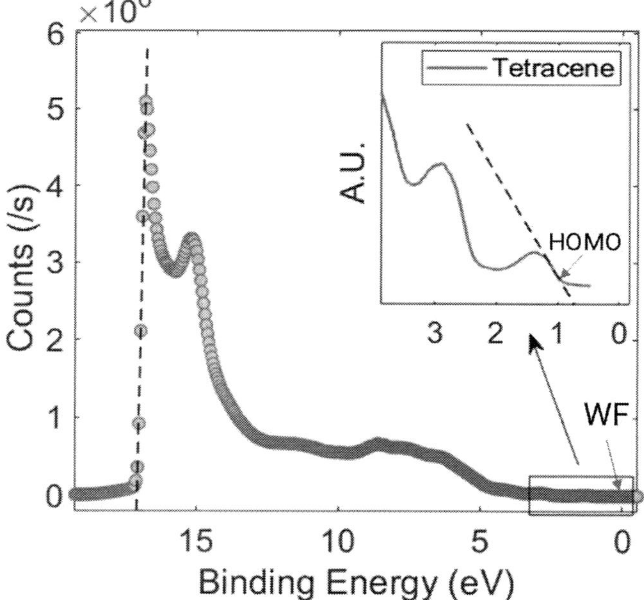

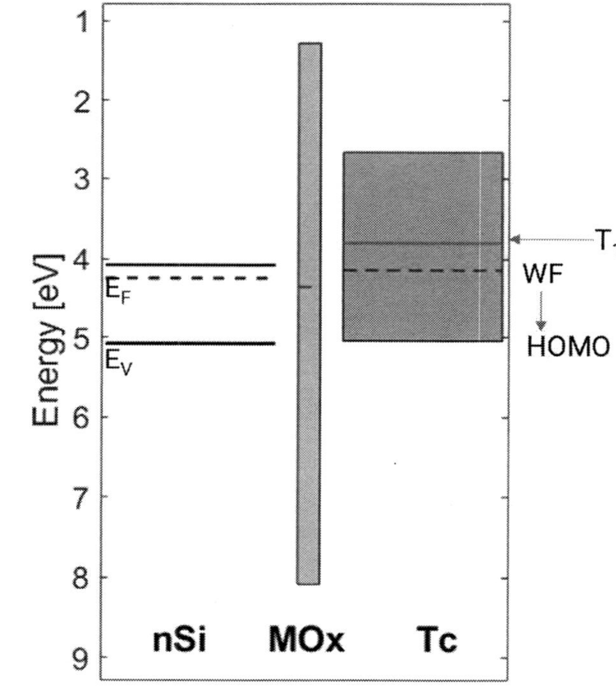

Full Details: N. Nagaya *et al.*, "Exciton fission enhanced silicon solar cell," *Joule*, vol. 0, no. 0, 2025, doi: 10.1016/j.joule.2025.101965.

020065-011

Si/MOx/Tc Band Alignment

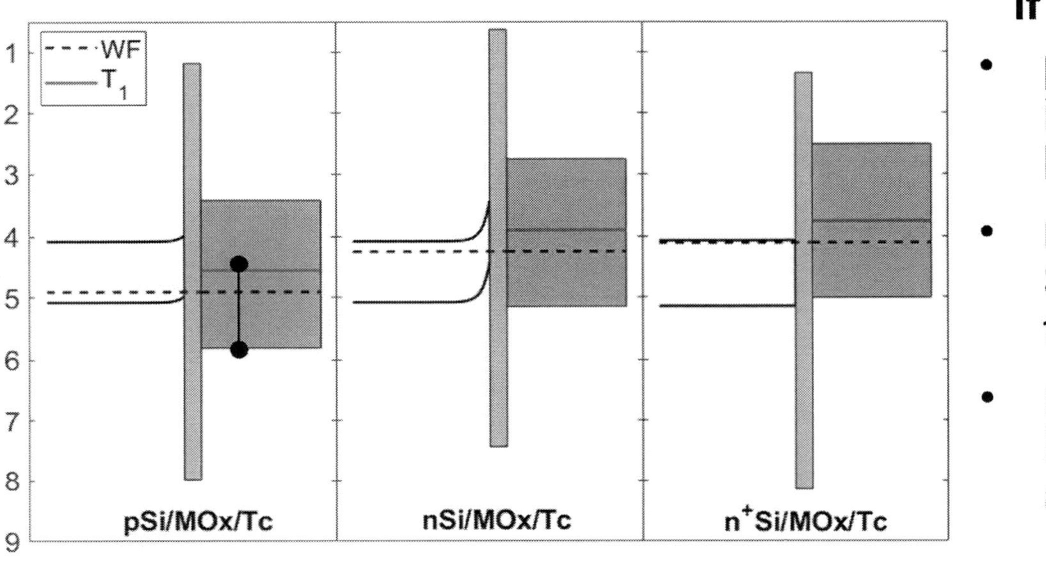

If Band Alignment is important:

- p (or p+) - triplet energy level is in the middle of the Si band gap. **Electrons Blocked**

- n-type – band bending in the Si results in slight barrier to triplets

- n+ removes the Si band bending **improving electron alignment**

Characterising SF devices:

- Magnetic Photoluminescence (MPL)

- Triplet generation can be 'turned off' by applying a magnetic field.

At High Field:

- ↑ Singlet Concentration = ↑ PL_{Tc}

- ↓ Fewer Triplets into the Si = ↓ PL_{Si}

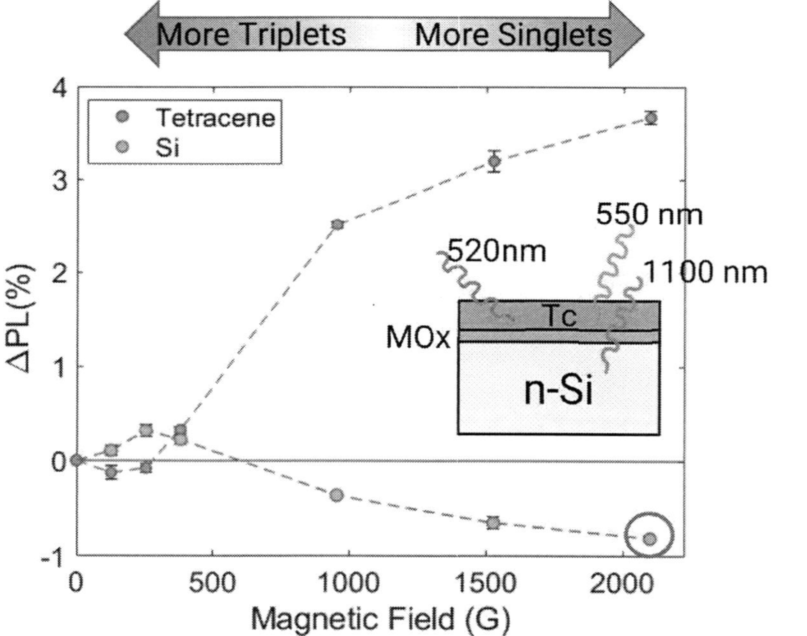

13 UNSW SYDNEY

Doping Study Results

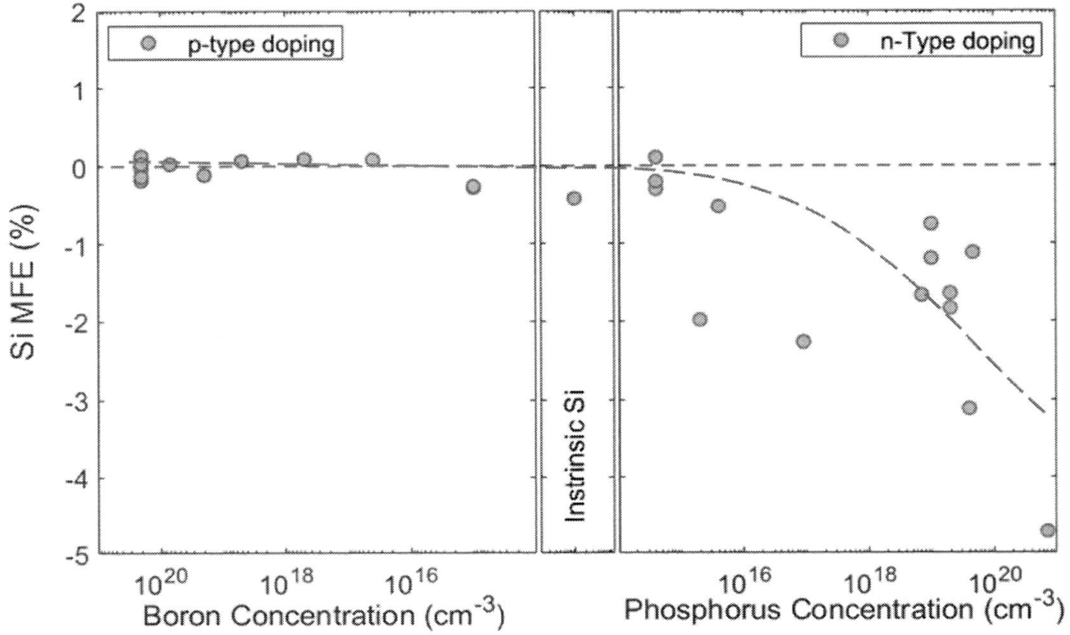

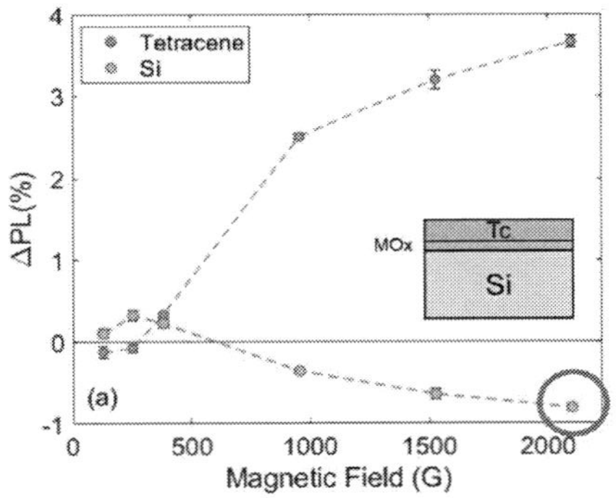

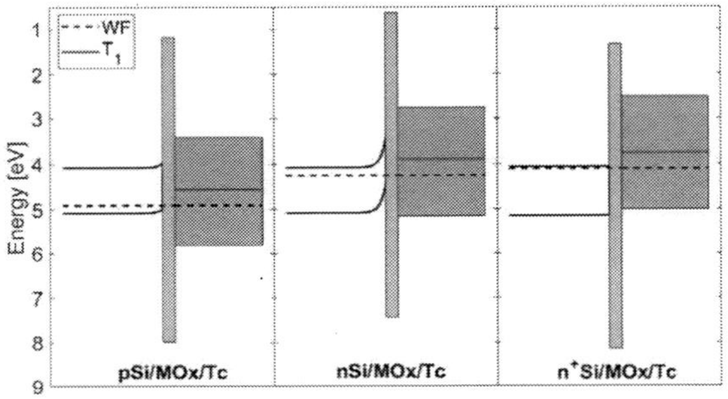

Clear trend with Si doping
In this system, the band alignment is important, suggesting a charge transfer mechanism

14

SF on Si cell device

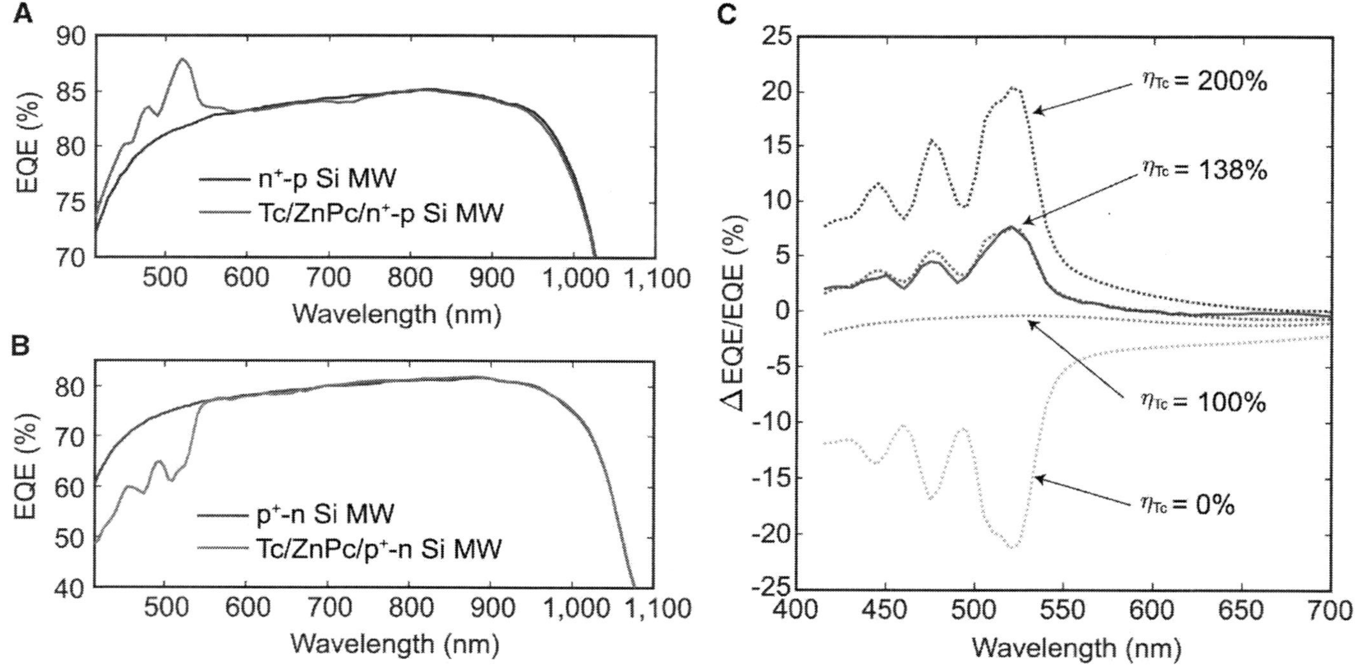

N. Nagaya *et al.*, "Exciton fission enhanced silicon solar cell," *Joule*, vol. 0, no. 0, 2025, doi: 10.1016/j.joule.2025.101965.

Conclusions

Singlet Fission on Silicon
- SF solar cells offer an alternative approach for **high efficiency** Si tandems
- **Simple** adaption to the industrial silicon technology

Si Cell Structure
- Certain cell structures will block exciton transfer
- **n+ Si front** surface best for triplet transfer
- PERC cells best for proof of concept

Moving Forward
- Enhancement in EQE has been demonstrated
- Further work to demonstrate on a higher efficiency device

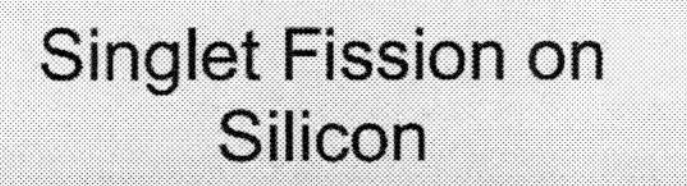

Thank you for listening
shona.mcnab@unsw.edu.au

16

Mechanisms for Energy transfer

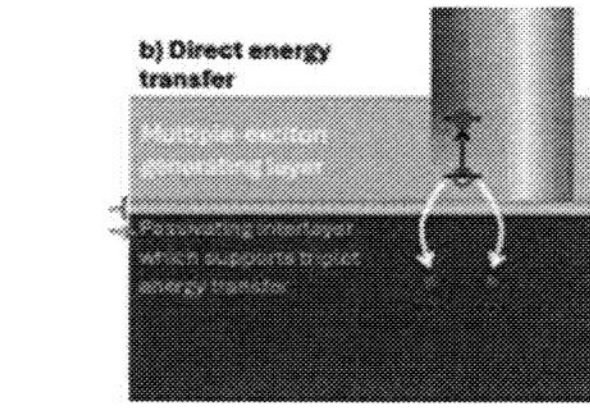

FRET Transfer

- $1/r6$ – up to 10nm in organics.

- Donor emission overlaps with acceptor absorption

- 'matching' resonances allows excited donor to transfer energy to acceptor.

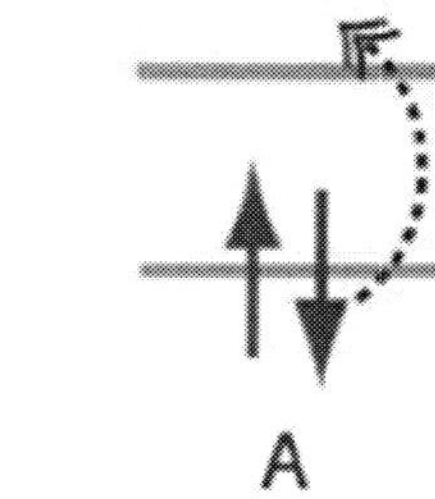

17 UNSW SYDNEY

Measuring Band Alignment

1. Si-MOx Alignment
- Kraut's Method[1]
- UV-vis

2. Band Bending in Si
- XPS Si2p Peak Shift[2]

3. Si-Tc Alignment
- UPS[2]

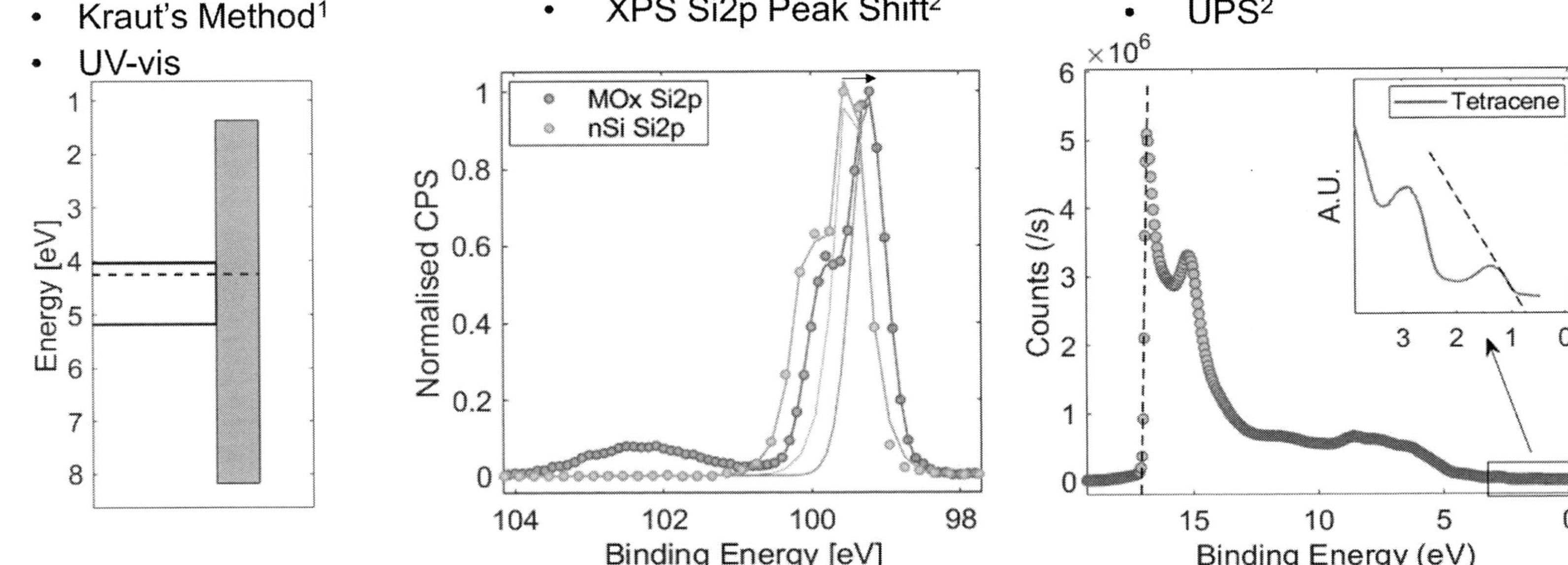

[1]Edris Khorani, Shona McNab; Optoelectronic properties of ultrathin ALD silicon nitride and its potential as a hole-selective nanolayer for high efficiency solar cells. APL Mater. 2020; 8 (11): 111106. https://doi.org/10.1063/5.0023336
[2]Baldo

18

UNSW SYDNEY

PERFORMANCE OF A 4-TERMINALS SPECTRAL SPLITTING ASYMMETRIC SOLAR CONCENTRATOR IN DIFFUSE SUNLIGHT: A NUMERICAL STUDY

Floriana Morabito[1], Daniela Fontani[2], Paola Sansoni[2], Mehdi Ahmadi[3], Salvatore Lombardo[3], Andrea Farina[1],
Silvia Maria Pietralunga[1*]
[1]CNR-IFN Milano, Piazza L. da Vinci 32 – 20133 Milano, Italy
[2]CNR-INO Largo E. Fermi, 6 – 50125 Firenze, Italy
[3]CNR-IMM Zona Industriale, Ottava Strada, 5 – 95121 Catania, Italy

*Corresponding author: silviamaria.pietralunga@cnr.it

ABSTRACT: We numerically analyze the performance of a spectral splitting low concentrator under diffuse sunlight. The optics is the core of a 4-Terminal (4T) dual-junction PV architecture, with a wedged right-angled prism asymmetric concentrator and NIR and VIS cells respectively coupled to the bottom and the rear sides of the wedge. The spectral splitting approach relaxes the geometrical and technological constraints typical of tandem configurations.
Light guiding is achieved by combining Total Internal Reflection and dichroic reflection, and skew incident rays become fully confined. Perfect optical coupling is supposed. Optical performance depends on the concentration ratio, set by the value of the apex angle of the wedge, on the input spectral content and on the spectral selection performed by the dichroic mirrors. Optical power ratio exceeding 60% can be achieved for diffuse input light. In the case of a HJT silicon cells and a GaAs single junction reference cell, by using license plate data for the electrical parameters of the cells, the Power Conversion Efficiency of the diffuse component in clear sky conditions amounts to around 30%, reaching up to 45% in case of overcast conditions. This geometry also minimizes self-shading and appeals to integrated and bifacial PV applications.
Keywords: photovoltaics, four-terminal, bifacial, diffuse light.

1 INTRODUCTION

The energy sustainability of life and human progress is undoubtedly one of the greatest contemporary challenges. Renewable energy sources are ideally inexhaustible and therefore are strategic resources in which to foster research and innovation. In this perspective, photovoltaic (PV) conversion of solar energy will likely maintain a key role in the global energetic portfolio [1]. However, it is also by economic competitiveness that PV will be able to gain a place of choice among the possible energy supply solutions. When considering the deployment of PV utility-scale plants, competitiveness comes with maximizing power conversion efficiency (PCE) of PV modules and optimization of soil usage, targeting at minimizing the levelized cost of energy. The need to cope with restrictions in terms of the surface available is even stronger in the case of Integrated PV (IPV) on buildings, but also on self-powered vehicles and devices, which face intrinsic limitations in dimensions. To increase the PCE at unitary area is therefore a key request also for the IPV market, where solutions are often customized for specific applications and may be quite diverse in terms of shape, size, optical design, and type of solar cell employed. Also, the stringent constraints in terms of cost that heavily affect the utility-scale market are somewhat relaxed in the IPV context, and the PV module itself becomes a design element of the final product. Functionality and esthetics can then coexist thanks to innovative designs, e.g., as discussed by Borja Block A. and co-authors in [2].

One approach to increase the PCE of PV modules at same occupied area is to use bifacial solar cells that collect backscattered radiation from the ground at their rear side. Silicon solar cells typically improve PCE by around 20%, in dependence on albedo level. Bifaciality may also be an added feature to multijunction PV systems that aim to overcome the Shockley–Queisser limit in PCE [3] by using several solar cells, each of which optimized for a specific spectral range [4]. In the specific case of the four-terminal (4T) dual-junction approach, a classically proposed configuration is made of two stacked cells. The top cell, with a higher bandgap, works in the visible (VIS) spectrum, and the bottom cell works in the near-infrared (NIR) one. Stacked cells have a common shape and are optically, but not electrically, "in series", with no need to integrate them monolithically. An alternative solution to cell stacking is spectral splitting, based on the spectral separation of light and cells [5]. This furtherly relaxes technological constraints, but typically suffers from larger dimensions of the module and poor land usage.

Recently, a solution for a low concentrating dual-junction 4-T PV system, which exploits spectral splitting at minimized footprint and can also profitably embed bifaciality, has been proposed [6,7]. In this paper we recall the design of the PV element, also to be considered as a "solar tile" for IPV solutions, and we specifically numerically analyze its performance in diffuse input light, by numerically evaluation of its PCE for the diffuse portion of input irradiation in selected conditions.

2 DESIGN AND ANALYSIS

2.1 Design of the asymmetric solar concentrator

We make reference to the geometry shown in Figure 1. More details on the conceptual design can be found in [6,7]. The core of the optics is made of a wedged right-angled prism of BK7 glass (refractive index $n = 1.5$) and apex angle φ. The longer cathetus is the input top side. The VIS solar cell is optically coupled to the rear side (short cathetus) and the NIR cell is coupled to the bottom side (hypothenuse). Ideally, we assume perfect optical coupling of all elements (no refractive index mismatches) and anti-reflection treatment at the top input surface. Numerical modelling is developed using a commercial 3D ray-tracing software, (ZEMAX OpticStudio, 22.2 Professional) in non-sequential mode and by performing data post-processing in MATLAB environment, as also detailed in [6]. The solar cells are modeled by detectors in ZEMAX environment. The PEC will be estimated by assuming the cells to be respectively a commercial silicon SHJ bifacial NIR cell ($V_{oc,Si}$ = 0.73V, FF_{Si}= 0.8) and a GaAs reference cell for the VIS-ReRa solutions B.V., ($V_{oc,GaAs}$=1V, FF_{Ga}= 0.82). Spectral splitting is obtained through two dichroic mirrors, one located on the bottom side (high reflection in the VIS) and one at the rear surface of the prism (high reflection in the NIR) and located right in front of the solar cells. Commercially available mirrors have been considered (Thorlabs Inc.) with a cutoff wavelength at 805 nm since it represents the crossing point of the curves of external quantum efficiencies (EQEs) of the two solar cells (from license plate data).

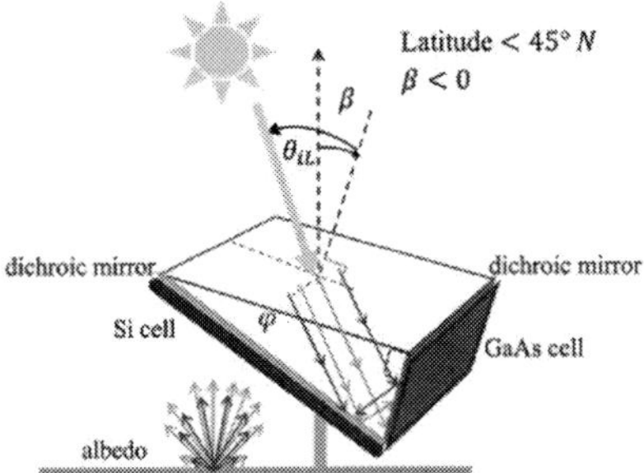

Figure 1: The conceptual design of the 4-T spectral splitting PV concentrator. VIS light (green rays) is absorbed at the VIS cell (here GaAs) and reflected off the NIR cell (here Si). The opposite occurs for the NIR light (dark red rays). Tilt angle β in the N-S direction is marked. At installation latitudes lower than 45° in the northern hemisphere, the top surface is north-side oriented (negative β values). Angle θ_{iL} is the limit incidence angle that guarantees confinement by TIR of direct VIS sunlight. In dependence on the latitude of installation, β may favor albedo collection from ground, also shown.

Low Concentration is obtained for VIS light in the North-South (NS) direction by combining Total Internal Reflection (TIR) at the top glass-air interface and the dichroic reflections. In order to guarantee TIR of light at the top surface, the internal incidence angle must exceed the limit angle for TIR (θ_L). In turn this introduces a limitation on the external incidence angle for light at the top surface, which must exceed a limit angle $\theta_{iL}= \theta_{iL}(n, \varphi)$. Different values for φ were here considered, also including φ = 14.5°, which corresponds to θ_{iL}=21° and to a geometrical concentration C_g = 4, φ = 25° that corresponds to C_g = 2.14 and to θ_{iL}= 0°, and φ = 30° [7]. Starting from $\varphi \geq 25°$ there is full acceptance of direct sunlight under in-field installation conditions; further increase of φ does not bring significant advantages.

It can be demonstrated that, whenever the refractive index of the wedge is n >1.4, TIR condition applies also to input skew rays with a component in the East-West direction, so that they are addressed to either solar cell according to the respective spectral band.

In case 3 < C_g < 5, stationary installation of the module can be considered, with no need for NS tracking. In this configuration, the best tilt angle β obeys the relation: $\beta = \left(90° - (\varphi_s + \theta_{iL})\right)$ where φ_s is the maximum sun elevation at summer solstice (at noon) at the latitude of installation. So installed, the input top surface becomes

more north-oriented than for a standard PV module, and this peculiar tilting also brings advantages for bifacial operation, since it reduces self-shading and increases the portion of albedo irradiation that can be collected from the ground. It has been shown that actually, by summing up direct irradiation and albedo contribution, the proposed 4-T geometry may outperform standard bifacial ones, especially at low latitudes [7].

2.2 Numerical method for diffuse light

To simulate input diffuse light, a rectangular light source has been activated in ZEMAX model, immediately outside of the input surface and randomly emitting rays Lambertian distributed in angle (cosine law). Firstly, the optical transfer function for diffuse input light was computed, by admitting a uniform input spectrum in the 410nm-1100nm range. In order to guarantee constant illumination, the area of the top input surface was kept fixed at 77mm x 20mm as the apex angle φ of the wedge varied. Full angular acceptance of input diffuse light leads to a thermodynamical concentration limit C_{MAX} = 1.5 [8]. Secondly, the diffused portion by Rayleigh scattering of a standard solar AM1.5G solar spectrum (clear-sky condition) is considered (www.nrel.gov/grid/solar-resource/spectra-am1.5.html/) and sampled on 175 equally spaced wavelength-points, with spectrally integrated power intensity of 1000 Wm^{-2}. The spectrum sampling was again performed in the wavelength range 410-1100 nm, according to the transparency spectrum of optical material and the operating range of silicon cells. As a third input, the Horizontal Irradiance (DHI) in overcast condition on a selected day was measured (in-field spectrum) at the installation site of Catania town (Sicily, Italy) and sampled.

Normalized input spectra are shown in Fig. 2. The outcast spectrum is richer in blue components and poorer in the VIS and NIR regions.

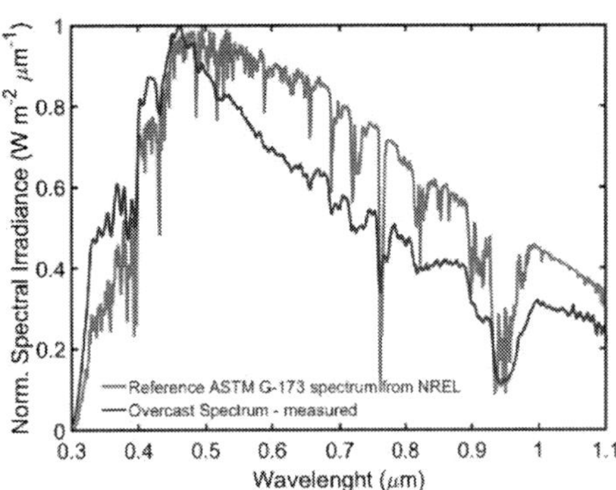

Figure 2: Input spectra used to estimate the PCE.

2.3 Performance evaluation

We rate the performance of the PV concentrator both optically and electrically. We define an optical Power ratio P_{ro} and an optical efficiency η_o as:

$$P_{ro} = \left(P_{out,VIS} + P_{out,NIR}\right)/P_{in} = \left(P_{ro,VIS} + P_{ro,NIR}\right) = \eta_{o-VIS} + \eta_{o-NIR} \quad (1)$$

where $P_{out,VIS/NIR}$ is the spectrally integrated optical power counted at the VIS/NIR detectors (representing the optical power reaching the solar cells), P_{in} is the spectrally integrated optical power at the input surface. The electrical performance is evaluated by computing the PCE as:

$$PCE =$$
$$= P_{out-Total,el}/P_{in,opt} = \qquad (2)$$
$$= ((I_{sc}V_{oc}FF)_{Si} + (I_{sc}V_{oc}FF)_{GaAs})/P_{in,opt}$$

where the short-circuit current is assumed to be equal to photocurrent at the cell and expressed as:

$$I_{sc} = \int_{selected\ spectrum} PhotonFlux_{cell}(\lambda) \cdot EQE(\lambda)d\lambda. \qquad (3)$$

The PhotonFlux at the specific cell in Eq. (3) is computed by dividing the spectral power density at the cell by the photon energy at each selected wavelength (λ).

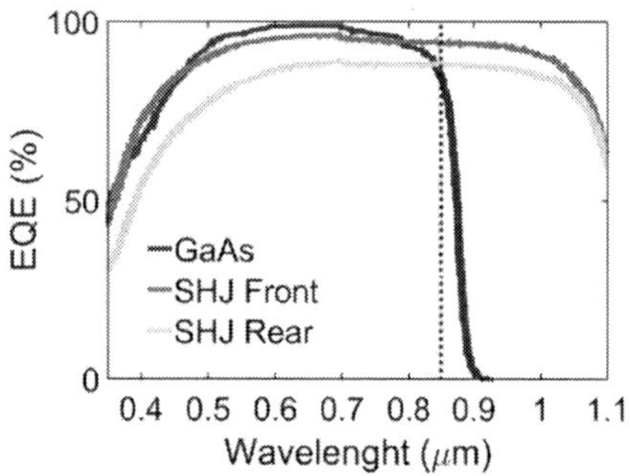

Figure 3: Plot of the EQE(λ) for the two cells and of the transmittance spectra for the dichroic mirrors.

3 RESULTS

The ray-tracing of VIS and IR diffuse light (green and black lines respectively) propagating in the wedged optics is shown in Fig. 4.

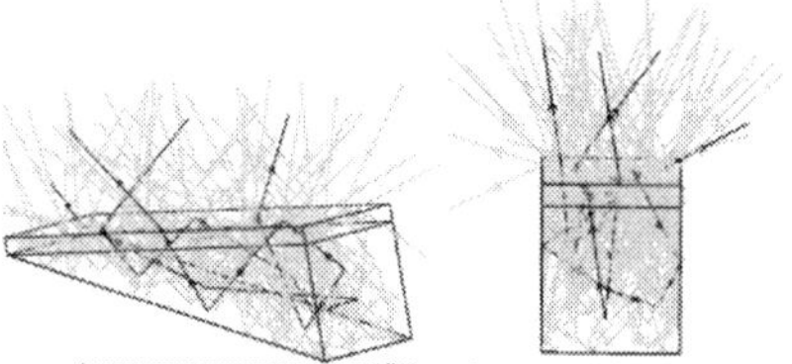

Figure 4: Ray tracing of diffuse light inside the wedged optics. Dichroic mirrors are embedded into the back and bottom sides. The E-W view shows confinement of skew rays.

The East-West view clearly shows how skew rays are confined inside the wedge. Some optical loss occurs at the top surface, due to those rays that do not undergo TIR. Differently from what happens in case of direct irradiation, the performance for diffuse irradiation at top surface is insensitive to sun elevation and to tilt angle. Instead, it still depends on the amplitude of the apex angle of the wedge, φ, which contributes to define θ_{iL} and the rate of input rays confinement by TIR. Depending on the choice of apex angle φ, optical power ratios have been obtained: for $\varphi = 25°$, $P_{ro,VIS} = 22\%$ and $P_{ro,NIR} = 42\%$ which amounts to total collection yield of diffused light equal to $P_{ro} = 64\%$.

The results for PCE are summarized in Tables I and II,

when considering both diffuse spectra, clear-sky and overcast, and different values for the apex angle φ (first column on the left). The values of output electrical power $P_{out,el}$ obtained on each solar cell are listed and summed up. In case of clear sky diffuse spectrum, input optical power is set at $P = 169mW$, corresponding to a fraction of 11% of the global irradiation over an illumination area at input equal to 15cm^2; for overcast spectrum the input optical power is estimated in $P = 226mW$, corresponding to a fraction of 35% of a global irradiation estimated in 42 mW/cm^2, over an illumination area at input equal to 15cm^2.

Table I: Computed Power Conversion Efficiency of the PV solution for diffuse irradiation (clear sky conditions)

	ASTM G-173 reference spectrum			
φ	$P_{out,el}\,(mW)$		T-$P_{out,el}(mW)$	PCE$_{diff}$
	Si	GaAs		
14.5°	16	21	37	22%
25°	15	27	42	25%
30°	16	35	51	30%
35°	15	38	53	31%
40°	15	42	58	34%
45°	15	42	58	34%

Table II: Computed Power Conversion Efficiency of the PV solution for diffuse irradiation (measured overcast spectrum)

	Overcast spectrum			
φ	$P_{out,el}\,(mW)$		T-$P_{out,el}(mW)$	PCE$_{diff}$
	Si	GaAs		
14.5°	39	35	74	33%
25°	37	45	82	36%
30°	41	59	100	44%
35°	37	64	101	45%
40°	37	72	109	48%
45°	37	72	109	48%

The rightmost columns report the global PCE of the diffuse fraction, respectively for the two input irradiation conditions. We notice that $\varphi = 14.5°$ corresponds to a $C_g \approx 4$ for VIS light, while at $\varphi = 45°$ no concentration occurs. The increase in $P_{out,el|GaAs}$ as the angle φ increases, is motivated by the fact that an increase in φ corresponds to a decrease in $C_{g|VIS}$ and, correspondingly, to the widening of the angular acceptance of the concentrator. In turn, this increases the photon flux at the cells and $I_{sc|GaAs}$, as can be expressed by Eq. 3. On the contrary, the $P_{out,el|Si}$ in the IR does not substantially change by increasing angle φ. Both input spectra show equivalent behaviors, with a saturation occurring for $\varphi > 40°$. Under the present conditions the PCE for the diffuse light component of input irradiation amounts up to 34% for blue-sky conditions and up to 48% for the overcast spectrum. If we recall however the fact that the assumptions underlying the choice of the size of the lower leg of the wedge prism, and therefore the size of the angle φ, are the dimensions of the high bandgap solar cell (here made of GaAs) we can set most probable conditions of $\varphi \leq 30°$. This in turn defines PCE values around 30% and 44% for the two spectral inputs. Evidently, the final contribution of PCE for diffuse light to the global PCE has to be rated by the fraction of diffuse irradiation over the total, in the specific weather condition.

4   CONCLUSIONS

A "solar tile" has been designed, also appealing for bifacial operation and that leverages the energy yield of diffuse irradiation component, in dependence on the performance of the VIS solar cell. It is conceived as a spectral-splitting 4-Terminal element, working as a LCPV in the VIS and its performance has been numerically evaluated. As a demonstration case, by assuming a SHJ bifacial cell for the NIR and a commercial GaAs cell for the VIS, in case of $\varphi = 25°$, the conversion efficiency of the diffused portion of input power is PCE_{diff} of 25% in case of clear sky diffused component (mostly Rayleigh scattering) and of 36% in case of typical overcast conditions. The case of $\varphi = 30°$ improves PCE_{diff} to 30% in case of clear sky and to 44% in case of overcast conditions. Further increase of φ might slightly improve PCE_{diff} up to saturation, coping with the thermodynamic limit (as shown in Table 1) but it is considered that the consequent aspect ratio of the PV element would lead to cost inefficiencies in manufacturing.

REFERENCES
[1] International Energy Agency (IEA). NetZeroby2050: A Roadmap for the Global Energy Sector. Paris (2023).
[2] A.B. Block, *et al.*, Energy Build. 314 (2024) 114253.
[3] W. Shockley and H.J.Queisser, J. Appl. Phys. 32 (1961) 510.
[4] M. Yamaguchi, *et al.*, J. Appl. Phys. 129 (2021) 240901.
[5] S. Rühle, *et al.*, J. Renew. Sustain. Energy. 1 (2009) 013106.
[6] A. Farina, *et al.*, Prog. Photovolt. Res. Appl. 31 (2023) 1299.
[7] F. Morabito *et al.*, Energies 18 (2025) 2044.
[8] G. Grasso *et al.*, Solar Energy 86 (2012) 1725.

ACKNOWLEDGMENTS
Present work has been funded by CNR-UVR AMICO2_PoC, through Next Generation EU PoC 2022 - PNRR (MIMIT-UIBM Mission 1 Component 2 Investment 6).

GAAS FOR THERMOPHOTONICS:
FROM THIN-FILM SOLAR CELLS TO HIGHLY EFFICIENT LEDS

N atasha Gruginskie[1], Peter Mulder[1], Gerard Bauhuis[1], Jani Oksanen[2], John Schermer[1]
[1]Radboud University – Nijmegen, The Netherlands; [2]Aalto University – Espoo, Finland
natasha.gruginskie@ru.nl

ABSTRACT: Thermophotonics (TPX) is a technology field that stems from thermophotovoltaics (TPV), in which the hot body of a conventional TPV system is replaced by a hot light-emitting diode (LED). Unlike a TPV system, the radiation from the emitter can be made super-thermal by electrically biasing the hot LED, enabling it to radiate more power than predicted by Planck's law. However, the realization of such a system requires the suppression of most of the non-radiative losses in the LED and extremely efficient light coupling to the photovoltaic absorber (PV). The high quality achieved by GaAs-based devices in the recent years and the advances in the LED industry indicate that this may now be achieved. This study presents the objectives of the *TPX-Power project*, a project that aims to investigate the feasibility of waste thermal energy recovery using TPX devices with the currently available and emerging semiconductor technologies. The experimental challenges associated with applying the well-established fabrication of III-V thin-film solar cells into the modified devices required for the realization of the TPX devices will be explored, and preliminary results will be shown. Finally, an overview of the required steps to fully develop this technology will be discussed.
Keywords: Light emitting diodes; Thermophotonics; III-V semiconductors; Thin-film devices.

1 INTRODUCTION

Light emitting diodes (LEDs) have long been known to convert ambient heat into emitted light [1-3]. This dual contribution to light generation opens up new possibilities for energy harvesting, particularly in the context of thermophotonic (TPX) systems, but yet the practical utilization of this effect has been limited due to the quality of the material and ohmic losses. In recent years, however, improvements in material quality and electronics fabrication suggest that TPX power conversion may now be feasible, and LEDs that convert more energy into light than the supplied electric energy have been recently demonstrated with cooling powers below 50 pW [4].

By combining a heated LED with a photovoltaic cell (PV) kept at a lower temperature, the emitted light can be captured and converted into electricity, as depicted in **Error! Reference source not found.** [5,6]. The project presented in this study aims to extend this concept to high power densities, in the range of 10-100 W/cm^2, and to demonstrate the proof-of-concept for a technology that converts thermal energy into electricity, making it ideal for industrial waste-heat reuse [7, 8]. To achieve this, highly efficient GaAs LEDs and (In)GaAs PV cells are developed. Limited literature exists on the fabrication of highly efficient GaAs LEDs or on the near-field coupling of real-life devices in this manner. This study will, therefore, outline a roadmap and the key technical challenges in developing this groundbreaking energy reuse technology.

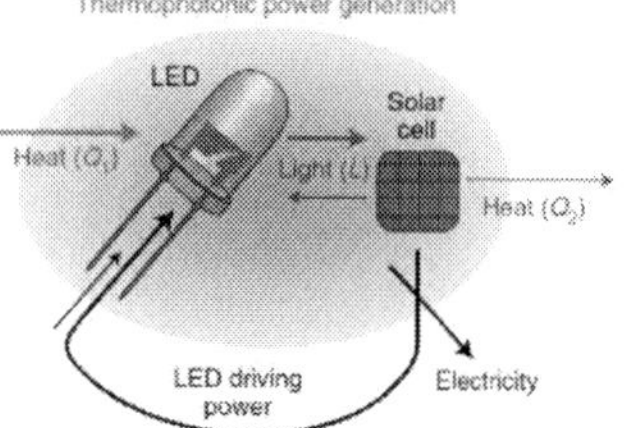

Figure 1: Schematic depiction of the thermophotonic power generation mechanism

2 MATERIALS AND METHODS

To realize these TPX devices, it is necessary to minimize all losses in the LED, as well as to maximize the light extraction and coupling to the PV component. In this context, GaAs LEDs are preferred due to their superior material quality and their high efficiency. The standard LED structure consists of a *p-i-n* junction with intrinsic GaAs as the active layer, sandwiched by two (*p*- and *n*-) InGaP confinement layers, as shown in the schematic depiction in **Error! Reference source not found.**a). During this project, several advances to this structure focused on increasing the devices internal radiative efficiency by reducing non-radiative recombination [9] and series resistance, as well as on increasing light extraction with the application of highly reflective scattering mirrors and current spreading layers [10].

The counterpart to the highly efficient LEDs developed in this project is the PV component (**Error! Reference source not found.**b), tailored to absorb nearly all the emitted light. Since the light absorption will be sub-optimal if the devices are completely symmetrical, i.e. if both the LED and the PV devices are GaAs, in this study we lower the bandgap energy of the PV device by introducing an *In* fraction of 9%. The lattice constant of In$_{0.09}$GaAs, however, differs from the GaAs growth wafer, and in order to fabricate devices with high enough efficiencies, a metamorphic buffer is applied. This entails the development of an inverted metamorphic (IMM) thin-film solar cell structure.

Both the LEDs and the solar cells in this study were fabricated similarly to previously reported techniques [11], and their performance is generally characterized by their dark characteristics and electroluminescence (EL) spectra and images.

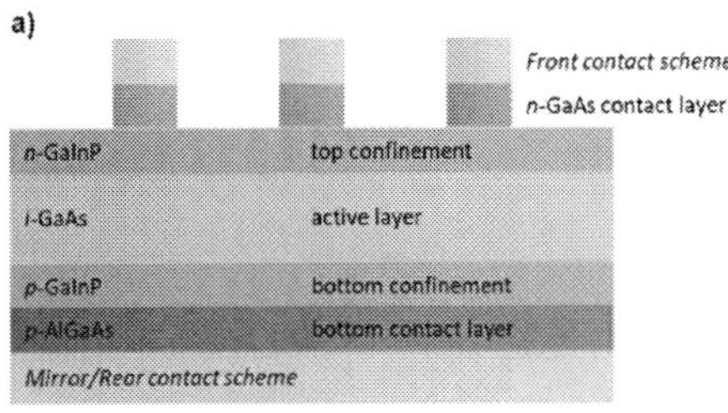

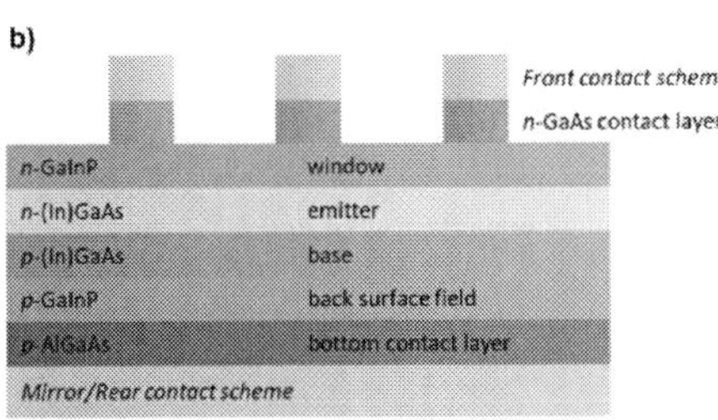

Figure 2: Schematic depiction of a) the basic LED and b) the basic solar cell structure developed in the projects.

3 RESULTS AND DISCUSSION

3.1 LED components

In order to increase light extraction, the application of highly reflective textured mirrors will be necessary, and therefore the rear contact of the LEDs will be patterned [12]. Because the LEDs' active layer is not doped and since the LEDs will be subjected to much higher current densities than solar cells usually operate, current spreading is a limiting mechanism in the LEDs. Several aspects of the front grid characterization and current spreading were discussed van der Krabben et al. [13], and similar considerations must be made to the rear contact when applying a point-contact array.

The dark curves in **Error! Reference source not found.**a) show a large difference in series resistance between the LEDs with planar and patterned rear mirrors, and the EL images show very defined contact points illuminated, indicating that most of the current does not diffuse laterally. A 500 nm highly doped p-InGaP layer was then introduced between the p-contact and bottom confinement layers, and the difference in series resistance between the two mirror architectures is significantly reduced. This is also represented in the more uniform illumination observed in the EL images.

3.2 PV cell component

In parallel to the LEDs development, the PV component must be tailored to absorb nearly 100% of the GaAs emission. The need for IMM (In)GaAs PV cells in this context is illustrated in *Figure 1*, with the external quantum efficiency (EQE) of an inverted lattice matched (ILM) thin-film GaAs solar cell shown together with the EQE of an inverted metamorphic $In_{0.09}GaAs$ cell and the emission spectrum of a standard thin-film GaAs LED at room temperature.

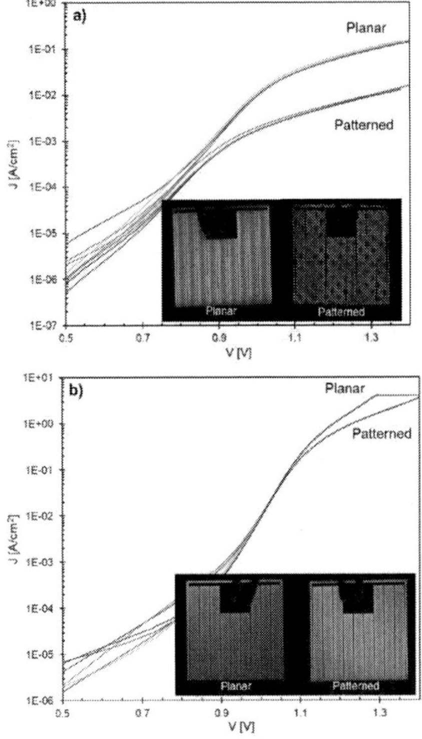

Figure 3: Schematic depiction of a) the basic LED and b) the basic solar cell structure developed in the projects.

The GaAs PV absorption is clearly very low and even zero for a significant portion of the LEDs emission, and this effect increases at higher temperatures, when there is a redshift in the emission peak of LEDs. It is important to note that in the presented curves both PV cells do not have an anti-reflection coating (ARC) applied to the front, and therefore an increase in absorption close to 30% is to be expected. This means that in the wavelength region of interest, the absorption of light by the $In_{0.09}GaAs$ PV with an ARC should be very close to unity.

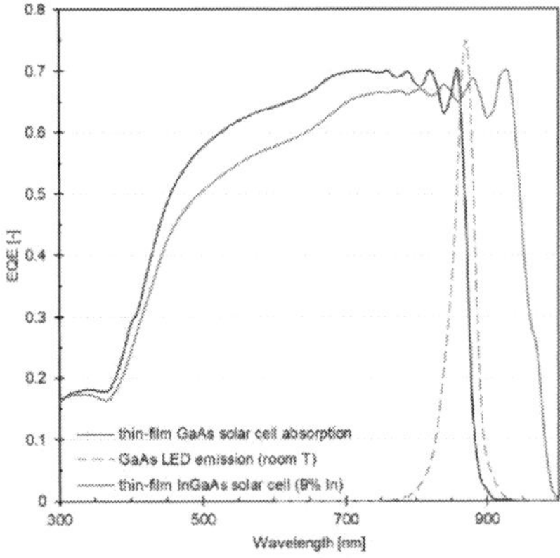

Figure 1: External quantum efficiency (EQE) of a GaAs and an $In_{0.09}GaAs$ solar cells. The emitted spectrum of a standard GaAs LED at room temperature is also depicted.

4   CONCLUSIONS AND OUTLOOK

This study demonstrated the feasibility of adapting thin-film GaAs device technology to thermophotonic applications. The quality of the epitaxial structures has been developed in parallel and pushed close to the limit of non-radiative recombination suppression, an essential step to enable electroluminescence cooling and thermophotonic power generation.

For the LED component, patterned rear mirrors were shown to strongly influence series resistance and current spreading, while the introduction of a p-InGaP current-spreading layer significantly reduced resistive losses while improving emission uniformity. For the PV component, inverted metamorphic $In_{0.09}GaAs$ solar cells were developed, providing the required bandgap offset and demonstrating sufficient spectral overlap with GaAs LED emission.

Taken together, these results establish the key design requirements for efficient TPX devices: suppression of resistive and non-radiative losses and maximization of light extraction While several fabrication bottlenecks have been identified, achieving light extraction efficiencies close to unity remains a major challenge and will be the focus of future work.

ACKNOWLEDGEMENTS

This work was supported by the European Research Council under the Horizon 2020 Future and Emerging Technologies program, under the projects OPTAGON (Grant Agreement No. 964698) and TPX-Power (Grant Agreement No. 951976).

REFERENCES

[1] Tauc, J. Czechoslovak Journal of Physics 7. PII: BF01688028, 275–276. issn: 0011-4626 (1957).

[2] Weinstein, M. A. Journal of the Optical Society of America 50, 597 DOI: 10.1364/JOSA.50.000597 (1960).

[3] Dousmanis, G. C. et al. Physical Review 133, A316–A318. DOI:10.1103/PhysRev.133.A316 (1964).

[4] Santhanam, P.et al. Physical review letters 108. 097403. DOI: 10.1103/PhysRevLett.108.097403 (2012).

[5] Chen, K.et al. Journal of Applied Physics 122, 143104. issn: 0021-8979 (2017).

[6] Zhao, B.et al. Nano letters 18, 5224–5230. eprint: 30016115 (2018).

[7] Sadi, et al. Nature Photonics 14. PII: 600, 205–214. issn: 1749-4885 (2020).

[8] *TPX-Power project* page: https://tpx-power-h2020.eu/

[9] Shahahmadi, S.A. et al. Appl. Phys. Lett. 124, 241105 (2024). DOI: 10.1063/5.0206166.

[10] van der Krabben, L.M. et al. Solar Energy Materials and Solar Cells 292 (2025) 113779. DOI: 10.1016/j.solmat.2025.113779

[11] Gruginskie, N. et al. Thin Solid Films 660 (2018) 10-18. DOI: 10.1016/j.tsf.2018.05.042

[12] van Eerden, M. et al. Prog Photovolt Res Appl. 2020;28:200–209. DOI: 10.1002/pip.3220

[13] van der Krabben, L.M. et al. ACS Appl. Electron. Mater. 2024, 6, 1483–1492. DOI: 10.1021/acsaelm.3c01816

LOW-ENERGY ELECTRON MULTIPLICATION ON NANOSTRUCTURED SOLAR CELLS: A NOVEL ROUTE TO OVERCOME SI-PV EFFICIENCY LIMITS

Mikaël Hosatte[1], Brice Rouffie[1], Zbigniew T. Kuznicki[1], Frédéric Milési[2], Bertrand Paviet-Salomon[3], Audrey Morisset[3], Philippe Wyss[3], Lejo J. Koduvelikulathu[4], Lazhar Rachdi[4], Lacramioara Popescu[4], Dominik Rudolph[4], Marek Basta[5], Andrzej Miszczuk[5], Martyna Majak[5], Beata Basta[5], Samuel Queste[6]

Corresponding author: mikael.hosatte@segton.com

[1] Segton Advanced Technology, 99 Boulevard de la Reine, Versailles 78000, France
[2] CEA-Leti, 17 avenue de Martyrs, 38054 Grenoble, France
[3] CSEM, Rue Jaquet-Droz 1, 2002 Neuchâtel, Switzerland
[4] ISC Konstanz e.V., Rudolf-Diesel-Straße 15, 78467 Konstanz, Germany
[5] Roltec, Swiety Marcin 29/8, Poznan 61-806, Poland
[6] Marie and Louis Pasteur University, 1 Rue Claude Goudimel, 25000 Besançon, France

ABSTRACT: Silicon photovoltaics, while dominating global photovoltaic production, are approaching the Shockley–Queisser efficiency limit. The LEEMONS project, funded by Horizon Europe (Grant 101172870), develops a novel nanostructured solar cell concept based on Low-Energy Electron Multiplication (LEEM). This process enables a single high-energy photon to generate multiple low-energy electrons, thereby reducing thermalisation losses and increasing photocurrent. The consortium integrates advanced ion implantation, annealing and metallisation techniques to demonstrate proof-of-concept prototypes using industrially relevant solar technologies such as heterojunction cells. Early results confirm the fabrication of ion-implanted nanostructured layers, validation of implantation masks and low-temperature metallisation alternatives. LEEMONS offers a scalable, industry-compatible pathway to higher Si-PV efficiencies, with strong alignment to EU goals on renewable energy, climate neutrality and technological sovereignty.
Keywords: Photovoltaics, electron multiplication, nanostructures, ion implantation, silicon solar cells

1 INTRODUCTION AND CONCEPT

Silicon photovoltaics have experienced remarkable cost reductions and global expansion over the past two decades. However, conventional Si solar cells remain constrained by the Shockley–Queisser limit [1]. As a result, further efficiency improvements through incremental advances are limited and new physical concepts are needed to sustain both performance gains and continued cost reductions.

The LEEMONS project (Low-Energy Electron Multiplication on Nanostructured Solar Cells) investigates a novel approach to carrier generation in nanostructured silicon. It is based on the concept of Low-Energy Electron Multiplication (LEEM), where high-energy photons generate multiple low-energy electrons instead of dissipating their excess energy through thermalisation. Nanostructuring is achieved through ion implantation, which locally amorphises the silicon, followed by specialised annealing that induces partial recrystallisation and interface flattening. This process reorganises atoms at the amorphous/crystalline (a-Si/c-Si) interfaces, enhancing electron multiplication through modifications of the electronic energy levels. This mechanism reduces thermalisation losses and enhances photocurrent, offering a disruptive pathway for efficiency improvements in silicon photovoltaics (Si-PV).

In contrast to tandem architectures, LEEM does not rely on new absorber materials and remains fully compatible with established silicon technology. Its scalable fabrication relies on industrial processes such as ion implantation, annealing and passivation, which are already widespread in semiconductor manufacturing.

2 ORGANISATION AND OBJECTIVES

LEEMONS (Project 101172870, Horizon Europe) is a 36-month RIA action running from November 2024 to October 2027. The consortium gathers six European partners across the value chain:

- **Segton Advanced Technology (Coordinator)** – development of the LEEM concept, communication and project management
- **CEA-Leti** – development of ion implantation and annealing processes
- **ISC Konstanz** – integration of LEEM layers into c-Si solar cells and optimisation
- **CSEM** – adaptation to back-contact solar cell architectures and characterisation
- **Roltec** – development of metallisation alternatives, lifetime studies, characterisation and simulation
- **Marie and Louis Pasteur University** – fabrication of silicon masks by Deep Reactive Ion Etching (RIE)

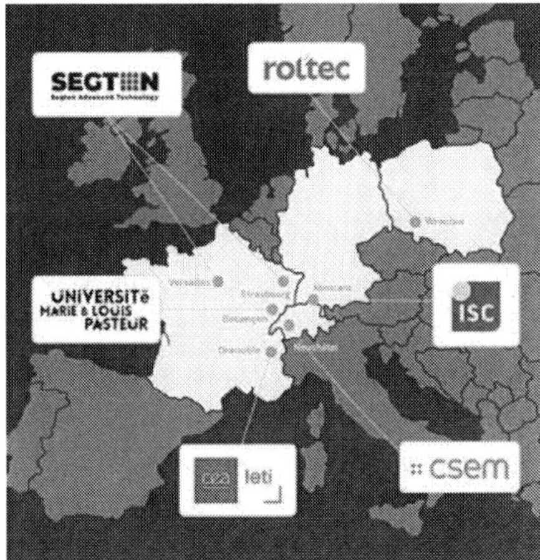

Figure 1: Overview of the LEEMONS partners.

Objectives:

1. Prototype a game-changing photovoltaic innovation through nanotechnology
2. Demonstrate lab-scale proof-of-concept devices on PERC and HJT cells.
3. Ensure high compatibility with industrial Si PV lines (80–95%).
4. Deliver cost-effective, sustainable solutions aligned with EU climate neutrality and strategic autonomy

3 TECHNOLOGY

The LEEMONS technology builds on the principle of LEEM in ion-implanted nanostructures embedded in crystalline silicon. Instead of dissipating the excess energy of above-bandgap photons as heat, impact ionisation generates multiple electron–hole pairs per absorbed photon. This mechanism directly enhances the photocurrent and reduces thermalisation losses, offering a fundamentally new route to surpass the efficiency limits of conventional Si-PV.

In contrast to tandem architectures or external conversion layers (based on photon up- or down-conversion), LEEM is fully compatible with crystalline silicon. It requires no additional absorber materials and relies on established industrial processes such as ion implantation, annealing and low-temperature metallisation. These features position LEEM as a scalable and cost-effective innovation pathway, building on the strengths of mature Si-PV manufacturing.

3.1 Fundamental Principle of Electron Multiplication

Electron multiplication in semiconductors is generally associated with impact ionisation [2], where a high-energy carrier generates a secondary electron–hole pair once its kinetic energy exceeds a threshold. In bulk silicon, the probability of such events is low due to rapid carrier thermalisation. By introducing nanostructured regions with controlled disorder and confinement, the LEEM approach modifies scattering dynamics and increases the probability of secondary pair generation before thermalisation occurs.

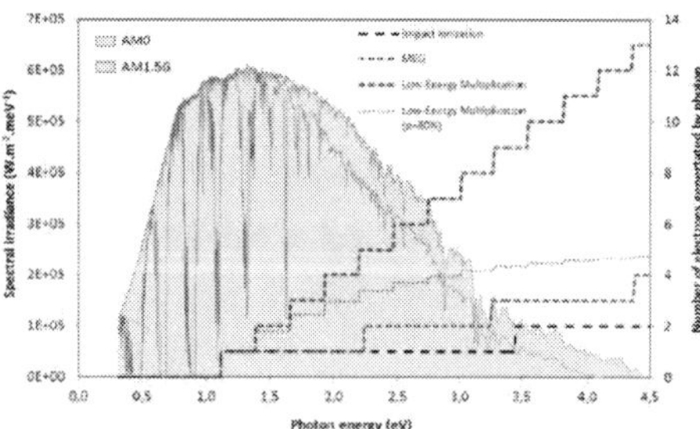

Figure 2: Theoretical comparison between impact ionisation, Multiple Exciton Generation (MEG) [3-5] and the LEEM mechanism. The staircase-like curves represent the stepwise increase in electrons per photon as photon energy rises. In the LEEM scenario, assuming a constant probability of secondary generation of 80%, the average carrier multiplication exceeds that of standard impact ionisation. Standard reference solar spectra AM0 and AM1.5G [6] are indicated in light green and light blue

respectively.

3.2 Nanostructuring by Ion Implantation

The enabling step of the LEEM concept is the controlled introduction of amorphised silicon (a-Si) nanolayers within a c-Si matrix. This is achieved by ion implantation at carefully selected energies and doses, followed by annealing. The process generates buried amorphised regions, which may be continuous or spatially modulated, acting as active sites for carrier multiplication. Subsequent annealing partially recrystallises the matrix, stabilising the nanostructures while preserving their electronic functionality.

Transmission electron microscopy (TEM) confirms the structural integration of these buried layers. Preliminary experiments at CEA-Leti have demonstrated discontinuous nanometre-scale layers without compromising the crystalline quality of the surrounding silicon. Such precise nanostructuring within standard wafers represents a key innovation of LEEMONS, leveraging microelectronics-derived implantation tools for photovoltaic applications.

3.3 Precision Implantation Using Hard Masks

Efficient LEEM layers require nanostructuring that supports electronic transport while enabling carrier multiplication. Electrical carriers must be able to cross the amorphised silicon regions through crystalline passages and the feature sizes must remain small since hot electrons in silicon thermalise extremely rapidly, within tens to a few hundred femtoseconds [7]. This ultrafast relaxation imposes strict constraints on the spatial scale of implanted features. To meet these requirements, LEEMONS employs hard masks for ion implantation. Two complementary approaches are being developed:

- Ultra-thin silicon masks, fabricated at UMLP using Deep Reactive Ion Etching (RIE). These masks, with ~10 μm apertures, enable the definition of patterned implantation zones over large wafer areas.

- Metallic mesh masks, consisting of ~7 μm-wide metallic wires assembled into large-area meshes. These masks are robust and compatible with industrial wafer sizes.

Compared to conventional photoresist patterning, hard masks avoid surface contamination and damage while enabling discontinuous implantation at scale. Early results demonstrate that such masks can generate buried amorphised layers with periodicity, enabling reproducible definition of electron multiplication zones.

3.4 Integration into Device Architectures

For LEEM technology to demonstrate its industrial impact, it must be integrated into the mainstream silicon solar cell designs that dominate current and emerging production. The project therefore focuses on three representative architectures:

- PERC (Passivated Emitter Rear Contact): long established as a leading industrial architecture, PERC continues to represent a very large share of global production. Its widespread adoption makes it a relevant platform for demonstrating the compatibility of LEEM layers with mass manufacturing.

- HJT (Heterojunction): offering excellent passivation quality and high open-circuit voltages, HJT is increasingly seen as a pathway to higher efficiency. LEEM layers must be integrated in a way that preserves the low-temperature processing conditions required by this architecture.

- IBC-HJT (Interdigitated Back Contact HJT): combining advanced metallisation with the benefits of heterojunction passivation, IBC-HJT represents one of the most promising high-end cell architectures. Demonstrating LEEM compatibility in this configuration paves the way toward next-generation devices.

Across all these device types, the key challenges are to minimise defect-induced recombination, maintain effective passivation and adapt metallisation strategies.

3.5 Metallisation and Passivation Challenges

Metallisation and passivation are critical bottlenecks for LEEM cell integration. Conventional high-temperature metallisation (>400 °C) risks modifying or erasing the implanted nanostructures. To address this, low-temperature alternatives are developed by ISC and Roltec to preserve the integrity of the LEEM layers while delivering high conductivity.

Passivation within the LEEM framework is approached as a coupled materials and process optimisation problem. Investigations consider alternative dielectric layers, modified deposition conditions and engineered interface treatments to accommodate the presence of ion-implanted nanostructures. Particular attention is given to how implantation, annealing and passivation steps interact, since process sequencing strongly influences both carrier lifetimes and structural stability.

Advances in metallisation and passivation are therefore central to validating the feasibility of LEEM integration. Establishing stable and reproducible processes in these areas will define the boundary conditions under which LEEM can be considered alongside other emerging concepts for high-efficiency silicon photovoltaics.

3.6 Advantages over Tandem and Other Novel Concepts

Several approaches are currently being investigated to overcome the efficiency limitations of single-junction silicon solar cells. Tandem devices combine absorbers with different bandgaps and have demonstrated high laboratory efficiencies, but they require the integration of heterogeneous materials, additional interconnection layers and significant modifications to production infrastructure. Photon conversion layers, which aim to modify the incident spectrum through up- or down-conversion processes, remain limited by incomplete conversion efficiencies and coupling losses. Hot-carrier solar cells represent another direction of research, although their practical implementation is hindered by the lack of absorber materials capable of sustaining slow carrier cooling.

The LEEM concept differs from these strategies by altering the response of silicon itself. Ion implantation and thermal treatments create nanostructured regions that enhance impact ionisation and allow multiple charge carriers to be generated from a single high-energy photon. This approach does not rely on supplementary absorbers or external spectral modification, but instead employs processes already established in the semiconductor and photovoltaic industries.

From a manufacturing perspective, this compatibility with existing equipment and process flows is a central advantage. LEEM offers the possibility of enhancing photocurrent generation while maintaining continuity with established crystalline silicon technology, thereby extending the scope of efficiency improvements within a familiar industrial framework.

4 PROGRESS AND RESULTS

4.1 Nanostructured Layer Fabrication

During the first year of the project, ion implantation experiments at CEA-Leti successfully produced discontinuous amorphised silicon layers embedded in crystalline silicon. However, the preliminary silicon masks used to create these discontinuities were not yet optimised. Their rough geometry generated extensive shadowing effects and limited the formation of buried discontinuous amorphised layers, making detection with standard ellipsometry techniques more challenging.

Therefore, complementary characterisation methods such as Raman spectroscopy, backscattered electron spectroscopy and TEM had to be employed to confirm the structural integration of the amorphised layers.

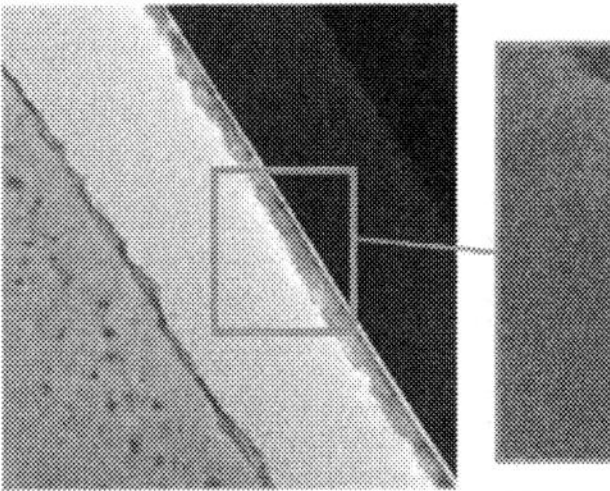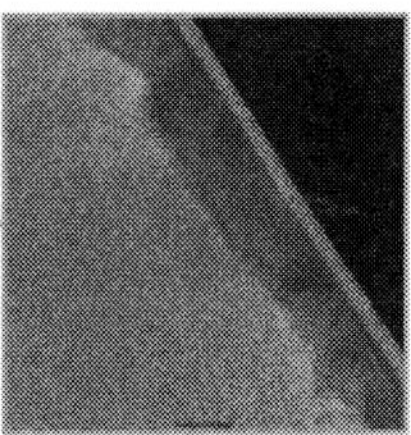

Figure 3: TEM image of an a-Si layer embedded into c-Si by ion implantation for LEEMONS project.

4.2 Hard Mask Development

UMLP developed ultra-thin silicon masks with 10 μm apertures using a deep-RIE process. These masks were successfully tested at CEA-Leti, marking the first validated milestone of the LEEMONS project. Early experiments in Grenoble demonstrated for the first time the feasibility of fabricating discontinuous buried amorphised layers using hard masks with 10 μm apertures.

In parallel, a second masking approach has been designed to enable smaller apertures (up to 7μm) and thinner masks. This method adapts standard metallic stencil printing masks, which are modified and coated to prevent contamination and to operate inside an ion implantation chamber. Production of these metallic mesh masks began in September 2025 in Japan, followed by final assembly in Spain and specialised coating in France.

These hard masks enable discontinuous ion implantation without the need for photoresist deposition and removal, thereby avoiding potential damage to wafers.

Figure 4: Ultra-thin mesh mask (~7μm stainless steel wires) that allows discontinuous ion implantation.

4.3 Low-Temperature Metallisation

At ISC Konstanz, several metallisation alternatives have been investigated to reduce thermal budgets and preserve the integrity of the implanted nanostructures. Initial lab-scale trials included contact resistance measurements across different metallisation pastes and temperature profiles, as well as mini-cell experiments using three test structures with varied diffusions. These experiments provided the first comparative data on how peak firing temperature influences performance.

In parallel, the amorphised nanostructure resistance tests were initiated in September 2025. SEGTON and CEA provided two implanted wafers that were subjected to optimised metallisation temperature curves. Ongoing characterisation will determine the maximum thermal budget that LEEMONS nanostructures can withstand.

Alternative metallisation routes are also under assessment. For example, LECO firing with adapted pastes is planned, although its compatibility with mini-Zebra architectures is still being evaluated due to the back-contact design. These exploratory trials aim to identify metallisation schemes that minimise process temperature while ensuring good electrical contact quality.

Roltec conducted multiple metal contact deposition trials and demonstrated the fabrication of electrodes with ohmic contact on silicon at process temperatures below 100 °C using silver deposition by magnetron sputtering. This approach allows the formation of contacts for Zebra IBC solar cells under low-temperature metallisation conditions, thereby preserving the structural integrity of the LEEMONS nanostructures.

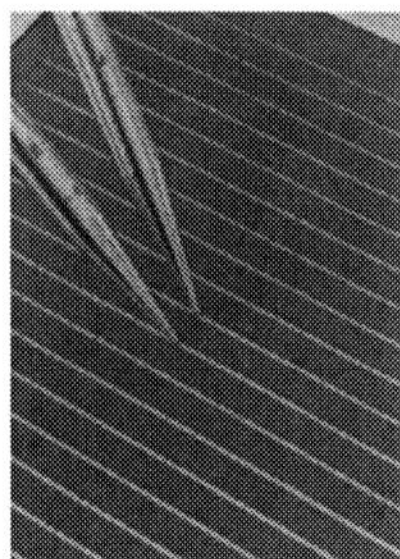

Figure 5: Measuring electrodes on an alternatively metallised sample prepared for LEEMONS.

4.4 Passivation optimisation tests on-going

The first integration steps have combined ion-implanted nanostructured layers with n-type crystalline silicon cells, marking the transition from material-level experiments to device-level validation. Passivation optimisation is currently ongoing at ISC Konstanz and CSEM, with multiple complementary approaches under investigation.

CEA-Leti's July 2025 implantation campaign provided wafers that are now being characterised and prepared for passivation at CSEM. Two diffusion routes are under evaluation: $POCl_3$ diffusion with etch-back and PECVD SiOx:P diffusion, both yielding promising profiles for front surface fields. CSEM has initiated lifetime studies to compare their effectiveness, with first results showing alignment with the LEEMONS concept.

Overall, the passivation optimisation campaign aims to balance effective suppression of recombination with seamless integration into the LEEMONS nanostructuring process, laying the foundation for functional PERC and HJT prototypes in the next phases.

5 IMPACT AND RELEVANCE

The LEEMONS concept addresses critical challenges in the PV industry:

- Sustainability: process relies on recyclable materials and minimises additional steps.
- Industrial compatibility: integration with existing PERC/HJT production lines avoids costly infrastructure changes.
- EU policy alignment: supports strategic autonomy and climate neutrality targets.

If successful, LEEMONS could extend the relevance of Si-PV, enabling higher efficiencies without the complexity of tandems and positioning Europe at the forefront of next-generation solar innovation.

6 CONCLUSIONS

LEEMONS introduces a fundamentally novel PV concept based on low-energy electron multiplication in nanostructured silicon. Initial progress validates ion implantation masks, amorphised layers and metallisation alternatives, laying the groundwork for full device integration. The upcoming project phases will focus on integrating LEEM layers into PERC and HJT prototypes, benchmarking performance and assessing scalability.

By coupling scientific innovation with industrial relevance, LEEMONS aims to deliver a disruptive, cost-effective pathway to higher Si-PV efficiency and long-term sustainability.

7 ACKNOWLEDGEMENTS

This project has received funding from the European Union's Horizon Europe research and innovation programme under grant agreement No. 101172870

8 REFERENCES

[1] W. Shockley, H.J. Queisser, "Detailed Balance Limit of Efficiency of p-n Junction Solar Cells," J. Appl. Phys., 32 (1961), 510–519.

[2] Sabine Kolodinski, Jürgen H. Werner, Thomas Wittchen and Hans J. Queisser, "Quantum efficiencies exceeding unity due to impact ionization in silicon solar cells", Appl. Phys. Lett., Vol. 63, (1993), 2405.

[3] A. J. Nozik, "Spectroscopy and Hot Electron Relaxation Dynamics in Semiconductor Quantum Wells and Quantum Dots", Annu. Rev. Phys. Chem., Vol. 52, (2001), 193–231.

[4] D. Timmerman, J. Valenta, K. Dohnalova, W. D. A. M. de Boer and T. Gregorkiewicz, "Step-like enhancement of luminescence quantum yield of silicon nanocrystals", Nature Nanotechnology, Vol. 6, (2011), 710-713.

[5] N. M. Gabor, Z. Zhong, K. Bosnick, J. Park and P. L. McEuen, "Extremely Efficient Multiple Electron-Hole Pair Generation in Carbon Nanotube Photodiodes", Science, Vol. 325, (2009), 1367-1371.

[6] C. A. Gueymard, "SMARTS2, A Simple Model of the Atmospheric Radiative Transfer of Sunshine: Algorithms and performance assessment", Florida Solar Energy Center Report, (1995).

[7] A Sieradzki, M Basta, P Scharoch and J-Y Bigot, "Ultrafast Optical Properties of Dense Electron Gas in Silicon Nanostructures", Plasmonics, Vol. 9, No. 3, (2014), 545-551.

TAILORING CBTSSE SOLAR CELLS FOR INDOOR PHOTOVOLTAIC APPLICATIONS

Hitarth Narsi Patel*, Bindu Pamula, Deepak Joshi, Vivek Garg
*Optoelectronics2Application (O2A) Research Group, Department of Electronics Engineering,
S. V. National Institute of Technology Surat-395007, India*

ABSTRACT: These Solution-processed $Cu_2BaSn(S,Se)_4$ (CBTSSe) thin films have emerged as promising candidates for next-generation photovoltaics due to their earth-abundant and non-toxic constituents, as well as tunable bandgaps suitable for both outdoor and indoor applications. While significant progress has been made in optimizing CBTSSe-based solar cells for outdoor use, their potential for indoor energy harvesting, particularly for powering IoT devices, remains largely unexplored. This work investigates the performance of a CBTSSe-based device, originally designed for outdoor applications, under indoor light conditions. A baseline simulation model, calibrated against a 6.17% efficient experimental device, was developed using SCAPS. This model incorporates realistic material parameters and interface defect considerations. The absorber layer bandgap was optimized for indoor illumination (1.9 eV) and the impact of absorber thickness and defect density was systematically investigated. Furthermore, the buffer layer was modified by exploring different conduction band offsets and ultimately replacing Zn:CdS with ZnSe to enhance electron transport. Our simulations demonstrate a significant improvement in device performance under indoor WLED illumination (1000K lux), achieving a power conversion efficiency exceeding 30%. This study highlights the potential of CBTSSe as a viable material for high-performance indoor photovoltaics and contributes to the development of self-powered IoT devices
Keywords: CBTS, thin films, indoor photovoltaics, SCAPS

1 INTRODUCTION

Solution processable thin films have attracted significant amount of interest among researchers due to low cost and simple processing techniques. The existing thin film based devices such as CdTe and $CuInGaSe_2$ (CIGS) suffers from toxicity and rare earth element constitutes [1]. Various elemental substitution studies were performed to eliminate the toxic and rare earth elements. It was proposed to replace the rare earth Indium with Zinc and considerable efforts were made to establish a new absorber with Cu_2ZnSnS_4 (CZTS) elemental constituent [2], [3]. Despite tremendous decade long effort to maximize the performance of CZTS devices, the maximum achievable PCE is less than 14% [3]. The performance is effect due to antisite defects which causes band tailing. The effect of antisite defects arises due to similar atomic sizes of elements in CZTS. The elemental substitution of elements with different atomic sizes can mitigate this defect and improve the performance of the devices. Various Density function theory (DFT) studies have been studies to find the potential element to replace Zn in CZTS [4], [5]. It is proposed to replace Zn with Ba which results in an earth abundant and environment friendly material Cu_2BaSnS_4 (CBTS) which has proven in mitigating antisites defects while exhibiting desirable optoelectric properties for photovoltaic application [6], [7], [8]. CBTS has a wide bandgap of 2 eV and by adding selenium to it, the bandgap can be further reduced up to 1.44 eV thus making it suitable for single and multijunction solar cells [9]. $Cu_2BaSn(S,Se)_4$ (CBTSSe) has trigonal structure which deforms to orthorhombic if excess amount of selenium $(X = Se/(Se+S) > 0.75)$ is added to it [10]. The CBTSSe devices made using vacuum processing technique had PCE of 2.68% [11]. Various improvements in the device were proposed which boosted the PCE to 5% [12], [13]. The solution processing route was explored and after optimization, the PCE of 5% was achieved which is comparable to vacuum processed devices [14], [15]. Recently by modifying the cell structure, the PCE solution processed devices reach 6.17% [16]. Significant progress has been made in the development of Internet of Things (IoT) devices, many of

which require low-power operation. Indoor photovoltaics have emerged as a promising energy harvesting solution for these low-power IoT devices, potentially enabling self-powered operation. Consequently, research efforts have focused on identifying suitable materials for indoor solar cells to replace conventional silicon-based cells, which exhibit suboptimal performance in indoor environments. The low bandgap of silicon hinders its ability to effectively harvest energy from indoor light sources. For optimal performance in these environments, a bandgap of approximately 1.9 eV is desired. Materials possessing this bandgap are expected to exhibit maximum PCE. CBTS offer a tunable bandgap ranging from 1.44 to 2 eV, including the ideal 1.9 eV value. This tunability makes CBTS a promising candidate for indoor photovoltaic applications.

This work investigates the potential of a CBTSSe-based device, originally designed for outdoor applications, as an indoor energy harvesting solution. A baseline simulation model of the cell was developed and calibrated in SCAPS to accurately reproduce the performance of a fabricated counterpart, minimizing discrepancies [17]. This calibrated baseline model was then employed to systematically optimize each layer, exploring variations in thickness and defect density, and evaluating alternative materials. The scarcity of research on CBTS device performance in indoor photovoltaic applications highlights the significance of this work, which aims to contribute to the advancement of CBTS-based indoor energy harvesting technologies. The manuscript is further divided into three sections. Section 2 deals with baseline model development, Section 3 has results and discussions and Section 4 is devoted to conclusion of the work.

2 BASELINE MODEL DEVELOPMENT

The baseline model of 6.17% efficient is designed using Solar Cell Capacitance Simulator (SCAPS)[16]. The tool solves Poisson's equation and continuity equations and accurately predicts the performance of the solar cells. In the baseline model, Mo is used as back contact, CBTSSe is the absorber layer, Zn:CdS (ZCS) is the buffer layer, Mg:ZnO (ZMO) is the window layer, and Al:ZnO (AZO) is the front transparent conductive oxide (TCO) layer (Fig. 1(a)). The performance of the baseline model matches with the experimental device with minimal error. The baseline model is designed with material parameters listed in [18].

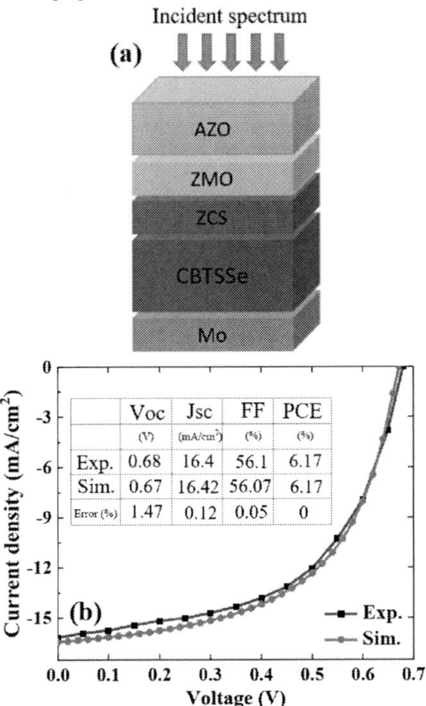

	Voc	Jsc	FF	PCE
	(V)	(mA/cm²)	(%)	(%)
Exp.	0.68	16.4	56.1	6.17
Sim.	0.67	16.42	56.07	6.17
Error (%)	1.47	0.12	0.05	0

Fig. 1(a): Schematic of CBTSSe cell structure, (b) J-V characteristics of experimental and simulated devices.

The interface defects were added at Absorber – Buffer interface to include the effect of surface recombination of charge carriers at the junction. The effect of reflectance encountered at the TCO is also added in the model [16]. The J-V characteristics of both, experimental and simulated cell, with standard AM 1.5G illumination with 1000 W/m² are shown in Fig. 1(b).

3 RESULTS AND DISCUSSION

3.1 Absorber layer optimization

The bandgap of CBTSSe can be tuned from 1.44 to 2 eV by modifying the composition ratio of S and Se (Fig. 2(a)) [18]. The baseline model is subject to indoor illumination of WLED spectrum with 1000K lux. The indoor spectrum has incident power of 53.31 W/m². The bandgap of absorber layer is set to 1.9 eV which is the optimum bandgap for indoor photovoltaics applications [19]. The performance of the cell are noted as PCE = 19.85%, Open circuit voltage (Voc) = 0.91 V, Short circuit current density (Jsc) = 1.66 mA/cm², and Fill factor (FF) = 69.61%.Optimizing absorber layer thickness and defect density is crucial for high-performance solar cells. High defect densities introduce trap states, increasing charge carrier recombination and consequently degrading device performance.

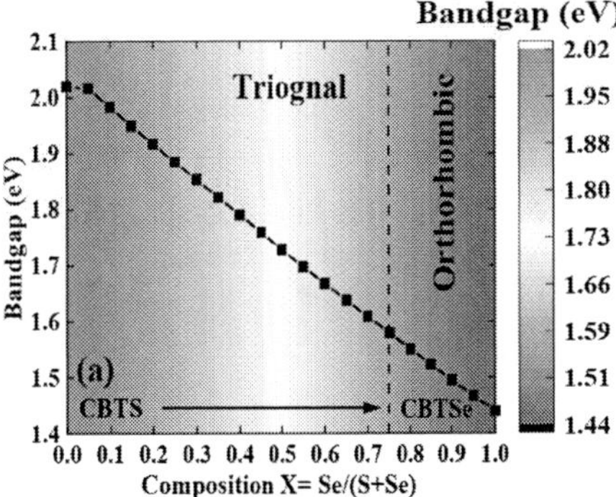

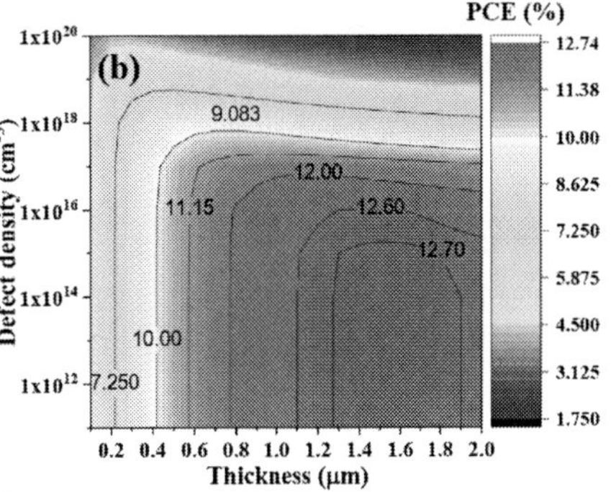

Fig. 2(a) Variation in Eg due to variation in X, (b) Effect on PCE due to variation in defect density and thickness of absorber layer

Defect density is inversely related to both carrier lifetime and diffusion length. While a thicker absorber layer promotes deeper light penetration and higher charge generation, these photo generated carriers must traverse the entire layer without recombining, a process governed by their diffusion length. Excessively thick absorbers can exhibit reduced fill factors due to increased bulk resistance encountered by carriers during transport. Therefore, absorber thickness is fundamentally limited by the carrier diffusion length. Since defect density directly influences diffusion length, it and absorber thickness are interdependent parameters requiring careful co-optimization. Both the parameters, thickness and defect density, are simultaneously varied from 0.1 to 2 µm and 10^{10} to 10^{20} cm⁻³, and the results are shown as contour plot in Fig. 2(b). From the plot the optimized thickness and defect density are found to be 1.5 µm and 10^{14} cm⁻³ respectively. This optimization balances the benefits of increased light absorption with the detrimental effects of increased recombination, ultimately determining the overall performance of the solar cell. With these modification, the PCE of the cell is boosted to 22.42% with Voc = 0.93 V, Jsc =1.74 mA/cm², and FF =73.66%.

3.2 Buffer layer modification

Buffer layer plays an important role in determining the performance of the cell. Buffer layer must ensure smoother movement of electrons and block the holes towards the front junction. The conduction band offset (CBO) analysis is performed to study the effect band alignment on performance of the cell. CBO is defined as the difference between the electron affinity of absorber and buffer layer.

The positive value of CBO exhibits a cliff structure which allows the electrons to flow from absorber layer to buffer layer and block the movement of the holes. Negative value of CBO generates spikes at the absorber-buffer junction which creates a barrier for the electrons to move toward the front contact and encourages their recombination.

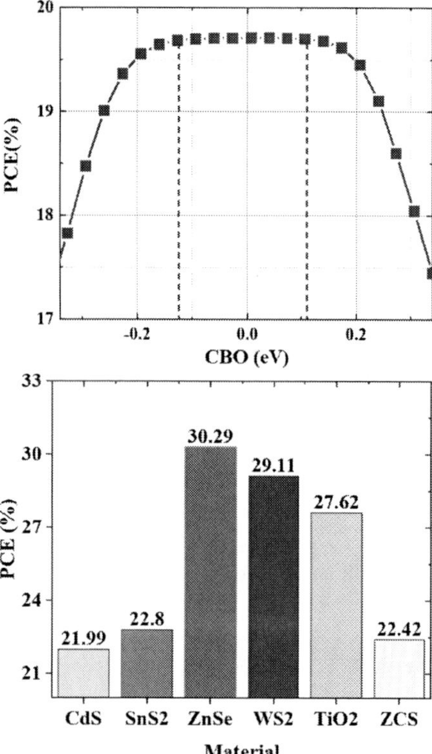

Fig. 3(a) Effect on PCE due to variation in CBO, (b) PCE of cells with various buffer layers

We vary CBO from -0.34 to 0.34 eV and its effect on the PCE of the cell is shown in Fig 3(a). The PCE of the cell shows minimal variation for the range of CBO values allowing an opportunity to replace the existing buffer layer with any alternate material whose electron affinity lies within the range. We investigated several promising electron transport layer (ETL) materials [20], [21] and propose replacing the existing ZCS with ZnSe to enhance the performance of the device (Fig. 3(b)). ZnSe has high doping density in order of 10^{19} cm^{-3} resulting in strong electric field. This field facilitates efficient charge carrier drift across the junction, minimizing recombination losses and enhancing overall device performance. The cell with structure as Mo/CBTSSe/ZnSe/ZMO/AZO has PCE of 30.29% with Voc = 1.12 V, Jsc =1.76 mA/cm^2, and FF =74.55%.

4 CONCLUSION

In this work, we have successfully demonstrated the potential of CBTSSe-based solar cells for high-performance indoor photovoltaic applications. Starting with a calibrated baseline model that accurately reflects the performance of a fabricated device, we systematically optimized the cell structure for indoor light conditions. Our investigations revealed the importance of tuning the absorber layer bandgap to 1.9 eV for optimal indoor performance. Through careful co-optimization of absorber thickness and defect density, we achieved a significant boost in efficiency. Furthermore, the modification of the buffer layer by replacing ZCS with ZnSe, enabled by an analysis of conduction band offset, led to a substantial improvement in charge transport and a further enhancement in device performance. Our simulations demonstrate a remarkable power conversion efficiency exceeding 30% under indoor WLED illumination. This research contributes to the growing field of indoor photovoltaics and paves the way for the development of self-powered devices for a sustainable future.

REFERENCES

[1] A. Wang, M. He, M. A. Green, K. Sun, and X. Hao, "A Critical Review on the Progress of Kesterite Solar Cells: Current Strategies and Insights," *Adv Energy Mater*, p. 2203046, Nov. 2022

[2] W. Wang *et al.*, "Device Characteristics of CZTSSe Thin-Film Solar Cells with 12.6% Efficiency," *Adv Energy Mater*, vol. 4, no. 7, p. 1301465, May 2014.

[3] D. B. Mitzi, O. Gunawan, T. K. Todorov, K. Wang, and S. Guha, "The path towards a high-performance solution-processed kesterite solar cell," *Solar Energy Materials and Solar Cells*, vol. 95, no. 6, pp. 1421–1436, Jun. 2011.

[4] C. Wang *et al.*, "Design of I 2 –II–IV–VI 4 Semiconductors through Element Substitution: The Thermodynamic Stability Limit and Chemical Trend," *Chemistry of Materials*, vol. 26, no. 11, pp. 3411–3417, Jun. 2014.

[5] S. Lie, M. Guc, V. Tunuguntla, V. Izquierdo-Roca, S. Siebentritt, and L. H. Wong, "Comprehensive physicochemical and photovoltaic analysis of different Zn substitutes (Mn, Mg, Fe, Ni, Co, Ba, Sr) in CZTS-inspired thin film solar cells," *J Mater Chem A Mater*, vol. 10, no. 16, pp. 9137–9149, 2022.

[6] F. Hong, *et al.*, "Trigonal Cu 2 -II-Sn-VI 4 (II = Ba, Sr and VI = S, Se) quaternary compounds for earth-abundant photovoltaics," *Physical Chemistry Chemical Physics*, vol. 18, no. 6, pp. 4828–4834, 2016.

[7] B. Teymur *et al.*, "Optoelectronic and material properties of solution-processed Earth-abundant Cu2BaSn(S, Se)4 films for solar cell applications," *Nano Energy*, vol. 80, p. 105556, Feb. 2021.

[8] J. Ge and Y. Yan, "Synthesis and characterization of photoelectrochemical and photovoltaic Cu2BaSnS4 thin films and solar cells," *J Mater Chem C Mater*, vol. 5, no. 26, pp. 6406–6419, Jul. 2017.

[9] J. Ge, Y. Yu, and Y. Yan, "Earth-abundant trigonal BaCu 2 Sn(Se x S 1−x) 4 (x = 0–0.55) thin films with tunable band gaps for solar water splitting," *J. Mater. Chem. A*, vol. 4, no. 48, pp. 18885–18891, 2016.

[10] J. Ge, Y. Yu, and Y. Yan, "Earth-Abundant Orthorhombic BaCu 2 Sn(Se x S 1− x) 4 (x ≈ 0.83) Thin Film for Solar Energy Conversion," *ACS Energy Lett*, vol. 1, no. 3, pp. 583–588, Sep. 2016.

[11] Y. Kim and D. B. Mitzi, "Growth and Photovoltaic Device Application of Cu2BaGe1−xSnxSe4 Films Prepared by Selenization of Deposited Precursors," *ACS Appl Eng Mater*, vol. 4, no.10, pp.11528–11536, Oct. 2021.

[12] D. Shin, E *et al.*, "Synthesis and Characterization of an Earth-Abundant Cu 2 BaSn(S,Se) 4 Chalcogenide for

Photoelectrochemical Cell Application," *J Phys Chem Lett*, vol. 7, no. 22, pp. 4554–4561, Nov. 2016.

[13]D. Shin, *et al.*, "Earth-Abundant Chalcogenide Photovoltaic Devices with over 5% Efficiency Based on a Cu $_2$ BaSn(S,Se) $_4$ Absorber," *Advanced Materials*, vol. 29, no. 24, p. 1606945, Jun. 2017.

[14]B. Teymur, *et al.*,"Influence of Copper Composition on Cu$_2$BaSn(S,Se)$_4$ Solution-Deposited Films and Photovoltaic Devices with Over 5% Efficiency," *ACS Appl Eng Mater*, vol. 5, no. 9, pp. 10645–10656, Sep. 2022.

[15]B. Teymur, *et al.*, "Solution-Processed Earth-Abundant Cu $_2$ BaSn(S,Se) $_4$ Solar Absorber Using a Low-Toxicity Solvent," *Chemistry of Materials*, vol. 30, no. 17, pp. 6116–6123, Sep. 2018.

[16]B. Teymur, *et al.*, "Top Stack Optimization for Cu $_2$ BaSn(S, Se) $_4$ Photovoltaic Cell Leads to Improved Device Power Conversion Efficiency beyond 6%," *Adv Energy Mater*, p. 2201602, Sep. 2022.

[17]M. Burgelman, *et al.*, "Modeling thin-film PV devices," *Progress in Photovoltaics: Research and Applications*, vol. 12, no. 23, pp. 143–153, Mar. 2004.

[18]H. N. Patel, *et al.*, "Bandgap engineering of earth-abundant Cu2BaSn(S1-xSex)4 for photovoltaic application: A systematic approach to double grading," *Solar Energy Materials and Solar Cells*, vol. 269, p. 112792, Jun. 2024.

[19]S. Mishra *et al.*, "Solution-processed next generation thin film solar cells for indoor light applications," *Energy Advances*, vol. 1, no. 11, pp. 761–792, 2022.

[20]A. Rumberg, *et al.*, "ZnSe buffer prepared by iodine-enhanced chemical vapour deposition for Cu(In,Ga)(Se,S)-based solar cells," *Solar Energy Materials and Solar Cells*, vol. 75, no. 1–2, pp. 1–8, Jan. 2003.

[21]H. N. Patel, *et al.*,, "Elucidating the Potential Strategies for Performance Improvement of CBTSSe-Based Solar Cells: A Pathway Toward 20% Efficiency," *Energy Technology*, vol. 12, no. 4, Apr. 2024.

Tailoring CBTSSe Solar Cells for Indoor Photovoltaic Applications

Hitarth Narsi Patel , Bindu Pamula, Deepak Joshi , Vivek Garg

Optoelectronics2Application (O2A) Research Group, Department of Electronics Engineering,
S. V. National Institute of Technology Surat-395007, India

Abstract

This study investigates the application of earth-abundant $Cu_2BaSn(S,Se)_4$ (CBTSSe) films for powering IoT devices through indoor photovoltaics. A calibrated SCAPS simulation model was used to optimize the device's performance. We tuned the absorber layer's bandgap to 1.9 eV and replaced the buffer layer with ZnSe to enhance electron transport. The simulations predict a significant improvement, with the PCE exceeding 30% under indoor WLED illumination. This work highlights CBTSSe as a promising material for indoor energy harvesting.

Device structure and simulation methodology

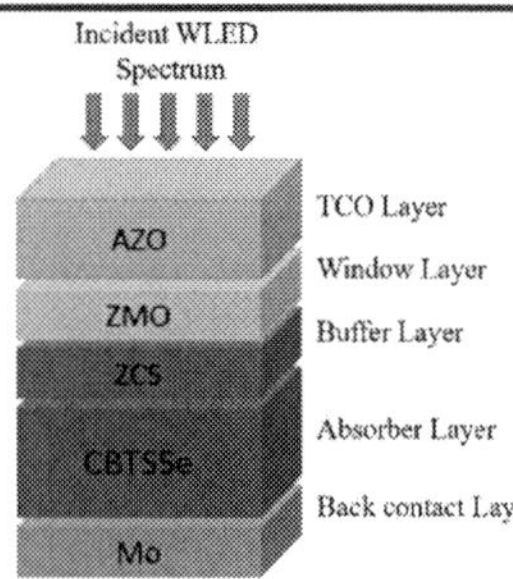

- SCAPS – 1D is used to design the base line model to replicate the behavior of the Simulation device with Experimental cell.
- The baseline model has error less than 1.5%.
- The baseline model is further calibrated to optimize the device.

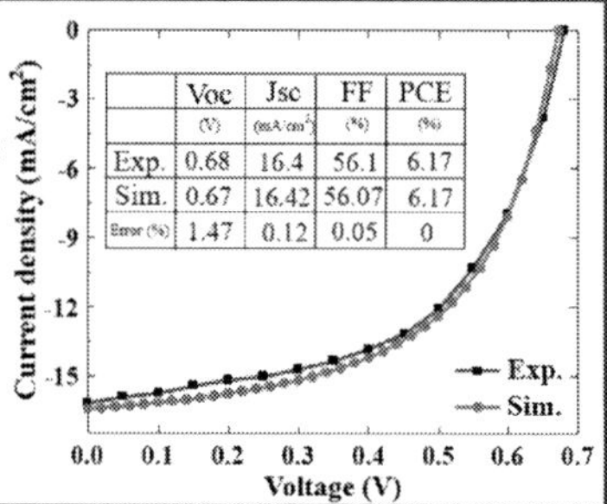

	Voc (V)	Jsc (mA/cm²)	FF (%)	PCE (%)
Exp.	0.68	16.4	56.1	6.17
Sim.	0.67	16.42	56.07	6.17
Error (%)	1.47	0.12	0.05	0

Bandgap optimization

- The Bandgap of CBTSSe is tuned from 1.44 to 2.02 eV by changing composition ratio (X) of S and Se
- CBTSSe shows trigonal structure for X < 0.75 and orthorhombic for X > 0.75.

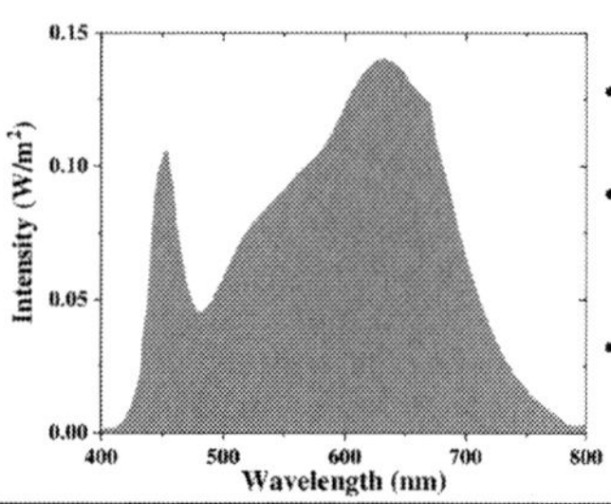

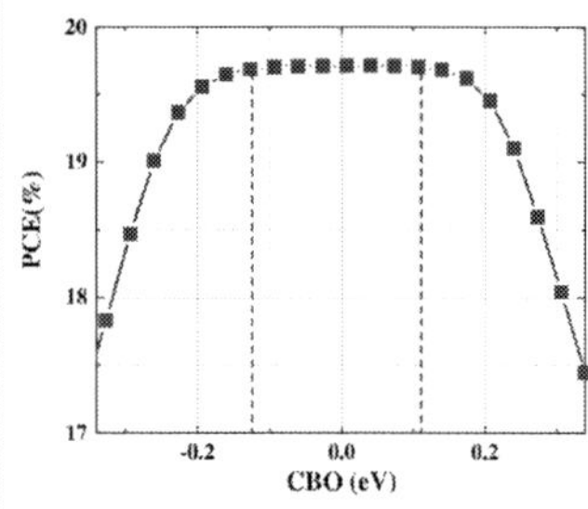

- The spectrum of indoor WLED is different then AM1.5G
- WLED spectrum has strong intensity in Visible - infrared region (600 to 700nm)
- We set the bandgap of CBTSSe to 1.9 eV for optimal spectrum utilization.

Absorber layer optimization

- The Absorber thickness and defect density were simultaneously varied.
- The optimum value of thickness and defect density are found to be 1.5μm and 10^{15} cm⁻³ respectively.

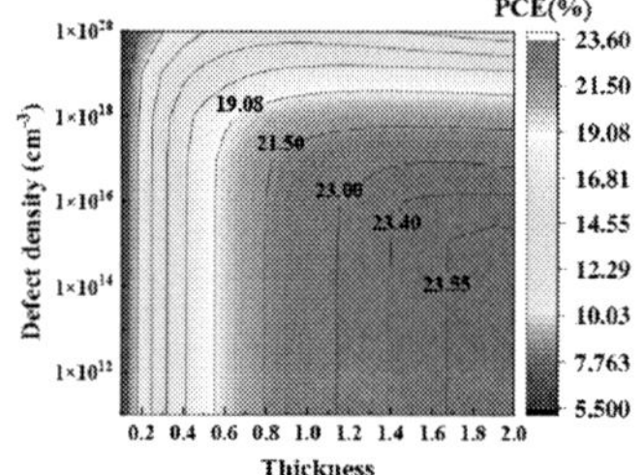

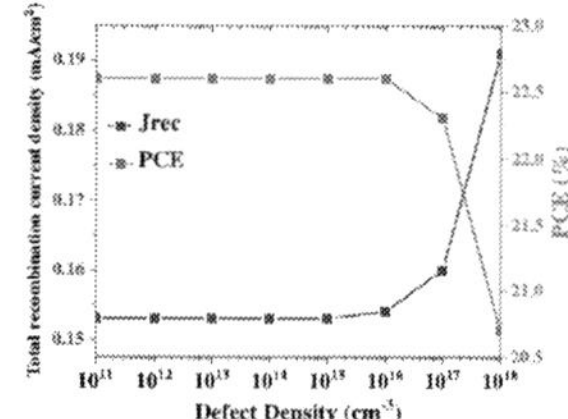

- As the defect density increases, the PCE of the cell reduces and recombination current density increases.

Buffer Layer optimization

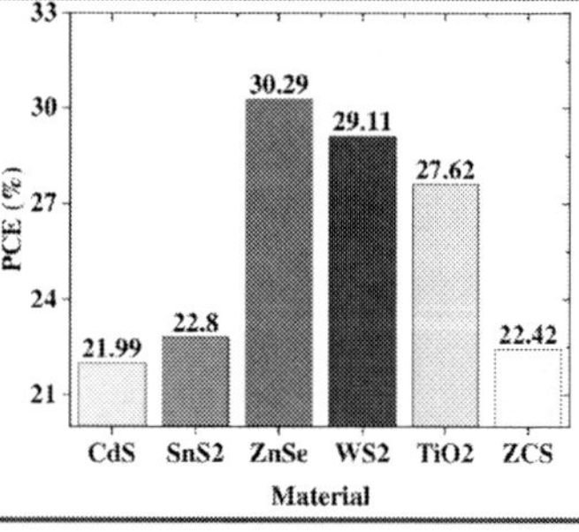

- Conduction band offset (CBO) is the difference in the electron affinity (EA) of absorber and buffer layer.
- The EA of buffer is varied while EA of absorber is kept constant to identify the effect on PCE.
- Materials within CBO range are replaced with existing buffer layer and their performance is analyzed.
- Cell with ZnSe buffer layer exhibits highest PCE of 30.29% Voc = 1.12 V, Jsc =1.76 mA/cm², and FF =74.55%.

Conclusion

- The bandgap of the absorber layer is tuned to 1.9 eV for efficient utilization of indoor spectrum.
- The Thickness and defect density of the absorber layer is optimized for maximizing performance.
- A suitable replacement of ZCS buffer layer is proposed using CBO analysis.
- The proposed device with cell structure Mo/CBTSSe/ZnSe/ZMO/AZO is 30.29% efficient.

References

- D. Shin, T. Zhu, X. Huang, O. Gunawan, V. Blum, and D. B. Mitzi, Adv. Mater., vol. 29, no. 24, p. 1606945, Jun. 2017.
- B. Teymur, Y. Kim, J. Huang, K. Sun, X. Hao, and D. B. Mitzi, Adv. Energy Mater., vol. 12, no. 40, p. 2201602, Oct. 2022.

Acknowledgement: The authors would like to thank Mr. Marc Burgelman from ELSI at University of Gent, Belgium for providing SCAPS-1D software and acknowledge financial support received from SVNIT - Surat

2BV.1.5

THEORETICAL INSIGHTS THROUGH DFT INTO AGBIS₂ THIN FILMS ABSORBER FOR PHOTOVOLTAIC APPLICATIONS

Dhruv Singh Thakur[1], Rajesh Kumar Sharma[2], Nithin Chatterji[3], Vivek Garg[4], Shivendra Yadav[5]
Department of Electronics Engineering, SVNIT, Surat-395007, India
ds22ec001@eced.svnit.ac.in, d21ec011@eced.svnit.ac.in, nithinc@eced.svnit.ac.in, vivekg@eced.svnit.ac.in,
shivendra.y@eced.svnit.ac.in

ABSTRACT: $AgBiS_2$ has emerged as a promising absorber material for thin-film solar cell applications due to its earth-abundant, non-toxic composition and tunable optical bandgap (Eg) (0.8–1.32 eV), making it suitable for low-cost and scalable production. This study comprehensively investigates the suitability of $AgBiS_2$ absorber for solar cells, emphasizing its structural, optoelectronic, and photovoltaic performance. Using density functional theory (DFT), we explore the electrical and optical properties, including Eg, absorption coefficient (α), dielectric constant, and refractive index. The result shows a very high 'α' of the order of ~106, and Eg (direct/indirect) calculated by MGGA and HSE method 1.18/0.63, and 1.55/0.99 respectively, which is very close to the experimental value ~1.0 eV. These insights highlight the potential of $AgBiS_2$ as a versatile absorber material, paving the way for advancements in thin film solar cell technologies.
Keywords: $AgBiS_2$, thin film, density functional theory, optoelectrical properties, QuantumATK

1   INTRODUCTION

A promising approach to improving solar cell technology is through the development of thin-film solar cells, which offer a much thinner absorber layer compared to conventional silicon-based solar cells. Ternary and quaternary chalcogenide or Matildite materials have recently attracted considerable research attention for their potential in photovoltaic applications. $AgBiS_2$ stands out as an environmentally friendly, abundant, and non-toxic material with excellent absorption properties, high mobility, and an optimal Eg range of 1–1.32 eV [1]. $AgBiS_2$ known as Matildite has two established crystal phases. The two crystal phases are the cubic α-$AgBiS_2$ and hexagonal β-$AgBiS_2$ phases. It belongs to the I–V–VI₂ family of compounds (where I = Cu/Ag/Au; V = As/Sb/Bi and VI = S/Se/Te) [2]. This article investigates the optical and electrical properties of $AgBiS_2$ using DFT simulations. By evaluating its optoelectronic performance, we aim to contribute valuable insights into the potential of $AgBiS_2$ in advancing eco-friendly and high-performance photovoltaic technologies.

2   COMPUTATIONAL METHOD

The linear combination of atomic orbitals (LCAO) calculator is utilized with Meta-generalized gradient approximation (MGGA) and Heyd-Scuseria-Ernzerhof (HSE) exchange-correlation (XC) function in the QuantumATK [3] to calculate the structural and optoelectronic properties of the $AgBiS_2$ compound. Based on DFT, this method is considered the most sophisticated computational technique for determining materials' ground state properties. The interactions of electron-ion are explained by the Vanderbilt-type pseudopotentials (PP). In the process of geometry optimization, the effects of XC interaction are calculated with the MGGA and HSE. We calculated the total energy, unit cell volume, and Eg of the AgBiS2 by taking the noncollinear spin, occupational method is Fermi-Dirac and Monkhorst (MP)-Grid k-point density 8×8×2 incorporated for the Brillouin-zone (BZ) sampling as shown in Fig. 1(c) with applying pseudoDojo PP. In the self-consistent iterative process, the criteria of convergence: the total difference in energy found within

1.0×10^{-6} eV/atom, the maximum stress within 0.02 GPa, the maximum atom displacement within 1.0×10^{-4}Å, and the maximum force within 0.01eV/Å.

3   RESULT AND DISCUSSION

3.1 Structural properties of $AgBiS_2$ compound

As shown in Fig.1(a), the β-$AgBiS_2$ crystal belongs to the space group P-3m1, No.164, which is a hexagonally symmetric structure. The placement of the ions is shown in (x, y, z) coordinates: Ag: (0, 0, 0), (0.3333, 0.6667, 0.672), Bi: (0, 0, 0.5), (0.3333, 0.6667, 0.163), S: (0, 0, 0.253), (0.3333, 0.6667, 0.406), (0.3333, 0.6667, 0.926). In this work, for optimization of geometry considering the cost of calculation time and accuracy requirements, we adopted a method to optimize the geometry of β-$AgBiS_2$ crystal, which is the MGGA. The Brillouin Zone is shown in Fig. 1(c) which describes the primitive cell in reciprocal space.

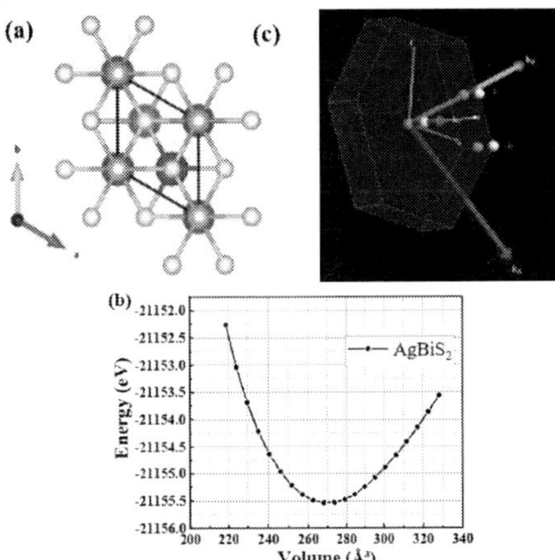

Figure 1: β-$AgBiS_2$ crystal (a) Structure (b) Volume optimization plot (c) Brillouin Zone

Table I reported the calculated lattice constants and other reported experimental and theoretical data for comparison. The calculated lattice constants a and c are 4.043 and 18.93 Å, respectively, with 0.66% and 0.68% deviation from the experimental values, the optimized volume and ground state energy for this compound is 267.97 Å³, -21155.5397 eV as shown in Fig.1(b), a favorable agreement by DFT standards as shown in Table I.

Table I: β-AgBiS$_2$ Crystal lattice constant a(Å), c(Å), and Eg (eV) compared to experimental and theoretical data.

Parameter		This study		Other study [1], [2]		Exp. [4], [6], [7]
		MGGA	HSE	PBE	HSE	
Lattice constant (Å)	a	4.043	-	4.0497, 4.02	---	4.07
	c	18.93	-	19.019, 19.05	---	19.06
Eg (eV) (Direct/ Indirect)		1.18/ 0.63	1.55/ 0.99	0.42, 0.46	1.54	0.9, 1.2

3.2 Electronic properties of AgBiS$_2$ compound

To analyze the electronic characteristics of β-AgBiS$_2$ crystal, we have to find out the electronic band structure. Fig. 2 shows the related results, from which we can observe that β-AgBiS$_2$ crystal having Eg (direct/indirect) obtained by MGGA and HSE method is 1.18/0.63 eV, and 1.55/0.99 eV respectively, which approximately matches to the experimental value 1.2 eV. The valence band (dashed blue line------) and conduction band (dashed red line------), for the AgBiS2 nanocrystals the Eg ($\sim$1.0 eV) blue-shifted due to the quantum confinement relative to that of the bulk phase of AgBiS$_2$.

(a)

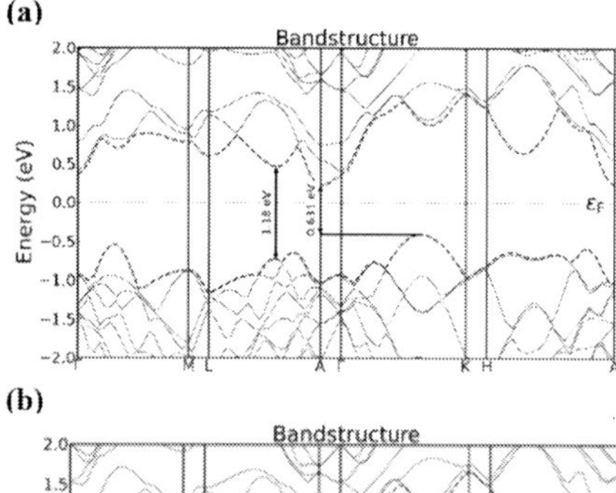

(b)

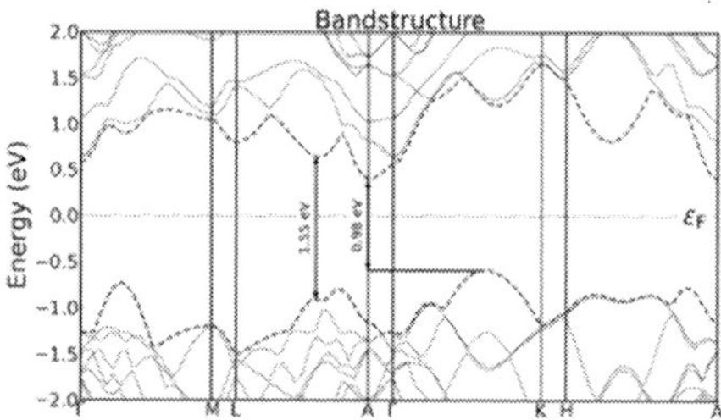

Figure 2: Band structure of β- AgBiS$_2$ (a) by MGGA (b) by HSE

3.3 Optical properties
(a) Absorption coefficient (α)

Optical characteristics are the behavior of materials when exposed to incident light. Optical parameters provide a deep understanding of the selected material and its behavior due to light interaction, highlighting their valuable contribution to the optic, solar technology, and photonic. The absorption coefficient $\alpha(\omega)$ is used to quantify the interaction between light and matter. The absorption coefficient $\alpha(\omega)$ is expressed by the following equation (1). where "c" is the speed of light.

$$\alpha(\omega) = \frac{\sqrt{2}\omega^2}{c}\left\{\sqrt{\varepsilon_1{}^2(\omega) - \varepsilon_2{}^2(\omega)} - \varepsilon_1(\omega)\right\}^{1/2} \quad (1)$$

Fig. 3(a), displays the $\alpha(\omega)$ curve obtained using the complex dielectric function $\varepsilon(\omega)$. The threshold energy for AgBiS$_2$ is $\sim$1 eV, indicating the point at which these substances begin to absorb electromagnetic radiation. Below the threshold energy, the material is transparent and absorbs no light in this energy range. AgBiS$_2$ compound reveals optical absorption starting in the near-infrared region and extending into the ultraviolet region. With increasing the photon energy, the absorption spectra increase and reaches peak value of 1.1×10^6 at 2.7 eV. The optical absorption as shown in Fig.3(a) starts in the UV region and spreads up to the infrared spectrum of light.

(b) Complex dielectric constant (ε)

The complex dielectric function $\varepsilon(\omega)=\varepsilon_1(\omega)+i\varepsilon_2(\omega)$ describes the complete optical response of a material. $\varepsilon_1(\omega)$ represents the degree of polarization of material under the external electric field, while $\varepsilon_2(\omega)$ is related to their behavior of light absorption. It can be observed from Fig. 3(b) that the first peak of AgBiS$_2$ is located at 1.66 eV, indicating that this material has strong electrical polarization behavior within the visible to near-infrared range. AgBiS$_2$ attains a negative value in $\varepsilon_1(\omega)$ at 2.4 eV to 4 eV, indicating that the materials completely reflect the incident photon. In addition, Fig.3(c) represents $\varepsilon_2(\omega)$, demonstrating the dissipation properties of the material. Incident photon energy of less than 1.0 eV of material shows no response. The point at which the absorption of energy in the material begins is called threshold value which is consistent with the band gap of AgBiS$_2$. AgBiS$_2$ exhibits the maximum value of $\varepsilon_2(\omega)$ = 26.96 at 2.36 eV, and the maximal peak of $\varepsilon_2(\omega)$ is the absorption peak, which shows that AgBiS$_2$ has good absorption capacity in visible light.

(a)

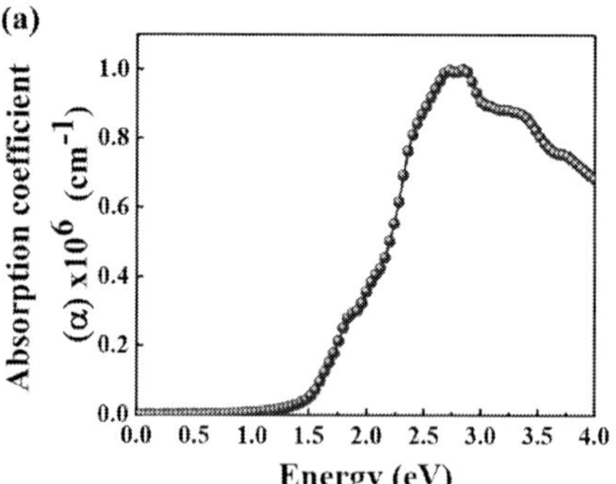

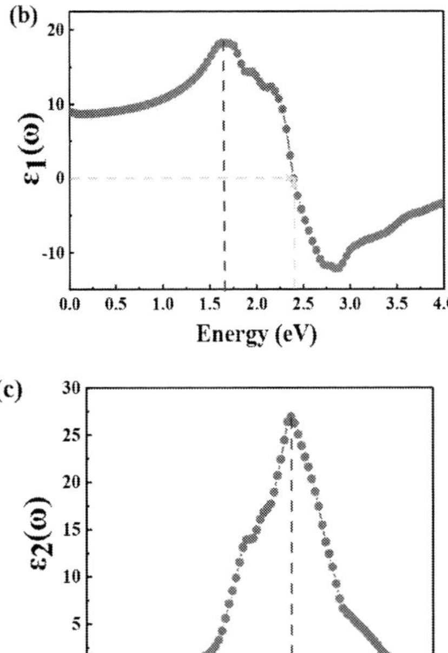

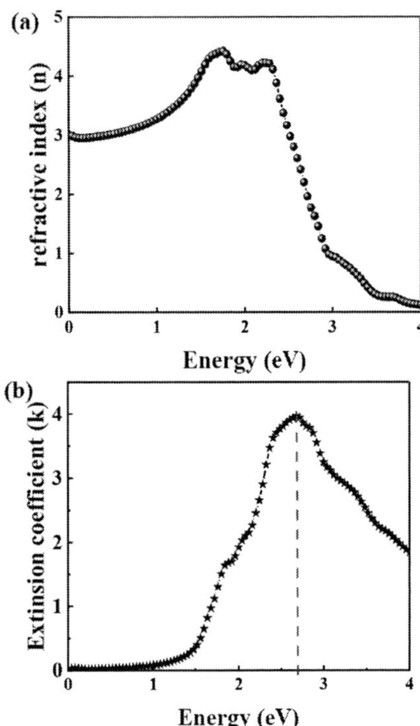

Figure 3: (a) absorption coefficient $\alpha(\omega)$ (b) real part of dielectric function ε_1 (c) imaginary part dielectric function ε_2 of AgBiS$_2$.

Figure 4: Calculated (a) refractive index $n(\omega)$ (b) extinction coefficient $k(\omega)$

(c)   Refractive index (n) and extinction coefficient (k)

The refractive index explains how light passes through materials and is influenced by their structure and composition. The refractive index and extinction coefficient of the material can be calculated by equation (2). Fig. 4(a) illustrates the refractive index for the AgBiS$_2$ compound. The static refractive index $n(0)$ is 3. The spectrum of n(ω) shows the highest peak value of $n(\omega) = 4.42$ around 1.76 eV. The $n(\omega)$ and the static refractive index are valuable for calculating light refraction and for applications in photoelectric devices. A refractive index greater than 1 indicates that photons slow down upon entering the material due to interaction with electrons. Higher values of $n(\omega)$ indicate greater delay in the passage of photons through the material. The peak of refractive index $n(\omega)$ within the visible or near-infrared region suggested that the compound used in devices is working in the visible or near-infrared region.

$$n(\omega) = \left\{ \frac{\varepsilon_1(\omega)}{2} + \frac{\sqrt{\varepsilon_1{}^2(\omega) - \varepsilon_2{}^2(\omega)}}{2} \right\}^{1/2} \quad (2)$$

$$k(\omega) = \left\{ -\frac{\varepsilon_1(\omega)}{2} + \frac{\sqrt{\varepsilon_1{}^2(\omega) - \varepsilon_2{}^2(\omega)}}{2} \right\}^{1/2} \quad (3)$$

Fig. 4(b) displays the extinction coefficient k(ω) for AgBiS$_2$ calculated by Equation (3). The extinction coefficient quantifies the light that is absorbed and scattered in the material, characterizing its ability to absorb light. Larger values of k(ω) indicate stronger absorption and intense scattering of light. The threshold energy for k(ω) is ~1 eV and the maximum value of the extinction coefficient is 3.967 at 2.68 eV.

4   CONCLUSION

In conclusion, AgBiS$_2$ demonstrates strong potential as a high-performance, eco-friendly absorber material for thin-film solar cells. Its structural properties, including optimized lattice constants (a = 4.043 Å, c = 18.93 Å), align closely with experimental values, confirming the accuracy of the MGGA method. The electronic band structure calculations match the experimental band gap of 1.2 eV, with values of 1.18/0.63 eV (MGGA) and 1.55/0.99 eV (HSE). The material exhibits excellent optical absorption from near-infrared to ultraviolet regions, peaking at 1.1×10^6 cm^{-1} at 2.7 eV. The refractive index, with a static value of 3 and a peak of 4.42 at 1.76 eV, indicates significant photon interaction, essential for photoelectric applications. The extinction coefficient shows strong light absorption, with a maximum of 3.967 at 2.68 eV. Overall, these properties make AgBiS$_2$ a promising candidate for efficient, cost-effective photovoltaic technologies.

REFERENCES

[1]   M. Bernechea, N. C. Miller, G. Xercavins, D. So, A. Stavrinadis, and G. Konstantatos, "Solution-processed solar cells based on environmentally friendly AgBiS2 nanocrystals," *Nat Photonics*, vol. 10, no. 8, pp. 521–525, Aug. 2016, doi: 10.1038/nphoton.2016.108.

[2]   T. Manimozhi, S. Kavirajan, K. Kamala Bharathi, E. Senthil Kumar, and M. Navaneethan, "Ultra-low thermal conductivity of AgBiS2 via Sb

substitution as a scattering center for thermoelectric applications," *Journal of Materials Science: Materials in Electronics*, vol. 33, no. 16, pp. 12615–12628, Jun. 2022, doi: 10.1007/s10854-022-08211-y.

[3] "Manual — | QuantumATK V-2023.12 Documentation." Accessed: Jun. 11, 2024. [Online]. Available: https://docs.quantumatk.com/manual/manual.html

[4] S. Geller and J. H. Wernick, " Ternary semiconducting compounds with sodium chloride-like structure: AgSbSe 2 , AgSbTe 2 , AgBiS 2 , AgBiSe 2 ," *Acta Crystallogr*, vol. 12, no. 1, pp. 46–54, Jan. 1959, doi: 10.1107/S0365110X59000135/FULL.

[5] F. Viñes, M. Bernechea, G. Konstantatos, and F. Illas, "Matildite versus schapbachite: First-principles investigation of the origin of photoactivity in AgBi S2," *Phys Rev B*, no. 23, Dec. 2016, doi: 10.1103/PhysRevB.94.235203.

[6] I. I. Golovach, V. S. Gerasimenko, V. Y. Slivka, N. I. Dovgoshei, M. I. Golovei, and A. V Bogdanova, "VITRIFICATION OF AND OPTICAL AND PHOTOFLI~CTRICAL PROPERTIES OF AgAsS 2, AgSbS2, AND AgBiS 2."

[7] B. Pejova, D. Nesheva, Z. Aneva, and A. Petrova, "Photoconductivity and relaxation dynamics in sonochemically synthesized assemblies of AgBiS2 quantum dots," *Journal of Physical Chemistry C*, vol. 115, no. 1, pp. 37–46, Jan. 2011, doi: 10.1021/jp106605t.

Dhruv Singh Thakur; Rajesh Kumar Sharma; Nithin Chatterji; Vivek Garg; Shivendra Yadav

Optoelectronics2Application (O2A) Research Group, Department of Electronics Engineering,
S. V. National Institute of Technology Surat-395007, India

2BV.1.6

Abstract

$AgBiS_2$ is a promising absorber for thin-film solar cells owing to its earth-abundance, non-toxicity, and tunable bandgap (0.8–1.32 eV), enabling low-cost scalable production. This study, based on density functional theory, evaluates its structural, electronic, and optical properties, revealing a high absorption coefficient (~10^6 cm⁻¹) and bandgaps (1.18/0.63 eV by MGGA, 1.55/0.99 eV by HSE) close to the experimental ~1.0 eV. These results establish $AgBiS_2$ as a versatile candidate for efficient photovoltaic applications.

Methodology

Linear combination of atomic orbitals (LCAO) calculator is utilized with Meta-generalized gradient approximation (MGGA) and Heyd-Scuseria-Ernzerhof (HSE) exchange-correlation (XC) function in the QuantumATK to calculate the structural and optoelectronic properties of the $AgBiS_2$ compound.

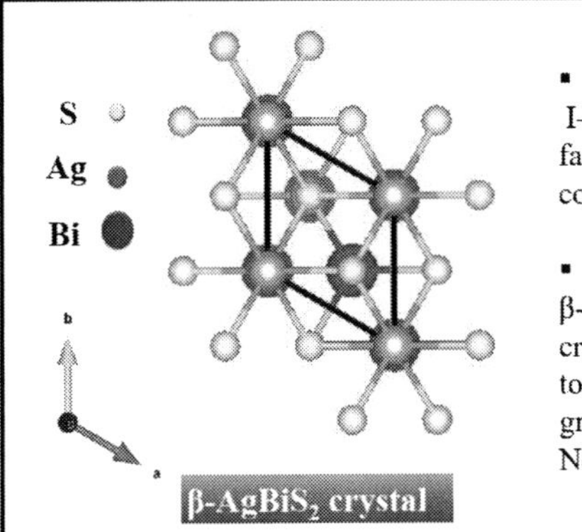

- It belongs to I–V–VI₂ family of compounds.
- Hexagonal β-AgBiS₂ crystal belongs to the space group P-3m1, No.164.

Material Structure Optimization

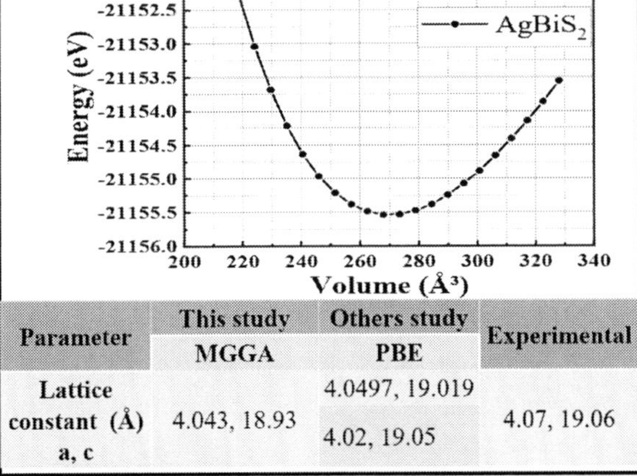

Parameter	This study	Others study	Experimental
	MGGA	PBE	
Lattice constant (Å) a, c	4.043, 18.93	4.0497, 19.019 / 4.02, 19.05	4.07, 19.06

Electronic properties

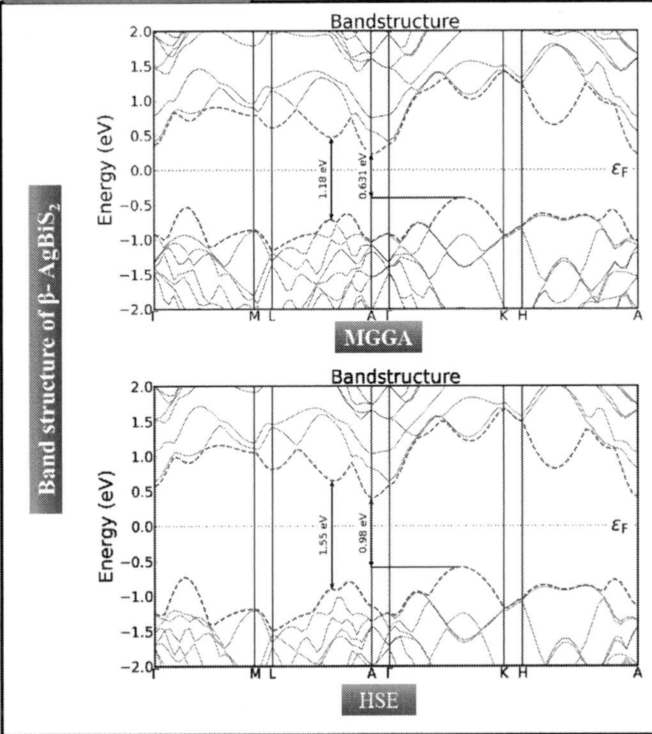

Optical Properties

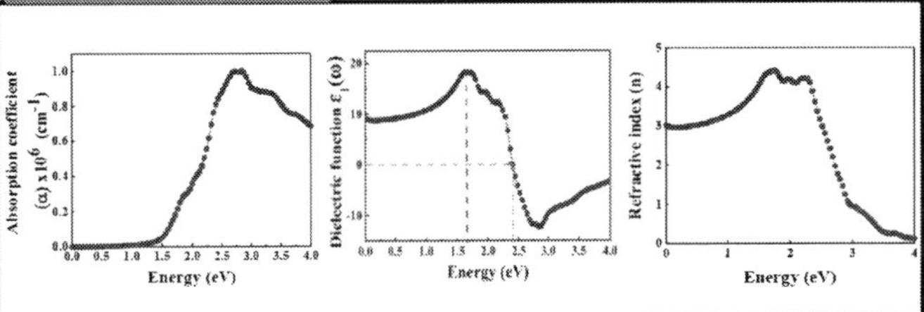

Conclusion

$AgBiS_2$ shows strong promise as an eco-friendly absorber for thin-film solar cells. Its optimized lattice constants (a,c = 4.043, 18.93 Å) closely match experimental values, validating the MGGA method. Electronic band structure results align with the experimental Eg, supported by MGGA and HSE calculations. The material exhibits excellent optical absorption (up to 1.1×10^6 cm⁻¹) across a wide spectral range, with high refractive index and extinction coefficient. Hence $AgBiS_2$ emerges as a low-cost, efficient candidate for next-generation photovoltaics.

Acknowledgement

The authors acknowledge the financial support from "SVNIT, Surat" under Grant No. Dean (R&C)/Seed Money/2021-22/10783, and "Divyasampark iHUB Roorkee for the Device Materials and Technology Foundation" under Grant Nos. 4-371 and 4-372.

References

[1] M. Bernechea et al., Nat Photonics, vol. 10, no. 8, pp. 521–525, Aug. 2016.
[2] S. Geller et al., Acta Crystallogr, vol. 12, no. 1, pp. 46–54, Jan. 1959.
[3] F. Viñes et al., Phys Rev B, no. 23, Dec. 2016.
[4] B. Pejova et al., Journal of Physical Chemistry C, vol. 115, no. 1, pp 37–46, Jan. 2011.

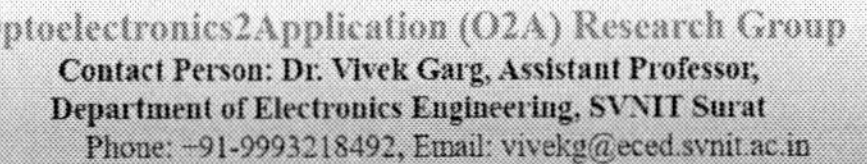

RÉPUBLIQUE FRANÇAISE
Liberté
Égalité
Fraternité

CLEO Project AZURSPACE esa

ONERA
THE FRENCH AEROSPACE LAB

NOVEL ENCAPSULATION MATERIALS : RADIATION TEST AND RESULTS

D. Lansade, S. Lewandowski, S. Duzellier, H. Gasse

Alternatives to coverglass
Specifications: wide spectral transparency, stable in radiative environment, mechanically flexible

---

PDMS composite/hybrid (nanoSi)

Embedding of vinyl-functionalized silica nanoparticles photonic crystal

Tunable (short-UV absorbers)
Provide basic shielding
Under scale-up process

Self-healing PDMS (PDMS-UI)

Intrinsic self-healing solution : 50% urea / 50% imine

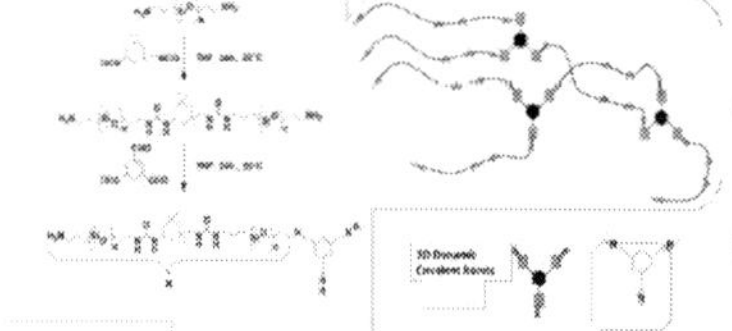

Urea/Tri-Imine:
Home-made 2-step synthesis
Dual crosslinking:
Dynamic covalent & hydrogen-bond

Self-healing theoretically unlimited
Large surface
Sprayable

Blend Polyimide + POSS (CORIN®)

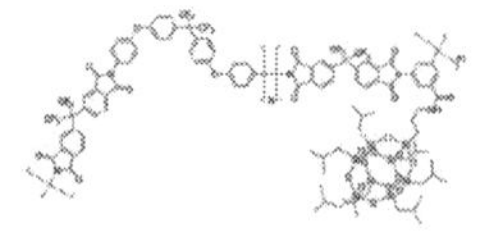

Polyhedral Oligomeric Silsesquioxane
Powder diluted into esters

Commercially available
Solvent-based liquid resin or powder form
Spray, dip or casting applications

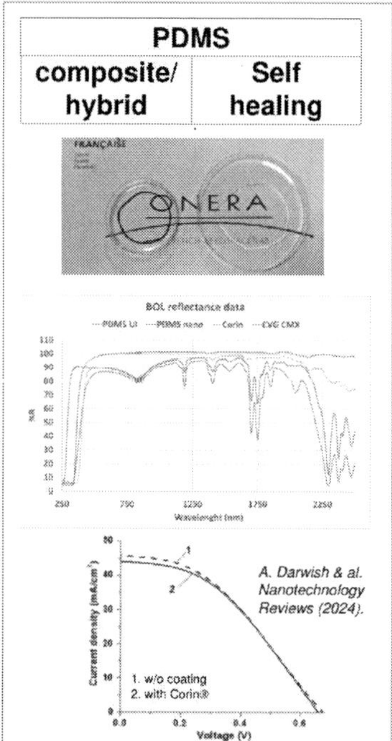

3.5 10^{15} 600keV e⁻/cm² (2 years GEO)

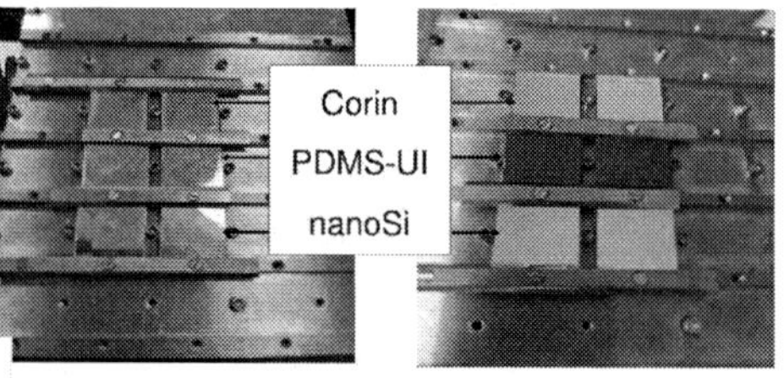

$$\alpha_s = \frac{\int_{250}^{2500} A(\lambda) I_s(\lambda) d\lambda}{\int_{250}^{2500} I_s(\lambda) d\lambda}$$

UV (200-400nm) ~1000esh

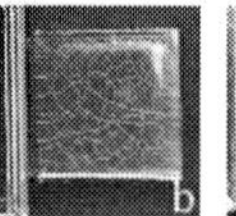

Si-nano 1 year GEO / p+

D. Lansade et al., Polym. Degrad. Stab. 176 (2020)

Conclusions:

✓ PDMS composite : high UV/electrons stability. Requires optimisation for proton (avoid cracking). Under industrialisation

✓ Self-healing PDMS : sensitive to UV & electrons. Partial recovery of degradation (with protons)

D. Yilmaz, DOI: 10.1021/acsami.4c02431

✓ Corin®: high stability to electrons. UV Sensitive. Test with protons shall be carried out

---

The authors would like to thank : AZUR SPACE Solar Power GmbH and ESA for their financial support in this project, the Organic Polymer Chemistry Laboratory, MAP Space Coatings and CNES for their collaboration in developing the PDMS solutions.

Correlated Disordered Nanostructures for Light Trapping in Ultrathin Solar Cells

L. DE ALMEIDA[1], I. REVOL[1], J-B. DOUCET[1], Mathieu ARRIBAT[1], G.ALMUNEAU[1], S. COLLIN[2]

[1]LAAS-CNRS, Laboratoire d'analyse et d'architecture des systèmes, 31400 Toulouse, France

[2]C2N, Centre de Nanoscience et de Nanotechnologie, 91120 Palaiseau, France

Nanostructuration and disorder

Light trapping is an important pathway in photovoltaic devices development that aims to **maximize the absorption of light** in a material. Increasing the optical path length of light in a material increases the probability of absorption.

For the past forty years, random texturing has been utilized for light trapping. In recent years, periodic nanostructures have emerged as an alternative. As a further alternative, **disordered correlated** or **amorphous** nanostructures have proven to improve scattering at various angles, to promote light trapping and allow to **reduce production cost** by increasing tolerance to fabrication defects.

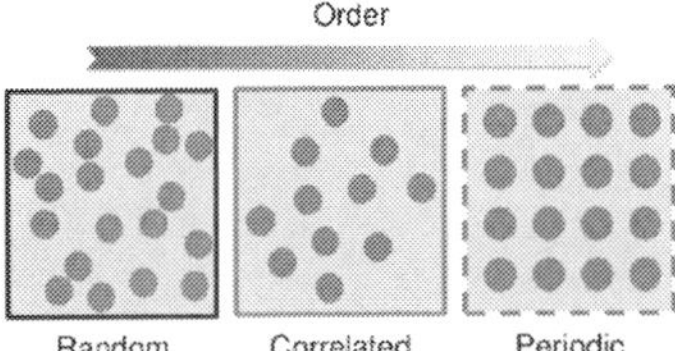

Order

Random — Correlated — Periodic

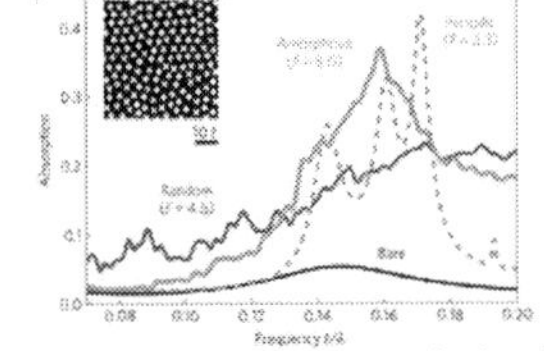

Absorption spectrum of two-dimensional structures of a-Si layer of 100 nm
The absorption of the **amorphous** structure is better than the absorption of the **periodic** and **random** structure at certain wavelengths. (see reference [1])

Objectives

My PhD: Nanostructure Si cell and understand disorder impact on optical and electrical parameters

O1: Low-cost and large surface process → Colloidal lithography

O2: Understanding the impact of disorder on optical properties of thin silicon films

O3: Integrating disordered light trapping strategies in silicon thin-film

O1: How to fabricate correlated disorder nanostructures?

Colloidal lithography process

Negatively charged PS-beads suspension + functionalization of particles

Positively charged substrate

Step 1: Beads deposition

Carboxyl

LAAS-CNRS — 5 µm

SEM Image of CL138 sample after beads deposition

Step 2: Deposition of the etch mask
Mask selection depends on etching, here 50 nm titanium for dry etching

Step 3: Colloidal removal
Adhesive tape and acetone

Step 4: Pattern transfer to substrate by ICP-RIE etching

Isotropic etching
SF_6
t_{etch} = 15 sec

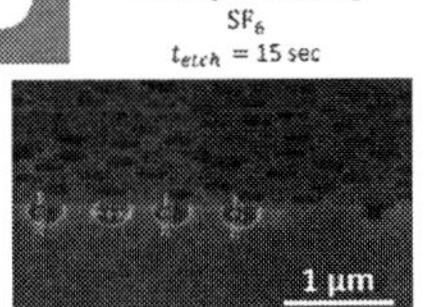

1 µm

SEM cross-section image of ET-Si-07 after etch mask removal

Anisotropic etching
SF_6, C_4F_8 and O_2
t_{etch} = 2 min 45 sec

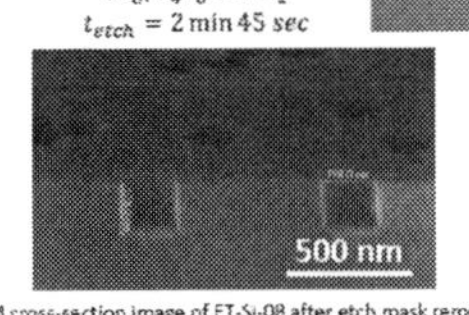

500 nm

SEM cross-section image of ET-Si-08 after etch mask removal

O2: How do we characterize disorder?

Structure factor

$S(q_x, q_y)$ - CL-TW2-01

$$S(q) = \frac{1}{N}\sum_m \sum_n \exp(iq \cdot (r_m - r_n))$$

Pair correlation function

$$g(r) = \left(\frac{2}{N^2}\sum_{m=1}^{N}\sum_{n=m+1}^{N}\delta(r_m)\delta(r_n - r)\right)$$

Table: summary of the various parameters used to characterize our arrangements

Sample	Pattern size (nm)	Pseudo-period g(r) (nm)	Pseudo-period S(q) (nm)
CL-TW2-01	210	410	342
CL-TW2-08	500	933	980
CL-TW2-09	210	410	345

O3: How do we characterize disordered light trapping strategies in silicon thin-film?

Objective: Characterization of correlated-disorder nanostructure

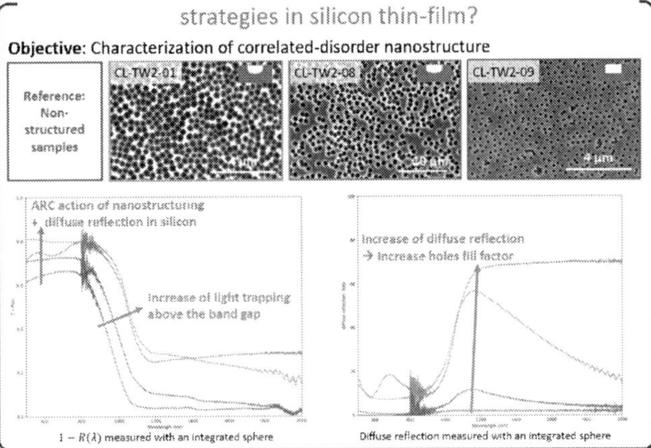

Reference: Non-structured samples

CL-TW2-01 — CL-TW2-08 — CL-TW2-09

ARC action of nanostructuring + diffuse reflection in silicon

increase of light trapping above the band gap

= Increase of diffuse reflection → Increase holes fill factor

$1 - R(\lambda)$ measured with an integrated sphere

Diffuse reflection measured with an integrated sphere

References

[1] Vynck, K., Burresi, M., Riboli, F. et al., Nature Mater 11, 1017–1022 (2012). https://doi.org/10.1038/nmat3442

[2] Massiot, I., Cattoni, A. & Collin, S., Nat Energy 5, 959–972 (2020). https://doi.org/10.1038/s41560-020-00714-4

[3] Terao, T., Nakayama, T., Phys. Rev. E 60, 7157 (1999). https://doi.org/10.1103/PhysRevE.60.7157

Conclusion & Outlook

Colloidal lithography

- Development of a repeatable experimental protocol
- Fabricating other geometries of etching profile with wet etching (inverted pyramid)

How does the pattern impact the optical performances?

Integration on silicon thin-film (10, 15, 25 and 50 µm)

- Preliminary optical measurements
- Observed redshift in transmission for structured samples
- Investigation of long-wavelength absorption mechanisms (ongoing work)

Outlook

- Comparison of the optical performance of these structures with periodic references and correlated disorder fabricated by polymer blend lithography.
- Understanding the impact of disorder on the optical performances

Acknowledgement

The authors acknowledge the support of the French Agence Nationale de la Recherche (ANR), under grant ANR-22-PETA-0005 (PEPR TASE, project IOTA).
This work is also partly supported by LAAS-CNRS micro and nanotechnologies platform, member of the French RENATECH network.

Laboratoire conventionné avec

LIGHTWEIGHT PHOTONIC COOLER WITH MULTI-LAYERED THIN FILM IR FILTERS AND ANTI-DUST PROPERTIES FOR PV APPLICATIONS IN DESERT ENVIRONMENTS

Brahim Aïssa*, M.I. Hossain
Qatar Environment and Energy Research Institute (QEERI), Hamad Bin Khalifa University (HBKU), Qatar Foundation,
Doha, 5825, Qatar
* baissa@hbku.edu.qa

ABSTRACT: The present research is dedicated to the design and fabrication of advanced multi-stacked thin-film structures composed of alternating metal-oxide and metallic layers. These engineered coatings are conceived as multifunctional photonic coolers, offering a combination of near-infrared (NIR) filtering, anti-dust, and anti-reflective properties that make them highly attractive for deployment in energy-intensive environments. The optimized configuration consists of three key components: titanium oxide (TiOx) as the outermost layer, nickel oxide (NiO) as an intermediate buffer, and silver (Ag) as the reflective hot-mirror layer. Each material in this architecture serves a distinct optical and functional role. The layers were deposited using thermal electron-beam (e-beam) evaporation under a controlled oxygen atmosphere, with a continuous vacuum environment maintained throughout the process to ensure dense, defect-free growth and reproducible film quality. One of the notable characteristics of the TiOx top layer is its inherent super-hydrophilicity. This property imparts both self-cleaning and anti-dust functionalities, critical for outdoor applications in desert climates where soiling can drastically reduce optical efficiency. In parallel, the multi-layer stacking strategy leverages the contrasting refractive indices of constituent oxides to fine-tune the spectral response. Low-refractive-index TiOx, when paired with high-refractive-index oxides such as NiO or molybdenum oxide (MoOx), creates constructive interference effects that enhance visible light transmission while simultaneously suppressing unwanted infrared radiation. Experimental results confirmed that bilayer combinations such as MoOx/TiOx and NiO/TiOx exhibited superior transmittance in the visible spectrum compared to single TiOx films, thereby optimizing light harvesting in photovoltaic and optical applications. The inclusion of a reflective metallic layer (Ag or, alternatively, Al) further enhanced performance, acting as an efficient hot-mirror with a wavelength cutoff beginning at ~800 nm. Beyond this threshold, the structure demonstrated the ability to reflect more than 70% of incident IR radiation, thereby effectively mitigating heat accumulation. This carefully engineered multi-stack thin-film structure not only provides efficient IR filtering but also functions simultaneously as an anti-reflective coating for visible light and as an anti-soiling surface layer. These multifunctional attributes significantly extend its commercial potential, particularly for integration into energy-efficient building envelopes, smart glazing, and large-scale photovoltaic systems operating under harsh and dusty environmental conditions. Furthermore, the reliance on scalable deposition techniques, such as e-beam evaporation, underscores the feasibility of adapting this approach for industrial-scale manufacturing. In sum, the multi-layer metal-oxide/metal-oxide/metal photonic cooler represents a versatile, durable, and scalable solution for managing the solar spectrum, mitigating heat, enhancing light utilization, and resisting environmental degradation. Its multifunctionality positions it as a promising candidate for next-generation energy-saving technologies in desert and other extreme climates.

1 INTRODUCTION

The solar radiation that reaches the Earth's surface is composed of three principal spectral regions: ultraviolet (UV), visible, and infrared (IR) light. Among these, the infrared portion represents the largest share, accounting for approximately 54% of the total incident solar energy. This dominant fraction plays a critical role in heat generation, as the IR wavelengths are efficiently converted into thermal energy upon interaction with materials and surfaces. Consequently, the substantial presence of IR radiation significantly increases the cooling load of buildings, a challenge that is particularly exacerbated in hot and arid desert climates where air conditioning systems already consume vast amounts of energy [1–6].

Given these circumstances, the development of thin-film technologies that can selectively reflect the IR spectrum, while simultaneously ensuring high optical transparency in the visible region, has emerged as a research priority. For applications in the photovoltaic (PV) sector, maintaining maximum transparency in the visible range is not merely desirable but essential, as this spectral region governs the efficiency of light harvesting and, ultimately, the electrical power output of solar devices. To meet this need, metallic layers, such as silver (Ag), aluminum (Al), and gold (Au), have been widely investigated for their potential to act as effective IR filters, owing to their strong capacity to absorb or reflect infrared radiation at resonance frequencies. However, these metallic films are hindered by intrinsic drawbacks, most notably their susceptibility to degradation, which compromises their optical and structural stability over time and thereby limits their long-term performance [7–10]. To mitigate these issues, researchers have proposed the use of composite "sandwich" structures in which the metallic layers are embedded between oxide layers. While such architectures offer improved protection, they remain vulnerable to key reliability challenges. Problems such as oxygen diffusion into the metal layers and the development of internal film stress during deposition can lead to structural cracking and, in turn, reduced optical transparency in the visible spectrum. A comprehensive body of work has identified a range of transition metal oxides, most notably TiOx, SnOx, MoOx, and NiOx, as promising candidates for the fabrication of IR filters, owing to their favorable electronic, optical, and chemical properties, as well as their compatibility with various device architectures [11–15]. These oxides have been successfully deposited using multiple thin-film deposition techniques, including magnetron sputtering, thermal or electron-beam vacuum evaporation, and atomic layer deposition (ALD). Among these, electron-beam (e-beam) evaporation has attracted particular attention for its versatility, scalability, and capacity to achieve high-quality multilayer coatings with controlled stoichiometry.

The overarching objective of the present work is therefore to design and fabricate a cost-effective, multilayered IR filter consisting of a metal-oxide/metal-oxide/metal configuration. The targeted device must simultaneously exhibit high optical transparency within the visible spectrum, thereby enabling adequate solar conversion efficiency in PV applications—and strong reflectivity within the IR region to suppress heat build-up. Furthermore, the filter is specifically conceived for deployment in harsh desert environments, where it must not only withstand elevated temperatures and intense solar flux but also resist dust accumulation. To this end, the multilayer system incorporates anti-soiling surface properties to enhance durability and operational lifetime [16–25].

The research methodology integrates both advanced numerical modeling and experimental validation, enabling systematic optimization of structural design, materials selection, and deposition parameters. A schematic representation of the proposed multilayer stack is provided in Fig. 1. Through this combined approach, the study demonstrates the potential of such engineered IR filters to contribute significantly to energy-efficient building envelopes, photovoltaic modules, and related technologies designed for hot and dusty climates. This work thus represents a critical step toward the broader integration of selective IR-reflecting coatings into sustainable energy systems tailored for some of the world's most challenging environmental conditions.

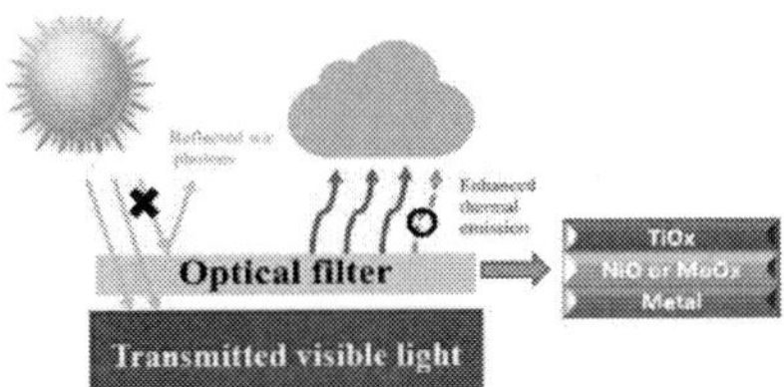

Figure 1: Schematic representation of the multilayered thin-film architecture designed for infrared (IR) filtering applications. The structure consists of sequentially deposited metal oxide and metallic layers, optimized to achieve high transparency in the visible spectrum while reflecting near-infrared (NIR) wavelengths. The inclusion of TiOx as the outermost layer provides anti-reflective and anti-soiling functionalities, NiO serves as a buffer/high-index oxide layer, and Ag (or Al) acts as the reflective hot-mirror layer. This configuration illustrates the functional integration of optical filtering, photonic cooling, and environmental durability within a scalable thin-film design.

2 METHODOLOGY

Metal oxide thin films, with a particular focus on nickel oxide (NiO) and titanium oxide (TiOx), were deposited via electron-beam (e-beam) evaporation under carefully controlled conditions. The depositions were carried out at room temperature while maintaining a constant flow of oxygen to ensure stoichiometric film growth and to minimize oxygen vacancies, which are known to critically influence both optical and electrical properties. In parallel, metallic layers such as aluminum (Al) and silver (Ag) were deposited under vacuum conditions without the introduction of oxygen flow. This deliberate differentiation in process atmospheres allowed for the preservation of metallic conductivity in Al and Ag layers, while simultaneously achieving the desired oxide stoichiometry in NiO and TiOx layers. The films were fabricated on both rigid glass substrates and flexible polyethylene terephthalate (PET) substrates, highlighting the adaptability of the process for applications ranging from conventional photovoltaic modules to lightweight and bendable optoelectronic devices.

A comprehensive suite of characterization techniques was employed to assess the structural, optical, and surface properties of the fabricated films. Ellipsometry and UV–Vis spectrophotometry were used to determine the refractive indices, extinction coefficients, and transmittance spectra of the multilayer structures, thereby enabling direct correlation between deposition parameters and optical performance. Contact angle measurements provided critical insights into the surface wettability and hydrophilicity of the coatings, an essential feature for evaluating anti-soiling and self-cleaning potential under real-world desert conditions. Surface morphology and roughness were investigated using a three-dimensional stylus profilometer (Dektak), which provided quantitative topographical mapping of the films. Complementary nanoscale imaging was performed using field-emission scanning electron microscopy (FESEM) and atomic force microscopy (AFM), offering detailed views of grain structure, uniformity, and surface features that influence scattering and light management within the films. Structural and chemical bonding analyses were conducted via X-ray photoelectron spectroscopy (XPS, Fig. 2), which not only confirmed the oxidation states of Ti and Ni but also provided evidence of stoichiometric stability across the different deposition conditions.

Initial optimization efforts were directed toward fine-tuning the thicknesses of each individual layer, as nanoscale variations strongly affect the interference patterns responsible for visible transmittance and infrared reflectance. By systematically varying thicknesses, it was possible to establish an optimized balance between high visible-light transparency and strong near-infrared rejection, while maintaining robust anti-reflective and anti-soiling characteristics. These optimizations lay the foundation for tailoring multilayered oxide/metal stacks for specific applications, whether as photonic coolers for buildings, protective coatings for photovoltaic panels, or multifunctional surfaces for flexible electronics.

The detailed deposition protocols, characterization results, and structure–property correlations will be presented and discussed extensively in the full version of this study. These findings not only underscore the versatility of e-beam evaporation in producing complex multi-functional thin films but also highlight the potential of such coatings to serve as scalable, durable, and high-performance solutions for next-generation energy and environmental technologies.

3 RESULTS AND DISCUSSIONS

The optical response of the NiO thin films was systematically investigated using UV–Vis spectroscopy over the broad wavelength range of 200–2000 nm. The absorptance (A) of the films was derived using the standard relationship:

$$A(\%) = 100 - (T+R)$$

where T denotes the transmittance and R the reflectance. The results demonstrated a strong dependence of optical behavior on film thickness. Ultra-thin films (~20 nm) exhibited exceptionally high transmittance, reaching values up to 85% for wavelengths above 500 nm, thereby maximizing visible-light penetration. In contrast, thicker films (>100 nm) displayed significantly higher absorptance and reflectance, confirming that careful control of thickness serves as a powerful tool to tailor the optical properties of NiO coatings.

A similar dependence on thickness was observed for metallic layers. For Al and Ag films, reflectance varied markedly between 10 nm and 15 nm, underscoring the critical influence of nanoscale thickness variations on spectral selectivity. Importantly, in hybrid NiO/metal multilayer configurations, such as NiO (100 nm)/Al (10 nm) and NiO (100 nm)/Ag (15 nm), the films simultaneously achieved low reflectance in the visible range, ensuring transparency, while exhibiting strong reflectance in the infrared (IR) region. This dual behavior is highly advantageous for near-infrared (NIR) filtering applications, where blocking thermal IR radiation while preserving visible transmittance is essential for photonic cooling and energy efficiency.

Microstructural characterization provided further insights into film quality and stability. Scanning electron microscopy (SEM) revealed that all evaporated multi-stacked layers were dense, homogenous, and devoid of pinholes or cracks—an essential prerequisite for reliable optoelectronic device performance. Surface roughness was strongly correlated with the thickness of the metallic interlayers. Specifically, NiO/metal (Al or Ag, 20 nm) samples exhibited an average surface roughness of ~17 nm, whereas NiO/metal (Al or Ag, 10 nm) layers displayed smoother surfaces with roughness values closer to ~10 nm. Interestingly, increased roughness was associated with smaller grain sizes, indicating that metallic layers not only determine optical reflectivity but also exert a decisive influence on the surface morphology of subsequent oxide layers. This microstructural control could, in turn, be harnessed to tailor surface wettability.

To further optimize the optical properties, additional experiments were conducted by depositing TiOx on top of NiO/Ag films fabricated on lightweight, flexible PET substrates. These TiOx-capped structures exhibited distinctly modified transmission, reflectance, and absorptance profiles across the measured spectrum. Configurations such as TiOx (50 nm)/NiO (100 nm)/Ag (20 nm) and TiOx (50 nm)/NiO (100 nm)/Ag (25 nm) were particularly promising, achieving enhanced reflectance (~20%) at wavelengths beyond 800 nm. This marked improvement in NIR rejection capability confirmed the effectiveness of the multi-stack approach in producing high-performance hot-mirror coatings.

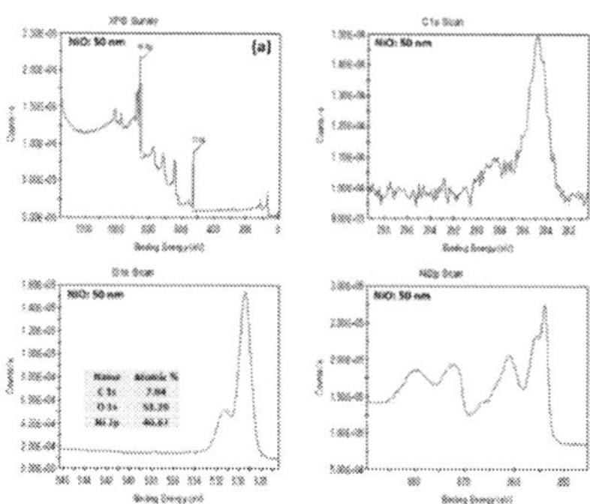

Figure 2: X-ray photoelectron spectroscopy (XPS) survey spectrum of NiO thin films with a thickness of 50 nm. The spectrum confirms the presence of characteristic Ni and O core-level peaks, validating the stoichiometry of the deposited films. The absence of extraneous peaks indicates high purity, while the well-defined Ni 2p and O 1s signals provide evidence of stable oxide bonding states. These results confirm the chemical integrity and quality of the NiO layers fabricated by e-beam evaporation under controlled oxygen flow.

The surface wetting behavior of the thin films was systematically assessed using contact angle (CA) measurements, an important indicator of anti-soiling potential. Films with CA values exceeding 60° were classified as suitable for mitigating dust adhesion in humid environments. Among the tested samples, the TiOx (50 nm)/NiO (300 nm)/Ag (25 nm) configuration displayed the highest degree of hydrophobicity, with a CA of ~104°, reflecting a robust anti-soiling surface. By contrast, the lowest CA (~61.3°) was recorded for the TiOx (50 nm)/NiO (300 nm)/Ag (5 nm) configuration, which was predominantly hydrophilic. These results demonstrated that wettability was intimately linked to surface roughness: higher roughness decreased surface tension, which in turn enabled the possibility of engineering super-hydrophobic surfaces for desert applications.

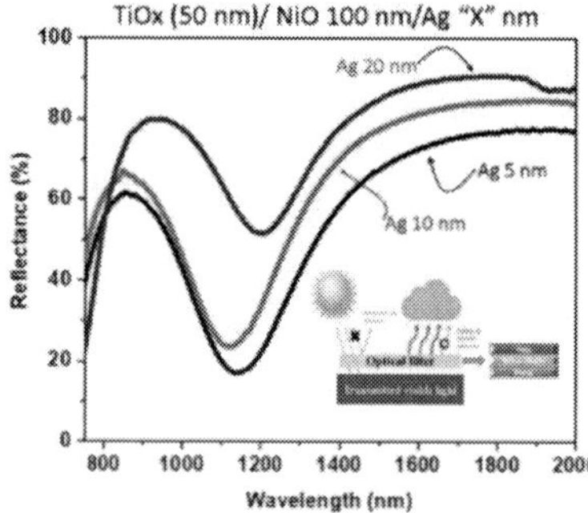

Figure 3: Reflectance spectra as a function of wavelength for multilayer structures incorporating silver (Ag) layers of varying thicknesses. The curves highlight the strong dependence of optical response on Ag thickness, with thinner layers exhibiting lower reflectance across the visible spectrum, while thicker layers enhance reflection in the near-infrared (NIR) region. This tunability demonstrates the critical role of metallic layer thickness in optimizing hot-mirror performance for selective IR filtering applications.

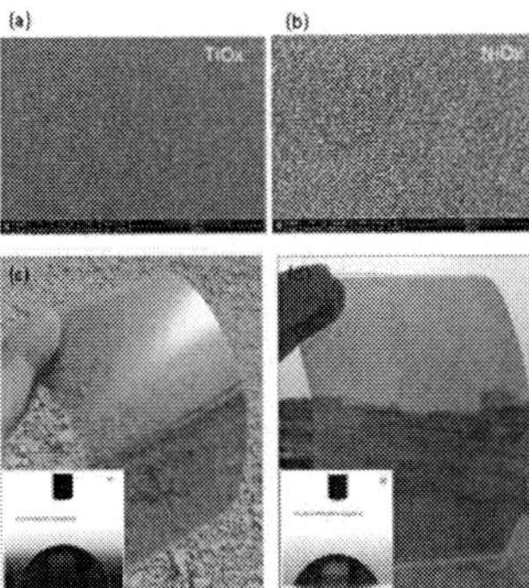

Figure 4: Scanning electron microscopy (SEM) images illustrating the dense, uniform, and pinhole-free morphology of TiOx thin films, alongside high-quality NiOx layers exhibiting smooth and homogeneous surface coverage. The figure also includes optical photographs of flexible multilayer filters deposited on PET substrates, highlighting the visual appearance and transparency of devices with varying silver (Ag) thicknesses. These images collectively confirm the structural integrity, morphological uniformity, and scalability of the fabricated multilayer coatings. Complementary outdoor field testing over a two-month period provided critical validation of the laboratory findings. Notably, the most hydrophilic configurations showed minimal dust accumulation during real-world exposure, in agreement with the measured CA values. These results emphasize the complex interplay between roughness, wettability, and environmental performance, suggesting that both hydrophilic and hydrophobic strategies may be viable depending on application-specific requirements.

In summary, the study confirms that the optical, morphological, and wetting properties of NiO/metal and TiOx/NiO/metal thin films can be finely tuned through precise control of thickness and material stacking. Such multi-functional coatings combine NIR filtering with anti-soiling behavior, and their scalability on both rigid and flexible substrates highlights their strong potential for integration into energy-efficient photovoltaic systems, smart windows, and other optoelectronic devices designed for operation in harsh desert environments.

The findings of this study clearly demonstrate the promise of optimized NiO/metal/TiOx multilayer configurations as highly effective near-infrared (NIR) filters. By carefully tuning the thickness and sequence of individual layers, these structures exhibit adjustable optical properties across the visible–NIR spectrum, while simultaneously offering controlled surface morphology and tailored wetting behavior. Such multifunctionality not only enhances their performance as hot-mirror coatings but also provides intrinsic anti-soiling characteristics, thereby extending their durability in harsh environmental conditions. Collectively, these attributes highlight the strong potential of the proposed designs for integration into advanced optoelectronic systems, including energy-efficient photovoltaic modules, smart glazing technologies, and photonic cooling applications in desert and other extreme climates.

4 CONCLUSIONS

Infrared (IR) spectrum filters play a critical role in suppressing the transmission of IR wavelengths, which are the dominant contributors to heat generation under solar illumination. By selectively reflecting the IR portion of the spectrum while maintaining acceptable levels of visible transparency, such filters can significantly reduce thermal loading, thereby improving the energy efficiency of photovoltaic (PV) modules and building envelopes, an aspect of particular importance in desert environments where cooling demands are exceptionally high. In this study, we report the successful development of multi-functional stacked thin-film structures that combine *infrared filtering, anti-reflective behavior, and anti-soiling properties* within a single photonic cooler design. The multilayer coatings were fabricated using reactive electron-beam (e-beam) evaporation, a process chosen for its scalability, reproducibility, and ability to precisely control oxide stoichiometry. In this configuration, silver (Ag) was employed as a seed layer with a nominal thickness of 20 nm, providing both reflectivity and a template for the subsequent growth of nickel oxide (NiO) and titanium oxide (TiOx) layers. Optical characterization revealed that the NiO (300 nm)/Ag (20 nm) stack exhibited the strongest IR filtering capability, achieving a pronounced infrared cut-off with more than 75% reflectance for wavelengths exceeding 750 nm. In contrast, the visible-light region maintained a transmittance peak of approximately 45% when the metallic layers were restricted to thicknesses between 5 nm and 20 nm. These results underscore the dual function of the architecture: maintaining sufficient visible transparency while effectively reflecting unwanted IR radiation. To further extend the applicability of the design, the multilayer coatings were also deposited on flexible polymer substrates. These flexible IR filters demonstrated enhanced multifunctionality, combining effective IR blocking with anti-reflective properties and dust-repellent behavior. In particular, the TiOx (50 nm)/NiO (300 nm)/Ag (25 nm) configuration achieved the highest measured hydrophobicity, with a contact angle (CA) of ~104°. This strong water-repellent surface confirmed excellent anti-soiling potential, which is essential for maintaining optical efficiency in arid and dusty outdoor environments.

Collectively, the findings confirm the feasibility of fabricating dense, defect-free, and scalable metal oxide/metal/metal oxide stacks via thermal e-beam evaporation. The resulting coatings simultaneously provide *near-infrared filtering, visible anti-reflection, and self-cleaning capabilities*, thereby addressing three critical challenges of optoelectronic devices deployed in harsh climates. Importantly, the scalability of this approach highlights its suitability for integration into miniaturized PV modules, smart window technologies, and advanced photonic cooling systems.

The detailed mechanism underlying the infrared cut-off, arising from the interplay between interference effects in the oxide layers and plasmonic reflection in the metal seed layer, together with its implications for PV module performance, will be comprehensively discussed in the full version of this paper.

5 REFERENCES

[1] N. Abundiz-Cisneros, R. Sanginés, R. Rodríguez-López, M. Peralta-Arriola, J. Cruz, and R. Machorro, *Energy and Buildings*, vol. 206, p. 109558, 2020.
[2] H. Sahm, C. Charton, and R. Thielsch, *Thin Solid Films*, vol. 455, pp. 819–823, 2004.

[3] M. I. Hossain, A. Khandakar, M. E. H. Chowdhury, S. Ahmed, et al., *Journal of Electronic Materials*, pp. 1–11, 2021.

[4] E. Stamate, *Nanomaterials*, vol. 10, no. 1, p. 14, 2020.

[5] W. K. Tan, A. Yokoi, G. Kawamura, A. Matsuda, and H. Muto.

[6] C.-H. Liang, S.-C. Chen, X. Qi, C.-S. Chen, and C.-C. Yang, *Thin Solid Films*, vol. 519, no. 1, pp. 345–350, 2010.

[7] J. T.-W. Wang, J. M. Ball, E. M. Barea, A. Abate, J. A. Alexander-Webber, J. Huang, et al., *Nano Letters*, vol. 14, no. 2, pp. 724–730, 2014.

[8] P. Pinpithak, H.-W. Chen, A. Kulkarni, Y. Sanehira, M. Ikegami, and T. Miyasaka, *Chemistry Letters*, vol. 46, no. 3, pp. 382–384, 2017.

[9] C. Liu, W. Li, J. Chen, J. Fan, Y. Mai, and R. E. Schropp, *Nano Energy*, vol. 41, pp. 75–83, 2017.

[10] K. Cao, Z. Zuo, J. Cui, Y. Shen, T. Moehl, S. M. Zakeeruddin, et al., *Nano Energy*, vol. 17, pp. 171–179, 2015.

[11] P. Baroch, J. Musil, J. Vlcek, K. Nam, and J. Han, *Surface and Coatings Technology*, vol. 193, no. 1–3, pp. 107–111, 2005.

[12] J. Velevska and M. Ristova, *Solar Energy Materials and Solar Cells*, vol. 73, no. 2, pp. 131–139, 2002.

[13] X. Yang, P. Zheng, Q. Bi, and K. Weber, *Solar Energy Materials and Solar Cells*, vol. 150, pp. 32–38, 2016.

[14] I. S. Kim, E.-K. Jeong, D. Y. Kim, M. Kumar, and S.-Y. Choi, *Applied Surface Science*, vol. 255, no. 7, pp. 4011–4014, 2009.

[15] X. J. Feng and L. Jiang, *Advanced Materials*, vol. 18, no. 23, pp. 3063–3078, 2006.

[16] M. I. Hossain, B. Aïssa, A. Samara, S. A. Mansour, C. A. Broussillou, and V. Bermudez Benito, *ACS Omega*, vol. 6, no. 8, pp. 5276–5286, 2021.

[17] L. L. Lebel, B. Aïssa, M. A. El Khakani, and D. Therriault, *Composites Science and Technology*, vol. 70, no. 3, pp. 518–524, 2010.

[18] W. Julia, C. Luis, R. Federico, et al., *Advanced Functional Materials*, vol. 23, pp. 5591–5598, 2013.

[19] D. T. H. Dalir, R. D. Farahani, V. Nhim, B. Aïssa, et al., *Langmuir*, vol. 28, no. 1, pp. 791–803, 2011.

[20] A. Ali, F. El-Mellouhi, A. Mitra, and B. Aïssa, *Nanomaterials*, vol. 12, no. 5, p. 788, 2022.

[21] R. D. Farahani, D. T. H. Dalir, V. Le Borgne, A. Loick, et al., *Composites Science and Technology*, vol. 72, no. 12, pp. 1387–1395, 2012.

[22] N. M. H. Gavi, B. D. Ngom, A. C. Beye, A. M. Strydom, B. Aïssa, V. V. Srinivasu, and M. Chaker, *Journal of Magnetism and Magnetic Materials*, vol. 324, no. 6, pp. 1172–1176, 2012.

[23] B. Aïssa and M. A. El Khakani, *Nanotechnology*, vol. 20, no. 17, p. 175203, 2009.

[24] M. A. Habib, M. Barkat, B. Aïssa, and T. Denidni, *Progress in Electromagnetics Research*, vol. 88, pp. 135–148, 2008.

[25] H. Zhao, H. Kimura, Z. Cheng, X. Wang, and T. Nishida, *Applied Physics Letters*, vol. 95, p. 232904, 2009. https://doi.org/10.1063/1.3271032.

Lightweight Photonic Cooler with Multi-Layered Thin Film IR Filters and Anti-Dust Properties for PV Applications in Desert Environments

Brahim Aissa*, and Mohammad I. Hossain

Qatar Environment and Energy Research Institute (QEERI)- Hamad Bin Khalifa University (HBKU), Doha, P.O. Box 34110, Education City, Doha, Qatar

*Contact: baissa@hbku.edu.qa

QEERI
معهد قطر لبحوث البيئة والطاقة
Qatar Environment & Energy Research Institute
جامعة حمد بن خليفة
HAMAD BIN KHALIFA UNIVERSITY

Abstract

- The overall objective of this work is to develop nano-structured thin films based on cost-effective oxide materials with an integration of very thin metal layer.
- High transmission (T>78%) in the visible light due to low refractive index/high refractive index stacked layer. High reflectance starting (R≈75%) from 800 nm in the IR region. Super hydrophilic TiOx acts as an anti-soiling coating due to photocatalytic behavior and our developed recipe. Scalability, stability. Technology transferable to flexible substrates. Multi-functionalities: IR filtering, anti-reflection coating in the visible range, and anti-soiling coating. Experimental realization and proof-of-concept.

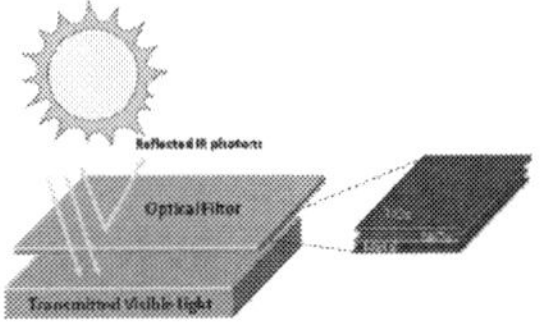

Figure 1: Schematic structure of infrared (IR) photonic filter

We present a novel "metal-oxide/metal-oxide/metal" multi-stack infrared (IR) filter, which incorporates various functionalities.

We use e-beam evaporation process that ensures precise control over the growth parameters.

To meet the desired criteria of achieving a high transmission yield (T%) in the visible spectrum and a high reflection yield (R%) in the IR region, we utilized numerical simulations based on experimental parameters.

Furthermore, we applied these results to perovskite solar cells, demonstrating the enhanced photovoltaic performance achieved through the implementation of IR filtration.

Optical properties:

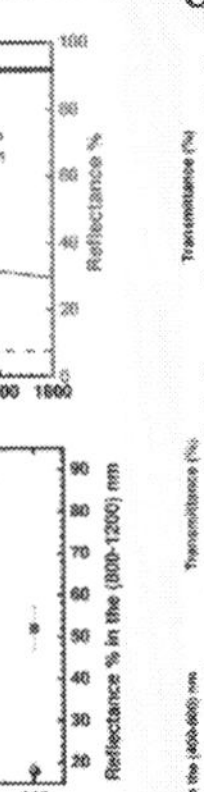

Figure 6: UV–vis of NiO, layers grown at 2 × 10⁻⁴ Torr with different thicknesses: (a) typical example of T % and R % of NiO, of 20 nm thickness and (b) summary of T % and R % of NiO, films with different thicknesses.

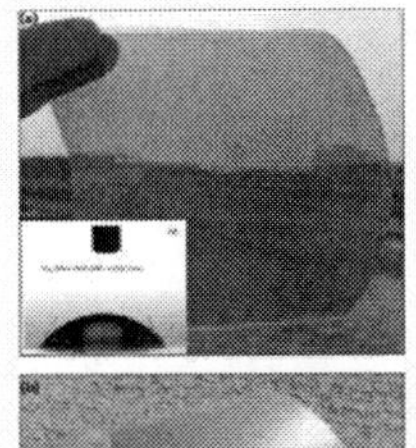

Figure 7: UV–vis results of NiO/metal layers grown with different thicknesses. (a) Transmittance (%) and reflectance (%) of 100 nm thick NiO deposited on (a) 10 nm of Al and (b) 10 nm of Ag layers. (c) Variation of both T % and R % with respect to the NiO film thicknesses for two metals, namely, Al and Ag.

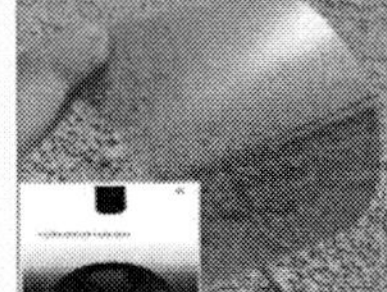

Optical photos of the filters along with the contact angle measurements performed on these flexible coatings.

1. Experimental Setup

NiO and TiOx metal-oxide layers were reactively evaporated at room temperature (RT) with a growth rate of 1 Å/s and a deposition pressure of 2 × 10-4 Torr, under a constant oxygen flow of 20 sccm, using a Denton™ e-beam evaporation. Later, Al and Ag metal layers were evaporated at the same growth rate without any oxygen supply.

specification	our development	ConverLight65 [i]	ConverLight75 [i]	oxide-based multilayer structure [ii]	nitride-based multilayer structure [ii]
fabrication technique	physical vapor deposition	physical vapor deposition	physical vapor deposition	physical vapor deposition	physical vapor deposition
cost	inexpensive due to the simple structure, no process temperature, and available materials	expensive due to the complex structure	expensive due to the complex structure	expensive due to the complex structure	expensive due to the complex structure
applications	broad (building windows to PV)	broad (building windows to PV)	broad (building windows to PV)	PV	PV
functionalities	NIR filter, daylight harvesting, and antisoiling coating	NIR filter	NIR filter	NIR filter	NIR filter
number of stacked layers	3	5	5	8	4

[i] https://chromogenics.com/dynamic-glass/
[ii] Lee, M. et al. Photonic structures in radiative cooling. Light: Sci. Appl. 2023, 12, 134

- The optical measurements were conducted using UV-Vis spectroscopy (PerkinElmer Lambda™) instrument.
- The wetting behavior was assessed through Kruss™ contact angle measurements.
- Surface topology using a Dektak™ 3D stylus.
- Microstructure and morphology using JEOL 7610™ FESEM.
- For structural characterization, XPS analysis was involved with a specific narrow bandwidth analysis at 20 eV with 10 scans for HRXPS.
- The spectral analysis and peak fitting were conducted using the "Avantage" software.

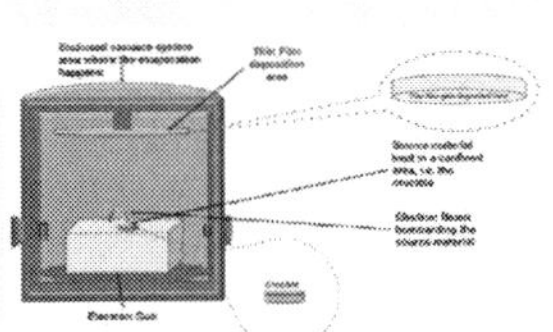

Figure 2: Schematic of the e-beam evaporation process

2. Results

Morphological and Structural properties

Figure 3: Top view SEM images of NiO/metal layers. (a) NiO (300 nm), (b) NiO (100 nm)/Al (10 nm), (c) NiO (300 nm)/Al (20 nm), (d) NiO (100 nm)/Ag (10 nm), (e) NiO (300 nm)/Ag (20 nm), and (f) TiOx (50 nm) on NiO (300 nm)..

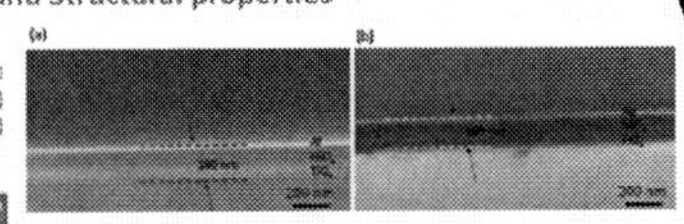

Figure 4: SEM images of NIR-stacked films: (a) TiO₂ stacked over NiO₂/Al and (b) TiO₂ stacked over NiO₂/Ag.

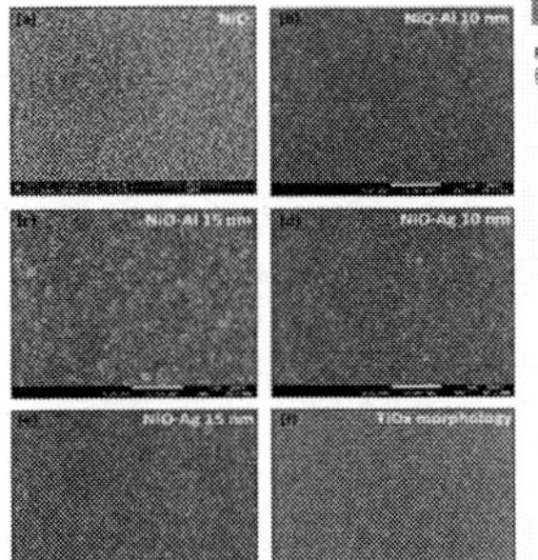

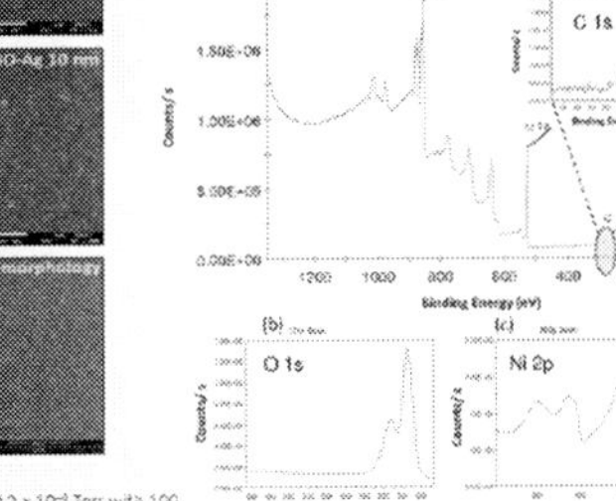

Figure 5: XPS survey of NiO layers grown at 2 × 10⁻⁴ Torr with 100 nm thickness. High-resolution XPS for (b) O 1s and (c) Ni 2p.

PV Properties :

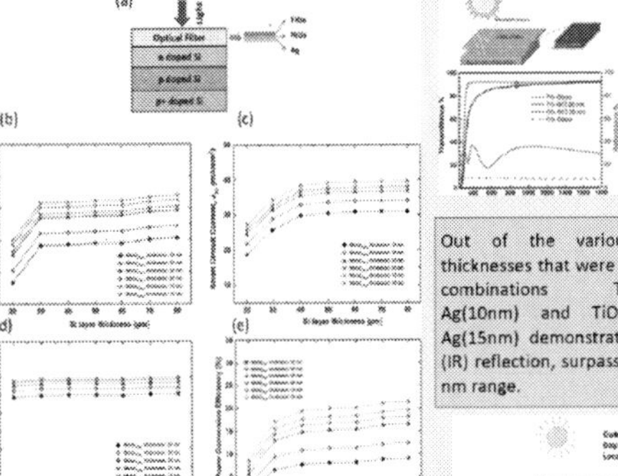

Out of the various configurations and thicknesses that were tested and analyzed, the combinations TiOx(50nm)/NiO(100nm)/Ag(10nm) and TiOx(50 nm)/NiO(100nm)/Ag(15nm) demonstrated the highest infrared (IR) reflection, surpassing 38% in the 750-1200 nm range.

Figure 8: Device performance simulation of Si solar cells using the optical properties of NIR filters

Figure 9: TiOx (50 nm)/NiO(100nm)/Ag(15nm) filters. The insets are examples of the contact angle measurements performed on these flexible coatings.

Figure 10: Temperature measurement vs time of the day performed on a quartz substrate placed in outdoor conditions, in cases with and without IR coating.

3. Summary:

- Photonic coolers based on IR filters are developed to cutoff wavelengths, which cause heat generation.
- In this work, stacked layers consisting of metal oxides and metal layers were developed by using a reactive e-beam evaporation process.
- The highest NIR cutoff was obtained for NiO (100 nm)/Ag (10 nm) layers with a value of 38% IR reflectance in the 750–1200 nm range while keeping a descent T % value above 50% in the vis range.
- Later, flexible substrates were used to develop such IR filters with other functionalities such as antireflection and antisoiling coatings. TiO₂ (50 nm)/NiO (100 nm)/Ag (10 nm) showed the highest hydrophobicity, with a CA of about 104°.
- These results confirm that the developed multistacked metal-oxide/metal-oxide/metal layers using thermal e-beam evaporation can be used as a flexible NIR light filter with a potential antidust ability and a large-scale fabrication feasibility.
- The preliminary experimental results confirmed the capability of such filters to reduce the temperature in outdoor conditions efficiently. Work is currently in progress to quantify this reduction accurately and correlate it with dusty and meteorological conditions.

4. References

1. Abundiz-Cisneros, N., R. Sanginés, R. Rodríguez-López, M. Peralta-Arriola, J. Cruz, and R. Machorro. "Novel Low-E filter for architectural glass pane." Energy and Buildings 206 (2020): 109558.
2. Zhao, Pin, Seohan Kim, Seonghwan Yoon, and Pungkeun Song. "Characteristics of indium zinc oxide/silver/indium zinc oxide multilayer thin layers prepared by magnetron sputtering as flexible transparent film heaters." Thin Solid Layers 665 (2018): 137-142.
3. Loka, Chadrasekhar, Kyoung Ryeol Park, and Kee-Sun Lee. "Multi-functional TiO2/Si/Ag (Cr)/TiNx coatings for low-emissivity and hydrophilic applications." Applied Surface Science 363 (2016): 439-444.
4. Hossain, M. I., A. Khandakar, M. E. H. Chowdhury, S. Ahmed, M. M. Nauman, and B. Aissa. "Numerical and Experimental Investigation of Infrared Optical Filter Based on Metal Oxide Thin Layers for Temperature Mitigation in Photovoltaics." Journal of Electronic Materials (2021): 1-11.

ENHANCING INDOOR PHOTOVOLTAICS: OPTIMIZATION OF DYE-SENSITIZED SOLAR CELLS FOR THE INTERNET OF THINGS

Giorgia Salerno[a] [b], David Roy Bradford [d], Alessio Dessi [c], Daniele Franchi[c] , Alessandro Abbotto[a],Ottavia Bettucci*[a], Marina Freitag* [d].

[a] Department of Materials Science, Solar Energy Research Center MIB-SOLAR and INSTM Milano-Bicocca Research Unit University of Milano-Bicocca,Via Cozzi 55, Milano I-20125, Italy, [b] Department of Information and Electrical Engineering and Applied Mathematics (DIEM) University of Salerno, Invariante 12/B, Via Giovanni Paolo II, 132, Fisciano (SA) I-84084, Italy; [c] National Council of Research – Institute for the Chemistry of Organometallic Compounds (CNR-ICCOM), Via Madonna del Piano 10, Sesto Fiorentino 50019, Italy; [d] School of Natural and Environmental Science, Bedson Building, Newcastle University, NE1 7RU, Newcastle upon Tyne, UK.

giorgia.salerno@unimib.it

ABSTRACT: The rapid expansion of the Internet of Things (IoT) and the increasing reliance on technology in the past decade have intensified the demand for sustainable and efficient energy solutions for powering small indoor devices. Low-light photovoltaics represents an innovative approach to harnessing ambient light in homes and workplaces, and among available technologies, Dye-Sensitized Solar Cells (DSSCs) stand out as a particularly promising option. DSSCs operate by mimicking photosynthesis and typically consist of a photosensitizing dye, a titanium dioxide (TiO_2) photoanode, and a redox couple electrolyte. Unlike conventional silicon-based photovoltaics, they can effectively capture diffuse indoor light, making them highly suited for powering sensors and low-power electronics. Their cost-effectiveness, structural flexibility, and ability to be tailored to specific light sources further enhance their appeal. A key factor in DSSC performance under indoor conditions is the compatibility between the dye's absorption spectrum and the emission spectrum of artificial lighting, such as LEDs and fluorescent lamps. Co-sensitization strategies and the use of dyes with D-π-A (push–pull) structures can significantly improve light harvesting under narrow-spectrum indoor sources. In this study, we focus on optimizing dye selection and co-sensitization to improve DSSC efficiency for indoor applications. Preliminary results show that specific dyes, such as Y123 and TP1, outperform others under particular indoor light sources due to superior spectral matching. Notably, TP1, an affordable and easily synthesized dye, achieved results comparable to the more expensive Y123 under indoor conditions These findings highlight the critical role of dye-lamp matching and device architecture in maximizing DSSC performance. Future work will extend testing to modern LED lamps and refine dye combinations to enhance stability, efficiency, and integration, contributing to the development of sustainable, cost-effective energy solutions for indoor IoT devices.

1 INTRODUCTION

The growing proliferation of the Internet of Things (IoT) and the rising energy demand of low-power indoor devices have driven intensive research into photovoltaic technologies capable of efficiently harvesting ambient light.[1] Among these, dye-sensitized solar cells (DSSCs) have emerged as a promising solution for indoor applications due to their ability to operate efficiently under diffuse and low-light conditions, their structural flexibility, and relatively low production costs. In a DSSC, light is absorbed by a dye anchored to a mesoporous titanium dioxide (TiO_2) layer, promoting electron excitation. The excited electrons are injected into the TiO_2 conduction band and subsequently transported to the fluorine-doped tin oxide (FTO) substrate, from where they flow through an external circuit to generate electricity. The oxidized dye molecules are regenerated by electrons supplied from a redox couple in the electrolyte, thus completing the circuit and enabling continuous energy generation.[2] Dye selection plays a critical role in optimizing DSSC performance under indoor lighting. In this work, we investigate TP1, a dye characterized by advantageous spectroscopic properties and a simpler, more cost-effective synthesis compared to widely used high-performance dyes such as XY1 and Y123.[3] While XY1 and Y123 are typically co-adsorbed with disaggregating agents like chenodeoxycholic acid (CDCA) to prevent dye aggregation on the TiO_2 surface, enhance molecular distribution, strengthen binding to the semiconductor, and improve device stability, recent studies have explored alternative additives such as Bufexamac (BPHA) and its analogue benzohydroxamic acid (BHA). These compounds have been shown to promote an even more orderly dye arrangement on titania. In this study, we examine the performance of TP1 in the presence of BPHA and BHA to assess their impact on the efficiency and stability of DSSCs under indoor illumination.[4]

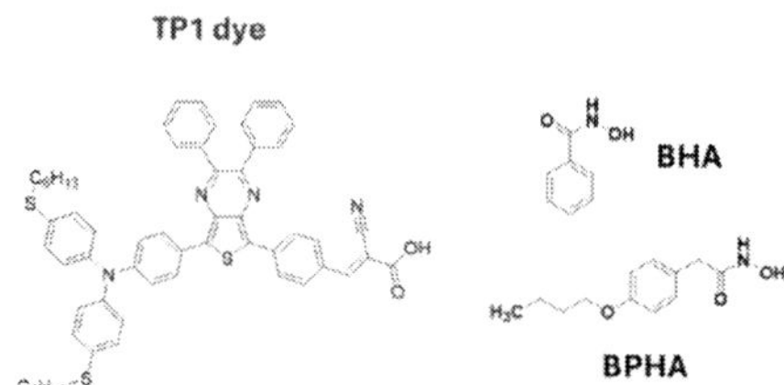

Figure 1: Dye and disaggregating agents used on this project

2 DSSCs DEVICES

2.1 CELL FABRICATION

Conductive glass substrates (Nippon Sheet Glass, Pilkington, 10 Ω sq⁻¹ sheet resistance) were sequentially cleaned in Hellmanex solution, deionized water, acetone, and ethanol, followed by UV–ozone treatment to remove residual contaminants. A compact TiO_2 blocking layer was then deposited by spray pyrolysis at 450 °C from a 0.2 M titanium tetraisopropoxide/2 M acetylacetone solution in isopropanol. Mesoporous TiO_2 photoanodes with active areas of 3.2 cm² (4 cm × 0.8 cm) or 8 cm² (8 cm × 1 cm) were subsequently screen-printed (Seritec Services SA, Corseaux, Switzerland) using DSL 30 NRD-T TiO₂ paste (30 nm, Dyesol/GreatCellSolar) to achieve a 4 μm thick film. For cells tested under AM 1.5G illumination, 18NR-AO Titania (GreatCellSolar) paste was employed. After drying at 120 °C, a 400 nm scattering layer (WER2-0, Dyesol/GreatCellSolar) was screen-printed on top of the mesoporous film and the substrates were gradually heated to 450 °C and sintered for 30 min. The resulting films were treated with 40 mM aqueous TiCl₄ at 70 °C for 30 min and sintered again at 450 °C for 30 min. After cooling to room temperature, the titania films were sensitized by immersion in the appropriate dye solution for 12 h. PEDOT counter electrodes were prepared by electro polymerization of 3,4-ethylenedioxythiophene from a 0.01 mM aqueous solution containing 0.1 M sodium dodecyl sulphate.[5] The redox electrolyte for liquid DSSCs consisted of 0.05 M Cu(tmby)₂TFSI, 0.02 M Cu(tmby)₂TFSl₂, 0.2 M lithium bis(trifluoromethanesulfonyl)imide, and 1.2 M 1-methylbenzimidazole in N-methyl-2-pyrrolidone (MPN).[6] Finally, the photoanode and counter electrode were assembled, and the electrolyte solution was introduced to complete the device.

2.2 PRELIMINARI RESULTS

For reference cells, a 0.1 M TP1 solution with 0.5 M chenodeoxycholic acid (CDCA) was employed, whereas in the alternative approach TiO₂ electrodes were first pretreated with Bufexamac (BPHA) or benzohydroxamic acid (BHA). Specifically, TiO₂ films were immersed in a 3 mM BPHA solution in ethanol for 30 minutes at room temperature, rinsed with ethanol, dried with compressed air, and subsequently sensitized in the TP1 dye solution at room temperature for 12 hours.

Once assembled, the cells were characterized under simulated sunlight using an AM 1.5 solar simulator to ensure comparable conditions. The photovoltaic parameters obtained (Table 1) indicate that the use of alternative co-adsorbents significantly affects device performance. The reference TP1–CDCA cell showed a power conversion efficiency (PCE) of 5.13 %, with Voc = 850 mV, Jsc = 9.23 mA cm⁻², and a fill factor (FF) of 0.66. By contrast, TP1–BHA achieved the best performance with a PCE of 6.55 %, Voc = 860 mV, Jsc = 10.6 mA cm⁻², and FF = 0.72, demonstrating both higher photocurrent and improved FF compared to the CDCA-based device. TP1–BPHA exhibited a moderate increase in Jsc (9.78 mA cm⁻²) and FF (0.70), resulting in a PCE of 5.37 %, although a lower Voc (790 mV) was recorded. These results confirm that pretreatment of TiO₂ electrodes with BHA or BPHA can improve dye organization and interfacial properties, leading to enhanced charge collection and higher device efficiency. In particular, BHA appears to be the most promising additive for TP1-based DSSCs, combining a simple procedure with a clear gain in performance.

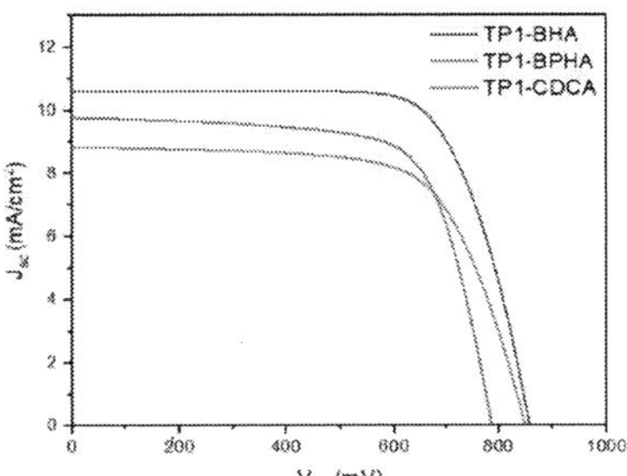

Figure 2: J/V curves of DSSCs sensitized by TP1 dye and the different types of disaggregating agents.

Table 1: J/V characteristics of DSSCs sensitized by TP1 dye and the different types of disaggregating agents.

Cell name	V_{oc} (mV)	J_{sc} (mA/cm²)	FF (%)	η(%)
TP1-CDCA	850 (840±10)	9.23 (8.72±0.7)	0.66 (0.65±0.6)	5.13 (4.87±0.3)
TP1-BHA	860 (830±30)	10.6 (10.5±0.1)	0.72 (0.71±0,1)	6.55 (6.1±0.4)
TPI-BPHA	790 (7700±20)	9.78 (9.16±0.3)	0.70 (0.71±0.4)	5.37 (5.1±0.4)

3 DEVICE CHARACTERIZATION

Current–voltage measurements (J/V) were carried out in ambient air under AM 1.5G illumination using Sinus-70 solar simulator (Wavelabs, Leipzig, Germany), calibrated with reference silicon device (RERA solutions). An X200 source meter (Ossila, Sheffield, UK) was used to assess solar cell performance (scan speed 100 mV s−1). A mask was employed to confine the active solar cell area to 0.196 cm².

4   CONCLUSIONS AND FUTURE DEVELOPMENTS

Building on the results obtained so far, the same optimization strategy will be extended to operation under low-light conditions. Once the fabrication protocol is fully optimized, the performance of the cells will be evaluated under artificial indoor illumination using two types of fluorescent lamps commonly employed in domestic and office environments (OSRAM 930 and OSRAM 765), which feature distinct emission spectra but are both largely covered by the absorption profile of the TP1 dye. In addition, a modern LED lamp will be included to reflect the current global trend in indoor lighting technologies. Finally, the pretreatment molecules identified as beneficial for the cost-effective TP1 dye will also be applied to DSSCs employing co-sensitization strategies with TP1 and other dyes, in order to enhance spectral matching between the dyes' absorption and the emission characteristics of indoor light sources.

7 KEYWORDS

DSSC, Indoor application, organic dyes.

8 REFERENCES

[1] H. Michaels, M. Rinderle, I. Benesperi, R. Freitag, A. Gagliardi, M. Freitag, *Chem. Sci.* **2023**, *14*, 5350-5360.

[2] A. B. Muñoz-García, I. Benesperi, G. Boschloo, J. J. Concepcion, J. H. Delcamp, E. A. Gibson, G. J. Meyer, M. Pavone, H. Pettersson, A. Hagfeldt, M. Freitag, *Chem. Soc. Rev.* **2021**, *50*, 12450-12550.

[3] G. Salerno, D. Franchi, A. Dessì, M. Bartolini, N. Manfredi, A. Abbotto, O. Bettucci, *ChemistryOpen*, *n/a*, e202400464.

[4] Y. Ren, D. Zhang, J. Suo, Y. Cao, F. T. Eickemeyer, N. Vlachopoulos, S. M. Zakeeruddin, A. Hagfeldt, M. Grätzel, *Nat.* **2023**, *613*, 60-65.

[5] N. Sakmeche, S. Aeiyach, J.-J. Aaron, M. Jouini, J. C. Lacroix, P.-C. Lacaze, *Langmuir* **1999**, *15*, 2566-2574.

[6] Y. Saygili, M. Söderberg, N. Pellet, F. Giordano, Y. Cao, A. B. Muñoz-García, S. M. Zakeeruddin, N. Vlachopoulos, M. Pavone, G. Boschloo, L. Kavan, J.-E. Moser, M. Grätzel, A. Hagfeldt, M. Freitag, *J. Am. Chem. Soc.* **2016**, *138*, 15087-15096.

Enhancing Indoor Photovoltaics: Optimization of Dye-Sensitized Solar Cells for the Internet of Things

Giorgia Salerno[a] [b], David Roy Bradford [d], Alessio Dessi [c], Daniele Franchi[c], Alessandro Abbotto[a], Ottavia Bettucci*[a], Marina Freitag* [d].

[a] Department of Materials Science, Solar Energy Research Center MIB-SOLAR and INSTM Milano-Bicocca Research Unit University of Milano-Bicocca, Via Cozzi 55, Milano I-20125, Italy; [b] Department of Information and Electrical Engineering and Applied Mathematics (DIEM) University of Salerno, Invariante 12/B, Via Giovanni Paolo II, 132, Fisciano (SA) I-84084, Italy; [c] National Council of Research – Institute for the Chemistry of Organometallic Compounds (ChR-ICCOM), Via Madonna del Piano 10, Sesto Fiorentino 50019, Italy; [d] School of Natural and Environmental Science, Bedson Building, Newcastle University, NE1 7RU, Newcastle upon Tyne, UK.

Low light photovoltaics is an innovative strategy to harness light inside homes and power small electronic devices that are part of the Internet of Things (IoT). Among existing photovoltaic devices, Dye Sensitized Solar Cells (DSSCs) are the most promising technology in this field. The core of a DSSC is an organic dye with a D-π-A structure (push-pull) whose absorption must be as compatible as possible with the emission spectrum of indoor lamps.

DSSCs DEVICE

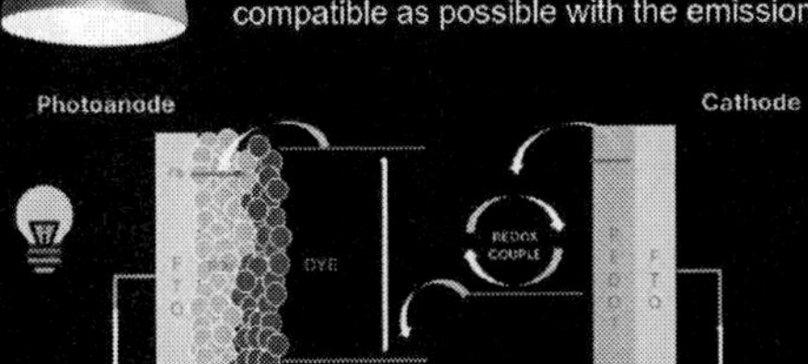

In a DSSC the light is caught by a dye anchored on the TiO_2 layer, exciting the electrons. The excited electrons are injected into the TiO_2 conduction band and then transferred to the fluorine-doped tin oxide glass (FTO) and finally flowing through an external circuit, generating electricity. The oxidized dye molecules are regenerated by electrons stemming from an electrolyte containing a redox couple. This step completes the circuit, allowing continuous electron flow and energy generation.

PURPOSE OF THE WORK

The dye selected for this work is the TP1 dye due to its interesting spectroscopic features and its relatively straightforward synthetic process simpler but also significantly more cost-effective compared to other highly efficient dyes such as XY1 and Y123, commonly used in indoor DSSCs studies. XY1 and Y123 are typically used in combination with a disaggregating agent like chenodeoxycholic acid (CDCA), which 1. prevent dye aggregation on the TiO_2 surface, 2. enhance the uniform distribution of dye molecules, 3. promote stronger binding to the semiconductor improving overall cell efficiency, and 4. improve the long-term stability of the solar cell. Recently, various alternative disaggregating molecules such as Bufexamac (BPHA) and its analogue benzohydroxamic acid (BHA), have been explored in the literature. These compounds fulfill the same role as CDCA, but studies have shown that they facilitate a more orderly arrangement of dye molecules on the titania surface. For these reasons, in this work dye TP1 has been tested in presence of BPHA and BHA to investigate changes in the DSSCs efficiencies. [1-3]

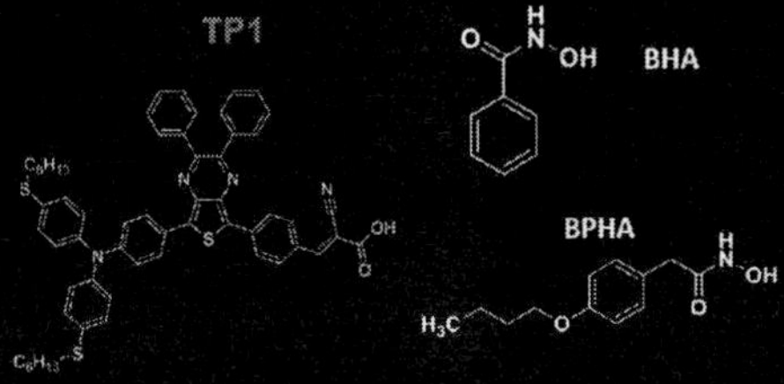

PRELIMINARY RESULTS

The cells were fabricated as described in the literature, using a 0.1 M solution of TP1 with 0.5 M chenodeoxycholic acid for the TP1-type cells. In contrast, for the molecules where pretreatments with BPHA and BHA were applied, TiO_2 electrodes were immersed in an EtOH solution containing 3 mM BPHA at room temperature for 30 minutes. Subsequently, the BPHA-coated TiO_2 electrodes were rinsed with EtOH and dried using compressed air. The BPHA-coated mesoporous TiO_2 films were then sensitized by immersion in the dye solutions at room temperature for 12 hours.

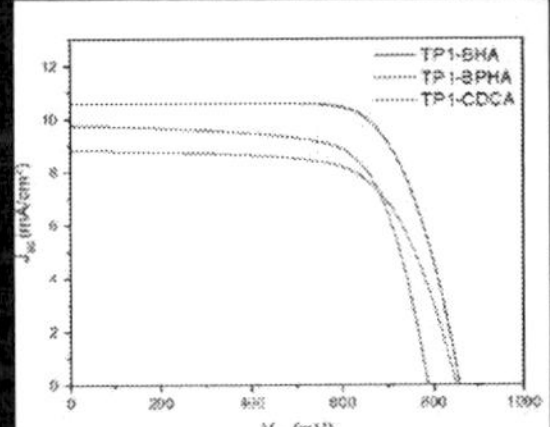

Cell name	V_{oc} (mV)	J_{sc} (mA/cm²)	FF (%)	η(%)
TP1-CDCA	850	9.23	0.66	5.13
	(840±10)	(8.72±0.7)	(0.65±0.6)	(4.87±0.3)
TP1-BHA	860	10.6	0.72	6.55
	(830±30)	(10.5±0.1)	(0.71±0,1)	(6.1±0.4)
TP1-BPHA	790	9.78	0.70	5.37
	(7700±20)	(9.16±0.3)	(0.71±0.4)	(5.1±0.4)

As can be seen from the *J/V* results, TP1 with a 0.5 M concentration of chenodeoxycholic acid produces a lower PCE% compared to the use of BHA and BPHA as pretreatments. The V_{oc} does not show significant differences, except in the case of TP1-BPHA, where it is lower. The current is higher in the case of TP1-BHA, and the fill factor (FF) is also better in the cells that were pretreated with BHA and BPHA.

FUTURE DEVELOPMENTS

Based on the previously described results, the same optimization will also be tested under low-light conditions. Once the fabrication process has been optimized, the cells will be tested using two types of fluorescent lamps commonly used in indoor environments (OSRAM 930 and OSRAM 765), which have different emission spectra but are both well covered by the absorption spectrum of the TP1 dye (see figures on the right). Additionally, a modern LED lamp will be used, reflecting the current global trend in indoor lighting technologies. Finally, the same pretreatment molecules used with the cost-effective TP1 dye could be applied to DSSC cells employing co-sensitization strategies with TP1 and other dyes, in order to enhance the spectral matching between the dyes' absorption and the emission spectra of indoor light sources.

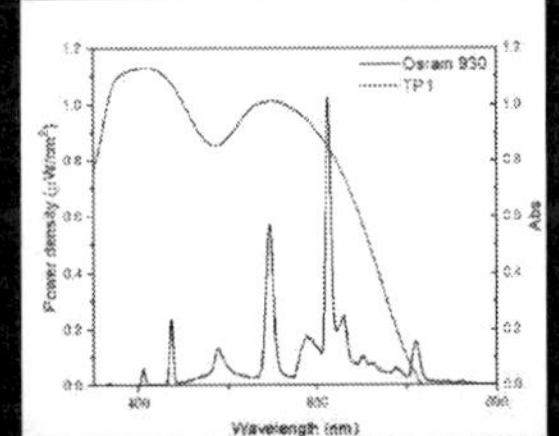

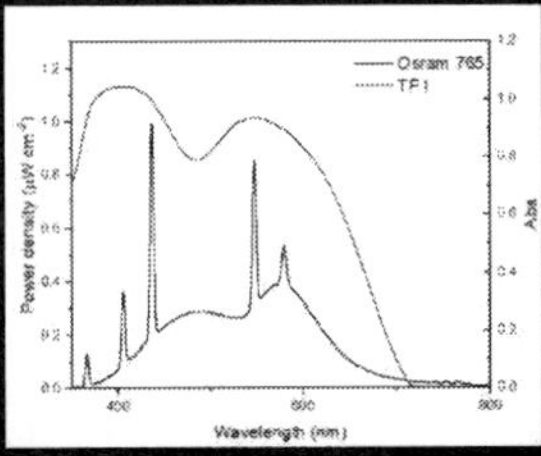

CONCLUSIONS

In conclusion, the TP1 dye had previously been synthesized and studied as a cost-effective alternative to conventional organic dyes such as Y123 and XY1, which are commonly used in DSSCs. Compared to these standard dyes, TP1 was identified as a more economical organic dye option. Moreover, the 1 sun efficiencies of TP1-based cells were improved using alternative co-adsorbents, specifically BHA and BPHA, rather than the commonly employed ones. In particular, BPHA had already been previously studied and demonstrated to enhance performance when used with other organic dyes.

ACKNOWLEDGMENTS

University of Milano-Bicocca, Ministero dell'Università e della Ricerca (PRIN2022 Mendeleev), and PNRR-Sustainable Mobility Center (CNMS), MOST – Sustainable Mobility Center (funding from the European Union Next-GenerationEU, Piano Nazionale di Ripresa e Resilienza (PNRR) – Missione 4 Componente 2, Investimento 1.4 – D.D. 1033 17/06/2022, CN00000023) for financial support

REFERENCES

1. Ren, Y. et al. Hydroxamic acid pre-adsorption raises the efficiency of cosensitized solar cells. Nat. 613, 60-65, doi:10.1038/s41586-022-05460-z (2023).
2. Salerno, G. et al. Optimizing DSSCs Performance for Indoor Lighting: Matching Organic Dyes Absorption and Indoor Lamps Emission Profiles to Maximize Efficiency. ChemistryOpen n/a, e202400464. (2024)
3. Muñoz-Garcia, A. B. et al. Dye-sensitized solar cells strike back. Chem. Soc. Rev. 50, 12450-12550, doi:10.1039/D0CS01336F ,(2021).

CONTACTS

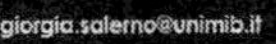

giorgia.salerno@unimib.it
www.linkedin.com/in/giorgia-salerno

SIC RECRYSTALLIZATION BY UV NANOPULSED LASER ANNEALING

Daniele Arduino [a b], Luciano Scaltrito [a], Sergio Ferrero [a], Andrea Ancillao [a]

[a] Department of Applied Science and Technology, Politecnico di Torino, Corso Duca degli Abruzzi 24, 10129 Torino, Italy.

[b] Department of Information Engineering, Electrical Engineering and Applied Mathematics, University of Salerno, Via Giovanni Paolo II 132, 84084 Fisciano, Italy

daniele_arduino@polito.it , luciano.scaltrito@polito.it , sergio.ferrero@polito.it , andrea.ancillao@polito.it

Corresponding Author: Daniele Arduino

ABSTRACT: This work explores the use of nanosecond UV pulsed laser annealing to induce localized recrystallization in amorphous silicon carbide (a-SiC) thin films, a strategic material for power electronics and photovoltaic applications. The experiment was conducted in a vacuum chamber (4.3×10^{-1} mbar) using a 355 nm Q-switched DPSS laser, with a spot size of about 80 μm and power ranging from 1.15 to 3.95 W. The films, 450–500 nm thick and deposited on crystalline 4H-SiC substrates, were irradiated under different combinations of fluence and scan speed. TEM analysis revealed that, under optimal conditions, nanocrystalline domains (5–15 nm) formed up to about 50 nm in depth, while preserving the substrate integrity and avoiding ablation effects. The results demonstrate the feasibility of a compact, selective thermal treatment compatible with fabrication workflows, opening perspectives for advanced devices and novel electronic architectures.

Keywords: Amorphous Silicon Carbide Crystallization, DPSS Q-switched Laser, UV Laser Annealing, Vacuum-Assisted Processing

1. INTRODUCTION

The growing adoption of technologies for sustainable energy and high-performance electronics has driven research toward materials and processes that offer efficiency, miniaturization, and operational robustness. In this context, silicon carbide (SiC) has emerged as one of the most promising semiconductors, thanks to its outstanding properties: wide bandgap, high thermal conductivity, excellent chemical and mechanical stability, and the ability to operate at high temperatures, voltages, and frequencies [1] [2]. These characteristics make SiC an ideal choice for next-generation power devices, particularly in applications such as photovoltaics, electric mobility, and energy conversion systems.

Depending on its crystal structure, SiC can exist in numerous polytypes (over 200), each with slightly different electronic properties [3]. Among them, 4H-SiC is one of the most widely used in microelectronics due to its high carrier mobility. Amorphous SiC (a-SiC) also shows significant potential for optoelectronic and high-frequency applications, thanks to its wider bandgap compared to silicon [1] [4] [5] [6] [7].

However, working with SiC still shows several challenges, particularly in the fabrication of high-quality crystalline layers starting from amorphous films or those damaged by ion implantation [5]. In many cases, a post-deposition thermal treatment is required to restore the crystalline order or to activate dopants [8] [9]. Conventional thermal treatments, typically performed in a furnace, allow for recrystallization and dopant activation, but involve heating the entire device. This can adversely affect already-processed regions, cause unwanted dopant diffusion, or damage existing metal interconnections, making such methods less suitable when localized modification of material properties is required. To overcome these limitations, there has been increasing interest in recent decades in alternative localized annealing techniques, particularly laser annealing. This method allows targeted thermal energy transfer to surface layers while keeping the underlying layers cool [10]. Several studies have explored the use of lasers to process SiC through additive approaches (annealing, doping, surface modification) or subtractive ones (ablation). A wide range of laser sources have been employed: from traditional excimer and Nd:YAG lasers [11] [12] [13] [14] [15] to more recent picosecond and femtosecond lasers [16] [17] [18].

In the context of laser annealing of amorphous SiC films, various studies have demonstrated that optical absorption of laser pulses can induce partial or complete recrystallization of the material through annealing mechanisms. Experiments using UV pulsed lasers (KrF, XeCl) have shown the formation of crystalline phases, with improvements in crystal quality observed via TEM [19] [20]. A KrF laser (248 nm) has been used to induce crystallization in a-SiC films, resulting in the formation of the cubic 3C-SiC phase [21]. At higher fluences, polycrystalline layers have been obtained on ion-implanted films [22]. More recently, visible laser sources such as ruby lasers (694 nm) and Nd:YAG lasers at 532 nm have also been tested with some success, although generally with lower efficiencies [23] [24].

The present study aims to explore a more compact and potentially more sustainable laser-based solution, using a DPSS Q-switched laser at 355 nm operating under controlled vacuum conditions. The use of vacuum helps reduce surface oxidation and improves thermal transfer efficiency, making the process cleaner and more reproducible. The main goal is to evaluate the feasibility of achieving localized and controlled recrystallization of thin amorphous SiC films, allowing selective post-treatment processes for advanced electronic devices and multilayer MEMS structures.

2. STUDY AIM

The main goal of this work was to explore whether it is possible to use localized thermal treatment, specifically laser annealing, to modify thin amorphous silicon carbide (a-SiC) films in a controlled way, aiming to trigger partial or full crystallization of the material. This type of approach could be particularly useful in the electronics field, especially for applications that require selective modifications at the microscale, such as in power devices. A key part of the study focused on testing a DPSS Q-switched laser operating at 355 nm under vacuum conditions, to evaluate whether this system could serve as a valid, and also possibly more compact and cost-effective, alternative to more complex laser technologies commonly used in previous research. Overall, the aim was to assess the feasibility of a selective post-treatment process for SiC, capable of targeting specific areas of the material without exposing the whole device to high thermal stress. If successful, this method could contribute to advancing fabrication techniques for power electronics, especially in scenarios where precision, miniaturization, and material integration are crucial.

3. MATERIALS AND METHODS

3.1 Samples

The experiment was carried out on samples made of amorphous silicon carbide (a-SiC) thin films, about 450 nm thick, deposited by Physical Vapor Deposition (PVD) onto 4H-SiC substrates. The substrates, 100 mm in diameter and 325–375 μm thick, were produced by Dow Corning and supplied by CNRS-SiMaP (Grenoble, France). The deposition was performed with a Si/C ratio of approximately 1.11, at a substrate temperature of 250 °C and a chamber pressure of 0.9 Pa. The plasma power was set to 450 W, and the process lasted 90 minutes, resulting in a growth rate of roughly 300 nm per hour.

3.2 Equipment

The thin films were then locally annealed using a Q-switched DPSS laser (model SOL 4W, 355 nm, Bright Solutions), operating at a wavelength of 355 nm. The repetition rate could be varied between 30 and 120 kHz, with output power ranging from 3.95 W (at 30 kHz) to 1.15 W (at 120 kHz). Depending on the repetition frequency, the pulse duration ranged from 11.9 ns to 31.4 ns. The laser beam had a Gaussian spatial profile, with a spot size of approximately 80 μm. The laser beam was directed onto the samples via a simple optical path that included a UV-enhanced aluminum mirror (Thorlabs PF10-03-F01) and a plano-convex fused silica lens with a 100 mm focal length, AR-coated for the 245–400 nm range (Thorlabs LA4380-UV). Samples were moved under the laser beam using a two-axis motorized stage (Misumi LX26 for X and LX20 for Y), allowing scan speeds between 40 and 100 mm/s. The whole process took place in a custom-built vacuum chamber, kept at a pressure of 4.3×10^{-1} mbar using a rotary vane pump (Varian SD90). The laser entered the chamber through a UV-grade fused silica window (Thorlabs WG42012-UV, Ø2", 12 mm thick, AR-coated for 245–400 nm) and was focused directly onto the sample surface.

3.3 Characterization techniques

After processing, the samples were analyzed to assess surface morphology and structural changes induced by the laser treatment. This characterization was performed using optical microscopy (Leitz Wetzlar Ergolux AMC Inspection Microscope) and transmission electron microscopy (TEM) with a Talos F200X system (Thermo Scientific).

3.4 Study protocol

To investigate how the laser treatment affects the material as a function of the irradiation parameters, a calibration table (see Table 1) was first created. This table links the duty cycle (ranging from 10% to 80%) with the laser repetition frequency (30–100 kHz), providing a mapping of the actual average output power for each combination. The resulting power values range from approximately 0.03 W up to a maximum of 2.97 W.

Calibration matrix	10%	20%	30%	40%	50%	60%	70%	80% duty cycle
30 kHz	0,06	0,25	0,55	0,95	1,39	1,84	2,37	2,97
40 kHz	0,05	0,18	0,41	0,74	1,12	1,58	2,03	2,5
50 kHz	0,04	0,14	0,33	0,59	0,93	1,3	1,75	2,2
60kHz	0,04	0,12	0,27	0,5	0,77	1,12	1,48	1,95
70kHz	0,04	0,1	0,23	0,42	0,66	0,95	1,3	1,66
80kHz	0,03	0,09	0,2	0,36	0,58	0,84	1,16	1,47
90kHz	0,03	0,08	0,18	0,32	0,5	0,74	1,04	1,38
100kHz	0,03	0,08	0,16	0,28	0,47	0,65	0,92	1,37
freq								

Table 1   Calibration table of the laser source

Using this table as a reference, a series of laser scan lines were produced on the a-SiC film, each one characterized by a different combination of power and scan speed. The scan speeds used were within the operational range of the system (40–100 mm/s), allowing the exploration of a wide set of experimental conditions.

After laser processing, all the lines were inspected under an optical microscope to evaluate their surface appearance. The most promising conditions were selected based on two main criteria: the uniformity of the line along its length and its optical appearance, the idea was trying to distinguish between lines that looked burnt or excessively dark (which could indicate damage) and those that showed contrast or reflectivity suggestive of a successful annealing effect.

Following this initial screening, a line was identified as representative of an effective treatment. This was then analysed by transmission electron microscopy (TEM) to investigate possible changes in the film's crystalline structure, in order to assess whether local crystallization of the amorphous SiC had occurred.

During the experiment, numerous sets of irradiation lines were produced, organized into labelled blocks (A–P), each characterized by a specific combination of repetition rate, average delivered power, and scanning speed (see Table 2). These combinations were designed to systematically explore a wide parameter space. The operating conditions were selected based on the laser calibration table obtained experimentally (see Table 1).

Block	Frequency [kHz]	Average Power (W)	Scan Speed (mm/s)	Fluence [J/cm²]
A	40	0,18-0,36	40-50	0,09-0,18
B	40-50	0,74-1,12	50-70	0,37-0,46
C	40	0,05-0,65	40	0,02-0,32
D	80	0,09-0,84	40	0,02-0,21
E	50	0,33-0,84	40-80	0,13-0,33
F	60	0,27-0,77	70-80	0,09-0,26
G	70	0,42-1,66	90-100	0,12-0,47
H	30	0,25-2,47	40-50	0,17-1,77
I	40	1,12-2,03	40-50	0,56-1,01
J	100	0,08-0,92	50	0,02-0,18
K	50-60	0,04-0,33	40	0,01-0,13
L	90	0,08-0,74	40	0,02-0,16
M	50-70	0,10-1,75	40	0,03-0,66
N	80-90	0,82-1,47	40	0,16-0,37
O	50	0,93-1,75	40	0,37-0,70
P	100	0,92-1,37	50	0,18-0,27

Table II   The different blocks of sample lines obtained with different combinations of parameters

4. RESULTS

4.1 Optical analysis

A series of laser scan lines were produced on the a-SiC thin film using different combinations of laser power and scan speed. After the treatment, all lines were initially examined via optical microscopy to assess changes in their visual appearance.

The lines obtained in the different blocks were inspected using optical microscopy. In many cases (e.g., blocks A and K), the lines were completely absent or barely perceptible, even at high magnifications, as visible in Figure 1 and Figure 2. This indicates that, under those parameter combinations, the energy delivered to the film was insufficient to trigger a detectable modification.

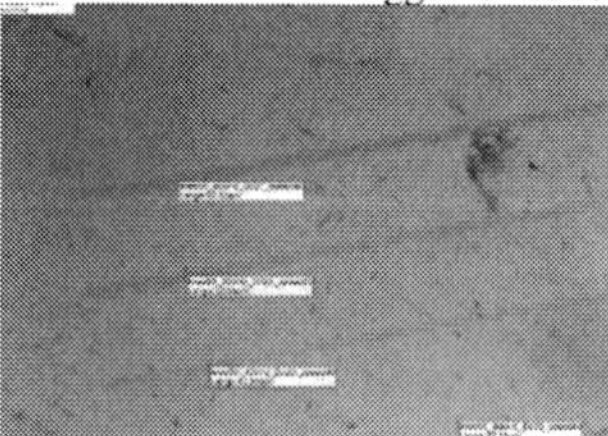

Figure 1 Some of the lines of Block A at the optical microscope: they are barely perceptible

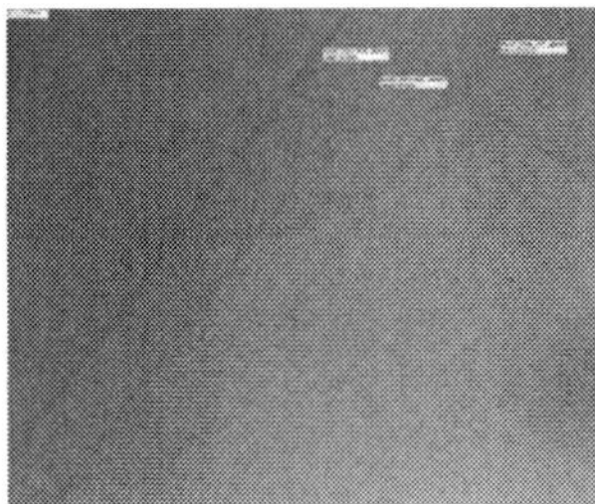

Figure 2 Some of the lines of Block K at the optical microscope: they are barely perceptible

Other blocks (e.g., B, H, I, N, O) showed visible lines, but with clear morphological issues: irregular edges, localized darkening, and discontinuities, potentially related to excessive fluence or thermal instabilities, as visible in the Figures 3-7. These effects suggest that, although sufficient energy was delivered, the irradiation regime was not optimized to ensure an orderly structural transformation.

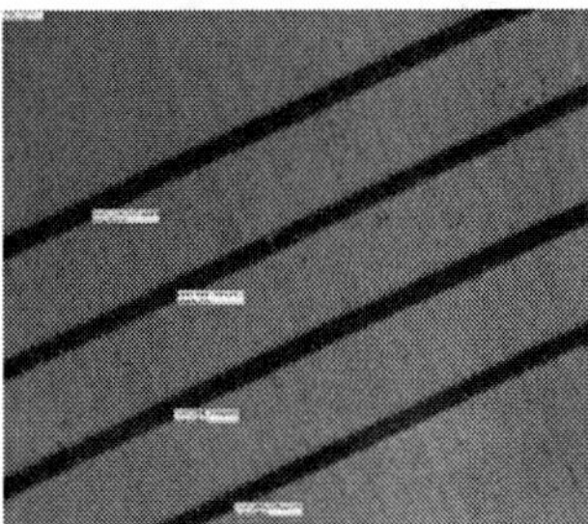

Figure 3 Some of the lines of Block B

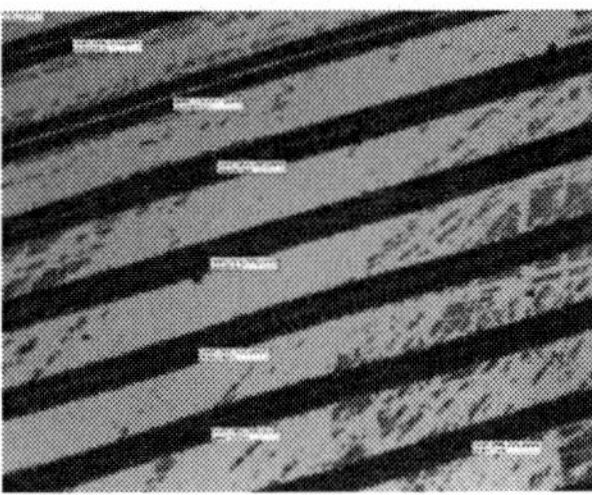

Figure 4 Some of the lines of Block H

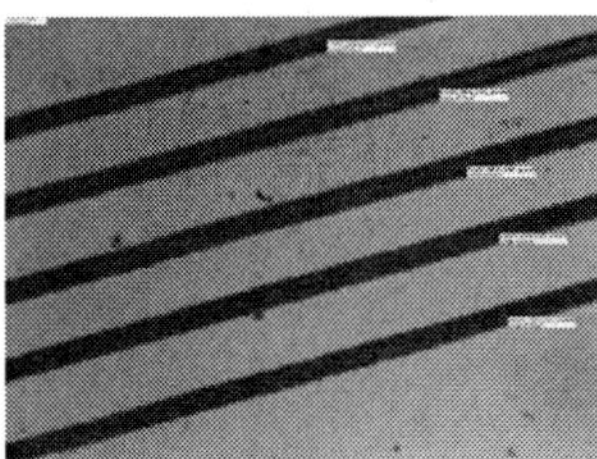

Figure 5 Some of the lines of Block I

Figure 6 Some of the lines of Block N

Figure 7 Some of the lines of Block O

As visible in Figure 8, in the block G there is a produced line (line β) that appeared significantly better. Line β was produced by using a power of 1,12 W , scan speed of 100 mm/s, frequency of 70 kHz, pulse width of 20,8 ns and fluence of 0,32 J/cm^2. This was characterized by sharp and uniform edges along its entire length, homogeneous visual contrast with respect to the untreated surface, and the absence of cracks, melting, or delamination. These features suggested an optimal balance between fluence and scanning speed, making it particularly promising for controlled material transformation. That line was selected for TEM analysis.

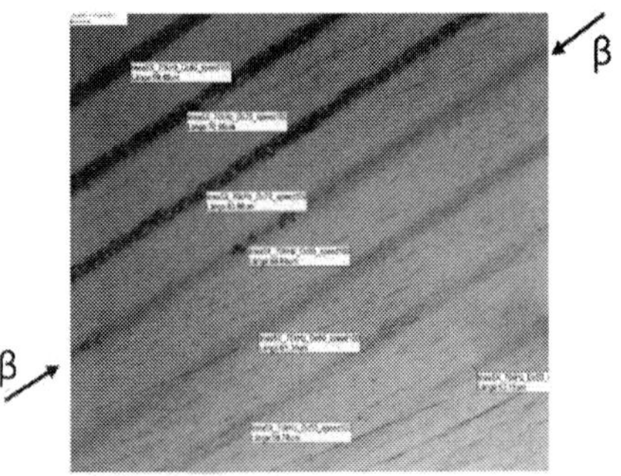

Figure 8 Some of the lines of Block G: line β is indicated by arrows

A part of the lines exhibited either excessive surface darkening or morphological irregularities, indicative of overheating. However, a subset of lines showed uniform width and a consistent surface contrast that suggested successful localized thermal treatment.

Among these, a specific line was selected for further analysis due to its clean edges, uniform contrast, and absence of visual damage such as cracking or melting. This line β was analysed by transmission electron microscopy (TEM) to investigate changes in the structural order of the a-SiC layer induced by laser irradiation.

4.2 TEM analysis

Cross-sectional TEM images revealed significant structural differences between the laser-treated (yellow circle) and untreated areas (blue circle), as visible in Figure 9. In the untreated regions, the a-SiC film appeared as a fully amorphous layer with no discernible lattice fringes. In contrast, the laser-processed zones showed the presence of nanocrystalline domains embedded within the amorphous matrix. These crystalline regions exhibited well-defined lattice fringes and were consistent in size and distribution across the treated area.

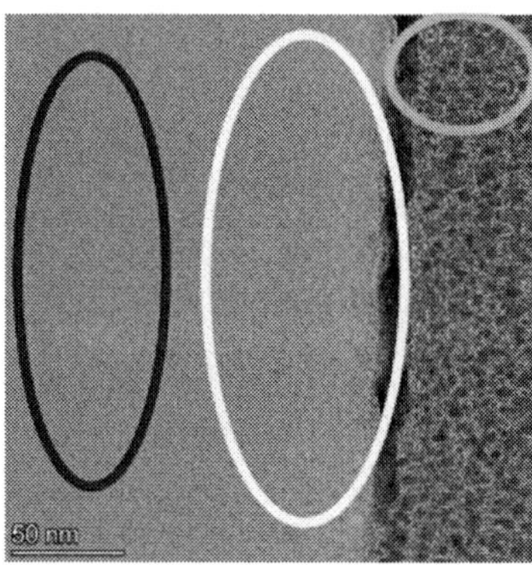

Figure 9 TEM image of the cross-section of line β: the laser-treated area (yellow circle) and untreated area (blue circle) and the protective Platinum layer used during TEM measurements (green circle)

Zoomed TEM images confirmed the presence of crystalline domains of 2–5 nm, indicating the onset of localized polycrystalline crystallization with random orientation. This treated area is from surface of SiC layer to about 50 nm of depth, as visible in Figure 10.

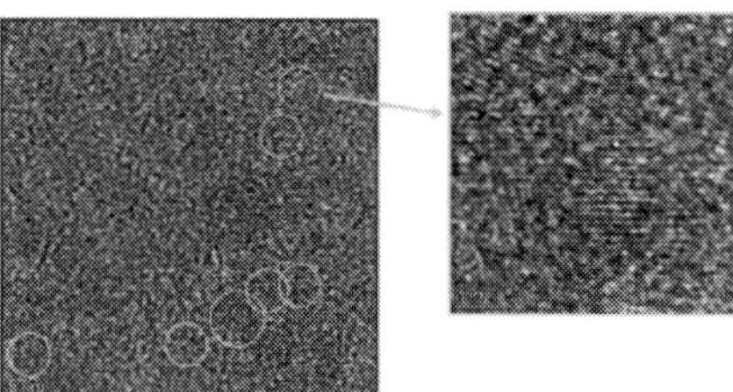

Figure 10 Zoomed TEM images of the treated area of line β

5. DISCUSSION

The results demonstrate that it is possible to induce a localized crystallization process in thin films of a-SiC using a compact DPSS Q-switched laser source at 355 nm, operating under vacuum conditions. The absence of macroscopic melting or visible cracking indicates that the process occurred in a controlled manner, remaining below the material's thermal damage threshold.

The behavior observed in the treated regions suggests a mechanism based on rapid, localized heating that provides sufficient thermal energy to initiate crystal nucleation, but remains limited in depth due to the short pulse duration (11.9–31.4 ns) and small optical spot size (~80 µm). The shallow modification depth (~50 nm) is consistent with a surface-level recrystallization process, which could be particularly useful for applications requiring functional changes in the upper layer without affecting the substrate or underlying layers.

The formation of disordered, nanometric crystalline domains without preferential orientation suggests that, at these fluence levels, the process does not result in complete or epitaxial recrystallization, but rather an initial structural reorganization. This outcome aligns with previous studies using excimer lasers such as KrF and XeCl [21], [22], which reported crystalline phase formation in a-SiC films at comparable fluences. However, the approach presented in this work offers significant advantages in terms of system compactness, optical simplicity, and operational costs, owing to the use of a more accessible commercial DPSS laser compared to excimer sources.

Additionally, the use of a custom vacuum chamber enhanced the energy efficiency of the process by reducing thermal dissipation and preventing surface oxidation or contamination—common issues in treatments performed in ambient air.

The proposed method is distinguished by its high spatial selectivity and by a lower system complexity compared to approaches based on excimer lasers, while at the same time showing significant potential for direct integration into electronic device manufacturing workflows. The results obtained demonstrate that this strategy is not only effective and selective, but also compatible with established technological processes, thereby outlining relevant application prospects in multilayer power electronics, next-generation MEMS, and high-efficiency photovoltaics.

The experimental observations open several directions for future research. A first line of development will focus on the fine optimization of laser parameters, aimed at extending the extent of crystallization and improving the control of the crystallographic orientation of the resulting domains. In this context, the use of shorter wavelengths, particularly in the deep ultraviolet range (<248 nm), could enhance surface absorption and consequently increase process efficiency.

Another research avenue will be the extension of the method to materials with similar structural and functional characteristics, such as SiNx or SiGe alloys, with the aim of assessing its universality and possible limitations. At the same time, it will be necessary to systematically address the challenges related to industrial scalability, including the adaptation of the treatment to larger surface areas or to more complex geometries, such as whole wafers or partially processed devices.

Finally, a strategic objective for technology transfer concerns the integration of the laser treatment into consolidated production lines, with particular reference to photovoltaic technologies and power electronics, where the potential application impact could be especially significant.

6. CONCLUSIONS

In this work, we have shown that it is possible to achieve localized crystallization in thin a-SiC films using a 355 nm UV DPSS Q-switched laser under vacuum conditions. The treatment produced nanocrystalline domains only in the surface layer, without damaging the film's structure or morphology, confirming that the technique can selectively modify the material's surface. Compared to excimer lasers, this approach is more compact, easier to handle, and operationally less complex.

The results also suggest that this strategy could be useful for applications such as power electronics, MEMS, and high-efficiency photovoltaics. Furthermore, the method provides a solid basis for future studies aimed at optimizing the treatment parameters and applying it to different materials and geometries, with potential developments toward integration into existing industrial processes.

Conflict of interest

The authors declare that they have no conflict of interest.

7. REFERENCES

[1] G. Foti, «Silicon carbide: from amorphous to crystalline material», *Appl. Surf. Sci.*, vol. 184, fasc. 1–4, pp. 20–26, dic. 2001, doi: 10.1016/S0169-4332(01)00751-6.

[2] R. Gharbi *et al.*, «Observation of negative capacitance in a-SiC:H/a-Si:H UV photodetectors», *Solid-State Electron.*, vol. 50, fasc. 3, pp. 367–371, mar. 2006, doi: 10.1016/j.sse.2006.02.009.

[3] X.-B. Li, E.-W. Shi, Z.-Z. Chen, e B. Xiao, «Polytype formation in silicon carbide single crystals», *Diam. Relat. Mater.*, vol. 16, fasc. 3, pp. 654–657, mar. 2007, doi: 10.1016/j.diamond.2006.11.078.

[4] J. Homberger, A. B. Lostetter, K. J. Olejniczak, T. McNutt, S. M. Lal, e A. Mantooth, «Silicon-carbide (SiC) semiconductor power electronics for extreme high-temperature environments», in *2004 IEEE Aerospace Conference Proceedings (IEEE Cat. No.04TH8720)*, Big Sky, MT, USA: IEEE, 2004, pp. 2538–2555. doi: 10.1109/AERO.2004.1368048.

[5] J. M. Melzak, «Silicon carbide for RF MEMS», in *IEEE MTT-S International Microwave Symposium Digest, 2003*, Philadelphia, PA, USA: IEEE, 2003, pp. 1629–1632. doi: 10.1109/MWSYM.2003.1210450.

[6] L. Scaltrito *et al.*, «Structural and electrical characterization of epitaxial 4H–SiC layers for power electronic device applications», *Mater. Sci.*

[7] S. Ferrero *et al.*, «Defect characterization of 4H-SiC wafers for power electronic device applications», *J. Phys. Condens. Matter*, vol. 14, fasc. 48, pp. 13397–13402, dic. 2002, doi: 10.1088/0953-8984/14/48/394.

[8] S. Kühnapfel, D. Amkreutz, C. Klimm, e N. H. Nickel, «Excimer laser crystallization of a-SiC$_x$ on glass», *Can. J. Phys.*, vol. 92, fasc. 7/8, pp. 709–712, lug. 2014, doi: 10.1139/cjp-2013-0571.

[9] U. Coscia *et al.*, «Laser annealing study of PECVD deposited hydrogenated amorphous silicon carbon alloy films», *Appl. Surf. Sci.*, vol. 254, fasc. 4, pp. 984–988, dic. 2007, doi: 10.1016/j.apsusc.2007.08.003.

[10] D. Arduino, S. Stassi, C. Spano, L. Scaltrito, S. Ferrero, e V. Bertana, «Silicon and Silicon Carbide Recrystallization by Laser Annealing: A Review», *Materials*, vol. 16, fasc. 24, p. 7674, dic. 2023, doi: 10.3390/ma16247674.

[11] D. Sciti e A. Bellosi, «Laser Micromachining of Silicon Carbide», *Key Eng. Mater.*, vol. 206–213, pp. 305–308, dic. 2001, doi: 10.4028/www.scientific.net/KEM.206-213.305.

[12] D. H. Lowndes e R. F. Wood, «Studies of pulsed laser melting and rapid solidification using amorphous silicon», *J. Lumin.*, vol. 30, fasc. 1–4, pp. 395–408, feb. 1985, doi: 10.1016/0022-2313(85)90068-7.

[13] M. Vivona *et al.*, «Effects of Excimer Laser Irradiation on the Morphological, Structural, and Electrical Properties of Aluminum-Implanted Silicon Carbide (4H-SiC)», *ACS Appl. Electron. Mater.*, vol. 4, fasc. 9, pp. 4514–4520, set. 2022, doi: 10.1021/acsaelm.2c00748.

[14] C. Calabretta *et al.*, «Laser Annealing of P and Al Implanted 4H-SiC Epitaxial Layers», *Materials*, vol. 12, fasc. 20, p. 3362, ott. 2019, doi: 10.3390/ma12203362.

[15] M. Vivona *et al.*, «Exploring UV-Laser Effects on Al-Implanted 4H-SiC», *Solid State Phenom.*, vol. 342, pp. 85–89, mag. 2023, doi: 10.4028/p-6jg806.

[16] J. Jandeleit, A. Horn, R. Weichenhain, E. W. Kreutz, e R. Poprawe, «Fundamental investigations of micromachining by nano- and picosecond laser radiation», *Appl. Surf. Sci.*, vol. 127–129, pp. 885–891, mag. 1998, doi: 10.1016/S0169-4332(97)00762-9.

[17] M. Farsari, G. Filippidis, S. Zoppel, G. A. Reider, e C. Fotakis, «Efficient femtosecond laser micromachining of bulk 3C-SiC», *J. Micromechanics Microengineering*, vol. 15, fasc. 9, pp. 1786–1789, set. 2005, doi: 10.1088/0960-1317/15/9/022.

[18] Y. Dong e P. Molian, «In-situ formed nanoparticles on 3C-SiC film under femtosecond pulsed laser irradiation», *Phys. Status Solidi A*, vol. 202, fasc. 6, pp. 1066–1072, mag. 2005, doi: 10.1002/pssa.200420015.

[19] Y. Hishida, M. Watanabe, K. Nakashima, e O. Eryu, «Excimer Laser Annealing of Ion-Implanted 6H-Silicon Carbide», *Mater. Sci. Forum*, vol. 338–342, pp. 873–876, mag. 2000, doi: 10.4028/www.scientific.net/MSF.338-342.873.

[20] S. Urban e F. Falk, «Laser crystallization of amorphous SiC thin films on glass», *Appl. Surf. Sci.*,

vol. 184, fasc. 1–4, pp. 356–361, dic. 2001, doi: 10.1016/S0169-4332(01)00517-7.

[21] D. K. Basa, G. Ambrosone, U. Coscia, e A. Setaro, «Crystallization of hydrogenated amorphous silicon carbon films with laser and thermal annealing», *Appl. Surf. Sci.*, vol. 255, fasc. 10, pp. 5528–5531, mar. 2009, doi: 10.1016/j.apsusc.2008.09.042.

[22] A. Hedler, S. Urban, F. Falk, H. Hobert, e W. Wesch, «Excimer laser crystallization of amorphous silicon carbide produced by ion implantation», *Appl. Surf. Sci.*, vol. 205, fasc. 1–4, pp. 240–248, gen. 2003, doi: 10.1016/S0169-4332(02)01071-1.

[23] P. Baeri, C. Spinella, e R. Reitano, «Fast Melting of Amorphous Silicon Carbide Induced by Nanosecond Laser Pulse», *Int. J. Thermophys.*, vol. 20, fasc. 4, pp. 1211–1221, lug. 1999, doi: 10.1023/A:1022623424614.

[24] G. Ambrosone *et al.*, «Crystallization of hydrogenated amorphous silicon–carbon films by means of laser treatments», *Appl. Surf. Sci.*, vol. 247, fasc. 1–4, pp. 471–476, lug. 2005, doi: 10.1016/j.apsusc.2005.01.051.

SiC recrystallization by UV nanopulsed laser annealing

Daniele Arduino

Supervisor: Prof. Luciano Scaltrito, Prof. Sergio Ferrero – Dr. Andrea Ancillao

Research context and motivation

The demand for sustainable energy is driving innovation in power electronics, with SiC as a key material thanks to its wide bandgap, high thermal conductivity and fast switching capabilities, making it ideal for next-gen photovoltaic devices [1]. Since SiC crystals are hard to produce, the crystallization of amorphous SiC by annealing can be an alternative solution [2]. Traditional furnace methods heat the entire device, risking damage to previously fabricated structures, therefore laser annealing was explored because it can heat locally, minimizing such effects [3]. While other studies used effective but costly excimer lasers, this research proposes a more compact, cost-efficient method using a DPSS Q-switched laser in vacuum. By optimizing parameters (frequency, power, pulse duration, scan speed), localized crystallization of amorphous SiC thin films was obtained, improving structural properties and supporting the development of SiC-based devices, especially for photovoltaics.

Adopted methodologies

Used samples

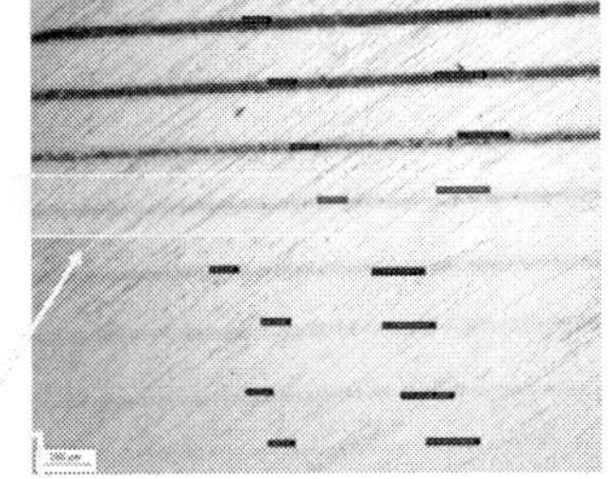
Experimental setup

The experimental set up consisted in a **DPSS Q-switched laser (355 nm).** The calibration matrix of frequency and duty cycle was used to control the actual laser power delivered to sample:

Calibration matrix	10%	20%	30%	40%	50%	60%	70%	80% duty cycle
30 kHz	0,06	0,25	0,55	0,95	1,39	1,84	2,37	2,97
40 kHz	0,05	0,18	0,41	0,74	1,12	1,58	2,03	2,5
50 kHz	0,04	0,14	0,33	0,59	0,93	1,3	1,75	2,2
60kHz	0,04	0,12	0,27	0,5	0,77	1,12	1,48	1,95
70kHz	0,04	0,1	0,23	0,42	0,86	0,95	1,3	1,66
80kHz	0,03	0,09	0,2	0,36	0,58	0,84	1,16	1,47
90kHz	0,03	0,08	0,18	0,32	0,5	0,74	1,04	1,38
100kHz	0,03	0,08	0,16	0,28	0,47	0,65	0,92	1,37
freq								

Annealing was performed under vacuum ($\sim 4.3 \times 10^{-1}$ mbar, granted by a rotary vane vacuum pump) in a custom-designed chamber to ensure clean and controlled conditions. Multiple annealing lines were written by varying frequency, power, and scan speed. They were inspected through an optical microscope. The two most promising conditions were selected for transmission electron microscopy (TEM) analysis to assess crystallinity.

Results

Optical characterization allowed the identification of the best result, obtained with the following settings:

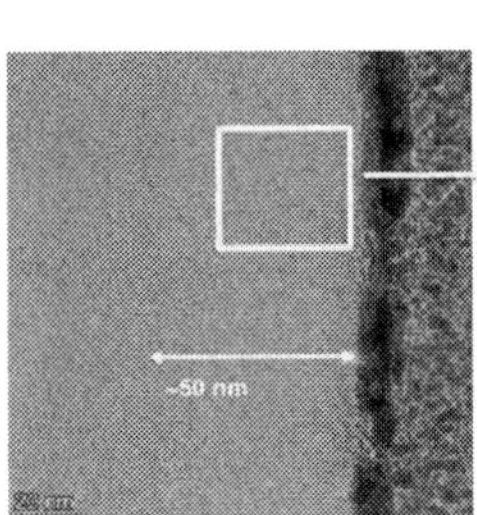

- Frequency: 70 kHz
- Pulse duration: 20,8 ns
- Duty cycle: 65%
- Power: 1.12 W
- Fluence: 0,32 J/cm²
- Scan speed: 100 mm/s

TEM analysis revealed **crystalline domains of 2–5 nm within the top 50 nm** of the film surface, indicating a localized polycrystalline crystallization with **random orientation**.

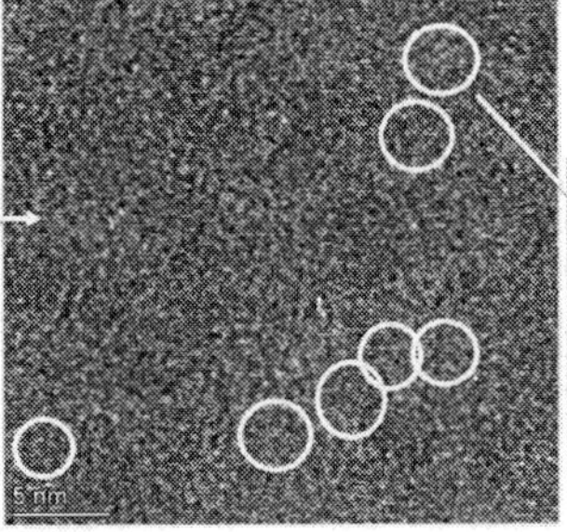

Future work

- Use **shorter-wavelength lasers** to improve annealing and SiC crystallization.
- Test **alternative SiC-like materials** to assess broader applicability
- **Optimize the process for full-wafer annealing**, enabling large-scale industrial use in photovoltaics and power electronics.

References

1. G. Foti, «Silicon carbide: from amorphous to crystalline material», *Appl. Surf. Sci.*, vol. 184, fasc. 1–4, pp. 20–26, dic. 2001, doi: 10.1016/S0169-4332(01)00751-6.
2. U. Coscia *et al.*, «Laser annealing study of PECVD deposited hydrogenated amorphous silicon carbon alloy films», *Appl. Surf. Sci.*, vol. 254, fasc. 4, pp. 984–988, dic. 2007, doi: 10.1016/j.apsusc.2007.08.003.
3. D. Arduino, S.Stassi, C.Spano, L.Scaltrito, S.Ferrero, V.Bertana, «Silicon and Silicon Carbide Recrystallization by Laser Annealing: A Review», *Materials*, vol. 16, fasc. 24, p. 7674, dic. 2023, doi: 10.3390/ma16247674

PhD program in
Photovoltaics
39th Cycle

EXPLORING THE CHARACTERISTICS ADDITION METHOD FOR ESTIMATING BIFACIAL EFFICIENCY IN Cs₃Sb₂I₉-BASED INDOOR PEROVSKITE SOLAR CELLS

Rajesh Kumar Sharma[1], Dhruv Singh Thakur[2], Deepak Joshi[3], Vivek Garg[4], Shivendra Yadav[5]
Department of Electronics Engineering, SVNIT, Surat, India
d21ec011@eced.svnit.ac.in[1], ds22ec001@eced.svnit.ac.in[2], d.joshi@eced.svnit.ac.in[3], vivekg@eced.svnit.ac.in[4],
shivendra.y@eced.svnit.ac.in[5]

The rapid growth of Internet of Things (IoT) devices has increased the demand for efficient indoor photovoltaics (IPV). Lead-free perovskite-inspired materials (PIMs), such as $Cs_3Sb_2I_9$, offer a promising alternative to conventional lead-halide perovskites due to their favourable electronic properties and non-toxic nature. Despite their potential, the bifacial performance of $Cs_3Sb_2I_9$ for indoor light harvesting remains largely unexplored. This study investigates $Cs_3Sb_2I_9$ as an absorber material in a bifacial solar cell with the optimized architecture AZO/TNT/$Cs_3Sb_2I_9$/$SrCu_2O_2$/Ni, designed for a bandgap of 1.95 eV. The monofacial reference device achieves a power conversion efficiency (PCE) of 3.7% under a 1000 lux WLED spectrum. Unlike previous studies that primarily report bifaciality factors, this work focuses on bifacial efficiency estimation. Results indicate that using 'steel' as the rear surface yields the highest PCE of 67.24%, demonstrating the potential of $Cs_3Sb_2I_9$-based bifacial solar cells for high-performance IPV applications.

Keywords: Bifacial efficiency, Characteristics Addition, Sb-Perovskite, SCAPS-1D, UV-Vis spectroscopy.

1 INTRODUCTION

The increasing demand for self-powered wireless devices, particularly in indoor environments with varying light conditions, has driven the development of IPV as a promising energy solution. Indoor light sources, such as fluorescent lamps and white LEDs (WLEDs), provide spectral ranges between 400 and 800 nm [1], [2], with typical illuminance levels of 200 to 1000 lux [3], [4]. However, conventional crystalline silicon solar cells, with their narrow bandgap of 1.12 eV, are not well-suited for indoor applications. While lead-based perovskites offer high efficiency, they pose significant environmental concerns [5], [6], and tin-based alternatives suffer from stability issues [7]. PIMs, particularly those with an $A_3B_2X_9$ structure, present a promising alternative by addressing both toxicity and stability challenges. Among them, $Cs_3Sb_2I_9$, with a bandgap of 1.95 eV, has shown potential for indoor applications. However, its reported PCE remains low at 3.7%, primarily due to poor film morphology and suboptimal device structures. While theoretical studies suggest possible improvements, significant gaps remain in optimizing $Cs_3Sb_2I_9$ for practical IPV applications.

In our previous study, the optimized AZO/TNT/$Cs_3Sb_2I_9$/$SrCu_2O_2$/Ni structure achieved a maximum PCE of 38.77% under front-side illumination (from the AZO side) with WLED light. In this work, for the first time, the optimized device is illuminated from the Ni contact (rear-side), achieving PCE of 38.88% under WLED illumination. Since SCAPS-1D simulations are limited to illuminating light from either side of the device independently, alternative modeling strategies are required to accurately determine bifacial efficiency. This study explores the characteristic addition (CA) method [8], providing deeper insights into the bifacial potential of $Cs_3Sb_2I_9$-based solar cells.

2 AIM AND APPROACH

Figure 1(a) illustrates the baseline device structure, while Figure 1(b) presents the JV characteristics of the experimental and simulated models. The baseline model was optimized in SCAPS-1D by adjusting absorber thickness, defect density, doping concentration, and interface properties for improved accuracy [9]. The enhanced AZO/TNT/$Cs_3Sb_2I_9$/$SrCu_2O_2$/Ni device achieves a PCE of 38.77% under front-side (AZO-side) WLED illumination. For the first time, the device is illuminated from the Ni contact (rear-side), yielding PCE of 38.88%. Figure 1(c) presents the JV characteristics for both cases, with performance parameters summarized in Table I. As SCAPS-1D only simulates single-sided illumination, alternative modeling is required for bifacial efficiency estimation.

Table I: Performance parameters of the proposed indoor bifacial device under front- and rear-side illumination with 100% incident light intensity.

Illu. side	V_{OC} [V]	J_{SC} [mA cm^{-2}]	FF [%]	η [%]
Front	1.47	1.55	89.08	38.77
Rear	1.47	1.55	89.21	38.88

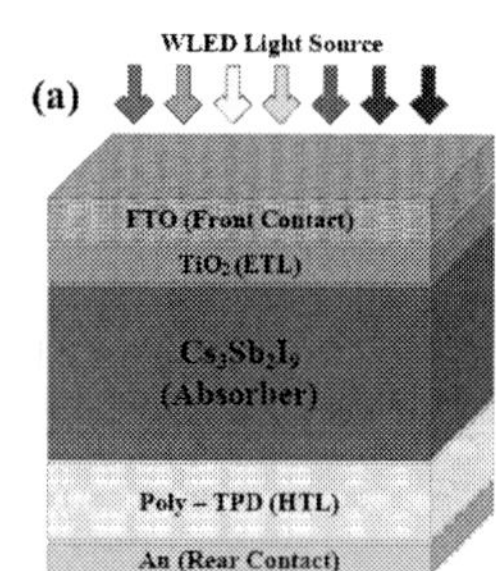

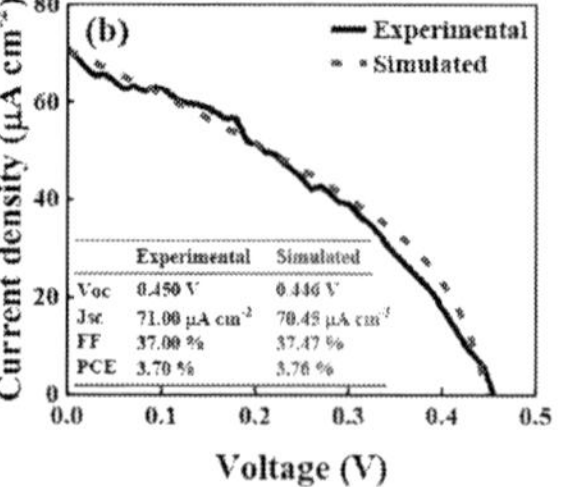

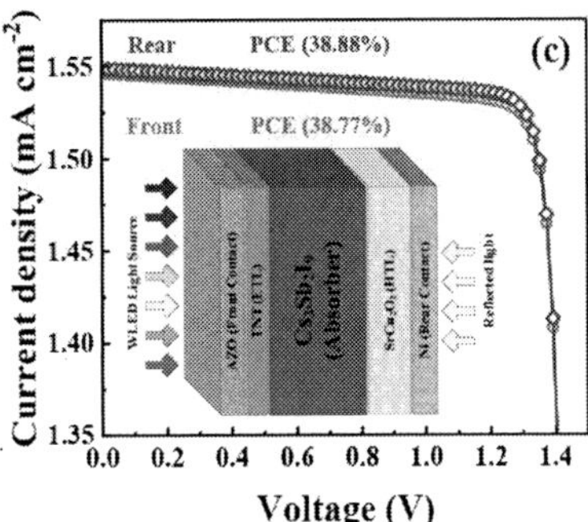

Figure 1: (a) Structure of the indoor monofacial device, (b) *J-V* characteristics of experimental and calibrated model, (c) proposed device with optimized front and rear-side *J-V* characteristics.

3 RESULTS AND DISCUSSION

In practical scenarios, bifacial solar cells are illuminated from both the front and rear sides simultaneously. However, due to SCAPS-1D's limitation to one-sided illumination, the bifacial *JV* characteristics are estimated using the CA method. In this method, the current densities for front and rear illumination, which include both light-generated and dark current components, are combined. To avoid double-counting the dark current, it is subtracted once, as shown by:

$$
\begin{aligned}
J_{bi}(V, P_f, P_r) &= J_D(V) + J_{L,f}(P_f) + J_{L,r}(P_r) \\
&= J_f(V, P_f) + J_r(V, P_r) - J_D(V)
\end{aligned}
\tag{1}
$$

Here, J_{bi} represents the bifacial current density as a function of voltage (V), front illumination intensity (P_f), and rear illumination intensity (P_r), while J_f and J_r represent current densities under front and rear illumination, respectively.

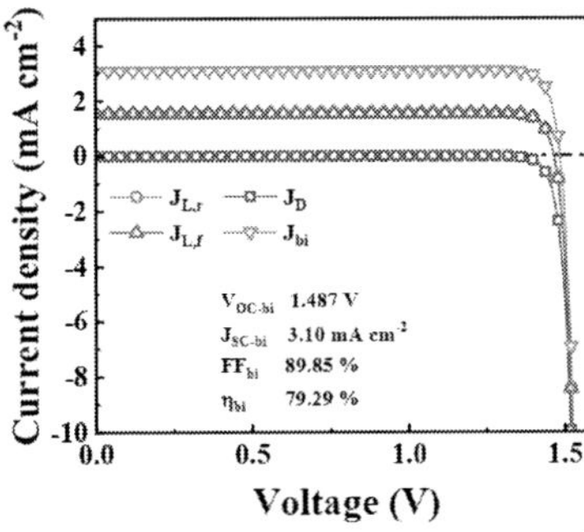

Figure 2: *J-V* characteristics of the proposed indoor bifacial device under dark conditions, rear and front illumination, along with the bifacial *J-V* curve estimated through the CA method.

Figure 2 presents the *JV* characteristics under dark conditions, front illumination, rear illumination, and the bifacial *JV* characteristics derived from the CA method

with 100% illumination intensity. Under ideal conditions, with equal 100% illumination from both sides, the proposed bifacial solar cell achieves a PCE of 79.29%. However, since rear-side illumination primarily consists of reflected light, which is not 100% intense, the device's performance was also analyzed under reduced rear-side illumination. The results highlight the significant impact of varying rear-side illumination intensities on bifacial efficiency, underscoring the need to consider realistic operating conditions in bifacial solar cell designs.

The rear-side light intensity is varied from 0% to 50% of the total WLED illumination. Figure 3(a) shows the *JV* curves for different rear-side illumination levels, while Figures 3(b)-(c) display the corresponding performance parameters. The PCE increases from 38.77% with front-side illumination only to 58.93% when the rear-side receives 50% illumination.

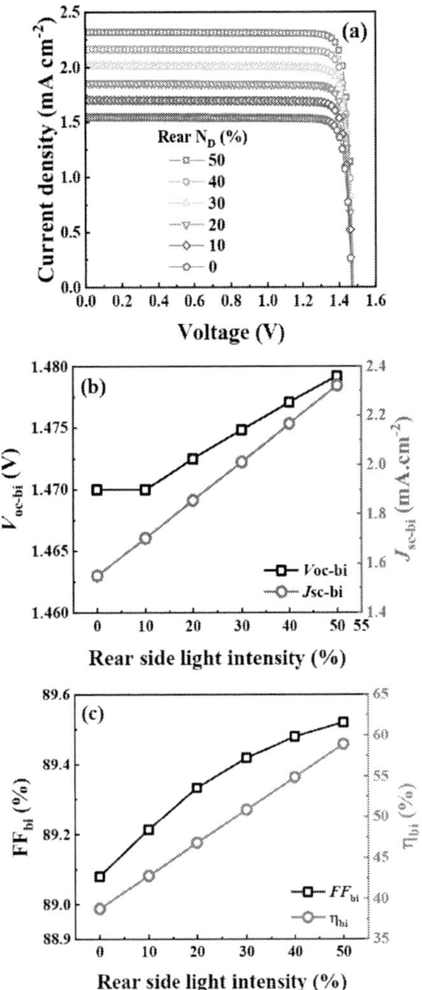

Figure 3: (a) *J-V* characteristics of the proposed bifacial device under varying rear illumination intensities, with N_D ranging from 0% to 50%, to analyze the device's behaviour, (b) $V_{OC\text{-}bi}$ and $J_{SC\text{-}bi}$ and (c) FF_{bi} and η_{bi} of the proposed device with N_D ranging from 0% to 50%.

The rear-side illumination varies with wavelength, influenced by the reflectance of indoor materials, as shown in Figure 4(a)-(b). This reflectance is measured using a UV-Vis fibre-optic spectrometer (Ocean Optics Inc.), as depicted in Figure 4(c). The measured reflectance spectrum acts as an optical filter, modifying the incident WLED light before it reaches the rear side of the device. To account for this effect, SCAPS-1D simulations are performed to extract the JV characteristics under rear-side illumination, incorporating the reflectance spectrum as a transmission filter.

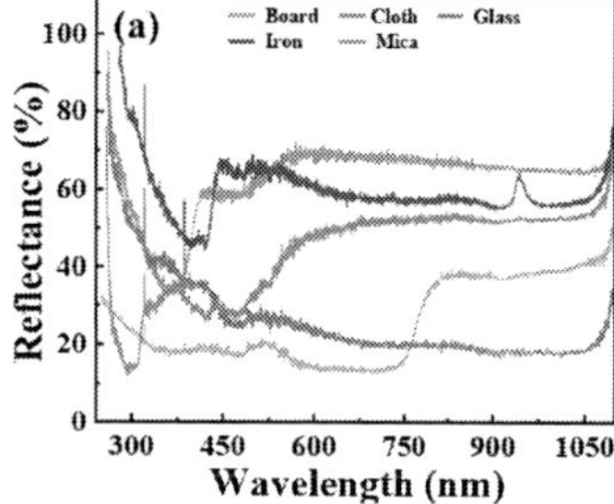

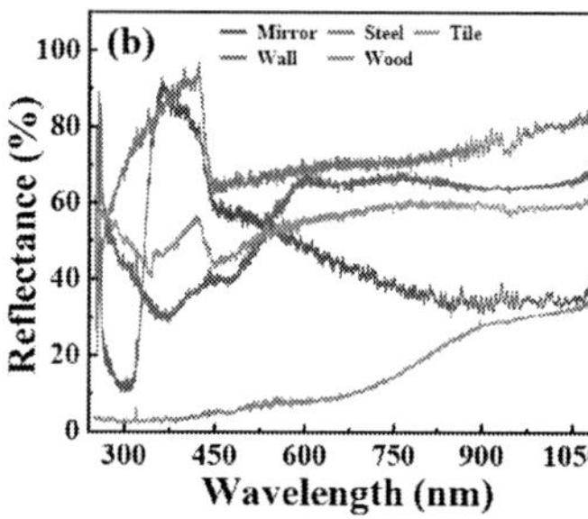

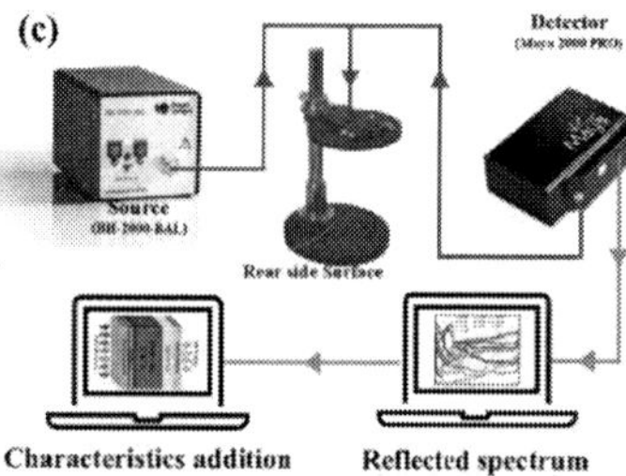

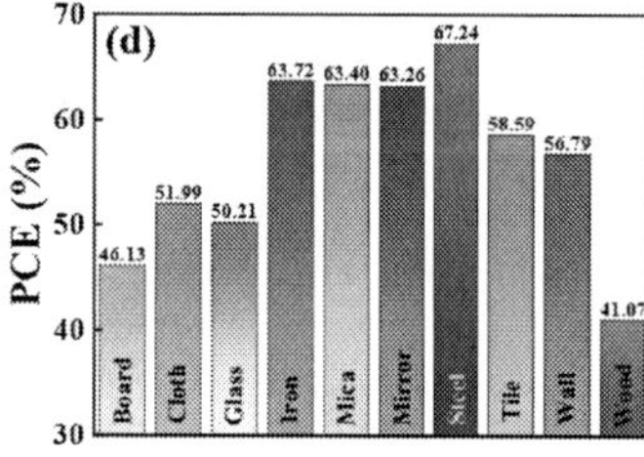

Figure 4: (a)-(b) Reflected spectra of different indoor surfaces, (c) schematic of the setup of bifacial parameter estimation, (d) bifacial PCE of the proposed device for different rear-side surfaces.

These JV characteristics are then combined with the front-side illumination JV characteristics using the CA method, which ensures accurate estimation of bifacial performance by eliminating redundant dark current components. The resulting bifacial JV characteristics are used to determine the efficiency of the proposed bifacial device under varying rear-side surfaces. As shown in Figure 4(d), the highest PCE of 67.24% is achieved when "steel" is used as the rear surface, demonstrating the significant influence of rear-side reflectance on device performance.

4 CONCLUSIONS

In conclusion, the bifacial efficiency of the proposed indoor bifacial device was estimated using the CA method, which combines JV characteristics from front and rear illumination while eliminating redundant dark current components. The method enabled precise evaluation of bifacial performance, revealing a maximum PCE of 79.29% under ideal conditions and 67.24% with steel as the rear surface. This study highlights the effectiveness of the CA method in modeling bifacial devices and underscores the importance of rear-side illumination and material reflectance in optimizing real-world performance.

ACKNOWLEDGMENTS

The authors would like to thank Marc Burgelman from ELSI at the University of Gent, Belgium, for providing the SCAPS-1D simulation software. They also acknowledge financial support from "SVNIT Surat" under Grant No. dean(R&C)/seed money/2021-22/10783 and "Divyasampark iHUB Roorkee for the Devices Materials and Technology Foundation" under Grant Nos. 4-371 and 4-372.

REFERENCE

[1] S. Biswas and H. Kim, "Solar Cells for Indoor Applications: Progress and Development," *Polymers 2020, Vol. 12, Page 1338*, vol. 12, no. 6, p. 1338, Jun. 2020, doi: 10.3390/POLYM12061338.

[2] B. P. Lechêne, M. Cowell, A. Pierre, J. W. Evans, P. K. Wright, and A. C. Arias, "Organic solar cells and fully printed super-capacitors optimized for indoor light energy harvesting," *Nano Energy*, vol. 26, pp. 631–640, Aug. 2016, doi: 10.1016/J.NANOEN.2016.06.017.

[3] K. W. Houser, "Something Happened on the Way to a Target Illuminance," *LEUKOS*, vol. 10, no. 1, pp. 1–2, 2014, doi: 10.1080/15502724.2014.841501.

[4] I. Mathews, S. N. Kantareddy, T. Buonassisi, and I. M. Peters, "Technology and Market Perspective for Indoor Photovoltaic Cells," *Joule*, vol. 3, no. 6, pp. 1415–1426, Jun. 2019, doi: 10.1016/J.JOULE.2019.03.026.

[5] F. Di Giacomo, A. Fakharuddin, R. Jose, and T. M. Brown, "Progress, challenges and perspectives in flexible perovskite solar cells," *Energy Environ Sci*, vol. 9, no. 10, pp. 3007–3035, Oct. 2016, doi: 10.1039/C6EE01137C.

[6]   P. D. Dissanayake *et al.*, "Environmental impact of metal halide perovskite solar cells and potential mitigation strategies: A critical review," *Environ Res*, vol. 219, p. 115066, Feb. 2023, doi: 10.1016/J.ENVRES.2022.115066.

[7]   L. Chen, S. Fu, Y. Li, N. Sun, Y. Yan, and Z. Song, "On the Durability of Tin-Containing Perovskite Solar Cells," *Advanced Science*, vol. 11, no. 1, p. 2304811, Jan. 2024, doi: 10.1002/ADVS.202304811.

[8]   R. K. Sharma, H. Narsi Patel, D. Singh Thakur, V. Garg, and S. Yadav, "Investigating ASnI2Br wide bandgap tin perovskite for bifacial solar cells: Modeling of bifacial efficiency with comparative analysis," *Solar Energy*, vol. 283, p. 113017, Nov. 2024, doi: 10.1016/J.SOLENER.2024.113017.

[9]   R. K. Sharma, R. Keshri, and S. Yadav, "Computational modeling of Cs3Sb2I9-based novel architecture under WLED illumination for indoor photovoltaic applications," *Optical and Quantum Electronics 2024 56:11*, vol. 56, no. 11, pp. 1–17, Nov. 2024, doi: 10.1007/S11082-024-07708-6.

Exploring the Characteristics Addition Method for Estimating Bifacial Efficiency in $Cs_3Sb_2I_9$-Based Indoor Perovskite Solar Cells

Rajesh Kumar Sharma, Dhruv Singh Thakur, Deepak Joshi, Vivek Garg, Shivendra Yadav

Department of Electronics Engineering, SVNIT, Surat-395007, India

2BV.1.47

Abstract

The rapid expansion of IoT devices has increased the need for efficient indoor photovoltaics (IPV). This study explores lead-free perovskite-inspired $Cs_3Sb_2I_9$ as a non-toxic absorber in a bifacial solar cell with the architecture $AZO/TNT/Cs_3Sb_2I_9/SrCu_2O_2/Ni$, optimized for a 1.95 eV bandgap. A monofacial reference device achieves 3.7% PCE under 1000 lux WLED. Unlike prior studies focused on bifaciality factors, we directly estimate bifacial efficiency, finding that a 'steel' rear surface yields a peak PCE of 67.24%, highlighting the strong potential of $Cs_3Sb_2I_9$-based bifacial solar cells for next-generation IPV systems.

Aim and approach

- Bifacial PSCs harvest light from both front and rear sides.
- SCAPS-1D supports only one-sided illumination.
- Adopted the Characteristics Addition (CA) method to model bifacial J-V.
- CA method avoids double-counting of dark current.
- J-V for front and rear illumination extracted separately under WLED.
- Indoor surface reflectance measured using UV-Vis fibre-optic spectrometer.
- Measured reflectance spectrum used as an optical filter in SCAPS-1D.

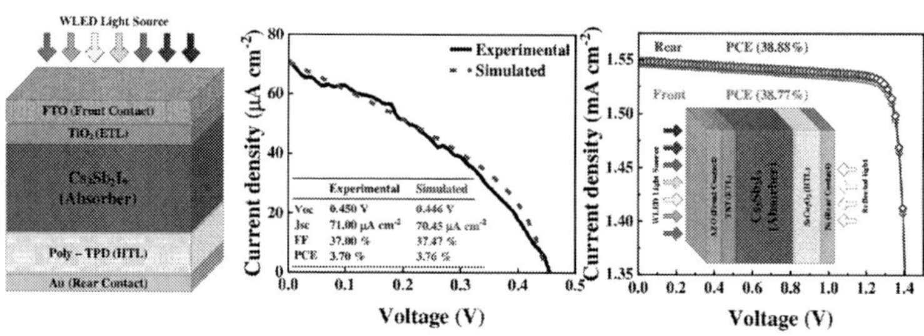

Result and Discussion

- **Ideal case:** With 100% light from both sides → PCE 79.29%.
- **Realistic case:** Rear-side illumination reduced due to reflectance.
- Simulated rear-side illumination from 0% to 50% of WLED.
- **Performance gain:**
  Front only → PCE 38.77% | Rear 50% → PCE 58.93%

- Rear illumination strongly boosts efficiency, even at partial levels.
- Reflectance spectrum (tiles, walls, surfaces) filters rear-side light.
- SCAPS simulations capture realistic bifacial behavior with filtered spectra.
- **Key insight:** Indoor bifacial PSC design must account for reflectance.

Performance Parameters

Illumination side	V_{OC} [V]	J_{SC} [mA cm^{-2}]	FF [%]	η [%]
Front	1.47	1.55	89.08	38.77
Rear	1.47	1.55	89.21	38.88

Characteristics Addition Equation:

$$J_{bi}(V, P_f, P_r) = J_D(V) + J_{L,f}(P_f) + J_{L,r}(P_r) = J_f(V, P_f) + J_r(V, P_r) - J_D(V)$$

J-V characteristics at different rear side intensities

$V_{OC\text{-}bi}$ 1.487 V
$J_{SC\text{-}bi}$ 3.10 mA cm^{-2}
FF_{bi} 89.85 %
η_{bi} 79.29 %

Rear N_D (%): 50, 40, 30, 20, 10, 0

Performance parameters at different rear side intensity

Reflectance extracted from UV-Vis Setup

UV-Vis Setup

PCE at different rear surfaces

Conclusion

Using the characteristics Addition (CA) method, the bifacial device achieved up to 79.29% PCE (ideal) and 67.24% with a steel rear surface. The study highlights the CA method's accuracy and the critical role of rear-side illumination and reflective materials in enhancing indoor bifacial solar cell performance.

References

[1] R. K. Sharma, H. Narsi Patel, D. Singh Thakur, V. Garg, and S. Yadav, "Investigating ASnI2Br wide bandgap tin perovskite for bifacial solar cells: Modeling of bifacial efficiency with comparative analysis," *Solar Energy*, vol. 283, p. 113017, Nov. 2024, doi: 10.1016/J.SOLENER.2024.113017.

[2] R. K. Sharma, R. Keshri, and S. Yadav, "Computational modeling of Cs3Sb2I9-based novel architecture under WLED illumination for indoor photovoltaic applications," *Optical and Quantum Electronics* 2024 56:11, vol. 56, no. 11, pp. 1–17, Nov. 2024, doi: 10.1007/S11082-024-07708-6.

Acknowledgement

The authors would like to thank Marc Burgelman from ELSI at the University of Gent, Belgium, for providing the SCAPS-1D simulation software. They also acknowledge financial support from "SVNIT Surat" under Grant No. dean(R&C)/seed money/2021-22/10783 and "Divyasampark iHUB Roorkee for the Devices Materials and Technology Foundation" under Grant Nos. 4-371 and 4-372.

Optoelectronics2Application (O2A) Research Group

Contact Person: Dr. Vivek Garg, Assistant Professor, Department of Electronics Engineering, SVNIT, Surat
Contact: +91 261-220-1707, Email: vivekg@eced.svnit.ac.in

020082-001

CERTAINLY I-V MEASUREMENT OF THE PEROVSKITE DEVICE UNDER DIM LIGHT INTENSITY

Yean-San Long1*, Yung-Tsung Liu, Min-An Tsai, Cho-Fan Hsieh
Center for Measurement Standards, Industrial Technology and Research Institute, Hsinchu 300, Taiwan.
Contact information*: mickeylong88@itri.org.tw

ABSTRACT: The measured I-V hysteresis is complicated by the vast array of different perovskite solar cell (PSC) device architectures. In our study, we used a dynamic I-V, RTOS method, for I-V then the results showed better accuracy by eliminating in real time the acceptance effect. We also used this method with the testing procedure to compare emerging PV hysteresis behavior under dim light intensity of solar simulator. Therefore, we will compare difference between delay-time and RTOS method under dim light intensity, there are shown RTOS method more certainly I-V measurement of PSC under the dim light intensity.
Keywords: PSC, Solar cell, Intensity

1 AIM AND APPROACH

Emerging PV include organic photovoltaic (OPV), dye-sensitized solar cell (DSSC) and Perovskite solar cell (PSC). The operation principle of OPV/DSSC/PSC is using layers of organic molecules subject to lighting after excitation electronic then pass to the inorganic/organic layer of the wide energy gap nano-layer and voltage. The major differences between OPV/DSSC/PSC and p-n junction solar cells are spectrum, absorption range, photoelectric conversion response time and AM1.5G for standard test condition (STC), etc.

OPV/DSSC/PSC is a high potential product used for energy harvesting, especially in the context of indoor illumination applications. It is important to enhance the quality and reliability of such products, and to overcome the measurement error caused by capacity effect like hysteresis problem. Industry needs a relatively unified international test specifications to make the experimental data are reliable. Therefore, it is necessary to standardize I-V (current − voltage) and SR (spectrum response) and indoor lighting simulator test methods of measurement for OPV/DSSC/PSC.

Therefore, with increasing applications in consumer electronics such as smart phones, laptops and tablet PCs, the need for pervasive computing with a requirement of lower power consumption is increasing every day. This opens the door for energy harvesting that could charge the batteries in these devices to keep them continually functioning in some useful state. There has been a lot of attention on flexible thin film solar cells, such as perovskite solar cell (PSC), given their low-cost and improving efficiency. Performance characterization of PSCs has been investigated, in order to clarify how to determine their performance accurately. Accurate characterization of PSC requires level lighting consideration on each very slow temporal response in the I-V curves of the DSC are clearly dependent on the voltage sweep direction, even when the sweep time is the order of seconds [1][2]. Furthermore, the temporal response is dependent on different level lighting consideration. This analysis showed to improve accuracy, measurement should be real time removing capacitance effect with a Real-Time One-Sweep Method (RTOSM) [3]. Additionally, RTOSM will be useful to measuring cell performance more accurately and rapidly when evaluating solar cell performance..

2 SCIENTIFIC INNOVATION AND RELEVANCE

The samples are perovskite solar cells (PSCs). All sample size are 4 cm2. These I-V curves were carried out by Keithley Source Meter (Model 2651), and 3A solar simulator, meet IEC 60904, SEMI PV57 and SEMI PV69 requirements. Auto-adjustable light intensity (range from Dark to 1,200 W/m2) by homemade-LabVIEW based program, non-uniformity less than 2 % (at 20 cm x 20 cm), and temporal instability less than 2 %. During the I-V measurement in the dark and under solar simulator, the scan direction was forward and backward, the sample temperature should be stablized at 25 ℃ with a fluctuation of less than 1 ℃ and the irradiance intensity were determined using a reference cell (WPVS), respectively.

The bias voltage we applied in the I–V measurement is changed stepwise from Isc to Voc (forward) or in the reverse direction (backward, Voc to Isc). When there is capacitance effect occurs in different level lighting, this measurement process will produce as Fig. 2 of the phenomenon. Its shows the stepwise applied voltage around Voc in a step of 10 mV with 1 point/ms sampling-rate and the transient photocurrent responses of the PSC both in forward and backward scans. I-V measured by RTOS method during the real-time monitoring chart (see Fig. 1) can be removed the capacitance effect of forward/backward under different level lighting. The first advantage can monitor I-V immediately without capacitive effect, available as Fig.1. The other advantage of forward over to backward in I-V curve is very closely to unity, more accurately and rapidly when evaluating sample performance, Ex. Pmax/Isc/Voc/FF (see Fig.1). In Fig. 1, the time constant for equilibrium of PSCs can be estimated by the measurement of the transient photocurrent under the application of a stepwise-changed voltage, an overshot current appears immediately after an abrupt increase of applied voltage, and then the current gradually decreases to an equilibrium state. The response time, which relies on lighting level and property of device, is to decrease while increasing level lighting in the forward and to keep constant in the backward. Because the external biased potential can affect device difference caused by the conversion step like capacitance effect of forward/backward under different level lighting, available as Fig. 1. While using the way of fixed delay time to get the I-V curve, it will cause different set benchmarks, and not enough to achieve complete removal of measurement errors caused by capacitance effect [2, 3]

3 RESULTS (OR PRELIMINARY RESULTS) AND CONCLUSIONS

In this work, we follow the testing flow in [3, 4] in the I-V measure as discussed in reference [1, 2], RTOS method can read simultaneously multi-point forming step after taking the optimization stabilizing test at a point on the I-V curve. The measured performance of sample is highly responsive to the external measurement condition. A reliable evaluation report requires the measurement to be performed under proper condition and the details of the measurement should be clearly described in the report. A list of proposals [2, 4] for the measurement of sample is given below:

In this work, RTOS method can real-time remove the capacity effect from high to low level lighting for I-V successfully (Fig. 5 and Table 1) and proposes the forward/backward schematic reaction mechanism for PSC (Fig. 3). This mean backward scan has a saturation in HUMO and forward scan has a saturation in LUMO, and its response time is shown to increase while decreasing level lighting in the forward and to keep constant in the backward. Thus using the way of fixed delay time to get the I-V curve under high to low level lighting, it is not enough to achieve complete removal of measurement errors caused by capacitance effect [2, 3]. Results also demonstrated the influence from capacitance during the measurement of I-V curves by using a steady-state simulator. Therefore, RTOS method certainly plays the better role than delay time method to get more reasonable characteristics of PSCs (Fig. 5 and Table 1)..

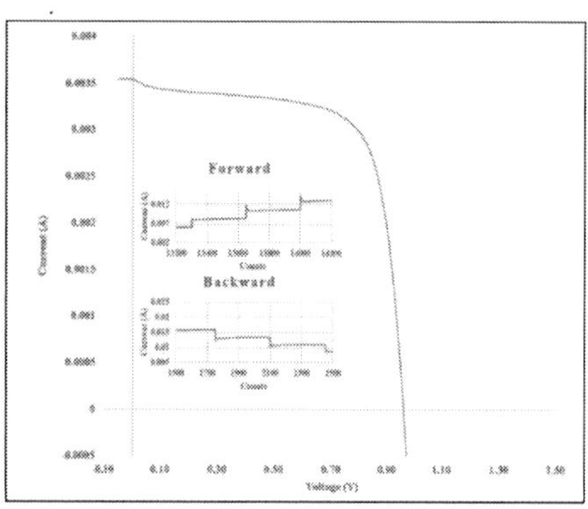

Fig. 1. Step-wised schematic of the RTOS method for I-V.

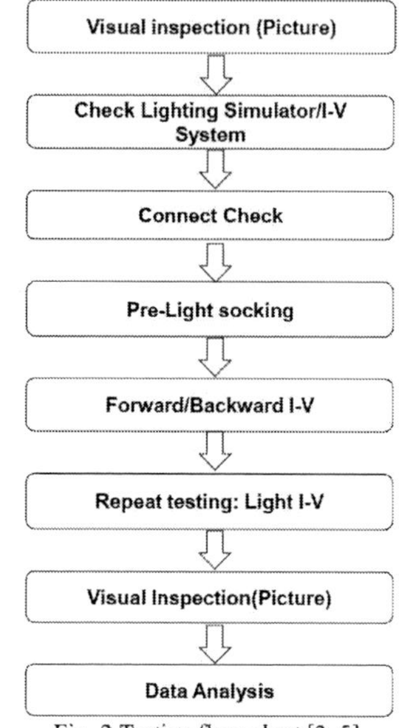

Fig. 2 Testing flow-chart [2, 5].

Fig. 3 Principle of operation and energy level scheme of the PSC device in forward/backward

4 References

[1] T. C. Wu, S. T. Hsu and Y. S. Long, "New Set-up Procedures and Integrated Measurement System for Organic Photovoltaic (OPV) Module", International Photovoltaic Science and Engineering Conference (PVSEC23), 2013.

[2] Y. S. Long, S. T. Hsu and T. C. Wu, "Induction of Internal Capacitance Effect in Performance Measurement of OPV (Organic Photovoltaic) Device by RTOSM (Real-Time One-Sweep Method)", Journal of Energy and Power Engineering, Vol 8, pp1059-1066, 2014.

[3] Y. S. Long, S. T. Hsu and T. C. Wu, "A Study of Capacitance Effect in DSC from High to Low Level Lighting by Real-Time One-Sweep Method", OPTIC2014.

[4] SEMI PV57-1214, Test Method for Current-Voltage (I-V) Performance Measurement of Organic Photovoltaic (OPV) and Dye-Sensitized Solar Cell (DSSC).

[5] US PTO. 8224598, Method for forming optimal characteristic curves of solar cell and system thereof.

Certainly I-V measurement of the perovskite device under dim light intensity

Yean-San Long[1*], Yung-Tsung Liu[1], **Min-An Tsai**[1], Cho-Fan Hsieh
Industrial Technology Research Institute (ITRI)[1]
*mickeylong88@itri.org.tw

ABSTRACT

The measured I-V hysteresis is complicated by the vast array of different perovskite solar cell (PSC) device architectures. In our study, we used a dynamic I-V, RTOS method, for I-V then the results showed better accuracy by eliminating in real time the acceptance effect. We also used this method with the testing procedure to compare emerging PV hysteresis behavior under dim light intensity of solar simulator. Therefore, we will compare difference between delay-time and RTOS method under dim light intensity, there are shown RTOS method more certainly I-V measurement of PSC under the dim light intensity.

The bias voltage we applied in the I–V measurement is changed stepwise from Isc to Voc (forward) or in the reverse direction (backward, Voc to Isc). When there is capacitance effect occurs in different level lighting, this measurement process will produce as Fig. 2 of the phenomenon. Its shows the stepwise applied voltage around Voc in a step of 10 mV with 1 point/ms sampling-rate and the transient photocurrent responses of the PSC both in forward and backward scans. I-V measured by RTOS method during the real-time monitoring chart (see Fig. 1) can be removed the capacitance effect of forward/backward under different level lighting. The first advantage can monitor I-V immediately without capacitive effect, available as Fig.1. The other advantage of forward over to backward in I-V curve is very closely to unity, more accurately and rapidly when evaluating sample performance, Ex. Pmax/Isc/Voc/FF (see Fig.1). In Fig. 1, the time constant for equilibrium of PSCs can be estimated by the measurement of the transient photocurrent under the application of a stepwise-changed voltage, an overshot current appears immediately after an abrupt increase of applied voltage, and then the current gradually decreases to an equilibrium state. The response time, which relies on lighting level and property of device, is to decrease while increasing level lighting in the forward and to keep constant in the backward. Because the external biased potential can affect device difference caused by the conversion step like capacitance effect of forward/backward under different level lighting, available as Fig. 1. While using the way of fixed delay time to get the I-V curve, it will cause different set benchmarks, and not enough to achieve complete removal of measurement errors caused by capacitance effect.

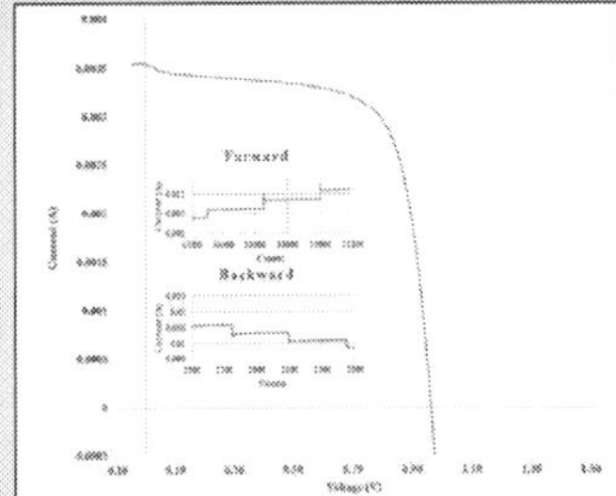

Figure 1: Step-wised schematic of the RTOS method for I-V

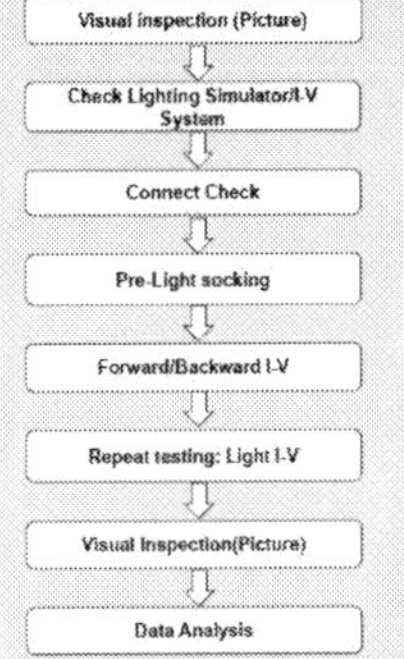

Figure 2: Testing flow-chart

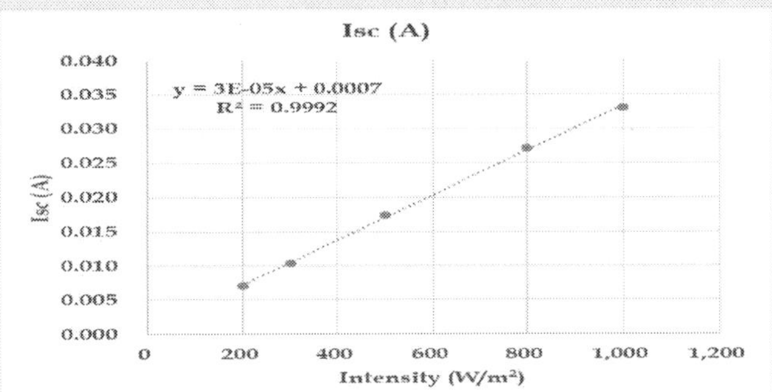

Isc (A)

$y = 3E\text{-}05x + 0.0007$
$R^2 = 0.9992$

Intensity (W/m²)

Figure 3: Principle of operation and energy level scheme of the PSC device in forward/backward

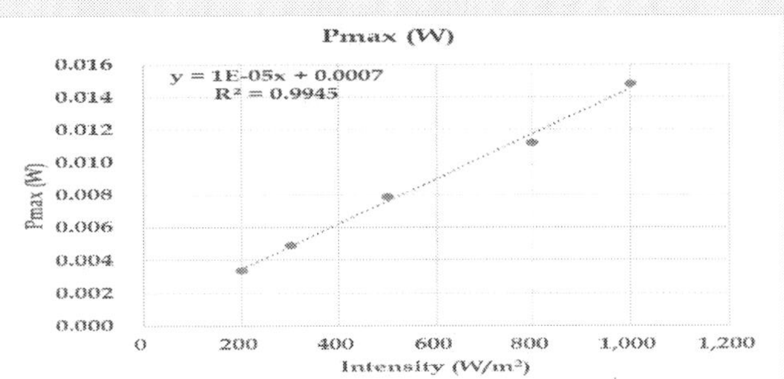

Pmax (W)

$y = 1E\text{-}05x + 0.0007$
$R^2 = 0.9945$

Intensity (W/m²)

Figure 5: Isc/Pmax under dim lighting.

Conclusions

In this work, RTOS method can real-time remove the capacity effect from high to low level lighting for I-V successfully (Fig. 5) and proposes the forward/backward schematic reaction mechanism for PSC (Fig. 3). This mean backward scan has a saturation in HUMO and forward scan has a saturation in LUMO, and its response time is shown to increase while decreasing level lighting in the forward and to keep constant in the backward. Thus using the way of fixed delay time to get the I-V curve under high to low level lighting, it is not enough to achieve complete removal of measurement errors caused by capacitance effect. Results also demonstrated the influence from capacitance during the measurement of I-V curves by using a steady-state simulator. Therefore, RTOS method certainly plays the better role than delay time method to get more reasonable characteristics of PSCs (Fig. 5).

INVESTIGATION OF CD-FREE SB2SE3 THIN-FILM SOLAR CELLS BY ALD-ZNSNO ELECTRON TRANSPORT LAYER

Luna Lázaro-Castrillón[1], Yudania Sánchez[2], David Payno[3], Umair Razi[2], Victor Bonal[3], Fátima Cabello[1], Beatriz Galiana[4], Alejandro Pérez-Rodríguez[2], José Manuel Merino[3], Raquel Caballero[1,*]

[1]Instituto de Óptica Daza de Valdés-CSIC, C/ Serrano 121, 28006 Madrid, Spain
[2]IREC, Catalonia Institute for Energy Research, C/ Jardins de les Dones de Negre 1, Barcelona 08930, Spain
[3]Universidad Autónoma de Madrid, C/ Francisco Tomás y Valiente 7, 28049 Madrid, Spain
[4]Universidad Carlos III de Madrid, Avda. Universidad 40, 28911 Leganés, Madrid, Spain
*raquel.caballero@csic.es

ABSTRACT: Most of the efficient Sb_2Se_3-based PV devices use CdS as electron transport layer (ETL) or/and an organic hole transport layer. With the objective of fabricating non-toxic and stable solar cells, we investigate substrate Sb_2Se_3 thin-film PV devices by the replacement of CdS by $Zn_{1-x}Sn_xO$ (ZTO) layer without using an organic material in the device structure. In this work, Sb_2Se_3 thin films have been grown by selenization of evaporated Sb layer onto Mo/SLG substrates. ZTO films are fabricated by atomic layer deposition (ALD) to develop Cd-free solar cells, while the reference CdS layer is deposited by chemical bath. The absorber presents an orthorhombic structure with [hk1] preferred orientation, and a compact structure free of pinholes. The different techniques used for the fabrication of the ETLs show the different CdS and ZTO morphologies, with a conformal growth and uniform surface for the ZTO. ITO/ZnO/CdS/Sb_2Se_3/Mo/SLG and ITO/ZnO/ZnSnO/Sb_2Se_3/Mo/SLG solar cells are fabricated. A total efficiency of 4.3 % for the CdS/Sb_2Se_3 solar cell and of 3.0 % for the Cd-free PV device are obtained. It is revealed that ZTO thickness is a critical parameter to optimize the heterojunction. In this work, 40 nm ZTO layer leads to higher device performances.

Keywords: Sb_2Se_3, ZnSnO, thin-film solar cells, chalcogenides

1 INTRODUCTION

Low-dimensional antimony-chalcogenide materials have received an outstanding interest for photovoltaic (PV) devices in the last years. They show high stability, low environmental impact, low cost, low carbon footprint and high technological flexibility. In particular, Sb_2Se_3 shows a high absorption coefficient $> 10^5$ cm^{-1}, allowing to reduce the film thickness to 50-500 nm, band gap energy E_g of around 1.2 eV, and, a much lower melting point than that of CIGSe, CdTe and CZTSSe, requiring lower processing temperatures. Nowadays, efficiencies above 10% have already been achieved for Sb_2Se_3-based solar cells [1]. However, most of the Sb_2Se_3-based thin-film solar cells use CdS as ETL and/or an organic material as hole transport layer (HTL).

In this work, we fabricate sustainable Sb_2Se_3-based PV devices using only inorganic materials avoiding the use of CdS. ZTO has attracted significant attention for its non-toxic and earth-abundant constituent elements, large and tunable band gap, and good control over the conduction band offset between the active and ETL layer. Here, Sb_2Se_3 thin films are grown by selenization of evaporated Sb layer. ZTO thin films fabricated by ALD are used as non-toxic ETL of the Sb chalcogenide solar cells. Total area efficiencies of 3.0 % are achieved for the Cd-free Sb_2Se_3 solar cells, and, these devices are compared with the standard CdS/Sb_2Se_3.

2 EXPERIMENTAL DETAILS

2.1 Sb_2Se_3 absorber layer growth

Sb_2Se_3 thin films were grown by selenization of Sb evaporated layers onto Mo/SLG substrates. Sb layers with different thicknesses were evaporated, resulting in Sb_2Se_3 films of around 400 and 800 nm after the selenization. The selenization process was carried out in a tubular furnace under Ar atmosphere using elemental Se at temperature of 340 °C for one hour.

2.2 Device fabrication

CdS layer was deposited by chemical bath (CBD) at 70 °C for 40 minutes [2]. The CdS layer presents a band gap energy of 2.4 eV. $Zn_{1-x}Sn_xO$ layer was grown by ALD using TDMASn and DEZ precursors. Varying the number of cycles, ZTO layers with thicknesses of 20, 40 and 60 nm were produced. The composition was slightly varied from x=[Sn]/([Sn]+[Zn]) = 0.25 to 0.33. A window layer composed of i-ZnO (50 nm) and In_2O_3:SnO_2 (ITO) (200 nm) layers was deposited by RF-pulsed sputtering deposition. Neither grids nor an anti-reflection coating were deposited onto the final photovoltaic devices. Moreover, no thermal treatment was performed to the solar cells.

2.5 Characterization techniques

Grazing incidence X-ray diffraction (GIXRD) was performed to study the structural properties of the chalcogenide thin films and to identify the different phases. GIXRD data were collected with a PANAlytical X´Pert Pro MPD diffractometer, using CuK_α radiation and a multilayer mirror to produce a parallel beam. Detector scans with incident angle of 4° were carried out. The morphology of the ETL/Sb_2Se_3/Mo/glass structure was analysed by SEM using a SEM FEI VERIOS 460, operating at 2 kV. EDX depth profile was performed in a Talos F200X field emission TEM/STEM operating at 200 keV with four symmetrical EDX detectors. Spectral reflectance of the completed PV devices was measured in the spectral range from 300 to 1200 nm with wavelength step of 10 nm using a VASE Woollam ellipsometer.

Current-Voltage (I-V) characteristics of the photovoltaic devices were measured by using a Sun 3000 class solar simulator (Abet Technologies Inc., Milford, Connecticut, USA) under standard test conditions (25°C, AM 1.5, 100 mW/cm^2). External quantum efficiency (*EQE*) of the solar cells was measured using a Bentham PVE300 system (Bentham Instruments Ltd., Berkshire, UK) calibrated with a Si and Ge photodiodes.

3 RESULTS AND DISCUSSION

3.1 Sb$_2$Se$_3$ thin films

Fig. 1.a. shows the X-ray diffraction patterns of Sb$_2$Se$_3$ thin film using grazing incidence angle of 4°. The absorber or active layer exhibits an orthorrombic crystal structure (JCPDS # 00-015-0861). Mo diffraction peaks are also detected and the formation of MoSe$_2$ phase cannot be ruled out. The texture coefficients (TC) of the main (hk0) and (hk1) planes in the range of 10 ° to 60 ° of the Sb$_2$Se$_3$ absorber layer were calculated (see Fig. 1.b.). Sb$_2$Se$_3$ thin film presents preferential orientation in the [hk1] direction, which is beneficial for the carrier's transport [3].

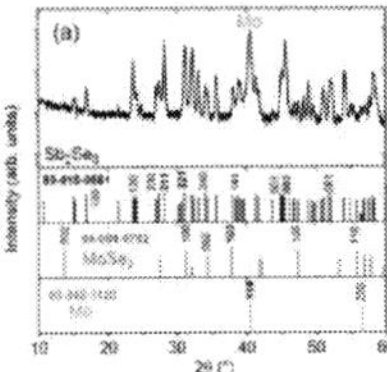
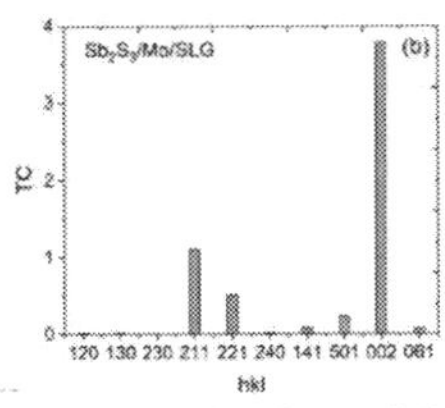

Figure 1: (a) XRD pattern using GI angle of 4° and (b) XRD texture coefficient (TC) of Sb$_2$Se$_3$ thin film grown on Mo/SLG.

Fig. 2.a. and 2.b. show the surface of the Sb$_2$Se$_3$ and the cross-sectional SEM picture of Sb$_2$Se$_3$/Mo structure. A smooth surface and a compact back interface structure free of pinholes is formed. EDX depth profile of Sb, Se and Mo is performed to investigate the elements distribution at the back region (see Fig.2.c.). A thin MoSe$_2$ layer seems to be formed at the Sb$_2$Se$_3$/Mo interface, as reported in [3].

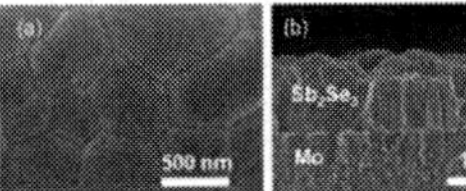
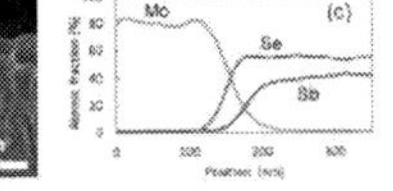

Figure 2: (a) Surface of the absorber layer, (b) cross-sectional SEM picture of Sb$_2$Se$_3$/Mo structure and (c) EDX depth profile of Mo, Sb and Se elements at the back interface.

3.2 Sb$_2$Se$_3$-based PV devices

Fig. 3 shows the surface of both ETLs used in this work, CdS and ZTO, as well as the cross-sectional SEM picture of the ETL/Sb$_2$Se$_3$ interfaces. It is clear that the morphology of the ETLs is very different. ZTO layer is characterized by a conformal growth and very uniform surface, related to the ALD technique. In both cases, the Sb$_2$Se$_3$ thin films are well covered by the ETLs.

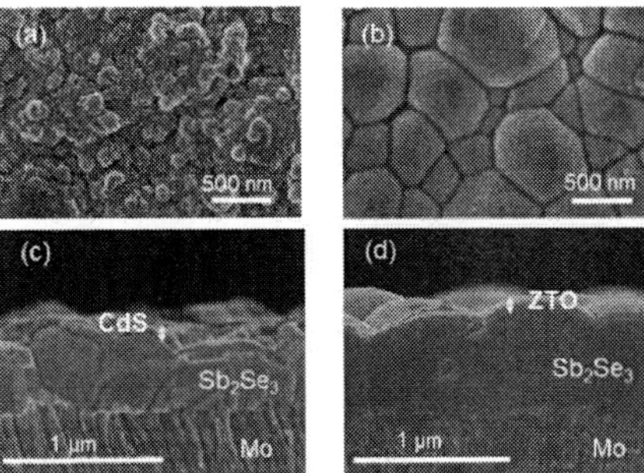

Figure 3: Surface of (a) CdS and (b) ZTO layers, and, (c) and (d) cross-sectional SEM picture of ETL/Sb$_2$Se$_3$ interfaces.

Table I shows the PV parameters of the best solar cells fabricated using CdS and ZTO as ETLs and two different thicknesses of Sb$_2$Se$_3$ absorber layer. The [Sn]/([Sn]+[Zn]) (TTZ) atomic ratio and thickness of the ZTO layer is also displayed. Open circuit voltage V$_{OC}$ and fill factor FF are much higher for the devices using CdS, leading to higher efficiencies. It is clear that the variation of the ZTO thickness has an important impact on the short circuit current density J$_{SC}$ and the FF of the devices. The increase of the ZTO thickness from 40 to 60 nm leads to a lower J$_{SC}$ and FF, resulting in a lower device performance in the Series of 400 nm Sb$_2$Se$_3$. However, in the Series of 800 nm Sb$_2$Se$_3$, the reduction from 40 to 20 nm ZTO thickness produced a significant decrease of solar cell efficiency from 3.0 to 1.8 % related to the lower J$_{SC}$ and FF due to a higher series resistance R$_s$. On the other hand, the slight variation of the TTZ atomic ratio, from 0.25 to 0.33, has not an influence on the PV parameters. Although promising results are achieved, Cd-free PV devices present lower device performances than those produced using CdS as ETL. Luo et al. [4] achieved a device performance of 3.44 % (V$_{OC}$ = 364 mV, J$_{SC}$ = 23.23 mA/cm^2 and FF = 40.63 %) for [Sn]/([Sn]+[Zn]) atomic ratio of 0.43 with the ZTO layer grown by co-sputtering. It is necessary to investigate higher [Sn]/([Sn]+[Zn]) atomic ratios than the used in the present work to optimise the band alignment of the heterointerface and improve device performance [3].

Fig. 4 shows the J-V characteristics of some of the solar cells of Table 1. In any case, a cross-over effect is observed, being clear that the interfaces are not yet fully optimized. As mentioned above, the formation of a thin MoSe$_2$ layer takes place at the back interface, that normally allows for a good ohmic contact and an improved carrier's transport. This is an indication that the heterojunction has to be improved.

Table I: PV parameters of the best solar cells using CdS and ZTO as ETLs, composition and thickness of the ZTO layers.

Sb_2Se_3 (nm)	ETL	[Sn]/([Sn]+[Zn])	ETL (nm)	V_{OC} (mV)	J_{SC} (mA/cm^2)	FF (%)	η (%)	R_s ($\Omega\cdot$cm^2)	R_{sh} ($\Omega\cdot$cm^2)
400	CdS	-	60	373	21.9	50.8	4.2	2.5	96.3
	ZTO	0.33	40	297	20.4	42.7	2.6	3.5	56.2
	ZTO	0.33	60	303	18.2	40.5	2.2	4.5	59.4
800	CdS	-	60	411	20.1	51.6	4.3	5.3	260.0
	ZTO	0.25	20	367	15.2	31.5	1.8	10.6	47.5
	ZTO	0.25	40	344	19.6	45.1	3.0	4.3	117.6
	ZTO	0.33	40	348	20.0	43.7	3.0	4.4	113.9

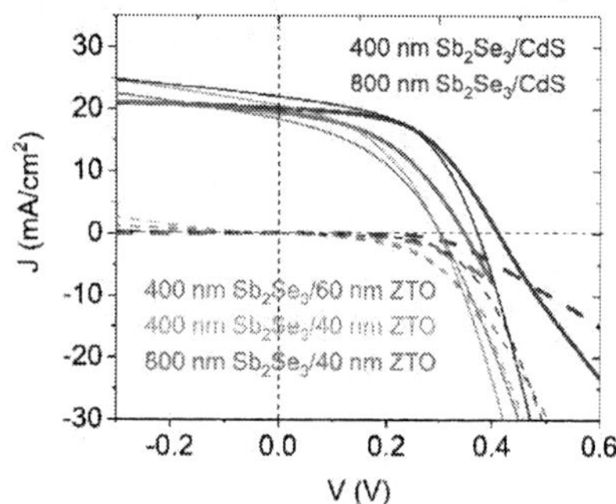

Figure 4: J-V characteristics of PV devices using CdS and ZTO as electron transport layers. All the ZTO layers presented a TTZ atomic ratio of 0.33.

Fig. 5 displays the external quantum efficiency (EQE) of representative Sb$_2$Se$_3$-based solar cells. A higher spectral response is measured at short wavelength range for the Cd-free solar cells related to a higher band gap energy of the ZTO layer of around 3.4 eV, while the CdS presents a band gap energy of 2.4 eV. The Cd-free PV devices are characterised by a lower spectral response starting from 550 nm, and a higher EQE is obtained for the case of thinner Sb$_2$Se$_3$ layer. Specular reflectance was measured for the PV devices. The Cd-free devices show a higher specular reflectance, being higher when the ZTO layer is thicker, of 60 nm (see inside Fig. 5), which in part is related to a rougher surface. Internal quantum efficiency (IQE) has been also plotted in Fig. 5.

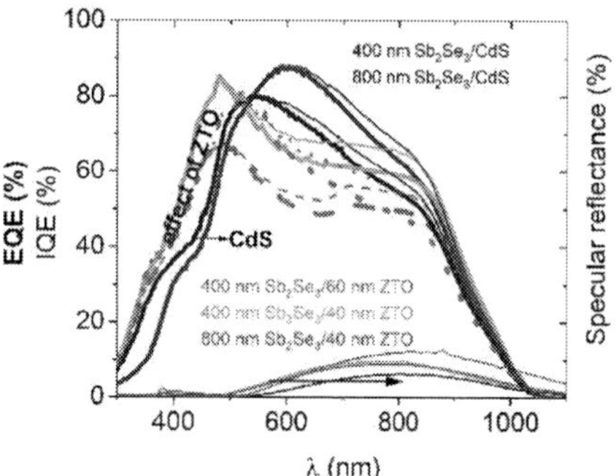

Figure 5: External (thicker line) and internal (thinner line) quantum efficiency measurements of the most representative PV devices. Specular reflectance of the completed devices is also plotted.

4 CONCLUSIONS

Cd-free Sb$_2$Se$_3$-based solar cells have been fabricated. Sb$_2$Se$_3$ thin films have been grown by a two-stage process, evaporation of Sb layer followed by a selenization process. Sb$_2$Se$_3$ single phase orthorhombic crystal structure oriented in the [hk1] is formed on Mo/SLG with a compact structure, free of pinholes. A comparison between Cd-free PV devices and using CdS as ETL is performed. The morphology of both ETLs is very different, outstanding the conformal growth and uniform surface of ZTO deposited by ALD. It is shown that the ZTO thickness is a key parameter to control the heterointerface. In this work, 40 nm of ZTO is the thickness that allows for higher performance. A higher spectral response in the range of the short wavelengths is obtained when using ZTO due to its higher band gap energy of 3.4 eV, and a lower quantum efficiency starting from 500 nm is measured related to the higher reflectance in this range. Although a high performance is achieved when using CdS, first promising results are obtained with ZTO deposited by ALD with a maximum total efficiency of 3.0 %. A further optimization of the composition and optical properties of the ZTO layer and the ZTO/Sb$_2$Se$_3$ band alignment will be the objective of a future work to enhance the Cd-free Sb$_2$Se$_3$ device performance.

Acknowledgments

This work was supported by SUNLIFE (PCI2024 155033-2) project funded by MICIU/AEI/10.13039/501100011033/UE, ASSESS (TED2021-129666B-C21 and TED2021-129666B-C22) project funded by MCIN/AEI/10.13039/501100011033 and by the "European Union Next Generation EU/PRTR" and InnoPV (PID 2022-140226OB-C3) funded by MICIU/AEI/10.13039/501100011033 and by "FEDER/UE". We also acknowledge the service from the MiNa Laboratory at IMN-CSIC, and funding from CM (project S2018/NMT-4291 TEC2SPACE), MINECO (project CSIC13-4E-1794) and EU (FEDER, FSE).

References

[1] Y. Zhao, S. Wang, Ch. Li, B. Che, X. Chen, H. Chen, R. Tang, X. Wang, G. Chen, T. Wang, J. Gong, T. Chen, X. Xiao, J. Li, Y. Zhao et al., Energy Environ. Sci. 15 (2022) 5118.

[2] M. Neuschitzer, Y. Sánchez, S. López-Marino, H. Xie, A. Fairbrother, M. Placidi, S. Haass, V. Izquierdo-Roca, A. Pérez-Rodríguez, E. Saucedo, Progress in Photovoltaics: Research and Applications 23(11) (2015)1660.

[3] X. Wen, Z. Lu, X. Yang, Ch. Chen, M.A. Washington, G.G. Wang, J. Tang, Q. Zhao, T.M. Lu, ACS Appl. Mater.

Interfaces 15 (2023) 22251.
[4] Y.D. Luo, M. Chen, R. Tang, M. Azam, S. Chen, Z.H. Zheng, Z.H. Su, P. Fan, H.L. Ma, G.X. Liang, X.H. Zhang, Solar Energy Materials and Solar Cells 240 (2022) 111721.

Investigation of Cd-free Sb_2Se_3 thin-film solar cells by ALD-$Zn_{1-x}Sn_xO$ electron transport layer

Luna Lázaro-Castrillón[1], Yudania Sánchez[2], David Payno[3], Umair Razi[2], Víctor Bonal[3], Fátima Cabello[1], Beatriz Galiana[4], Alejandro Pérez-Rodríguez[2], José Manuel Merino[3], Raquel Caballero[1,*]

[1]Instituto de Óptica-CSIC, Madrid, Spain
[2]IREC, Barcelona, Spain
[3]Universidad Autónoma de Madrid, Madrid, Spain
[4]Universidad Carlos III de Madrid, Madrid, Spain

*raquel.caballero@csic.es

Motivation

- Sb_2Se_3 is a promising candidate as an absorber material for thin-film solar cells due to its suitable band gap (1.2 eV), high absorption coefficient (>10^5 cm^{-1}), quasi 1D structure, high stability and low deposition temperature.
- The earth-abundant and non-toxic nature of its elements positions Sb_2Se_3 as a sustainable alternative to conventional photovoltaic materials.
- Sustainable PV devices require the replacement of CdS to avoid its toxicity and the use of inorganic materials to assure its stability.

Objective: Investigation of sustainable Sb_2Se_3-based substrate solar cells, replacing CdS by $Zn_{1-x}Sn_xO$ (ZTO) grown by atomic layer deposition (ALD).

Experimental details

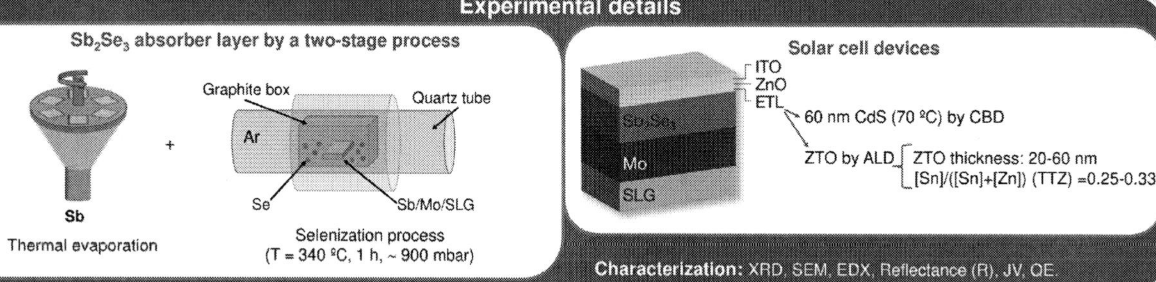

Characterization: XRD, SEM, EDX, Reflectance (R), JV, QE.

Sb_2Se_3 absorber layer

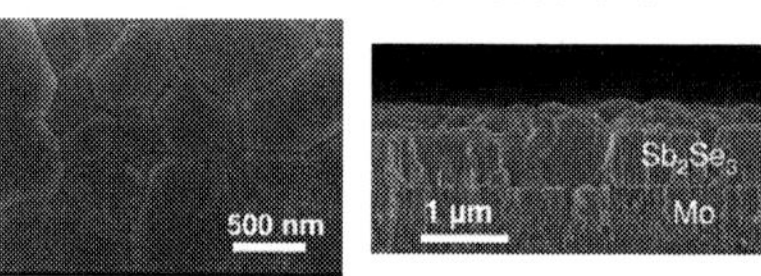

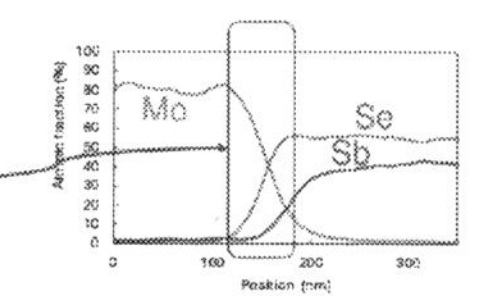

- Sb_2Se_3: Orthorhombic crystal structure with preferential orientation in the [kk1] direction, optimal for the carriers transport.
- Compact Sb_2Se_3/Mo structure, free of pinholes.
- $MoSe_2$ layer at the back interface.

Sb_2Se_3–based PV devices

Surface and cross-sectional SEM

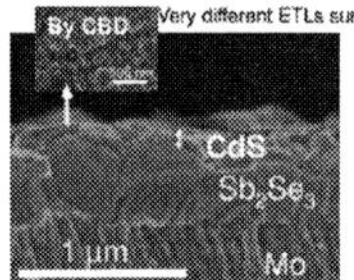

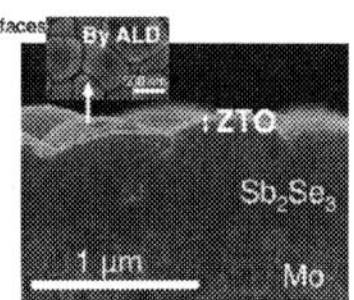

- Sb_2Se_3 thin films are well covered by both ETLs.
- Conformal growth and uniform surface of ZTO.

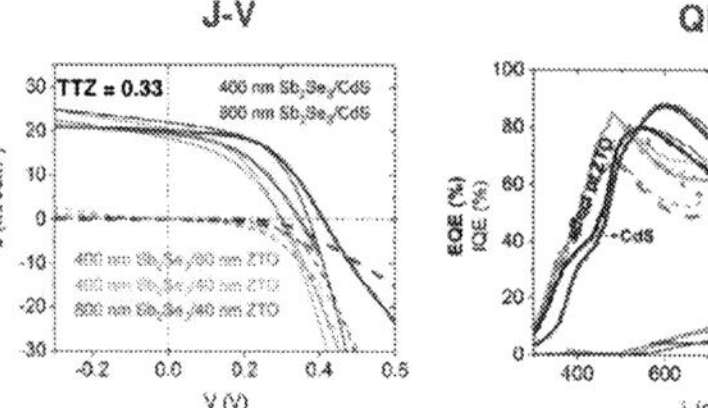

- A higher spectral response (SR) is measured at short λ range related to a higher band gap energy of the ZTO layer of ~ 3.4 eV.
- Lower EQE and higher specular reflectance from 500 nm for ZTO devices.
- Thicker ZTO layer ⇒ ↑ R and roughness.
- ↓ J_{SC} and FF due to ↑ R_s for thinner ZTO (20 nm) ⇒ ↓ η.
- ZTO thickness is the most critical parameter for the range of composition used.
- Cross-over effect in the J-V characteristics ⇒ interfaces are not fully optimized yet.

Effect of Sb_2Se_3 thickness

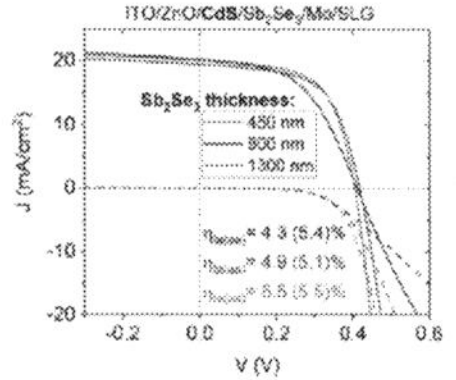

- In all cases, active area efficiency in the range of 5 %.
- Enhanced performance when using thinner absorber.

PV parameters

Sb_2Se_3 (nm)	ETL	[Sn]/([Sn]+[Zn])	ETL (nm)	V_{OC} (mV)	J_{SC} (mA/cm²)	FF (%)	η (%)	R_s (Ω·cm²)	R_{sh} (Ω·cm²)
400	CdS	-	60	373	21.9	50.8	**4.2**	2.5	96.3
	ZTO	0.33	40	297	20.4	42.7	2.6	3.5	56.2
	ZTO	0.33	60	303	18.2	40.5	2.2	4.5	59.4
800	CdS	-	60	411	20.1	51.6	**4.3**	5.3	260.0
	ZTO	0.25	20	367	15.2	31.5	1.8	10.6	47.5
	ZTO	0.25	40	344	19.6	45.1	3.0★	4.3	117.6
	ZTO	0.33	40	348	20.0	43.7	3.0★	4.4	113.9

Conclusions

- Sb_2Se_3 single phase orthorhombic crystal structure oriented in the [hk1] is formed on Mo/SLG with a compact structure, free of pinholes.
- Sb_2Se_3-based PV devices are fabricated using CdS by CBD and alternative ZTO by ALD as ETLs with efficiencies of 5.5 and 3.0 % respectively.
- Cd-free solar cells are characterized by a higher SR at the short wavelength due to the higher band gap energy of ZTO and a lower SR from 500 nm with a higher specular reflectance.
- The thickness of ZTO is a key parameter to enhance the Sb_2Se_3/ZTO interface. In this work, 40 nm ZTO leads to higher device performance.

This work was supported by ASSESS (TED2021-129666B-C21) project funded by MCIN/AEI/10.13039/501100011033 and by the "European Union Next Generation EU/PRTR", InnoPV (PID 2022-140226OB-C3) project funded by MICIU/AEI/10.13039/501100011033 and by "FEDER/UE" and SUNLIFE (PCI2024-155033-2) project funded by MICIU/AEI /10.13039/501100011033/UE.

NUMERICAL SIMULATION OF CADMIUM-FREE BUFFER LAYERS FOR COPPER-DOPED ANTIMONY SELENIDE SOLAR CELLS

Fabio Butrichi [a, b], Maurizio Acciarri [a], Giorgio Tseberlidis [a, c], Vanira Trifiletti [a], Michele Casappa [d], Stefano Rampino [d], Simona Binetti [a]

[a] Department of Materials Science and Solar Energy Research Center (MIB-SOLAR), University of Milano-Bicocca, Via Roberto Cozzi 55, Milano, Italy

[b] Department of Information and Electrical Engineering and Applied Mathematics, University of Salerno, Via Giovanni Paolo II 132, Fisciano (SA), Italy

[c] Institute of Science, Technology and Sustainability for Development of Ceramic Materials, National Research Council, Via Granarolo 64, Faenza (RA), Italy

[d] Institute of Materials for Electronics and Magnetism, National Research Council, Parco Area delle Scienze 37/A, Parma, Italy

ABSTRACT: Cu-doped Sb_2Se_3 is considered a promising absorber for photovoltaics. The main efficiency bottleneck is related to the n-type buffer layer: the commonly used CdS presents a strong parasitic absorption in the visible light and displays a non-optimal band alignment; moreover, CdS is toxic.

This modelling work presents the simulated performances of alternative buffer layers to overcome these issues: ZnSe, SnS_2 and $In_2(O_x,S_{1-x})_3$.

First, the experimental $Cu:Sb_2Se_3/CdS$ junction reported by some of the authors was simulated to obtain experimental values of Sb_2Se_3 simulation parameters.

ZnSe was found as very promising to substitute CdS; the optimal value of the thickness is dependent on the type of defectivity at the interface. SnS_2 also shows good potential, but strongly dependent on donor doping density, that should be as high as possible, considering the possibility of external doping too. For what concerns $In_2(O_x,S_{1-x})_3$, the outmatch on CdS is possible if the composition is optimized, sticking to the better ratio between oxygen and sulfur. The role of the defectivity at the surface is very important for all the buffer layers object of this work, therefore the selection of an adequate buffer layer and the control of the growth is mandatory to obtain a high-performing device.

Keywords: antimony selenide, buffer layers, Cd-free, thin films, photovoltaics

1 INTRODUCTION

Among absorber materials for thin film solar cells, Sb_2Se_3 has gained great attention in the research, thanks to its optimal direct band gap of about 1.2 eV coupled with an absorption coefficient $>10^5$ cm^{-1} and the abundance and safeness of its constituting elements [1].

The reported record efficiency for Sb_2Se_3-based solar cells is 10.57% [2].

One factor that has limited device efficiencies so far is the low p-type conductivity [3], which can be increased by extrinsic metal doping.

Another issue is related to the V_{oc} loss due to interface recombination. Indeed, the conventionally used buffer layer, CdS, displays a high absorption in the blue range of light and is made by a toxic element such as cadmium; moreover, it presents a high lattice mismatch with Sb_2Se_3 and Cd atoms tend to diffuse into Sb_2Se_3 [4].

Some of the authors of this contribution reported on a 5.25% efficient $Cu:Sb_2Se_3$ solar cell [5], with a high value of short circuit current but still a loss in the V_{oc}.

This work aims to overcome this issue, simulating the substitution of CdS with various alternative buffer layers, to determine how an increase in transparency and a more proper band-alignment could help to enhance the V_{oc} values of the experimental material, with its properties and defects. The simulated buffer layers will be all Cd-free, to gain also in sustainability.

The approach is based on a numerical simulation using the free simulation software SCAPS-1D [6].

2 SIMULATION METHODS

SCAPS-1D (Solar Cell Capacitance Simulator) free software, version 3.3.11, was used to carry out the J-V simulations reported in this work. The software was developed in the University of Gent by M. Burgelman and co-workers [6].

The continuity equation for holes and electrons and the Poisson equation are the basis for the calculations performed by SCAPS 1-D. J-V curves are therefore produced as output based on the solar cell's architecture.

Each component of the device is characterized by its thickness, band-gap and electronic properties, such as doping density and bulk defects; interfacial defectivity is also considered.

Standard test conditions (STC) are used for simulation performing, choosing a normal to the sample illumination from the top contact, characterized by 1.5 air mass and 100 mW/cm^2 power density.

3 RESULTS AND DISCUSSION

3.1 Experimental $Cu:Sb_2Se_3/CdS$ simulation

The simulations object of this work are not dealing with an optimized absorber but are grounded on experimental data from actual Sb_2Se_3-based solar cells.

Most of the important simulation parameters of Sb_2Se_3, such as the band-gap, the electron affinity (and hence the band position), the density, capture section and energy position of the defects, the density of doping and series and shunt resistance of the whole cell are directly taken from measurements on Sb_2Se_3 solar cell.

First, the experimental junction Sb_2Se_3/CdS already reported by some of the authors [5] has been modelled, to get the most accurate parameters of the absorber material under exam.

The architecture used of the solar cells was FTO/Sb$_2$Se$_3$/CdS/i-ZnO/AZO; the parameters for simulating CdS, i-ZnO and AZO have been chosen from literature [7] [8].

Figure 1 reports the simulated and experimental curves, while Table I reports their photovoltaic parameters. It's possible to appreciate how the theoretical and experimental curves are well matching; the photovoltaic parameters of the simulated and of the experimental solar cell are very similar, with a difference lower than 2 %.

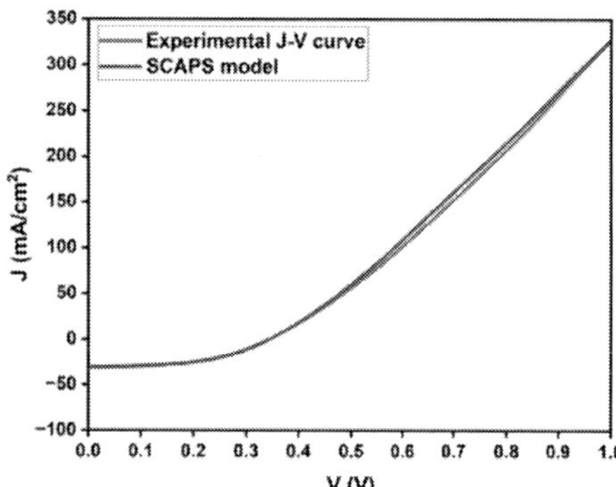

Figure 1: Comparison of simulated and experimental J-V curve of the junction Cu:Sb$_2$Se$_3$/CdS.

Table I: Comparison of simulated and experimental PV parameters of the junction Cu:Sb$_2$Se$_3$/CdS.

	Experimental	Simulated
V_{OC} (mV)	343.0	344.0
J_{SC} (mA/cm^2)	31.4	31.2
FF (%)	49.0	48.2
η (%)	5.25	5.18

The investigated buffer layers are ZnSe, SnS$_2$, and In$_2$(O$_x$S$_{1-x}$)$_3$. For each of them, three scenarios for the interface modelling have been formulated: no defects (ideal case), a situation of low defectivity starting from the interfacial defectivity energetic level reported in the literature, and a high-defectivity one (the same interface defects of the junction Cu:Sb$_2$Se$_3$/CdS).

3.2 Cu:Sb$_2$Se$_3$/ZnSe junction

ZnSe simulation optoelectronic parameters and defects have been taken from literature [9] [10] [11]. The energetic levels for the construction of the low defectivity interface were taken from [10].

Figure 2 reports the efficiency calculation as a function of ZnSe thickness. No defect and low defectivity scenarios present their maximum efficiency with buffer layer thickness between 20 and 25 nm, while the high defectivity one between 45 and 50 nm.

ZnSe is effectively able to outmatch CdS performance in the simulation, reaching η = 14.4 % and η = 8.5 % in the low and high defectivity scenario, respectively.

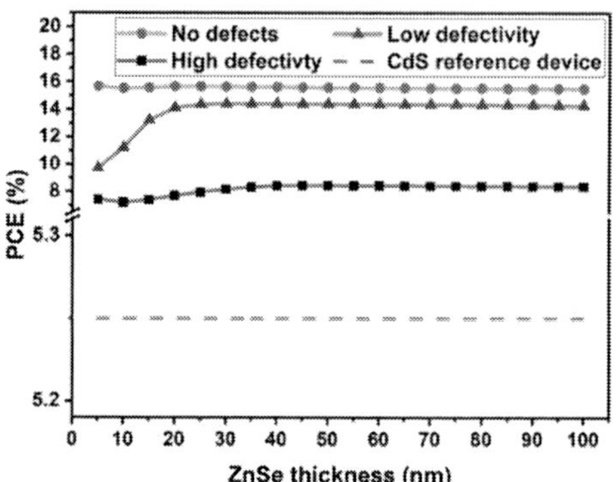

Figure 2: Simulated efficiency of the junction Cu:Sb$_2$Se$_3$/ZnSe as a function of ZnSe thickness.

3.3 Cu:Sb$_2$Se$_3$/SnS$_2$ junction

Also, SnS$_2$ shows very promising results as an alternative buffer layer. Simulation parameters and defects of SnS$_2$ have been taken from literature [12][13]; the energetic levels for the low-defectivity interface were taken from [13].

In literature, SnS$_2$ is reported to have the doping acceptor density between 10^{17} [14] and 10^{19} [15] cm^{-3}. Its effect is very impactful and can be appreciated in Table II (with a fixed thickness of 50 nm).

Table II: Simulated efficiency of the junction Cu:Sb$_2$Se$_3$/SnS$_2$ as a function of SnS$_2$ doping density.

Doping density (cm^{-3})	PCE (%) no defects	PCE (%) low defectivity	PCE (%) high defectivity
$1.0 \cdot 10^{17}$	15.95	9.70	4.55
$5.0 \cdot 10^{17}$	15.59	11.65	5.36
$1.0 \cdot 10^{18}$	15.63	12.05	5.79
$5.0 \cdot 10^{18}$	15.70	12.74	7.77
$1.0 \cdot 10^{19}$	15.72	12.94	9.14
$5.0 \cdot 10^{19}$	15.76	13.29	13.44

The calculated efficiency as a function of the thickness is reported in figure 3 (fixing doping density at the average value of 10^{18} cm^{-3}). In this case also, the optimal point corresponds to a thickness of 10-20 nm for no or low defectivity and to 45-55 nm for high defectivity scenario, confirming the same trend as for ZnSe.

SnS$_2$ is able to outmatch CdS too, but the delivered efficiency is strongly influenced by the doping density, as described above, and by the level of interface defectivity.

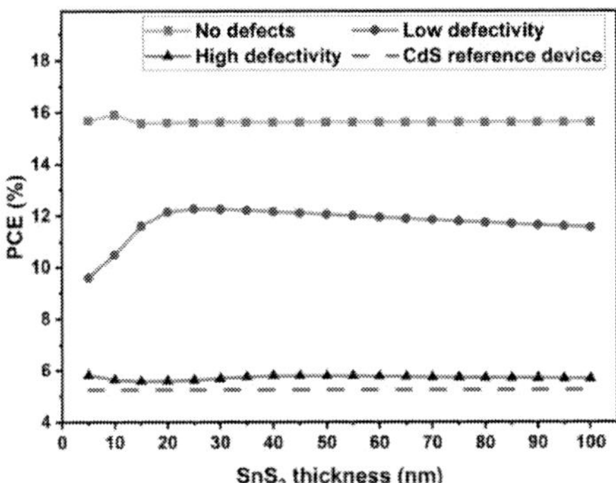

Figure 3: Simulated efficiency of the junction Cu:Sb₂Se₃/SnS₂ as a function of SnS₂ and thickness.

3.4 Cu:Sb₂Se₃/In₂(OₓS₁₋ₓ)₃ junction

In₂(OₓS₁₋ₓ)₃ has also been simulated as an alternative buffer layer, focusing on a low value of x. The value of In₂(OₓS₁₋ₓ)₃ simulation parameters as a function of composition and energy levels of interface defects in low-defectivity hypothesis were taken from [16].

Efficiency was simulated as a function of composition (figure 4) finding an optimal value of x=0.107 both for low and high defectivity situations, with the final composition In₂(O₀.₁₁S₀.₈₉)₃.

It was not possible to obtain the last two points of the high defectivity curve because the simulation didn't converge for the largest quantities of oxygen.

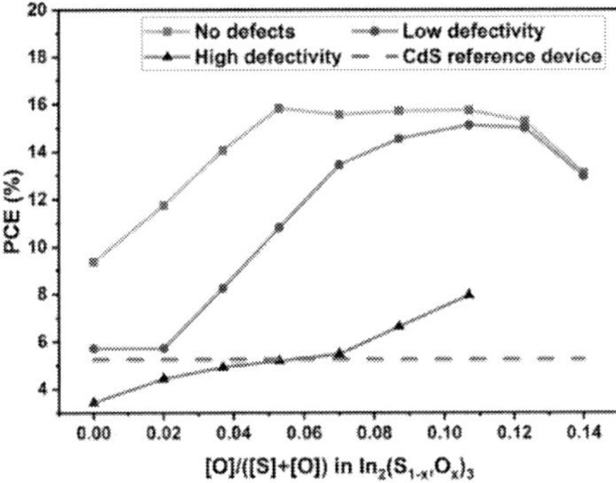

Figure 4: Simulated efficiency of the junction Cu:Sb₂Se₃/In₂(OₓS₁₋ₓ)₃ as a function of In₂(OₓS₁₋ₓ)₃ composition (A).

The optimal value of x=0.107 was used to simulate the efficiency as a function of the thickness of the buffer layer (figure 5), finding thickness >60 nm optimal for both low and high defectivity hypotheses.

In₂(OₓS₁₋ₓ)₃ is the most performing buffer layer reported in this study, reaching η = 15.1 %, in low defectivity scenario

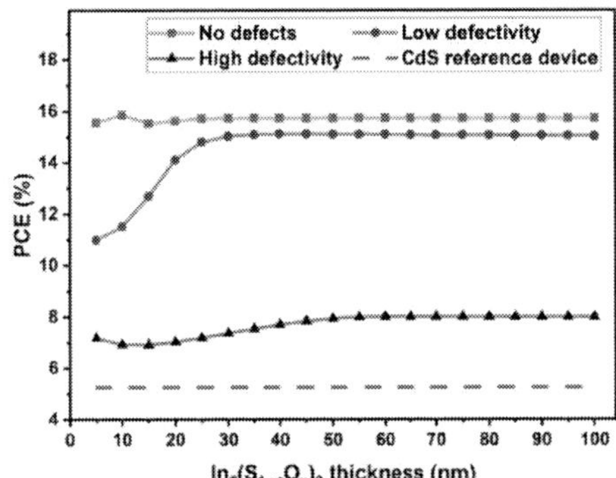

Figure 5: Simulated efficiency of the junction Cu:Sb₂Se₃/In₂(OₓS₁₋ₓ)₃ as a function of In₂(OₓS₁₋ₓ)₃ thickness.

4 CONCLUSIONS

The intention to find alternative buffer layers with better performances than CdS (experimental η = 5.25%) was fully addressed.

The performance of SnS₂ is strongly related to the doping density, reaching η ≈ 13% in the best doping density conditions of 10^{19} cm⁻³; if this layer is to be used, it could be helpful to consider the addition of an external dopant.

ZnSe demonstrated to be able to overcome the CdS standard in all the defectivity scenarios and thicknesses, reaching η ≈ 8% and η ≈ 14% in high defectivity and low defectivity scenario, respectively.

In₂(OₓS₁₋ₓ)₃ needs to be prepared very carefully, because its better performances are restricted to a very narrow interval of composition; if the stoichiometry requirement is met and the interface defectivity is low, Cu:Sb₂Se₃/In₂(OₓS₁₋ₓ)₃ junction could reach η = 15.1%, the highest efficiency value (not in ideal defectivity scenario) reported in this study.

In₂(OₓS₁₋ₓ)₃ is able to reach the highest efficiency, ZnSe, whose efficiency is about only 1 % lower, could be considered the most promising alternative buffer layer studied in this work since it is indium-free and hence cheaper and critical raw material free, is easier to prepare (being binary without the anion ratio to tune) and the performances are more robust to the possible interface defectivity.

Finally, the differences between the three scenarios of defectivity show how important the choice of the buffer layer and the control of its growth process are in avoiding or reducing defects at the interface as much as possible.

5 REFERENCES

[1] C. Chen et al., Solar RRL, vol. 6, no. 7, p. 2200094, Jul. 2022.
[2] Y. Zhao et al., Energy Environ Sci, vol. 15, no. 12, pp. 5118–5128, 2022.
[3] Y. B. Kim et al., Energy Environ Sci, vol. 11, no. 9, pp. 2540–2549, 2018.
[4] A. Mavlonov et al., Solar Energy, vol. 201, pp. 227–246, 2020.
[5] R. Jakomin et al., Solar, vol. 4, no. 1, pp. 83–98, Feb. 2024.
[6] M. Burgelman et al., Thin Solid Films, vol. 361–362, pp. 527–532, 2000.
[7] A. Basak et al., Solar Energy Materials and Solar

Cells, vol. 230, p. 111184, 2021.
[8] C. Gobbo et al., Energies (Basel), vol. 16, no. 10, May 2023.
[9] S. H. Zyoud et al., International Review on Modelling and Simulations, vol. 16, no. 3, pp. 120–128, 2023.
[10] R. Kumari et al., ACS Omega, vol. 8, no. 1, pp. 1632–1642, 2022.
[11] A. Rahmoune et al., Optik (Stuttg), vol. 283, p. 170875, 2023.
[12] T. Garmim et al., Mater Today Proc, vol. 66, pp. 146–150, 2022.
[13] B. M. Sakunde et al., ACS Appl Energy Mater, vol. 7, no. 14, pp. 5691–5697, Jul. 2024.
[14] Md. F. Hossain et al., Opt Commun, vol. 559, p. 130410, 2024.
[15] T. Garmim et al., Mater Today Proc, vol. 66, pp. 146–150, 2022.
[16] E. Moradi Haghighi et al., Opt Laser Technol, vol. 169, p. 110107, 2024.

Numerical simulation of cadmium-free buffer layers for copper-doped antimony selenide solar cells

Fabio Butrichi [a,b], Maurizio Acciarri [a], Giorgio Tseberlidis [a,c], Vanira Trifiletti [a], Michele Casappa [d], Stefano Rampino [d], Simona Binetti [a]

[a] Department of Materials Science and Solar Energy Research Center (MIB-SOLAR), University of Milano-Bicocca, Milano, Italy
[b] Department of Information and Electrical Engineering and Applied Mathematics, University of Salerno, Fisciano (SA), Italy
[c] Institute of Science, Technology and Sustainability for Development of Ceramic Materials, National Research Council, 48018, Faenza (RA), Italy
[d] Institute of Materials for Electronics and Magnetism, National Research Council, 43124, Parma, Italy

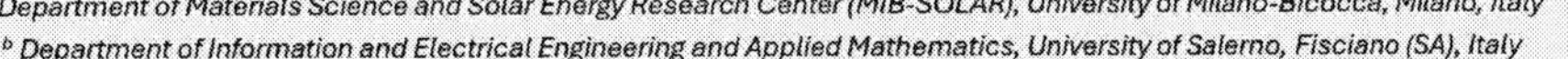

Cu-doped Sb_2Se_3 is considered as a promising p-type semiconductor for photovoltaic applications. The main efficiency bottleneck is related to the choice of n-type buffer layer: the commonly used CdS presents a strong parasitic absorption in the visible range of light and displays a non-optimal band alignment; moreover, CdS is very toxic.

This simulation work presents the possible performances of alternative buffer layers to overcome these issues: ZnSe, SnS_2 and $In_2(O_x S_{1-x})_3$.

First, the experimental $Cu:Sb_2Se_3/CdS$ junction reported by some of the authors was simulated to obtain experimental values of Sb_2Se_3 parameters.

ZnSe has been found as very promising to substitute CdS; the precise value of the thickness, important for the performance, is dependent on the type of defectivity at the interface. SnS_2 also shows good potential, but strongly dependent on donor doping density, that should be as high as possible, also considering the possibility of an external doping. For what concerns $In_2(O_x S_{1-x})_3$, the outmatch on CdS is possible if the composition is optimized, sticking to the better ratio between oxygen and sulfur. The role of the defectivity at the surface is very important for all the buffer layers object of this work, therefore the selection of an adequate buffer layer and the control of the growth is mandatory to obtain a high-performing device.

$Cu:Sb_2Se_3/CdS$

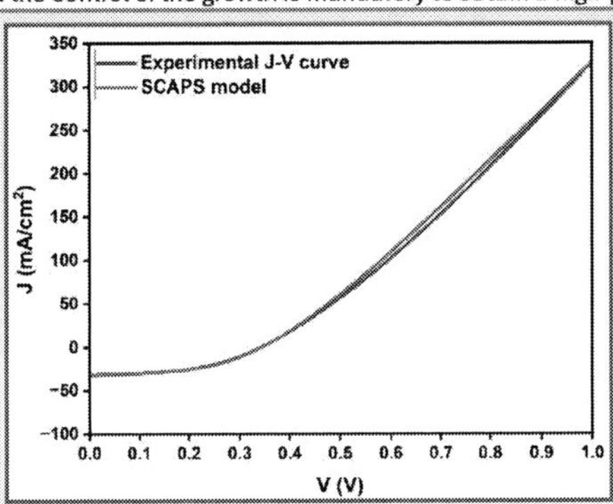

	Experimental	SCAPS model
V_{OC} (mV)	343.0	344.0
J_{SC} (mA/cm²)	31.4	31.2
FF (%)	49.0	48.2
PCE (%)	5.25	5.18

- Very good agreement between experimental and simulated data

- Reliable $Cu:Sb_2Se_3$ optoelectronic parameters for buffer layer substitution study

$Cu:Sb_2Se_3/In_2(S_{1-x}O_x)_3$

- Efficiency value strongly dependent on stoichiometry (low oxygen quantity range)
- Best composition considering low defectivity level is: $In_2(S_{0.89}O_{0.11})_3$

- Optimal thickness value dependent on defectivity level
- Increase of series resistance at high thickness underrated in SCAPS modelling

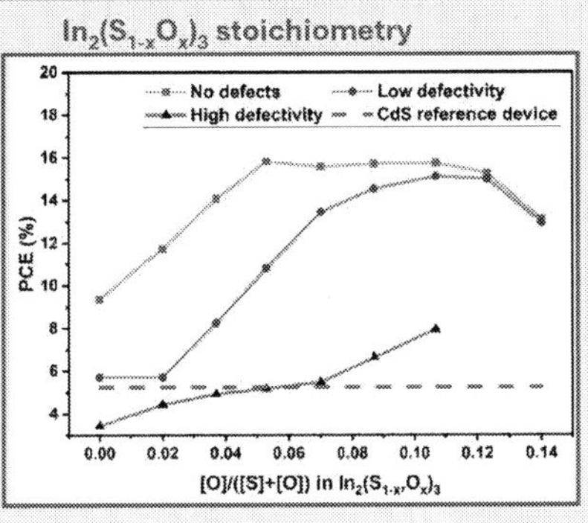

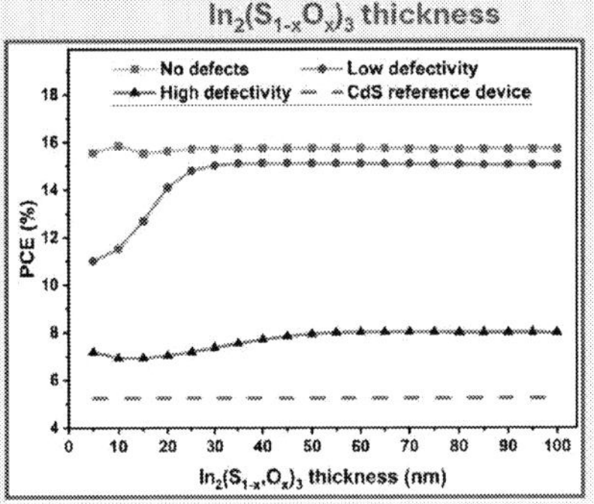

$Cu:Sb_2Se_3/ZnSe$

- Optimal thickness around 30 nm
- Increase of series resistance at high thickness underrated in SCAPS modelling

- The most promising alternative buffer layer, considering also low cost and easy preparation

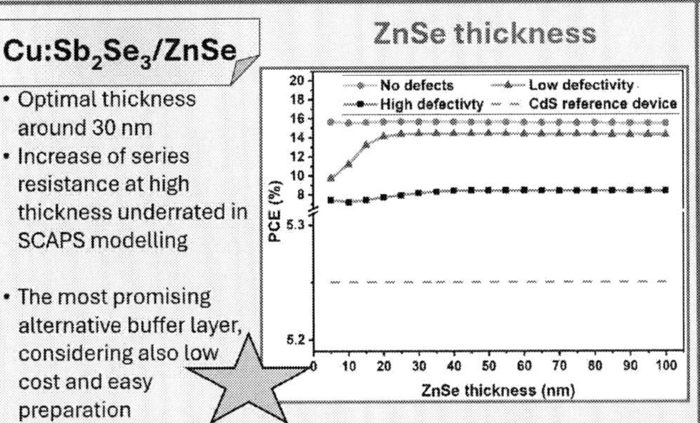

$Cu:Sb_2Se_3/SnS_2$

- Optimal thickness around 30 nm

- Strong **dependence on doping density**

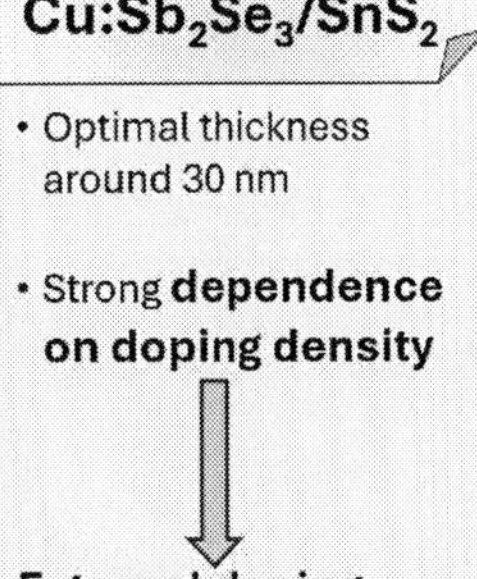

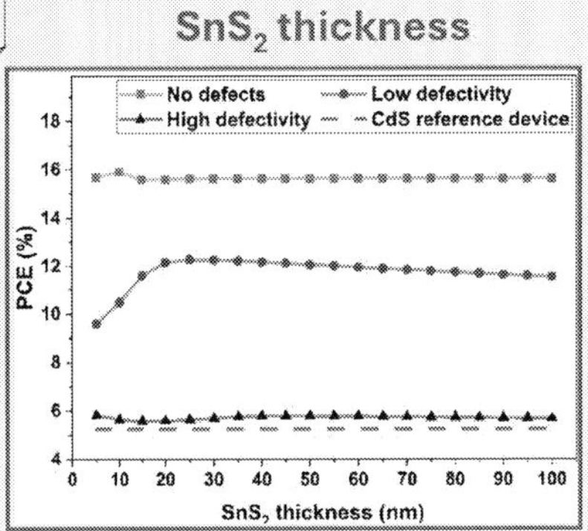

This study is a result of the research project CANVAS, funded by the Italian Ministry of the Environment and the Energy Security, through the Research Fund for the Italian Electrical System (type-A call, published on G.U.R.I. n. 192 on 18-08- 2022) and of the COST Action Research and International Networking project "Emerging Inorganic Chalcogenides for PVs (RENEW-PV)," CA21148. The author F. B. acknowledges the Dottorato di Interesse Nazionale "Photovoltaics".

The effect of thickness on the Sb₂Se₃ superstrate solar cells.

N. Torabi[1], J.M. Delgado-Sanchez[2], E. Artegiani[1], P. Jakuza[3], M. Meneghini[3,4], A. Romeo[1*]

[1] LAPS-Laboratory for Photovoltaics and Solid-State Physics, Department of Computer Science, University of Verona, Ca' Vignal 1, Strada Le Grazie 15, 37134 Verona, Italy.

[2] Department of Applied Physics, University of Seville, Ctra. Utrera km 1, Seville, Spain

[3] University of Padova Department of Information Engineering via Gradenigo 6/B 35131 Padova, Italy

[4] University of Padova, Department of Physics and Astronomy, via Marzolo 8, 35131 Padova, Italy

Abstract — In this study, we analyze the impact of different thickness of antimony selenide thin films on the electrical properties of the absorber and on the efficiency of the finished solar cells. Sb_2Se_3 absorbers have been deposited with thickness from 400 nm to 1200 nm, grown by thermal evaporation on CdSe buffer layer in superstrate configuration.

The highest efficiency has been delivered by the lowest thickness, with a large absorption spectra and higher quantum efficiency response as well as a higher carrier concentration. Moreover, a post-annealing treatment in air at 150 °C, improves the efficiency of the cells with a larger impact on the thinnest absorber, increasing the Voc and correcting the rollover effect observed in the J-V of the thicker absorber layers.

I. INTRODUCTION

Antimony selenide (Sb_2Se_3) possesses an optimal band gap of around 1–1.2 eV and has a high absorption coefficient ($>10^5 cm^{-1}$), making it a cost-effective option for thin-film solar cells [1]. It is made of earth-abundant and low-toxic elements but what is more interesting, it is the quasi-one-dimensional (Q-1D) crystal structure, that limits the effects of the grain boundaries [2], [3].

Driven by the high absorption coefficient and by the accurate control of the deposition rate of our thermal evaporation system, both absorbers and finished devices with different Sb2Se3 layer thicknesses have been analyzed and compared. The Sb_2Se_3 films where grown by thermal evaporation with a thickness of 400, 800, and 1200 nm, in a superstrate device structure of glass/SnO₂: F/SnO₂/CdSe/Sb₂Se₃/Au. Also, a post-annealing treatment (PAT) in air has been applied to the finished device. The optimized annealing temperature and time were defined as respectively 150°C and 20 min.

The best results have been delivered by the thinner absorber that, together with the post deposition annealing, show a higher current density and higher open circuit voltage, which was found to be driven by higher quantum efficiency response and high carrier concentration.

II. METHODS

A. Fabrication

Sb_2Se_3 solar cells are fabricated in a superstrate configuration, utilizing a glass/SnO₂:F (FTO)/SnO₂/CdSe/Sb₂Se₃/Au structure. The commercial coated glasses (NSG TEC 12D) were used as substrates, where 60 nm of the buffer layer, CdSe, is thermally evaporated at 340°C under a pressure of $1*10^{-5}$ bar. Subsequently, Sb_2Se_3 is evaporated from a graphite crucible at 500-600°C, with a pressure of $2*10^{-6}$ mbar and an evaporation rate of 0.15 nm/sec. Annealing in vacuum is applied to enhance the crystallinity by heating the stack in the evaporation chamber at 350°C for 30 minutes. A 30 nm thick gold layer with a cell area of 0.13 cm² is thermally evaporated on top of the absorber as back contact. The devices are labeled T400, T800, and T1200 according to their absorber thickness. Finally, one device from each batch undergoes a post-annealing treatment (PAT) in the oven at a temperature of 150 °C for 20 min, resulting in T400-PAT, T800-PAT, and T1200-PAT.

B. Characterization Techniques

Current density–voltage (JV) characteristics are collected with a Keithley Source Meter 2420, under an AM 1.5 spectrum at 100 mW/cm², using a LOT Quantum Design Europe solar simulator LS0306.

X-ray diffraction (XRD) and grazing angle x-ray diffraction (GXRD) patterns were obtained on a Bruker D8 Advance instrument equipped with a Cu K_α radiation source operating at 40 kV and 30 mA. The diffractograms were measured in the range of 3-70º 2θ, with step time of 0.1 s and step size of 0.015º.

The morphology and elemental composition of the crystalline phases were analyzed by scanning electron microscopy (SEM/EDX), using a JEOL microscope (JSM 5400 Model) and working 20 kV. This equipment is connected to an energy dispersive system X-ray (EDX) (Oxford Link ISIS) which allows chemical analysis of samples using a detector of Si/Li with a Be window. The external quantum efficiency (EQE) spectra were acquired using a commercial LOANA solar cell analysis system, calibrated with a silicon reference sample with known EQE using an incident spotlight of 1 mm × 2 mm area. An HP4284A LCR, controlled by a specific in-house software, was applied for capacitance-voltage, drive-level capacitance profiling, and admittance spectroscopy.

10.4229/EUPVSEC2025/2BV.2.3
020089-001

III. ANALYSIS AND RESULTS

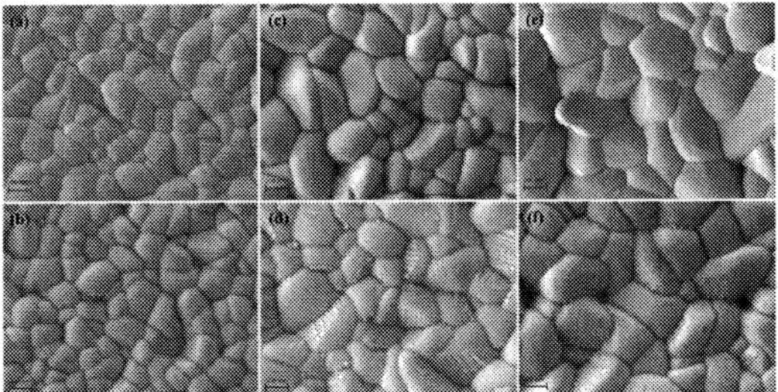

Figure 1: Top-view SEM images of (a) T400, (b) T400-PAT, (c) T800, (d) T800-PAT, (e) T1200, and (f) T1200-PAT Sb_2Se_3 films.

Scanning electron microscope pictures of different thick Sb_2Se_3 films show grain enlargement as the film thickness increases (see figure 1. a, c, and e), with the average grain size developing from 200 to 300 nm. After post-annealing treatment (PAT) (figure 1. b, d, and f), the grain boundaries become more defined, and the average grain size increases slightly. Additionally, some aggregations are present at the grain boundaries in the thicker films. These appear as needle-shaped in the T800-PAT film but as localized particles in the T1200-PAT film. The small size of the aggregations, a few nanometers, make it difficult to detect by EDX (not shown here), XRD. Fleck et al. [4] have reported the formation of α-Sb_2O_3 on the surface through simple air exposure to the samples or annealing in air.

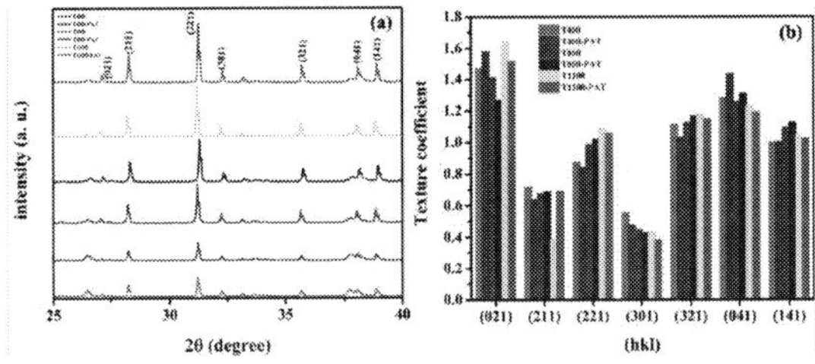

Figure 2: (a) XRD peaks, and (b) texture coefficient of different thick Sb_2Se_3 films before and after PAT.

The X-ray diffraction (XRD) patterns of all the absorber confirm the orthorhombic crystal structure (JCPDS No. 15-0861) of Sb_2Se_3 (Figure 2 (a)). (211) and (221) planes are the preferred orientations due to their large angle to the surface [5].
A TC diffraction value larger than one indicates a preferential orientation of the grains along that direction.

Accordingly, our films are orientated along (hk1) planes, but they are textured along (021) and (041) planes, which have a smaller angle to the surface compared to (211) and (221) planes. Increasing the thickness and PAT increase the texturizing along these orientations and has a larger impact on the T400 film.

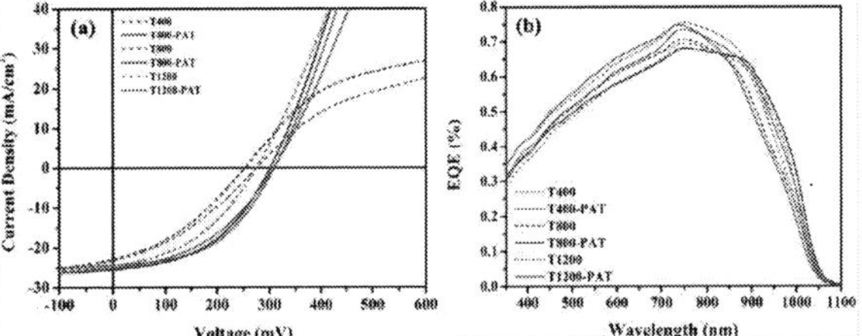

Figure 3: (a) Current-Voltage curves, and (b) EQE response of the various thick Sb_2Se_3 solar cells before and after PAT.

The current-voltage (J-V) characteristics (Figure 3 (a) and Table 1, representing the most efficient solar cells) demonstrate that the T400 cell shows the highest efficiency, while after PAT, the efficiency increases of at least 1% absolute efficiency for all cases. Chen et al. shows that the minimum thickness to capture all photons is 800 nm, however we demonstrate here that 400 nm allows a very efficient absorption of the spectrum [1]. J_{sc} exhibits smaller values for thicker layers of Sb_2Se_3 solar cells, although theoretically, it should increase. This could offer enhancement of defect density in the thicker Sb_2Se_3 films during the growth process. After PAT, J_{sc} has improved except for the T400 cell, where we did not observe the aggregation at the grain boundaries. Although V_{oc} and FF exhibit the highest value in the T400 cell, these parameters have enhanced after PAT in all devices. We can see a similar trend for shunt and series resistances, showing more favorable values of the ultra-thin Sb_2Se_3 solar cells.

Table 1: Photovoltaic parameters of different thick Sb_2Se_3 solar cells before and after PAT.

Sample	J_{sc} (mA/cm²)	V_{oc} (mV)	FF (%)	η (%)
T400	24.3	279	41.2	2.8
T400-PAT	24.3	314	48.4	3.7
T800	22.6	258	35.2	2
T800-PAT	25.4	307	45.6	3.5
T1200	23	279	34.6	2.2
T1200-PAT	25	314	42.1	3.3

Also, the rollover effect at higher bias voltage in the J-V curves of T800 and T1200 solar cells (Figure 3 (a)) vanishes after PAT. It has been shown that a thin Sb_2O_3 layer on the surface of Sb_2Se_3 acts as a barrier, improving the hole extraction, while a thicker layer would negatively impact increasing series resistance [4]. Similarly, the PAT reduces the rollover effect and decreases the series resistance.

Sb$_2$Se$_3$ solar cells, in all cases, exhibit comparable carrier collection in the whole spectrum, as shown in the EQE curves in Figure 3 (b). The lower response of EQE before 600 nm and after 800 nm could be explained by the parasitic absorption of the CdSe and by the recombination due to deep defects, respectively. The broad increase of EQE in the whole spectrum of the T1200-PAT cell supports the higher J$_{sc}$ via an enhanced carrier collection. Although Jsc exhibits similar values after PAT for T400 cells, the EQE drops after 700 nm, which could be associated with a slight reduced absorption of the thinner Sb$_2$Se$_3$ layer.

Capacitance-voltage (CV) and deep-level capacitance profiling (DLCP), see Figure 4, identify carrier concentrations of T400, T800, and T1200 cells respectively of 4.6x10^{16} cm^{-3}, 2.6x10^{16} cm^{-3}, and 2.2x10^{16} cm^{-3}. The 400 nm thick Sb$_2$Se$_3$ solar cell shows the highest doping density and, consequently, the smallest SCR width.

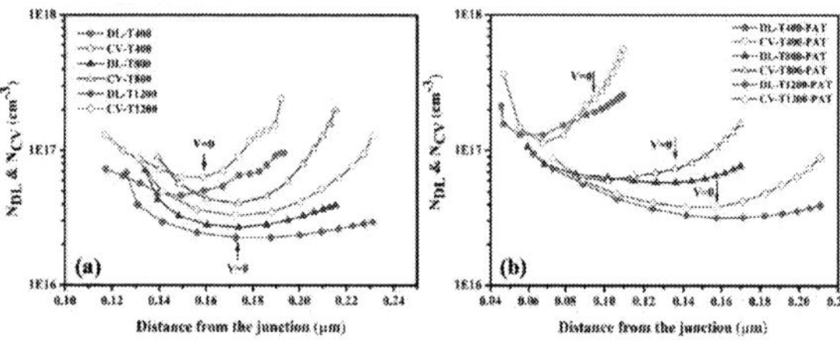

Figure 4: capacitance-voltage (CV) and deep-level capacitance profiling (DLCP) of different thick Sb2Se3 solar cells (a) before and (b) after PAT.

The differences between CV and DLCP profiles are distinct, particularly for thicker absorber layers confirming the presence of deep defects. The carrier concentration of T400-PAT, T800-PAT, and T1200-PAT cells increases to 1.3x10^{17} cm^{-3}, 5.8x10^{16} cm^{-3}, and 3.1x10^{16} cm^{-3}, respectively, resulting in a shrunk SCR width, which is shown at V=0 on the graph. The larger difference between CV and DLCP profiles seen before the annealing, disappears after the annealing and the profiles result almost superposed after PAT. This suggests that the annealing may act as a passivation layer.

IV. CONCLUSIONS

This work demonstrates that reducing the Sb$_2$Se$_3$ absorber thickness down to 400 nm in a superstrate glass/FTO/SnO$_2$/CdSe/Sb$_2$Se$_3$/Au configuration leads to superior device performance compared to thicker (800 nm and 1200 nm) layers. The thinner absorber delivers the highest efficiency thanks to higher carrier concentration, enhanced quantum efficiency, and improved open-circuit voltage. Post-annealing treatment in air at 150 °C for 20 min further boosts performance across all thicknesses, most notably for the 400 nm films, by increasing carrier density, reducing deep-level defects, and suppressing the J–V rollover effect.

These results indicate that very thin Sb$_2$Se$_3$ absorbers, combined with a mild air annealing step, can effectively absorb the solar spectrum while minimizing defect density and series resistance.

V. ACKNOWLEDGMENTS

This work has been partially funded by ACT-FAST project, n. CETP22_00039 within CET-partnership program. The Italian Ministry of Research is thankfully acknowledged. Cariverona foundation is thankfully acknowledged for partially funding this project Ref. 2022.0094 – ID 52271 – CUP B33C22001760007.

REFERENCES

[1] C. Chen *et al.*, "Optical properties of amorphous and polycrystalline Sb2Se3 thin films prepared by thermal evaporation," *Appl Phys Lett*, vol. 107, no. 4, Jul. 2015, doi: 10.1063/1.4927741.

[2] A. Mavlonov *et al.*, "A review of Sb2Se3 photovoltaic absorber materials and thin-film solar cells," May 01, 2020, *Elsevier Ltd*. doi: 10.1016/j.solener.2020.03.009.

[3] Y. Zhou *et al.*, "Thin-film Sb2Se3 photovoltaics with oriented one-dimensional ribbons and benign grain boundaries," *Nat Photonics*, 2015, doi: 10.1038/nphoton.2015.78.

[4] N. Fleck *et al.*, "How Oxygen Exposure Improves the Back Contact and Performance of Antimony Selenide Solar Cells," *ACS Appl Mater Interfaces*, vol. 12, no. 47, pp. 52595–52602, Nov. 2020, doi: 10.1021/acsami.0c14256.

[5] F. Pattini *et al.*, "Role of the substrates in the ribbon orientation of Sb2Se3 films grown by Low-Temperature Pulsed Electron Deposition," *Solar Energy Materials and Solar Cells*, vol. 218, no. June, p. 110724, 2020, doi: 10.1016/j.solmat.2020.110724.

TRANSFER OF GAAS SOLAR CELLS TO UNPRECEDENTED FLEXIBLE POLYMERIC BASES OF PVC:PMMA:DOP MODIFIED WITH EG

Graciana S. Sousa[1]; Luciana D. Pinto[2]; Fabiele C. Tavares[3]; Guillermo J. N. Soares[4]; Rudy M. S. Kawabata[5]; Rogério Valaski[6]; Maurício P. Pires[7]; Roberto Jakomin[8]; Guilherme M. Torelly[9]; Patrícia L. Souza[10]

[1,2,7,10]Instituto de Física - Universidade Federal do Rio de Janeiro, Rio de Janeiro, Brazil; [3,4,8]Campus Duque de Caxias - Universidade Federal do Rio de Janeiro, Duque de Caxias, Brazil; 5,9Laboratório de Semicondutores (LabSem) - Pontifícia Universidade Católica do Rio de Janeiro, Rio de Janeiro, Brazil; 6Laboratório de Fenômenos de Superfície/DIMAT - Instituto Nacional de Metrologia, Rio de Janeiro, Brazil.

graciana.sousa@ifpa.edu.br; dornnelas@yahoo.com.br; fabieletavares@hotmail.com; guillermo.nog9@gmail.com; rudykawarudykawa@gmail.com; rvalaski@inmetro.gov.br; pires@if.ufrj.br; roberto.jakomin@gmail.com; torelly@puc-rio.br; plsouza@if.ufrj.br

ABSTRACT: Single GaAs solar cells, Produced by Metalorganic Vapor Phase Epitaxy (MOVPE) on a rigid GaAs substrate, were transferred to an unprecedented flexible polymer blend of PVC:PMMA:DOP (1.0:1.0:0.5) modified with exfoliated graphene (EG). The exfoliated graphene was employed to enhance properties such as thermal and mechanical resistance of the polymeric bases. The blend with EG adhered perfectly to the solar cells, providing the necessary mechanical support. The current–voltage measurements on the rigid cells and after their transfer to flexible substrates showed that the cell's efficiency remained unchanged following the transfer. Therefore, we can conclude that PVC:PMMA:DOP blends modified with EG show great potential for use as a flexible base in high-efficiency photovoltaic cells.
Keywords: solar cells, PVC-PMMA blends, flexible substrate, flexible solar cells

1 APPLICABLE TOPIC AND SUB-TOPIC NUMBER

High-efficiency solar cells are commonly produced by Metalorganic Vapor Phase Epitaxy (MOVPE) on rigid monocrystalline Gallium Arsenide (GaAs) substrates, which are responsible for eighty percent of the production cost [1,2]. Solar cells based on these III-V materials hold the current world records for photovoltaic conversion efficiency [3] due to their high photon absorption capability and high crystalline quality. The rigid monocrystalline substrate is indispensable as crystallographic base and mechanical support in the fabrication process of the solar cell structure but it is not active during the photovoltaic operation [4].

Removing the rigid substrate and reusing it for sequential depositions may substantially reduce the overall cost of the solar cells [2,5].There is a growing interest in technologies that allow the commercialization of solar cells on light, flexible, and low-cost substrates, expanding not only the range of applicability but also reducing production, transport, and installation costs [6,7]. The transfer of solar cell structures from GaAs substrates to flexible bases has become a growing focus of interest within the scientific community, as highlighted in various studies [8,12]. In our research group, we developed a methodology for the transfer process of III-V solar cells onto flexible copper substrates obtained through electrodeposition and onto copper adhesive tape [13,14].

Polymeric blends are a cost-effective alternative to be used as flexible bases for III-V photovoltaics. Recentely, we have prepared and characterized polymeric blends using poly(vinyl chloride) (PVC) and poly(methyl methacrylate) (PMMA) with plasticizing agents such as dioctyl adipate (DOA) and dioctyl phthalate (DOP) to be used as unprecedented flexible polymeric bases for III-V photovoltaics [15,16]. The properties of PVC:PMMA polymer blends [17-19], incorporated with these plasticizers [20-22], are being extensively studied. The incorporation of rigid and stiff PMMA into PVC partially plasticized with DOP further improves its flexibility and enhances its mechanical and thermal properties [22]. We successfully performed the transfer of InGaAs/GaAs heterostructures onto two different polymer blend compositions, modified with exfoliated graphene (EG) [16]. Photoluminescence measurements confirmed that the III-V structures were not damaged by the transfer process. The emission peak energy of InGaP, after the transfer process, remained steady at approximately 1.85 eV, corresponding to the bandgap energy of bulk InGaP. The exfoliated graphene (EG) was introduced into the blend with the aim of increasing mechanical and thermal resistance, as well as enhancing the adhesion of the polymers to III-V materials [23]. Blends containing exfoliated graphene are optimal candidates as substrates for solar cells, presenting a new opportunity for reducing the cost of high-efficiency devices and expanding the range of photovoltaic applications. In this work, single GaAs solar cells, produced by MOVPE on a rigid GaAs substrate, were transferred to an unprecedented flexible polymer blend of PVC:PMMA:DOP (1.0:1.0:0.5) modified with exfoliated graphene (EG).

2 EXPERIMENTAL DEVELOPMENT

2.1 Process of preparing polymeric blends

The blend PVC:PMMA:DOP (1.0:1.0:0.5) + EG (Fig. 1) was prepared by solution-casting technique in dimethylformamide (DMF) [15,16]. The preparation consists of the gradual dissolution of the polymers in DMF at 60 °C, under magnetic stirring. After 1 hour the plasticizer DOP is added. After 4 hours under stirring, the solution is poured into a Petri dish. The blends were dried under vacuum at 60 °C for 24 hours.

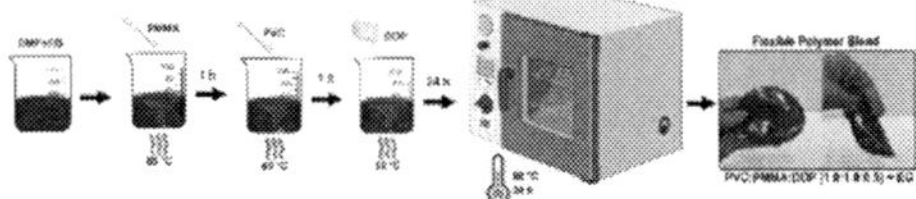

Figure 1: Preparation of the PVC:PMMA:DOP (1.0:1.0:0.5) + EG blend.

2.2 Transfer of GaAs solar cells to polymeric blends

The transfer of solar cell from the GaAs substrates to polymer blends was based on complete etching of the GaAs substrate [13,14], Fig. 2. The process consisted of the following steps: first, a temporary glass substrate was glued over the active layer of the solar cell to ensure mechanical stability. Then, the GaAs substrate was chemically etched using a basic solution of hydrogen peroxide (H_2O_2) and ammonium hydroxide [13,14]. After the etching process, the thin III-V film was ready to be transferred onto the flexible base.

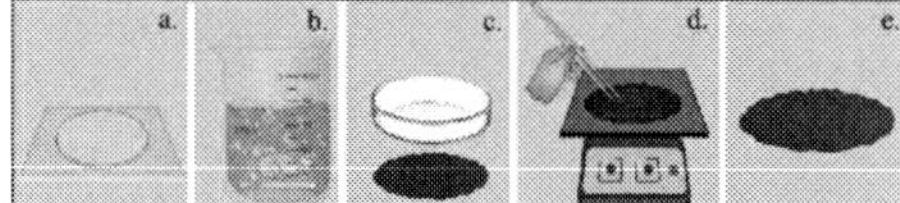

Figure 2: General transfer methodology. a) Temporary substrate bonding (glass); b) complete etching of the GaAs substrate; c) flexible bases adhesion; d) removal of the temporary substrate; e) sample on a flexible substrate [13,14].

GaAs solar cells were transferred to the blend PVC:PMMA:DOP (1.0:1.0:0.5) + EG. The adhesion of the flexible bases to the III-V solar cell occurs during the drying process of the blends, with slow solvent evaporation in a vacuum oven at 60 °C [15,16]. Fig. 3(a) illustrates the structure of a GaAs single-junction solar cell fabricated via MOVPE on a rigid GaAs substrate. Figure 3(b) presents the design of the solar cell mask, while Figure 3(c) shows an image of small solar cells successfully transferred onto the flexible polymer blend. The polymer blend, enriched with EG, adhered seamlessly to the solar cells, providing the required mechanical support. Remarkably, the cells remained intact throughout the entire transfer process.

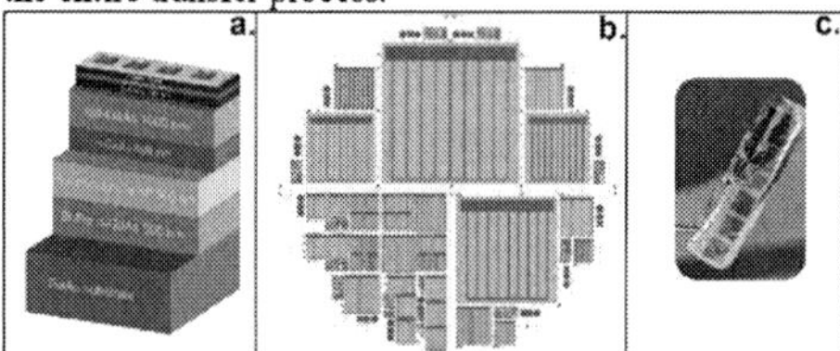

Figure3: (a) Structure of a single GaAs solar cell; (b) Design of a solar cell mask; (c) III-V solar cells transferred onto the blend PVC:PMMA:DOP (1.0:1.0:0.5) + EG.

3 RESULTS AND DISCUSSIONS

The current–voltage measurements were performed using an AM1.5G filter and an incident optical power of 300 W, corresponding to an irradiance of 100 mW/cm², on the rigid cells while still on the GaAs substrate and after their transfer to flexible substrates. The I–V curve measurements in Figure. 4 showed that, after the transfer, the cell's efficiency and other figures of merit, such as open-circuit voltage (Voc), short-circuit current (Isc), and fill factor (FF), showed no significant changes, indicating that the transfer did not compromise the cell's performance.

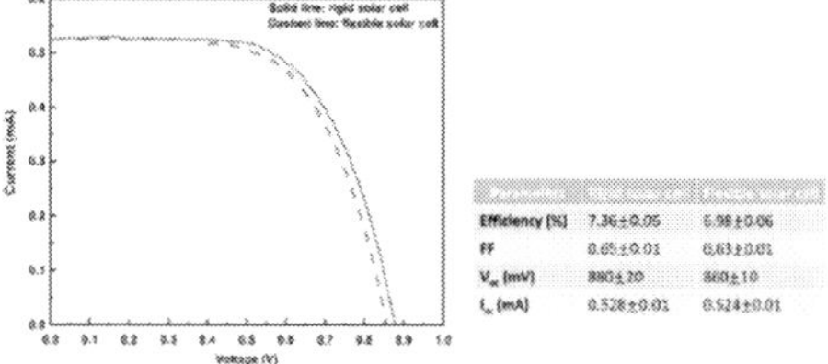

Fig 4. I-V measurements at room temperature under the light of the solar simulator with an AM1.5G filter and incident optical power of 300 W.

4 ADDITIONAL COMPONENTS

The GaAs solar cells were successfully transferred onto the flexible PVC:PMMA:DOP (1.0:1.0:0.5) blend modified with exfoliated graphene. The incorporation of graphene into the polymer blend enhanced its thermal resistance and improved its mechanical strength, providing the necessary stability during the transfer process. Current–voltage (I-V) measurements, conducted under AM1.5G solar simulation, showed that the photovoltaic efficiency and other figures of merit were unchanged after the transfer onto flexible substrates. These parameters are essential for assessing the efficiency and overall behavior of solar cells. The fact that all these metrics remained unaltered reinforces the effectiveness of the transfer process and the feasibility of using the graphene-modified flexible blend as a base for high-efficiency solar cells. These results demonstrate that PVC:PMMA:DOP blends modified with exfoliated graphene are promising alternatives for use as flexible substrates in III-V solar cells. The ability to maintain solar cell performance after transferring to flexible substrates marks a significant advancement in making high-efficiency photovoltaic technologies to be used in a wider range of applications. Additionally, we will epitaxially grow new structures for high-efficiency III-V solar cells, and we will explore their transfer onto other polymer blends integrated with with graphene, with the goal of expanding the potential applications of flexible photovoltaic devices.

4.1 References

[1] Lee, Kyusang et al. Reuse of GaAs substrates for epitaxial lift-off by employing protection layers. Journal of Applied Physics, Vol. 111, n. 3, p. 033527, 2012.

[2] Ward, J. Scott et al. Techno-economic analysis of three different substrate removal and reuse strategies for III-V solar cells. Progress in Photovoltaics: Research and Applications, Vol. 24, n. 9, p. 1284-1292, 2016.

[3] NREL.gov, "Best Research-Cell Efficiency Chart," National Renewable Energy Laboratory, 2023, <https://www.nrel.gov/pv/cell-efficiency.html>. Accessed 10 April 2023.J. Clerk Maxwell, A Treatise on Electricity and Magnetism, 3rd ed., vol. 2. Oxford: Clarendon, 1892, pp.68–73.

[4] El-ATab, Nazek; Hussain, Muhammad M. Flexible and stretchable inorganic solar cells: Progress, challenges, and opportunities. MRS Energy & Sustainability, Vol. 7, 2020.

[5] Cheng, Cheng-Wei et al. Epitaxial lift-off process for gallium arsenide substrate reuse and flexible electronics. Nature communications, Vol. 4, n. 1, p. 1-7, 2013.

[6] Schubert, Markus B.; WERNER, Jürgen H. Flexible solar cells for clothing. Materials today, Vol. 9, n. 6, p. 42-50, 2006.

[7] Masuda, Taizo et al. Highly Decorative, Lightweight Flexible Solar Cells for Automotive Applications. SAE Technical Paper, 2019.

[8] Yun, Y., Moon, S., Kim, S., & Lee. J. Flexible fabric-based GaAs thin-film solar cell for wearable energy harvesting applications. *Solar Energy Materials and Solar Cells*, 246, 2022.

[9] Junhua Long, Xuefei Li, Qiangjian Sun, Pan Dai, Yi Zhang, Jingjing Xuan, Feixue Chen, Minghui Song, Shinya Honda, Shiro Uchida, Shulong Lu.. Simple Processing and Analysis of Flexible III–V Multijunction

Solar Cells Using Low-Temperature Transfer Technology. RRL Solar, Volume5, Issue7, 2021.

[10] Bin Zhao, Xian-Sheng Tang, Wen-Xue Huo, Yang Jiang, Zi-Guang Ma, Lu Wang, Wen-Xin Wang, Hong Chen, Hai-Qiang Jia. Characteristics of InGaP/GaAs double junction thin film solar cells on a flexible metallic substrate. Solar Energy, Volume 174, Pages 703-708, 2018.

[11] Moon, S., Kim, K., Kim, Y., Heo, J., & Lee, J. (2016). Highly efficient single-junction GaAs thin-film solar cell on flexible substrate. *Scientific reports*, 6(1), 1-6, 2016.

[12] Y.H. Lee, K.W. Park, S.J. Kang, C.I. Yeo, J.B. Kim, E.K. Kang, Y.M. Song, Y.T. Lee. Fabrication and analysis of thin-film GaAs solar cell on flexible thermoplastic substrate using a low-pressure cold-welding, Current Applied Physics, Volume 15, Issue 11, Pages 1312-1317, 2015.

[13] B. V. Rocha, M. O. Silva, L. D. Pinto and P. L. Souza, "III-V solar cells transferred to flexible substrates based on Cu," *36th Symposium on Microelectronics Technology (SBMICRO)*, Porto Alegre, Brazil, 2022, pp. 1-4, 2022.

[14] M. O. Silva, "Células de multijunções de alta eficiência: Metodologias para transferência de materiais semicondutores III-V de forma reprodutível para substrato flexível," (master's dissertation). Departamento de Engenharia Elétrica, PUC-Rio, 2021.

[15] G. S. Sousa, L. D. Pinto, F. C. Tavares, P. L. Souza, *et al.*, "Preparation and characterization of PVC-PMMA polymer blends as flexible bases for III–V photovoltaics," *2023 37th Symposium on Microelectronics Technology and Devices (SBMicro)*, Rio de Janeiro, Brazil, 2023, pp. 1-4, 2023.

[16] G. S. Sousa *et al.*, "Transfer of InGaP/GaAs thin-film to unprecedented flexible polymeric bases of PVC:PMMA:DOP modified with EG for solar cell applications," *2024 38th Symposium on Microelectronics Technology and Devices (SBMicro)*, Joao Pessoa, Brazil, 2024, pp. 1-4, 2024.

[17] V. V. Soman, and D. S. Kelkar, "FTIR Studies of Doped PMMA - PVC Blend System". Macromolecular Symposia: POLYCHAR – 16 World Forum on Advanced Materials, vol. 277, pp. 152 – 161, March 2009.

[18] M. S. Khan, R. A. Qazi, and M. S. Wahid, "Miscibility studies of PVC/PMMA and PS/PMMA blends by dilute solution viscometry and FTIR," African Journal of Pure and Applied Chemistry, vol. 2, pp. 41 – 45, April 2008.

[19] S. Ramesh, and CW. Liew, "Development and investigation on PMMA– PVC blend-based solid polymer electrolytes with LiTFSI as dopant salt," Polymer Bulletin, vol.70, pp. 1277–1288, April 2013.

[20] Thamil Selvi Velayutham, Miscibility and immiscibility in PVC-based blends, IPNs, and gels, Editor(s): Sabu Thomas, H. Akhina, Poly(vinyl chloride)-based Blends, Interpenetrating Polymer Networks (IPNs), and Gels, Elsevier, Pages 377-400, 2024.

[21] Hofmann, G.H. (1985). Polymer Blend Modification of PVC. In: Walsh, D.J., Higgins, J.S., Maconnachie, A. (eds) Polymer Blends and Mixtures. NATO ASI Series, vol 89. Springer, Dordrecht.

[22] R. Chakrabarti, M. Das and D. Chakraborty, Physical, mechanical, and thermal properties of PVC/PMMA blends in relation to their morphologies. J. Appl. Polymer Science 93, 2721, 2004.

[23] Razaq, A. *et al.* Review on Graphene-, Graphene Oxide-, Reduced Graphene Oxide-Based Flexible Composites: From Fabrication to Applications. Materials, 15(3), 1012, 2022.

Transfer of GaAs solar cells to unprecedented flexible polymeric bases of PVC:PMMA:DOP modified with EG

Graciana S. Sousa[1]; Luciana D. Pinto[1]; Fabiele C. Tavares[2]; Guillermo J. N. Soares[2]; Rudy M. S. Kawabata[3]; Guilherme M. Torelly[3]; Rogério Valaski[4]; Maurício P. Pires[1]; Roberto Jakomin[2]; Patrícia L. Souza[1]

[1]*Instituto de Física - Universidade Federal do Rio de Janeiro*, Rio de Janeiro, Brazil;
[2]*Campus Duque de Caxias - Universidade Federal do Rio de Janeiro*, Duque de Caxias, Brazil;
[3]*Laboratório de Semicondutores (LabSem) - Pontifícia Universidade Católica do Rio de Janeiro*, Rio de Janeiro, Brazil;
[4]*Laboratório de Fenômenos de Superfície/DIMAT - Instituto Nacional de Metrologia* Rio de Janeiro, Brazil.

I. Introduction

- High-efficiency solar cells based on III-V materials, such as Gallium Arsenide (GaAs) have a high production cost, with the **substrate accounting for 80% of this value**.
- A promising cost-reduction strategy is to transfer the solar cell structure to a **low-cost, flexible base**, which allows for the reuse of the original substrate.
- We developed polymeric blends of poly(vinyl chloride) (**PVC**), poly(methyl methacrylate) (**PMMA**) with a dioctyl phthalate (**DOP**) plasticizer, modified with exfoliated graphene (**EG**).
- Exfoliated graphene enhances mechanical resistance and thermal stability, as well as adhesion of the polymeric blend to the thin film solar cell.

II. Objectives

Transfer GaAs solar cells, produced by Metalorganic Vapor Phase Epitaxy (MOVPE) on a rigid GaAs substrate, to a flexible polymer blend of PVC:PMMA:DOP (1.0:1.0:0.5) modified with exfoliated graphene (EG).

III. Materials and Methods

- **Preparation of polymeric blend**

  The blend PVC:PMMA:DOP (1.0:1.0:0.5) + EG was prepared by solution-casting technique in dimethylformamide (DMF) [1, 2].

  The preparation consists of the gradual dissolution of the polymers in DMF at 60 °C, under magnetic stirring. After 1 hour the plasticizer DOP is added. After 4 hours under stirring, the solution is poured into a Petri dish.

  The blends were dried under vacuum at 60 °C for 24 hours.

- **Preparation of the solar cell for substrate transfer**

  A p-i-n solar cell was grown by MOVPE on a GaAs substrate with an InGaP stop-etch layer. This layer enables selective etching of the substrate without damaging the active region.

- **Substrate transfer**

  Prior to etching, the solar cell's front-side is attached to a temporary glass substrate using a removable glue.

  The substrate is then completely etched under controlled conditions.

  On a petri dish, the liquid blend is poured over the backside of the solar cell. After drying for 24 hours in a vacuum oven at 60°C, the blend is stable and the glass is removed from the solar cell's front side.

- **Solar cell characterization**

  The current–voltage measurements were performed under AM1.5g illumination, before and after flexibilization of the solar cells

IV. Results and Conclusion

- GaAs single-junction cells were successfully transferred onto a flexible blend: PVC:PMMA:DOP + EG (1.0:1.0:0.5).
- The blend adhered perfectly to the III-V semiconductor films, providing the necessary mechanical support.
- I–V measurements on the rigid and flexible cells, indicate preserved optoelectronic and photovoltaic performance after the transfer.
- The PVC:PMMA:DOP blends with EG have great potential to be used as a flexible base for III-V solar cells.

Next steps:

- Transfer III-V cells to novel blends with.
- Fabricate a GaAs solar cell with a selective sacrificial layer for epitaxial lift-off and substrate reuse.

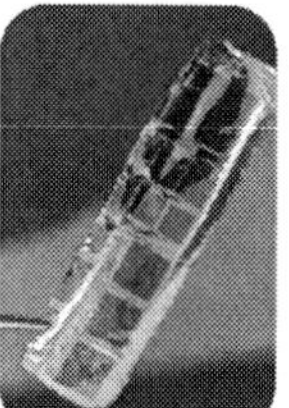

Base solar cell structure — Rigid GaAs solar cell — Structure after substrate etching and polymer casting — Flexible GaAs solar cell

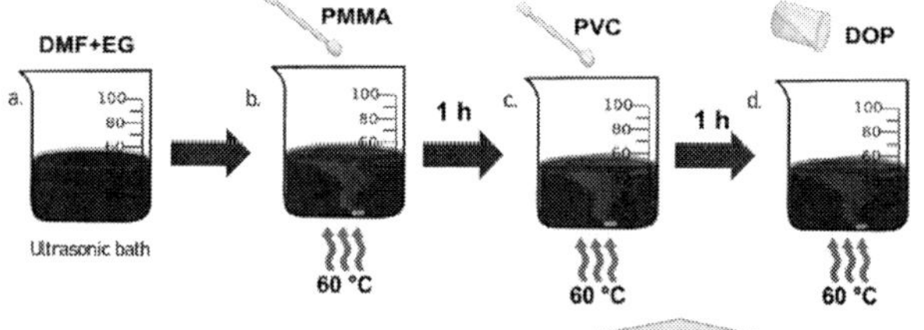

Preparation of the PVC:PMMA:DOP blend with exfoliated graphene

a. Exfoliated graphene is mixed to DMF in an ultrasonic bath;
b. PMMA is added to the solution;
c. PVC is added to the solution;
d. DOP is added to the solution;
e. The blend is dried under vacuum at 60°C for 14 hours;
f. The flexible polymer blend is obtained.

Substrate transfer procedure

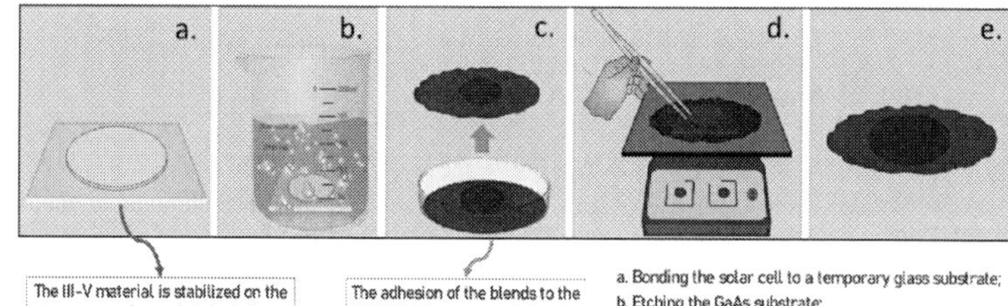

The III-V material is stabilized on the temporary glass substrate before etching, and different flexible bases can be adhered.

The adhesion of the blends to the III-V thin films occurs during the drying of the blend in a vacuum oven at 60 °C for 24 hours.

a. Bonding the solar cell to a temporary glass substrate;
b. Etching the GaAs substrate;
c. Casting the polymeric blend;
d. Removing the temporary substrate;
e. Flexible solar cell.

Photovoltaic parameters of solar cell B before and after transfer to flexible substrates.

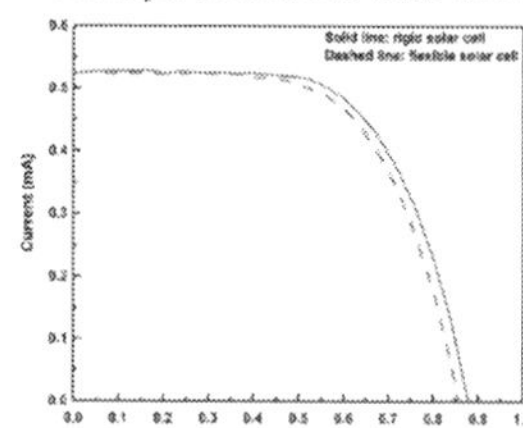

Parameters	Rigid	Flexible
Efficiency (%)	7.36±0.05	6.98±0.06
FF	0.65±0.01	0.63±0.01
V_{oc} (mV)	880±20	860±10
I_{sc} (mA)	0.528±0.01	0.524±0.01

References

[1] G. S. Sousa, L. D. Pinto, F. C. Tavares, P. L. Souza, et al., "Preparation and characterization of PVC-PMMA polymer blends as flexible bases for III–V photovoltaics," *2023 37th Symposium on Microelectronics Technology and Devices (SBMicro)*, Rio de Janeiro, Brazil, 2023, pp. 1-4, 2023.

[2] G. S. Sousa et al., "Transfer of InGaP/GaAs thin-film to unprecedented flexible polymeric bases of PVC:PMMA:DOP modified with EG for solar cell applications," *2024 38th Symposium on Microelectronics Technology and Devices (SBMicro)*, João Pessoa, Brazil, 2024, pp. 1-4, 2024.

Acknowledgments

This work was sponsored by the National Council for Scientific and Technological Development – CNPq, via the grant 444979/2024-7.
Financiadora de Estudos e Projetos (FINEP) - Brazil.
Fundação de Amparo à Pesquisa do Estado do Rio de Janeiro (FAPERJ) - Brazil.
Coordenação de Aperfeiçoamento de Pessoal de Nível Superior (CAPES) – Brazil.
The authors would like to thank Daniel N. Micha (Nokia Bell Labs), Bráulio S. Arcanjo (UFRJ), Maria Luiza Rocco (UFRJ) and Clara M. Almeida (INMETRO) for their collaboration to the research

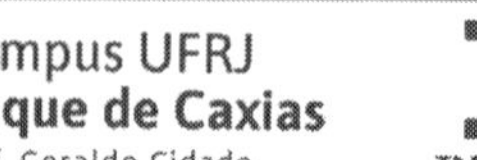

Development and Characterization of a Glued GaAs/Si Tandem Solar Cell in Four-Terminal Configuration

W. M. M. Bazilio[1*], R. M. S. Kawabata[1], L. D. Pinto[2], D. N. Micha[3,1], P. L. Souza[2], G. M. Torelly[1]

[1] Department of Electrical Engineering - PUC-Rio, Rio de Janeiro, RJ, Brazil
[2] Institute of Physics - UFRJ, Rio de Janeiro, RJ, Brazil
[3] Department of Physics - CEFET/RJ, Petrópolis, RJ, Brazil
willian.m.bazilio@aluno.puc-rio.br

ABSTRACT: This work demonstrates a cost-effective fabrication method for a four-terminal (4T) GaAs/Si tandem solar cell using a commercial epoxy for mechanical stacking. The process involves the fabrication of individual cells, removal of the original GaAs substrate, and subsequent bonding. We characterized the electrical and optical properties of both subcells before and after integration.

After bonding, the silicon cell showed a significant performance drop, with an 81% loss in efficiency and an 88% reduction in short-circuit current density. The GaAs cell's performance was less affected, with a 17% decrease in efficiency. The final combined efficiency of the tandem device reached approximately 7%, which is lower than the initial 9.4% efficiency of the standalone Si cell.

The performance degradation is primarily attributed to optical losses from Fabry-Perot interference and increased surface roughness after processing. This initial study validates the bonding approach and identifies clear pathways for improvement, such as implementing anti-reflective coatings and optimizing the GaAs cell structure, to advance III-V/Si integration.

Keywords: Tandem solar cell; Epoxy bonding; III-V/Silicon; Substrate Removal; GaAs/Si

1 INTRODUCTION

The combination of III-V semiconductors with silicon has garnered significant interest in optoelectronic research due to their superior optical properties for photon absorption and versatility in tuning the energy gap. These same semiconductors, on the other hand, are constrained by high production costs and fabrication complexity, in contrast to Si which is abundant, cost-effective, and benefits from advanced technological development and large-scale manufacturing.

The integration of III-V semiconductors with Si for photovoltaic applications was first explored in the 1980s [1, 2], driven by advancements in epitaxial growth techniques that enabled high-efficiency optoelectronic devices. However, the high cost of III-V solar cells limited their use to niche applications, such as space stations and satellites. Currently, approximately 95% of global solar cell production relies on Si [3, 4], and through innovations such as PERC, TOPCon, and HJT technologies, Si solar cell experimental efficiencies have come closer to the theoretical limit of 30% [5]. Meanwhile, III-V solar cells have achieved record efficiencies in the past decades [6]. To overcome the theoretical efficiency limit of single-junction solar cells, tandem structures combining III-V and Si have emerged as a promising solution and have already achieved efficiencies above the 30% barrier [7,8].

Although direct epitaxial growth of III-V materials on silicon has been explored, the results have been limited due to factors such as the mismatch in lattice parameters, which makes it difficult to achieve high crystal quality and induces defects in the structure, thereby affecting device performance. Additionally, the difference in thermal expansion coefficients hinders stability during growth and/or integration, and an optimized structure is required to ensure proper current matching between the different materials [9]. Another approach being studied involves direct bonding of the devices without intermediate adhesives. However, this technique requires specialized equipment for substrate cleaning and polishing, as well as a controlled environment with specific pressure and temperature conditions for the bonding process, which increases the cost of the device [10]. A more viable alternative involves growing III-V solar cells on III-V substrates and transferring the active layers onto silicon solar cells through bonding with glass and epoxy adhesive. This configuration, operating in a four-terminal arrangement, enables optical coupling while maintaining electrical insulation between the devices [11,12].

In 2015, Essig et al. [13] used a transparent epoxy adhesive (TRA-BOND-931-1) to mechanically bond an InGaP cell to a Si cell in a four-terminal configuration, achieving an efficiency of 27%. In 2017, process improvements, including antireflection coatings and the replacement of the original substrate with a glass slide, increased the efficiencies of tandem cells to 32.8% (GaAs/Si) and 35.9% (InGaP/GaAs/Si) [14,15]. More recently, in 2023, Fraunhofer ISE, in collaboration with the AMOLF Institute, set a record efficiency of 36.1% in a tandem solar cell composed of InGaP and InGaAsP layers, featuring a metal-dielectric reflector to enhance light trapping in the bottom cell, as well as a metal/polymer nanocoating. The bottom cell was a state-of-the-art Si (TOPCon) solar cell, integrated through surface-activated wafer bonding [16].

In this study, we fabricated a GaAs/Si tandem solar cell in a four-terminal configuration and performed electrical and optical characterization of the device. We investigated the performance of both the Si and GaAs solar cells prior and after the integration was made to analyze their individual behavior. In this arrangement, the devices operate independently, since the epoxy layer and glass slide ensure electrical insulation post-integration. An advantage to analyzing the system in this approach over a two-terminal configuration is that the currents generated by the individual cells are not constrained to a series connection, enabling optimization of both solar cells independently.

2 AIM AND APPROACH

The Si solar cell was fabricated at the Photovoltaic Solar Energy Laboratory (LB-Solar) at PUC-RS, with dimensions of 2×2 cm^2. It features a PERT (n^+pp^+) structure, a silicon dioxide passivation layer, and a thin titanium dioxide film as an anti-reflective coating. The GaAs solar cell was fabricated at LabSem/PUC-Rio, with dimensions of 2×2 cm² and an active area of 1.5×1.5 cm². Its layered structure consists of a top contact (GaAs-*p*), a 30 nm thick window layer (AlGaAs-*p*), a 200 nm thick emitter (GaAs-*p*), a 1 μm thick base (GaAs-*nid*), a 800 nm thick back contact (GaAs-*n*), a 500 nm thick sacrificial layer (GaInP-*n*), and a 500 nm buffer layer (GaAs-*n*) grown on a GaAs-n substrate. The structure does not include an anti-reflective coating or a back surface field (BSF) layer.

The photolithographic mask used in processing was designed to allow access to both contacts from the top of the device. The metallic contacts consisted of Ti/Pt/Au : 20/100/200 nm for the front; and Ni/Ge/Au : 25/55/150 nm for the back contact.

We initially performed the electrical and optical characterization of both the Si and GaAs solar cells prior to forming the tandem device. A solar simulator system (SF300A, Sciencetech) was used as the light source, and a semiconductor parameter analyzer (HP 4145B) was employed to measure the *IV*-curve from which we extract the figures of merit J_{SC}, V_{OC}, FF, and efficiency (η). The quantum efficiency and the optical properties (in this case, transmittance) were measured using a white light source, a monochromator, and a calibrated Si sensor (SM05PD3A, Thorlabs) as can be seen in Figure 1(c). After bonding the solar cells (Figure 1(a)), we performed electrical characterization in a four-terminal configuration to simulate a real operating condition (Figure 1(b)). For this purpose, a semiconductor parameter analyzer was used to apply a constant voltage of 0.74 V to the GaAs cell, corresponding to its point of maximum extracted power. Subsequently, the parameters of the Si cell were measured using a programmable power supply and a multimeter, both controlled by a Python-based software developed at LabSem-PUC-Rio.

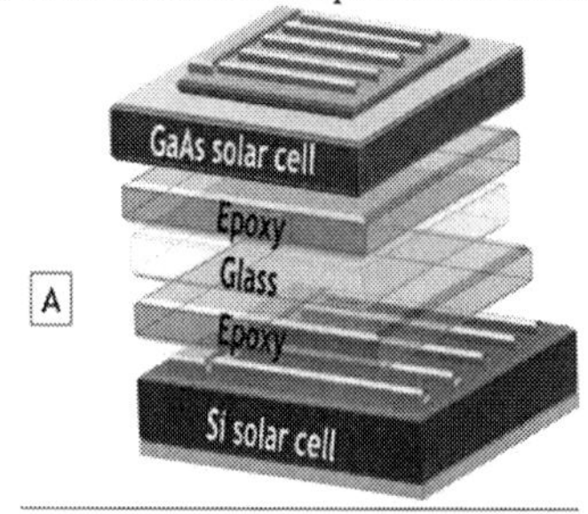

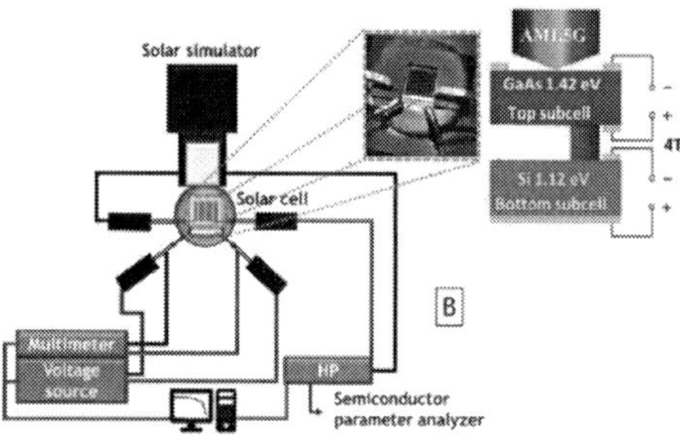

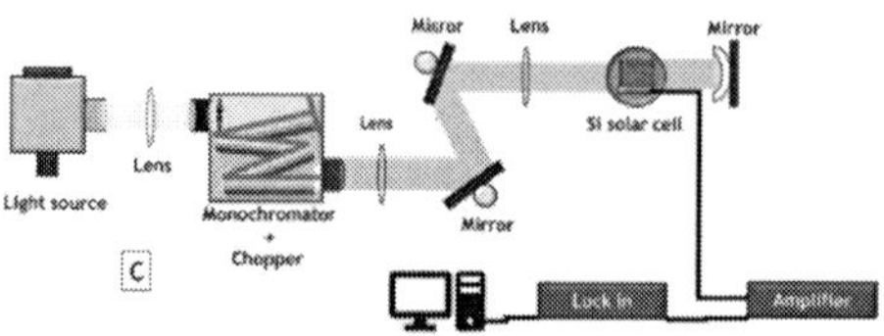

Figure 1: (a) the exploded schematic of the GaAs/Si tandem solar cell, (b) the setup to measure the solar cell's I-V curve, and (c) the setup employed to measure the optical and optoelectronic properties of the solar cells, the epoxy and the glass slide.

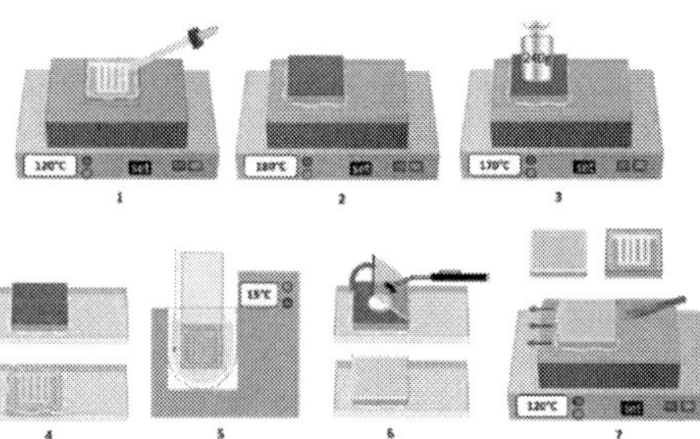

Figure 2: Steps for the processing of the GaAs/Si tandem solar cell.

In this investigation we have analyzed the influence of the GaAs substrate and the impact of its removal, resulting in a 55% increase in J_{SC}, 23% in V_{OC}, 21% in FF, and 72% in efficiency of the Si subcell after integration. For the removal of the GaAs substrate, the GaAs solar cell was attached to a glass substrate with the use of a temporary adhesive (WaferBOND HT-10.10).

The aforementioned adhesive was applied using spin coating for uniformity (350 RPM for 30 seconds) and cured under 120, 180 and 170 °C while a 214 g weight was applied (Figure 2(1, 2, 3)). For its removal, the next step was to etch the GaAs substrate down to the InGaP layer using a solution of hydrogen peroxide and ammonium hydroxide. The solution's temperature was maintained constant at 15 °C throughout the procedure using a chiller (Figure 2(5)), and the etching process took 1 hour and 45 minutes.

After the etching procedure, the GaAs solar cell thin film was bonded to a glass slide with epoxy (EPO-TEK 353 ND), and is represented in Figure 2(6). Once the GaAs thin film was stabilized on this glass slide with epoxy, the temporary adhesive and its glass substrate could be removed. A hotplate at 120 °C cured the epoxy in 5 minutes but required an additional 10 minutes to soften the temporary adhesive. The removal of the GaAs solar cell from the glass substrate was performed by mechanically sliding it after the adhesive softened, as illustrated in Figure 2(7). Remaining adhesive residue was removed using a proprietary solvent (HT-10.10). Finally, the GaAs solar cell with epoxy and glass slide was bonded to the Si solar cell with the same epoxy using the same procedure, reaching the final schematic represented in Figure 1(a).

3   RESULTS AND CONCLUSIONS

We probed the performance of the Si and GaAs solar cells individually before and after bonding. We obtained their *I-V* curves and quantum efficiencies shown in Figure 3, from which we extracted the parameters J_{SC}, V_{OC}, FF, and η, as shown in Table 1.

Table I: Parameters of Si and GaAs cells before and after bonding

Si SC	Bonding		Δ (%)
	Before	After	
J_{sc} (mA/cm²)	26.0	5.7	-88
V_{oc} (V)	0.50	0.48	-4
FF (%)	72	65	-10
η (%)	9.4	1.8	-81
GaAs SC	**Before**	**After**	**Δ (%)**
J_{sc} (mA/cm²)	9.8	8.7	-11
V_{oc} (V)	0.92	0.96	+4
FF (%)	68	61	-10
η (%)	6.2	5.1	-17

The Si solar cell, whose *I-V* curve is shown in magenta in Figure 3, exhibited initial values of J_{SC} = 26.0 mA/cm², V_{OC} = 0.50 V, FF = 72%, and $\eta \approx$ 9.4%. After coupling, these values dropped to J_{SC} = 5.7 mA/cm², V_{OC} = 0.48 V, FF = 65%, and $\eta \approx$ 1.8% (extracted from the dark yellow curve in Figure 3). This corresponds to a reduction of approximately 88% in J_{SC}, 10% in FF and 4% in V_{OC}, leading to a total loss of 81% in efficiency. The integral quantum efficiency of the silicon solar cell after integration (shown in dark yellow in Figure 4) decreased by approximately 39% in the 870–1100 nm wavelength range with respect to its value before integration (in magenta in Figure 4).

The GaAs solar cell before integration, whose *I-V* curve is shown in blue in Figure 3, presented J_{SC} = 9.8 mA/cm², V_{OC} = 0.92 V, FF = 68%, and η = 6.2%. Its quantum efficiency is far below unity (light blue curve in Figure 4) in the useful spectral range due to a non-optimal design of the structure and the lack of an anti-reflective coating in the front surface. The post-coupling *I-V* curve (orange in Figure 3) shows that the GaAs solar cell experienced reductions of 11% in J_{SC}, 10% in FF, and 17% in efficiency. Its quantum efficiency curve (light blue in Figure 4) showed that the GaAs solar cell exhibited a 26% reduction compared to the same cell after substrate removal (shown in orange).

The deterioration in performance observed in both solar cells can be attributed to several factors. The largest performance loss occurred in the J_{SC} of the Si solar cell. This drop can be attributed to two factors: the thickness of the GaAs top cell (~2 μm) and the absence of anti-reflective coatings. The lack of coatings leads to destructive Fabry-Perot interference, which compromises the device's overall efficiency. The oscillations observed in the spectral range absorbed by the Si cell, revealed in the dark yellow curve in Figure 4, result from the Fabry-Perot interferences of the light crossing the GaAs solar cell. This effect is one of the main factors responsible for

the reduction in the available light for the Si cell. Another critical factor is the roughness of the thinned GaAs cell surface introduced upon removal of the temporary glass substrate. This roughness increases light reflection on the front surface, preventing uniform incidence and further degrading the device's performance. Furthermore, the analysis of the quantum efficiency curve of the Si cell below 870 nm in tandem configuration (tail in the dark yellow curve in Figure 4) reveals that the GaAs cell does not fully absorb the solar spectrum with wavelengths below its bandgap, which reinforces the need for optimization of its structure. Nonetheless, this shows the benefit and the effectiveness of the process used for the top solar cell thinning, as approximately 7% of the useful sunlight was lost to the GaAs substrate prior to the processing and integration.

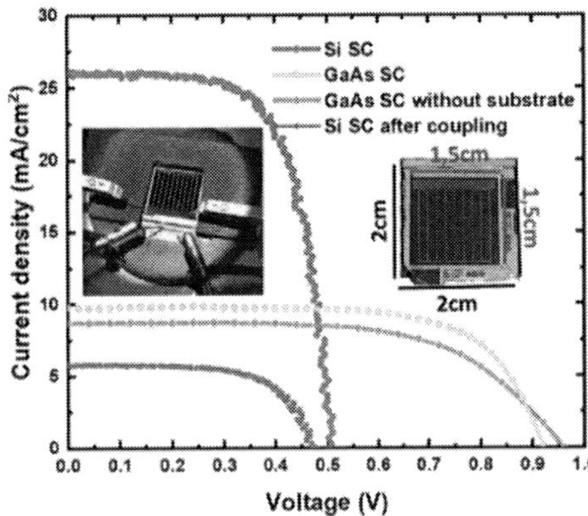

Figure 3: I-V curves of the GaAs and Si solar cells before and after the tandem formation.

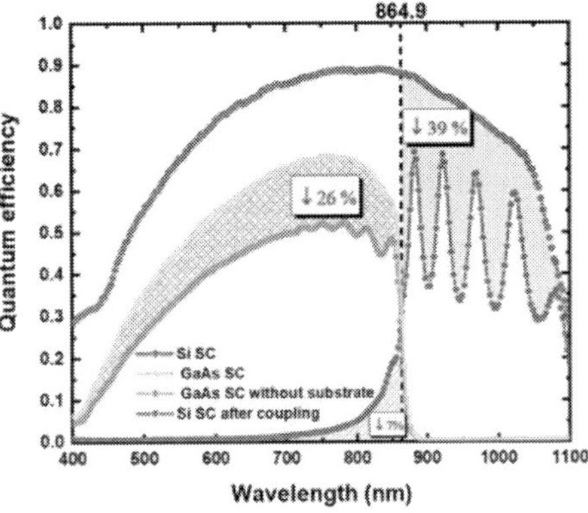

Figure 4: Quantum efficiency of the GaAs and Si solar cells before and after the tandem formation.

This study demonstrated the successful fabrication of a 4T bonded GaAs/Si tandem solar cell using commercially available and low-cost materials, such as epoxy and glass. Despite the 7% combined efficiency, which is lower than that of the standalone silicon cell (9.4%), the results provided valuable insights for future optimizations in the GaAs cell structure and the substrate transfer process. Based on transmittance and quantum efficiency measurements, it will be possible to design optimized anti-reflective coatings for the air/GaAs (front) and GaAs/epoxy+glass (rear) interfaces, reducing optical losses associated with Fabry-Perot destructive interferences. Structural improvements also include optimizing the GaAs active layer thickness for efficient absorption below 870 nm, incorporating a BSF layer to minimize recombination near the back contact, optimizing the layer doping levels and refining the fabrication process of the silicon cells to improve optical and electrical matching, while reducing shading after integration. Another critical aspect to be investigated is the surface roughness observed after the GaAs cell transfer, which affects reflectance and overall device performance.

Implementing these improvements is essential to achieve higher efficiencies in both devices and further establishing the bonding technique as a competitive approach for III-V/Si tandem cell integration. In addition to improving the individual cells' performance in the tandem configuration, we aim to include other techniques to reduce the cost of III-V integrated solar cells, such as epitaxial lift-off and light management techniques to reduce the required volume of materials.

4   References

[1] Gee, J. M. et al. 31%-efficient GaAs/Si mechanically stacked MJ solar cell. *IEEE PVSC*, 1:754–758, 1988.

[2] Jain, N. et al. III–V/Si multijunction integration: Challenges and outlook. *Energy Harvest. Syst.*, 1(3-4):121–145, 2014.

[3] Fraunhofer ISE. *Photovoltaic Report*, 2021.

[4] SolarPower Europe. *Global Market Outlook for Solar Power 2021-2025*, 2021

[5] Shockley, W., Queisser, H. J. Detailed balance limit of pn junction efficiency. *J. Appl. Phys.*, 32(3):510–519, 1961.

[6] NREL. *Cell Efficiency Chart*. Disponível em: https://www.nrel.gov/pv/cell-efficiency.html.

[7] Green, M. A. et al. Solar cell efficiency tables (version 62). *Prog. Photovolt: Res. Appl.*, 29:657, 2021.

[8] Schygulla, P. et al. High-efficiency III-V/Si tandem cells. *Prog. Photovolt: Res. Appl.*, 30:869, 2021.

[9] Green, M. A. et al. Solar cell efficiency tables (version 64). *Prog. Photovolt: Res. Appl.*, 31(7):651–663, 2023.

[10] Tanabe, Katsuaki. "Semiconductor Wafer Bonding for Solar Cell Applications: A Review." *Advanced Energy and Sustainability Research* 4.11 (2023): 2300073.

[11] Bazilio, W. M. M. et al. Epoxy bonding techniques for III-V/Si tandem cells. *SBMicro*, IEEE, 2024.

[12] Zhang, P. et al. Intermediate connection of subcells in Si-based tandem cells. *Small Methods*, 8:2300432, 2024.

[13] Essig, S. et al. Progress in III-V/Si tandem solar cells. *Energy Procedia*, 77:464, 2015.

[14] Essig, S. et al. Advances in III-V/Si tandem cell fabrication. *IEEE J. Photovolt.*, 6:1012, 2016.

[15] Essig, S. et al. Development of high-efficiencytandem cells. *Nat. Energy*, 2:17144, 2017.

[16] Fraunhofer ISE & AMOLF. Silicon-based MJ cell reaches 36.1% efficiency, 2023. Disponível em:https://www.ise.fraunhofer.de. [Acesso em: 23 jan. 2025].

Comparison of Flexible Molybdenum Foil and Sputtered Molybdenum Back Contacts for CZTSSe Solar Cells.

Ikram Anefnaf, Giorgio Tseberlidis[+], Simona Binetti[+], Alessandro Veneri, Elisa Artegiani, and Alessandro Romeo

LAPS-Laboratory of Photovoltaic and Solid-State Physics, Department of Computer Science, University of Verona, Strada Le Grazie 15, 37134 Verona, Italy
[+]Milano-Bicocca Solar Energy Research Center (MIB-SOLAR), Dipartimento di Scienza dei Materiali, Università degli Studi di Milano-Bicocca

Abstract —
Molybdenum foil (MoF) flexible substrates have attracted significant interest in fabricating kesterite thin-film solar cells, thanks to their potential for lightweight, flexible, and large-scale applications. However, one of the main key challenges with MoF is the absence of sodium, typically introduced from soda-lime glass (SLG) substrates, which is critical in enhancing CZTSSe film quality. To address this, a thin layer of NaF has been deposited on top of the MoF to balance the absence of sodium and thus enable enhanced grain growth and crystallinity. In this paper, the deposition processes were optimized systematically with respect to absorber quality and device performance. Solar cells have been characterized, and their performance has been compared with reference devices processed on sputtered Mo. Preliminary results showed low-performing devices based only on Mo foil. However, upon incorporating the pre-deposited NaF layer, efficiency increased to 2.5%. These preliminary results suggest that Mo foil is a promising substrate for flexible CZTSSe solar cells and, upon optimization, could reach performance comparable to standard devices on sputtered Mo back contacts.

I. Introduction

The performance of the CZTSSe-based solar cells has been significantly improved by enormous efforts in these years, which therefore stands out as one of the most promising alternatives to traditional silicon-based photovoltaics. Among various influencing factors that determine the performance of CZTSSe solar cells, the quality of the back contact plays a leading role [1], [2], [3].

The back contact is vital in effective charge collection, reducing resistive losses, and ensuring optimal device performance. The molybdenum foil (MF) is emerging as a promising alternative because it offers several advantages, such as low cost, flexibility, ease of fabrication and improved thermal stability [4], [5]. the MF as a back contact material may provide unique opportunities for optimizing the performance of CZTSSe solar cells; however, its impacts on

the overall efficiency and performance are still under investigation. Although promising, further research is needed to understand it completely.

The primary objective of the present work is to analyze the performances of the CZTSSe solar cells using different back contact substrates comparatively. By analyzing the resulting device characteristics, we aim to identify the advantages and challenges of using Mo foil as an alternative to the traditionally used sputtered Mo. This study is still ongoing, and several optimizations during the deposition and characterization as well are under active investigation, with extensive characterizations for a better understanding of how changing the back contact affects the overall performance of devices. One of the key focuses of this work was to tackle the back contact defects, one of the major issues that limit the efficiency and performance of CZTSSe-based solar cells.

II. Materials and Device Fabrication

A. CZTS ink preparation

The CZTS ink is prepared by dissolving zinc acetate dihydrate, copper acetate monohydrate, tin chloride, and thiourea in 2-methoxyethanol at room temperature. The precursor is then deposited on a previously RF-sputtered Mo thin glass by spin coating.

B. Thin film and device fabrication

For the fabrication of devices, three batches of samples were prepared. Sputtered Mo was used as the back contact in the first batch, deposited through RF-magnetron sputtering on soda lime glass substrates. The prepared CZTS ink was spin-coated onto the sputtered Mo stack at 2400 rpm for 15 seconds and then dried in the air on a hotplate at 310 °C for 5 minutes. The samples were subsequently annealed in a

10.4229/EUPVSEC2025/2BV.2.10
020093-001

tubular furnace under a selenium atmosphere to form the CZTSSe absorber. This step was followed by depositing a thin 50 nm CdS layer using chemical bath deposition (CBD) and an i-ZnO/ITO stack via sputtering to complete the solar cell structure.

The second batch followed the same deposition conditions, but molybdenum foil was employed as a flexible substrate. The third batch used the same process as the second batch, with minor differences, incorporating a thin coating of NaF formed by thermal evaporation over an MoF-flexible substrate.

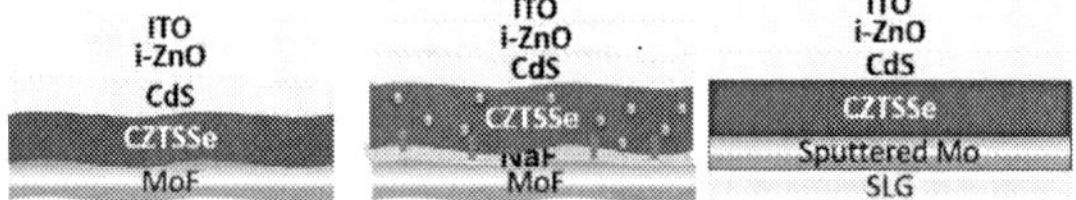

Fig. 1. Schematic illustration of CZTSSe solar cells based on different back contact substrates used in this work.

III.   RESULTS AND DISCUSSIONS

AFM images of CZTSSe thin films deposited on flexible Mo foil and sputtered Mo substrates are shown in Figure 2: in all cases, homogeneous coverage can be obtained: (a) CZTSSe absorber deposited on MoF, (b) CZTSSe absorber deposited on evaporated Na-coated Mo foil, and (c) CZTSSe absorber deposited on sputtered Mo.

The uniformity of grains on substrates can also be collected from the topography of the surface. In particular, the sputtered Mo and Na-coated MoF samples greatly influence grain size and coverage quality within the substrate. However, the sample using only MoF shows an inhomogeneity of grain distribution. Although this comparative study highlights the effect of the sodium incorporation on the grain size and overall absorber quality.

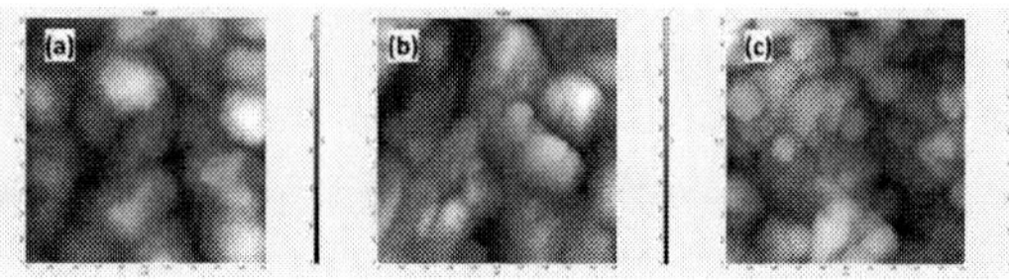

Fig. 2. 2D AFM micrographs of the CZTSSe deposited on different back contact: (a) MoF (b) MoF/Na, and (c) sputtered Mo

The Raman results of CZTSSe absorbers (see figure 3) show the characteristic peaks corresponding to the kesterite phase: the peaks located at 173, 197, and 243 cm^{-1} correspond to the B mode, A mode, and E mode of CZTSSe, respectively. Notably, the Na-coated MF sample shows sharper and more intense peaks than the other back contact samples, indicating increased crystallinity. This enhancement is most possibly

due to the sodium ability to passivate grain boundaries and promote crystal formation, as also AFM results support.

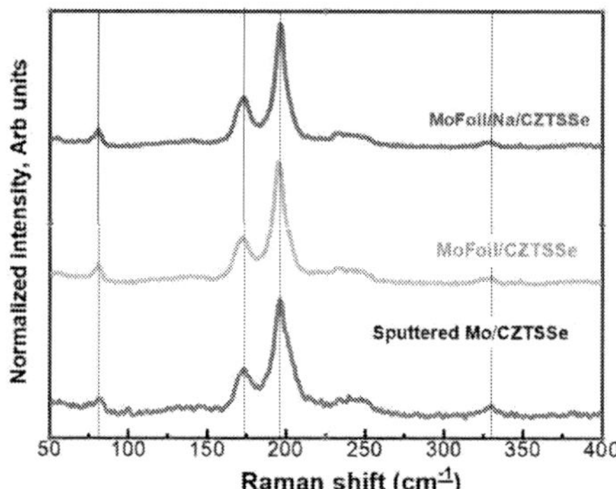

Fig. 3. Raman spectra of the CZTSSe deposited on different back contacts (a) MoF (b) MoF/Na, and (c) sputtered Mo

Figure 4 presents a set of box plots statistics comparing the photovoltaic performance metrics of the efficiency (η), open-circuit voltage (V_{OC}), short-circuit current density (J_{sc}) and fill factor (FF) for CZTSSe devices fabricated on different Mo substrates. The best device performance is achieved with sputtered Mo, as detailed in Table 1.

The devices using an MoF back contact substrate exhibit significantly lower performance, indicating interface defects that limit their performances. However, adding a thin layer of NaF leads to a remarkable enhancement in all optoelectronic parameters. this enhancement is likely due to the sodium role in passivating interface defects and promoting absorber quality, which agrees with AFM and Raman results.

Kee Jeong et al. prove that incorporating a 10 nm layer of NaF on flexible MoF for kesterite solar cells leads to enhanced kesterite-based solar cells' performance [6]. Additionally, several research has demonstrated that MoF flexible MoF substrate-based kesterite solar cells with an additional NaF layer have higher mechanical stability and optoelectronic properties [7], [8].

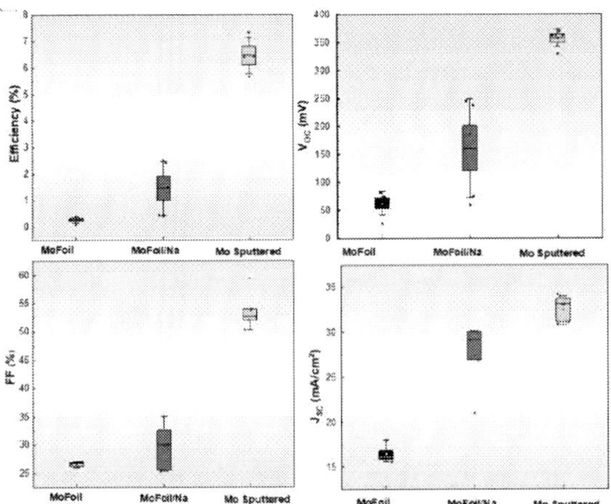

Fig. 4. Device characteristics of CZTSSe thin-film solar cells with various back contact substrates. The parameters given here represent the best of five cells' different substrates.

Table I: Best photovoltaic parameters of CZTSSe solar cells on different substrates.

Sample	V_{oc} (mV)	J_{sc} (mA/cm^2)	FF (%)	Eff (%)
Sputtered Mo	375	33.0	58.3	7.2
MF	82.5	16.8	28.6	0.4
MF/Na	279	23.3	41.3	2.6

IV.   CONCLUSIONS

In this work, we evaluated the performance of CZTSSe solar cells deposited by spin coating on different back contact substrates: MF, Na-coated MF, and sputtered Mo. The obtained results reveal that the sample with only MF sample shows very poor results related to optoelectronic parameters. This poor performance is primarily related to the absorber quality, with smaller grain sizes and higher defect densities, leading to increased charge carrier recombination and minimize device performance. However, a significant performance enhancement is achieved when the thin Na layer is incorporated on the MoF substrates. This incorporation of Na significantly affected the morphological and structural properties of the absorbers, increasing the grain size and minimizing the grain boundaries.

The best performance achieved devices using sputtered Mo back contacts with PCE around 7.3%. This achievement can be related to the diffusion of Na diffusion from the soda-lime glass substrate in the annealing process.

V.   ACKNOWLEDGMENTS

Cariverona foundation is thankfully acknowledged for partially funding this work with INSOBILD project Ref. 2022.0094 – ID 52271 – CUP B33C22001760007. The Italian Ministry of Research through CANVAS project is thankfully acknowledged.

REFERENCES

[1] Nisika, K. Kaur, and M. Kumar, "Progress and prospects of CZTSSe/CdS interface engineering to combat high open-circuit voltage deficit of kesterite photovoltaics: a critical review," *J. Mater. Chem. A*, vol. 8, no. 41, pp. 21547–21584, 2020, doi: 10.1039/d0ta06450e.

[2] V. Karade *et al.*, "Insights into kesterite's back contact interface: A status review," *Sol. Energy Mater. Sol. Cells*, vol. 200, p. 109911, Sep. 2019, doi: 10.1016/j.solmat.2019.04.033.

[3] J. Fu *et al.*, "Defect engineering enabling p-type Mo(S,Se)2:TM (TM = V, Nb, Ta) towards high-efficiency kesterite solar cells," *Chem. Eng. J.*, vol. 457, p. 141348, Feb. 2023, doi: 10.1016/j.cej.2023.141348.

[4] K.-J. Yang *et al.*, "The alterations of carrier separation in kesterite solar cells," *Nano Energy*, vol. 52, pp. 38–53, Oct. 2018, doi: 10.1016/j.nanoen.2018.07.039.

[5] E. Jo, M. G. Gang, H. Shim, M. P. Suryawanshi, U. V. Ghorpade, and J. H. Kim, "8% Efficiency Cu2ZnSn(S,Se)4 (CZTSSe) Thin Film Solar Cells on Flexible and Lightweight Molybdenum Foil Substrates," *ACS Appl. Mater. Interfaces*, vol. 11, no. 26, pp. 23118–23124, Jul. 2019, doi: 10.1021/acsami.9b03195.

[6] K.-J. Yang *et al.*, "Flexible Cu2ZnSn(S,Se)4 solar cells with over 10% efficiency and methods of enlarging the cell area," *Nat. Commun.*, vol. 10, no. 1, Jul. 2019, doi: 10.1038/s41467-019-10890-x.

[7] H. K. Park *et al.*, "Flexible kesterite thin-film solar cells under stress," *Npj Flex. Electron.*, vol. 6, no. 1, Nov. 2022, doi: 10.1038/s41528-022-00221-4.

[8] N. M. Espinel Pérez, E. Vera López, J. A. Gómez Cuaspud, and J. B. Carda Castelló, "A review of recent advances of kesterite thin films based on magnesium, iron and nickel for photovoltaic application: insights into synthesis, characterization and optoelectronic properties," *Clean Energy*, vol. 8, no. 2, pp. 217–238, Apr. 2024, doi: 10.1093/ce/zkad093.

MONOLITHIC INTERCONNECTION OF THIN FILM MINIMODULE PREPARED BY A CNC MECHANICAL SCRIBING.

David Payno[1], Jacob Andrade-Arvizu[2], Marta Miró-Llorente[2], Pedro Vidal-Fuentes[2], Raquel Caballero[1,3], Víctor Izquierdo-Roca[2], Alejandro Perez-Rodriguez[2]

1 - Universidad Autónoma de Madrid, Madrid, Spain. 2 – Institut de Recerca en Energia de Catalunya (IREC), Barcelona, Spain 3 – Instituto de Óptica Daza de Valdés, Consejo Superior de Investigaciones Científicas (CSIC), Madrid, Spain.

ABSTRACT: Monolithic interconnection is a key strategy for thin-film photovoltaic (PV) modules, enabling dense series-connected cell arrays without external wiring. Conventional laser scribing, however, requires complex optimization and can be unsuitable for high-melting-point or highly transparent materials. This work demonstrates a low-cost, flexible alternative based on fully mechanical scribing using a computer numerical control (CNC) system. Kesterite (Cu₂ZnSnSe₄) thin-film minimodules with Mo/CZTSe/CdS/ZnO/ITO architecture were fabricated and interconnected into an 8-cell series configuration. By selecting scribing tips of different hardness, specific layers were selectively removed without damaging underlying contacts, achieving effective P1–P2-P3 patterning. The interconnected module delivered a total open-circuit voltage of 2.65 V, consistent with the sum of individual cell voltages, while maintaining comparable current and shunt resistance. Main performance losses arose from increased series resistance and reduced active area, limiting power conversion efficiency to 2% for the module, 3.1% for the module active area, versus a efficiency of 6% for an individual reference cell. These results highlight mechanical scribing as a practical method for early-stage PV technologies and a potential complement to laser scribing in industrial applications.

Keywords: Thin-film, Photovoltaics, Monolithic Interconnection

1 INTRODUCTION

The monolithic interconnection has been the standard adopted technique to interconnect for thin film photovoltaics, since it allows for densely packaged arrays of cells, without the need of wiring and minimising the use of front metallic contacts [1], [2], [3]. However, laser scribing can be inconvenient to use with high melting point materials and/or very transparent materials, like Molybdenum, ZnO or SiO₂. Moreover, the development of a laser monolithic interconnection typically requires a fine-tuning of a set of lasers that must be studied for each material and technology to get a good and reproducible result. For this reason, monolithic interconnection is typically implemented only in mature PV technologies. As a means of accelerating the monolithic integration at earlier stages, we have developed a simple method of mechanically scribed monolithic interconnection as a low-cost, fast and flexible alternative. A mechanically scribed interconnection can be easily applied in the early stages of thin film technology, in a wide variety of materials, and has the potential to expand and complement the laser scribing methods in the late stages of any PV technology.

In this work, a fully mechanical method for monolithic interconnection has been developed, using a computer numerical control (CNC) system, successfully demonstrating a series interconnection of 8 thin-film solar cells based on kesterite. By simply choosing the materials of the scribing tip with an appropriate hardness, the layers to be removed can be easily selected without damaging the bottom layers, and therefore having a minimum impact on the optoelectronic parameters of the cells.

2 EXPERIMENTAL PROCEDURE

Interconnected thin-film solar cells were prepared following a Mo/CZTSe/CdS/ZnO/ITO configuration. The scribing lines were prepared using a CNC machine, following the pattern of **Figure 1a**, and a spring-loaded tool, as shown in **Figures 1b** and **1c**.

2.1 Sample preparation

First, a layer of Molybdenum was deposited by DC sputtering on a clean soda-lime glass substrate. The P1 was then scribed on the molybdenum film, using a hard tungsten carbide tip, to disconnect and delimitate the back contact. Then, Cu₂ZnSnSe₄ absorber was prepared by sequentially sputtering Cu, Zn and Sn metals, followed by a selenization treatment in argon on a quartz furnace. A MoSe₂ layer is naturally formed during the selenization between the molybdenum and the absorber layers. A CdS buffer layer was prepared by chemical bath deposition, followed by a ZnO window layer prepared by RF sputtering. At this stage, the P2 was scribed using a soft nickel tip, selectively removing the absorber and buffer/window layers without damaging the molybdenum back contact. A conductive and transparent ITO layer was deposited by RF sputtering, acting as the front contact and connecting at the same time the front and the back contacts of consecutive cells. A P3 scribing process was performed to isolate the front contacts, using the nickel tip. A perpendicular P4 is used with the hard WC tip, isolating 8 different rows of cells and preventing shunts in the edges. A complete scheme of the process is shown in **Figure 1d**.

10.4229/EUPVSEC2025/2BV.2.13
020094-001

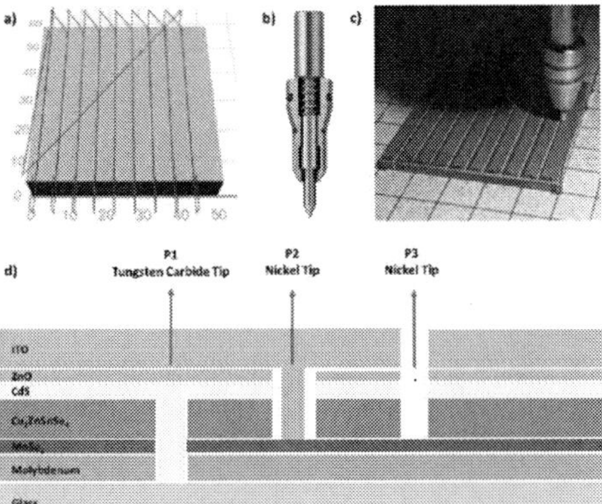

Figure 1. a) Scribing pattern used. b) Scheme of the spring-loaded tool. c) Image of the scribing process. d) Scheme of sample layer stack.

2.2 Characterization

The I-V curves of the cells were characterized under illumination of 1 sun AM1.5, individually and interconnected. Single cells were measured by directly contacting the negative electrode with the ITO of the cell to be measured, while contacting the positive electrode with the ITO of the previous cell. The negative electrode was moved to the subsequent cells to measure all the monolithically interconnected cells between the electrodes.

3 RESULTS AND DISCUSSION

The resulting sample contains 8 rows of 8 monolithically interconnected cells, each cell having a total area of 5x5 mm², and an active area of 3.5x4.7 mm², as shown in **Figure 2**. The dead area will be the sum of the width of the lines (0.3 mm) and the space between them, adding a total of 8.55 mm². Therefore, there is a 34% loss of active area, which counts as the main factor of losses.

First, the optoelectronic parameters of individual cells were measured to observe the inhomogeneities caused by the monolithic interconnection process. As can be observed in Figure 3a and 3b, the process keeps a good homogeneity on the sample, with the parameters of columns A, E and H being slightly affected, likely caused by an incomplete scribing.

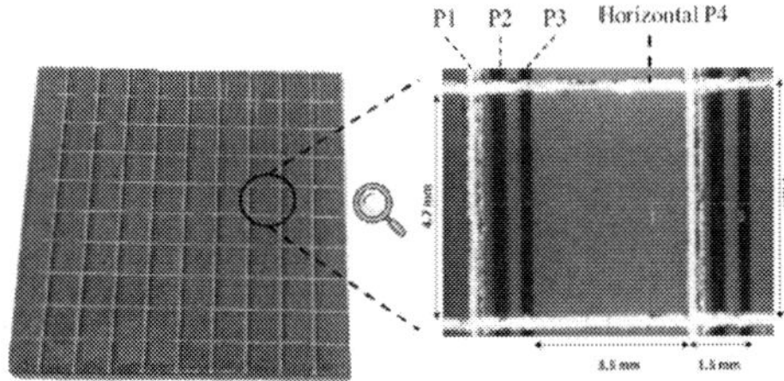

Figure 2. Image of the sample, with a close view of the scribed lines and its dimensions.

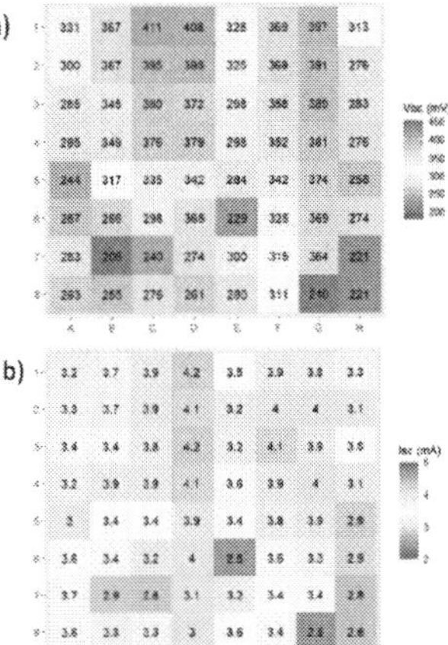

Figure 3. a) Mapping of V_{oc} and b) J_{sc} of individual cells in the sample.

The characteristic IV curves of the interconnected cells were obtained as a function of the number of cells connected, shown in **Figure 4**, from which the optoelectronic parameters were extracted and shown in **Table I**. It can be observed that the V_{oc} increase proportionally to the number of cells connected, with only a loss of 39 mV with respect to the sum of individual cells' V_{oc}, demonstrating a complete and effective interconnection. The small increase in current and R_{sh} suggests that the values obtained are affected by the measurement method, and the losses are mitigated when all the cells connected are measured, reaching values comparable with the reference sample.

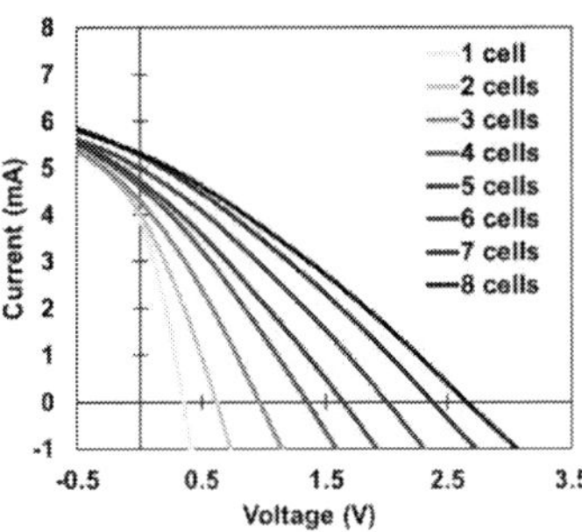

Figure 4. I-V curves as a function of the number of monolithically interconnected cells.

Table I. Parameters measured under AM1.5 of interconnected cells.

	I_{sc} (mA)	V_{oc} (mV)	FF (%)	PCE (%)	R_s (Ω)	R_{sh} eff (Ω cm²)
Reference	4.11	392	61.0	6.0	10	220
1 cell	3.87	349	30.6	2.5	52	47
2 cells	4.01	621	28.9	2.2	113	73
3 cells	4.29	976	28.9	2.4	167	94
4 cells	4.61	1351	28.9	2.7	214	110
5 cells	4.73	1635	28.5	2.7	274	117
6 cells	5.00	1993	29.2	3.0	306	162
7 cells	5.28	2374	28.9	3.1	353	171
8 cells	5.31	2657	29.0	3.1	388	200

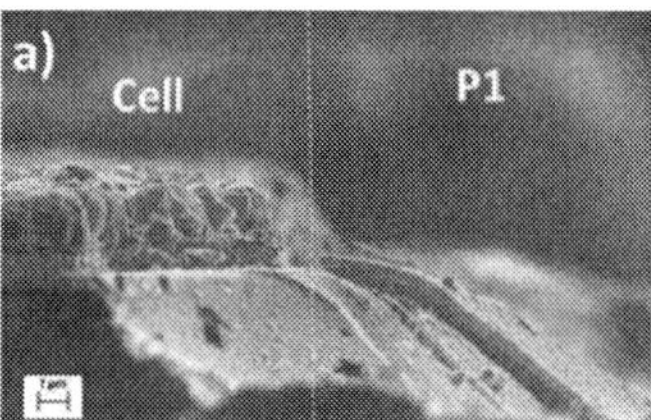

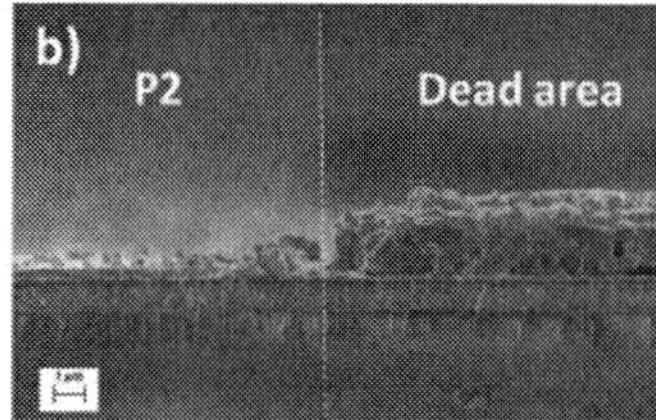

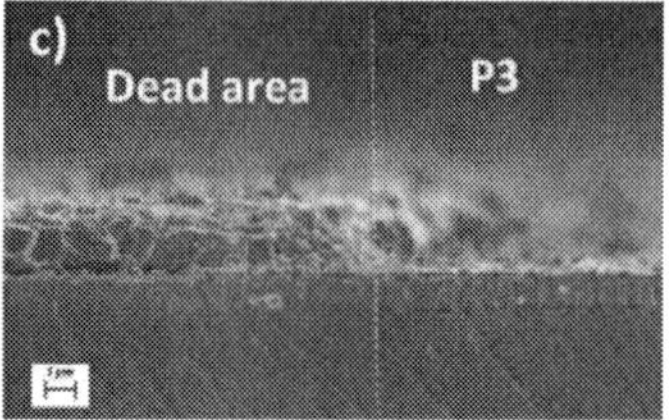

Figure 5. Cross secttional SEM of the area where it can be observed a) the P1 b) P2 and c) P3.

By comparing the mini-module of 8 cells with a reference cell isolated without any interconnection, it can be observed that the main losses come from an increase in the series resistance proportionally with each connected cell, adding 38.5 Ω/cell on average, severely affecting the FF and limiting the power conversion efficiency (PCE).

A close inspection on **Figure 5** of the scribed lines reveals that all layers have been successfully removed in the case of P1, while the molybdenum layer is still intact in the case of P2 and P3, and a smooth deposition of ITO over the Mo can be observed in the P2. Therefore, the observed increase of Rs can be caused by two effects: A non-ohmic contact between the ITO and Mo, due to the $MoSe_2$ interlayer (marked in blue), and a high ITO laminar resistance, both of which are added with each cell connected. These problems can be addressed in future work by the application of better contact material, such as Ag or Cu, in the P2, and the addition of a conductive finger to improve the laminar conductivity. In any case, these problems are independent of the method used to make the scribing. Taking into account the losses of the active area, the total mini-minimodule efficiency drops from 3.1% to 2%, so more efforts are required to reduce the dead area.

4 CONCLUSIONS

We demonstrate that a fully mechanical scribed monolithic interconnection can be prepared without the use of laser scribing, which can be an advantage in certain technologies and a simpler approach for a laboratory and small scale, since it does not require high process optimization. Mechanical scribing can also complement laser scribing with certain types of materials, and be competent for industrial and large-scale. By an appropriate choice of the tip scriber material, a soft nickel tip successfully removed the cell layers, keeping intact the molybdenum back contact, while a hard tungsten carbide tip could easily remove the molybdenum layer as well.

By analyzing both the individual cells and the arrays, we demonstrate that the cells have been successfully connected, reaching a V_{OC} of 2.65 V with 8 cells of 300 - 400 mV individual V_{OC}, maintaining in the array the efficiency of the best individual cell. Other parameters, such as the current and the shunt resistance, are maintained in the array of cells to similar levels as in the reference cell. Main electrical losses come from an increase in the series resistance, affecting the fill factor, due to a high ITO laminar resistance, and non-ohmic TCO/Metal contact in the P2 connection, while a significant loss of active area limits the overall efficiency of the array. Future work will focus on improving and mitigating these losses while reducing and compacting the thickness of the scribed lines.

REFERENCES

[1] K. Li *et al.*, "One-dimensional Sb2Se3 enabling ultra-flexible solar cells and mini-modules for IoT applications," *Nano Energy*, vol. 86, p. 106101, Aug. 2021, doi: 10.1016/J.NANOEN.2021.106101.

[2] G. Heise *et al.*, "Demonstration of the monolithic interconnection on CIS solar cells by picosecond laser structuring on 30 by 30 cm2 modules," *Progress in Photovoltaics: Research and Applications*, vol. 23, no. 10, pp. 1291–1304, Oct. 2015, doi: 10.1002/PIP.2552.

[3] J. Perrenoud, B. Schaffner, S. Buecheler, and A. N. Tiwari, "Fabrication of flexible CdTe solar modules with monolithic cell interconnection," *Solar Energy Materials and Solar Cells*, vol. 95, no. SUPPL. 1, pp. S8–S12, May 2011, doi: 10.1016/J.SOLMAT.2010.11.019.

ACKNOWLEGEMENTS

This project has received funding from the European Union's Horizon 2020 research and innovation programme under grant agreement No 952982 (Custom-Art) and the Project ASSESS (TED2021-129666B-C21) funded by MCIN/AEI/ 10.13039/501100011033

Monolithic interconnection of thin film minimodule prepared by CNC mechanical scribing

David Payno[1], Jacob Andrade-Arvizu[2], Marta Miró-Llorente[2], Pedro Vidal-Fuentes[2], Raquel Caballero[3], Victor Izquierdo-Roca[2], Alejandro Perez-Rodriguez[2]

[1] Universidad Autónoma de Madrid, Madrid, Spain. [2] Institut de Recerca en Energia de Catalunya (IREC), Barcelona, Spain [3] Instituto de Óptica Daza de Valdés, Consejo Superior de Investigaciones Científicas (CSIC), Madrid, Spain.

1 Abstract

The monolithic interconnection is the adopted standard for thin films:

- ✓ Densely packed arrays of cells.
- ✓ Front metal contacts reduced or avoided.

Laser is fast and scalable, but:

- ✗ Requires optimization for every layer.
- ✗ Produce heat damage and shunts.
- ✗ Not compatible with some materials.
- ✗ Hazardous vapors.

Mechanical: **Is it possible? Is it effective?**

- Easy to adapt.
- Ideal for laboratory scale.
- Scalable to industrial.
- Less hazardous.

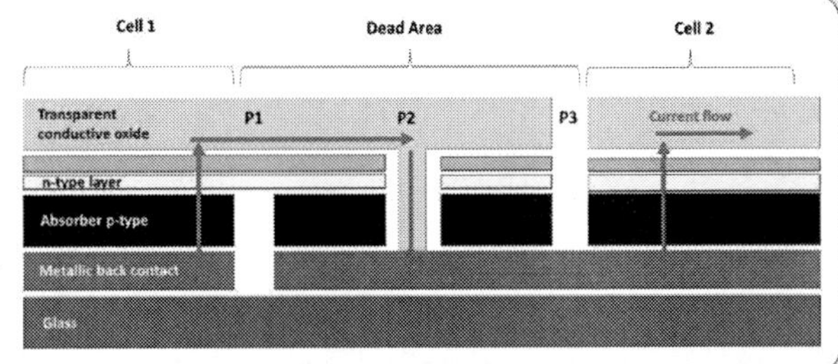

3 Close inspection

8 rows of 8 cells connected in series

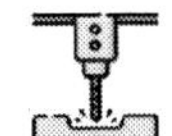
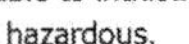

Total Area = 25 mm²

Dead area = 8.55 mm²

Cell active area = 16.45 mm²

Loss of active area = 34 %

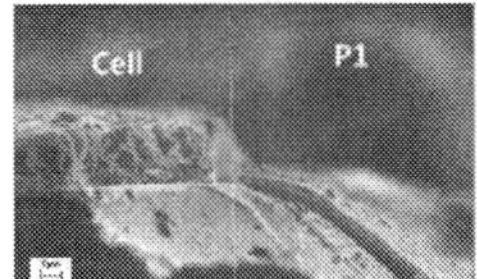

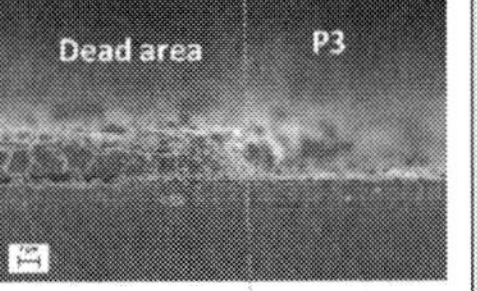

2 Method: Mechanical Scribing

Choose the TIP: **WC** tip to engrave hard layers.

Nickel tip to engrave soft materials without damaging the bottom layers.

Loading pattern on a CNC

Exchangeable spring-loaded tip

Deposit the next layer

Scribe the pattern

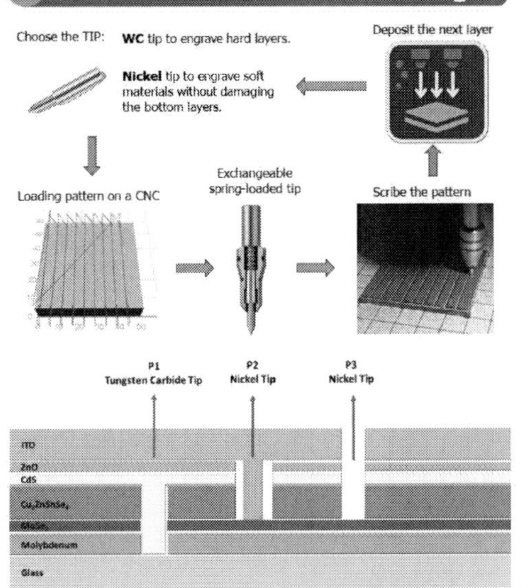

4 PV analysis

Flexible measurements of individual and consecutive connected cells

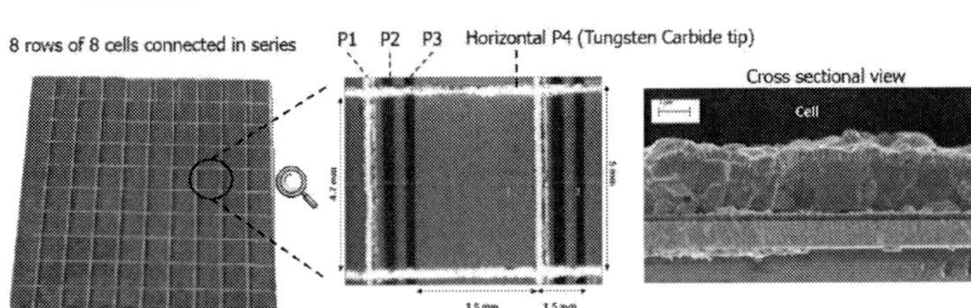

Individual measurements of each cell

I-V curves under AM 1.5 illumination

	I_{sc} (mA)	V_{oc} (mV)	FF (%)	Efficiency (%)	R_s (Ω)	R_{sh} effective (Ω cm²)
Reference	4.11	392	61.0	6.0	10	220
1 cell	3.87	349	30.6	2.5	52	47
2 cells	4.01	621	28.9	2.2	113	73
3 cells	4.29	976	28.9	2.4	167	94
4 cells	4.61	1351	28.9	2.7	214	110
5 cells	4.73	1635	28.5	2.7	274	117
6 cells	5.00	1993	29.2	3.0	306	162
7 cells	5.28	2374	28.9	3.1	353	171
8 cells	5.31	2657	29.0	3.1	388	200

Sum of individual 8 cells V_{oc} = 2696 mV

ONLY 39 mV of Voc loss

Average cells adds R_s = 48.5 Ω

Considering the full area of the array efficiency = 2 %

Highly successful:

- V_{oc} minor loss.
- No losses in I_{sc}.
- The effective shunt resistance increases with the connected cells until reference → Minor shunting problems in the array.

Mayor loses:

- Increase of series resistance proportionally to the number of connected cells → Reduction of FF.
- Loss of active area.
- The effect of scribing is slightly inhomogeneous.

5 How to improve

Minimize the dead area:

1. Bring the lines closer together.
2. Sharper tips to reduce the width of the scribed lines.
3. Wider cells.

Improve resistances:

- A. Introduce a metal contact in P2.
- B. Thin horizontal metal fingers.
- C. Isolation and passivation on P1 and P3.

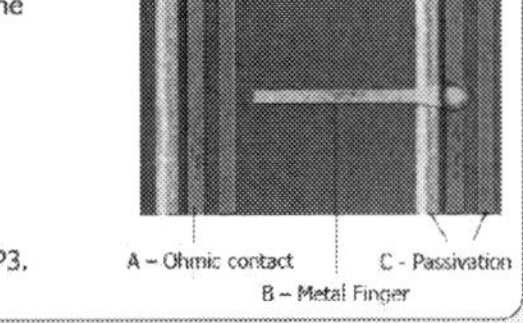

6 Conclusions

- Functional photovoltaic array of series-connected cells prepared by only mechanical scribing.
- Mechanical scribing controlled by CNC is highly precise and can be complementary to laser scribing in industrial processes.
- A soft Nickel tip is used to effectively scribe on soft materials, avoiding damage to the back contact.
- Demonstrated a very low shunt, current and voltage losses.
- Main losses of the process are associated with an increase in the series resistance, due to a high resistance of the TCO, and non-ohmic contact between the top and back contacts.
- Optimization to reduce the dead area is required.

References

1) Heise, G.; Börner, A.; Dickmann, M.; Englmaier, M.; Heiss, A.; Kemnitzer, M.; Konrad, J.; Moser, R.; Palm, J.; Vogt, H.; Huber, H. P. Demonstration of the Monolithic Interconnection on CIS Solar Cells by Picosecond Laser Structuring on 30 by 30 Cm2 Modules. Progress in Photovoltaics: Research and Applications 2015, 23 (10), 1291–1304. https://doi.org/10.1002/PIP.2552.

2) Perrenoud, J.; Schaffner, B.; Buecheler, S.; Tiwari, A. N. Fabrication of Flexible CdTe Solar Modules with Monolithic Cell Interconnection. Solar Energy Materials and Solar Cells 2011, 95 (SUPPL. 1), S8–S12. https://doi.org/10.1016/J.SOLMAT.2010.11.019.

3) qLi, K., Li, F.; Chen, C.; Jiang, P.; Lu, S.; Wang, S.; Lu, Y.; Tu, G.; Guo, J.; Shui, L., Liu, Z.; Song, B.; Tang, J. One-Dimensional Sb2Se3 Enabling Ultra-Flexible Efficient Mini-Modules for IoT Applications. Nano Energy 2021, 86, 106101. https://doi.org/10.1016/J.NANOEN.2021.106101.

Contact david.payno@uam.es / david.payno@csic.es

Acknowledgments

This project has received funding from the European Union's Horizon 2020 research and innovation programme under grant agreement No 952982 (Custom-Art) and the Project ABSESS (TED2021-129666B-C21) funded by MCIN/AEI/ 10.13039/501100011033

020095-001

KINETIC MORPHOLOGY EVOLUTION OF NON-FULLERENE BULK HETEROJUNCTION BLENDS: THE ROLE OF SOLVENT ADDITIVES IN THERMAL STABILITY

Tzu-Yen Huang[1*], Anton P. Le Brun[2]

[1]Neutron Group, National Synchrotron Radiation Research Center, Hsinchu 30092, Taiwan
[2]Australian Centre for Neutron Scattering, Australian Nuclear Science and Technology Organization, New South Wales
2234, Australia
*Email: huang.ty@nsrrc.org.tw

ABSTRACT: The thermal stability of bulk heterojunction (BHJ) active layers is a critical factor in determining the long-term performance of non-fullerene organic solar cells (OSCs). In this study, the kinetic morphology of PffBT4T-2OD: ITIC BHJs was systematically investigated under varying annealing temperatures. Pristine PffBT4T-2OD films demonstrated excellent thermal stability, while ITIC thin films exhibited diffusive interfaces and morphological changes when annealed above 120°C. For PffBT4T-2OD: ITIC BHJs, elevated temperatures at 120°C induced the migration of ITIC clusters toward the air interface, accompanied by the formation of a PffBT4T-2OD-rich layer near the substrate. To address this thermal instability, we incorporated the 1,8-diiodooctane (DIO) as a solvent additive into the BHJs. The addition of DIO significantly enhanced the intermixing of donor and acceptor materials, resulting in a uniform morphology of the active layer and improved thermal stability up to 120°C. These findings confirm that solvent additives effectively mitigate thermal-induced phase separation and prolong the stability of BHJs.
Keywords: Organic solar cells, solvent additives, thermal annealing, stability

1 INTRODUCTION

Organic solar cells (OSCs) have emerged as a promising technology owing to their compatibility with solution-process, roll-to-roll production, and potential for low-cost, lightweight, and flexible devices.[1-3] The bulk heterojunction (BHJ) device configuration, in which electron donor and acceptor materials are intimately blended, enables efficient separation of photogenerated excitons and transport of charge carriers through pure phases to the respective electrodes. Strategies such as thermal annealing and the use of solvent additives are widely applied to reorganize the nanoscale morphology, thereby improving exciton dissociation, charge collection, and overall device efficiency.

Poly[(5,6-difluoro-2,1,3-benzothiadiazol-4,7-diyl)-alt-(3,3'''-di(2-octyldodecyl)-2,2';5',2'';5'',2'''-quaterthiophen-5,5'''-diyl)] (PffBT4T-2OD) is a narrow-band-gap polymer (1.65 eV) with high charge-carrier mobility ($\sim 10^{-2}$ cm^{2}V^{-1}s^{-1}) and demonstrated power conversion efficiencies up to 11%.[4] In recent years, non-fullerene acceptors (NFAs) have become an important class of OSC materials due to their strong optical absorption, tunable electronic structures, and ability to synergistically improve device performance when paired with low-band-gap polymers.[5, 6] Among these, 3,9-bis(2-methylene-(3-(1,1-dicyanomethylene)-indanone))-5,5,11,11-tetrakis(4-hexylphenyl)-dithieno[2,3-d:2',3'-d']-s-indaceno[1,2-b:5,6-b']dithiophene (ITIC) is a well-known NFA with energy levels ideally matched to PffBT4T-2OD. In preparing the BHJ thin films, high-boiling-point solvent additives are frequently introduced to promote nanoscale mixing between donor and acceptor phases, facilitating an optimized morphology for enhanced device performance. [7] Our previous studies have shown that in PffBT4T-2OD: ITIC BHJs, thermal annealing can induce aggregation of ITIC molecules within the polymer matrix, resulting in interfacial diffusion and an increase in surface roughness.[8] We propose that limited initial miscibility between donor and acceptor phases creates a thermodynamic driving force for phase separation upon heating. However, the extent to which solvent additives influence vertical phase organization, as well as the kinetics of morphological evolution under different annealing temperatures and durations, remains unclear.

Neutron reflectometry (NR) offers sub-nanometer resolution for probing vertical composition profiles and interfacial structure in thin films.[9-11] In this work, we employ NR to examine PffBT4T-2OD: ITIC BHJ films prepared with and without the solvent additive 1,8-diiodooctane (DIO). By monitoring temperature- and time-dependent morphological changes, we aim to provide new insights into phase behavior in OSCs.

2 EXPERIMENTAL PROCUDUES

2.1 Preparation of PffBT4T-2OD: ITIC Blend Films

The DIO concentrations of 0.25 v/v% were dissolved in a 1,2-dichlorobenzene: chlorobenzene (1:1 v/v%) co-solvent mixture and used to prepare the PffBT4T-2OD: ITIC blend (Solarmer Energy Inc.) solutions at a total concentration of 10 mg/ml. The solutions were stirred at 90°C overnight to ensure complete dissolution. Both the blend solutions and substrates were then maintained at 90°C to prevent severe aggregation during thin-film preparation. The active layer solution was then spin-coated onto the Si wafers under a nitrogen environment (1000 rpm for 60 s). Each sample was subsequently placed in a vacuum chamber and annealed at RT, 90°C, 120°C, and 150°C while NR measurements were performed at the first incident angle.

2.2 Neutron Reflectometry Measurements.

The NR measurements were performed on the Spatz time-of-flight neutron reflectometer at the Australian Nuclear Science and Technology Organization (ANSTO) OPAL reactor (proposal nos. P18686 & P20060).[12] A chopper pairing of choppers 1 and 2 with a separation of 480 mm and a rotation speed of 25 Hz provides a wavelength resolution ($\Delta\lambda/\lambda$) of $\sim$5%. The NR curves were collected at the first incident angles of 0.70° (1 hr) and the second incident angle will be collected at 3.50° (3 hrs) to cover the momentum transfer (Q) range of $0.008 \leq Q \leq 0.24$ Å^{-1}. The momentum transfer is defined as $Q = 4\pi \sin(\theta)/\lambda$, where θ is the incident angle and λ is the neutron wavelength. An illuminated footprint of 18 mm long and 20 mm wide was used. The reduction procedure involves considering detector efficiency, converting the time-of-flight data to wavelength, and then calculating Q range, re-binning the data to instrument resolution, stitching the datasets from the two incident angles at the overlap region to provide a complete reflectivity profile, and scaling the critical edge equal to unity. The NR data were analyzed using the *refnx* software.[13] Parameters defining the properties of the different layers were varied using a differential evolution algorithm until the difference between the experimental and model data was minimized. The fitting parameters for NR mesasurements are summarized in Table 1.

3 RESULTS AND DISCUSSION

The thermal stability and morphological evolution of BHJs are critical factors in improving the performance of OSCs. Our previous work has shown that elevated annealing temperatures promote interfacial diffusion and increase surface roughness due to ITIC aggregation within the polymer matrix.[8] NR was employed to probe the vertical morphology of BHJ thin films during thermal annealing. Based on an assumed bulk density of 0.90 g cm^{-3}, the scattering length density (SLD) values of PffBT4T-2OD and ITIC are calculated to be 0.65×10^{-6} Å^{-2} and 1.44×10^{-6} Å^{-2}, respectively. Our findings indicate that the highly flexible side chains of PffBT4T-2OD do not significantly contribute to vertical morphological changes at temperatures above 90°C, confirming its intrinsic thermal stability under annealing. In contrast, ITIC thin films exhibit the onset of diffusive interface formation at 120°C, suggesting that thermal annealing promotes the formation of ITIC nanocrystal aggregates, thereby altering the vertical morphology. This behavior persists at 150°C. The observed onset temperature for thermal instability is consistent with literature reports on diffusion-limited crystallization, providing further insight into the morphological evolution of ITIC-based BHJs under thermal treatment.[14]

Figures 1(a) and 1(b) present the NR patterns and SLD profiles of pristine PffBT4T-2OD: ITIC (6:4) BHJ films. The NR fringes remained unchanged upon annealing up to 90°C, with the SLD profiles indicating a uniform film of thickness 802 ± 2 Å and surface roughness of 64 ± 9 Å. The fringes are shifted within the Q range of 0.01-0.03 Å^{-1} at 120°C, consistent with the trend observed at 150 °C, indicating similar morphology changes in the film at both temperatures. As shown in Figure 1(b), the SLD profiles reveal the onset of vertical phase segregation above 120°C, forming a two-layer structure. A PffBT4T-2OD-rich layer

$(235 \pm 16$ Å, SLD $= 0.67 \times 10^{-6}$ Å^{-2}) developed adjacent to the substrate, while an ITIC-rich layer $(544 \pm 19$ Å, SLD $= 1.45 \times 10^{-6}$ Å^{-2}) formed at the air interface, with an accompanying surface roughness of 68 ± 3 Å. This stratification persisted at 150°C, yielding a PffBT4T-2OD-rich layer of 250 ± 13 Å and a ITIC-rich layer of 518 ± 16 Å, with a surface roughness of 63 ± 2 Å. Although the ITIC molecules were reported to have a higher surface energy than PffBT4T-2OD polymers, the observed thermal behavior is consistent with previous findings.[8] Excess thermal energy activates ITIC molecule diffusion toward the air interface rather than accumulation at the substrate.

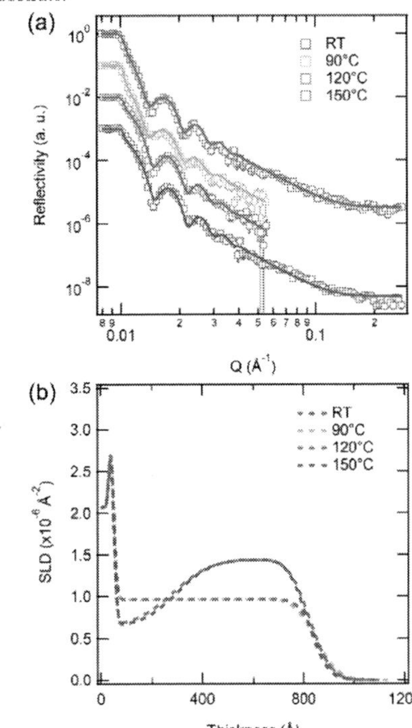

Figure 1. The NR curves and the corresponding SLD profiles for (a, b) pristine PffBT4T-2OD: ITIC (6:4) BHJ films on Si wafers annealed from RT to 150°C. The individual data points and solid lines represent the experimental data and fitting results respectively.

Solvent additives are widely used to promote donor-acceptor intermixing and to achieve a favorable blend morphology for stable device performance. To examine

Table 1. The fitting parameters are summarized from the NR results.

Substrates	Thickness (Å)	SLD (Å^{-2})	Roughness (Å)
BHJ layer (D:A = 6:4) /Si @ RT	802 ± 2	0.97 ± 0.01	57 ± 2
BHJ layer (D:A = 6:4) /Si @ 90°C	802 ± 3	0.97 ± 0.01	70 ± 2
BHJ layer (D:A = 6:4) /Si @ 120°C	544 ± 19	1.45 ± 0.04	68 ± 3
	235 ± 16	0.67 ± 0.02	120 ± 9
BHJ layer (D:A = 6:4) /Si @ 150°C	518 ± 16	1.45 ± 0.04	63 ± 2
	250 ± 13	0.65 ± 0.02	111 ± 8
BHJ layer (D:A = 5:5, 0.25 v/v% DIO) /Si @ RT	739 ± 3	1.05 ± 0.02	52 ± 2
BHJ layer (D:A = 5:5, 0.25 v/v% DIO) /Si @ 90°C	739 ± 2	1.05 ± 0.01	48 ± 2
BHJ layer (D:A = 5:5, 0.25 v/v% DIO) /Si @ 120°C	741 ± 2	1.05 ± 0.01	54 ± 2
BHJ layer (D:A = 5:5, 0.25 v/v% DIO) /Si @ 150°C	337 ± 13	1.19 ± 0.04	92 ± 6
	460 ± 11	0.76 ± 0.02	96 ± 13

whether poor initial mixing contributes to the thermal instability of ITIC molecules upon annealing, 0.25 v/v% DIO was incorporated into PffBT4T-2OD: ITIC (5:5) BHJ films. Figures 2(a) and 2(b) show the corresponding NR curves and SLD profiles. The NR fringes remained well-defined after annealing up to 120°C, indicating enhanced thermal stability with DIO incorporation. The SLD profiles at this stage reveal a uniform donor-acceptor distribution, with a total film thickness of 740 ± 1 Å and surface roughness of 51 ± 3 Å. At 150°C, however, the fringes became less distinct, suggesting morphological changes. Extended annealing induced vertical phase segregation, producing a PffBT4T-2OD-rich bottom layer (460 ± 11 Å, SLD = 0.76×10^{-6} Å^{-2}) adjacent to the substrate and a top layer (337 ± 13 Å, SLD = 1.19×10^{-6} Å^{-2}) at the air interface. The slightly higher SLD of the top layer compared to the uniform BHJ indicates only modest ITIC enrichment after prolonged annealing. At an annealing temperature of 150°C, the NR fringes of BHJ (6:4) films (*see Figure 1(a)*) remain more pronounced than those of BHJ (5:5) films with 0.25 v/v% DIO, which can be attributed to the higher fraction of thermally stable PffBT4T-2OD in the blends, leading to a more robust vertical morphology. Overall, these results demonstrate that solvent additives promote efficient PffBT4T-2OD: ITIC mixing and significantly improve the thermal stability of BHJ thin films.

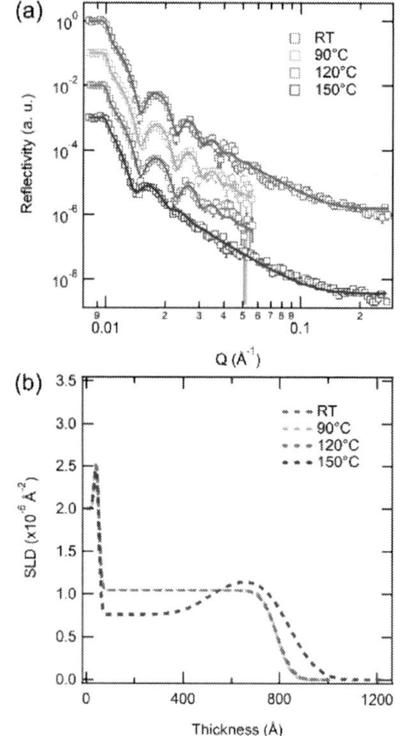

Figure 2. The NR curves and the corresponding SLD profiles for (a, b) PffBT4T-2OD: ITIC (5:5) BHJ films with 0.25% DIO on Si wafers annealed from RT to 150°C. The individual data points and solid lines represent the experimental data and fitting results respectively.

To identify phase stratification after thermal annealing, Figure 3 presents the NR fitting results for PffBT4T-2OD:

ITIC (5:5) BHJ films processed with 0.25 v/v% DIO and annealed at 150°C. Pronounced fringes are observed in the Q range of 0.01 - 0.03 Å^{-1}. The one-layer model does not reproduce the experimental data in this range, indicating that the active layer undergoes non-uniform structural changes upon heating. In contrast, a two-layer model provides a better description of the thermal behavior, as further supported by the residual plots, which show improved agreement near Q ~ 0.01 Å^{-1}. These results reveal that thermal annealing promotes the formation of an ITIC-rich layer at the air interface, while the PffBT4T-2OD-rich layer preferentially accumulates adjacent to the substrate.

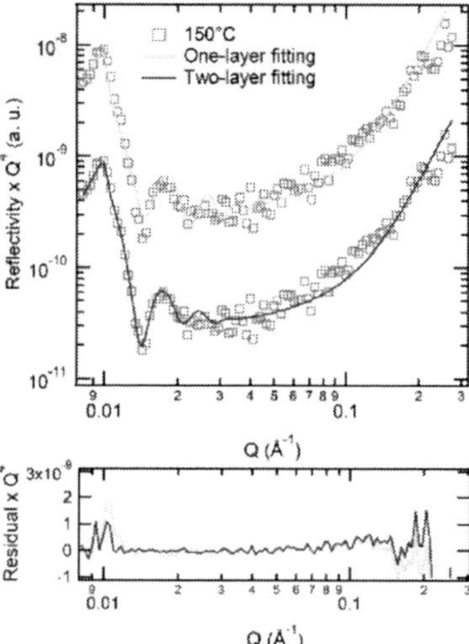

Figure 3. The NR curves and residual plots of PffBT4T-2OD: ITIC (5:5) bulk heterojunction (BHJ) films containing 0.25 v/v% DIO, annealed at 150°C. The solid lines correspond to fits using one-layer and two-layer models, respectively.

4 CONCLUSIONS

We have investigated the vertical morphology of PffBT4T-2OD: ITIC BHJs by varying the annealing temperature. For pristine BHJs, NR analysis revealed that excess thermal energy activates ITIC molecules to diffuse toward the air interface, leading to the formation of an ITIC-rich top layer and a PffBT4T-2OD-rich bottom layer adjacent to the substrate. This vertical phase segregation was evident above 120°C and persisted at 150°C, indicating that the morphology becomes thermally unstable at elevated temperatures. To address this instability, we incorporated the solvent additive, DIO, to enhance donor-acceptor intermixing and achieve a favorable blend morphology. Our results demonstrate that DIO incorporation promotes a more uniform vertical distribution of PffBT4T-2OD and ITIC, as evidenced by stable NR fringes and consistent SLD profiles up to 120°C. This enhanced miscibility delays the onset of phase segregation and significantly improves the thermal stability of the BHJs. These findings confirm our hypothesis that insufficient initial mixing contributes to the thermal instability of ITIC-based blends, and that use of solvent additives can mitigate this effect. Incorporating DIO not only improves the intermixing during film formation but also prolongs the thermal stability of the active layer, offering a viable strategy for enhancing the operational stability of organic solar cell devices.

5 REFERENCES

[1.] M. Kaltenbrunner, M.S. White, E.D. Głowacki, T. Sekitani, T. Someya, N.S. Sariciftci, S. Bauer, Nat. Commun. 3 (2012) 770.

[2.] C. Lungenschmied, G. Dennler, H. Neugebauer, S.N. Sariciftci, M. Glatthaar, T. Meyer, A. Meyer, Sol. Energy Mater. Sol. Cells 91 (2007) 379.

[3.] L.H. Rossander, H.F. Dam, J.E. Carlé, M. Helgesen, I. Rajkovic, M. Corazza, F.C. Krebs, J.W. Andreasen, Energy Environ. Sci. 10 (2017) 2411.

[4.] Y. Liu, J. Zhao, Z. Li, C. Mu, W. Ma, H. Hu, K. Jiang, H. Lin, H. Ade, H. Yan, Nat. Commun. 5 (2014) 5293.

[5.] C. Yan, S. Barlow, Z. Wang, H. Yan, A.K.Y. Jen, S.R. Marder, X. Zhan, Nat. Rev. Mater. 3 (2018) 18003.

[6.] H. Sun, F. Chen, Z.-K. Chen, Mater. Today 24 (2019) 94.

[7.] B. Arredondo, J. Carlos Pérez-Martínez, L. Muñoz-Díaz, M.d.C. López-González, D. Martín-Martín, G. del Pozo, E. Hernández-Balaguera, B. Romero, J. Lamminaho, V. Turkovic, M. Madsen, Sol. Energy 232 (2022) 120.

[8.] T.-Y. Huang, A.P. Le Brun, B. Sochor, C.-M. Wu, Y. Bulut, P. Müller-Buschbaum, S.V. Roth, Y.-L. Yang, ACS Appl. Nano Mater. 7 (2024) 17588.

[9.] B. Morgan, M.D. Dadmun, J. Polym. Sci., Part B: Polym. Phys. 55 (2017) 1142.

[10.] S.J. Rinehart, G. Yuan, M.D. Dadmun, Soft Matter 16 (2020) 1287.

[11.] L.-M. Wang, Q. Li, S. Liu, Z. Cao, Y.-P. Cai, X. Jiao, H. Lai, W. Xie, X. Zhan, T. Zhu, ACS Appl. Mater. Interfaces 12 (2020) 24165.

[12.] A.P. Le Brun, T.-Y. Huang, S. Pullen, A.R.J. Nelson, J. Spedding, S.A. Holt, J. Appl. Crystallogr. 56 (2023) 18.

[13.] A.R.J. Nelson, S.W. Prescott, J. Appl. Crystallogr. 52 (2019) 193.

[14.] L. Yu, D. Qian, S. Marina, F.A.A. Nugroho, A. Sharma, S. Hultmark, A.I. Hofmann, R. Kroon, J. Benduhn, D.-M. Smilgies, K. Vandewal, M.R. Andersson, C. Langhammer, J. Martín, F. Gao, C. Müller, ACS Appl. Mater. Interfaces 11 (2019) 21766.

ON THE VIABILITY OF CIGS TECHNOLOGY FOR SILICON BASED TANDEM SOLAR CELLS

Juan C. Jimeno[1], Vanesa Fano[1], Eneko Cereceda[1], Aloña Otaegi[1], Nekane Azkona[1], Rubén Gutiérrez[1],
Federico Recart[1], Velia Rodríguez[1], Carlos del Cañizo[2] & David Fuertes[2]
[1] Technological Institute of Microelectronics, University of the Basque Country UPV/EHU, 48013, Bilbao, Spain
[2] Universidad Politécnica de Madrid, Instituto de Energía Solar,
ETSI Telecomunicación, Ciudad Universitaria, E-28040 Madrid, Spain
jc.jimeno@ehu.eus

ABSTRACT: This work models the efficiency obtainable from tandem structures with a silicon bottom cell and a CIGS top cell. Its results are based on the characteristics obtained by different authors on single CIGS solar cells, modelling their dependence of V_{oc} on E_G and the dependence of V_{oc} on recombination mechanisms with kT or 2kT dependence. Results are modelled for different connection strategies: 4 terminals, with independent bias conditions for top and bottom cells; 3 terminals, with a parallel interconnection of both sub-cells (one top in parallel with a series of two bottoms); 2 terminals as conventional tandem cells with series connection. The work shows the viability of CIGS / Silicon tandem cells for any configuration with different band gap targets for optimum conversion efficiency, upgrading the efficiency of a single high efficiency silicon solar cell.
Keywords: Tandem solar cell, CIGS, Silicon

1 INTRODUCTION

Crystalline silicon cells are currently the workhorse of photovoltaics. However, the efficiency of industrially manufactured cells is approaching its theoretical maximum. It is now widely accepted that solar cells of the future will need to make a more intelligent use of the solar spectrum, perhaps by including two or more pn junctions, each suited to a region of the solar spectrum.

CIGS cells have shown exceptional characteristics in the past, very close to those of the best silicon cells, with the best of them having efficiencies of over 23.3% [1]. In addition, they have other advantages such as being able to be made in thin films, with the savings in material that this entails. Furthermore, their stability and their manufacturability are well demonstrated. However, their efficiency has always been slightly lower than that of silicon cells and the brutal reduction in the cost of the latter has made them a minority option today. The best CIGS cells are made based on materials with E_G close to that of silicon cells, from 1.1 to 1.2 eV, so they do not appear to be a good complement to these in tandem structures. However, their E_G can be modulated in a range of 1 to 2 eV, which has not been sufficiently explored in tandem structures.

In conventional tandem cells connected in series, the useful photons of the solar spectrum must be distributed equally among all the cells composing the tandem structure. This greatly limits the materials to be combined, even more so when one of them, the silicon of the bottom cell, appears today as invariant. Our group presented a three-terminal tandem solar cell structure [2] based on an IBC-type silicon cell whose sensitivity to E_G mismatches between the top and bottom cells is very small, making it useful for structures even with very mismatched E_Gs. This structure was quickly adopted by other groups [3] and today constitutes one of the basic structures in the design of tandem cells, whether based on silicon, perovskites or other materials [4].

This work models the recombination characteristics that appear in the best CIGS cells made so far, trying to establish relationships between the obtainable V_{oc}, their E_G, and the dominant recombination type in the device.

2 THE SOLAR SPECTRUM

Tandem cells have a higher sensitivity to the incident light spectrum than conventional cells. In conventional single-junction solar cells, all collected electrons are extracted at the same voltage, and at most one electron is extracted for each photon. Tandem cells use different materials, each capable of capturing photons only from a certain energy level. For each photon absorbed, a single electron can be extracted, identically to conventional cells, at a voltage directly related to the threshold energy required to capture them, E_G. Screening photons according to their energy allows for better use of the light spectrum. The theoretical limit for converting light to electric current is 68% [5] using a large number of materials. Efficiencies close to 38% [6] have been obtained for three materials, and close to 33% for two junctions [7]. All these record results correspond to cells made of III-V materials, which, due to their high cost, are usually reserved for space applications. For single junction cells the efficiency limit is close to 30% for GaAs cells [8], followed by silicon cells with efficiencies close to 27.5% [9]. Due to their low cost and efficiency close to theoretical limits it seems very likely that silicon cells will continue to dominate the market, but increasing their efficiency requires their combination with other cells in tandem structures.

This work focuses on tandem cells with only two junctions. The study was conducted for the AM1.5G spectrum. The cell with the lowest E_G corresponds to a 1.1 eV silicon cell, assuming a conservative efficiency of 25%. The top cell will be a CIGS cell. The current collected by each cell is a function of the E_G of the top cell (Fig. 1). The voltage it provides is also a function of the band (red to green line) in Fig. 2. The region in which it is located depends on the technology and imperfections of this top cell. The green line corresponds to the maximum obtainable open circuit voltage, V_{oc}, for a solar cell according to our models (the best cell technologies of III-V materials fit well to this green line) and can be roughly expressed as:

$$V_{oc} = \frac{E_G}{q} - 0,4$$

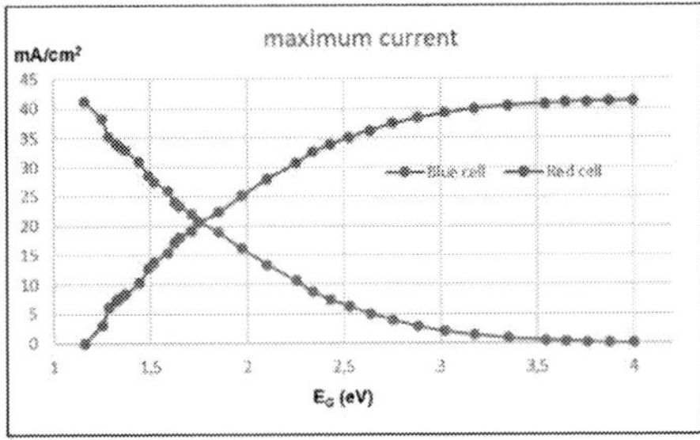

Figure 1: Maximum photocurrents obtainable by the top cell, in blue, and the bottom cell, in red, when the latter is a silicon cell

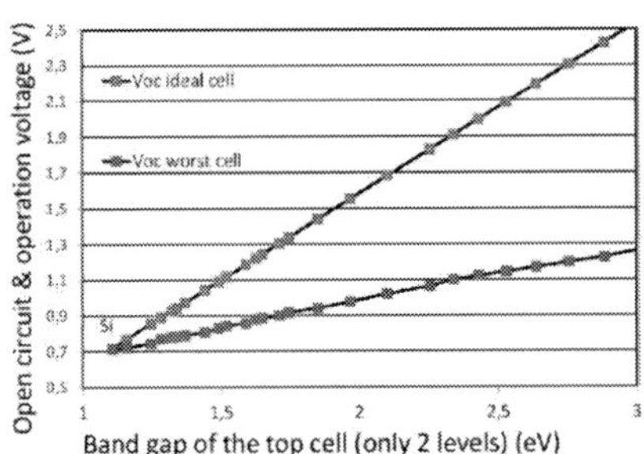

Figure 2: V_{oc} values for the top cell, in green the maximum possible and in red the minimum admissible

The red line represents the minimum V_{oc} voltage required for a top cell, the cell with the highest E_G, to not degrade the performance of a tandem cell based on a silicon bottom cell. In other words, this represents the minimum V_{oc} value required for the bottom cell for the tandem assembly to achieve an efficiency of at least 25%.

3 INTERCONNECTION TOPOLOGIES

In tandem cells, the top cell is used as an optical filter for the bottom cell, so that the most energetic photons are collected in the former, while the lowest-energy ones are collected in the latter. Therefore, the top cell sits above the latter. However, electrical interconnections can vary.

The most common is shown in Fig. 3, in which both cells are connected in series. Its current is limited by the poor cell, which, according to Fig. 1, restricts the E_G range for the top cell from 1.6 to 1.9 eV. Figure 4 shows the maximum efficiency obtainable for a tandem cell as a function of the E_G value of the top cell for the case where the bottom cell is a silicon cell with 25% efficiency.

The 4-terminal connection allows the behavior of each cell to be independent (Fig. 5) and provides the highest efficiencies but requires placing the cells in two different electrical circuits.

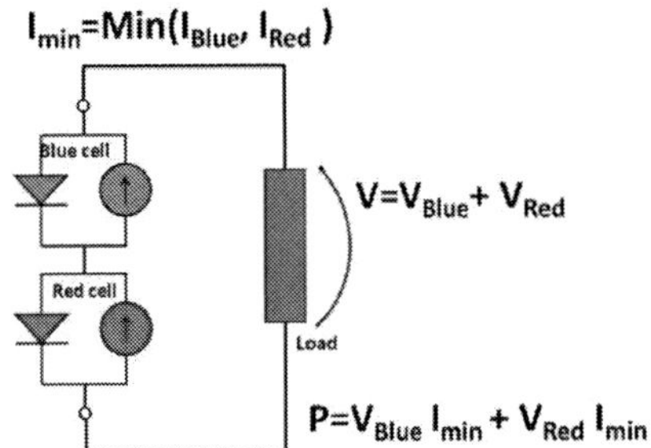

Figure 3: Two-material tandem solar cell with series interconnection

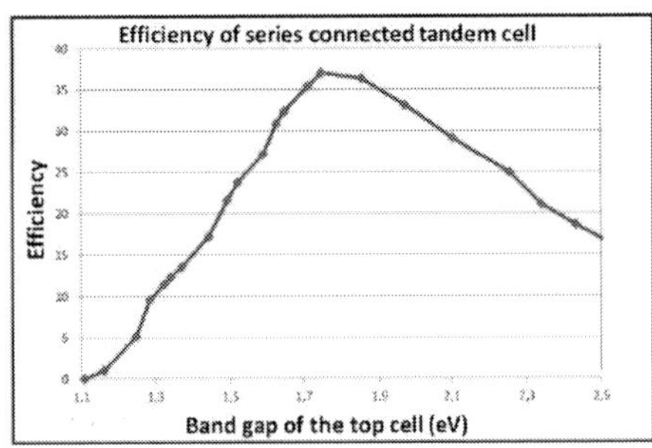

Figure 4: Maximum efficiency is achievable for a series connected tandem cell with a silicon bottom cell and depending on the E_G of the top cell

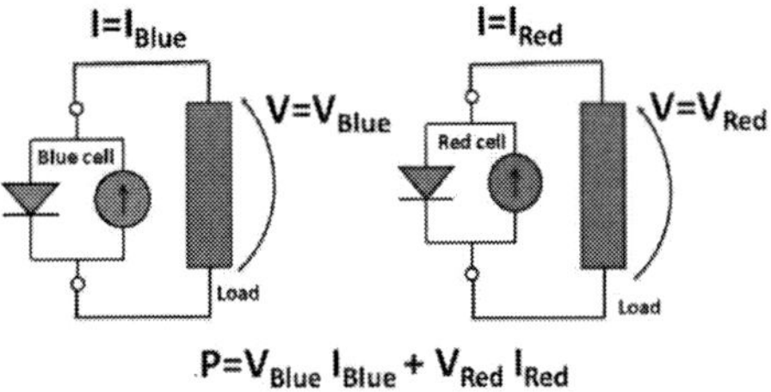

Figure 5: 4-terminal tandem solar cell with two materials without interconnection between them

The parallel connection of the cells (Fig. 6) is limited by the cell voltage. Identically to the case of the series connection, figure 7 shows the maximum efficiency obtainable for a tandem cell as a function of the E_G value of the top cell for the case where the bottom cell is a silicon cell with 25% efficiency. It can be seen that this kind of interconnection offers better adaptability than the series connection. However, it would require implementing 3 pn junctions per cell. A completely equivalent simplification is the 3-terminal cell (Fig. 8), from which modules with tandem cells in parallel can be built.

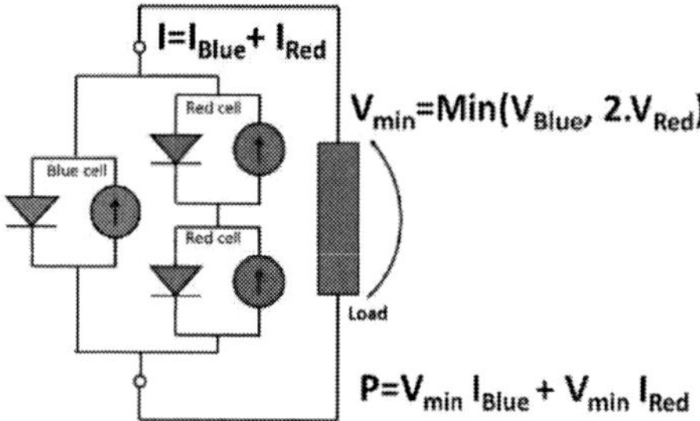

Figure 6: Two-material tandem solar cell with parallel interconnection

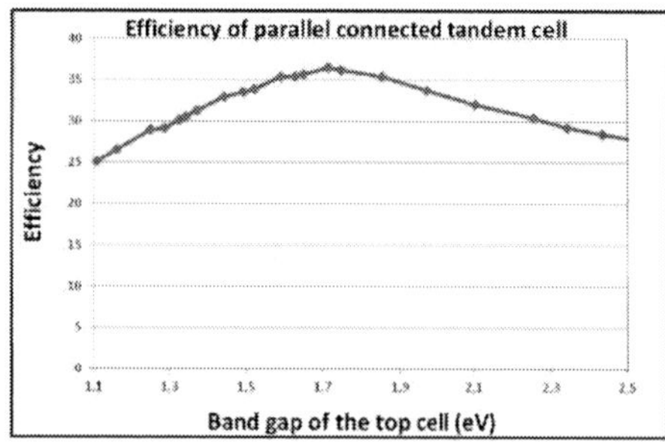

Figure 7: Maximum efficiency achievable for a parallel connected tandem cell with a silicon bottom cell and depending on the E_G of the top cell

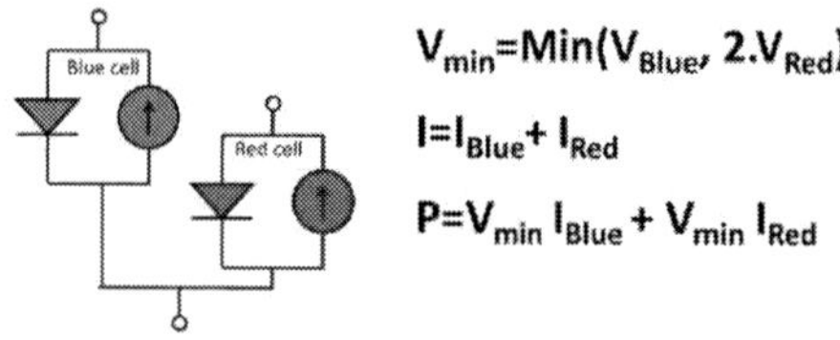

Figure 8: 3-terminal tandem solar cell with two materials and parallel interconnection

4 MODELLING THE CIGS TECHNOLOGY

Currently, there are no models for how CIGS cell characteristics vary depending on E_G. Furthermore, some studies refer to technologies from 10 years ago, and current cells are much better. It is also unknown whether CIGS cells behave with m=1 or 2, which is crucial for the performance of tandem cells.

In order to make a model that covers all possibilities, but always considering the maximum achievable, we have considered the results reported by 3 different authors, Nakamura in 2019 [1] with CIGS cells with record efficiency of 23.35%, Barreau in 2020 [10] and W.N. Shafarman [11]. This last work is the one with the best analysis of CIGS cells in terms of their band-gap, however, as it is almost 25 years old, its results have been clearly surpassed by the other two previously presented.

In order to obtain a valid model for all situations, two extreme behaviors have been considered, depending on whether the V_{oc} was limited by m=1 or m=2 effects. A fit of the best results of the 3 papers presented has been performed. Figure 9 shows the excellent fit of both models to the reported V_{oc} voltages. The recombination models obtained can be expressed as:

$$J = 1.5 \ 10^{-4} \exp\left(\frac{-E_G}{2\,V_T}\right).\exp\left(\frac{V}{V_T}\right) \ A/cm^2$$

$$J = 4 \ 10^{-4} \exp\left(\frac{-E_G}{4.5\,V_T}\right).\exp\left(\frac{V}{2\,V_T}\right) \ A/cm^2$$

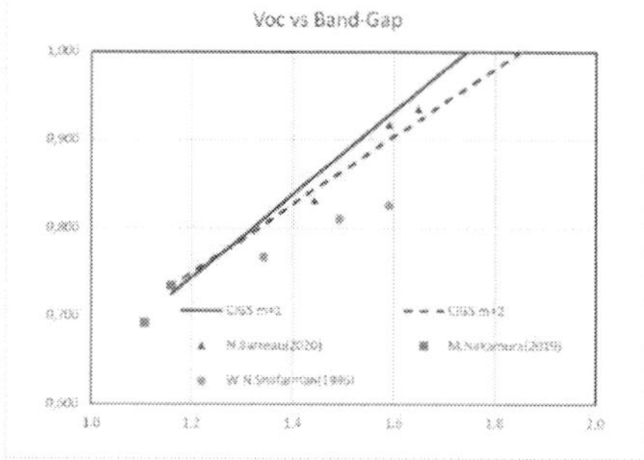

Figure 9: Recombination model for CIGS technology in the cases of m=1 and m=2 vs. experimental data

For the I_{sc} (Fig. 10) small discrepancies are found in the region of high E_G values, above 1.65 eV, which could mean that the optical band gap (obtained as a projection of V_{oc} at T = 0 K) is perhaps larger than this value. In this case the model should be refined a bit more.

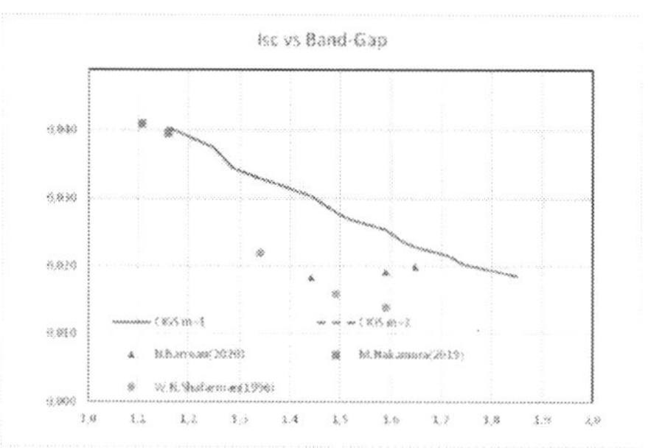

Figure 10: Photogeneration model for CIGS technology vs. experimental data

It should be noted that the fill-factors, shown in figure 11, are highly variable and always depend on parasitic effects. In the fit of the characteristics shown in figure 11 a series resistance, R_s, value of 0.5 $\Omega \cdot cm^2$ has been applied for the case of m=1 and of 3 $\Omega \cdot cm^2$ for the case of m=2. Even if these differences in R_s are not taken into account, the high FF values for the low band-gap cells suggest a behavior close to m=1 and closer to m=2 in the high band-gap cases. Identical conclusions would be obtained from comparison of results from CIGS perovskite technologies. As example for 1.55 eV of E_G the CIGS cell [12] presents a FF of 72,2 % (for a V_{oc} of 0.92 V) compared to 84.0% (for a V_{oc} of 1.19 V) of their equivalent perovskite [13] cell, suggesting that the m=2 behavior of CIGS cells may be the main cause of their low FF and V_{oc} values.

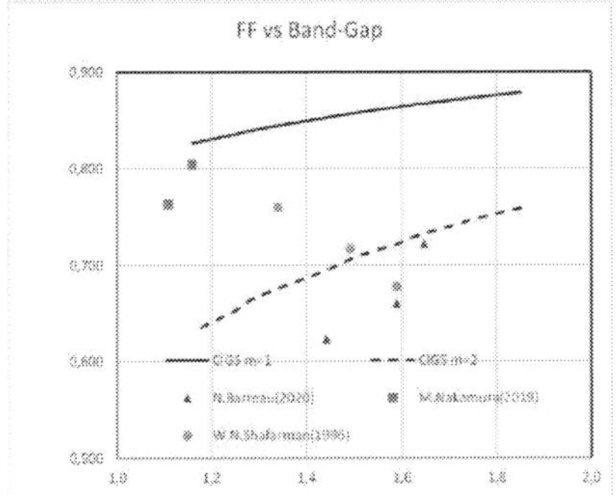

Figure 11: Fill-Factor model for CIGS technology in the cases of m=1 and m=2 vs. experimental data

5 OBTAINED RESULTS

Numerical simulation of tandem cells with a silicon bottom cell and efficiency 25% and a CIGS top cell according to the models in Figure 9 and their corresponding recombination has led to the results in figures 12, 13 and 14 for 4-terminal cells (Fig. 12), 2-terminal cells and series connection (Fig. 13) and 2 or 3-terminal cells and parallel connection (Fig. 14).

The best results are obviously obtained for 4-terminal cells (Fig. 12), where a clear improvement is obtained for tandem structures with CIGS cells. The maximum efficiency obtainable for a tandem structure in these circumstances, on a silicon cell with 25% efficiency and a CIGS top cell behaving like the m=1 model, is 30.3% for band-gaps between 1.85 and 1.95 eV and 28.5% for identical band-gaps under the m=2 model. This indicates that there is a net gain between 3.5 and 5.3 absolute points compared to a silicon cell without a tandem. For an E_G of 1.65 eV the gain is between 2.8 and 4.6 absolute points (efficiencies of 27.8 to 29.6 %).

For cells connected in series (Figure 13), a narrow net gain region appears located between 1.63 and 1.97 eV of E_G, reaching theoretical efficiencies of up to 30.3% for 1.75 eV of E_G, the same as with 4-terminal structures. For the case of m=2, the results are also similar to those obtained for 4 terminals but restricted to the region from 1.65 to 1.9 of E_G. For values outside this range, the CIGS cell causes a deterioration of the results of the tandem cell.

For parallel-connected cells (Fig. 14), there are virtually no restrictions on the window in which the improvement occurs, but it is less spectacular than in series connections, being limited to 2 to 4.5 absolute points of

improvement and, for a practical E_G range, perhaps only 1 to 2 points of improvement. We believe this is due to the fact that high-E_G CIGS cells (at least those we studied) have operating voltages that are not as high as they should be.

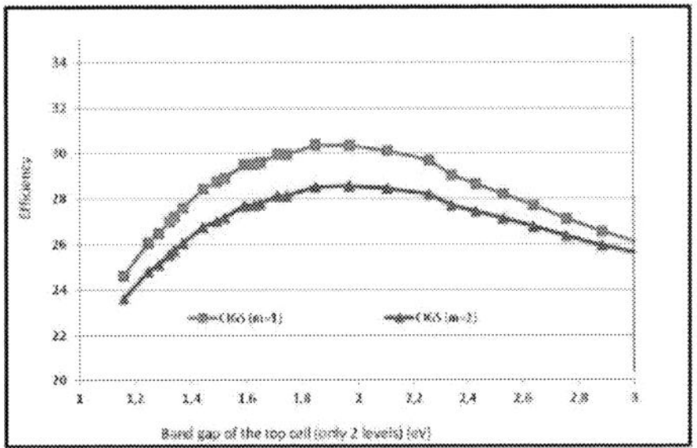

Figure 12: Efficiencies achievable for 4-terminal tandem cells of a silicon bottom cell with 25% efficiency and a CIGS top cell for models m=1 and m=2

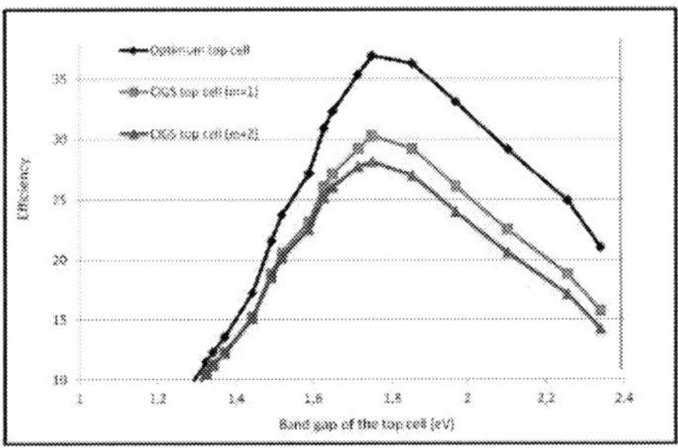

Figure 13: Efficiencies for tandem cells for a silicon bottom cell and 25% efficiency and a top cell according to the CIGS cell model with m=1 and m=2, in cases where cells are interconnected in series

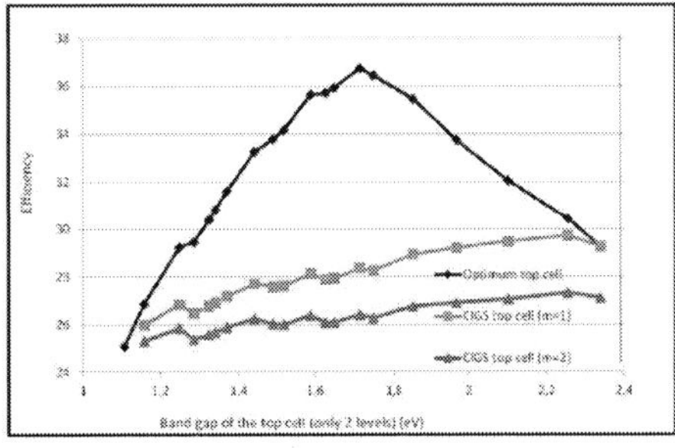

Figure 14: Efficiencies for tandem cells for a silicon bottom cell and 25% efficiency and a top cell according to the CIGS cell model with m=1 and m=2, in cases where cells are interconnected in parallel

5 CONCLUSIONS

CIGS solar cells can be a real and easily industrializable alternative for the development of tandem solar cells based on a silicon bottom cell. In conventional series interconnection configurations, they present a narrow region with the potential for more than 5 absolute points of improvement over the silicon cell. For parallel configurations, they are more limited, but the restrictions on the E_G required for the CIGS cell disappear, opening up a significant area for research and ongoing improvement.

Precise characterization of the behavior of CIG cells is essential, and it is necessary to clearly determine in which cases their recombination depends on m=1 or m=2. The results of this work indicate that the final efficiency will largely depend on this factor, which not only determines the device's operating voltage but also its fill factor.

Finally, Figure 15 represents an overview of the regions and magnitudes in which CIGS technology can represent an advance over conventional silicon technologies.

This work has not taken into account the degradation that the joint manufacture of silicon and CIGS cells can produce in the former, which are clearly technological aspects that must be addressed.

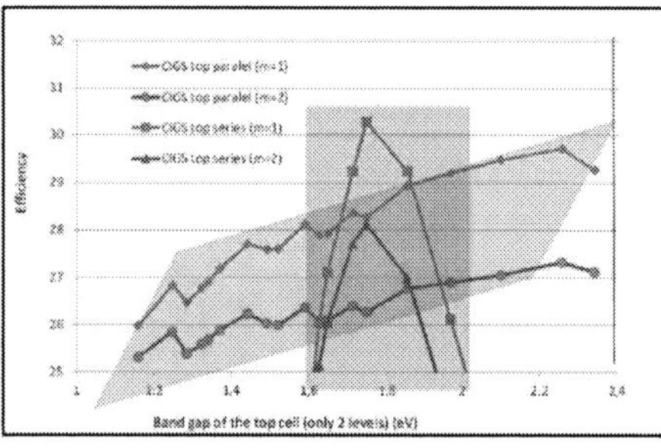

Figure 15: Efficiencies for tandem cells for a silicon bottom cell and 25% efficiency and a top cell according to the CIGS cell model with m=1 and m=2, in cases where cells are interconnected in series or parallel

6 ACKNOWLEDGEMENT
Acknowledgement

This research was supported by the M-ERA.NET Consortium under the 2024 Joint Call, with funding through the PARACELSis Project from the Agencia Vasca de Innovación (Innobasque), the Spanish Research Agency MICIU/AEI/10.13039/501100011033 (PCI2025-16314), the Hazitek ZL-2025/00146 and the European Union.

7 REFERENCES

[1] M. Nakamura, K. Yamaguchi, Y. Kimoto, Y. Yasaki, T. Kato and H. Sugimoto, "Cd-Free Cu(In,Ga)(Se,S)2 Thin-Film Solar Cell With Record Efficiency of 23.35%," in IEEE Journal of Photovoltaics, vol. 9, no. 6, pp. 1863-1867, Nov. 2019, doi: 10.1109/JPHOTOV.2019.2937218.

[2] Juan. C. Jimeno, Rubén Gutierrez, Vanesa Fano, Ahmed Habib, Carlos del Cañizo, Muhammad A. Rasool, Aloña Otaegi, "A 3 Terminal Parallel Connected Silicon Tandem Solar Cell". Energy Procedia, Volume 92, August 2016, Pages 644-65. doi:10.1016/j.egypro.2016.07.031

[3] Emily L. Warren, Michael G. Deceglie, Michael Rienacker, Robby Peibst, Adele C. Tamboli and Paul Stradinsa, "Maximizing tandem solar cell power extraction using a three-terminal design". Sustainable Energy & Fuels, 2018. doi: 10.1039/c8se00133b

[4] Xingliang Li, Qiaojing Xu, Lingling Yan, Chengchao Ren, Biao Shi, Pengyang Wang, Sayantan Mazumdar, Guofu Hou, Ying Zhao and Xiaodan Zhang, "Silicon heterojunction-based tandem solar cells: past, status, and future prospects". Nanophotonics 2021; 10(8): 2001–2022. doi: 10.1515/nanoph-2021-0034

[5] J. F. Geisz, R. M. France, K. L. Schulte, M. A. Steiner, A. G. Norman, H. L. Guthrey, M. R. Young, T. Song, and T. Moriarty, "Six-junction III-V solar cells with 47.1% conversion efficiency under 143 suns concentration," Nat. Energy 5, 326 (2020).

[6] K. Sasaki, T. Agui, K. Nakaido, N. Takahashi, R. Onitsuka, and T. Takamoto, "Development of InGaP/GaAs/InGaAs inverted triple junction concentrator solar cells," AIP Conf. Proc. 1556, 22 (2013).

[7] M. A. Green, E. D. Dunlop, J. Hohl-Ebinger, M. Yoshita, N. Kopiakis, and X. Hao, "Solar cell efficiency tables (version 57)," Prog. Photovoltaics 29, 3 (2021).

[8] Kayes BM, Nie H, Twist R, Spruytte SG, Reinhardt F, Kizilyalli IC, Higashi GS. 27.6% conversion efficiency, a new record for single-junction solar cells under 1 sun illumination. Proceedings of the 37th IEEE Photovoltaic Specialists Conference, 2011.

[9] https://www.longi.com/en/news/

[10] N. Barreau et al., "High efficiency solar cell based on Cu(In,Ga)S2 thin film grown by 3-stage process," 2020 47th IEEE Photovoltaic Specialists Conference (PVSC), Calgary, AB, Canada, 2020, pp. 1715-1718. doi: 10.1109/PVSC45281.2020.9300598.

[11] W. N. Shafarman, R. Klenk and B. E. McCandless, "Characterization of Cu(InGa)Se/sub 2/ solar cells with high Ga content," Conference Record of the Twenty Fifth IEEE Photovoltaic Specialists Conference - 1996, Washington, DC, USA, 1996, pp. 763-768, doi: 10.1109/PVSC.1996.564240.

[12] Hiroi H, Iwata Y, Adachi S, Sugimoto H, Yamada A. New World-record efficiency for pure-sulfide Cu(In,Ga)S2 thin-film solar cell with Cd-free buffer layer via KCN-free process. IEEE Journal of Photovoltaics 2016; 6(3): 760-763.

[13] Jung EH, Jeon NJ, Park EY, et al. Efficient, stable and scalable perovskite solar cells using poly(3-hexylthiophene). Nature. 2019; 567(7749): 511-515.

ON THE VIABILITY OF CIGS TECHNOLOGY FOR SILICON BASED TANDEM SOLAR CELLS

Juan C. Jimeno[1], **Vanesa Fano**[1], **Eneko Cereceda**[1], **Aloña Otaegi**[1], **Nekane Azkona**[1], **Rubén Gutiérrez**[1], **Federico Recart**[1], **Velia Rodríguez**[1], **Carlos del Cañizo**[2] & **David Fuertes**[2]

[1] Technolgical Institute of Microelectronics (TiM), UPV/EHU, Bilbao, Spain. **email: jc.jimeno@ehu.eus**
[2] Instituto de Energía Solar (UPM), Universidad Politécnica de Madrid, Madrid, Spain

Aim & objectives

- Future increases in solar cell efficiencies will require tandem structures
- Crystalline silicon cells cover 95% of global production; their low cost, high efficiency and stability suggest that they will continue to dominate the market, even in tandem structures.
- CIGS presents an industrial mature technology, with efficiencies of up to 23%, close to silicon and its E_G can be varied from 1 to 2 eV
- The objective of this work is to analyze the feasibility of making CIGS tandems on silicon-based cells

Current and voltages in tandem cells

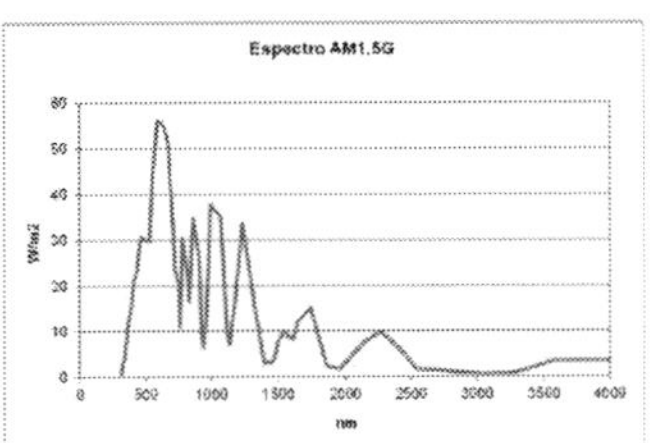

Fig. 1

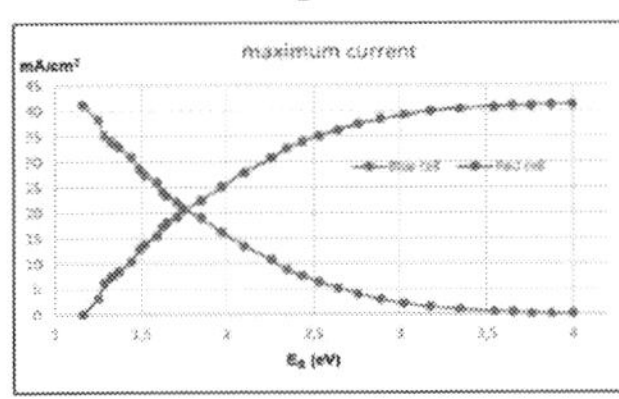

Fig. 2

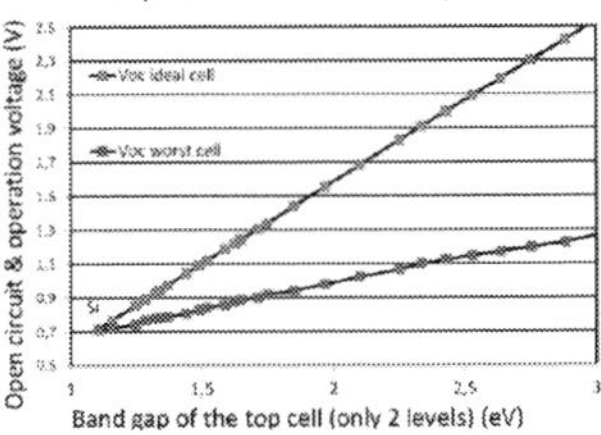

Fig. 3

This work focuses on tandem cells with only two junctions. The study was conducted for the AM1.5 spectrum (**Fig. 1**). The cell with the lowest E_G corresponds to a 1.1 eV silicon cell, assuming an efficiency of 25%. The top cell will be a CIGS cell. The current collected by each cell is a function of the E_G of the top cell (**Fig. 2**). The voltage it provides is also a function of the band (red to green line) in **Fig. 3**. The region in which it is located depends on the technology and imperfections of this top cell.

Tandem cell structures and philosophies

2 terminal series connected tandem cell

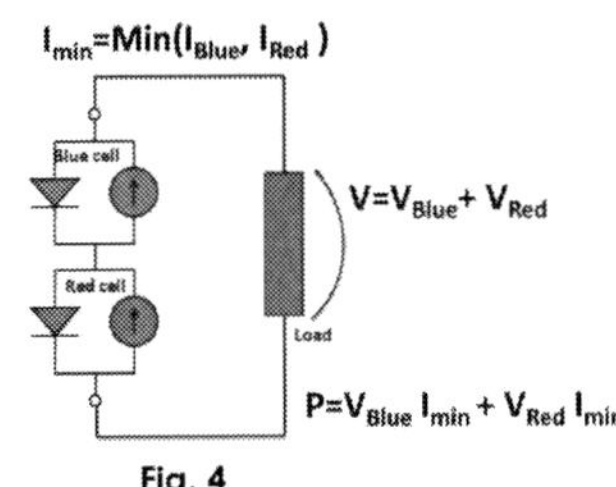

Fig. 4

4 terminal series connected tandem cell

Fig. 5

2 terminal parallel connected tandem cell

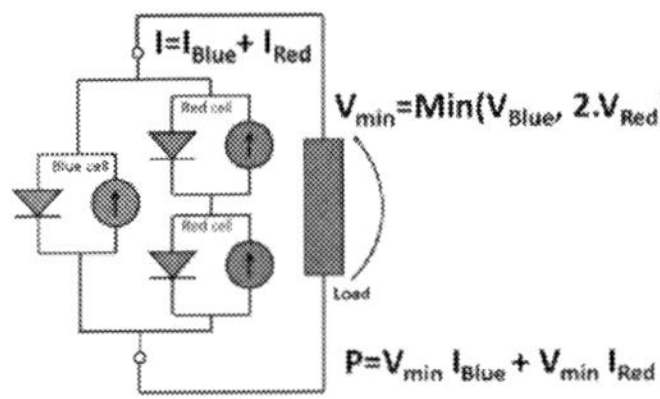

Fig. 6

3 terminal parallel connected tandem cell

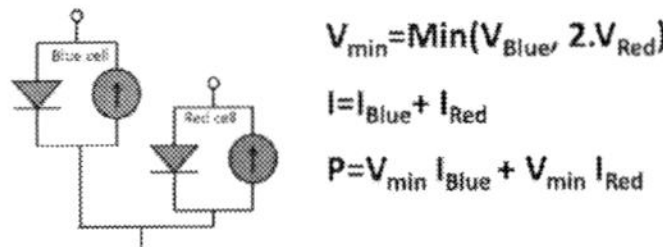

Fig. 7

In tandem cells are different electrical connection possibilities:

The most common is shown in **Fig. 4**, in which both cells are connected in series. Its current is limited by the poor cell, which, according to **Fig. 2**, restricts the E_G range for the TOP cell from 1.6 to 1.9 eV. The 4-terminal connection allows the behavior of each cell to be independent (**Fig. 5**) and provides the highest efficiencies but requires placing the cells in two different electrical circuits.

The parallel connection of the cells (**Fig. 6**) is limited by the cell voltage, but it offers better adaptability than the series connection. However, it would require implementing 3 pn junctions per cell. A completely equivalent simplification is the 3-terminal cell (**Fig. 7**), from which modules with tandem cells in parallel can be built.

Modelling the CIGS Technology

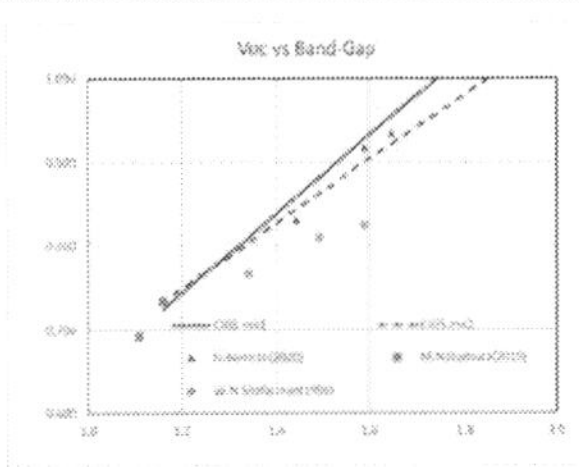

Fig. 8

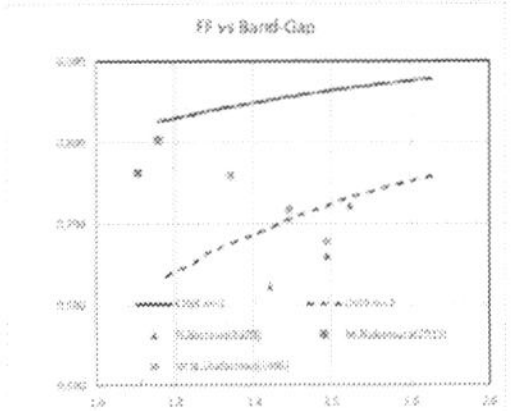

Fig. 9

Currently, there are no models for how CIGS cell characteristics vary depending on E_G. Furthermore, some studies refer to technologies from 10 years ago, and current cells are much better. It is also unknown whether CIGS cells behave with m=1 or 2, which is crucial for the performance of tandem cells. The solution was to fit the best cells to two models, one with m=1 and the other with m=2. The result can be seen in **Fig. 8** and the following equations.

$$J = 1.5\ 10^{-3} \exp\left(\frac{-E_G}{2\,V_T}\right)\cdot\exp\left(\frac{V}{V_T}\right)$$

$$J = 4\ 10^{-4} \exp\left(\frac{-E_G}{4.5\,V_T}\right)\cdot\exp\left(\frac{V}{2\,V_T}\right)$$

Comparison of the actual and modelled Fill-Factors (**Fig. 9**) suggests that low E_G cells (<1.3 eV) may have m close to 1, while high E_G cells may be close to 2.

Modelling Results of Tandem Structures

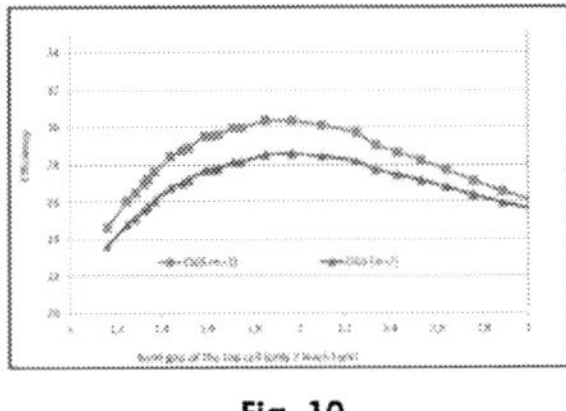

Fig. 10

Numerical simulation of tandem cells with a silicon bottom cell and efficiency 25% and a CIGS top cell according to the models in **Figure 8** and the previous equations, has led to the results in **Figures 10, 11** and **12** for 4-terminal cells (**Fig. 10**), 2-terminal cells and series connection (**Fig. 11**) and 2 or 3-terminal cells and parallel connection (**Fig. 12**).

The best results are obviously obtained for 4-terminal cells (**Fig. 10**), where a clear improvement is obtained for tandem structures with CIGS cells with an E_G greater than 1.4 eV. For the series-connected cells (**Fig. 11**), a narrow window of 1.65 to 1.95 eV is obtained in which the tandem cell with CIGS outperforms a standard silicon cell. For parallel-connected cells (**Fig. 12**), there are virtually no restrictions on the window in which the improvement occurs, but it is less spectacular than in series connections, being limited to 2 to 4.5 absolute points of improvement and, for a practical E_G range, perhaps only 1 to 2 points of improvement. We believe this is due to the fact that high-E_G CIGS cells (at least those we studied) have operating voltages that are not as high as they should be.

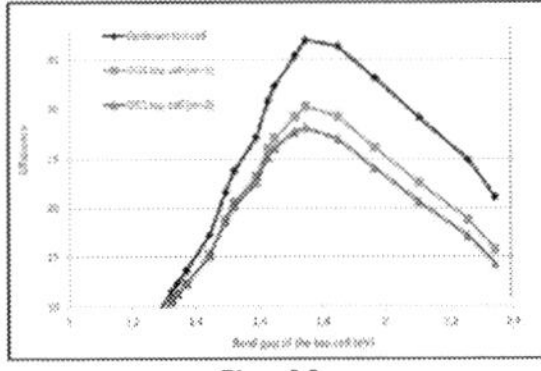

Fig. 11

Fig. 12

CONCLUSIONS

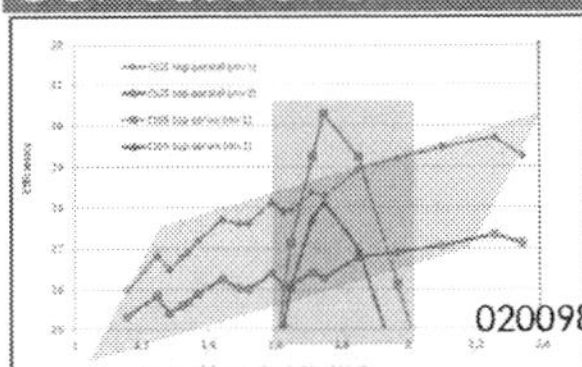

- CIGS technology appears to be a clear opportunity for the development of tandem cells in silicon. It could produce efficiency improvements of up to 5.5 absolute points for 4-terminal structures.
- For 2-terminal structures, the gains range from 3 to 5 points for a very narrow range of E_G values in the case of series connections and are somewhat lower in efficiency but without E_G restrictions for parallel connections. The figure on the left is a summary of what has been discussed here.
- A greater effort must be done in modelling high E_G CIGS cells.

UNIVERSITAT POLITÈCNICA DE VALÈNCIA

Study of the effect of precursor solution aging on Bismuth-based Chalcohalide Thin Films by Solution Method for Photovoltaic Applications

Benjamín Fritz Muñoz, Giulia Longo, Bernabé Marí Soucasé

Instituto de Diseño y Fabricación - Universitat Politècnica de València

Introduction / Objectives

The search for non-toxic and stable alternatives to lead-based perovskites has brought pnictogen-based chalcohalides to the forefront as promising candidates for next-generation photovoltaic absorbers[1]. Among these, **bismuth sulfo-bromide (BiSBr)** stands out as a particularly attractive material due to its earth-abundant composition, intrinsic thermodynamic stability, and suitable optoelectronic properties for single-junction solar cell applications, such as a direct bandgap in the range of ~1.6–1.8 eV and a high absorption coefficient ($>10^5$ cm^{-1}).[2,3]

In this work, our objectives are :

- Preparation of BiSBr films using a solution-processing method adapted from the synthesis[4] of SbSI.
- Study in the impact of precursor solution aging on the quality of resulting films.

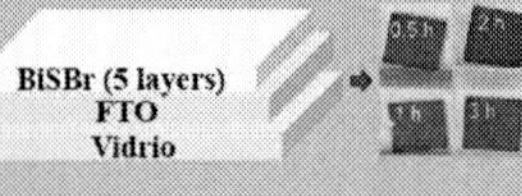

BiSBr (5 layers)
FTO
Vidrio

Fig 1 a) Schematic architectures of the BiSBr film prepared with precursors solution aged 0.5, 1, 2 and 3 hours with corresponding pictures.
b) Solutions A and B after 3 hours of stirring. c) Solution A and B after one night.
d) Mixed solution after one day

Methods

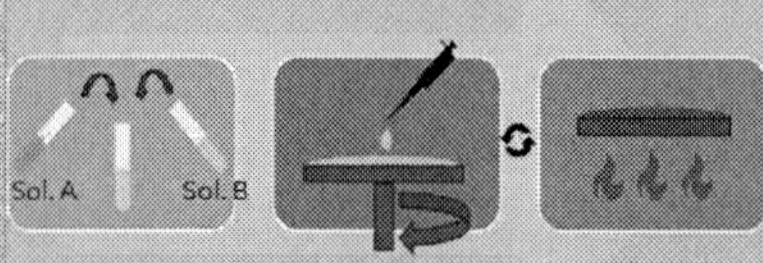

Sol. A   Sol. B

Solution synthesis   Dripping & Spin Coating   Annealing

Solution A:
$\begin{cases} 0,4\ mmol\ BiCl_3 \\ 0,1\ mmol\ BiBr_3 \\ 1,25\ mmol\ TU \end{cases}$
in 2 mL DMF for 2 hours at 80°C

Solution B:
0,5 mmol $BiBr_3$ in 1 mL DMSO for 2 hours at 80°C

Fig 2 Thin film BiSBr preparation

The two solution were mixed in a ratio A:B = 4:1 and then heated at 80°C for 0.5, 1, 2 and 3 hours, then deposited on FTO by spincoating in air, casting 75 µl at 4000 rpm for 60 sec.
The BiSBr film was then annealed at 160°C for 15 min each layer.

Results

Effect of aging solution

In the figure 3, The GIXRD diffractograms show increasing crystallinity as the stirring time increases. The samples left 0,5 and 1 hour of stirring show the appearance of the characteristic peaks of BiSBr, even if with very low intensity and with evidence of amorphous phase present. As the time of stirring is increased, the crystallinity of the film is higher, and clear presence of BiSBr can be appreciated. After 1 hour, no evident changes can be appreciated with increasing of stirring time.
The field-emission scanning electron microscopy (FESEM) images reveal a significant change in the surface morphology.

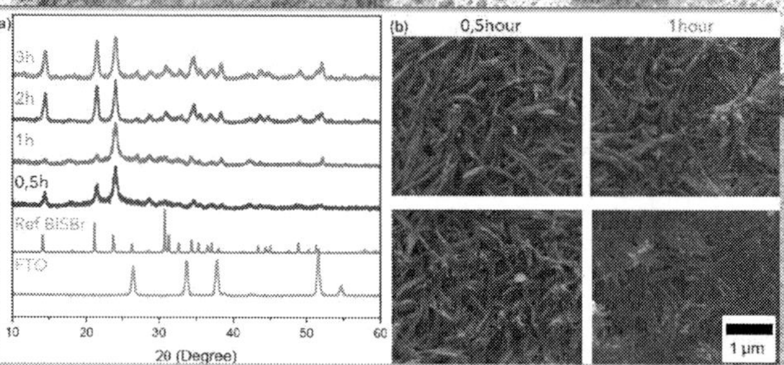

Fig 3 a) GIXRD diffractograms of the BiSBr thin films formed by solution with different aging times
b) FESEM images of the same films

Table 1 a) Distribution of Bi, S and Br taken from EDS of 0,5, 1, 2 and 3 h

Element	0,5 hour	1 hour	2 hours	3 hours
S (%)	40,4	41,9	34,7	30,2
Br (%)	27,6	26,4	34,3	36,3
Bi (%)	32,0	31,7	31,0	33,5

EDS quantifications (table 1) show significant changes in the film composition as stirring time increases. It also reveals that at short stirring times a S-rich phase is preferentially formed. As aging time increases, Br concentration increases, becoming predominant after 3h. Almost stoichiometric composition was found with 2h stirring.

Conclusions

BiSBr shows strong potential as a photovoltaic absorber, it presents several challenges that must be addressed. Our work demonstrates the importance of controlling the aging of the precursor solution as it influences the composition and morphology of the obtained BiSBr films, and contributes to a better understanding of its processing behavior and offers initial solutions for morphological control, paving the way for more effective integration into solar cell devices

Future work

The influence of stoichiometry on the precursor solution is essential, and the aging of precursor solutions with different stoichiometry will be analyzed as follow up work. In particular, variation in Br concentration will be analysed in solution A.

References

1. J. He, X. Hu, Z. Liu, W. Chen, G. Longo, Prospect for Bismuth/Antimony Chalcohalides-Based Solar Cells. Adv. Funct. Mater. 2023, 33, 2306075. https://doi.org/10.1002/adfm.202306075
2. Xiaoyu Guo, Yi-Teng Huang, Hugh Lohan, "Air-Stable Bismuth Sulfobromide (BiSBr) Visible-Light Absorbers: Optoelectronic Properties and Potential for Energy Harvesting" J. Mater. Chem. A, 2023, 11, 22775-22785, https://doi.org/10.1039/D3TA04491B
3. S. Li, Z. Huang, Y. Ding, C. Zhang, J. Yu, Q. Feng, J. Feng, Growth of BiSBr Microsheet Arrays for Enhanced Photovoltaics Performance. Small 2024, 20, 2306964. https://doi.org/10.1002/smll.202306964
4. Choi, Y.C.; Jung, K.-W. One-Step Solution Deposition of Antimony Selenoiodide Films via Precursor Engineering for Lead-Free Solar Cell Applications. Nanomaterials 2021, 11, 3206. https://doi.org/10.3390/nano11123206

020099-001

THIN-FILMS CELL FABRICATION:
A PRACTICAL APPROACH TO TEACHING PHOTOVOLTAICS FUNDAMENTALS

**Alessia Núñez-Osorio[a] , María José García-Salinas[b] , Manuel Pérez-García[b,c] , ,
Joaquín Alonso-Montesinos [b,c], Antonio M. Puertas-López[b,c] María Jesús Ariza-Camacho [b,c]**

Teaching Innovation Group in Photovoltaic Solar Cells, University of Almería, Spain

[a] Master's Student in Advanced Chemistry Laboratory, Faculty of Experimental Sciences. University of Almería, C/ Sacramento s/n Almería, 04120, Almería, Spain. davidale970@gmail.com

[b] Applied Physics Section; Dept. of Chemistry and Physics, University of Almería, C/ Sacramento s/n Almería, 04120, Almería, Spain. mjariza@ual.es, mjgarcia@ual.es, apuertas@ual.es, mperez@ual.es, joaquin.alonso@ual.es

[c] CIESOL Solar Energy Research Centre. Joint Centre UAL-CIEMAT. University of Almería, C/ Sacramento s/n Almería, 04120, Almería, Spain

ABSTRACT: Despite being one of the reference renewable energy, photovoltaic solar technology currently faces important challenges. One of them is the potential development of non-silicon-based materials solar cells, which, in addition to the need of tackling operational constrains as durability, introduces the need to adapt the current teaching contents on the fundamentals, fabrication and performance of solar cells taught in science and engineering university programs.
This work outlines a teaching-oriented methodology developed by our research group for the straightforward design, fabrication and performance assessment of dye-sensitized solar cells (DSSCs) using titanium dioxide pastes. We propose a complete manufacturing process and subsequent cell characterization, investigating various methods at each stage: paste preparation, photoelectrode fabrication, counter-electrode fabrication, cell assembly, electrolyte incorporation, and finally, assessment of the efficiency of the obtained cell. The entire methodology was developed to ensure feasibility and reproducibility within academic teaching and research laboratories. Finally, as a complementary resource, practical guides have been developed and interactive simulations implemented, and this material has been organized and consolidated into an web resource. This platform was specifically designed to provide structured access to educational materials, promoting both ease of access and self-learning.
Keywords: Photovoltaic solar energy, dye sensitized solar cells, educational resources, laboratory practices.

1 INTRODUCTION

Producing energy through renewable resources is a key component in achieving some of the most significant targets established by the Sustainable Development Goals (SDGs) concerning the fight against climate change. One of the most widely accepted technologies within solar energy is photovoltaic solar systems. This is constantly progressing and embracing innovations, including the use of solar cells made from alternative materials to silicon that can reduce the environmental impact of their manufacturing. The nature of some of these new materials also offers a highly interesting novelty: cells can be prepared from easily accessible substances through simple, manageable processes in teaching laboratories.

In this context, this paper presents an adaptation of the authors' previous research [1-3] on Dye-Sensitized Solar Cells (DSSCs) [4-6] intended for university-level teaching in undergraduate and specialized master's degrees. The aim of this paper is to provide methods and resources for educational lab-friendly DSSC fabrication and characterization.

2 PROCEDURES

Having in mind this educational aim for university students, we have designed laboratory practices and virtual simulations, written manuals for both, and integrated the whole material comprising a complete didactic unit. This unit has been organized as a set of procedures and guides for laboratory experiences as well as an HTML web-based resource repository including theoretical fundamentals and interactive simulations, called "Plataforma Educativa de Energía Solar" [7]. This platform offers students a global comprehensive learning experience in photovoltaic solar energy.

2.1 Laboratory experience 1: Fabrication of DSSC.

Our simplified method for fabricating a dye-sensitized solar cell begins with the preparation of the working electrode. This involves applying a layer of titanium dioxide (TiO_2) nanoparticle paste onto a fluorine dopped tin oxide (FTO) coated (conductive) glass slide using the "doctor-blade" method [5]. This layer is then sintered at high temperatures (450 °C for 1 hour) to consolidate the nanoparticles structure. Subsequently, the electrode is immersed in a dye solution so that the TiO_2 adsorbs the light-sensitive molecules. In parallel, the counter electrode is prepared by applying a thin layer of graphite onto another FTO glass. Both electrodes are assembled by facing the TiO_2 layer with the graphite one, leaving a gap that is filled with an iodine/iodide-based electrolyte. The active electrode area was around 0.36 cm^2. Further details regarding cell fabrication can be found in [1].

2.2 Laboratory experience 2: Characterizing a DSSC

The freshly assembled cell is then characterized to evaluate its efficiency by measuring the I-V (current vs. voltage) curve under artificial light and/or natural sunlight. The accurate acquisition of I-V curves is one of the key aspects in the characterization and optimization of photovoltaic systems. These curves are obtained through various methodologies; we have used the variable resistance method [1] and the charging capacitor method. The latter uses the energy generated by the cell or photovoltaic module to charge a capacitor and the current and voltage are measured during the charging process [8].

2.3 Web resource repository

A web platform, developed in HTML, compiles educational tools for learning about photovoltaic solar energy. The tools combine theoretical instruction with a rich practical experience gathering the virtual didactic material and the experimental guides. In a first step, the students can access educational materials to study the fundamentals. Next, they will gain practical experience through Virtual Labs (online simulations). Finally, students are prepared to conduct laboratory experiences 1 and 2 in the teaching and research laboratory, where they can fabricate real DSSCs, and analyse the efficiency of their own devices. With this aim, the platform integrates both virtual and physical lab methodologies, an approach that has proven highly effective in engineering and applied sciences.

The Virtual Labs are online simulations that allow students to experiment with photovoltaic systems in a controlled, virtual environment without the need for physical equipment. The Physical Labs are in-person guided sessions using real equipment like multimeters and signal generators to conduct live experiments and take real-time measurements.

2.4 Teaching experience

Laboratory experience 1 and 2 were developed at the University of Almería (Andalusia, Spain) between 2023 and 2025 as part of the University Teaching Innovation Project "Manufacture of a dye-sensitized solar cell (DSSC) and measurement of its characteristic parameters" (UAL PID 24_25_1_43C). Currently there are eight workspaces available for these teaching experiments, and students taking the Photovoltaic Solar Systems course in the Master's Degree in Solar Energy have already carried them out in the 2023-24 and 2024-25 academic years. Prior to conducting these practical experiments, the course's program includes 10 hours of classroom theory to study the basic concepts of solar cell operation and characterization, using silicon cells as a model and also describing the fundamentals of DSSC operation.
In this master's degree program, classes last 2.5 hours. Students manufacture the cell (experience 1) in the first 2.5-hour session. In the next session, they measure the characteristic curves (experience 2) of the cells they have manufactured themselves, as well as those of a commercial silicon cell and a laboratory photovoltaic panel. Students are also encouraged to measure series and parallel combinations of the cells they have manufactured and to use different lighting conditions.

3 RESULTS

After studying the theory and practicing in virtual labs, the real lab experiences follow: 1) Students fabricate the DSSC through a process involving photoelectrode and nanostructure creation, counter-electrode preparation, dye adsorption, and assembly with an electrolyte; 2) the I-V curve is then measured under natural or artificial sunlight using straightforward techniques, such as the variable resistance method and/or the capacitor charging method.

Regarding this practical section, the laboratory work can be completed in multiple sessions. We propose on-site some variations in methodology or materials, encouraging students to critically compare their own results with those obtained by their classmates.

3.1 Laboratory experience 1: Fabrication of DSSC.

A summary of this first part is shown in Fig. 1, with pictures of some of the steps done by the students.

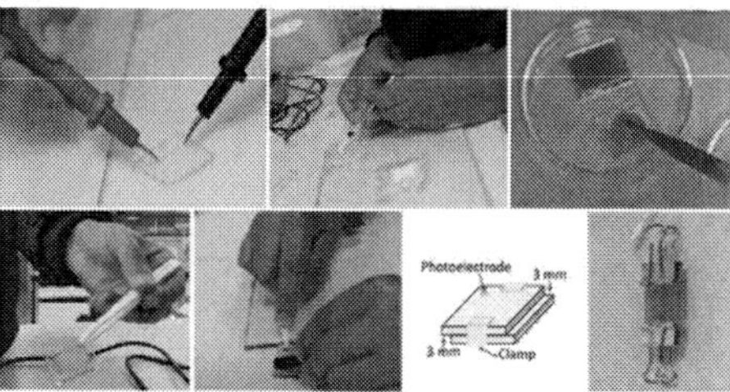

Figure 1: Steps in cell fabrication. Pictures taken by the students during their practical experience.

During lab experience 1), cell fabrication, it is important that students do not simply follow a recipe, systematically adhering to pre-established steps. While these steps should be provided, there should be some freedom to choose options and critically evaluate the consequences afterwards. The initial session is focused on preparing the electrolyte solution, the dye solution, and the nanoparticle paste. Students will gain practical experience in substance extraction, mixture preparation, and solution creation, using appropriate instruments to measure volumes and masses. Furthermore, students will already face a series of decision-making challenges: Which type of semiconducting nanoparticles to use? How to prepare the paste? Which electrolyte to use? Which type of dye, and if natural, what extraction method to employ? Alternatively, these products can be purchased pre-prepared (e.g., Solaronix [11]) which is advisable if time is short. In any case, we recommend providing several options for dyes and/or pastes. This allows students to choose how to fabricate their solar cell and then critically compare the quality obtained with each combination of materials. For example, the titanium dioxide nanoparticle paste can be prepared using high-purity chemicals (nitric acid and ethyl cellulose) or common household products (vinegar and soap).

3.2 Laboratory experience 2: Characterizing a DSSC

In lab experience 2) students apply acquired knowledge to obtain data, plot the I-V curve and calculate the cell characteristic parameters.

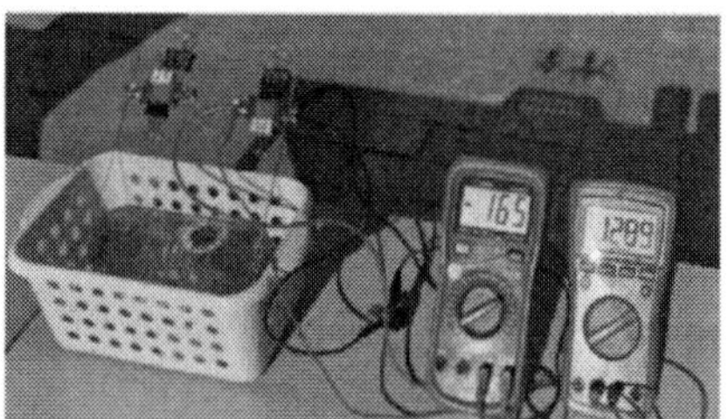

Figure 2: DSSC cell characterization. Method: variable resistance and natural sunlight. Picture taken by the students during their practical experience.

Fig. 2 shows a picture of the I-V data acquisition by using the variable resistance method with natural sunlight, while Fig. 3 shows the I-V curve obtained by a group of students using their own freshly manufactured cell. Analysis of these data leads to critical evaluation of the fabricated cell's performance enabling the determination of its energy conversion efficiency. Furthermore, they can compare different fabrication methods and dye characteristics, providing a comprehensive understanding of DSSC technology.

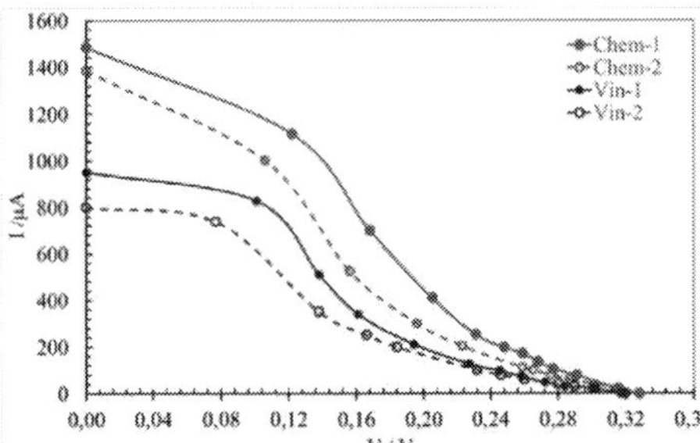

Figure 3: I-V curves obtained by a group of students using their own recently manufactured cell. Method: variable resistance and natural sunlight. Chem-1 and Chem-2: two cells using chemicals in the paste; Vin-1 and Vin-2: other two cells using vinegar and soap.

Alternatively, the I-V curve can be acquired using the capacitor charging method, which presents some challenges. First, the process takes place in a few seconds, so data acquisition devices are needed. Second, due to the low intensity values to be measured in the case of the students DSSC, the current sensors must have high resolution or amplification instruments must be used [12].

The experimental design to obtain measures with this method uses a data logger with voltage and current sensors and a 1100 or 4700 µF capacitor, as illustrated in Fig. 4.

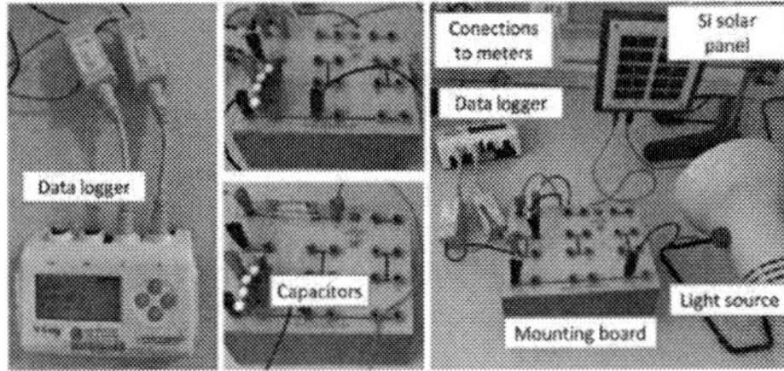

Figure 4: Materials and equipment for measuring I-V curve by the charging capacitor method for a DSSC or photovoltaic Si panel (right). Details of the capacitors (middle) and V-Log meter for data acquisition (left).

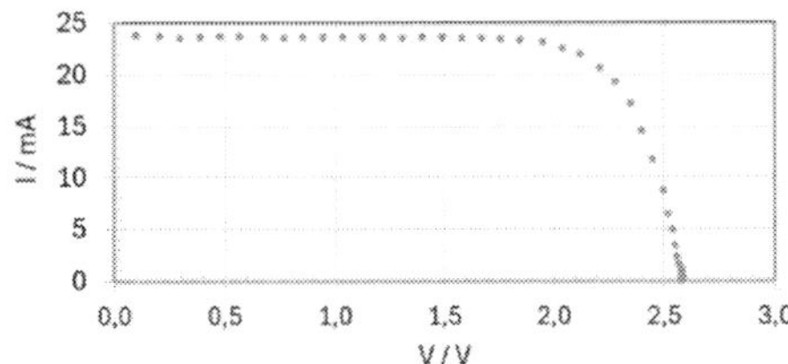

Figure 5: I-V curve for a Si PV cell. Method: charging capacitor with artificial light.

Fig. 5 depicts an example of I-V curve of a silicon panel obtained by the charging capacitor method with the equipment shown in Fig. 4. Moreover, both methods are compared in Fig. 6 for a DSSC. In this case, an instrumental amplifier has been used to measure the intensity of the DSSC using the capacitor method.

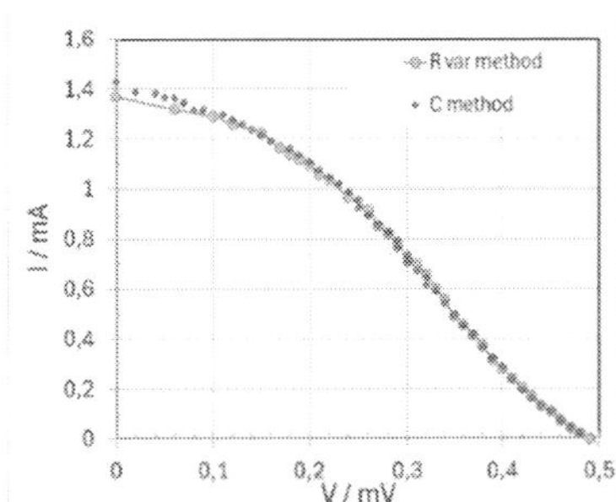

Figure 6: Comparison of the I-V curves of a DSSC measured using the variable resistance method and the charging capacitor method. Natural sunlight, 690 W/m².

3.3 Web Resource repository

All the didactic material can be found in a free-access web site [7]. This web platform is organized into a user-friendly interface with drop-down menus for easy navigation. The homepage includes these six main sections:

i) Home: Provides a general introduction to the platform and includes example simulations showing how irradiance and temperature affect I-V curves.

ii) Didactic Units: Contains structured modules with theoretical and practical content, covering everything from basic to advanced concepts.

iii) Virtual Labs: Provides interactive simulations and digital tools for virtual experimentation. Fig.s 7 and 8 show screen captures of some of the virtual labs.

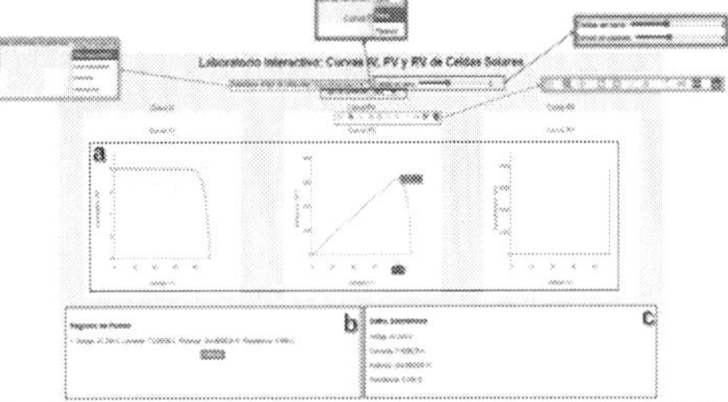

Figure 7: Display of the Solar Cell Simulation Lab in series and parallel – IV, RV, and PV Curves.

iv) In-person Labs: Offers guides for hands-on experiments in physical labs, allowing students to apply concepts in a controlled setting.

v) Videos: Features short, dynamic videos like demonstrations and tutorials to complement theoretical and practical learning.

vi) Simulation Guides: Offers supporting documents and materials to help students understand lab procedures and reinforce learning. Each guide includes a Doc file with instructions and an HTML file with the necessary functions for the simulation.

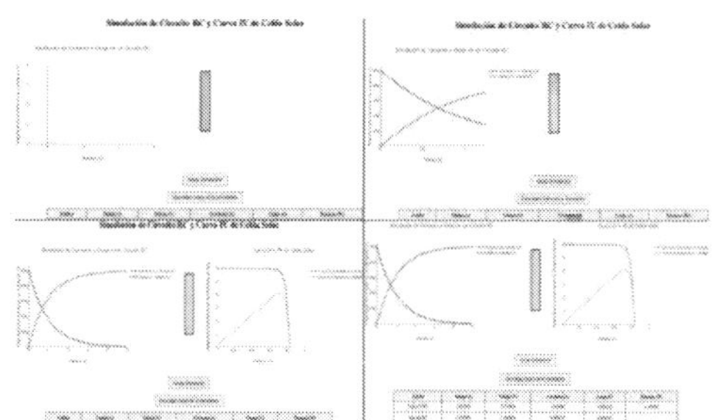

Figure 8: Capacitor Charging Lab with a Photovoltaic Panel - Relationship of the RC Circuit Curve, IV, and PV.

3.4 Teaching experience

So far, 24 students have taken part in the experiment (out of 33 enrolled in the two academic years). Their academic results have been good, with an average grade of 7.4/10 in the assessment of this part of the course. The students' opinion was evaluated through a survey, giving it an overall satisfaction rating of 4.7/5. Sixty percent of them found the cell manufacturing part more interesting, compared to 40% who preferred the cell and module characterization part. As suggestions for improvement, they propose increasing the time allotted to both cell manufacturing and characterization, so that more different cases can be explored in both experiences.

The optimization and adaptation of the DSSC manufacturing process to a 2.5-hour session was carried out in a Trabajo Fin de Carrera (similar to a Bachelor Thesis) for the Degree in Mechanical Engineering at the University of Almería [9], where basic concepts of photovoltaics are also taught. The method for measuring the characteristic curve of the cell with the charging of a capacitor was developed in a Master's Thesis [10], in which the web resource repository presented above was created. All these teaching tools are available at the Renewable Energy Laboratory of the Department of Chemistry and Physics at the University of Almería.

Future work aims to enable master's students to measure characteristic curves using the capacitor method. To do this, workstations must be equipped with a sufficiently fast data logger and current meters suitable for the characteristic curve of DSSCs. In addition, the number of workstations will be increased in order to schedule these experiments in large classes, such as those in undergraduate programs.

4 CONCLUSIONS

This paper presents practical work for degree or master students consisting in fabricating Dye-Sensitized Solar Cells, DSSC, from the elaboration of pastes to the final use and characterization. TiO_2 thin films are to be prepared using an accurate method to achieve an optimal nanostructure in the photoelectrode. In addition, counter-electrode preparation, dye adsorption, and assembly with an electrolyte are carried out with different procedures to finally obtain the highest possible efficiencies.

Overall, students approach research work: they study, design, and fabricate their own DSSC device, then measure I-V curve for their device and explore, analyse, and compare results.

In addition to the manuals and procedures for DSSC fabrication and characterization by students, the innovation introduced in this work is a complete didactic unit with all the material organized in a HTML web-based resource repository including theoretical fundamentals, practical guidelines and interactive simulations.

The innovative approach of this project lies in empowering students to not only grasp the fundamentals of solar energy but also actively participate in the fabrication and evaluation of solar cells. This methodology promotes deep learning and fosters critical thinking regarding emerging technologies in solar photovoltaics. Students who have already taken the course gained valuable hands-on experience and demonstrated increased motivation and interest in photovoltaic solar energy. They have expressed great satisfaction and achieved good academic results.

The results indicate that this didactic approach can be an excellent tool for teaching about renewable energies and encouraging innovation in solar device design.

Acknowledgements

Financial support from Universidad de Almería, under projects P_LANZ_2024/002 and UAL PID 24_25_1_43C is acknowledged. We thank Prof. Gázquez for his assistance with the charging capacitor method.

References:

[1] A.I. Maldonado-Valdivia, E.G. Galindo, M.J. Ariza, M.J. Garcia-Salinas, Solar Energy 91 (2013) 263-272. DOI: 10.1016/j.solener.2013.02.009

[2] M.J. García-Salinas, M.J. Ariza, Appl. Sci. 9 (2019) 2515. DOI:10.3390/app9122515

[3] M.J. Ariza-Camacho, M.J. García-Salinas, M. Pérez-García M. "Metodología docente para diseño, construcción y caracterización de células solares de colorante". XIX Congreso Ibérico y XV Congreso Iberoamericano de Energía Solar (CIES'2024), 2024.

[4] B. O'Regan, M. Grätzel, Nature 353 (1991), 737–740. DOI: 10.1038/353737a0

[5] S. Ito, T.N. Murakami, P.Comte, P. Liska, C. Grätzel, M.K. Nazeeruddin, M. Grätzel, Thin Solid Films 516 (2008), 4613–4619. DOI:10.1016/j.tsf.2007.05.090

[6] O. Mohiuddin, M. Obaidullah, C. Sabah, Opt. Quant. Electron 50 (2018), 377. DOI: 10.1007/s11082-018-1647-1

[7] https//w3.ual.es/grupodocente/labsolar

[8] Z. Chen, Y. Lin, L. Wu, S. Cheng, P. Lin, Energy Conversion and Management, 226 (2020) 113521. DOI: 10.1016/j.enconman.2020.113521

[9] C. Rodríguez-Martínez, *Experiencia de Fabricación de una célula fotovoltaica para la práctica docente.* Bachelor's Thesis in Mechanical Engineering Degree, Universidad de Almería (Spain), July 2025.

[10] D. A. Núñez-Osorio, *Desarrollo de un banco de recursos didácticos y simulaciones en HTML para la enseñanza y aprendizaje de curvas I-V de células fotovoltaicas obtenidas mediante la carga de un condensador.* Master's Thesis in Solar Energy, Universidad de Almería (Spain), January 2025.

[11] https://www.solaronix.com/materials/kits/ Solaronix. Available on May 2025.

[12] J. A. Gázquez-Parra, M. Fernández-Ros, N. Novas-Castellano, R. M. García-Salvador, IEEE Trans. Instrum. Meas. 64, 10 (2015) 2759-2768. DOI: 10.1109/TIM.2015.2420376

nicolas.otto@htw-berlin.de
nicolas.otto@helmholtz-berlin.de

OPTIMIZING INTERCONNECTION STRATEGIES FOR 2T PEROVSKITE-CIGSE TANDEM SOLAR MODULES: 3-STEP VS. 4-STEP LASER PATTERNING

Nicolas Otto[1,2], Christof Schultz[1], Guillermo Farias-Basulto[2], Wuai Zhang[3,4], Ayman Maqsood[2], Tadeus Ranisch[1], Yoko Schirmer[1], Jonas Preuschoff[1], Stefan Gall[4], Emil List-Kratochvil[3,4], Rutger Schlatmann[1,2], Bert Stegemann[1]

1. HTW Berlin - University of Applied Sciences, D-12459 Berlin, Germany
2. PVcomB, Helmholtz Zentrum Berlin für Materialien und Energie, D-12489 Berlin, Germany
3. Humboldt-Universität zu Berlin, Institut für Physik, Institut für Chemie und Center for the Science of Materials Berlin, D-12489 Berlin, Germany
4. Helmholtz-Zentrum Berlin für Materialien und Energie GmbH, D-14109 Berlin, Germany

MOTIVATION & BACKGROUND

- Perovskite and CIGSe: adjustable bandgaps → high-efficiency tandem cells
- Low-cost roll-to-roll processing on flexible substrates
- Record efficiencies of perovskite-CIGSe tandems demonstrated (2025) [1]
- Challenge: Simple module fabrication with minimal electrical and dead area losses requires adapted laser patterning [2]
- Key question: Can thin-film tandem modules be realized with only 3 patterning steps, reducing process complexity and costs?

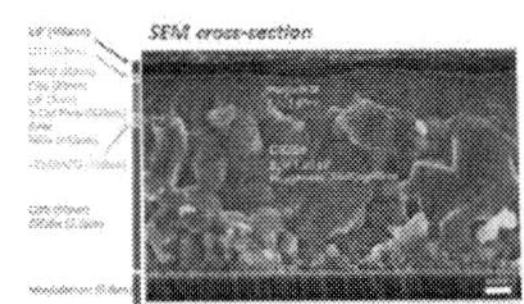

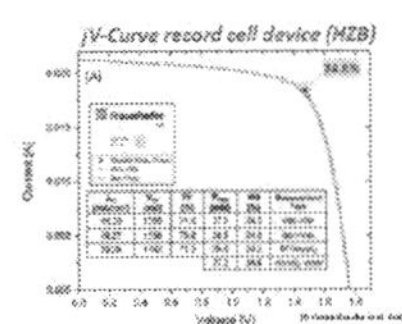

MINI-MODULE LAYOUT

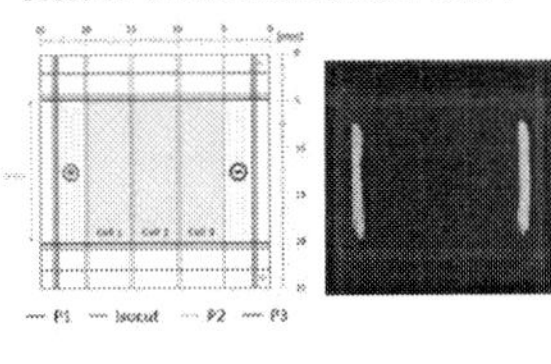

- Substrate size: 25x25 mm²
- Number of interconnected cells: 3
- Cell size: 5 mm x 15 mm
- GFF ~ 90 %

PROCESS DEVELOPMENT

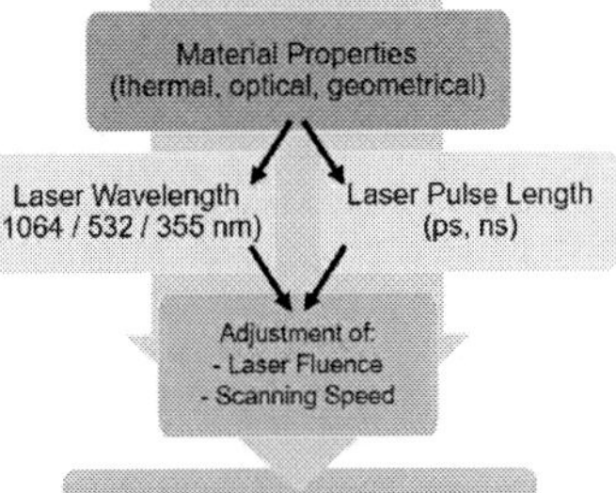

CLASSIC 3-STEP APPROACH

Principle of the 3-step interconnection (P1–P3)

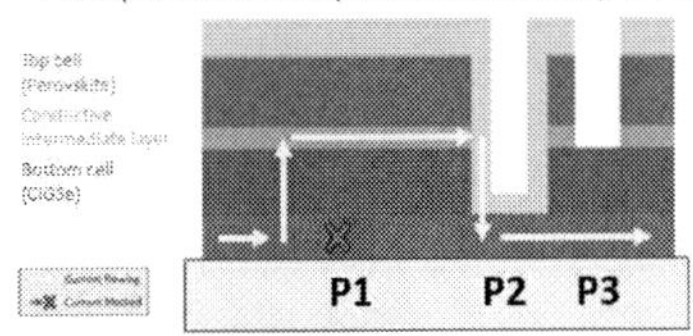

SEM cross-section at P1   jV curve

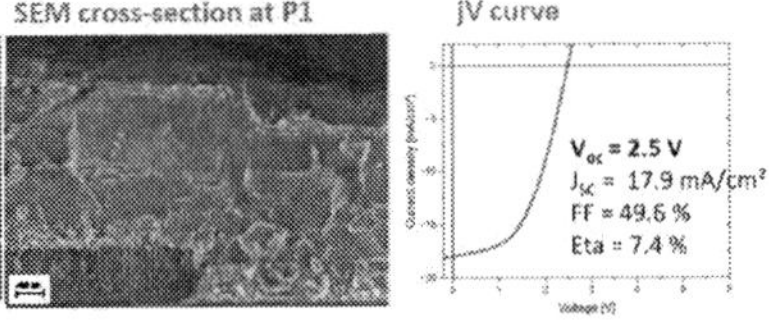

→ physical implementation/ structural details

→ proves voltage losses (reduced V_{oc})

Electroluminescence / Photoluminescence

- top cell PL image: clear signal
- top cell EL image: no signal
- bottom cell EL image: clear signal
- → visual evidence of the bypassing effect

→ alternative interconnection approach required

→ electrical separation of conductive inter-connection layer

ADDING THE *ISOCUT*

→ selective removal of the conductive interlayer

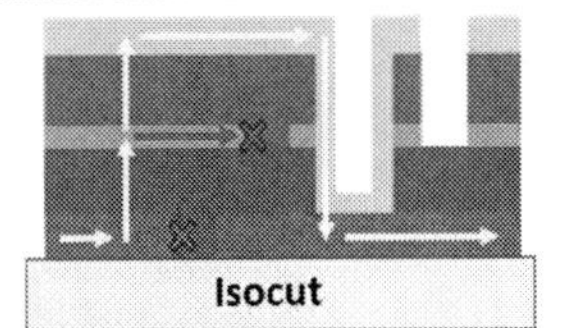

SEM cross-section at Isocut   jV curve

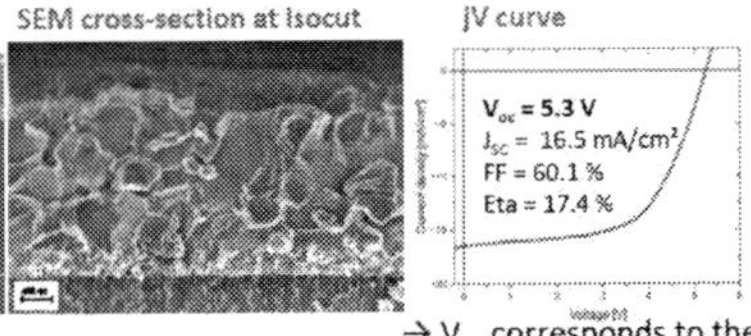

→ visual confirmation of the selective removal

→ V_{oc} corresponds to the expected value of three series-connected cells

Laser Scanning Microscopy / Photoluminescence

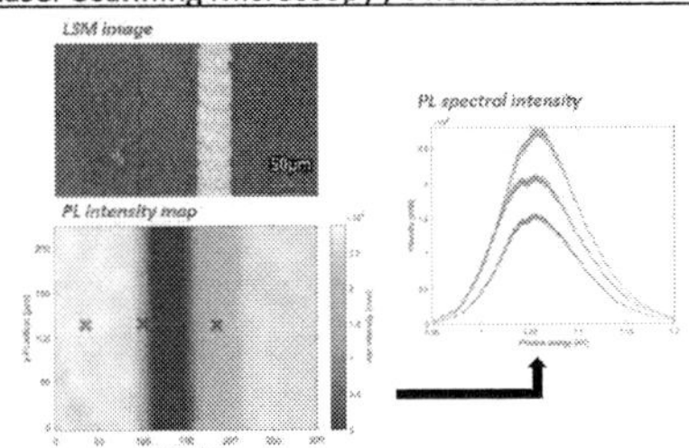

Near P1 scribe line → decrease in intensity, but no change in spectral shape
Within Isocut region → clear change in spectral profile (blue line) → local alteration of CIGSe absorber

→ Isocut step can overcome the voltage loss issue observed in the 3-step approach
→ increase of overall process complexity
→ inherent risk of unintended material modifications

BACK TO 3 STEPS?

→ combine P1 and Isocut into a single step → P1Iso

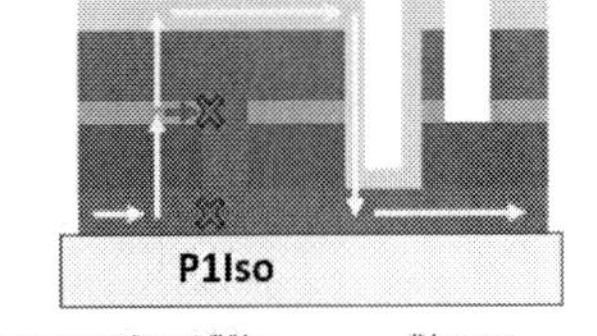

SEM cross-section at P1Iso   jV curve

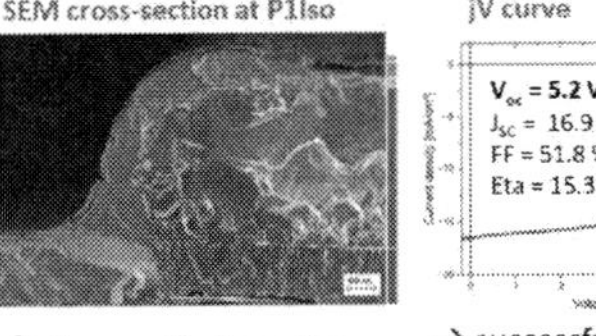

→ steep scribe line edge due to substrate-side patterning

→ successful series interconnection with performance close to the 4-step approach

Laser Scanning Microscopy / Photoluminescence

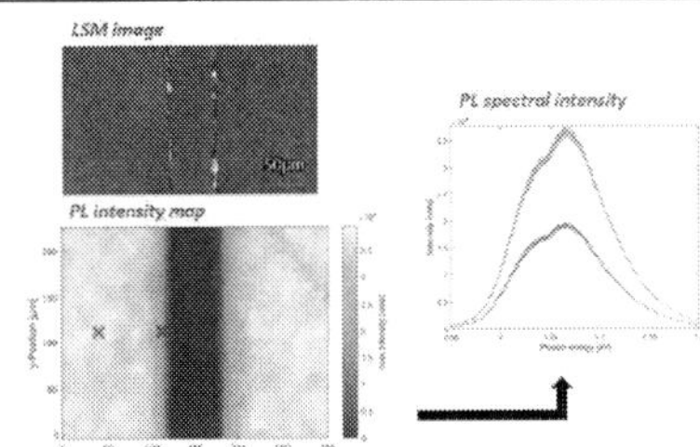

Reduced intensity near the P1 scribe line, but no spectral changes → CIGSe absorber composition remains unaffected by patterning through glass

→ promising compromise:
- simplifies processing
- preserves absorber quality
- ensures efficient series interconnection

- 3-step (P1 - P3): Causes bypassing of the perovskite top cell, leading to reduced V_{oc} and inferior jV characteristics.
- 4-step with Isocut: Prevents bypassing and provides excellent electrical performance. Trade-offs: higher process complexity and larger dead area
- P1Iso (P1 + Isocut combined): Separates the conductive intermediate layer while saving one step, simplifying fabrication and reducing the dead area. Electrical behavior is comparable to the 4-step approach, just slightly behind the best Isocut results.
- **Next step:** Evaluate 3-step patterning approach including the P1Iso on flexible substrates vs. the sequential 4-step process

[1] Farias-Basulto et al., submitted for publication
[2] C. Schultz et al., EPJ Photovoltaics, 2023, 14, 16

020101-001

Acknowledgement:
This research has received funding from the European Union Horizon Europe Energy program, project 101122288 — SolMates

Funded by the European Union

This presentation was selected by the Sc. Committee of the EU PVSEC 2025 for submission of a full paper to one of the EU PVSEC's collaborating peer-reviewed journals.

ELUCIDATING THE PROCESS OF ACCURATE SPECTRAL CALIBRATION FOR TANDEM I-V MEASUREMENT USING MULTI-LAMP LIGHT SOURCES

Antoine Bourgeois[1,2], Stella Hadiwidjaja[1], Zoltan Nicot-Senneville[1,3], Ye Jiayi[1], Choi Kwan Bum[1], Zhou Qilin[1], Hou Yi[1]

[1]Solar Energy Research Institute of Singapore, National University of Singapore (NUS), [2]Ecole Polytechnique, [3]Centrale Marseille

ABSTRACT: Reproducing the reference spectrum, AM1.5G, using solar simulators is essential for reporting the I-V performance of tandem solar cells. The International Electrotechnical Commission (IEC) presents the classification of solar simulators spectra in IEC 60904-9 and the spectral calibration for tandem devices in IEC 60904-1-1. However, implementation of these standards using multi-lamp light sources can be challenging.

This study presents a process for fulfilling both IEC standards using a multi-lamp light source with 21 tunable intensity channels of different peak wavelengths. A spectrum fitting method based on Gram-Schmidt orthonormalisation is introduced to approximate the AM1.5G spectrum from a known set of LED inputs, enabling forward modelling of the output spectrum. Non-linearity and spectral shift corrections ensure that the modelled spectrum remains accurate. A calibration process is presented to satisfy both solar simulator classification and the IEC-defined spectral mismatch factor and matching factor thresholds.

The method is validated on three perovskite–silicon tandem cells, all of which achieved | 1-M | < 0.05 and |1-Z | < 0.03 and for both sub-cells. This framework enables standard-compliant spectral simulation of AM1.5G for I-V of perovskite-based tandem devices.

Keywords: multi-source solar simulator; IEC 60904; tandem cell characterisation

1 DEADLINES AND DELIVERY

Perovskite-based tandem technologies are expected to become a commercial technology in the next 5-10 years [1][2]. With this momentum comes an increasing demand for accurate and reproducible characterisation of tandem devices. Among all characterisation metrics, the current–voltage (I–V) measurement under Standard Testing Conditions (STC) remains the most critical benchmark.

However, I–V measurements of tandem devices are sensitive to the spectral characteristics of the incident illuminated: the reference spectrum AM1.5G (E_{ref}). Discrepancy between E_{ref} and the laboratory-simulated spectrum (E_{sim}) distorts I-V results, affecting not only short-circuit current (I_{sc}), but also Fill Factor (FF) [3].

For reliable I–V measurements, E_{sim} must: 1) be a close replication of AM1.5G, 2) incite a similar tandem device response. These two conditions were formalised by standards issued by in IEC 60904-9 and 60904-1-1 [4] [5].

Laboratory simulated spectra can be generated by multi-lamp solar simulators, many of which feature 20, or more independently tunable (LED) lamps. The spectral irradiance of each lamp j can be defined as $E_j = \alpha_j e_j(\lambda)$ where α_j is its adjustable intensity and $e_j(\lambda)$ is its emission spectrum at full intensity. The total simulator spectrum is a superposition of all m lamps:

$$E_{\text{sim}}(\lambda) = \sum_{j=1}^{m} \alpha_j e_j(\lambda)$$

Multi-lamp simulators offer significant flexibility, allowing for precise control to fulfill the conditions set out in IEC 60904-1-1 and IEC 60904-0 [6]. However, the procedure delineating how to use multi-lamp light sources to fulfil these conditions is often overlooked [3]. Calibration for tandem devices of a solar simulator with light sources were discussed in several works although non proposed a non-iterative method [7] [8]. This study aims to build a non-iterative spectrum fitting and calibration process to target the requirements both IEC 60904-1-1 and IEC 60904-9 simultaneously, such that the process can be easily replicated by any multi-lamp solar simulator.

2 MATERIALS AND METHODS

2.1 Materials

The essential equipment for the proposed method includes: a multi-lamp solar simulator, a spectrometer and reference cells (RCs) matched to the spectral response of the tandem sub-cells. The required data are: the spectral response (SR) of each sub-cell of the tandem device under test (DUT) (IEC 60904-9) and E_{ref} = AM1.5G spectrum (IEC 60904-3).

2.2 Methods

2.2.1 Accounting for LED Non-Linearity

Lamps have a non-linear relationship between the input intensity command α_{in} and the actual optical output α_{out}, which was characterised. Polynomial functions were fitted to characterised data to model this behavior (Figure 1, $\alpha_{\text{out}} = P(\alpha_{\text{in}})$). This polynomial was inverted and integrated into the spectrum fitting algorithm to apply a correction $\alpha_{in} = P^{-1}(\alpha_{\text{out}})$, ensuring the achieved spectrum matched the intended spectrum based on the input commands.

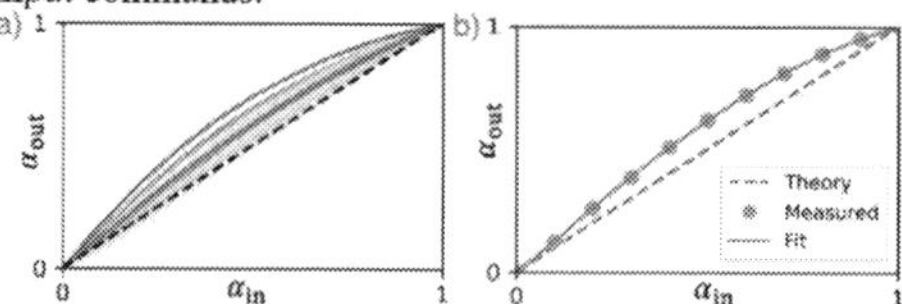

Figure 1: a) $\alpha_{\text{in}} e_j \neq \alpha_{\text{out}}$ for various lamps (shown in different colours). b) Interpolated α_{out} for lamp 19.

2.2.2 Spectrum Fitting using Orthonormal Basis Projection

A non-iterative spectral fitting method was developed to generate E_{sim}. E_{ref} is projected onto an orthonormal basis generated from e_j using the Gram-Schmidt process (Figure 2). This provided a fast, non-iterative estimate for α_j. This method can be used independently or as a stable first-guess for other iterative optimisation routines.

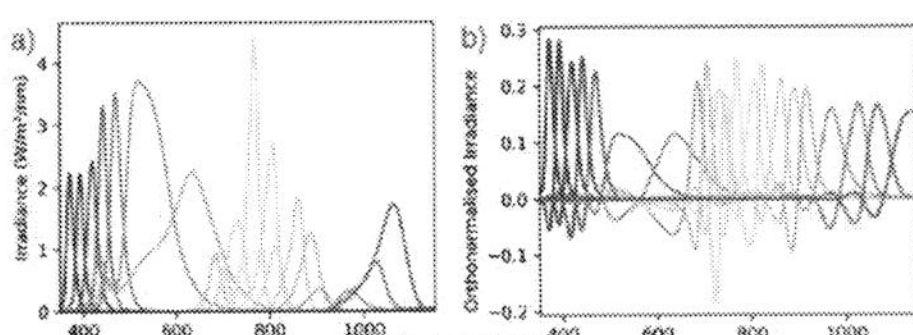

Figure 2: a) lamp spectra e_j b) basis by Gram-Schmidt orthonormalisation.

2.2.3 Calibration for Tandem Device Measurement

The calibration procedure to meet IEC 60904-1-1 requirements for tandem cells follows an adapted version of the calibration method proposed in [9], hereby referred to as Meusel's method. The m lamps are split into two virtual light sources (Figure 3), which are calibrated by Meusel's method. This results in multiple spectra which are then chosen according to the flowchart in Figure 4. The final calibrated spectrum is validated by measuring the I_{sc} of the RCs under E_{sim} to calculate Z. A successful calibration is achieved when $|1 - Z_{top,bot}| < 0.03$.

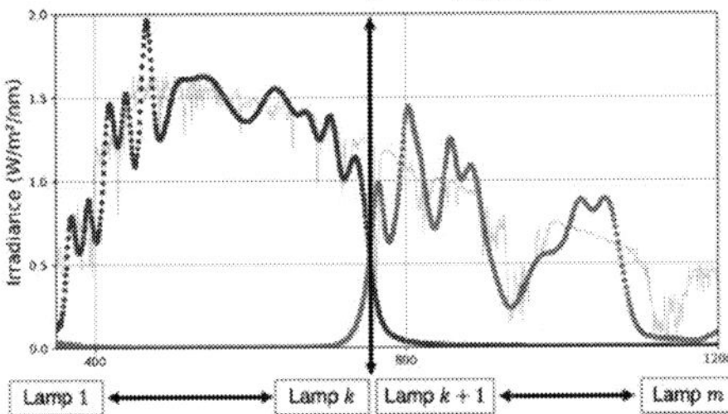

Figure 3. Example of splitting E_{sim} (at lamp $k = 16$).

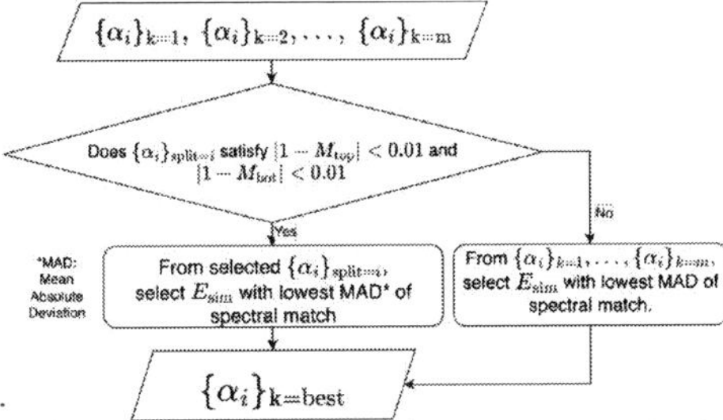

Figure 4. Decision flowchart for selecting the optimal spectrum.

3 RESULTS

The calibration method was tested on three perovskite-silicon tandem solar cells, referred to as Cell A, B and C. The resultant calibrated spectrum of each cell is shown in Figure 5. The uncalibrated calibrated spectra's M and Z are shown in Table 1.

Table I. Calibrated and Uncalibrated Spectra M, Z.

	Cell	$\|1 - Z_{top}\|$	$\|1 - Z_{bot}\|$	$\|1 - M_{bot}\|$	$\|1 - M_{bot}\|$
Uncali brated	A	0.015	0.032	0.002	0.009
	B	0.016	0.027	0.004	0.004
	C	0.017	0.060	0.004	0.035
Calibra ted.	A	0.010	0.001	0.005	0.006
	B	0.006	0.005	0.005	0.004
	C	0.013	0.007	0.005	0.016

For Cell A and B, the SR of the cells and the RCs were well-matched, achieving $|1 - M_{top,bot}| < 0.01$. For Cell C, whilst the top cell was well matched ($|1 - M_{top}| < 0.01$), the bottom cell's SR compared to RC_{bot} differed, resulting in a higher mismatch, but within the $|1 - M_{bot}| < 0.05$ threshold. For each tandem solar cell, a spectrum fulfilling the criterion of $|1 - Z_{top,bot}| < 0.03$ was achieved.

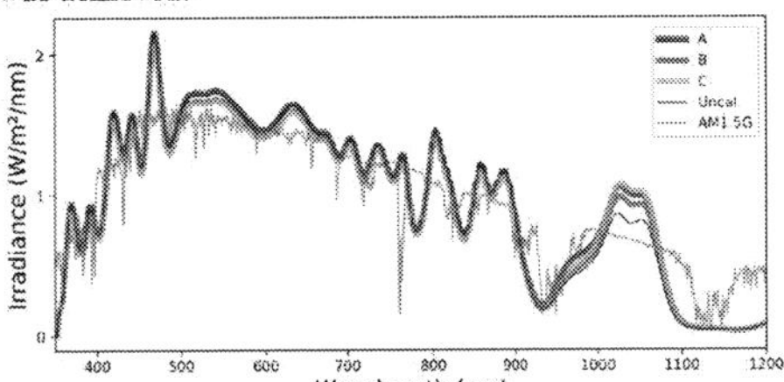

Figure 5. Calibrated spectrum of Tandem Cell A, B, C.

4 CONCLUSION

We developed a method to fit and calibrate the spectrum of a multi-lamp solar simulator for accurate tandem cell measurement. After accounting for lamp non-linearity through polynomial interpolation, we use the Gram-Schmidt orthonormalisation process to provide a stable fit to the AM1.5G spectrum. The calibration procedure then adapts the method from [9] for multi-lamp systems by virtually splitting the lamps into two and choosing the best spectrum from the resultant spectra. Validation on perovskite-silicon tandems achieved M within 1±5% and Z within 1±3%, fulfilling the IEC 60904-1-1 requirements.

5 ACKNOWLEDGEMENTS

SERIS is a research institute at the National University of Singapore (NUS). SERIS is supported by NUS, the National Research Foundation Singapore (NRF), the Energy Market Authority of Singapore (EMA) and the Singapore Economic Development Board (EDB). The author AB acknowledges financial support from EDF in the framework of the research and teaching Chair «Sustainable energies » at Ecole Polytechnique.

6 REFERENCES

[1] ITRPV, "International Technology Roadmap for Photovoltaics (ITRPV)," ITRPV, VDMA, 2024.
[2] H. Li and W. Zhang, Chemical Reviews, vol. 120, no. 18, pp. 9835-9950, 2020.
[3] S. Tao et al., Performance? A Calibration Lab's Perspective," Solar RRL, vol. 6, no. 12, p. 2200800, 2022.
[4] IEC, IEC60904-9: Classification of solar simulator characteristics, 2020.
[5] IEC, IEC60904-1-1: Measurement of current-voltage characteristics of multi-junction photovoltaic (PV) devices, 2020.
[6] M. Turek, et al., Solar Energy Materials and Solar Cells, vol. 194, pp. 142-147, 2019.
[7] D. Chojnak, et al., Silicon PV 2022, Konstanz, Germany, 2023.
[8] S. K. Reichmuth, et al., IEEE 46th Photovoltaic Specialists Conference (PVSC), Chicago, 2019.
[9] M. Meusel, et al., Progress in Photovoltaics: Research and Applications, vol. 10, no. 4, pp. 243-255, 2002.

Elucidating the Process of Accurate Spectral Calibration for Tandem I-V Measurement using Multi-Lamp Solar Simulators

Antoine BOURGEOIS[1,2], Stella HADIWIDJAJA[1], Zoltan NICOT-SENNEVILLE[1,3],
YE Jiayi[1], CHOI Kwan Bum[1], ZHOU Qilin[1], HOU Yi[1]
[1]Solar Energy Research Institute of Singapore, National University of Singapore
[2]École Polytechnique, [3]Centrale Méditerranée

Motivation & Introduction

- A 'mismatched' AM1.5G spectrum can mislead the I-V of a 2-terminal tandem solar cell due to current mismatch [1].
- We propose a non-iterative method to achieve an accurate spectrum using multi-lamp solar simulators.

- For tandem I-V to be accurate, the AM1.5G spectrum requires:
  - **Spectrum Fitting** to achieve Spectral Match "A" (IEC 60904-9).
  - **Calibration** for adequate 'matching factors (Z)' and 'mismatch factors (M)' (IEC 60904-1-1).

Spectrum Fitting

Multi-lamp solar simulators

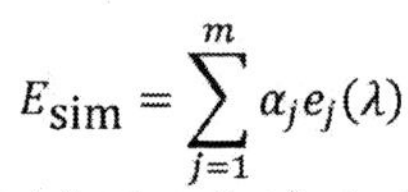

$$E_{sim} = \sum_{j=1}^{m} \alpha_j e_j(\lambda)$$

- E_{sim} : Spectral irradiance
- α_j : Intensity of Lamp j
- $e_j(\lambda)$: Spectrum of Lamp
- m : Number of lamps

Eq 1: Spectrum of a solar simulator.

- Spectrum fitting is done by finding α such that $E_{ref} = E_{sim}$.

Accounting for lamp non-linearity

- Lamps do not scale linearly (Fig. 1a).
- Polynomial interpolation $\alpha_{out} = P(\alpha_{in})$ accounts for non-linearity (Fig. 1b, Fit) and allows bi-directional control, i.e. $\alpha_{in} = P^{-1}(\alpha_{out})$.

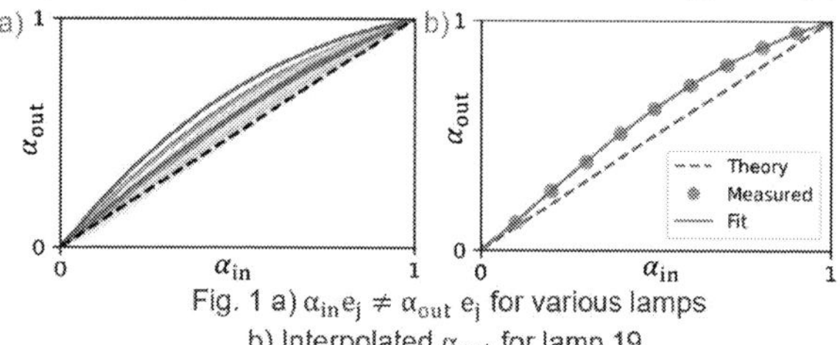

Fig. 1 a) $\alpha_{in}e_j \neq \alpha_{out} e_j$ for various lamps
b) Interpolated α_{out} for lamp 19.

Fitting through Gram-Schmidt Orthonormalisation.

- Using the Gram-Schmidt orthonormalisation algorithm [2], we generate a basis (Fig. 2b) from the measured spectra α (Fig. 2a).
- Project E_{ref} = AM1.5G on the orthonormal basis to find $\{\alpha\}$.

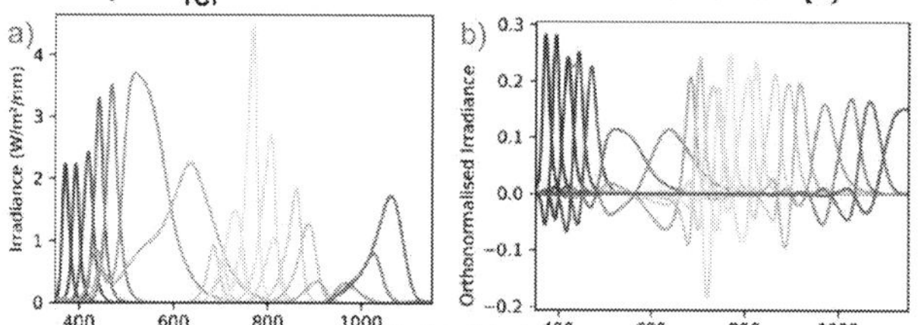

Fig 2. a) lamp spectra b) basis by Gram-Schmidt orthonormalisation.

Results

- Method validated on 3 tandem solar cells (Cell A,B,C, Fig. 5).

☑ Good spectral match   ☑ $|1 - Z| < 0.03$ ☑ $|1 - M| < 0.05$

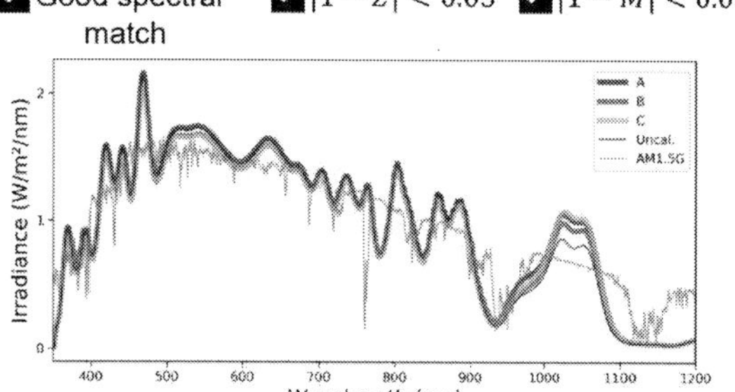

Fig. 5) Calibrated spectrum of Tandem Cell A, B, C.

Calibration

$$M = \frac{\int_\lambda E_{sim}\,SR_{DUT}\,d\lambda \int_\lambda E_{ref}\,SR_{RC}\,d\lambda}{\int_\lambda E_{ref}\,SR_{DUT}\,d\lambda \int_\lambda E_{sim}\,SR_{RC}\,d\lambda} \qquad Z = \frac{I_{RC}^{sim}}{I_{RC}^{ref}M}$$

Eq 2. M considers discrepancies of the spectral response (SR) of the reference cells (RC), SR of the device under test (DUT), E_{ref} and E_{sim}. Eq 3. Z represents the spectral accuracy of the measurement.

- *Meusel et al.* [2] calibrates $m = 2$ lamps, solving for $\{\alpha\}$ by the equations of photo-currents of two-junctions.
- With $m > 2$, but still only two junctions, we 'split' m into 2, and apply Meusel's method (Fig. 3).
- The best spectrum is chosen by assessing the spectral match and mismatch factor M (Eq. 2, Fig. 4).
- Z is measured using two reference cells (Eq. 3).

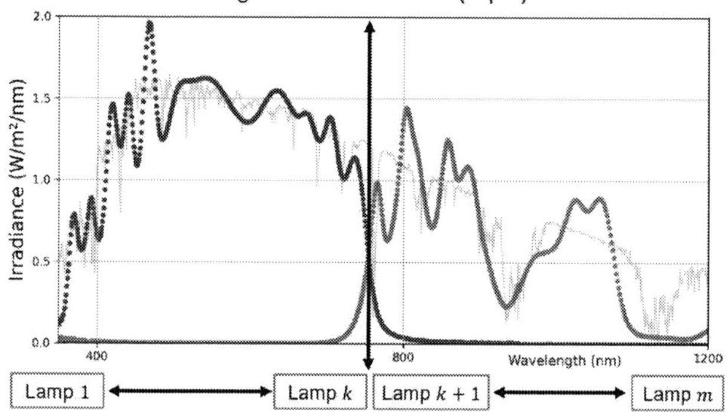

Fig. 3) Example of splitting E_{sim} (at lamp $k = 16$).

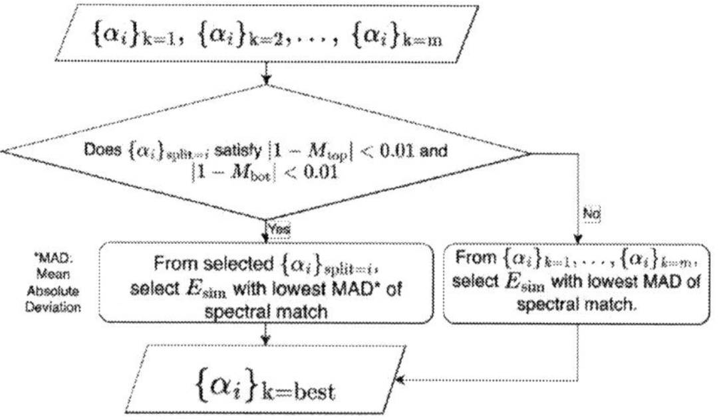

Fig. 4) Decision flowchart for selecting the optimal spectrum.

Conclusion and Discussion

- IEC-compliant spectrum is achieved through fitting and calibration.
- Calibration depends on the spectral compatibility of the available reference cells, the number of lamps and their spectra.
- Method can be extended to multiple junctions.

References
1. Song et al., 2022. Solar RRL, 6(12):2200800
2. Cheney & Kincaid, 2009. Linear Algebra, ISBN 978-0-7637-5020-6.
3. Meusel et al., 2002. Prog Photovolt Res Appl, 10(4):243–255

SERIS is a research institute at the National University of Singapore (NUS). SERIS is supported by NUS, the National Research Foundation Singapore (NRF), the Energy Market Authority of Singapore (EMA) and the Singapore Economic Development Board (EDB).

ACHIEVING IMPROVED LIGHT TRAPPING IN CIGS/PEROVSKITE SOLAR CELLS WITH GRATING-ENHANCED BILAYER HETEROJUNCTIONS: OPTICAL-ELECTRICAL STUDY

Mohammad Hossein Mohammadi*, Narendra Bandaru, Rasmus Schmidt Davidsen
Department of Electrical and Computer Engineering, Aarhus University, Denmark

ABSTRACT: This work investigates a cost-effective and less toxic alternative solar cell design: a CIGS/perovskite bilayer heterojunction integrated with photonic nanostructures. The bilayer structure reduces thermalization losses by combining a high-bandgap perovskite ($CH_3NH_3PbI_3$, 1.55 eV) top cell with a lower-bandgap CIGS (1.2 eV) bottom cell, enabling efficient spectrum utilization. CIGS is selected over silicon due to its direct bandgap, allowing reduced absorber thickness, lower material use, and potentially lower costs. The bilayer achieved a short-circuit current density of 25.98 mA/cm^2 and a power conversion efficiency (PCE) of 22.98%, representing a 15% improvement over single-junction perovskite cells. Further enhancement is achieved with convex grating light-trapping structures, raising the simulated PCE to 25.54%. Device performance was analyzed through coupled optical and electrical modeling using the finite element method in COMSOL Multiphysics, highlighting the potential of bilayer heterojunctions with photonic gratings for high-efficiency, scalable photovoltaics.
Keywords: CIGS/perovskite solar cell, Light trapping (LT), Photonic-nanostructure, Grating structure, COMSOL

1 INTRODUCTION

The rapid decline in the levelized cost of photovoltaics (PV) has driven global installed capacity from less than 50 GW in 2010 to over 2000 GW by 2025 [1]. To sustain this growth, research is increasingly focused on new materials and advanced light-management strategies, addressing the limited absorption of ultra-thin active layers used in flexible, cost-effective devices. Organic–inorganic hybrid perovskite solar cells (PSCs) have reached efficiencies up to 26% [2], owing to their direct bandgap, long carrier diffusion lengths, and high optical absorption [3]. PSCs are fabricated in mesoporous, dye-sensitized, HTL-/ETL-free, and planar (p–i–n, n–i–p) configurations [4], but single-junction devices are limited by the Shockley–Queisser efficiency threshold [5].

Tandem architectures are a promising pathway to surpass this limit by combining wide- and narrow-bandgap absorbers. Notable examples include perovskite/silicon [6], perovskite/CIGS [7], and all-perovskite tandems [8], with reported efficiencies above 30% in advanced configurations [9]. Among these, CIGS/perovskite tandems stand out due to tunable bandgaps, compatibility as thin-film technologies, and suitability for flexible devices. Record efficiencies of 24.6 (2T) and 29.36% (4T) have been reported. However, planar devices still suffer from reflection losses, necessitating optical management strategies.

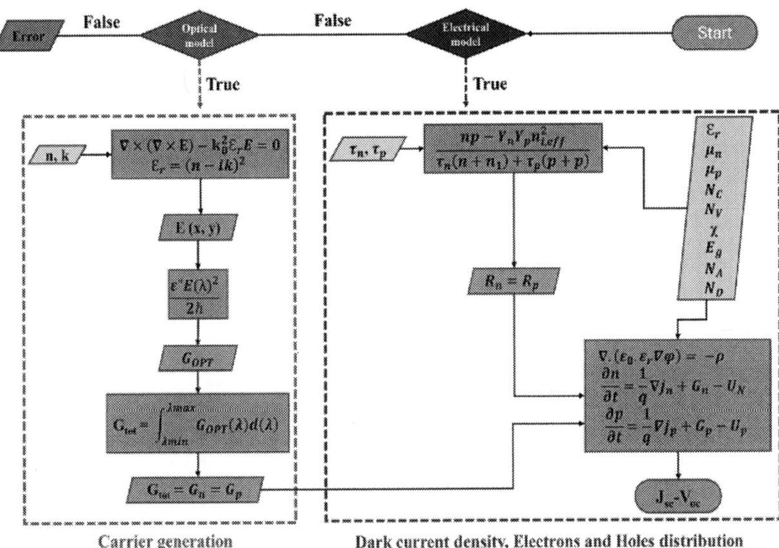

Fig. 1. The algorithm involves solving the electrical and optical models. In the optical part, k_0 denotes the free-space wave number, ε'' represents the imaginary component of the permittivity, and $\hbar$ is the reduced Planck constant. Within the electrical part, ρ is the charge density, φ is the electrostatic potential, ε_0 is the vacuum permittivity, Y_p and Y_n correspond to the hole and electron degeneracy factors, respectively.

Table 1. Electrical parameters required for PSC.

Parameter	TiO$_2$	CH$_3$NH$_3$PbI$_3$	CIGS	CuSCN
ε_r	9	6.5	13.6	9
N_C (cm^{-3})	1.00×10^{19}	1.66×10^{19}	2.2×10^{18}	2.5×10^{18}
N_V (cm^{-3})	1.00×10^{19}	5.41×10^{19}	1.9×10^{18}	1.8×10^{18}
μ_n/μ_p (cm^2/V)	20/10	50/50	100/25	$2.00\times10^{-4}/2.00\times10^{-4}$
χ (eV)	4.00	3.93	4.5	2.1
E_g (eV)	3.2	1.55	1.2	3.4
N_A (cm^{-3})	-	5.00×10^{13}	1.00×10^{16}	1.00×10^{17}
N_D (cm^{-3})	5.00×10^{18}	-	-	-
τ_n/τ_p (ns)	5/2	8/8	25/25	5/5

Light-trapping (LT) nanostructures—such as nanocones, gratings, and plasmonic nanoparticles—enhance scattering, reduce reflection, and extend the optical path length. These designs mitigate the trade-off between absorption and electrical performance, improve carrier collection, and reduce material consumption, thereby addressing stability and toxicity concerns in perovskite systems. Recent studies combining bilayer heterojunctions with nanophotonic designs, such as nano-prisms or convex gratings, have achieved efficiency gains exceeding 30% compared to planar references [10-12].

In this work, a planar PSC was simulated as a baseline, yielding 19.58% efficiency. Introducing a 500 nm CIGS layer increased PCE to 22.98%. Further enhancement was achieved by implementing patterned convex gratings at all interfaces, which improved light absorption, reduced reflection, and optimized field distribution, leading to significant improvements in device performance.

2 THEORY

In this study, two complementary models were employed to determine the optoelectronic design parameters: an optical model to describe light behavior within the device and an electrical model to evaluate charge transport and collection. The optical model was based on solving the Helmholtz equation (Fig. 1), yielding the electric field (E), from which the absorbed optical power and carrier generation rate were derived. The electron (G_n) and hole (G_p) generation rates were obtained by integrating the optical generation rate (G_{opt}) over a unit volume, using the real and imaginary components of the refractive index (n, k) from established literature sources

[50–58]. The electric field distribution and vector field plots were computed using the frequency-domain electromagnetic wave (EWFD) interface in COMSOL Multiphysics. Maxwell's equations were solved in the frequency domain, accounting for the complex refractive indices of each layer. A 2D bilayer heterojunction model, with and without light-trapping (LT) gratings, was analyzed under periodic boundary conditions and perfectly matched layers (PML) to minimize reflection artifacts. Incident plane waves spanning 300–1200 nm (10 nm steps) were simulated to evaluate field behavior across the visible and near-infrared spectrum.

The electrical model solved Poisson's equation together with the electron–hole continuity equations, incorporating recombination rates for electrons (R_n) and holes (R_p). Input parameters included relative permittivity (ε_r), carrier mobilities (μ_n, μ_p), conduction and valence band densities of states, electron affinity (χ), doping concentrations, and Shockley–Read–Hall (SRH) lifetimes (τ_n, τ_p), as listed in Table 1. Breakdown voltage was determined under dark conditions ($G_n = G_p = 0$) using the SRH recombination model. The optical and electrical models were coupled to calculate current density: photons absorbed within the layers generated electron–hole pairs, while increased applied voltage enhanced recombination. Continuity equations including generation and recombination terms were then used to extract the hole and electron current densities (J_p, J_n).

3 RESULTS AND DISSCUSIONS

To optimize spectrum utilization, the bilayer device employs CH$_3$NH$_3$PbI$_3$ perovskite (1.55 eV) as the top

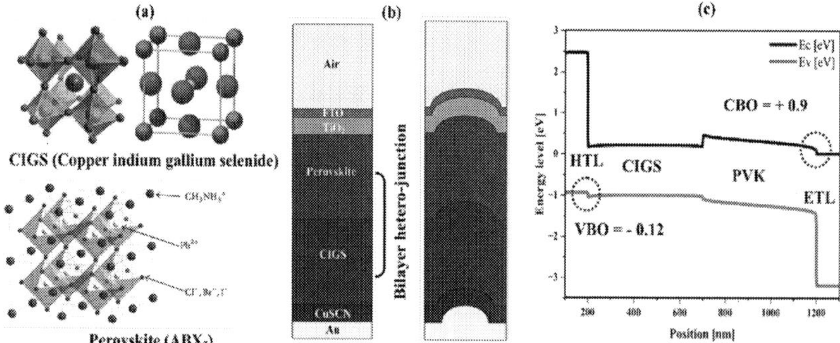

Fig. 2. Schematic representations of: (a) the CIGS crystal structure and the perovskite crystal structure, (b) the bilayer heterojunction configuration (c) the corresponding energy band diagram of the bilayer structure. Crystal structure drawings in (a) are borrowed from [13] with permission.

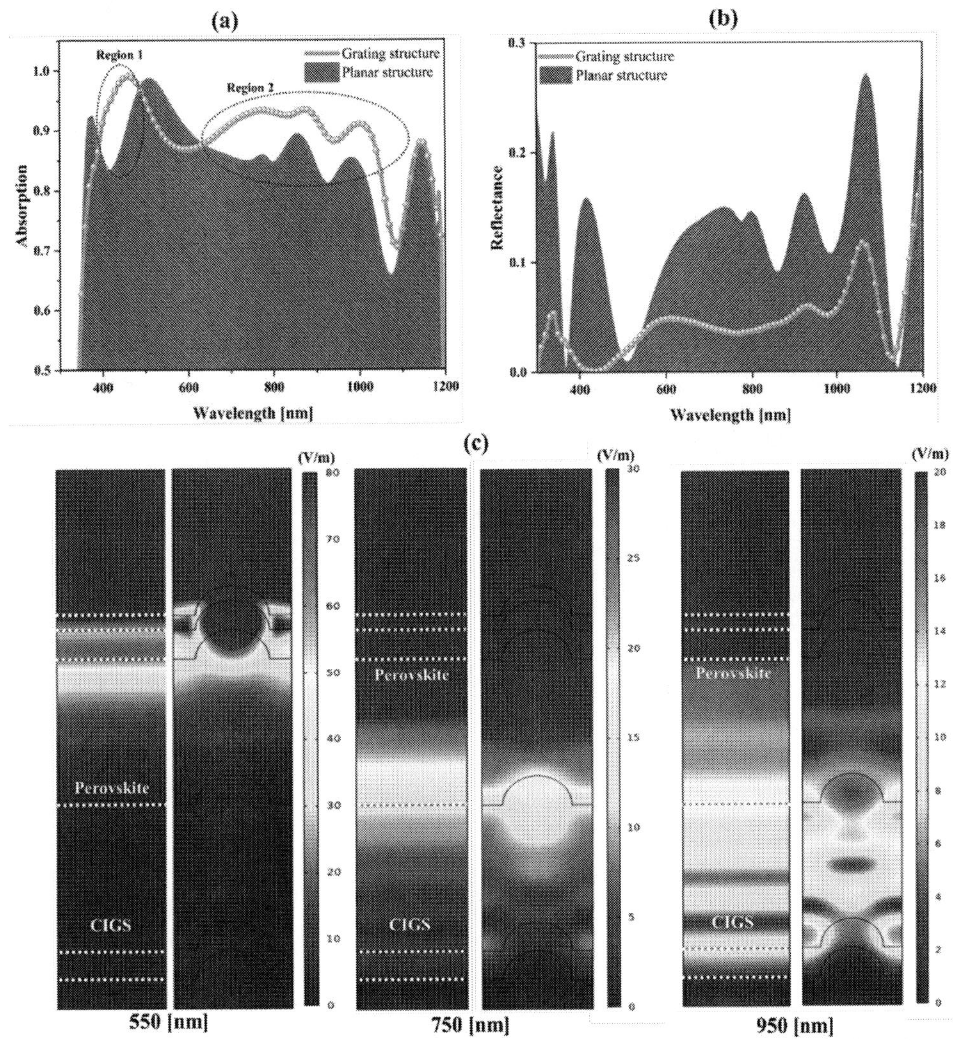

Fig. 3. Diagram showing (a) the absorption spectrum and (b) the reflection rate as functions of wavelength for both planar and LT structures. Electric field distributions across all PSC layers for (c) the planar and LT structure.

absorber for high-energy photons and CIGS (1.2 eV) as the bottom absorber for low-energy photons (Fig. 2a) [68]. An n–i–p configuration was adopted, offering improved V_{oc}, light absorption, and charge separation [13]. The final stack (Fig. 2b) consists of FTO/TiO$_2$/CH$_3$NH$_3$PbI$_3$/CIGS/CuSCN/Au, with energy-band alignment shown in Fig. 2c. A small negative valence-band offset at CuSCN/CIGS ($\approx$ –0.12 eV) promotes hole extraction, while a slightly positive conduction-band offset at TiO$_2$/perovskite ($\approx$ +0.9 eV) enhances electron collection. FTO serves as the transparent front electrode, and Au as the back contact due to their conductivity and stability.

This section analyzes the simulation results of the light-trapping (LT) structure. Figure 3a shows that converting the planar design into an LT configuration enhances absorption in both active layers, particularly in the 400–500 nm and 650–1100 nm regions. A reduction in absorption between 500–650 nm is observed, caused by strong optical confinement in the TiO$_2$ layer due to close grating spacing, which limits transmission into the perovskite absorber. Thus, while gratings improve broadband absorption, over-trapping can be counterproductive. Using gratings with a radius and height of 100 nm promoted effective confinement, though further optimization is required to maximize spectral performance.

The LT design also reduces reflection, as shown in Fig. 3b, confirming that light penetrates more efficiently into the active layers and is retained within them. Electric field distributions (Fig. 3c) illustrate this effect: at 550 nm, the LT structure channels more light into the perovskite compared to the planar case; at 750 nm, stronger coupling is observed in both perovskite and CIGS layers; and at 950 nm, field localization deep in the CIGS demonstrates enhanced infrared absorption. These features mitigate parasitic losses while improving confinement on both sides of the grating.

Table 2. Electrical parameters for CIGS/perovskite incorporating LT structure comparing to planar structure.

Structure	J_{sc} (mA/cm^2)	V_{oc} (V)	FF (%)	PCE (%)
Planar	25.98	1.012	87.37	22.98
LT	27.02	1.012	87.18	23.85

Coupling the optical and electrical models confirmed these gains: the higher optical generation (G_{opt}) in the LT design increased J_{sc} from 25.98 to 27.02 mA/cm^2, improving PCE by ~3.8% relative to the planar device (Table 2). This demonstrates that incorporating LT gratings into CIGS/perovskite bilayer solar cells can significantly enhance performance by reducing reflection and boosting carrier generation. A parametric study was conducted to evaluate the impact of nanostructure dimensions on photovoltaic performance by varying the height (h) and radius (r) of the convex gratings. The heatmaps in Fig. 4b reveal that J_sc and PCE are highly sensitive to grating height, with optimal results obtained for taller features (h > 140 nm) combined with smaller radii (r ≈ 40–60 nm). The best performance was achieved at h = 140 nm and r = 60 nm, yielding J_sc = 28.85 mA/cm^2, V_oc = 1.011 V, FF = 87.45%, and PCE = 25.54%. This represents a significant enhancement driven by improved light trapping, extended optical path lengths, and more efficient carrier extraction.

Two regimes of optical behavior were identified. Wider gratings (large r) promote initial absorption by allowing more light transmission into the device, while narrower gratings (small r) enhance confinement and internal scattering, leading to longer optical paths and stronger absorption. Table 3 confirms that the optimized geometry provides a ~7% relative increase in PCE compared to the non-optimized grating and a substantial improvement over the planar device. These findings highlight the effectiveness of precision nanostructure tuning for maximizing solar cell efficiency.

4 CONCLUSION

This work presents a performance-enhanced design for CIGS/perovskite solar cells by combining a bilayer heterojunction architecture with grating-assisted light trapping. Finite-element simulations (COMSOL Multiphysics) demonstrated the effectiveness of pairing a high-bandgap perovskite top absorber with a low-bandgap CIGS bottom absorber in a planar n–i–p stack, enabling complementary spectral absorption and improved J_sc and PCE.

Introducing a convex periodic grating further boosted performance by reducing reflection losses and extending optical path lengths through photon confinement and constructive interference. This nanophotonic modification increased PCE from 22.98% (planar bilayer) to 25.54% (optimized grating), representing an ~11% relative gain. Importantly, the nanostructured device maintained its advantage under realistic fabrication constraints, highlighting both robustness and manufacturability.

Overall, this study underscores the promise of light-trapping strategies for advancing thin-film photovoltaics. The proposed design offers a scalable, cost-effective pathway toward high-efficiency, lightweight, and flexible solar cells, providing a strong basis for future experimental validation and commercialization of nanostructured CIGS/perovskite devices.

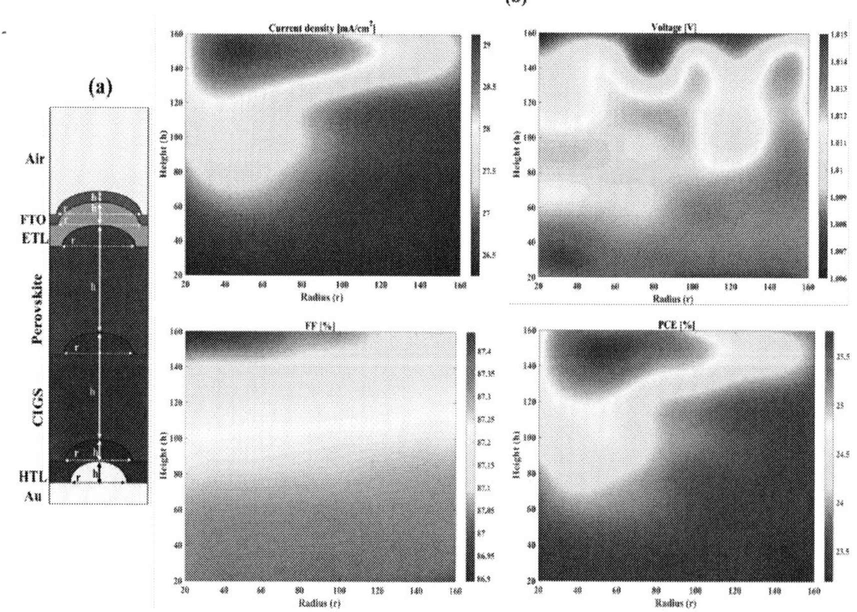

Fig. 4. Schematic (a) cross-section and (b) performance contour maps of a nanostructured CIGS/perovskite solar cell with embedded convex grating structures.

Table 3. Electrical parameters for CIGS/perovskite incorporating optimized grating structure comparing to planar and non-optimized structure.

Structure	J_{sc} (mA/cm^2)	V_{oc} (V)	FF (%)	PCE (%)
Planar	25.98	1.012	87.37	22.98
Non-optimized structure	27.02	1.012	87.18	23.85
Optimized structure	28.85	1.011	87.45	25.54

5 ACKNOLOWDGNENT

This research is financially supported by the CuSun project, funded by the Energy Technology Development and Demonstration Program (EUDP) in Denmark, under grant number 640231-510356.

6 COMPETING INTREST

The authors declare no competing interests.

7 REFERENCES

[1] L. Marroyo and E. L. Pigueiras, "Module Temperature Dispersion Within a Large PV Array: Observations at the Amareleja PV Plant," 2025.

[2] J. Tao *et al.*, "Suppressing non-radiative recombination for efficient and stable perovskite solar cells," *Energy & Environmental Science*, vol. 18, no. 2, pp. 509-544, 2025.

[3] J.-P. Correa-Baena *et al.*, "Promises and challenges of perovskite solar cells," *Science*, vol. 358, no. 6364, pp. 739-744, 2017.

[4] Y. Dai, X. Ge, B. Shi, P. Wang, Y. Zhao, and X. Zhang, "Enhancing Ultraviolet Stability and Performance of Wide Bandgap Perovskite Solar Cells Through Ultraviolet Light-Absorbing Passivator," *Small Methods*, vol. 9, no. 1, p. 2301793, 2025.

[5] J. Li, K. Wang, J. Liu, Y. Ye, and S. Liu, "Union of Perovskite and Silicon: Overcoming Electrical Losses for Surpassing Shockley–Queisser Limit," *Advanced Energy Materials*, p. 2500114.

[6] C. Kan *et al.*, "Efficient and stable perovskite-silicon tandem solar cells with copper thiocyanate-embedded perovskite on textured silicon," *Nature Photonics*, vol. 19, no. 1, pp. 63-70, 2025.

[7] L. Zeng, L. Tang, Z. Luo, J. Gong, J. Li, and X. Xiao, "A review of perovskite/copper indium gallium selenide tandem solar cells," *Solar RRL*, vol. 8, no. 21, p. 2301059, 2024.

[8] Z. Liu *et al.*, "All-perovskite tandem solar cells achieving> 29% efficiency with improved (100) orientation in wide-bandgap perovskites," *Nature Materials*, pp. 1-8, 2025.

[9] A. Abbasiyan and S. Golmohammadi, "Back contact optimization of both sub-cells in bifacial perovskite/silicon tandem solar cell," *Renewable Energy*, vol. 242, p. 122402, 2025.

[10] M. He *et al.*, "Enhancing Flexible Perovskite Photovoltaic Cells and Modules Through Light-Trapping and Light-Shifting Strategies," *Small Methods*, p. 2401954, 2025.

[11] N. Solhtalab, M. H. Mohammadi, M. Eskandari, and D. Fathi, "Efficiency improvement of half-tandem CIGS/perovskite solar cell by designing nano-prism nanostructure as the controllable light trapping," *Energy Reports*, vol. 8, pp. 1298-1308, 2022.

[12] M. H. Mohammadi, M. Eskandari, and D. Fathi, "Design of optimized photonic-structure and analysis of adding a SiO2 layer on the parallel CH3NH3PbI3/CH3NH3SnI3 perovskite solar cells," *Scientific Reports*, vol. 13, no. 1, p. 15905, 2023.

[13] M. W. Bouabdelli, F. Rogti, M. Maache, and A. Rabehi, "Performance enhancement of CIGS thin-film solar cell," *Optik*, vol. 216, p. 164948, 2020.

Achieving Superior Light Trapping in Perovskite/CIGS Solar Cells with Grating-Enhanced Bilayer Heterojunctions

42nd European Photovoltaic Solar Energy Conference and Exhibition

Mohammad Hossein Mohammadi*, Narendra Bandaru, Rasmus Schmidt Davidsen

Department of Electrical and Computer Engineering, Aarhus University, Denmark

Department of Electrical and Computer Engineering

2CV.3.22-304

Abstract

❖ A CIGS/perovskite bilayer heterojunction paired with convex periodic gratings offers a lower-cost, robust, and lower-toxicity route to higher performance than many alternative architectures.

❖ Complementary bandgaps 1.55 eV perovskite top absorber for shorter wavelengths and 1.2 eV CIGS bottom absorber for near-infrared—expand spectral harvesting, cut thermalization losses, and boost current.

❖ FEM simulations in COMSOL with coupled optical–electrical models show that grating-assisted light trapping reduces reflection, lengthens optical paths, and improves carrier collection.

❖ Performance improves from J_{sc} = 25.98 mA cm^{-2}, PCE = 22.98% (bilayer planar) to PCE = 25.54% with gratings, an ≈11% relative gain and ~15% above a single-junction perovskite baseline—supporting scalable, flexible thin-film PV.

Introduction

❖ Falling PV costs drove global capacity from <50 GW (2010) to >2000 GW (2025), pushing research toward thin, flexible absorbers and advanced light management to overcome limited optical absorption.

❖ Perovskites combine direct bandgaps, long diffusion lengths, and strong absorption (single-junction PCE ≈ 26%), but are SQ-limited and miss much of the 700–2500 nm irradiance.

❖ Tandems address this via complementary bandgaps; CIGS/perovskite is attractive for thin-film, flexible devices, with reported records around 24.6% (2T) and 29.36% (4T) and prior studies showing texture-enabled current matching.

❖ Light-trapping photonic structures (e.g., gratings, textures, nanocones, plasmonic features) reduce reflection and extend optical paths, boosting absorption and often aiding carrier transport—though precise, scalable patterning is a fabrication challenge.

Theory

Modeling Framework

➤ Optical model: Helmholtz equation solved for light absorption and carrier generation across 300–1200 nm.

➤ Electrical model: Poisson and continuity equations solved for charge transport and recombination.

➤ Both integrated in COMSOL Multiphysics using FEM.

Device Structure

➤ n–i–p bilayer heterojunction

➤ Perovskite (1.55 eV) captures higher-energy photons; CIGS (1.2 eV) captures lower-energy, near-IR photons.

➤ Convex grating nanostructures added at interfaces for enhanced light trapping.

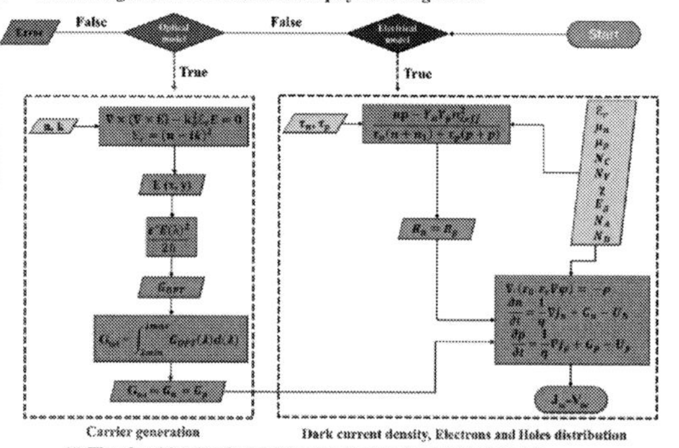

(1) The algorithm involves solving the electrical and optical models.

Carrier generation — Dark current density, Electrons and Holes distribution

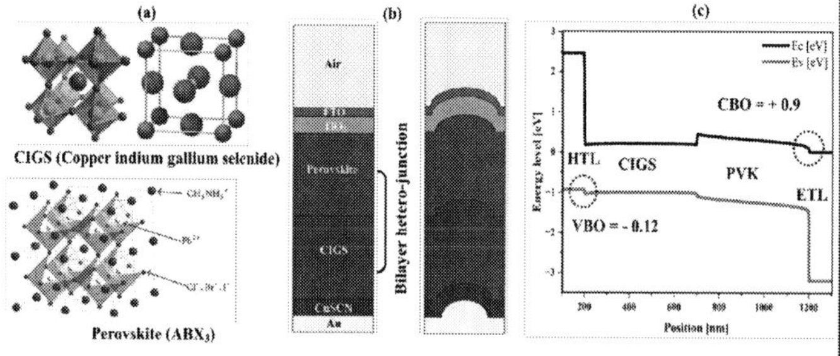

(2) (a) CIGS crystal structure and the perovskite crystal structure (b) the bilayer heterojunction configuration (c) energy band diagram of the bilayer structure.

Results

Table 1. Electrical parameters for CIGS/perovskite incorporating LT structure comparing to planar structure.

Structure	J_{sc} (mA/cm²)	V_{oc} (V)	FF (%)	PCE (%)
Planar	25.98	1.012	87.37	22.98
LT	27.02	1.012	87.18	23.85

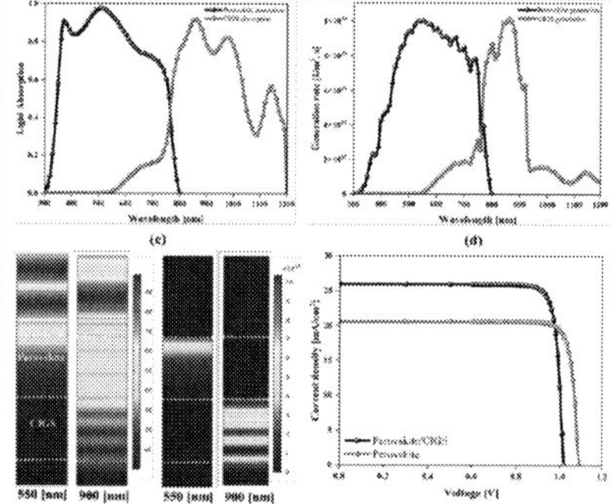

(3) (a) light absorption of perovskite/CIGS and (b) carrier generation rate versus wavelength (c) Electric field and carrier generation rate profiles (d) J–V characteristics.

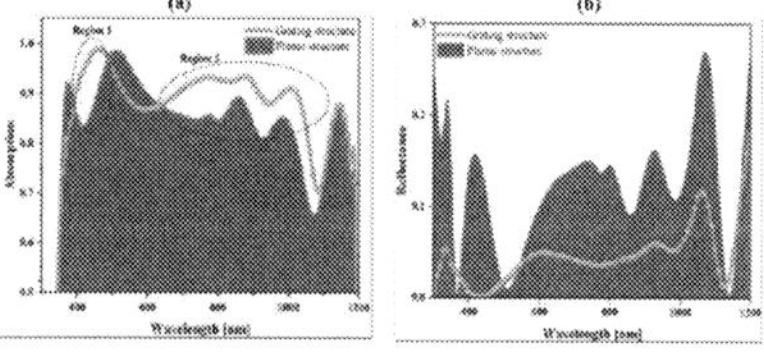

(4) (a)Absorption (b) reflection spectra (planar vs. grating)

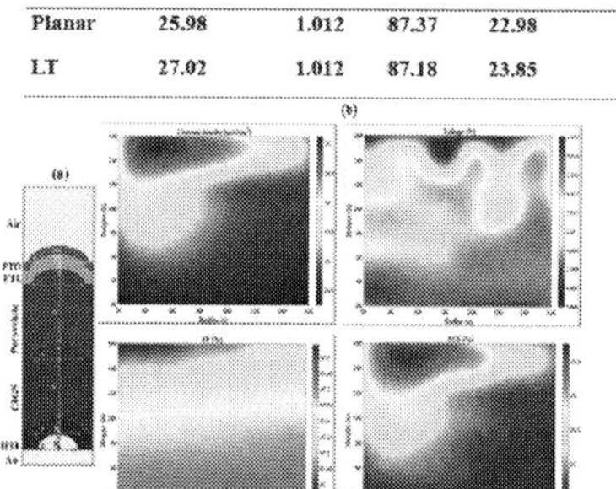

(6) (a) Schematic (a) cross-section and (b) performance contour maps of a nanostructured CIGS/perovskite solar cell with embedded convex grating structures.

Table 2. Electrical parameters for CIGS/perovskite incorporating optimized grating structure comparing to planar and non-optimized structure.

Structure	Jsc (mA/cm2)	Voc (V)	FF (%)	PCE (%)
Planar	25.98	1.012	87.37	22.98
Non-optimized	27.02	1.012	87.18	23.85
Optimized	28.85	1.011	87.45	25.54

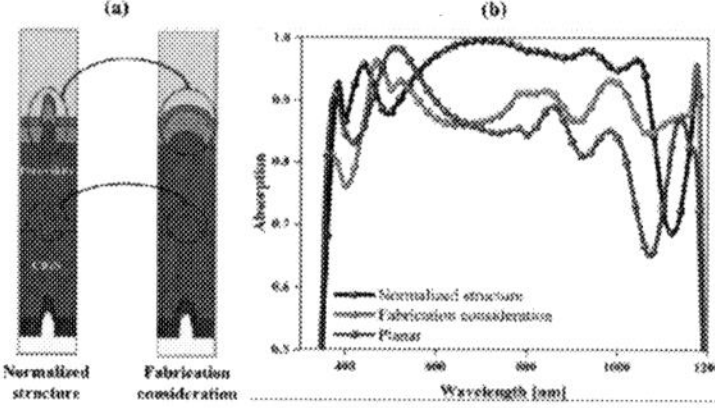

(7) (a) Front view of the modified CIGS/perovskite solar cell structure, illustrating both the sharp-edged and smooth-edged configurations, based on realistic fabrication considerations. (b) Corresponding absorption rate comparison for both the idealized (normalized) and fabrication-aware structures, highlighting the optical impact of edge rounding due to deposition conditions.

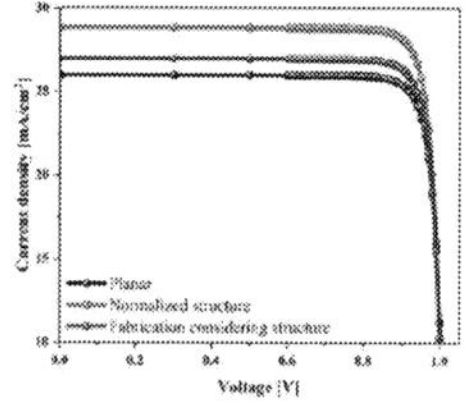

(8) Comparison of J–V curves for three different CIGS/perovskite solar cell configurations: planar structure (baseline), normalized structure (ideal sharp edges) and fabrication considering structure (with realistic smooth edges).

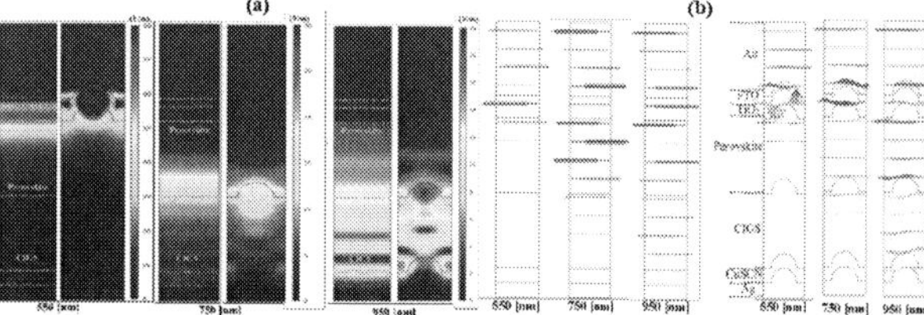

(5) (a) Electric field distributions across all PSC layers for (b) vector field simulations of the electric field intensity

Conclusion

❖ A bilayer heterojunction stacks a high-bandgap perovskite top absorber over a low-bandgap CIGS bottom absorber in a planar n–i–p layout, enabling complementary spectral absorption and higher J_{sc} and PCE.

❖ FEM simulations in COMSOL optimize a convex periodic grating that traps light via photon confinement and constructive interference, cutting reflection and extending optical path length.

❖ PCE rises from 22.98% (bilayer planar) to 25.54% with the optimized grating, an ≈11% relative efficiency while remaining robust under realistic fabrication tolerances.

❖ The nanostructured, grating-assisted design is cost-effective and scalable, supporting flexible, lightweight thin-film photovoltaics and guiding experimental development toward commercial CIGS/perovskite cells.

Acknowledgements

❖ This research is financially supported by the CuSun project, funded by the Energy Technology Development and Demonstration Program (EUDP), Denmark, under grant number 640231-510356.

Funding: AARHUS UNIVERSITY · EUDP · 020105-001

Contact email : moh@ece.au.dk

FABRICATION OF
BENDABLE PEROVSKITE/SILICON HETEROJUNCTION BIFACIAL TANDEM SOLAR CELLS

Kimihiko Saito*, Kanji Takahashi, Hirotaka Shishido, Ryousuke Ishikawa, Makoto Konagai
Tokyo City University, Advanced Research Laboratories
1-28-1 Tamatsutsumi Setagaya-ku Tokyo 158-8557, Japan
Phone +81-3-5707-2769 e-mail: kisaitou@tcu.ac.jp

ABSTRACT: We report the fabrication of a flexible bifacial monolithic perovskite (PVK)/silicon heterojunction (SHJ) tandem solar cell consisting of a $Cs_{0.05}FA_{0.95}PbI_3$ top cell (bandgap ~1.54 eV) and an ~80 μm-thick SHJ bottom cell. External quantum efficiency (EQE) measurements showed a top-cell current of 22.1 mA (1 cm^2 aperture) and a current mismatch of 8.0 mA between the sub-cells, which can be compensated by rear-side illumination of ~27 mW/cm^2, as indicated by bifacial SHJ single-cell results. Current–voltage characterization showed a linear increase in short-circuit current up to ~12.3 mW/cm^2, followed by saturation without achieving current balance with the top cell, accompanied by pronounced hysteresis. Extrapolation of the linear regime yielded a balancing irradiance of ~29 mW/cm^2, in good agreement with both the EQE-based estimate and reported simulations. In contrast, the four-terminal tandem exhibited no saturation, with the bottom-cell current scaling linearly with rear-side irradiance. These findings indicate that interfacial imperfections at the PVK/hole-transport layer interface may play a critical role in hindering current balancing in monolithic PVK/SHJ tandems.
Keywords: Si heterojunction, perovskite, bifacial, tandem solar cell

1 INTRODUCTION

From the perspective of mitigating greenhouse gas emissions, photovoltaic (PV) technology, as a major renewable energy source, has continued to expand worldwide [1]. In Japan as well, deployment has progressed significantly over the past decade [2]. However, available land for the installation of large-scale PV power plants is becoming increasingly scarce. As a result, policies promoting PV installation on buildings—particularly rooftops and façades in urban areas—are being actively pursued [3]. Perovskite (PVK) solar cells have attracted considerable attention in this context, as they offer advantages such as lightweight design, mechanical flexibility, and high-power conversion efficiency [4]. Furthermore, tandem integration with silicon heterojunction (SHJ) solar cells has achieved efficiencies approaching 35% [5]. It has also been reported that thinning the Si substrate and applying suitable edge treatment can render SHJ solar cells flexible [6]. These developments suggest that lightweight, flexible PVK/SHJ tandem cells employing thin SHJ bottom cells offer strong potential as building-integrated photovoltaics where installation area is limited. Indeed, efficiencies approaching 30% have already been reported [7], and we have also previously demonstrated exceeding 26% efficiency [8,9]. For further efficiency improvement of PVK/SHJ tandem cells, increasing the current density of the SHJ bottom cell—which tends to be lower than that of the PVK top cell—is a critical challenge. This issue becomes even more pronounced in thin SHJ cells. One proposed approach to address this limitation is the use of bifacial PVK/SHJ tandem architectures [10], and such devices have already been demonstrated [11,12]. Simulation studies have further indicated that PVK bandgap narrowing to increase the top cell current, combined with rear-side illumination (albedo) to enhance the SHJ bottom cell current for current matching, can achieve higher efficiencies [13–15]. For example, with an albedo of 30%, the optimal PVK bandgap has been suggested to be ~1.52 eV. In addition, from the viewpoint of long-term stability, which remains a key issue for the practical deployment of PVK solar cells, using a single-halide composition to avoid halide segregation, such as the iodine–bromine phase separation often observed in wide-gap perovskites [16], is a promising strategy [12].

Based on these insights, we fabricated bendable bifacial monolithic (two-terminal) PVK/SHJ tandem cells consisting of an ~80 μm-thick SHJ bottom cell and of a $Cs_{0.05}FA(Formamidine)_{0.95}PbI_3$ PVK top cell with a bandgap of ~1.54 eV. We investigated the dependence of cell performance on rear-side illumination intensity. For comparison, we also examined the bifacial characteristics of a PVK single-junction cell fabricated on glass substrates, a thin SHJ cell with the same structure as that used in the monolithic tandem cells, and a four-terminal PVK/SHJ tandem cell constructed from these cells.

2 EXPERIMENTS

2.1 Fabrication of SHJ cells

A Si substrate was thinned to ~80 μm by KOH etching, after which a micro-texture with a height of <1 μm was formed on the front (top-cell) side and a texture with a height of 2–3 μm was formed on the rear side. A rear-emitter-type SHJ cell with a 1 cm^2 active area defined by the front and rear indium tin oxide (ITO) electrodes was then fabricated. Details of the fabrication procedures are described in our previous report [17]. To enable bifacial operation, Ag electrodes were patterned into grids on both the front and rear ITO layers.

2.2 Fabrication of PVK cells

For single-junction cells, commercially available ITO-coated glass substrates (~200 nm, ~6 Ω/sq) were used. The ITO surfaces were treated with UV/O$_3$ cleaning, after which a hole transport layer (HTL) of [2-(3,6-dimethoxy-9H-carbazol-9-yl)ethyl] phosphonic acid (MeO-2PACz) was spin-coated at 3000 rpm and subsequently annealed at 105 °C for 10 min. A perovskite precursor solution was then spin-coated at 5000 rpm using anisole as the antisolvent, followed by a two-step annealing at 105 °C for 45 min and 150 °C for 10 min. Both spin-coating and annealing steps for the HTL and PVK layers were performed in a glovebox filled with nitrogen. A 20 nm-thick C_{60} film was deposited by thermal evaporation as an electron transport layer (ETL), followed by 20 nm-thick SnO_2 deposited by atomic layer deposition (ALD). Subsequently, a transparent electrode was formed to realize a bifacial cell structure, in which a 1 cm² ITO layer was sputtered, followed by evaporating Ag grid electrodes and a MgF_2 antireflection layer.

For tandem cells, a 7 nm-thick ITO recombination layer with a size of 1 cm² was sputtered onto the n-type a-Si:H layer of the SHJ bottom cell. The PVK top cell was then fabricated using the same procedure as for the single-junction cell, however, due to the surface micro-texture of the SHJ bottom cell, the PVK precursor solution was spin-coated at 3000 rpm.

2.3 Characterization of bifacial cell performance

External quantum efficiency (EQE) measurements were carried out in air at 25 °C using a Bunkoukeiki CEP-25NLT, in which a 1 cm² aperture mask was applied to the front side and a black antireflection film (reflectance <1%) was placed behind the rear side of the cell. For tandem cells, appropriate bias light and bias voltage were applied to the top and bottom subcells during EQE measurements. Current–voltage (I-V) characterization was performed in air at room temperature using an EKO MP-180 source measure unit, with 1 cm² aperture masks attached to both the front and rear sides of the bifacial single-junction and tandem cells. Standard 1-sun, AM1.5G illumination was applied from both the front and rear sides using an EKO LP-50A and a SAN-EI ELECTRIC XES-40S1 solar simulator, respectively, and the albedo level of rear-side illumination was adjusted by inserting neutral-density (ND) filters with transmittances of 6%, 12%, 25%, and 50% between the simulator and the rear surface of the cell. The actual rear-side irradiance for each ND filter condition was calibrated using an EKO Solar Simulator Spectroradiometer LS-100 in advance. In measurements without rear-side illumination, a black antireflection film was placed behind the cell, as in the EQE measurements. The front illumination intensity for the bifacial I-V measurement was then adjusted to match the EQE current under this dark rear-side condition, which, in the case of a tandem cell, corresponded to the smaller EQE current, namely that of the bottom cell.

3   RESULTS AND DISCUSSIONS

Fig. 1(a) shows the schematic structure of the bifacial PVK single-junction cell fabricated in this study. In this configuration, the transparent electrode consisting of an MgF_2 antireflection layer, an Ag grid electrode, and an ITO layer was placed on the front side, while the glass substrate was located on the rear side. Fig. 1(b) displays its EQE spectrum. From the plot of EQE^2 versus photon energy in this figure, the bandgap of the PVK layer was estimated to be ~1.54 eV, at which the photocurrent of the PVK top cell balances that of the Si bottom cell under an albedo of ~27%, according to the bifacial PVK/Si tandem simulations introduced in the Introduction [13-15]. Figures 1(c) and 1(d) display the I–V curves and cell characteristics under varying rear-side illumination intensities. As the rear illumination intensity increased, the short-circuit current (I_{sc}) rose linearly, and the open-circuit voltage (V_{oc}) also increased with the enhanced photocurrent. In contrast, the fill factor (FF) exhibited a decreasing trend, which can likely be attributed to an

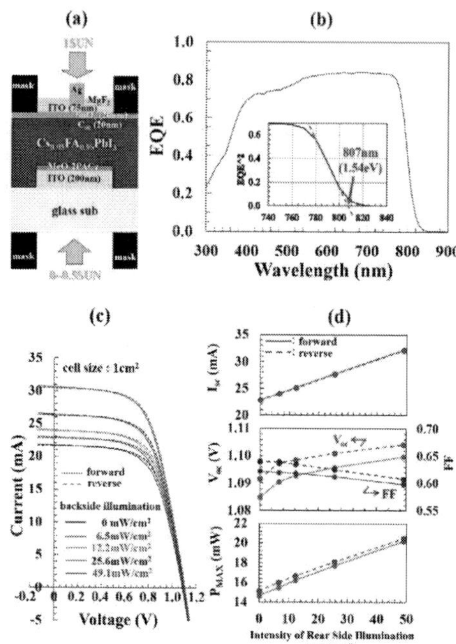

Figure 1: (a) Schematic structure of the bifacial PVK single-junction cell, (b) the EQE spectrum without rear-side illumination, (c) the I–V curves, and (d) cell properties measured under varying rear-side illumination.

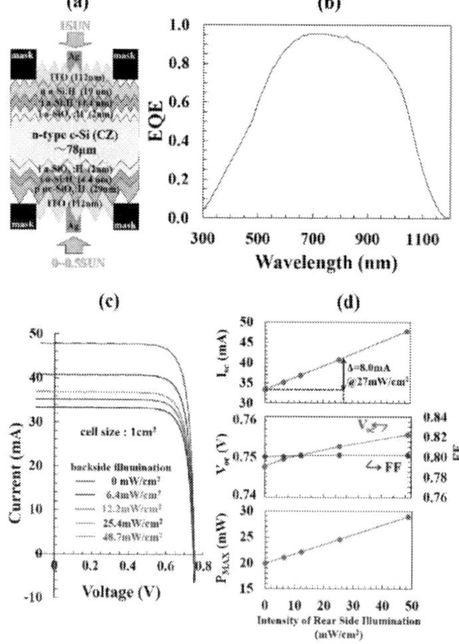

Figure 2: (a) Schematic structure of the bifacial SHJ single-junction cell, (b) the EQE spectrum without rear-side illumination, (c) the I–V curves, and (d) cell properties measured under varying rear-side illumination.

increase in the series resistance with higher photocurrent. Despite a small hysteresis depending on the voltage sweep direction, a power conversion efficiency (PCE) of 15% without rear illumination and maximum output power (P_{MAX}) of 18 mW at 25% albedo was obtained.

Figures 2(a) and 2(b) show the schematic structure and EQE characteristics of the SHJ single-junction cell fabricated in this study, respectively. Due to the use of an a-Si:H n-layer on the front side, the short-wavelength response is low. However, at longer wavelengths above 750 nm, which are meaningful for tandem operation as a bottom cell, high sensitivity was obtained even with a thin substrate with a thickness of 78 μm due to the light-trapping effect enhanced by the front-side micro-texture [17]. Figures 2(c) and 2(d) present the I-V curves and cell characteristics under different rear illumination intensities. Similar to the PVK single-junction cell, I_{sc} increased linearly with rear-side illumination, also causing an increase in V_{oc} due to higher photocurrent. As a result, the P_{MAX} improved from 19.9 mW without rear illumination (corresponding to 19.9% PCE) to 24.6 mW at 25% albedo.

A monolithic PVK/SHJ tandem cell was fabricated based on these PVK and SHJ cells, and its schematic structure together with photographs of the bent state and of the front and rear sides with the measurement attachment are shown in Fig. 3(a). To achieve higher current output from the top cell, not only the bandgap of the PVK material but also its layer thickness is an important factor. In this tandem cell, the PVK layer planarized the underlying micro-texture with a non-uniform thickness, exceeding 1 μm in the valleys and reducing to a few hundred nanometers at the pyramid tips [9,17]. Although the PVK layer exhibited non-uniform thickness, we consider that the coverage is sufficient to ensure reliable current generation in the top cell. This consideration is supported by the top-cell photocurrent of 22.1 mA for a 1 cm² aperture area, which was 8.0 mA higher than that of the bottom cell, as estimated from the EQE spectrum shown in Fig. 3(b). Furthermore, as indicated by the SHJ single-cell results in Fig. 2(d), this current deficit can be compensated by rear-side illumination at an intensity of 27 mW/cm², a value that agrees well with the simulation prediction of the albedo required for current matching between a 1.54 eV PVK top cell and a Si bottom cell [13-15]. Figure 3(c) presents the I–V characteristics of the tandem cell under varying rear illumination intensities. In this study, we did not apply any passivation treatment to the PVK layer [8,18]. The measured V_{oc} of 1.73 V without rear illumination was consistent with the correlation between I_{sc} and V_{oc} observed for the single-junction cells (Figs. 1(d), 2(d)). This indicates that the MeO-2PACz self-assembled monolayer (SAM), which acts as the HTL, is conformally formed on the ITO deposited on the textured surface, resulting in the normal operation of the tandem cell under zero-albedo conditions, as demonstrated in our previous studies [9]. With rear illumination, the output current increased with illumination intensity up to about 12.3 mW/cm². At higher intensities, however, the current did not change and significant hysteresis appeared in the I–V curves. Figure 3(d) summarizes the cell characteristics as a function of rear-side illumination intensity. I_{sc} exhibited saturation beyond ~12.3 mW/cm², and at 25.6 and 49.9 mW/cm²—where I_{sc} had already saturated—pronounced reductions in V_{oc} and FF were observed, particularly during forward (increasing voltage) sweeps. By extrapolating the linear low-intensity region of I_{sc}, the rear-

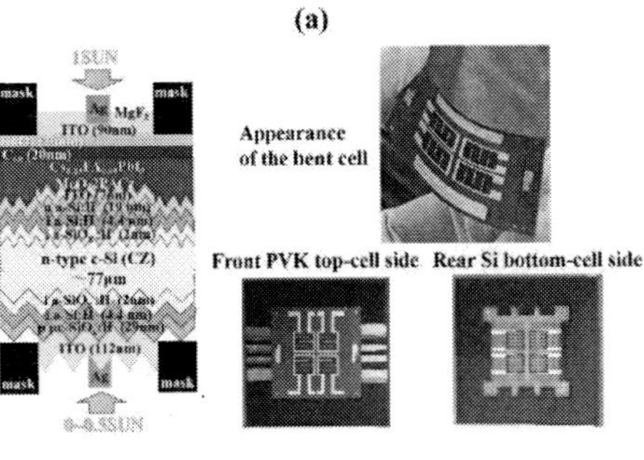

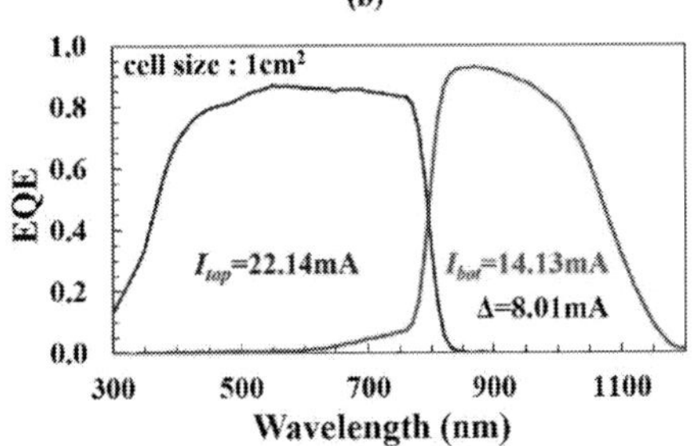

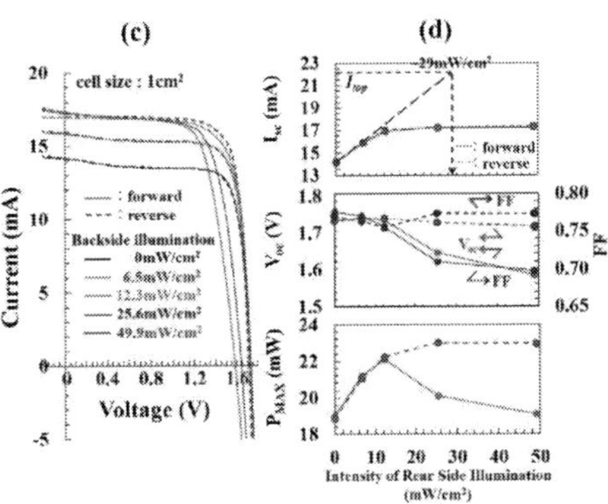

Figure 3: (a) Schematic of the bifacial PVK/SHJ tandem cell and photographs of its bent state and front/rear sides with the measurement attachment, (b) the EQE spectrum without rear-side illumination, (c) the I–V curves, and (d) cell properties measured under varying rear-side illumination.

side illumination required to reach the EQE-derived top-cell current of 22.1 mA was estimated to be ~29 mW/cm², which closely matches the simulated and expected balance point of 27 mW/cm² mentioned above. These results suggest that, although the tandem output should ideally increase up to the top-cell current, some limiting mechanism suppresses the current increase before reaching this value.

To verify this, a four-terminal PVK/SHJ tandem configuration was assembled using the PVK and SHJ single cells characterized in Figs. 1 and 2, as illustrated in Fig. 4(a). In this measurement, the front illumination intensity was adjusted so that the current matched the EQE current of the PVK single-junction top cell. The dependence of each subcell on rear illumination is shown

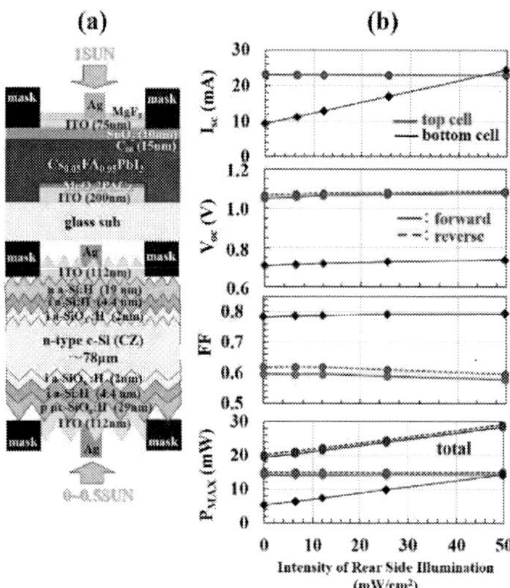

Figure 4: (a) Schematic structure of the four-terminal PVK/SHJ bifacial tandem cell, (b) the top and bottom cell properties measured under varying rear-side illumination.

in Fig. 4(b). The PVK top cell exhibited a constant I_{sc} of 23 mA regardless of rear illumination, indicating that the additional photons incident from the rear side were absorbed almost entirely by the SHJ bottom cell, while the current generated under front illumination remained unchanged. In contrast, without rear illumination, the bottom cell showed an I_{sc} of only 9.4 mA, significantly lower than the monolithic tandem value of 14.1 mA derived from the EQE spectrum. This reduction is attributed to transmission losses, which arise from parasitic absorption in the thick (200 nm) rear ITO electrode of the top cell and reflection at the rear side of the top cell due to the presence of the glass substrate and the air gap in the four-terminal configuration. Nevertheless, the bottom-cell I_{sc} increased linearly with rear illumination, consistent with the behavior observed for the bifacial SHJ single-junction cell, and reached a value comparable to the top-cell current of 24.3 mA at 49.7 mW/cm².

These results suggest that, in the monolithic tandem, the observed saturation of output current before current matching is caused by insufficient recombination of holes from the top cell with electrons from the bottom cell once the bottom-cell current exceeds a certain threshold. Although the HTL-SAM should be conformally formed on the ITO recombination layer as mentioned above, we fabricated tandems employing a thicker ITO recombination layer (20 and 50nm) to rule out concerns about possible inhomogeneity in the quality or thickness of the thin ITO layer (7 nm), which could introduce pinholes. However, even with the thicker ITO recombination layer, the same saturation tendency as that observed in the tandem cell with the 7-nm-thick ITO layer was obtained. This implies that the ITO recombination layer is not the origin of the saturation of output current before current matching. Furthermore, pronounced hysteresis in the I–V characteristics appeared simultaneously, indicating the involvement of ion migration in the PVK layer, which may lead to charge accumulation at the PVK/HTL interface, and/or to charge

trapping and delayed release at the same interface [19-22]. Both phenomena can hinder efficient hole supply; therefore, interfacial defects at the PVK/HTL interface may be the root cause of the observed saturation and hysteresis. On the other hand, phenomena such as the saturation of output current before current matching, accompanied by hysteretic I–V curves, were not observed in reports on bifacial PVK/SHJ tandem cells [11,12]. Moreover, monofacial PVK/SHJ tandem cells have achieved I_{sc} values exceeding 20 mA/cm² with well-balanced top and bottom cell currents [5,23-25]. These findings suggest that the limited output power observed in our bifacial cells, which did not increase as expected with higher albedo, is not a problem inherent to the bifacial architecture, but rather arises from imperfections at the PVK/HTL interface due to our unoptimized fabrication process. Therefore, to fully realize the potential of bifacial performance, precise control of both the PVK/ETL and PVK/HTL interfaces in the PVK top cell is likely to be essential.

Based on these considerations, we further explored replacing the HTL with alternative materials, specifically a mixture of MeO-2PACz and [4-(3,6-dimethyl-9H-carbazol-9-yl)butyl]phosphonic acid (Me-4PACz), aiming to achieve fast hole extraction and minimized nonradiative recombination at the PVK/HTL interface [23]. However, the issue persisted, and further studies are underway to clarify the underlying mechanisms and develop effective solutions.

4 SUMMARY

We fabricated a bendable bifacial monolithic tandem solar cell consisting of a Cs₀.₀₅FA₀.₉₅PbI₃ perovskite (PVK) top cell with an estimated bandgap of ~1.54 eV (derived from the EQE spectrum of the single cell) and an ~80 μm-thick SHJ bottom cell. EQE measurements of a 1 cm² tandem device, with the rear side masked by a black anti-reflection film, revealed that the bottom-cell EQE current was 8.0 mA lower than that of the top cell. Based on the dependence of I_{sc} on rear-side illumination intensity in a bifacial SHJ single cell with the same ~80 μm thickness and structure as the bottom cell, this current deficit corresponds to a rear-side irradiance of ~27 mW/cm² under simulated sunlight. In contrast, I–V measurements of the tandem cell under varying rear-side illumination intensities showed that I_{sc} increased linearly with intensity up to 12.3 mW/cm², but saturated at higher intensities, accompanied by pronounced hysteresis in the I–V curves. Extrapolation of the linear regime yielded a balancing irradiance of ~29 mW/cm², which agrees well with both the EQE-based estimate (~27 mW/cm²) and reported simulation values. Furthermore, bifacial characteristics were evaluated in a four-terminal tandem configuration, composed of a bifacial PVK single cell fabricated on a glass substrate and a bifacial SHJ single cell of ~80 μm thickness identical to the bottom cell. In this case, the bottom-cell I_{sc} increased linearly with rear-side illumination intensity without saturation. Overall, these results suggest that, in the monolithic architecture, ion migration in the PVK layer, which may cause charge accumulation, and/or trapping and delayed release at the PVK/HTL interface can hinder the supply of holes needed for recombination with electrons from the bottom cell, and may therefore underlie the observed saturation and hysteresis. While these findings point to the imperfect

PVK/HTL interface as a possible origin of the observed issues, the precise mechanisms remain under investigation.

ACKNOWLEDGEMENT

This work was supported by New Energy and Industrial Technology Development Organization (NEDO) under the project code JPNP20015.

REFERENCES

[1] https://www.iea.org/energy-system/renewables/solar-pv

[2] https://www.fit-portal.go.jp/PublicInfoSummary

[3] https://www.meti.go.jp/shingikai/energy_environment/perovskite_solar_cell/pdf/20241128_1.pdf

[4] Y. Wu, G Xu, Y. Shen, X. Wu, X Tang, C Han, Y Chen, F Yang, H. Chen, Y. Li and Y Li, Adv. Mater. 36 (2024) 2403531

[5] L. Jia, S. Xia, J. Li, Y. Qin, B. Pei, L. Ding, J. Yin, T. Du, Z. Fang, Y. Yin, J. Liu, Y. Yang, F. Zhang, X. Wu, Q. Li, S. Zhao, H. Zhang, Q. Li, Q. Jia, C. Liu, X. Gu, B. Liu, X. Dong, J. Liu, T. Liu, Y. Gao, M. Yang, S. Yin, X. Ru, H. Chen, B. Yang, Z. Zheng, W. Zhou, M. Dou, S. Wang, S. Gao, L. Chen, M. Qu, J. Lu, L. Fang, Y. Wang, H. Deng, J. Yu, X. Zhang, M. Li, X. Lang, C. Xiao, Q. Hi, C. Xue, L. Ning, Y. He, Z. Li, X. Xu and B. He, Nature (2025) https://doi.org/10.1038/s41586-025-09333-z

[6] W. Liu, Y. Liu, Z. Yang, C. Xu, X. Li, S. Huang, J. Shi, J. Du, A. Han, Y. Yang, G. Xu, J. Yu, J. Ling, J. Peng, L. Yu, B. Ding, Y. Gao, K. Jiang, Z. Li, Y. Yang, Z. Li, S. Lan, H. Fu, B. Fan, Y. Fu, W. He, F. Li, X. Song, Y. Zhou, Q. Shi, G. Wang, L. Guo, J. Kang, X. Yang, D. Li, Z. Wang, J. Li, S. Thoroddsen, R. Cai, F. Wei, G. Xing, Y. Xie, X. Liu, L. Zhang, F. Meng, Z. Di and Z. Liu, Nature 617 (2023) 717

[7] Y. Sun, F. Li, H. Zhang, W. Liu, Z. Wang, L. Mao, Q. Li, Y. He, T. Yang, X. Sun, Y. Qian, Y. Ma, L. Zhang, J. Du, J. Shi, G. Wang, A. Han, N. Wang, F. Meng, Z. Liu and M. Liu, Nat. Commun., 16 (2025) 5733

[8] K. Saito, K. Takahashi, H. Shishido and R. Ishikawa, Proceedings in 35th International Photovoltaic Science and Engineering Conference, We2b-Oc1-03 (2024)

[9] H. Shishido, R. Sato, D. Ieki, G. Matsuo, K. Saito, M.Konagai and R. Ishikawa, Sol. RRL, 9 (2025) 2400899

[10] R. Asadpour, R. V. K. Chavali, M. R. Khan and M. A. Alam, Appl. Phys. Lett., 106 (2015) 243902

[11] M. D. Bastiani, A. J. Millabelli, Y. Hou, F. Gota, E. Aydin, T. G. Allen, J. Troughton, A. S. Subbiah, F. H. Isikgor, J. Liu, L. Xu, B. Chen, E. V. Kerschaver, D. Baran, B. Fraboni, M. F. Salvador, U. W. Paetzold, E. H. Sargent and S. D. Wolf, Nat. Energy., 6 (2021) 167

[12] M. R. Golobostanfard, M. Othman, D.Turkay, K. Artuk, X. Y. Chin, M. D. Mensi, D. A. Jacobs, Q. Jeangros, C. M. Wolff, A. Hessler-Wyser and C. Ballif, Nano Energy, 131 (2024) 110269

[13] J. Chantana, Y. Kawano, T. Nishimura, A. Mavlonov and T. Minemoto, Sol. Energy, 220 (2021) 163

[14] M. R. Khan and M. A. Alam, Appl. Phys. Lett., 107 (2015) 223502

[15] A. Onno, N. Rodkey, A. Asgharzadeh, S. Manzoor, Z. J. Yu, F. Toor and Z. C. Holman, Joule, 4 (2020) 580

[16] R. Wang, X. Liu, S. Yan, N. Meng, X. Zhao, Y. Chen, H. Li, S. M. H. Qaid, S. Yang, M. Yuan and T. He, Nat. Commun., 15 (2024) 8899

[17] K. Saito, H. Shishido and R. Ishikawa, Proceedings in 40th European Photovoltaic Solar Energy Conference and Exhibition, 1AO.6.6 (2023) 020009-001

[18] D. B. Khadka, Y. Shirai, M. Yanagida, H. Ota, A. Lyalin, T. Taketsugu and K. Miyano, Nat. Commun., 15 (2024) 882

[19] H. J. Snaith, A. Abate, J. M. Ball, G. E. Eperon, T. Leijtens, N. K. Noel, S. D. Stranks, J. T-W, Wang, K. Wojciechowski and W. Zhang, J. Phys. Chem. Lett., 5 (2014) 1511

[20] B. Chen, M. Yang, S. Priya and K. Zhu, J. Phys. Chem. Lett., 7 (2016) 905

[21] S. Meloni, T. Moehl, W. Tress, M. Franckevicius, M. Saliba, Y. H. Lee, P. Gao, M. K. Nazeeruddin, S. M. Zakeeruddin, U. Rothlisberger and M. Graetzel, Nat. Commun., 7 (2016) 10334

[22] S. A. L. Weber, I. M. Hermes, S-H Turren-Cruz, C. Gort, V. W. Bergmann, L. Gilson, A. Hagfeldt, M. Graetzel, W. Tress and R. Berger, Energy Environ. Sci., 11 (2018) 2404

[23] A. Al-Ashouri, E. Kohnen, B. Li, A. Magomedov, H. Hempel, P. Caprioglio, J. A. Marquez, A. B. M. Vilches, E. Kasparavicius, J. A. Smith, N. Phung, D. Menzel, M. Grischek, L. Kegelmann, D. Skroblin, C. Gollwitzer, T. Malinauskas, M. Jost, G. Matic, B. Rech, R. Schlatmann, M. Topic, L. Korte, A. Abate, B. Stannowski, D. Neher, M. Stolterfoht, T. Unold, V. Getautis and A. Albrecht, Science, 370 (2020) 1300

[24] X. Y. Chin, D. Turkay, J. A. Steele, S. Tabean, S. Eswara, M. Mensi, P. Fiala, C. M. Wolff, A. Paracchino, K. Artuk, D. Jacobs, Q. Guesnay, F. Sahli, G. Andreatta, M. Boccard, Q. Jeangros and C. Ballif, Science, 381 (2023) 59

[25] E. Aydin, E. Ugur, B. K. Yildirim, T. G. Allen, P. Dally, A. Razzaq, F. Cao, L. Xu, B. Vishal, A. Yazmaciyan, A. A. Said, S. Zhumagali, R. Azmi, M. Babics, A. Fell, C. Xiao and S. D. Wolf, Nature, 623 (2023) 732

[...] Amalraj [...] bc, Neda Neykova [bc], Jakub Holovský *[bc]

[a] Department of Physics, Faculty of Science, University of Jaffna, Jaffna 40000, Sri Lanka
[b] SOLar cell MATerial laboratory, Faculty of Electrical Engineering, Czech Technical University in Prague, Technická 2, 166 27 Prague, Czech Republic
[c] Institute of Physics, Czech Academy of Sciences, v. v. i., Cukrovarnická 10, 162 00 Prague, Czech Republic

* Contact: e-mail: amalraj@univ.jfn.ac.lk, stankte3@fel.cvut.cz, jakub.holovsky@fel.cvut.cz,

FACsPbI$_3$ Perovskite Solar Cells:
Ethylammonium Bromide Both as an Additive and Surface Passivation

Why stability matters?
- High efficiency, but poor long-term stability[1]
- FACsPbI$_3$ suffers from defects & degradation[2]

Dual Role of EABr
- Additive in precursor → larger grains
- Surface passivation → defect suppression
- Goal: improve efficiency & stability

Process of fabrication

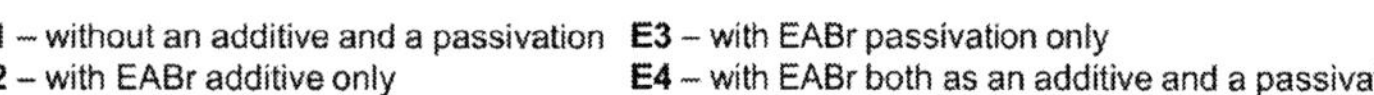

E1 – without an additive and a passivation
E2 – with EABr additive only
E3 – with EABr passivation only
E4 – with EABr both as an additive and a passivation

Grains and defects (SEM, AFM, XRD)

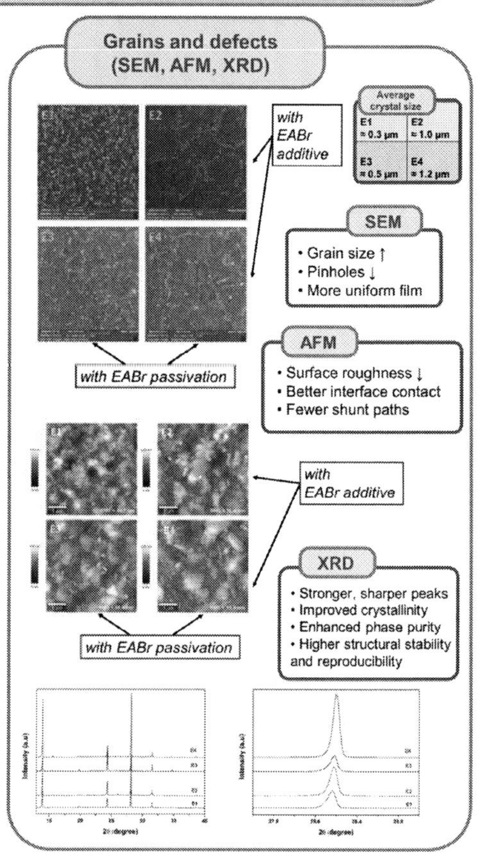

SEM
- Grain size ↑
- Pinholes ↓
- More uniform film

AFM
- Surface roughness ↓
- Better interface contact
- Fewer shunt paths

XRD
- Stronger, sharper peaks
- Improved crystallinity
- Enhanced phase purity
- Higher structural stability and reproducibility

Longer Carrier Lifetime (TRPL)

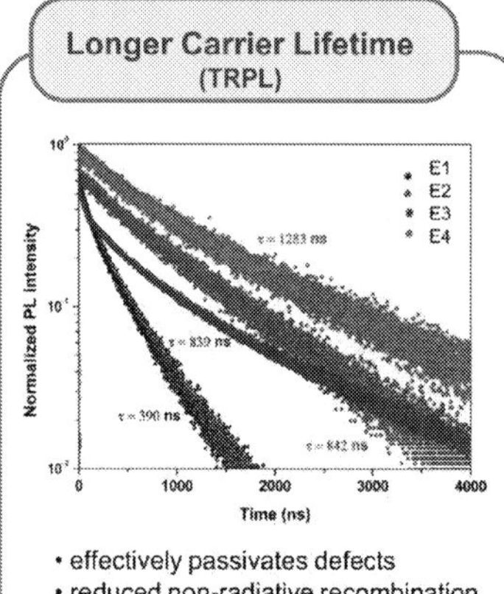

- effectively passivates defects
- reduced non-radiative recombination

Efficiency and stability gains with EABr (J–V Results)

Efficiency

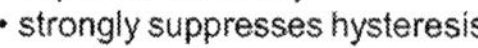

- improves efficiency
- strongly suppresses hysteresis

Stability (1 month test)

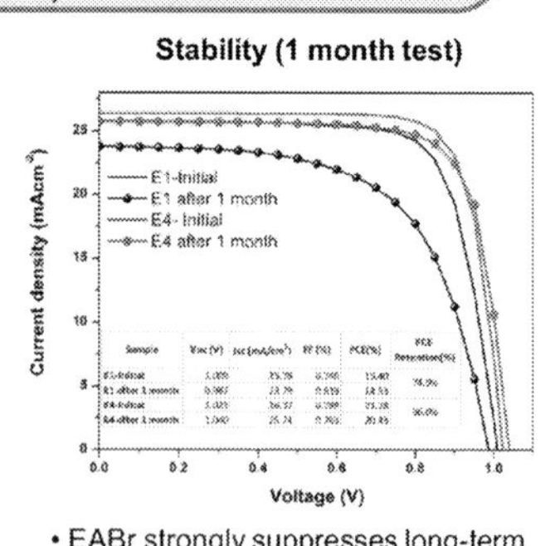

- EABr strongly suppresses long-term degradation

ACKNOWLEDGMENT:
We acknowledge Czech Science Foundation project 23-06543S and CTU student grant SGS24/135/OHK3/3T/13

References:
[1] Yan, Genghua, et al. "Visualizing performances losses of perovskite solar cells and modules: from laboratory to industrial scales." Advanced Energy Materials 15.3 (2025): 2403706.
[2] Guo, Zhendong, et al. "Understanding defects in perovskite solar cells through computation: current knowledge and future challenge." Advanced Science 11.20 (2024): 2305799.

Long-Term Degradation Analysis of Perovskite Solar Cells Over Three Years

Mohammad Istiaque Hossain*, Yongfeng Tong, Brahim Aissa

Qatar Environment and Energy Research Institute (QEERI), Hamad Bin Khalifa University (HBKU), Qatar Foundation, P.O. Box 34110, Doha, Qatar

*E-mail: mhossain@hbku.edu.qa

ABSTRACT: Power-conversion efficiencies (PCEs) in perovskite solar cells (PSCs) have risen to levels that now rival established photovoltaic technologies. Yet translation to market hinges not on peak efficiency alone, but on rigorous demonstrations of operational and long-term stability. The literature remains fragmented: many stability studies are short in duration, poorly harmonized, and therefore difficult to compare or interpret. Because PSCs possess materials properties and degradation pathways distinct from conventional semiconductors, their durability may need to be assessed against adapted, technology-specific criteria rather than by direct analogy. Here we examine the influence of storage on PSC aging over a three-year horizon. Devices with the architecture glass/FTO/compact-TiO₂/mesoporous-TiO₂/perovskite/Spiro-OMeTAD/Au were fabricated and stored in nitrogen gloveboxes under inert atmosphere. Despite the ostensibly benign conditions, ToF-SIMS and XRD analyses reveal progressive layer disintegration that correlates with a decline in PCE from an initial ~17% to ~8% after three years. A salient feature of the aging process is the time-dependent diffusion of lead species toward the metallic back contact, which emerges as a dominant pathway for interfacial degradation. Complementary photoluminescence measurements show pronounced emission quenching in the perovskite layer, consistent with the formation of nonradiative recombination centers associated with ion migration. Taken together, these results underscore the need for stability protocols that capture PSC-specific failure modes, especially interfacial evolution and ion-driven defect formation, even under inert storage. By clarifying how materials transport and interface chemistry govern performance loss over multi-year timescales, this study provides actionable guidance for lifetime engineering and the reliable scale-up of PSC technology toward commercialization.

1 INTRODUCTION

Halide perovskites have emerged as compelling semiconductors for high-performance optoelectronic devices, owing to their exceptional combination of strong light absorption, long carrier diffusion lengths, defect tolerance, and facile, low-temperature processing [1–5]. These attributes have propelled rapid gains in device metrics—most notably the remarkable rise in power-conversion efficiency (PCE) for perovskite solar cells (PSCs) over the past decade—placing the technology squarely in contention with incumbent photovoltaics. Yet, the same soft, ionic nature that enables such impressive optoelectronic behavior also renders perovskites vulnerable to environmental and operational stressors. Oxygen, ambient moisture, and sustained photon flux can trigger phase instabilities and stoichiometric drift, while thermal cycling and built-in fields encourage mobile ionic species to redistribute within the device stack [1–5]. Together, these processes complicate lifetime predictions and impede reliable scale-up.

A central durability concern arises from light-induced redox chemistry and field-assisted ion migration. Even in the absence of an applied bias, continuous illumination generates quasi-steady-state carrier populations and local electrochemical potentials that can drive halide migration, A-site reorganization, and metal/halide interdiffusion. In lead-based compositions, the presence of Pb species further introduces possible pathways for defect formation and interfacial reactions under persistent sunlight and electrical stress, accelerating performance loss [1–5]. Considerable insight has been gained into degradation mechanisms within the perovskite absorber itself, spanning photo-oxidation, halide segregation, and lattice decomposition [6–8], but translating those materials-level findings into robust device-level guidance still demands a systematic account of storage conditions, interfacial chemistry, and the coupled dynamics of ions and carriers across the full stack.

In this work, we focus on a representative FAMAPbI₃ perovskite solar cell architecture to disentangle how storage and illumination shape long-term stability in the absence of external electrical bias. By isolating the contributions of dark storage versus controlled light exposure, we delineate the role of non-equilibrium carriers and mobile ions in driving slow, cumulative changes at and near the top surface of the perovskite film[10–12]. Over time, we observe that photo-generated carrier populations and the drift of lead-related ionic species to the illuminated interface foster defect formation, precipitate surface reconstruction, and erode radiative efficiency, degradations that ultimately manifest as declines in open-circuit voltage, fill factor, and PCE [13–15].

Our approach emphasizes a device-centric perspective: storage state (ambient vs. inert, dark vs. illuminated), thermal history, and interfacial energetics are treated as co-equal variables alongside materials composition. By coupling structural and chemical probes with optical and electrical diagnostics, the study maps a coherent pathway from ion-/carrier-driven microstructural evolution to macroscopic performance decay. The resulting framework complements prior absorber-focused mechanistic studies [6–8] and offers practical guidance for stabilizing PSCs: tailoring interfaces to suppress ionic accumulation, engineering barriers to metal/halide interdiffusion, and defining stability protocols that reflect the technology's unique, illumination-activated degradation modes. We anticipate that these insights will aid researchers and engineers in designing storage, encapsulation, and operating regimes that extend device lifetime, thereby smoothing the path from laboratory demonstrations to durable, bankable perovskite photovoltaics.

2 METHODOLOGY

Fluorine-doped tin oxide (FTO)–coated glass substrates were sequentially cleaned three times by ultrasonication in soapy water, deionized (DI) water, and isopropyl alcohol (IPA), 15 min per bath. The rear (non-conductive) sides were masked with adhesive tape. To define the active area, one edge of the FTO was selectively etched using 4 M HCl in the presence of zinc powder, after which the substrates were thoroughly rinsed with DI water and dried under nitrogen. A compact TiO_2 layer was deposited by dip-coating twice from a precursor prepared by mixing 6 mL titanium diisopropoxide bis(acetylacetonate) with 54 mL IPA. The coated substrates were first dried/annealed at 200 °C for 10 min, followed by a high-temperature anneal at 450 °C for 30 min. A mesoporous TiO_2 layer based on ~30 nm particles was applied by spin coating. A dispersion was prepared by mixing 150 mg of TiO_2 paste (Dyesol 30 NR-D) with 1 mL ethanol. The slurry was spin-coated at 4000 rpm for 20 s with an acceleration ramp of 2000 rpm s^{-1}. (Subsequent thermal steps followed the compact-layer schedule above.) The perovskite precursor solution was prepared by dissolving PbI_2 (508 mg mL^{-1}), methylammonium iodide (MAI; 67.1 mg), and formamidinium iodide (FAI; 180.5 mg) in 1.0 mL of solvent (DMF:DMSO = 800:200 µL). Films were deposited using a two-step spin program: 1000 rpm for 10 s, then 4000 rpm for 30 s. During the second step, 300 µL chlorobenzene was dispensed onto the spinning substrate 20 s before the end of the program to promote smooth film formation.Completed devices had the stack: glass/FTO/compact-TiO_2/mesoporous TiO_2/perovskite/Spiro-OMeTAD/Au.

3 RESULTS AND DISCUSSIONS

Devices with the architecture glass/FTO/c-TiO_2/m-TiO_2/perovskite/Spiro-OMeTAD/Au exhibited strong initial performance, with Jsc = 22.26 mA cm^{-2}, Voc = 1.054 V, FF = 71.6%, yielding a PCE = 16.78%. The short-circuit current density integrated from the EQE spectrum agreed with the current–voltage (I–V) measurement (within experimental uncertainty), confirming optical-electrical consistency. Under nominally inert storage (N_2-filled desiccator), devices nevertheless showed a pronounced efficiency loss over time: Jsc fell to 15.10 mA cm^{-2} while Voc remained near 1.054 V at intermediate aging, indicative of transport and collection penalties (and likely FF erosion) preceding any major change in quasi-Fermi-level splitting. After three years, samples measured either in ambient air or in desiccators without continuous nitrogen purge displayed ohmic I–V characteristics, consistent with catastrophic shunting attributed to time-dependent ionic diffusion and interfacial degradation.
Structural and morphological probes tracked this evolution from intact to aged states. XRD patterns collected over three years showed reflections at 14.8°, 20.0°, 28.1°, and 40.1°, assigned to the (110), (200), (220), and (224) planes of the tetragonal perovskite phase, respectively. Notably,

PbI_2 signatures intensified most strongly in N_2-stored devices, whereas air-stored films exhibited diminished perovskite crystallinity and the emergence of the δ-$FAPbI_3$ (yellow, non-perovskite) phase, pointing to distinct degradation pathways under dry-inert versus humid/oxygenated conditions. Cross-sectional SEM of pristine devices revealed uniform, dense, and continuous layers; aged cross-sections showed interfacial roughening, local voiding, and film discontinuities consistent with diffusion-driven delamination and phase segregation.
Spectroscopic diagnostics corroborated the microstructural picture. PL spectra exhibited strong quenching with aging, evidencing the growth of nonradiative recombination channels associated with defect formation and interfacial disorder. Depth-resolved chemical analyses by ToF-SIMS and XPS demonstrated elemental redistribution across the stack, implicating halide and metal species transport (including Pb-related ions) through the TiO_2/perovskite/Spiro-OMeTAD interfaces. The chemical gradients and intermixing captured by depth profiling align with the observed transition from diode-like to ohmic behavior, as migrating ions lower interfacial barriers, dope transport layers locally, and eventually form conductive pathways.

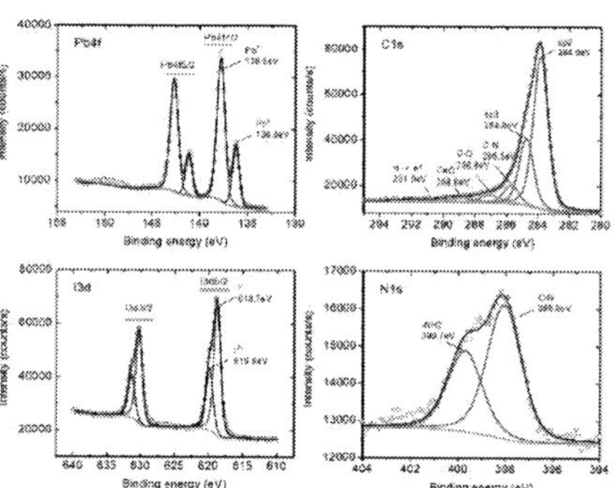

Figure 1: X-ray Photoelectron Spectroscopy (XPS) analysis of the perovskite films. The spectra reveal the characteristic elemental states and interfacial chemical interactions within the device stack. Distinct peaks corresponding to Pb^{2+}, I^-, PbO, and IO_2^- species are observed, evidencing partial oxidation of iodine and the formation of lead oxides. The evolution of these features with increasing depth indicates strong interfacial reactions between the perovskite absorber and the underlying TiO_2 layer, leading to the gradual decomposition of the perovskite lattice and the emergence of metallic Pb at deeper regions. These findings highlight the critical role of interfacial chemistry in governing the stability and degradation pathways of perovskite materials.

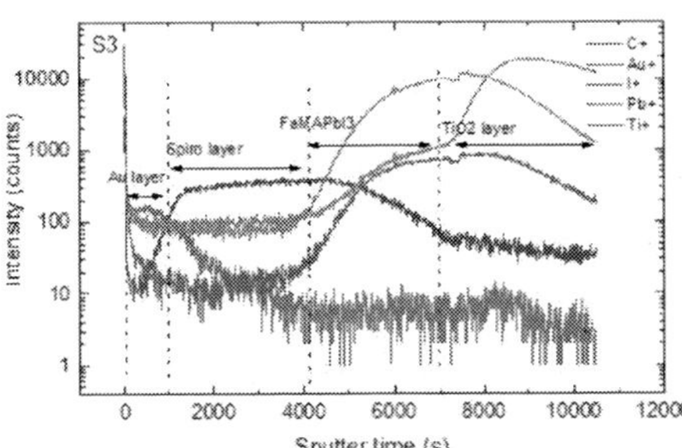

Figure 2: Time-of-Flight Secondary Ion Mass Spectrometry (ToF-SIMS) analysis of the perovskite devices. The depth profiles illustrate the elemental distribution and diffusion behavior across the multilayer device architecture. Noticeable variations in the Pb/I ratio, along with the migration of iodine ions toward the surface and lead diffusion across the interfacial regions, are evident after prolonged operation or environmental exposure. This ionic redistribution disrupts the stoichiometric balance of the perovskite layer, facilitating the formation of secondary non-perovskite phases such as lead iodide hydrates. The observed interdiffusion between layers underscores the dynamic nature of ion transport within the device stack and its pivotal contribution to structural degradation, compositional instability, and the eventual decline in photovoltaic performance.

Photoluminescence (PL) analyses revealed a progressive quenching of emission intensity over time, attributed to an increased density of trap states, accelerated charge-carrier recombination, and the migration of lead and halide ions toward non-radiative recombination centers. Complementary X-ray photoelectron spectroscopy (XPS) depth profiling identified the presence of Pb^{2+}, I^{2-}, PbO, and IO_2^- species, confirming iodine oxidation and strong interfacial interactions with the TiO_2 scaffold at deeper layers. These observations point to the gradual disintegration of the perovskite lattice into metallic lead. Time-of-Flight Secondary Ion Mass Spectrometry (ToF-SIMS) further revealed variations in the Pb/I ratio, extensive elemental interdiffusion across device layers, and pronounced iodine migration toward the surface. This ionic redistribution disrupted the stoichiometry and facilitated the emergence of non-perovskite secondary phases, including lead iodide hydrates. Collectively, these results demonstrate that ion migration, lattice distortion, and environmental stressors act synergistically to degrade the perovskite structure—manifested as a drastic decline in power conversion efficiency (PCE) from 17% to 8% within two years, accompanied by structural decomposition and elevated defect formation. Mitigating ionic migration thus remains pivotal to ensuring the long-term operational stability and performance of perovskite solar cells.

4 CONCLUSIONS

Ion migration in halide perovskites remains a central bottleneck to device reliability. In this study, we present a multi-year degradation analysis of n–i–p perovskite solar cells with the architecture glass/FTO/compact-TiO_2/mesoporous-TiO_2/perovskite/Spiro-OMeTAD/Au. The crystalline structure and surface morphology of the as-fabricated devices were verified by X-ray diffraction (XRD) and scanning electron microscopy (SEM). Over a two-year period, the power-conversion efficiency (PCE) declined from ~17% to ~8%, accompanied by a pronounced quenching of the photoluminescence (PL) emission—signatures consistent with the emergence of nonradiative recombination pathways and an increased defect density in the perovskite absorber. Depth-resolved chemical analyses using time-of-flight secondary ion mass spectrometry (ToF-SIMS) and X-ray photoelectron spectroscopy (XPS) reveal progressive elemental redistribution across the transport and absorber layers, indicating interlayer diffusion consistent with ion migration processes. Taken together, the electrical, optical, structural, and compositional data delineate a coherent degradation pathway driven by slow ionic motion and interfacial evolution. The work provides a rigorous long-term assessment of perovskite material stability at the device level and highlights the need for diffusion-blocking interfaces, robust encapsulation, and stability protocols tailored to the unique ionics of halide perovskites.

5 REFERENCES

[1] F. H. Isikgor, S. Zhumagali, L. V. T. Merino, M. De Bastiani, I. McCulloch, and S. De Wolf, "Molecular engineering of contact interfaces for high-performance perovskite solar cells," *Nature Reviews Materials*, vol. 8, no. 2, pp. 89–108, 2023.

[2] A. S. R. Bati, Y. L. Zhong, P. L. Burn, M. K. Nazeeruddin, P. E. Shaw, and M. Batmunkh, "Next-generation applications for integrated perovskite solar cells," *Communications Materials*, vol. 4, no. 1, p. 2, 2023.

[3] D. Yu, F. Cao, C. Su, and G. Xing, "Exploring, identifying, and removing the efficiency-limiting factor of mixed-dimensional 2D/3D perovskite solar cells," *Accounts of Chemical Research*, 2023, pp. 14558–145.

[4] T. Nie, Z. Fang, X. Ren, Y. Duan, and S. Liu, "Recent advances in wide-bandgap organic–inorganic halide perovskite solar cells and tandem application," *Nano-Micro Letters*, vol. 15, no. 1, p. 70, 2023.

[5] S. Liu, V. P. Biju, Y. Qi, W. Chen, and Z. Liu, "Recent progress in the development of high-efficiency inverted perovskite solar cells," *NPG Asia Materials*, vol. 15, no. 1, p. 27, 2023.

[6] M. I. Hossain, B. Aïssa, A. Samara, S. A. Mansour, C. A. Broussillou, and V. Bermudez Benito, *ACS Omega*, vol. 6, no. 8, pp. 5276–5286, 2021.

[7] L. L. Lebel, B. Aïssa, M. A. El Khakani, and D. Therriault, *Composites Science and Technology*, vol. 70, no. 3, pp. 518–524, 2010.

[8] W. Julia, C. Luis, R. Federico, *et al.*, *Advanced Functional Materials*, vol. 23, pp. 5591–5598, 2013.

[9] D. T. H. Dalir, R. D. Farahani, V. Nhim, and B. Aïssa, *et al.*, *Langmuir*, vol. 28, no. 1, pp. 791–803, 2011.

[10] A. Ali, F. El-Mellouhi, A. Mitra, and B. Aïssa, *Nanomaterials*, vol. 12, no. 5, p. 788, 2022.

[11] R. D. Farahani, D. T. H. Dalir, V. Le Borgne, A. Loick, *et al.*, *Composites Science and Technology*, vol. 72, no. 12, pp. 1387–1395, 2012.

[12] N. M. H. Gavi, B. D. Ngom, A. C. Beye, A. M. Strydom, B. Aïssa, V. V. Srinivasu, and M. Chaker, *Journal of Magnetism and Magnetic Materials*, vol. 324, no. 6, pp. 1172–1176, 2012.

[13] B. Aïssa and M. A. El Khakani, *Nanotechnology*, vol. 20, no. 17, p. 175203, 2009.

[14] M. A. Habib, M. Barkat, B. Aïssa, and T. Denidni, *Progress in Electromagnetics Research*, vol. 88, pp. 135–148, 2008.

[15] H. Zhao, H. Kimura, Z. Cheng, X. Wang, and T. Nishida, *Applied Physics Letters*, vol. 95, p. 232904, 2009. https://doi.org/10.1063/1.3271032.

ENHANCING SEMI-TRANSPARENT PEROVSKITE SOLAR CELL EFFICIENCY IN HARSH ENVIRONMENTS WITH SiO₂/ITO TRANSPARENT CONTACTS AND ANTI-SOILING COATINGS

Mohammad Istiaque Hossain*, Yongfeng Tong, Brahim Aissa

Qatar Environment and Energy Research Institute (QEERI), Hamad Bin Khalifa University (HBKU), Qatar Foundation, P.O. Box 34110, Doha, Qatar

*E-mail: mhossain@hbku.edu.qa

ABSTRACT: Indium tin oxide (ITO) thin films remain the cornerstone among transparent conductive oxides (TCOs) for semi-transparent perovskite solar cells (ST-PSCs), where high optical transparency and electrical conductivity are essential for efficient light harvesting and charge transport. However, conventional ITO processing typically requires high-temperature (>200 °C) annealing to achieve sufficient crystallinity, carrier mobility, and film densification. Such thermal dependence restricts their use on heat-sensitive or flexible substrates, posing a major limitation for scalable device integration and next-generation building-integrated photovoltaics (BIPVs). In this study, we demonstrate a room-temperature RF magnetron sputtering approach to fabricate SiO₂/ITO bilayer transparent electrodes with finely controlled structural, optical, and electronic characteristics. The SiO₂ overlayer functions as both a protective and optical-engineering layer, enhancing light transmission, minimizing surface defects, and imparting hydrophilic, anti-soiling behavior, crucial for maintaining optical clarity and stability under real-world environmental exposure. The underlying ITO film, optimized through precise control of sputtering pressure and RF power, exhibits superior crystallinity and uniform grain morphology even without post-deposition annealing. Comprehensive analyses using Hall effect measurements, X-ray diffraction (XRD), X-ray photoelectron spectroscopy (XPS), transmission electron microscopy (TEM), and atomic force microscopy (AFM) confirm the films' outstanding quality. The optimized SiO₂/ITO structures deliver an average optical transmittance of ~91% in the 400–1000 nm range, a sheet resistance below 45 Ω sq⁻¹, and a surface roughness under 1 nm, underscoring their excellent trade-off between transparency and conductivity. These results establish a scalable, energy-efficient, and substrate-independent route for producing high-performance transparent electrodes suitable for flexible, semi-transparent perovskite solar cells and other optoelectronic devices, enabling the transition toward low-temperature, sustainable photovoltaic manufacturing.

1 INTRODUCTION

Semi-transparent solar cells (ST-SCs) represent a rapidly emerging class of photovoltaic devices that combine light transmission and electrical power generation, enabling their integration into architectural elements such as building façades, smart windows, greenhouses, and tandem photovoltaic modules. Their dual functionality positions them at the forefront of next-generation energy-harvesting and daylight-management systems, where both aesthetic transparency and energy conversion efficiency are paramount. The performance and stability of ST-SCs are critically determined by the quality of their transparent conductive electrodes (TCEs), which must simultaneously exhibit high optical transmittance, low sheet resistance, strong mechanical adhesion, and chemical durability. Among available TCEs, indium tin oxide (ITO) remains the benchmark material owing to its high carrier mobility, wide optical bandgap (~3.5–4.0 eV), and excellent transparency across the visible and near-infrared spectra. However, conventional ITO deposition typically requires high-temperature (>300 °C) annealing, which restricts its application to heat-sensitive substrates such as polymers or hybrid perovskite layers. This thermal limitation has hindered the scalability of flexible and large-area semi-transparent perovskite solar cells (ST-PSCs).

In this study, we report a room-temperature RF magnetron sputtering approach for the fabrication of SiO₂/ITO bilayer transparent electrodes, designed to function as dual-purpose optical and electrical interfaces for ST-PSCs operating under ambient conditions. The SiO₂ capping layer serves multiple critical roles: it acts as an anti-reflective coating, enhances light incoupling, and imparts anti-soiling, self-cleaning, and environmental protection capabilities, thereby improving both optical performance and long-term durability in harsh environments. Furthermore, the SiO₂ overlayer mitigates surface defect density and promotes uniform energy band alignment at the perovskite interface, suppressing charge recombination and enhancing device stability. Meanwhile, the underlying ITO layer, deposited under optimized low-pressure (2 mTorr) and moderate RF power conditions, ensures efficient charge transport and optical transparency exceeding 85%, with a sheet resistance as low as ~45 Ω sq⁻¹. The resulting SiO₂/ITO stacks exhibit smooth, compact morphologies (AFM roughness < 1 nm) and high structural integrity without any post-deposition annealing. This low-temperature process therefore enables scalable, cost-effective fabrication of flexible, lightweight, and high-efficiency ST-PSCs, suitable for deployment in real-world building-integrated photovoltaics and adaptive energy-harvesting systems.

2 METHODOLOGY

At room temperature (RT), metal–oxide thin films were deposited via reactive electron-beam (e-beam) evaporation using a Denton™ system. The deposition was conducted under a base pressure of approximately 2×10^{-4} Torr, with an oxygen flow rate of 20 sccm and a growth rate of 1 Å/s, ensuring uniform layer formation and controlled stoichiometry. The optical properties of the resulting films were characterized using UV–Vis spectrophotometry (PerkinElmer Lambda™), enabling precise assessment of transmittance and absorption across the visible spectrum. Krüss™ contact angle measurements were employed to evaluate surface wettability and infer the degree of hydrophilicity or hydrophobicity of the coatings. Surface topology and roughness were analyzed using a Dektak™ 3D stylus profilometer, providing quantitative thickness and morphology data.

Microstructural and morphological features were further investigated by field emission scanning electron microscopy (FESEM, JEOL 7610™), revealing surface texture and grain distribution at high resolution. Finally, X-ray photoelectron spectroscopy (XPS) was employed to determine the elemental composition, oxidation states, and chemical bonding environments within the films, offering comprehensive insights into their structural and electronic characteristics.

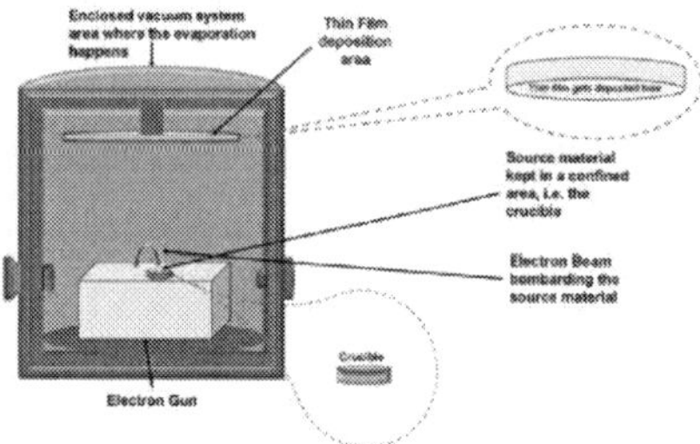

Figure 1: Schematic illustration of the RF magnetron sputtering deposition chamber used for SiO$_2$/ITO thin-film fabrication. The system comprises independently controlled SiO$_2$ and ITO targets, a rotating substrate holder to ensure uniform film thickness, and an oxygen–argon reactive gas inlet maintaining a constant flow of 20 sccm. The base pressure was maintained at 2×10^{-4} Torr, and deposition was performed at room temperature with a growth rate of 1 Å s^{-1}. The configuration allows precise control of plasma parameters, enabling low-temperature deposition of highly transparent, conductive oxide layers.

3 RESULTS AND DISCUSSIONS

Room-temperature sputtered indium tin oxide (ITO) films exhibited a dominant (222) diffraction peak centered around 31°, accompanied by secondary reflections consistent with the cubic bixbyite phase of In$_2$O$_3$. Depositions conducted under low argon pressure (2 mTorr) and moderate RF power (100–200 W) produced a marked enhancement in the (222) peak intensity, signifying improved crystallinity and enlarged grain domains—key contributors to higher electrical conductivity and optical transparency. X-ray photoelectron spectroscopy (XPS) confirmed the formation of highly pure, stoichiometric oxides with negligible carbon contamination. Both the 2 mTorr and 10 mTorr depositions displayed stable oxygen incorporation (SiO$_{1.91}$ for SiO$_2$), and the measured work function of ~3.94 eV indicated excellent electronic alignment for optoelectronic interfaces. Deconvolution of the XPS spectra revealed distinct and well-resolved In 3d, Sn 3d, O 1s, and Si 2p peaks, confirming precise stoichiometric control and chemical purity across all

compositions. Optical analyses via UV–Vis–NIR spectroscopy demonstrated an average transmittance exceeding 85% for the 2 mTorr films, with lower RF power favoring the highest transparency and minimal absorption losses. A clear thickness-dependent trade-off emerged: thinner layers enhanced visible transparency, whereas thicker ones yielded improved electrical conductivity, reflecting the intrinsic balance between optical and electrical performance. Surface characterization further highlighted the influence of process parameters. Films grown at low pressure (2 mTorr) and low RF power exhibited smaller contact angles and atomic force microscopy (AFM) roughness values below 1 nm, indicating exceptionally smooth, compact, and hydrophilic surfaces—highly advantageous for self-cleaning and anti-fouling functionalities. In contrast, increasing deposition pressure and power led to rougher morphologies, enlarged grains, and higher hydrophobicity, revealing the delicate interplay between plasma energy, adatom mobility, and surface texture.

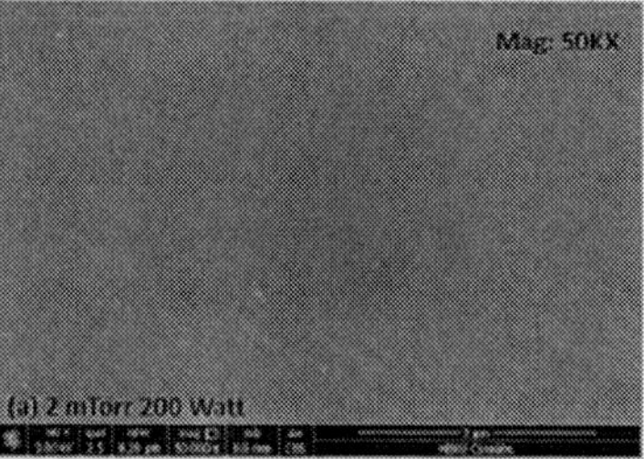

Figure 2: FESEM micrographs of ITO thin films deposited at two different sputtering pressures. At low pressure (2 mTorr), the film exhibits a dense, compact, and uniform granular structure with well-defined boundaries, indicative of enhanced adatom mobility and improved crystallinity. In contrast, deposition at higher pressure (10 mTorr) results in a rougher and less homogeneous surface, characterized by larger, irregular grains and increased porosity due to enhanced scattering and reduced kinetic energy of arriving species. These morphological differences directly influence the films' optical transparency, conductivity, and wetting behavior.

Probing the nanoscale architecture of our films, we found that the room-temperature sputtering process yields a crystalline structure of remarkable integrity. High-resolution TEM analysis revealed dense and sharply defined and ITO layers, with clear lattice fringes throughout the ITO bulk indicating a high-quality crystalline formation. This visual evidence was solidified by SAED patterns, which confirmed the film's structure as the highly conductive cubic bixbyite phase. We discovered that the key to this structural excellence lies in gentle deposition conditions,low pressure and low power—which promote the growth of large, well-aligned grains with minimal defects. This superior microstructure is the very foundation of the exceptional properties achieved, directly linking the atomic arrangement to the film's macroscopic function. Electrically, the films are powerful n-type conductors, boasting a high free carrier concentration on the order of magnitude. By carefully tuning the process to a low pressure of 2 mTorr and a moderate RF power, we optimized the interplay between carrier concentration and mobility, achieving a state-of-the-art resistivity of 2.79 10 $\Omega \cdot cm$ and a high carrier mobility of 35.5 $cm^2/V \cdot s$. Deviating from this optimum, for instance by increasing RF power, introduces a critical trade-off: while the creation of more oxygen vacancies boosts the carrier concentration and thus conductivity, it simultaneously degrades mobility due to increased electron scattering at grain boundaries, ultimately hindering overall performance. This deep understanding allows for the deliberate engineering of TCOs with tailored, superior properties for the most demanding applications.

4 CONCLUSIONS

This investigation unveils a facile and scalable RF magnetron sputtering methodology for the fabrication of robust transparent conductive electrodes, specifically designed for next-generation optoelectronics destined for harsh environmental deployment. By forgoing conventional high-temperature annealing, we have successfully synthesized a durable silicon dioxide/indium tin oxide () bilayer at room temperature. The deposition, meticulously controlled at a low pressure of 2 mTorr and a moderate RF power between 100–200 W, yields films possessing an exceptional synergy of properties: a luminous optical transmittance of approximately 90%, a low sheet resistance of ~, and an exquisitely smooth surface topography with an AFM-measured roughness below one nanometer. The strategically deposited overlayer serves as a multifunctional vanguard, imparting anti-reflective, protective, and self-cleaning characteristics. This capping layer demonstrates remarkable resilience against ultraviolet degradation, humidity ingress, and dust accumulation, thereby preserving pristine optical clarity over extended periods. Ultimately, these findings illuminate a pathway toward developing high-performance, mechanically flexible, and environmentally resilient transparent conductive electrodes, poised to significantly enhance the durability and efficiency of devices such as perovskite solar cells operating in challenging outdoor conditions.

5 REFERENCES

[1] Z. Ying, et al., "Sputtered indium-zinc oxide for buffer layer free semitransparent perovskite photovoltaic devices in perovskite/silicon 4T-tandem solar cells," Advanced Materials Interfaces, vol. 8, 2020, Article 2001604.
[2] B. Shi, et al., "Semitransparent perovskite solar cells: From materials and devices to applications," Advanced Materials, vol. 32, 2020, Article 1806474.
[3] S. An, et al., "Cerium-doped indium oxide transparent electrode for semi-transparent perovskite and perovskite/silicon tandem solar cells," Solar Energy, vol. 196, pp. 409–418, 2020.
[4] F. Kurdesau, et al., "Comparative study of ITO layers deposited by DC and RF magnetron sputtering at room temperature," Journal of Non-Crystalline Solids, vol. 352, pp. 1466–1470, 2006.
[5] K. Wang, et al., "ITO films with different preferred orientations prepared by DC magnetron sputtering," Optical Materials, vol. 134, p. 113040, 2022.
[6] M. I. Hossain, B. Aïssa, A. Samara, S. A. Mansour, C. A. Broussillou, and V. Bermudez Benito, ACS Omega, vol. 6, no. 8, pp. 5276–5286, 2021.
[7] L. L. Lebel, B. Aïssa, M. A. El Khakani, and D. Therriault, Composites Science and Technology, vol. 70, no. 3, pp. 518–524, 2010.
[8] W. Julia, C. Luis, R. Federico, et al., Advanced Functional Materials, vol. 23, pp. 5591–5598, 2013.
[9] D. T. H. Dalir, R. D. Farahani, V. Nhim, and B. Aïssa, et al., Langmuir, vol. 28, no. 1, pp. 791–803, 2011.
[10] A. Ali, F. El-Mellouhi, A. Mitra, and B. Aïssa, Nanomaterials, vol. 12, no. 5, p. 788, 2022.
[11] R. D. Farahani, D. T. H. Dalir, V. Le Borgne, A. Loick, et al., Composites Science and Technology, vol. 72, no. 12, pp. 1387–1395, 2012.
[12] N. M. H. Gavi, B. D. Ngom, A. C. Beye, A. M. Strydom, B. Aïssa, V. V. Srinivasu, and M. Chaker, Journal of Magnetism and Magnetic Materials, vol. 324, no. 6, pp. 1172–1176, 2012.
[13] B. Aïssa and M. A. El Khakani, Nanotechnology, vol. 20, no. 17, p. 175203, 2009.
[14] M. A. Habib, M. Barkat, B. Aïssa, and T. Denidni, Progress in Electromagnetics Research, vol. 88, pp. 135–148, 2008.
[15] H. Zhao, H. Kimura, Z. Cheng, X. Wang, and T. Nishida, Applied Physics Letters, vol. 95, p. 232904, 2009. https://doi.org/10.1063/1.3271032.

STUDY OF THE INFLUENCE OF Pb SUBSTITUTION BY Zn^{2+} IONS ON THE PROPERTIES OF $CsPbBr_{3-x}I_x$ THIN FILMS

G. Gordillo[1], O.G. Torres[1] y Julian C. Pena-Bermudez[2],
[1] Departamento de Física, Universidad Nacional, Bogotá, Colombia
[2] Universidad del Caribe (UNICARIBE), Santo Domingo, Dominican Republic

ABSTRACT: In this work is reported results of a study on optical and structural properties of thin films of cesium lead bromide iodide mixed perovskite ($CsPbBr_{3-x}I_x$), synthesized by sequential evaporation of precursors (CsBr, $PbBr_2$, PbI_2). Thin films of $CsPbBr_{3-x}I_x$ with a high degree of reproducibility of both the molar composition and the photovoltaic properties were achieved, using an electronic system with facilities to control the growth of the samples with the help of PID and PWM algorithms. Special emphasis was put in evaluating the effect that the substitution of the Pb cation by Zn^{2+} ions onto its optical, morphological and structural properties through transmittance, photoluminescence, Scanning Electron Microscopy (SEM) and Urbach Energy measurements.

1. INTRODUCTION

Organic-inorganic hybrid perovskite solar cells have been intensively investigated since their discovery, mainly due to their good optical and electronic properties [1], including high absorption coefficients [2], long carrier diffusion lengths [3] and low trap density [4]. A look made to the certified efficiencies reported in the popular NREL photovoltaic chart (Version 64), shows us some interesting trends [5]. The information associated with this chart reveals the following progress made so far [6]. The first single junction $MAPbI_3$ based solar cell, reported by researchers of EPFL, certified in 2013, had an efficiency of 14.1% [7]. This result motivated the researchers worldwide who put their resources into further improving the PCE of PSCs in order to achieve greater efficiency to compete with Si based PV devices. In a period of ten years, the record efficiency of 26.7% was achieved; this record was reported in 2024 by the University of Science and Technology of China (USTC) [8]. Another remarkable development in Perovskite based solar cells research has arisen in recent years. At the 2024 SNEC Expo in Shanghai, LONGi Green Energy Technology Co., Ltd., announced a major breakthrough in the development of its silicon-perovskite tandem solar cells [9]. According to authoritative certification by the European Solar Test Installation (ESTI), this cell's photovoltaic conversion efficiency has reached 34.6%. This achievement once again breaks the world record for silicon-perovskite tandem cell efficiency previously set by the LONGi team. Despite these progress, the presence of Pb is a major limiting to its commercialization [10]. A good candidate for lead replacement is Zn.

In this work, a study was conducted with the purpose of preparing thin films of $CsPbBr_{3-x}I_x$ using a route that includes sequential evaporation of their precursors ($PbBr_2/PbI_2/CsBr$) followed by annealing under normal environmental conditions. Through XRD, SEM, photoluminescence and spectral transmittance measurements carried out on samples prepared by varying the main synthesis variables (ratio of evaporated masses of precursors, precursor deposition rate and annealing temperature) varied in a wide range, conditions were found to grow thin films with composition $CsPbBr_{2.73}I_{0.27}$ that presented good optical, morphological and structural properties. Additionally, a study was conducted to evaluate the effect that the substitution of the Pb cation by Zn^{2+} ions onto its optical, morphological and structural properties through XRD, SEM, transmittance, photoluminescence and Urbach Energy measurements.

2. EXPERIMENTAL DETAILS

Initially thin films of $CsPbBr_{3-x}I_x$ were prepared by sequential evaporation of its precursors ($PbBr_2$, PbI_2,CsBr), where the chemical composition of the resulting compound is adjusted by varying the thickness ratio of precursors, which is determined with the help of a thickness monitor. Sequential evaporation was performed following a routine that includes initial evaporation of PbI_2 followed by evaporation of $PbBr_2$ and CsBr, keeping their respective deposition rates in the range of 4-6 Å/s. The Precursors are evaporated at room temperature from Knudsen cell-type evaporation sources and after the deposition, these are annealed at normal ambient air conditions at temperatures around 250^0C, for 20 minutes. Good reproducibility of both the composition and properties of samples with composition $CsPbBr_{2.73}I_{0.27}$ was achieved using equipment with facilities to control electronically the evaporation temperature and deposition rate of precursors, by means of PID and PWM algorithms. Details of equipment used to prepare the $CsPbBr_{2.73}I_{0.27}$ films is described in a previously published paper (see Ref. [11]), where a similar setup was used to deposit thin films of $MAPbI_3$ by sequential evaporation of precursors. After obtaining conditions to grow thin films with composition $CsPbBr_{2.73}I_{0.27}$, a study was carried out to evaluate the influence that the partial substitution of Pb by Zn^{2+} (obtained by additional evaporation of a layer of ZnBr) produces on the optical and structural properties.

The samples prepared were characterized by means of transmittance and reflectance measurements performed using a Varian–Cary 5000 spectrophotometer, as well as by XRD measurements performed with a Philips X'Pert Pro PANalytical diffractometer, using the radiation Cu-Kα (1.540598 Å), an acceleration voltage of 40 KV and a current 40 mA, and the film thickness was determined using a Veeco Dektak 150 surface profiler. The morphological characterization was performed with an electronic scanning microscope TESCAN, model Vega 3.

3. RESULTS AND DISCUSSION

3.1 Optical characterization

The influence that the substitution of Pb by Zn^{2+} ions on the optical properties of a reference $CsPbBr_{2.73}I_{0.27}$ sample was investigated through photoluminescence, and spectral transmittance and reflectance measurements. The samples were prepared using a route based on sequential evaporation of the precursors (PbI_2, $PbBr_2$, $ZnBr$, $CsBr$), described previously.

Fig. 1 shows typical transmittance and reflectance spectra of a reference film with composition $CsPbBr_{2.73}I_{0.27}$ in which Pb was replaced by Zn in percentages varying between 0 and 13%, as well as absorption coefficient (α) vs λ and Tauc $(\alpha h v)^2$ vs $h v$ curves. The absorption coefficient was estimated using the relation [12]: $\alpha = -(1/d) \ln \frac{T(\lambda)}{1 - R(\lambda)}$ and the Eg value was obtained from the intercept with the axis $h v$ of the curve of $(\alpha h v)^2$ vs $h v$.

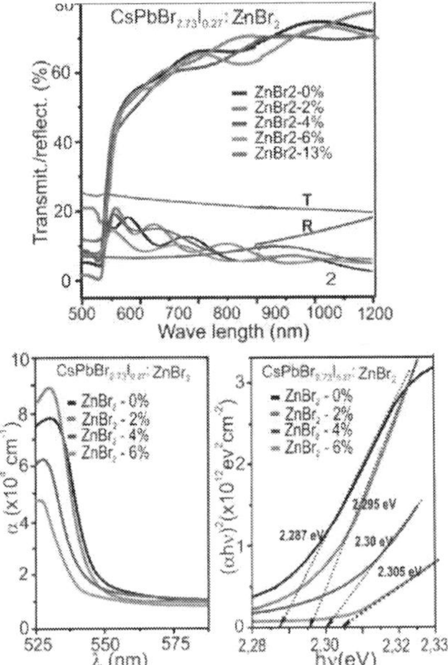

Fig. 1: Transmittance, reflectance, α vs λ and $(\alpha h v)^2$ vs $h v$ curves of a reference sample with composition $CsPbBr_{2.73}I_{0.27}$, in which the Pb cation was replaced by Zn in different percentages.

The results in Fig.1 show that the substitution of Pb by Zn at low concentrations has little effect on the energy gap Eg of the $CsPbBr_{2.7}I_{0.27}$ sample, indicating that under these conditions the band structure is not significantly affected; however, when the substitution of Pb by Zn is high (greater than 10%), the transmittance decreases strongly and interference maxima and minima are not observed,

indicating that this type of samples present a high degree of crystalline disorder that gives rise to high dispersion of the incident radiation that destroys the coherence of the rays that overlap to generate constructive interference. On the other hand, it is observed that the slope of the transmittance curves is slightly affected when Pb is substituted by Zn; this behavior can be explained by assuming that the substitution of Pb by Zn generates structural defects because the ionic radius of Pb (1.20 Å) is quite larger than that of Zinc (0.74Å); this situation generates band tail states within the gap that cause this decrease in the slope of the transmittance curves.

To evaluate the effect of the percentage of Pb by Zn substitution on the structural disorder in the perovskite films, the Urbach energy E_U was calculated from the α vs λ curves near the band edge, using the relation $\alpha_U = \alpha_0 exp \left[\frac{h v - E_l}{E u}\right]$ [13]. Where E_U is the Urbach Energy, E_l and α_0 are constant. Thus, a plot of $\ln(\alpha)$ vs. $h v$ should be linear and Urbach Energy can be obtained from the slope.

In Fig. 2 is shown , $\ln(\alpha)$ vs $h v$ curves (near the band edge) of a perovskite sample with composition $CsPbBr_{2.7}I_{0.27}$ in which Pb was substituted by Zn in a percentage that varied between 0 and 6% are presented; the E_U value calculated from the slopes of the $\ln(\alpha)$ vs $h v$ curves is shown in inset of Fig. 2; the E_U value obtained is less than 44 meV for samples in which Pb was substituted by Zn in a percentage $\leq$ 4%, indicating that they exhibit good crystalline quality; on the contrary, when a high Pb by Zn substitution is made ($\geq$ 6%) the E_U value increases strongly, indicating that this case presents high structural disorder.

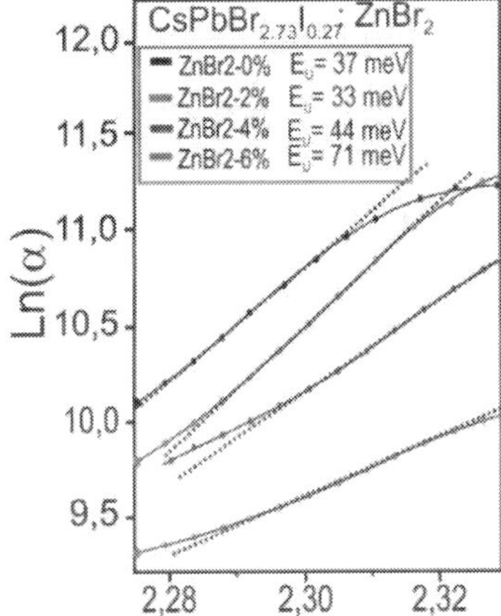

Fig. 2: Curves of $\ln(\alpha)$ vs $h v$, showing Eu values calculated for the sample $CsPbBr_{2.7}I0.27$ in which Pb was replaced by Zn in a percentage that varied between 0 and 6%.

The influence of replacing the Pb cation by Zn on the photoluminescence (FL) emitted by a $CsPbBr_{2.73}I_{0.27}$ sample was also studied in this work. Fig. 3 shows typical FL emission spectra of a $CsPbBr_{2.73}I_{0.27}$ thin film in which Pb was replaced by Zn in percentages ranging from 0 to 6%. These results show that the substitution of Pb by Zn slightly affects the optical gap of the $CsPbBr_{2.73}I_{0.27}$ film, results that agree with those previously obtained from the Tauc curves. It can also be observed that the FL spectrum of films prepared by replacing Pb by Zn in percentages lower than 4% is quite symmetrical, but this symmetry is lost when the substitution of Pb by Zn is increased to percentages higher than 4%. This behavior could be explained by assuming that the emission produced by samples prepared by replacing Pb with Zn in percentages less than 4% is mainly due to fundamental transition between states of the conduction and valence bands, while samples prepared by replacing Pb with Zn in higher percentages emit, in addition to fundamental radiation, radiation induced by transitions via energy levels within the gap associated with native defects and impurities.

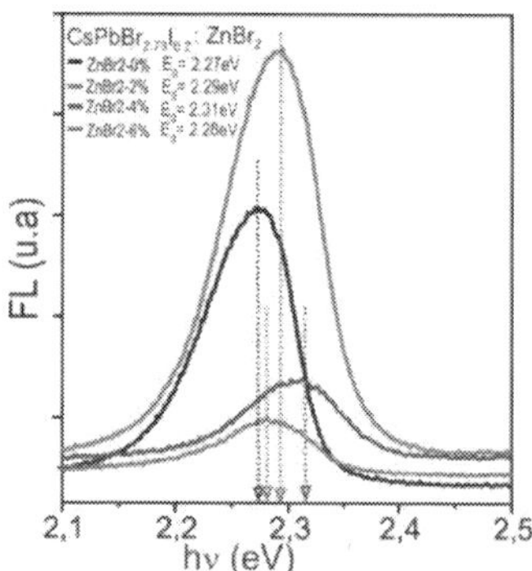

Fig. 3: Photoluminescence spectra of $CsPbBr_{2.7}I_{0.27}$ thin films prepared by varying the percentage of Pb substitution by Zn.

It is also observed that $CsPbBr_{2.73}I_{0.27}$ films prepared by replacing Pb with Zn in percentages greater than or equal to 4% exhibit a very low FL intensity; this behavior could be explained by poor crystalline quality and by the generation of non-radiative recombination centers associated with deep emission levels, induced by the excess substitution of Pb with Zn.

3.2 Structural properties

In Fig. 4a is compared the XRD spectrum of the reference $CsPbBr_{2.73}I_{0.27}$ sample with those in which Pb was replaced by Zn in a percentage that varied between 0 and 6%. These results reveals that the $CsPbBr_{2.73}I_{0.27}$ exhibit only reflections corresponding to the cubic-phase (PDF 96-451-0746), and when Zn ions substitute the Pb cation, the crystalline structure does not change; however, the reflections observed in the XRD pattern shift towards larger 2θ values, when the percentage of substitution of Pb by Zn increases. This shift is due to the fact that the ionic radius of Zn^{2+} is smaller than that of Pb^{2+}, which causes a reduction in the size of the unit cell and according to Bragg's law ($n\lambda=2d\sin\theta$) [14] for the relationship to be preserved, the angle θ must increase. Fig. 4b shows the effect that the substitution of Pb by Zn produces on the shift towards larger 2θ values of of the characteristic peak of the phase $CsPbBr_{2.73}I_{0.27}$,

observed at $2\theta = 21.5^0$ when the percentage of substitution of Pb by Zn increases. On the other hand, effect of substituting Pb by Zn on the crystallite size was estimated using the Scherrer equation [15]. ($D=k\lambda/(\beta\cos\theta$, where D is the crystallite size, $k = 0.94$, $\lambda_{Cu} = 1.5418$ Å, β is the FWHM and θ is the Bragg angle). It was found that in the range of Pb by Zn substitution studied (% Zn: 0 - 6), the crystallite size is not significantly affected, obtaining a value around 24 nm, which is a typical value for perovskites based on lead halides. The effect of substituting Pb for Zn on the microstrain ϵ of the $CsPbBr_{2.73}I_{0.27}$ sample was also estimated using the Williamson-Hall equation given by the relationship $\beta\cdot\cos\theta=Dk/\lambda+4\cdot\epsilon\cdot\sin\theta$ [16]. It was found that in the range of Pb by Zn substitution studied (% Zn: 0 - 6), the microstrain has a value of the order of $\epsilon=3.3\times10^{-4}$

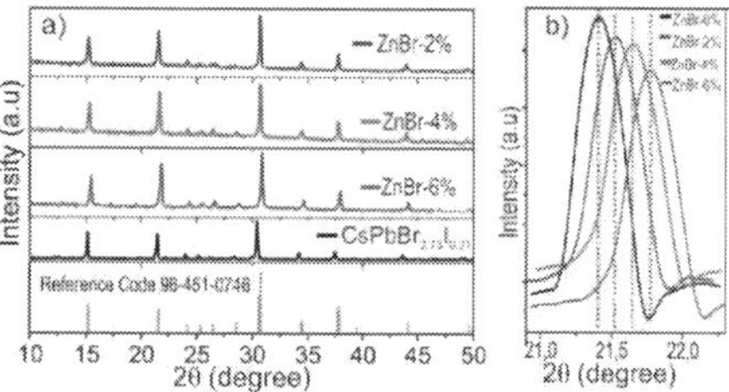

Fig. 4 : Effect that the substitution of Pb by Zn produces on a) the XRD spectra and b) on the shift of the characteristic peak of the phase $CsPbBr_{2.73}I_{0.27}$, observed at $2\theta = 21.5^0$.

3.3 Influence of partial substitution of Pb by Zn^{2+} on morphology of $CsPbBr_{3-x}I_x$ thin films

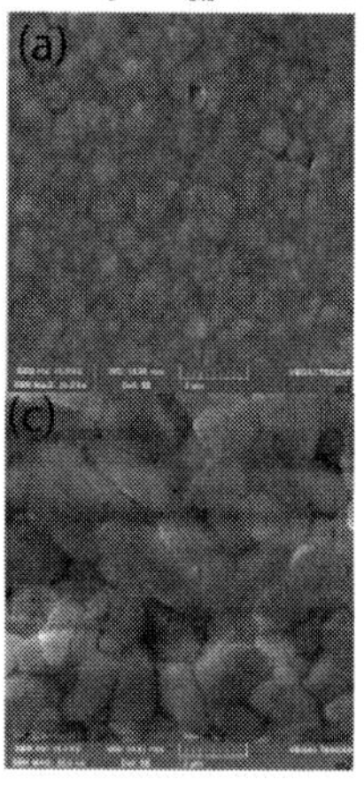
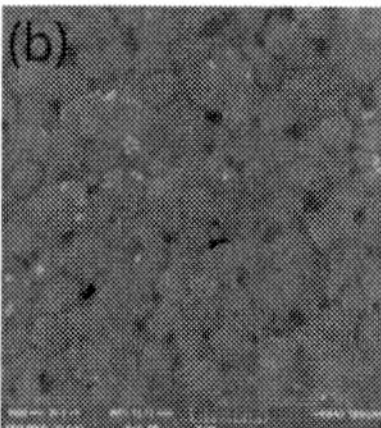

Fig. 5: SEM images of a thin film of $CsPbBr_{2.73}I_{0.27}$ in which Pb was partially replaced by Zn at concentrations of: a) 0, b) 0.2, c) 0.4 %

The effect of partially replacing the Pb cation with Zn in the structure of a reference sample with composition CsPbBr2.73I0.27 on its morphology was studied through scanning electron microscopy (SEM) measurements. Fig. 5 shows SEM micrographs of the reference sample in which Pb was replaced by Zn at concentrations ranging from 0 to 4%. These results reveal that the sample not doped with Zn presents a morphology consisting of very small grains and the formation of clusters of different sizes; the substitution of Pb by Zn significantly improves its morphology; this type of sample presents a morphology characterized by compact grains whose size increases significantly with increasing percentage of Pb atoms substituted by Zn.

4. CONCLUSIONS

The effect that the substitution of the Pb cation by Zn^{2+} ions on the optical, morphological and structural properties of perovskites thin films with composition $CsPbBr_{2.73}I_{0.27}$ which were synthesized by sequential evaporation of their precursors ($PbI2$, $PbBr2$, $CsBr$), was evaluated through XRD, SEM, spectral transmittance, photoluminescence, and Urbach Energy measurements. From these studies it was found that the substitution of Pb by Zn at low concentrations, does not significantly affect the electronic structure; however, when the substitution of Pb by Zn is greater than 10%, the samples present a high degree of crystalline disorder. On the other hand, it was observed that the substitution of Pb by Zn generates structural defects because the ionic radius of Pb is quite larger than that of Zinc; this situation generates band tail states within the gap that participate in the absorption processes.

XRD characterization revealed that the $CsPbBr_{2.73}I_{0.27}$ exhibit only reflections corresponding to the cubic-phase and when Zn ions substitute the Pb cation, the crystalline structure does not change; however the reflections shift towards larger 2θ values, when Pb is substituted by Zn due to the fact that the ionic radius of Zn^{2+} is smaller than that of Pb_{2+}. On the other hand, photoluminesence measurements indicated that the emission produced by samples prepared by replacing Pb with Zn in percentages less than 4% is mainly due to fundamental transition, while samples prepared by replacing Pb with Zn in higher percentages emit, in addition to fundamental radiation, radiation induced by transitions via energy levels within the gap associated with native defects and impurities.

ACKNOWLEDGEMENTS

This work was funded by the Research and Extension Division (DIEB) of the National University of Colombia - Bogotá Campus, project 59845. GMS & ES Research Group, Faculty of Sciences - Department of Physics - Cra 45 # 26-85, Bogotá, Postal Code 111321 – Colombia

REFERENCES

[1] Ansari, M.I.H.; Qurashi, A.; Nazeeruddin, M.K. Frontiers, Opportunities, and Challenges in Perovskite Solar Cells: A Critical Review. J. Photochem. Photobiol. C Photochem. Rev. 2018, 35, 1–24.

[2] Chen, Z.; Dong, Q.; Liu, Y.; Bao, C.; Fang, Y.; Lin, Y.; Tang, S.; Wang, Q.; Xiao, X.; Bai, Y.; et al. Thin Single Crystal Perovskite SolarCells to Harvest Below-Bandgap Light Absorption. Nat. Commun. 2017, 8, 1890.

[3] Xing, G.; Mathews, N.; Sun, S.; Lim, S. S.; Lam, Y. M.; Grätzel, M.; Mhaisalkar, S.; Sum, T. C., Long-Range Balanced Electronand Hole-Transport Lengths in Organic-Inorganic CH3NH3PbI3, Science 2013, 342, 344-347.

[4]. Juarez-Perez, E.J.; Hawash, Z.; Raga, S.R.; Ono, L.K.; Qi, Y. Thermal Degradation of CH3NH3PbI3 Perovskite into NH3 and CH3I Gases Observed by Coupled Thermogravimetry-Mass Spectrometry Analysis. Energy Environ. Sci. 2016, 9, 3406–3410.

[5] Martin A. Green, Ewan D. Dunlop, Masahiro Yoshita, Nikos Kopidakis, Karsten Bothe,Gerald Siefer, David Hinken, Michael Rauer, Jochen Hohl-Ebinger, Xiaojing Hao, Solar cell efficiency tables (version 64), Prog Photovolt Res Appl. 2024;32:425–441.

[6] NREL, PIP & NREL data, Cell Effiency Data Table, https://www.nrel.gov/pv/assets/docs/cell-effiency-data-table.xlsx (Last accessed: December 10, 2023

[7] Park, N.-G. Organometal Perovskite Light Absorbers Toward a 20% Efficiency Low-Cost Solid-State Mesoscopic Solar Cell. J. Phys.Chem. Lett. 2013, 4, 2423–2429

[8] http://en.ustc.edu.cn/info/1007/4676.htm

[9] https://www.longi.com/en/news/2024-snec-silicon-perovskite-tandem-solar-cells-new-world-efficiency/

[10] Babayigit, A.; Ethirajan, A.; Muller, M.; Conings, B., Toxicity of organometal halide perovskite solar cells. Nat. Mater. 2016, 15, 247-251.

[11] M. A . Reinoso, C. A. Otálora and G. Gordillo, Improvement Properties of Hybrid Halide Perovskite Thin Films Prepared by Sequential Evaporation for Planar Solar Cells, Materials 2019, 12, 1394

[12] J. I. Pankove. Optical Processes in Semiconductors, Dover Inc. New York, 1975.

[13] M.V. Kurik, Review of Urbach's tail. Phys. *Status Solidi A*, vol. 8, No. 9, 1971.

[14] R. Sharma, N. Hooda, A. Hooda, S. Khasa, Physica B : Condensed Matter Structural , dielectric and magnetic study of double perovskite La_2CoMnO_6, Phys. B Condens. Matter 673 (2024) 415473. https://doi.org/10.1016/j.physb.2023.415473.

[15] B.W. Kim, S.H. Im, Supersaturated Antisolvent-Assisted Crystallization for Highly Efficient Inorganic Perovskite Light-Emitting Diodes, ACS Nano 18 (2024) 28691–28699. https://doi.org/10.1021/acsnano.4c06465.

[16] M. Elhamel, Z. Hebboul, M. Elhabib, A. Draoui, A. Benghia, M. Benali, S. Goumri-, L.P. Mat, Journal of Solid State Chemistry Experimental synthesis of double perovskite functional nano-ceramic Eu_2NiMnO_6 : Combining optical characterization and DFT calculations, J. Solid State Chem. 323 (2023) 124022. https://doi.org/10.1016/j.jssc.2023.12402

Comparative Analysis and Efficiency Optimization of Sulfur-based Chalcogenide Perovskites (MgHfS$_3$, CaZrS$_3$, BaZrS$_3$) via Interface Engineering for High-Performance Solar Cells

Anees Ur Rehman*, Kung Ding, Jingwei Zhang, Xiang Chen

College of Mechanical and Electrical Engineering, Hohai University, China

Abstract

Chalcogenide perovskites (CP) present a stable and promising alternative to hybrid halide perovskites due to their strong visible-light absorption. This study investigates three sulfur-based chalcogenide absorbers—MgHfS$_3$, CaZrS$_3$, and BaZrS$_3$ —in Perovskite solar cells using SCAPS-1D simulations. CaZrS$_3$ is established as the most efficient absorber. Performance is further enhanced through interface (IF) engineering using 3C–SiC and graphene, achieving a power conversion efficiency of 23.13%.

Scientific Innovation

This study introduces several innovative aspects that contribute to the advancement of stable, high-performance solar cells:

Novel Absorber Focus:

MgHfS$_3$, CaZrS$_3$, and BaZrS$_3$ have seen limited exploration in photovoltaic research. This work provides the first detailed comparative performance analysis and optimization of these three sulfur-based chalcogenide perovskites.

Device Architecture Innovation:

The use of CSTO (CaSnTiO$_3$) as an ETL is unconventional yet effective, offering wide bandgap characteristics and good band alignment with CP.

Interface Engineering Strategy:

We introduce a dual-layer interface engineering approach using 3C–SiC and graphene, which has not been widely applied to CP-based PSCs. These materials help suppress interfacial recombination and enhance charge transport, which are considered critical factors in pushing device efficiency beyond current limits.

ETL	CBO (eV)	VBO (eV)
CSTO/ CaZrS$_3$	0.1	0.9
CSTO/ MgHfS$_3$	0.2	1.27
CSTO/ BaZrS$_3$	0.2	0.8

HTL	CBO (eV)	VBO (eV)
CaZrS$_3$/nPb	1	-0.5
MgHfS$_3$/nPb	1.1	-0.13
BaZrS$_3$/nPb	1.1	-0.6

$$CBO = X_{PER} - X_{CTL}$$
$$VBO = X_{CTL} - X_{PER} + E_{gCTL} - E_{gPER}$$

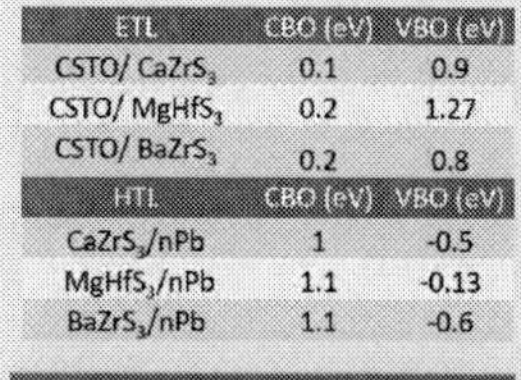

Fig. 1. Energy level diagram of the proposed PSCs without interfacial layers

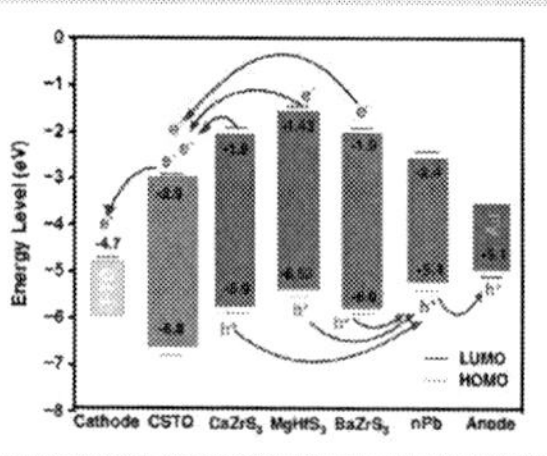
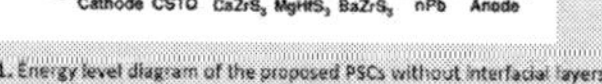

Fig. 2. Optical Absorption of the layers

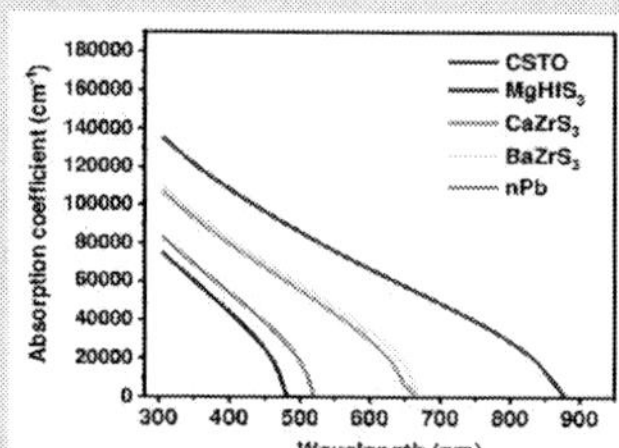
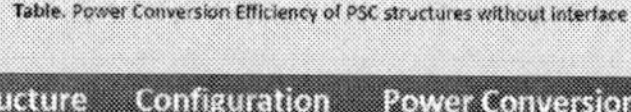

Table. Power Conversion Efficiency of PSC structures without interface

Structure No.	Configuration	Power Conversion Efficiency
Structure-1	CSTO/ CaZrS$_3$/nPb	21.07%
Structure-2	CSTO/ MgHfS$_3$/nPb	15.30%
Structure-3	CSTO/ BaZrS$_3$/nPb	10.73%

> Optimization of layer thickness of proposed PSCs without Interface Layers

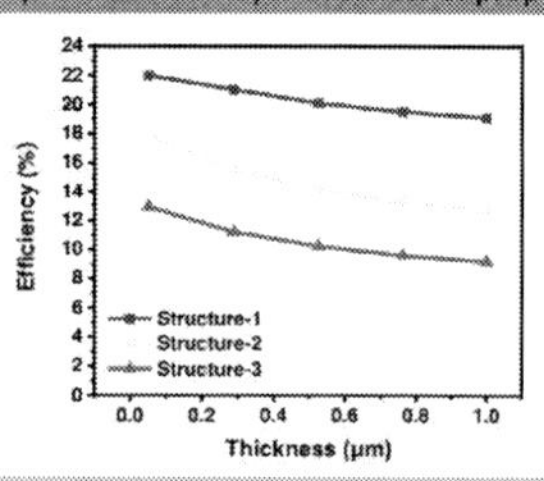

Fig. 3. Effect of Absorber layer thickness on proposed PSCs

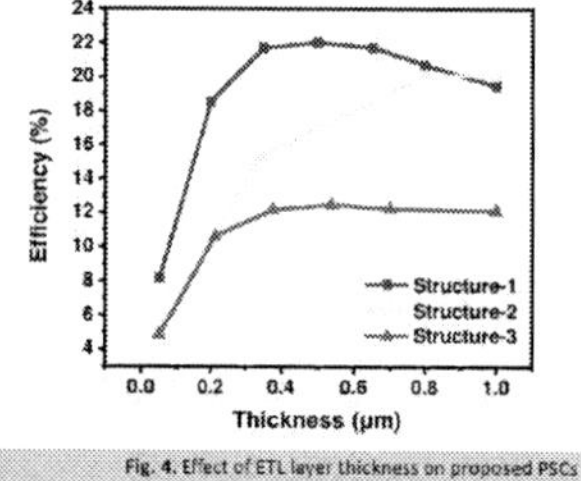

Fig. 4. Effect of ETL layer thickness on proposed PSCs

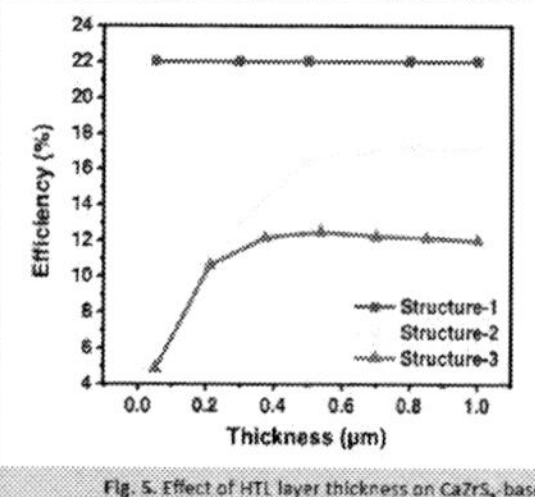

Fig. 5. Effect of HTL layer thickness on CaZrS$_3$-based PSC

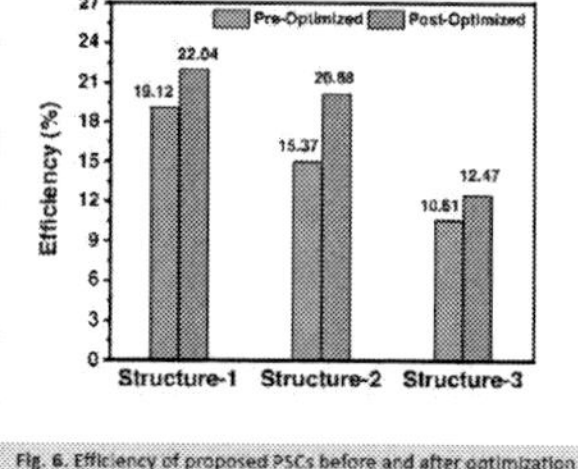

Fig. 6. Efficiency of proposed PSCs before and after optimization

> Optimization of CaZrS$_3$-based PSC with Interface Layers

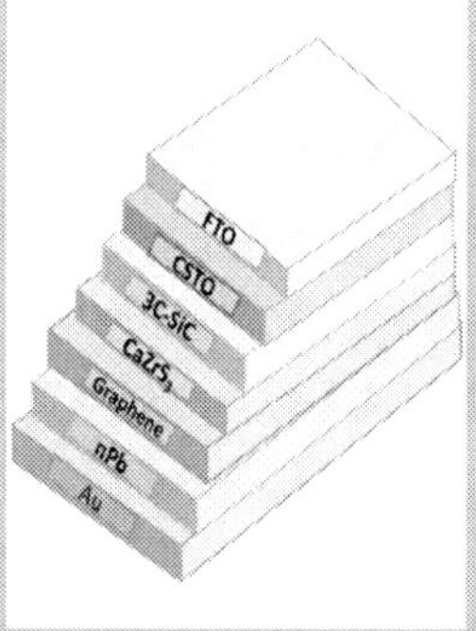

Fig. 7. Layer-by-layer diagram of CaZrS$_3$-based PSC with IF layers.

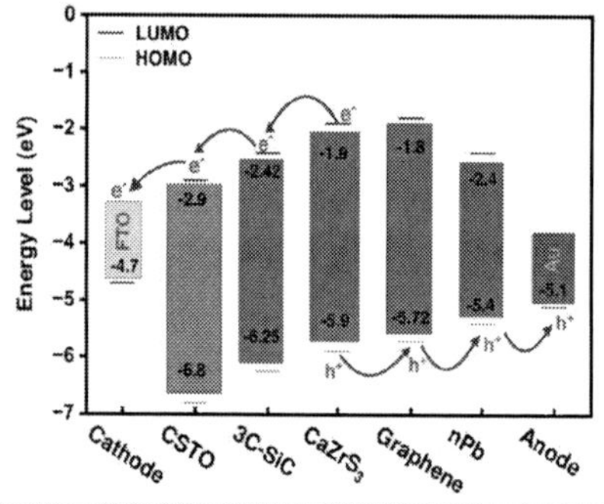

Fig. 8. Energy level diagram of the CaZrS$_3$-based PSC with IF layers

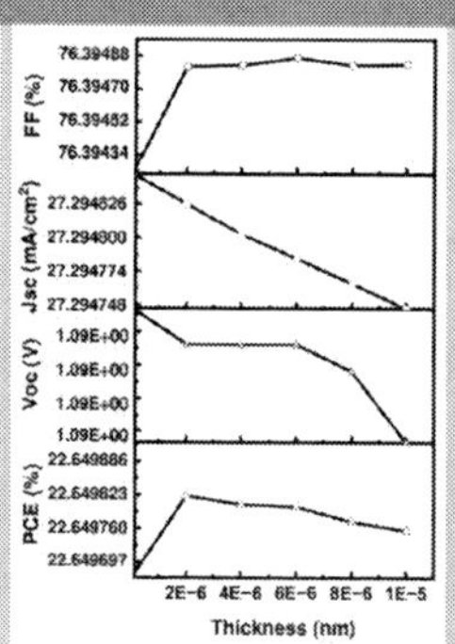

Fig. 9. Effect of varying thickness of 3C-SiC IF layer

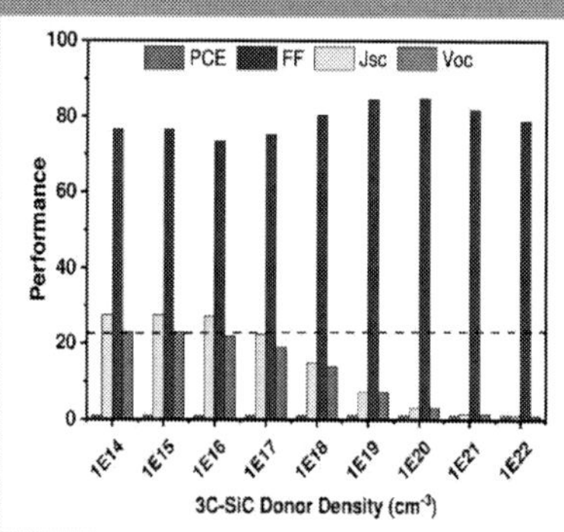

Fig. 10. Effect of varying doping densities of 3C-SiC IF layer

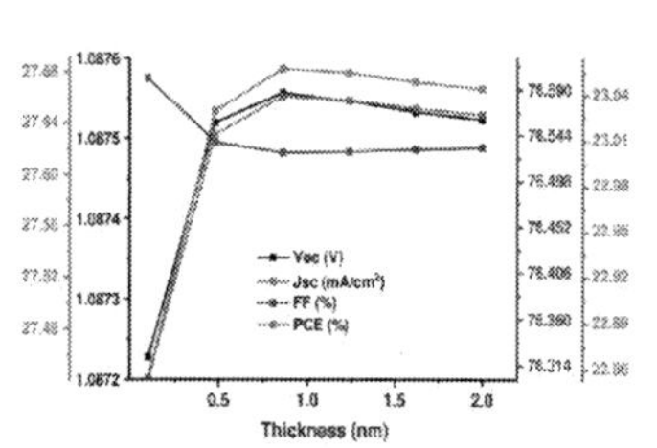

Fig. 11. Effect of varying thickness of graphene IF layer.

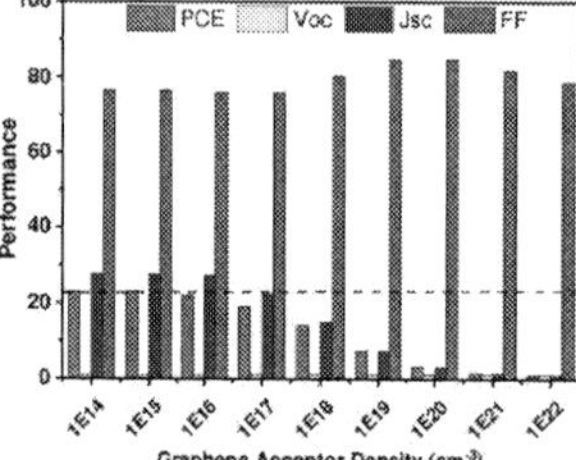

Fig. 12. Effect of varying doping densities of graphene IF layer

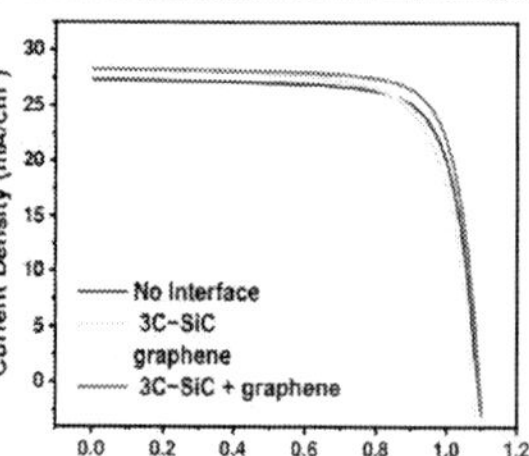

Fig. 13. I-V characteristics of the optimized PSCs structure with various IF layers

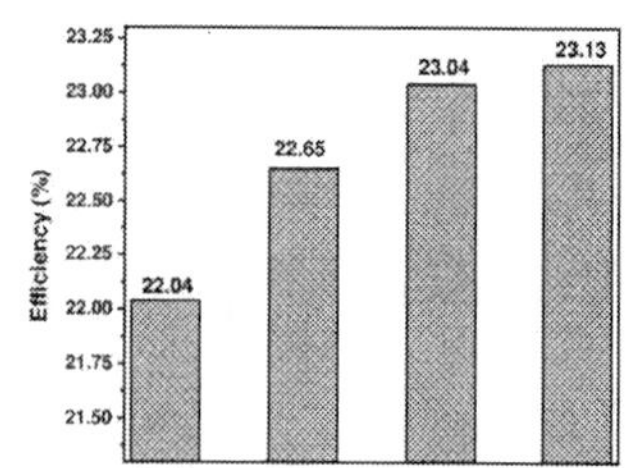

Fig. 14. Efficiency of CaZrS$_3$-based PSCs with & without IF layers

Conclusion

This study establishes CaZrS$_3$ as a promising sulfur-based chalcogenide absorber for efficient and stable PSCs. It also demonstrates the critical role of interface engineering in suppressing recombination losses and enhancing overall performance. These findings provide a scalable and sustainable pathway for future photovoltaic technologies based on environmentally friendly materials.

Funding

This work is supported by the Fundamental Research Funds for the Central Universities, China under grant BC250201180.

Development of Inorganic Perovskite CsPbI₃ with Heterojunction Engineering at the Buried Interface for Enhanced Stability and Performance.

42nd European Photovoltaic Solar Energy Conference and Exhibition

Syed Fawad Ali Shah[1*], Hyeonwook Park[1], Muhammad Rehan[2], Donghyeop Shin[2], Kihwan Kim[2*], Jae Ho Yun[1*]

[1] Korea Institute of Energy Technology (KENTECH), Naju-Si, 58277, South Korea
[2] Korea Institute of Energy Research (KIER), Daejeon, 34129, South Korea

Abstract

In recent years, there has been a significant surge in interest in all inorganic cesium lead triiodide ($CsPbI_3$) perovskite, primarily due to its exceptional thermal and light stability, a various range of fabrication methods and an optimal bandgap of 1.71 eV, making it a promising candidate for the development of tandem devices alongside silicon or other low-bandgap perovskite solar cells (PSCs). The reported power conversion efficiency (PCE) of $CsPbI_3$ PSCs has witnessed a remarkable increase, escalating from a mere 2.9% in 2015 to a substantial 21.15% at present, indicating its strong potential for practical application. However, it is essential to acknowledge that $CsPbI_3$ perovskite exhibits multiple phases (α, β, γ) and is prone to converting into the yellow phase (δ) at room temperature, leading to the formation of numerous defects, such as vacancy, interstitial, and antistite defects. The undesired phase transition is often initiated at the buried interface.

Here, we show that the spontaneously formed two-dimensional Ruddlesden Popper phase of $Cs_2PbI_2Cl_2$ at the buried interface improved electron transfer and phase stability of $CsPbI_3$. Perovskite solar cells based on $CsPbI_3/Cs_2PbI_2Cl_2$ light absorbers exhibit a power conversion efficiency of 20.6% under simulated solar illumination. Furthermore, un-encapsulated devices maintained about 90% of their initial efficiency after continuous light exposure during 1000 hrs.

Introduction

Inorganic Perovskite has

- high thermal stability
- lack of halide segregation
- anti-solvent free synthesis process
- high potential possibilities for efficiency improvement

Volatile organic cations MA/FA Unstable at high temperature

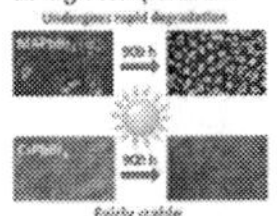

Three degradation pathways:
(1) CH_3NH_3 + HI (identified as the reversible path).
(2) NH_3 + CH_3I (the irreversible or detrimental path).
(3) a reversible Pb(0) + I_2(g) photodecomposition reaction.

Experimental Details

→ Crystal structure of the different phases and their relative phase transitions

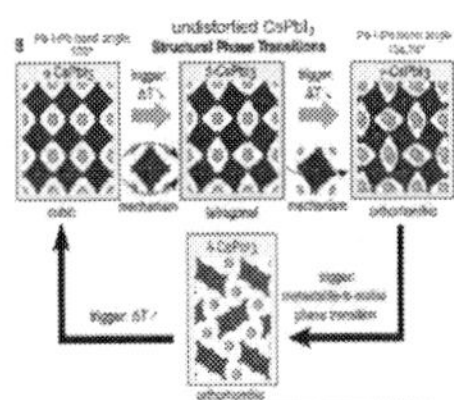

- Phase instability → smaller size of the Cs
- tolerance factor 0.847
- lattice strain induced from the ion size mismatch
- three-dimensional (3D) to one-dimensional (1D) non perovskite phase.

→ **Computational Analysis**

Comparison of properties between existing materials and halogen-mixed materials.

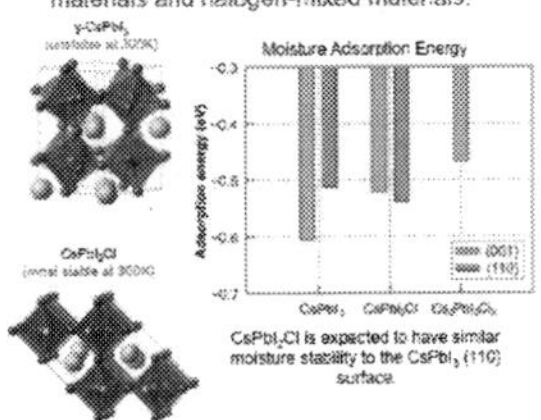

$CsPbI_2Cl$ is expected to have similar moisture stability to the $CsPbI_3$ {110} surface.

$CsPbI_2Cl$ is predicted to exhibit superior properties compared to $CsPbI_3$ in terms of moisture stability.

→ **Halides Incorporation in precursor solution**

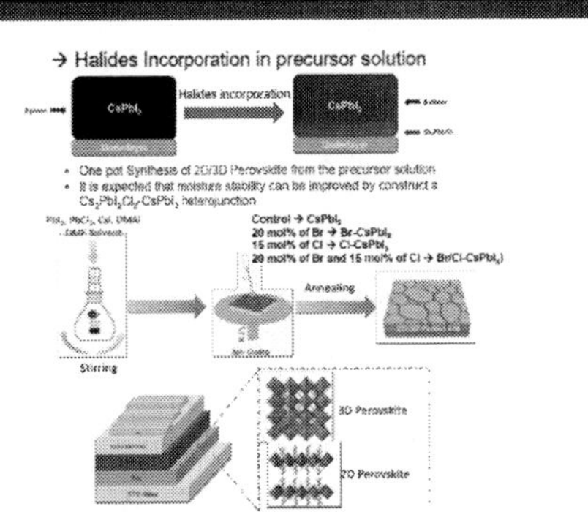

- One pot Synthesis of 2D/3D Perovskite from the precursor solution
- It is expected that moisture stability can be improved by construct a $Cs_2PbI_2Cl_2$-$CsPbI_3$ heterojunction

Control → $CsPbI_3$
20 mol% of Br → Br-$CsPbI_3$
15 mol% of Cl → Cl-$CsPbI_3$
20 mol% of Br and 15 mol% of Cl → $BrCl$-$CsPbI_3$

Results & Discussion

Morphological & Structural Analysis

- SIMS Analysis

Anion-targeted ToF-SIMS depth profiling

3D redistribution of Cl obtained by (ToF-SIMS)

- δ-phase $CsPbI_3$
- stable 2D RP $Cs_2PbI_2Cl_2$ at the buried interface
- enhanced β-phase stability of Cl-$CsPbI_3$

Device Performance

IV curve of the champion device

External quantum efficiency (EQE) spectra of the best-performing solar cells

- Steady state power output (SPO)
- Space Charge Limiting Current (SCLC)

Photovoltaic Performance

V_{oc}, FF and PCE improved incase of Cl-$CsPbI_3$

Device stability

- **Phase Stability at 65% RH**

The Cl-$CsPbI_3$ maintained its black phase even after 16 h of exposure to moisture.

2D $Cs_2PbI_2Cl_2$ phase at the buried interface improved the phase stability.

- Light illumination stability

9% reduction in PCE after 1000 hrs of un-encapsulated device in inert atmosphere

- Moisture Stability @75% RH

12.3% reduction in PCE after 700 hrs

Optical properties

- UV-Vis Analysis

$CsPbI_3$ = 1.7 eV
Cl-$CsPbI_3$ = 1.708 eV
Br-$CsPbI_3$ = 1.71 eV
Cl/Br-$CsPbI_3$ = 1.712 eV

- PL Analysis

Cl-$CsPbI_3$ high PL Intensity Longer Life time

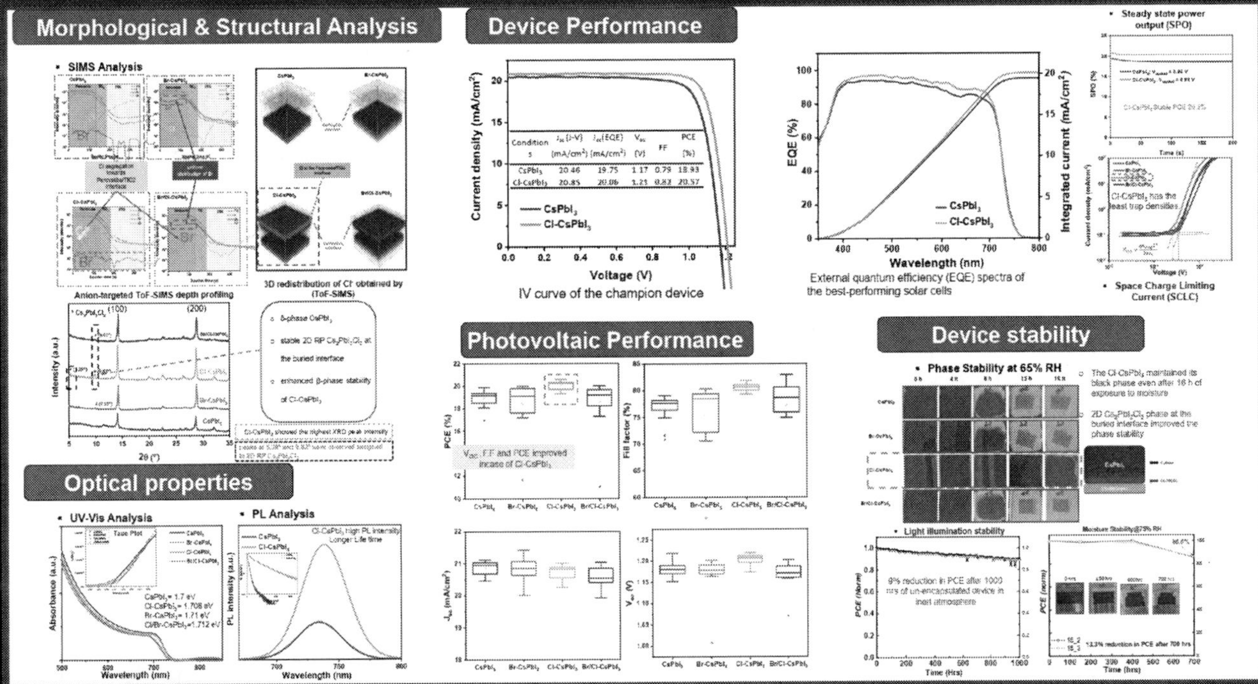

Conclusions

- Addition of Cl into $CsPbI_3$ induced the spontaneous formation of stable 2D RP $Cs_2PbI_2Cl_2$ at the buried interface.
- $Cs_2PbI_2Cl_2$ enhanced crystallinity, reduced trap densities, and improved phase stability of $CsPbI_3$
- Reduced interfacial lattice distortion leading to enhanced charge transfer and improved phase stability.
- Improved device performances and operational stabilities.
- These studies highlight the importance of buried interfacial Engineering.

PMDL.
NEXT-GENERATION PV MATERIALS
AND DEVICES LAB

References

[1] X. Gu, W. Xiang, Q. Tian, S. Liu, *Angewandte Chemie International Edition* 2021, 60, 23164.

[2] S. S. Mali, J. V. Patil, J.-Y. Shao, Y.-W. Zhong, S. R. Rondiya, N. Y. Dzade, C. K. Hong, *Nature Energy* 2023, 8, 989.

[3] Y. Cui, J. Shi, F. Meng, B. Yu, S. Tan, S. He, C. Tan, Y. Li, H. Wu, Y. Luo, D. Li, Q. Meng, *Advanced Materials* 2022, 34, 2205028.

Scan for Lab Introduction

020112-001

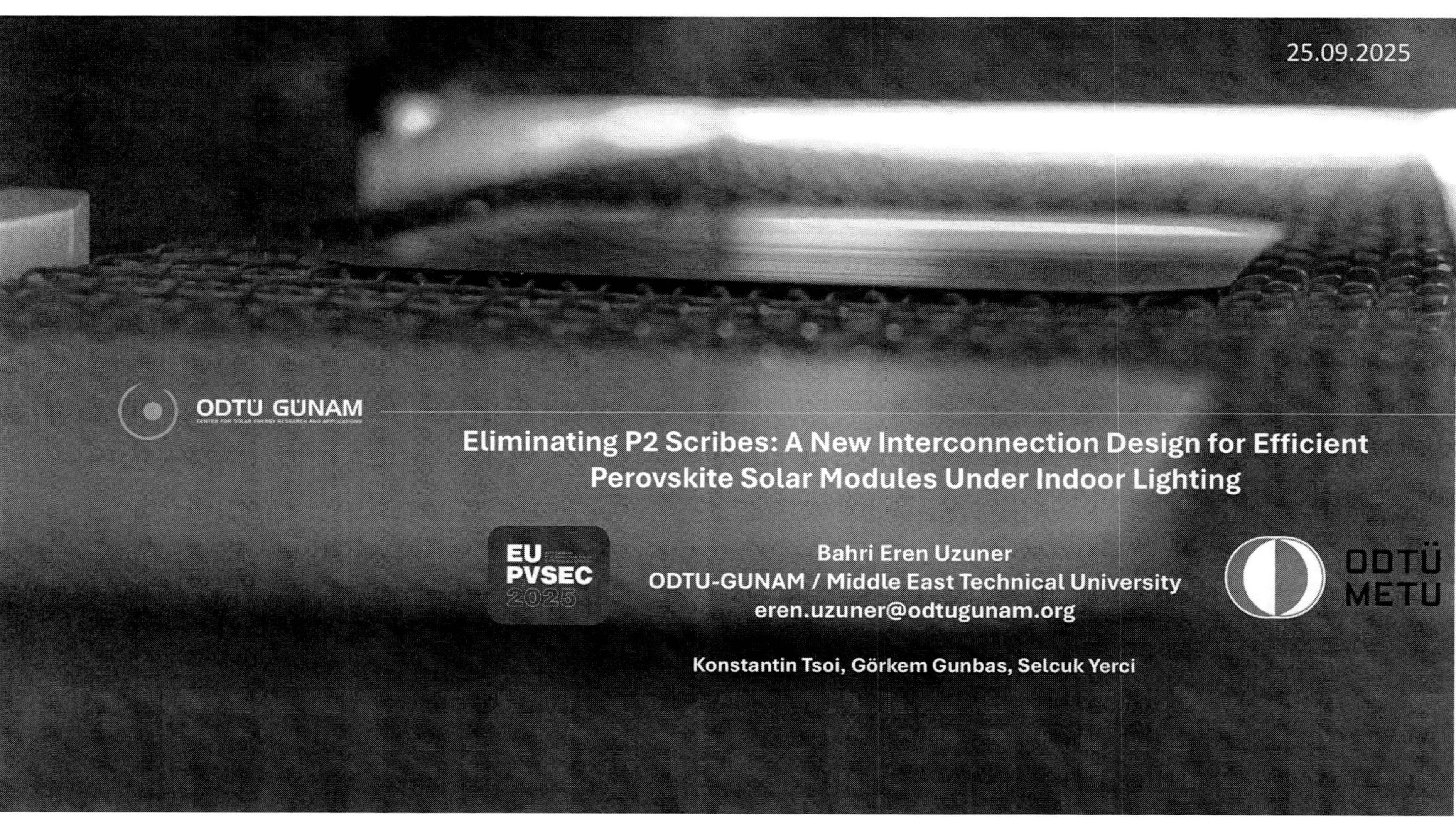
25.09.2025
ODTÜ GUNAM
CENTER FOR SOLAR ENERGY RESEARCH AND APPLICATIONS
Eliminating P2 Scribes: A New Interconnection Design for Efficient Perovskite Solar Modules Under Indoor Lighting
EU PVSEC 2025
Bahri Eren Uzuner
ODTU-GUNAM / Middle East Technical University
eren.uzuner@odtugunam.org
ODTÜ METU
Konstantin Tsoi, Görkem Gunbas, Selcuk Yerci

Introduction

- **Up-scaling** and efficient **interconnection** of perovskite solar cells are essential steps towards their commercial use.

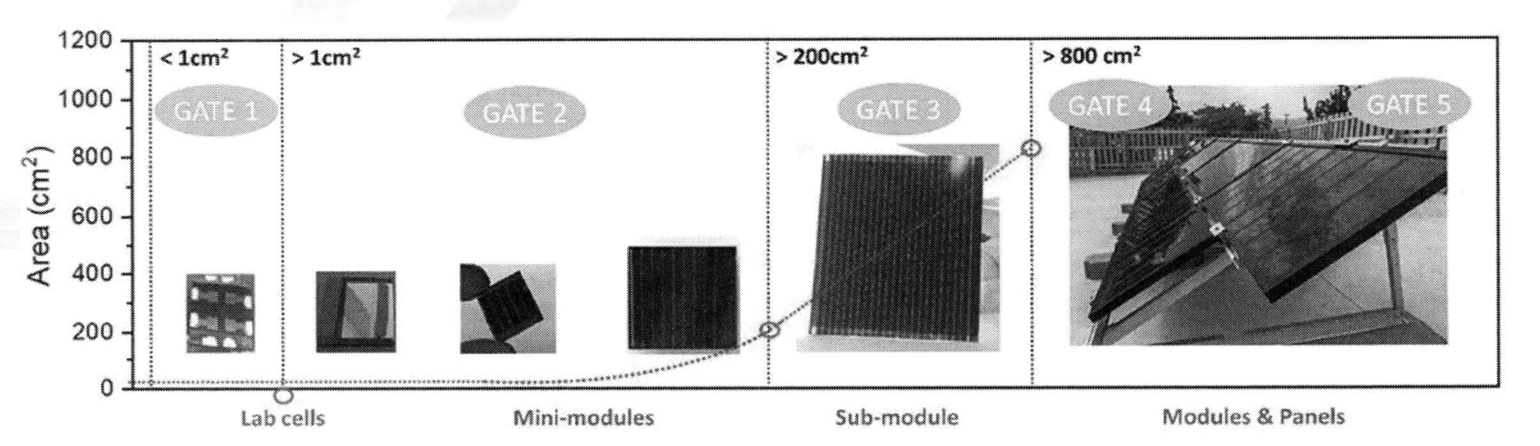

1. Forberich, K. et. al. (2025). Adv. Ene. Mat. 15(13).

1

Introduction

- **Up-scaling** and efficient **interconnection** of perovskite solar cells are essential steps towards their commercial use.

- **Monolithic series interconnection** holds promise from an **electrical perspective**

  - V_{oc} addition / J_{sc} limitation

  - $P_{loss} = J_{sc,\ module}^{2} \times R$

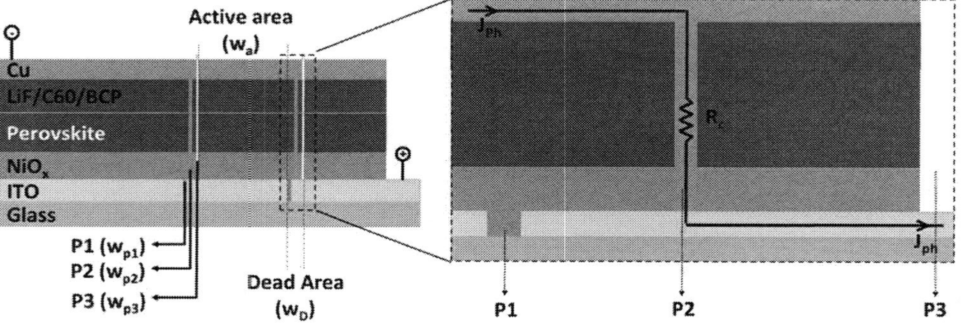

020113-003

Introduction

- **Up-scaling** and efficient **interconnection** of perovskite solar cells are essential steps towards their commercial use.

- **Monolithic series interconnection** holds promise from an **electrical perspective**

  - V_{oc} addition / J_{sc} limitation

  - $P_{loss} = J_{sc,\,module}^{2} \times R$

- It is formed by **3 adjacent laser scribes**;

  - Isolation of the front contact (**P1**)

  - Interconnection path of adjacent cells (**P2**)

  - Isolation of the back contact (**P3**)

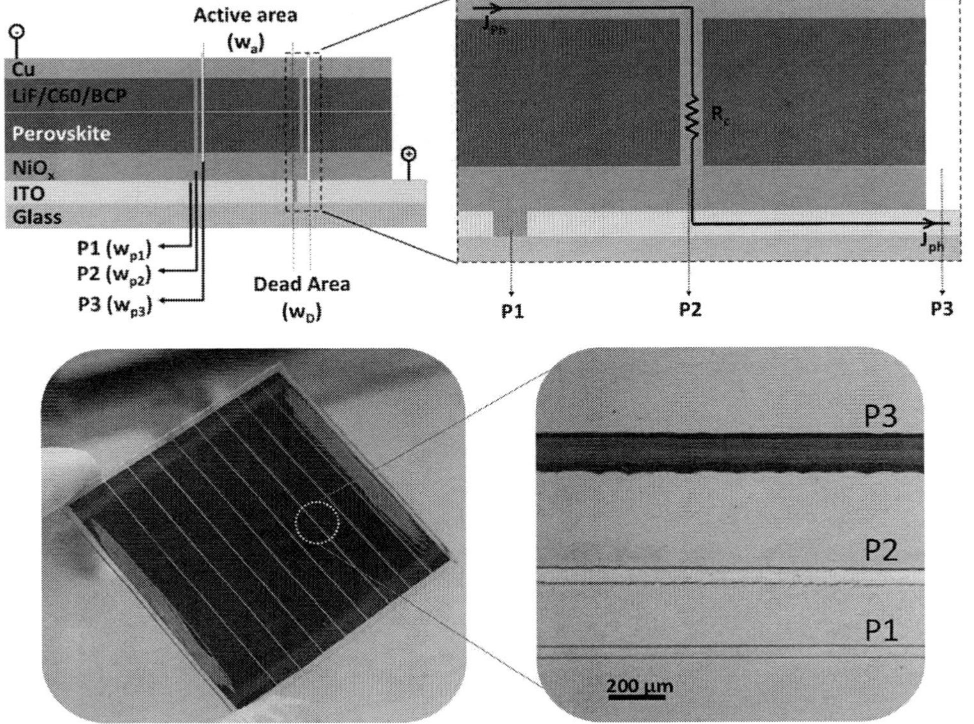

Benchmarks in the interconnection geometries

- **Full-cell-length (FCL) trench scribing**

  - State-of-the-art for the most thin-film module technologies

  - Typically yields >90% geometrical fill factor (GFF)

  - Requires material removal

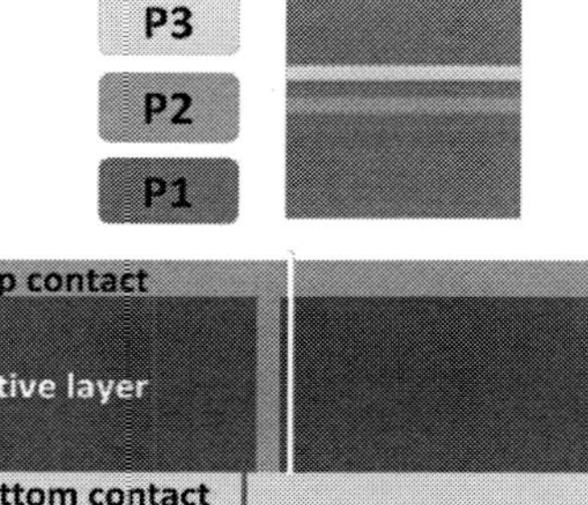

(A)

2. Meng, R. et. al. (2022). npj Flex. Elect. 6, 39.
3. Ma, Q. et. al. (2023). Device 1, 100174.
4. Zhang, B. et. al. (2024). Ener. Env. Sci 17, 2935–2944.
5. Feng, E. et. al. (2024). ACS Nano 18, 28026–28037.
6. Uzuner, B.E. et. al. (2025). Sol. Ener. Mat. and Sol. Cells 292, 113793.

ODTÜ GÜNAM — EU PVSEC 2025 — ODTÜ METU — www.odtugunam.org

Benchmarks in the interconnection geometries

- **Full-cell-length (FCL) trench scribing**
  - State-of-the-art for the most thin-film module technologies
  - Typically yields >90% geometrical fill factor (GFF)
  - Requires material removal
- **Dot or discontinuous line trenches**
  - Very high GFF can be achieved (>99%)
  - Requires material removal

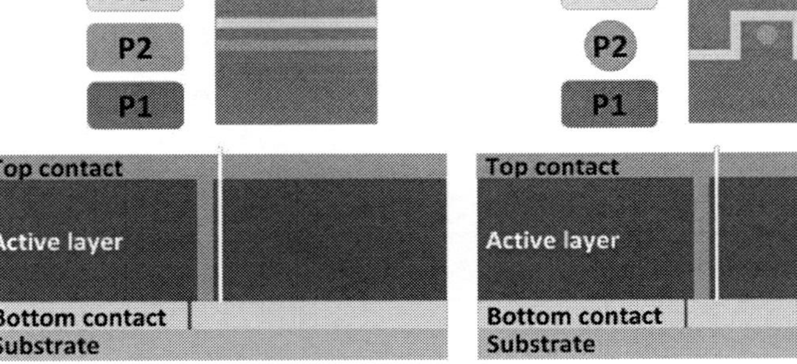

7. Haas, S. et. al. (2013). Prog. in Phot. 21, 972–979.
8. Rakocevic, L. et. al. (2020). Prog. in Phot. 28, 1120–1127.
9. Jiang, E. et. al. (2024). Solar RRL 8.
10. Di Giacomo, F. et. al. (2024). Adv Energy Mater 14.

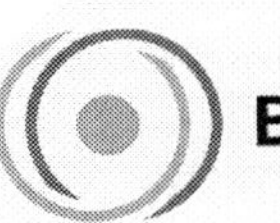

Benchmarks in the interconnection geometries

- **Full-cell-length (FCL) trench scribing**
  - State-of-the-art for the most thin-film module technologies
  - Typically yields >90% geometrical fill factor (GFF)
  - Requires material removal
- **Dot or discontinuous line trenches**
  - Very high GFF can be achieved (>99%)
  - Requires material removal
- **Chemical or laser-based contact modification**
  - Material removal is not necessary
  - Yields in decent contact resistance and GFF

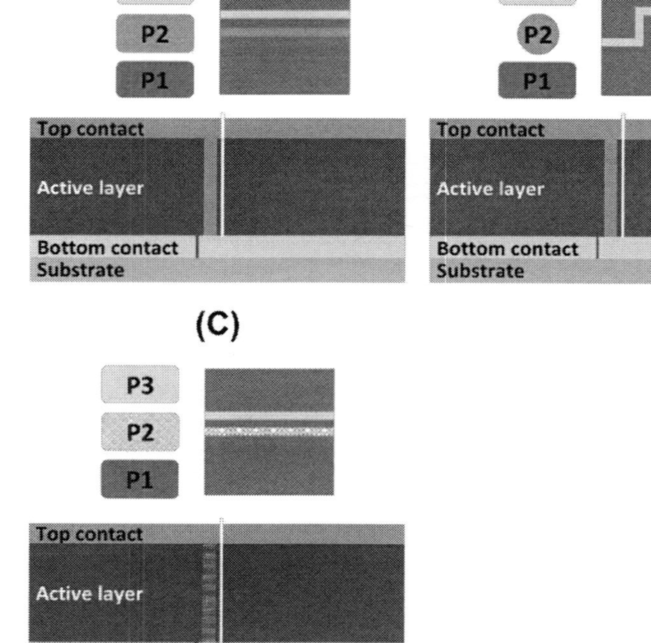

11. Westin, P.-O. et. al. (2008). Sol. Ener. Mat. and Sol. Cells 92, 1230–1235.

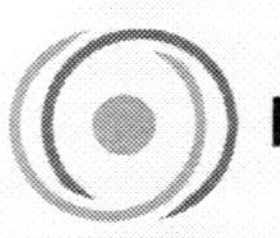

ODTÜ GUNAM

EU PVSEC 2025

 ODTÜ METU   www.odtugunam.org

Circuitry of a standard interconnection (FCL)

- In the standard model, photo-generated current flows **through the P2 contact** to the adjacent cell

  - Parallel resistances of R_{1-2} and R_{2-3} are **much higher**.

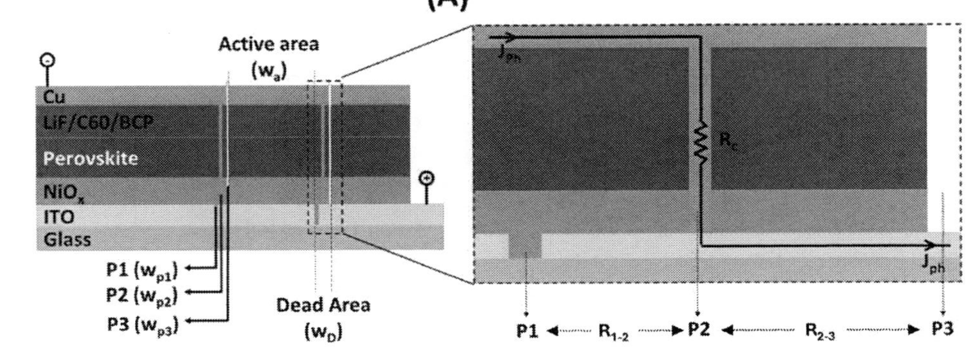

"Missing part" of the circuitry of a standard interconnection

- In the standard model, photo-generated current flows **through the P2 contact** to the adjacent cell

  - Parallel resistances of R_{1-2} and R_{2-3} are **much higher**.

- The so-called **safe zones** in between the P1-P2 and P2-P3 laser scribes have all layers to form a **"solar cell"**

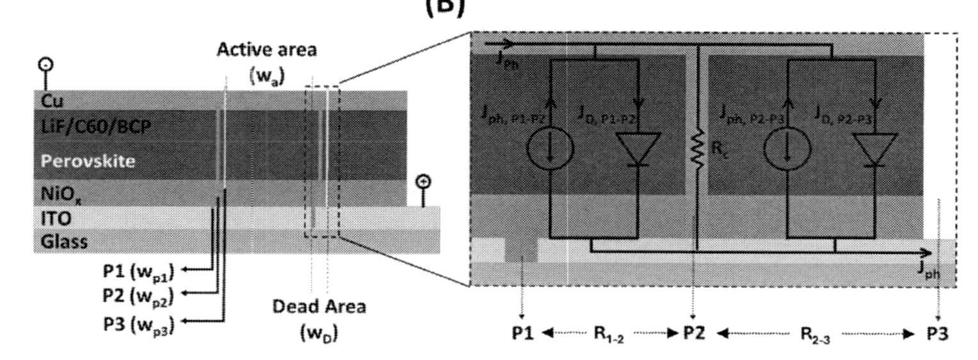

020113-009

"Missing part" of the circuitry of a standard interconnection

- In the standard model, photo-generated current flows **through the P2 contact** to the adjacent cell
  - Parallel resistances of $R_{1\text{-}2}$ and $R_{2\text{-}3}$ are **much higher.**
- The so-called **safe zones** in between the P1-P2 and P2-P3 laser scribes have all layers to form a **"solar cell"**
- Emission detected in the electroluminescence images of the safe zones as the applied bias is **reversed.**
  - Meaning that the PSCs at $R_{1\text{-}2}$ and $R_{2\text{-}3}$ are connected reversely to the active areas

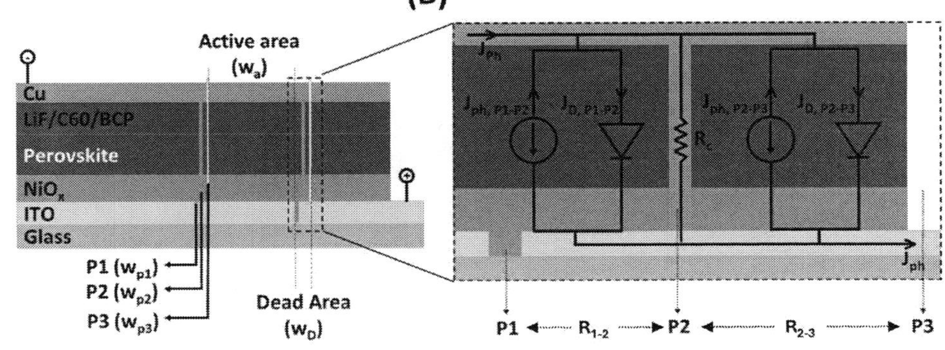

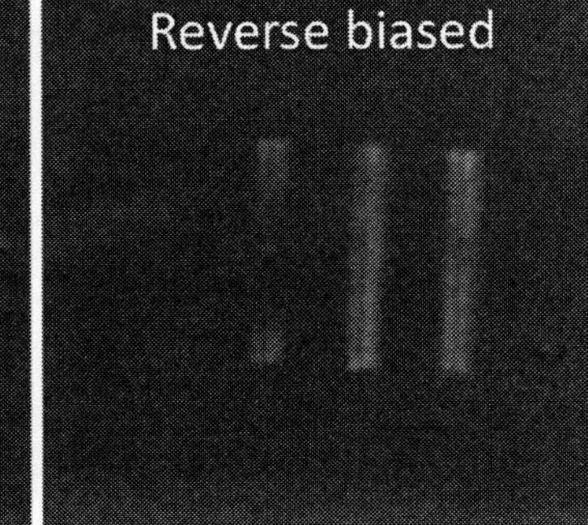

$R_{2\text{-}3}$: Safe zone between the P2 and P3; $R_{1\text{-}2}$: Safe zone between the P1 and P2

020113-010

Electrical modeling – Silvaco

- Test structure consisting of active area, interconnection, and R_{2-3} was simulated in Silvaco.

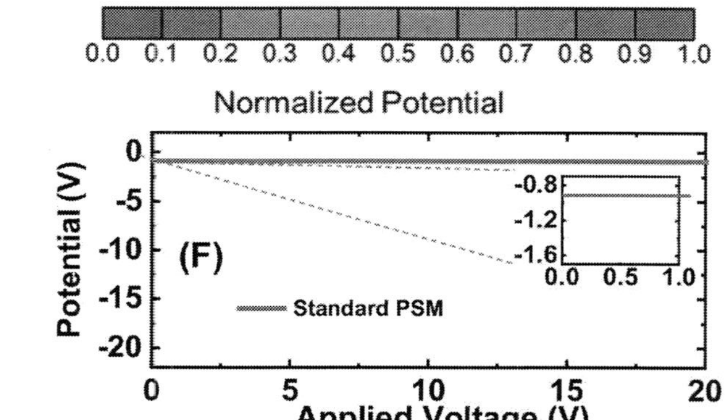

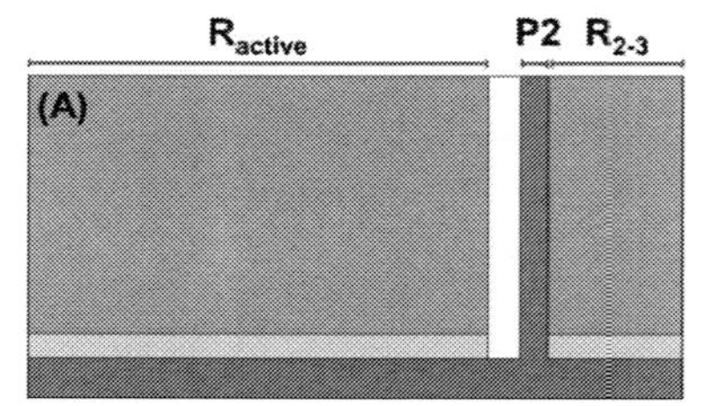
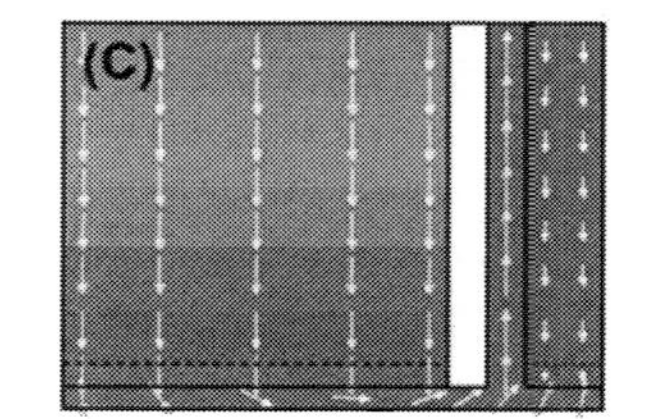

Silvaco simulations were done by **Konstantin Tsoi**

R_{2-3}: Safe zone between the **P2** and **P3**; R_{1-2}: Safe zone between the **P1** and **P2**

Electrical modeling – Silvaco

- Test structure consisting of active area, interconnection, and R_{2-3} was simulated in Silvaco.

- Safe-zones experience **reverse-bias** as the standard module is operated under **forward-bias.**

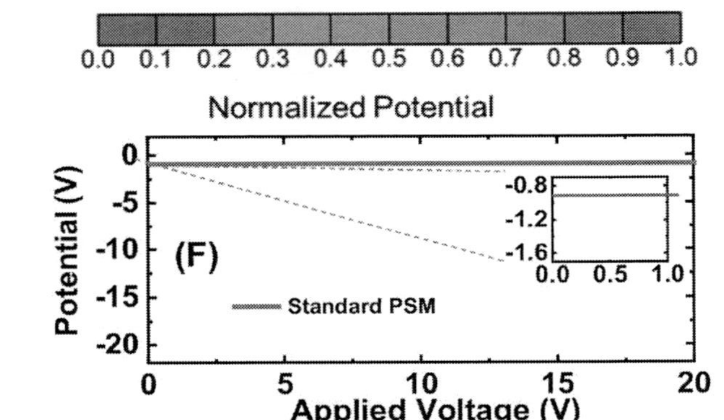

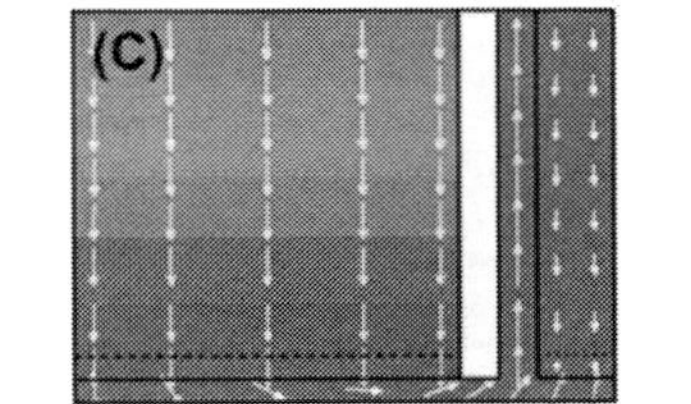

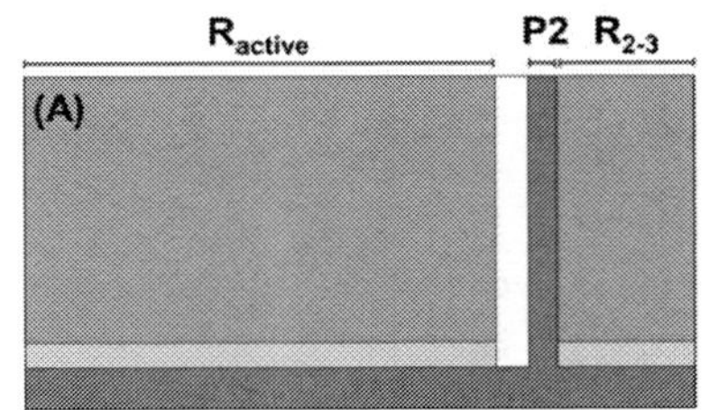

ODTÜ GUNAM   EU PVSEC 2025

Silvaco simulations were done by **Konstantin Tsoi**
R_{2-3}: Safe zone between the **P2** and **P3**; R_{1-2}: Safe zone between the **P1** and **P2**

ODTÜ METU   www.odtugunam.org

Electrical modeling – Silvaco

- Test structure consisting of active area, interconnection, and R_{2-3} was simulated in Silvaco.

- Safe-zones experience **reverse-bias** as the standard module is operated under **forward-bias.**

- The existence of a reverse bias in safe zones offers a prospect of achieving a **breakdown** within the dead region (R_{1-3}).

  - In the **absence of the P2 scribe.**

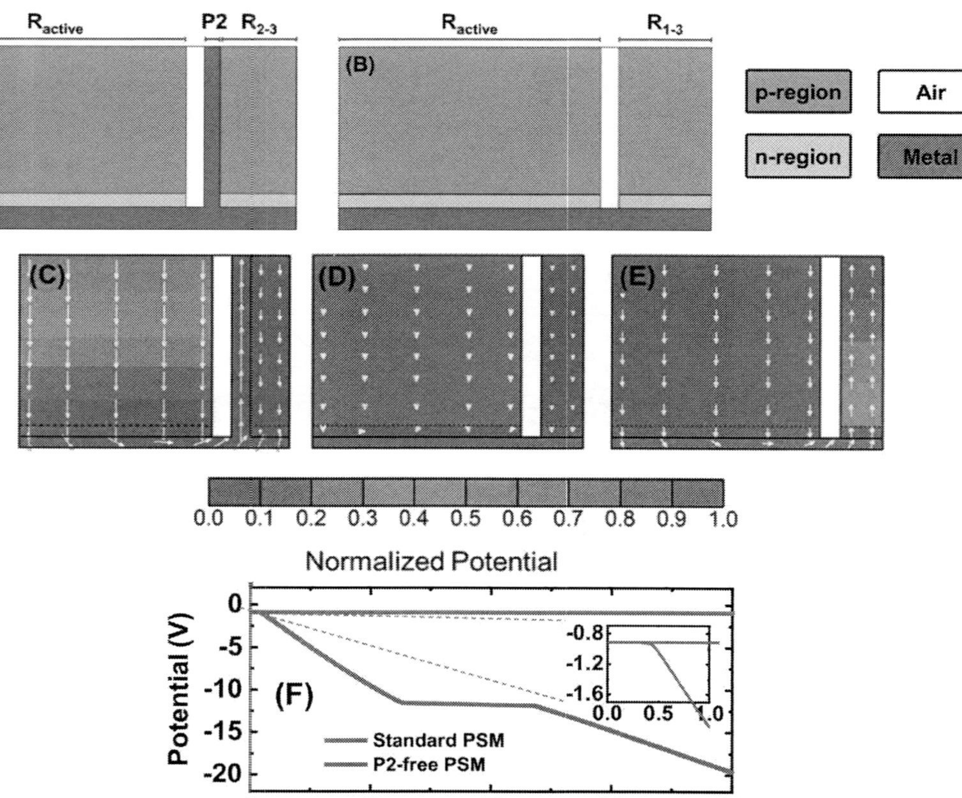

Electrical modeling – Silvaco

- Test structure consisting of active area, interconnection, and R_{2-3} was simulated in Silvaco.

- Safe-zones experience **reverse-bias** as the standard module is operated under **forward-bias.**

- The existence of a reverse bias in safe zones offers a prospect of achieving a **breakdown** within the dead region (R_{1-3}).

  - In the **absence of the P2 scribe.**

- Reverse-broken-down PSC $\rightarrow$ **Resistor**

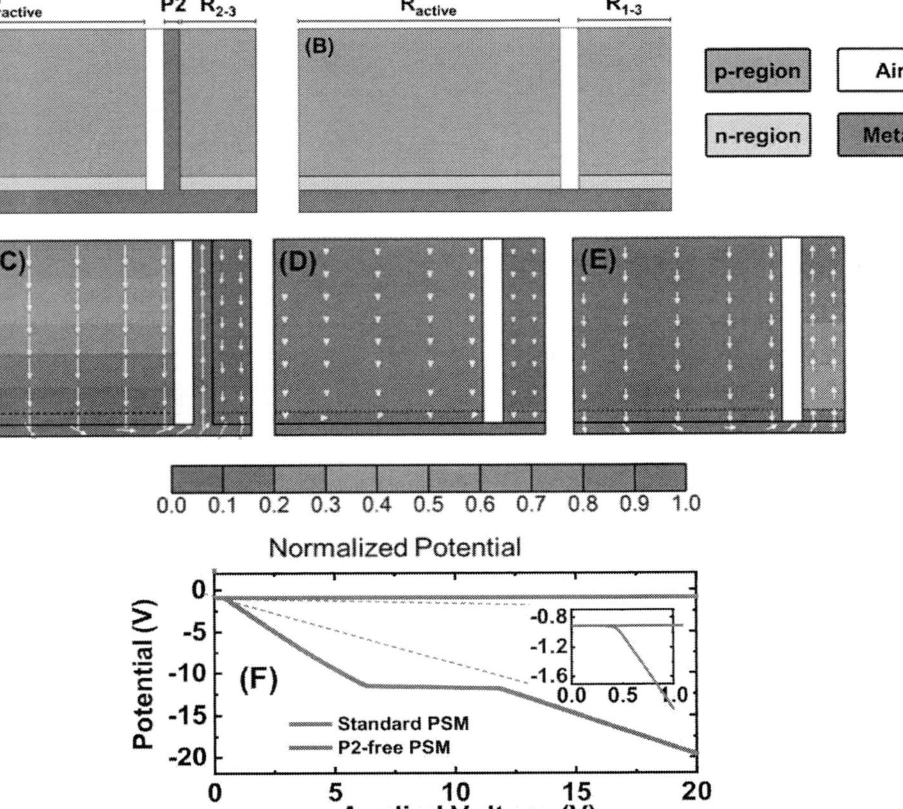

12. Johnson, S. et. al. (2025). Joule. 102102.
13. Jiang, F. et. al. (2024). Nat Energy 9, 1275–1284.

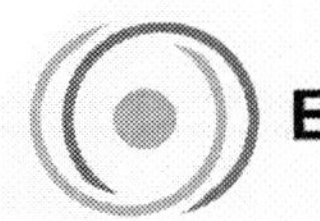

ODTÜ GUNAM

*Silvaco simulations were done by **Konstantin Tsoi***

*R_{2-3}: Safe zone between the **P2** and **P3**; R_{1-2}: Safe zone between the **P1** and **P2***

ODTÜ METU

www.odtugunam.org

020113-014

Electrical modeling – Reverse breakdown

- Fabricated PSCs possess **ohmic** behavior upon reverse breakdown ~@-3.5V

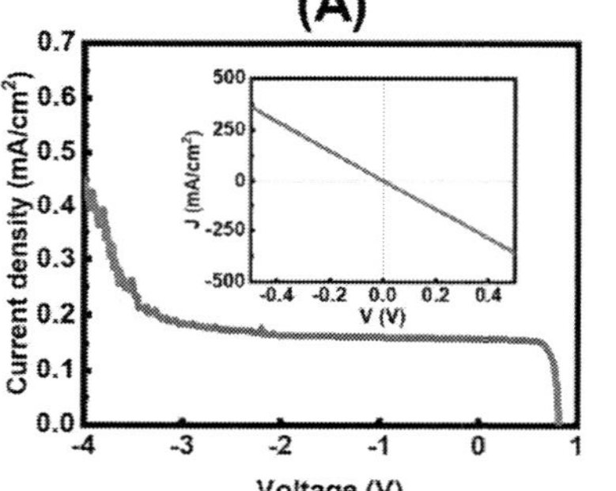

Electrical modeling – Transfer length method (TLM)

- Fabricated PSCs possess **ohmic** behavior upon reverse breakdown ~@-3.5V

- The contact resistivity of the broken-down PSCs was determined with TLM

  - ~1.25 $\Omega.cm^2$

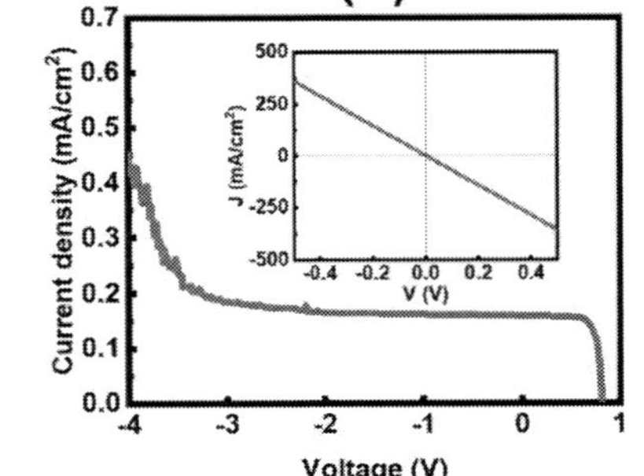

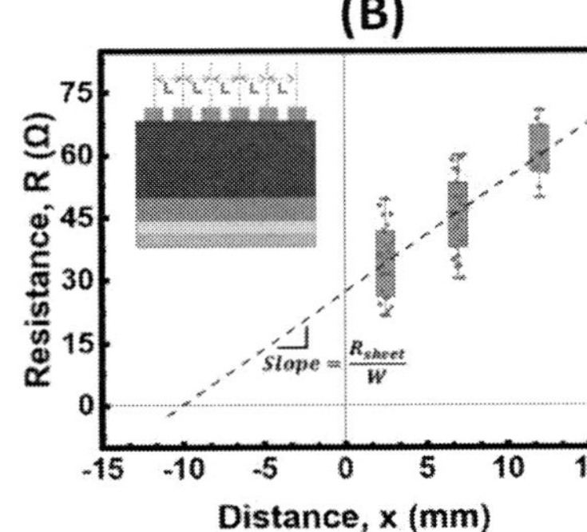

Electrical modeling – Single diode model

- Fabricated PSCs possess **ohmic** behavior upon reverse breakdown ~@-3.5V

- The contact resistivity of the broken-down PSCs was determined with TLM

  - ~1.25 $\Omega.cm^2$

$$J_{PH} \sim 20 \text{ mA/cm}^2$$

$$I = I_{sc} - I_0\exp\left(\frac{q(V + IR_s)}{nkT}\right) - \frac{V + (IR_s)}{R_{sh}}$$

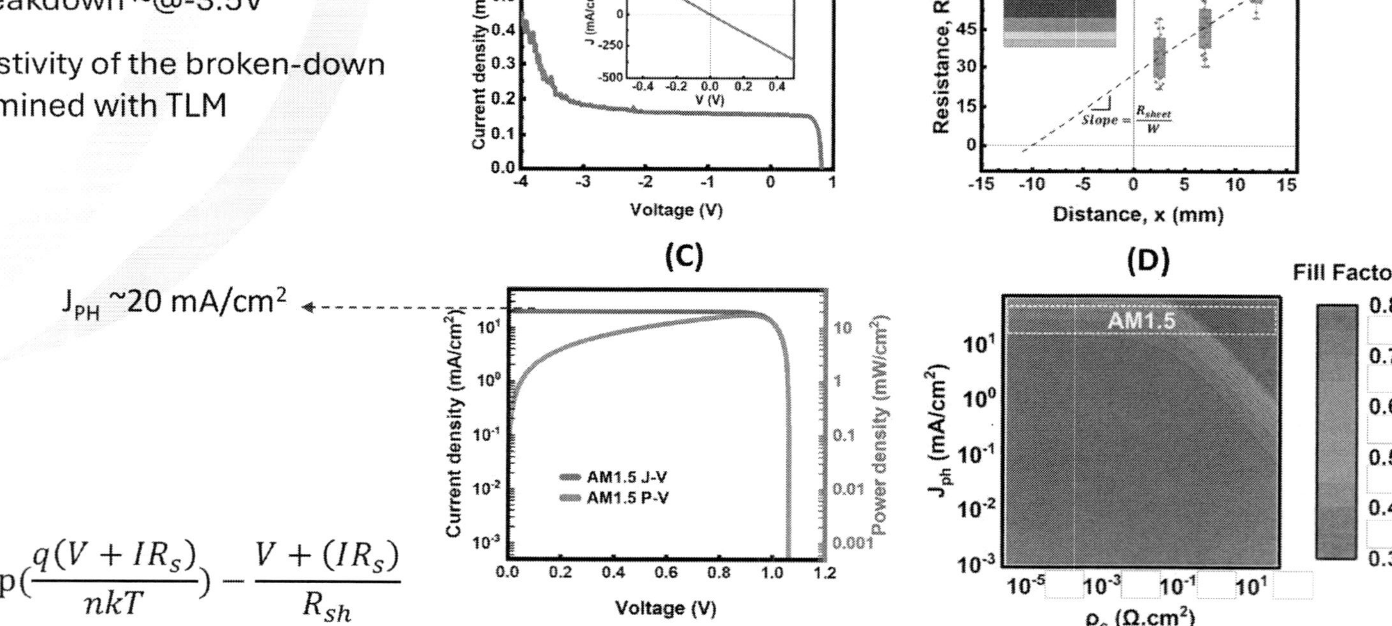

020113-017

Electrical modeling – Single diode model

- Fabricated PSCs possess **ohmic** behavior upon reverse breakdown ~@-3.5V

- The contact resistivity of the broken-down PSCs was determined with TLM

  - **~1.25 Ω.cm²**, **far lower** than the required interval, based on the single-diode model

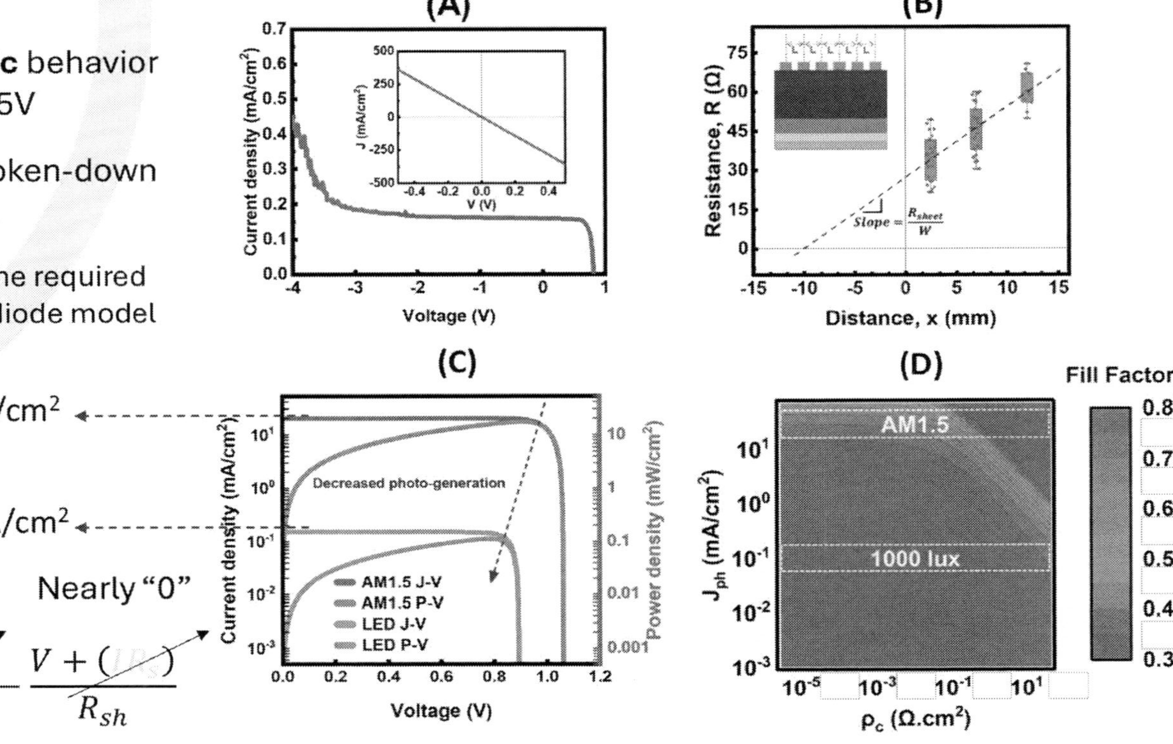

J_{PH} ~20 mA/cm²

J_{PH} ~0.1 mA/cm²

Nearly "0"

$$I = I_{sc} - I_0\exp\left(\frac{q(V + IR_s)}{nkT}\right) - \frac{V + (IR_s)}{R_{sh}}$$

P2-Free Perovskite Solar Modules

- Expectedly the geometrical fill factor (GFF) increase significantly.
  - **90% → 95%**

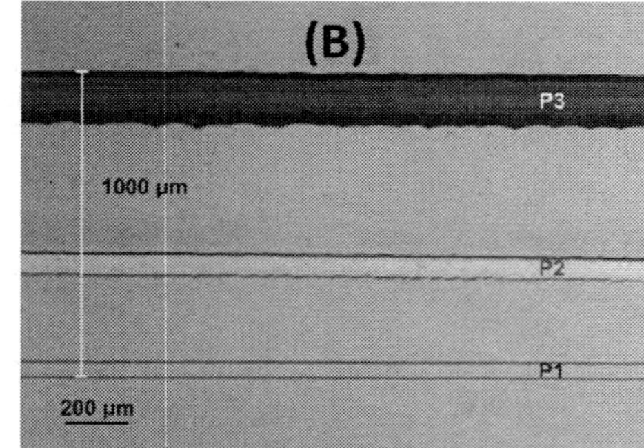

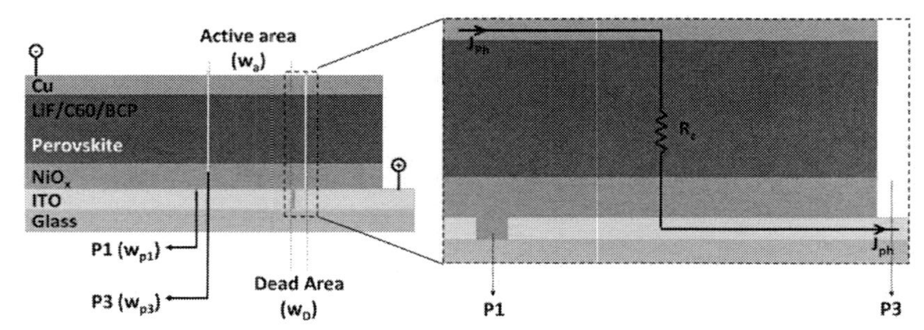

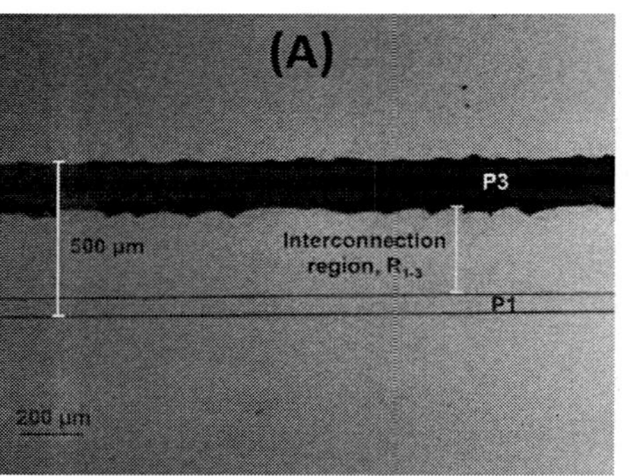

P2-Free Perovskite Solar Modules

- Expectedly the geometrical fill factor (GFF) increase significantly.

  - **90% → 95%**

- P2-free PSMs demonstrated exceptional performance under indoor illumination

  - **>82 % FF** and **>32% PCE**.

- No electrical loss was observed in compared to the reference cells.

Aperture Area (cm²)	Cell width / Cell number	V_{OC} (V)	Apt. Area J_{SC} (µA/cm²)	FF (%)	Act. Area PCE (%)	GFF (%)
	5 mm / 4	**3.67**	**31.33**	**82.65**	**32.17**	**90**
	5 mm / 4 / Standard	3.31	27.25	81.46	30.65	80
4.00	10 mm / 2	**1.72**	**66.02**	**82.66**	**32.80**	**95**
	10 mm / 2 / Standard	1.65	62.59	80.76	30.05	90
0.12	- / 1	0.97	152.67	82.06	33.60	-
2.50	- / 1	0.89	150.50	80.75	30.01	-

P2-Free Perovskite Solar Modules

- Expectedly the geometrical fill factor (GFF) increase significantly.

  - **90% → 95%**

- P2-free PSMs demonstrated exceptional performance under indoor illumination

  - **>82 % FF** and **>32% PCE.**

  - No electrical loss was observed in compared to the reference cells

- Air-ambient storage stability of standard and P2-free PSM;

  - **P2-free PSM** kept **~94%** of the initial PCE, whereas **standard PSM** kept **~80%** of the initial PCE

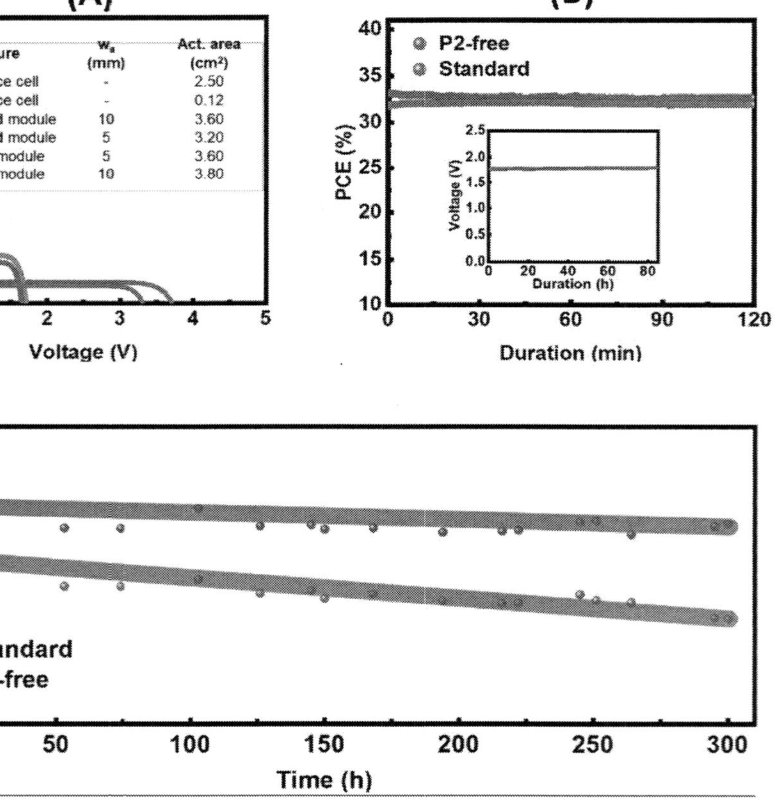

Conclusion

- **P2-free PSMs hold great promise**

  - Reduced fabrication **time**

  - Potentially opens a path for **laser-free** monolithic interconnection

  - Potential use for AM1.5 operations if the contact resistance can be further reduced.

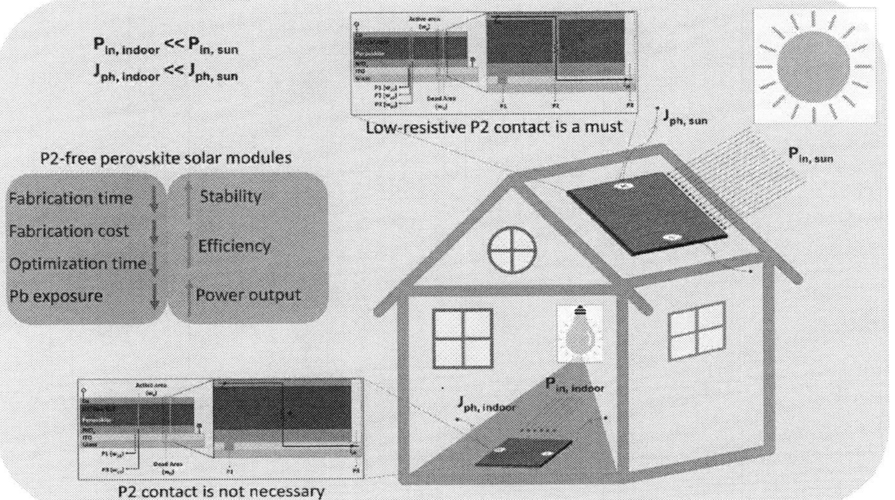

Conclusion

- **P2-free PSMs hold great promise**

  - Reduced fabrication **time**

  - Potentially opens a path for **laser-free** monolithic interconnection

  - Potential use for AM1.5 operations if the contact resistance can be further reduced.

- **>99% GFF could easily be achieved.**

  - Due to the limitations in our nanosecond laser system, GFFs were limited to the presented values.

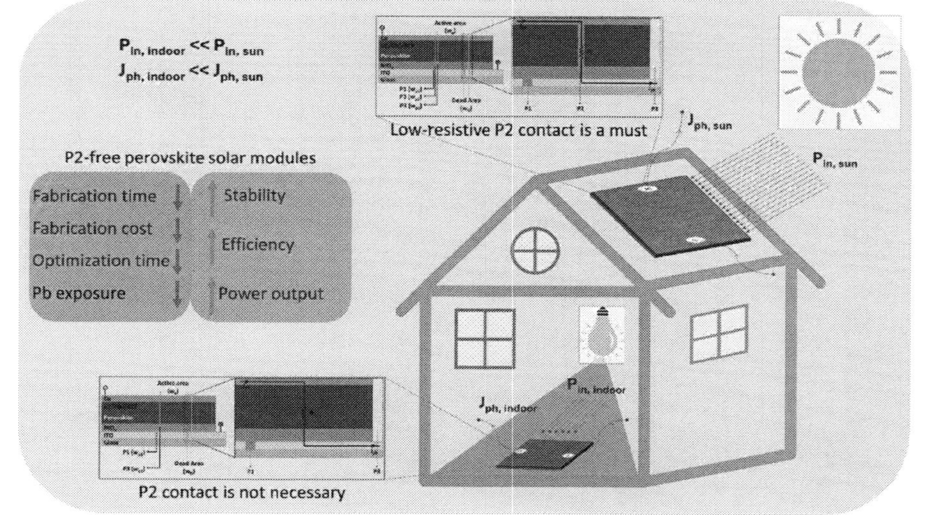

Conclusion

- **P2-free PSMs hold great promise**

  - Reduced fabrication **time**

  - Potentially opens a path for **laser-free** monolithic interconnection

  - Potential use for AM1.5 operations if the contact resistance can be further reduced.

- **>99% GFF could easily be achieved.**

  - Due to the limitations in our nanosecond laser system, GFFs were limited to the presented values.

- **Avoiding Pb exposure during P2-scribing**

  - Unlike P1 and P3, ablation of the perovskite is a must during P2.

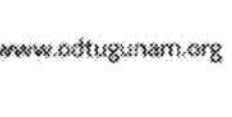

Acknowledgement

Thanks to the attendees, colleagues and co-workers of this study.

Funded by the Scientific and Technological Research Council of Türkiye (**TÜBİTAK**), Grant No. **221M472**, **22AG041**, and **124F194**.

Thanks to the **TÜBİTAK 6550** programme.

www.odtugunam.org

020113-025

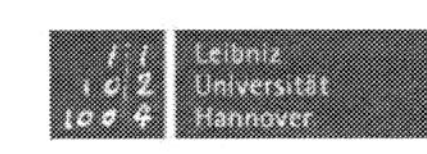

Evaporated self assembled monolayer (SAM) hole transport layers for scalable perovskite solar cells

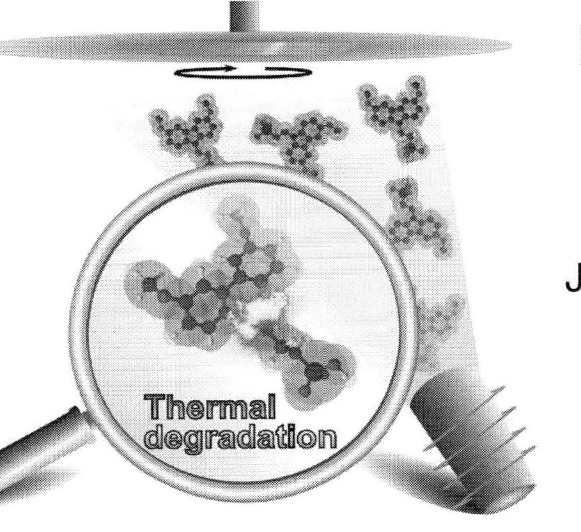

Joachim Vollbrecht[1], Verena Barnscheidt[1], Roland Clausing[1], Johannes Löhr[1], Larissa Mettner[1], Adam Neuba[2], Annika Raugewitz[1], Jessica Strey[1], Robby Peibst[1,3]

[1] Institute for Solar Energy Research Hamelin (ISFH), Emmerthal, DE
[2] Inorganic Chemistry - Analytics, Dept. of Chemistry, Paderborn University, Paderborn, DE
[3] Leibniz University Hannover, Institute of Electronic Materials and Devices, Hannover, DE

„SAM" based HTLs – overview

- SAM: **S**elf **A**ssembled **M**onolayer

- Since ca. 2018 used as HTLs in record breaking organic and perovskite (Pk) PV[1]

- Vast amount of organic molecules:[2] structure with head, linker, anchor groups

- Solution based deposition common

- Thickness of „SAM" HTL[3,4] : $d \approx 3$ nm

$\rightarrow$ **More than one layer of molecules**

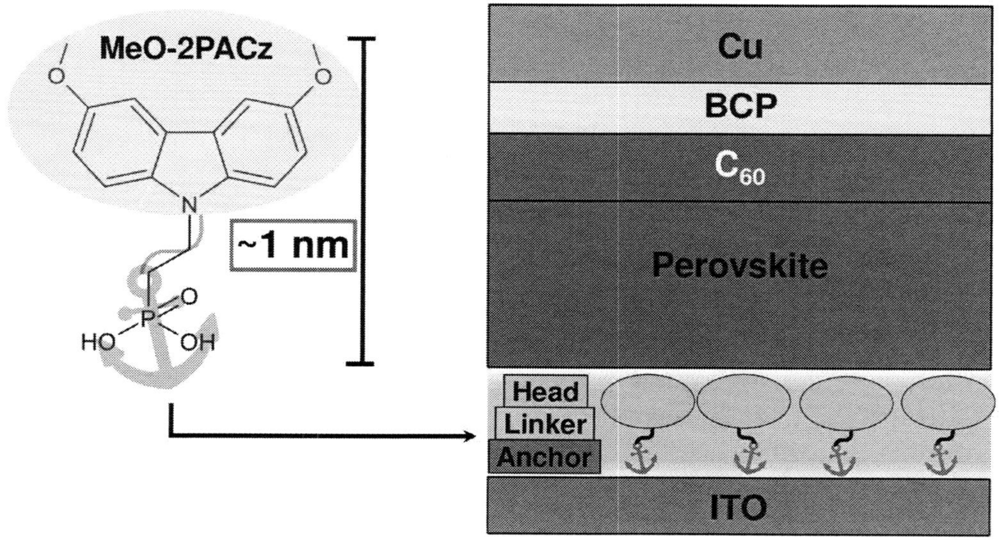

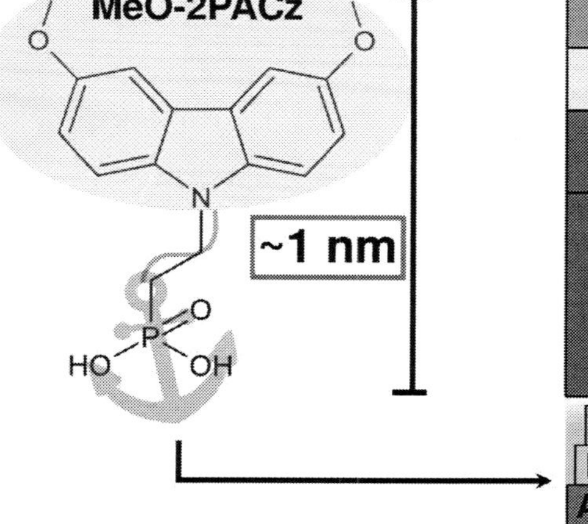

[1] A. Magomedov *et al. Adv. Energy Mater.* 2018, 1801892

[2] D. Yeo *et al. Nanomaterials* 2024, **14**, 175

[3] H. Xu *et al. Adv. Energy Mater.* 2024, 2401262

[4] O. Er-Raji *et al. Small Methods* 2025, 2401758

020114-002

Thermal evaporation of 2PACz, MeO-2PACz, Me-4PACz

- **T**hermal **E**vaporation (TE) possible, but uncommon

- First results for PACz based compounds published with 5 nm thick layers[5]

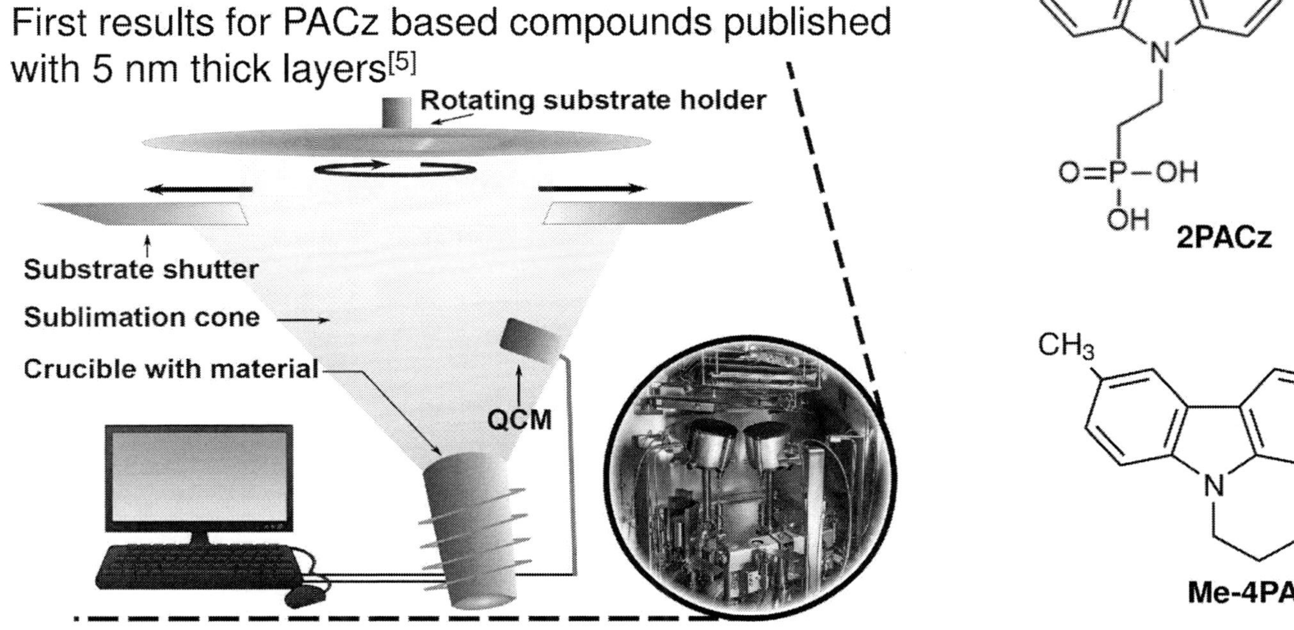

[5] A. Farag *et al. Adv. Energy Mater.* 2023, 2203982

020114-003

Thermal evaporation of MeO-2PACz – *JV* results

- Spin coated (SC) vs. 5 nm evap. with fresh MeO-2PACz (1st TE) vs. 5 nm evap. with residual MeO-2PACz (2nd TE)

- SJ Pk solar cells: MeO-2PACz variation, $Cs_{0.05}MA_{0.17}FA_{0.78}Pb(I_{0.78}Br_{0.17}Cl_{0.05})_3$ (E_g=1.67eV), ETL, Cu

Method [a]	V_{OC} (mV)	J_{SC} (mA·cm^{-2})	FF (%)	η (%)
SC	**1101** (1161)	**21.3** (21.7)	**66.4** (73.6)	**15.9** (18.1)
1st TE	**1066** (1110)	**20.6** (21.2)	**67.5** (72.8)	**14.9** (16.9)
2nd TE	**1016** (1091)	**20.6** (21.0)	**64.4** (67.6)	**13.5** (15.4)

[a] arithmetic means: **X**; maximum values in brackets

- Downward trend in efficiency η with each TE

→ **Degradation of MeO-2PACz during TE?**

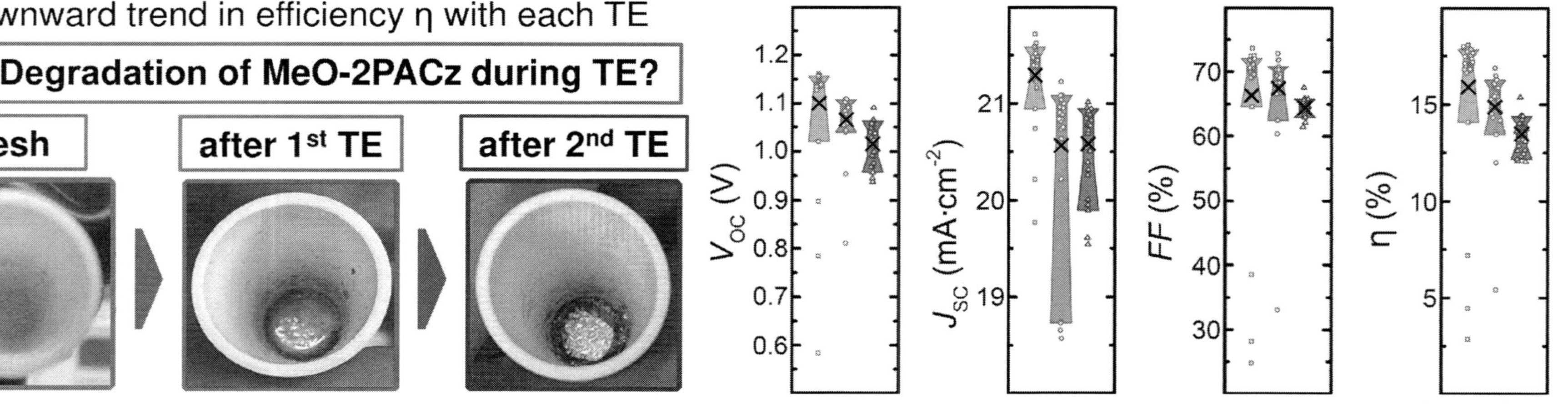

020114-004

Thermal evaporation of MeO-2PACz – MS results

ISFH

- Degradation of MeO-2PACz during TE?

- Samples of fresh MeO-2PACz and after 1st TE

- Time-of-flight mass spectrometry with electrospray ionization (TOF MS ES) in methanol

- Fragment of carbazole increased after 1st TE

→ **Adjustment of processing parameters necessary**

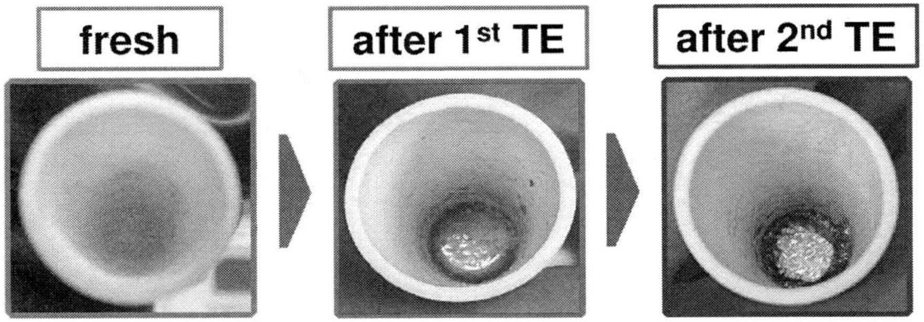

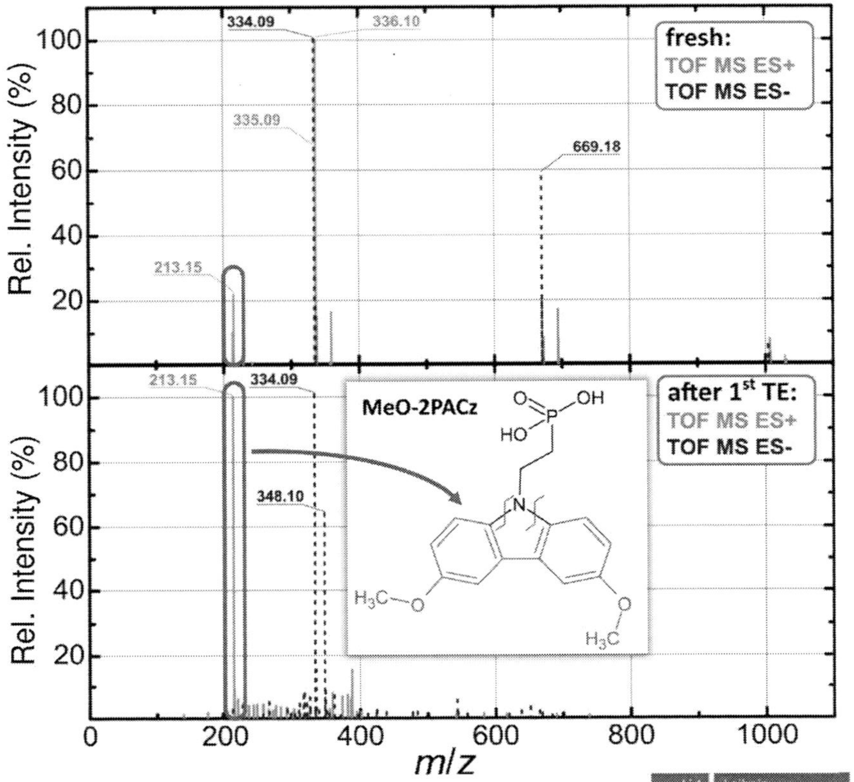

Leibniz Universität Hannover

020114-005

Thermal evaporation of MeO-2PACz – processing

- Adjustments of processing paramaters:

temperature T, rate v, time t, thickness d

Leibniz
Universität
Hannover

020114-006

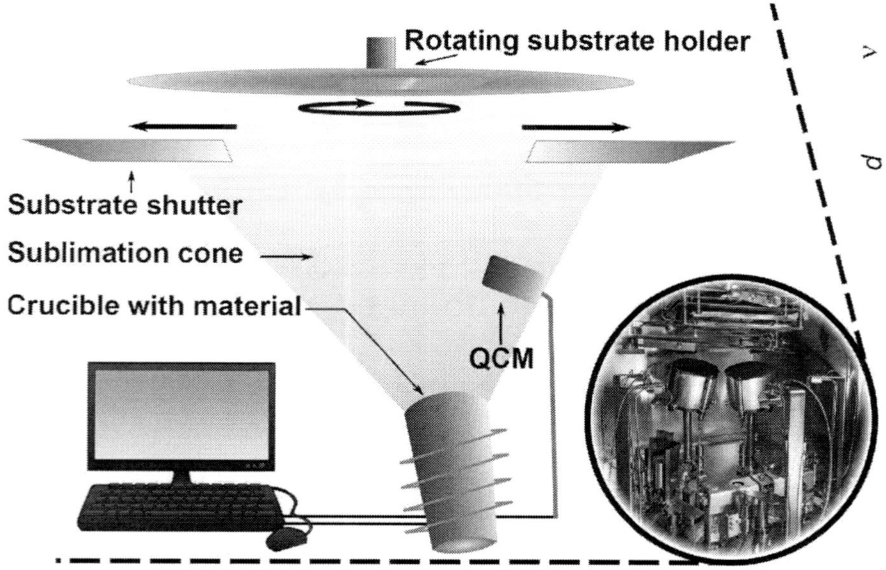

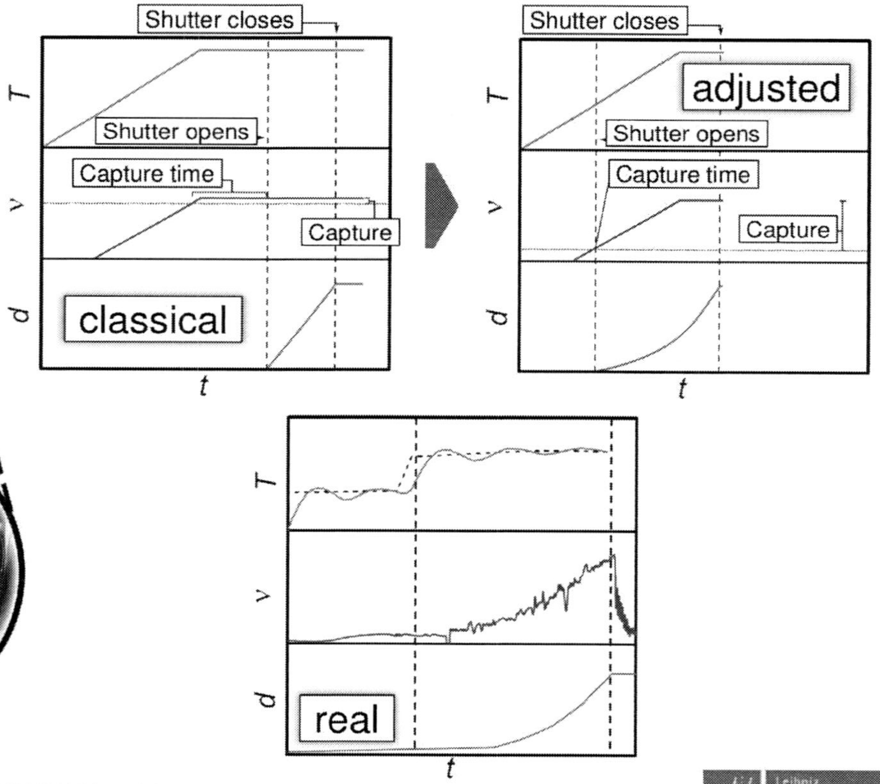

Adjusted TE of MeO-2PACz – *JV* results

- MeO-2PACz via:
  - SC as reference
  - 1 nm TE as „true" monolayer
  - **3 nm** TE for similar thickness as SC
  - 3.5 nm TE „complete" evaporation

- SJ Pk solar cells: MeO-2PACz variation, $Cs_{0.05}MA_{0.17}FA_{0.78}Pb(I_{0.78}Br_{0.17}Cl_{0.05})_3$ (E_g=1.67eV), $EDAI_2$ passivation, ETL, Cu

- SC and 1 nm TE similar efficiency η

- **3 nm** and **3.5 nm** TE higher variation in η

→ **MeO-2PACz via TE for evaporated absorber?**

Method [a]	V_{OC} (mV)	J_{SC} (mA·cm^{-2})	FF (%)	η (%)
SC	**1166** (1214)	**21.3** (21.9)	**75.5** (82.6)	**19.1** (21.5)
1 nm TE	**1196** (1224)	**20.9** (21.7)	**79.6** (82.7)	**19.9** (20.8)
3 nm TE	**1140** (1209)	**19.5** (21.5)	**77.1** (82.7)	**17.2** (20.6)
3.5 nm TE	**1141** (1198)	**20.9** (21.2)	**72.4** (77.4)	**17.7** (20.6)

[a] arithmetic means: **X**; maximum values in brackets

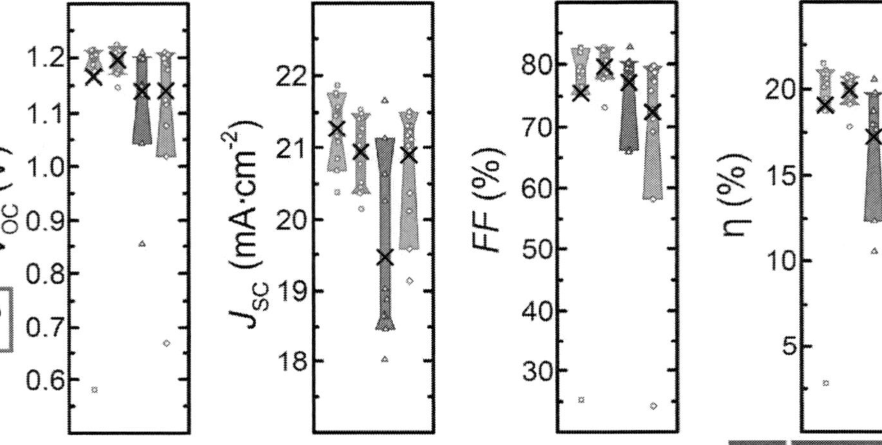

020114-007

MeO-2PACz for fully solvent free Pk solar cells

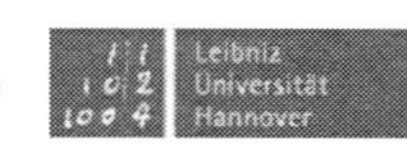

- 3 nm MeO-2PACz via adjusted TE

- No washing or annealing of MeO-2PACz layer

- Two different co-evaporated Pk absorbers deposited in dedicated, separate evaporation chamber

- No additional passivation

Absorber	E_g (eV)	V_{OC} (mV)	J_{SC} (mA·cm^{-2})	FF (%)	η (%)
$Cs_{0.065}FA_{0.935}Pb(I_{0.95}Cl_{0.05})_3$	1.56	1041	24.4	73.6	18.7
$Cs_{0.065}FA_{0.935}Pb(I_{0.8}Br_{0.2})_3$	1.62	1149	20.87	73.5	17.6

020114-008

Conclusions

- SAM based HTLs can be evaporated, but material degradation a problem
- Adjusted evaporation parameters lead to similar results as solution processing
- Fully solvent free Pk SJ solar cells with SAM based HTLs possible

Solar RRL

WILEY VCH

Solar RRL

RESEARCH ARTICLE

Less is more: Enabling Solvent-Free Fabrication of Perovskite Solar Cells via Thermal Evaporation of Ultrathin Self-Assembled Monolayers

Joachim Vollbrecht[1] | Verena Barnscheidt[1] | Roland Clausing[1] | Johannes Löhr[1] | Larissa Mettner[1] | Adam Neuba[2] | Annika Raugewitz[1] | Jessica Strey[1] | Robby Peibst[1,3]

[1]Photovoltaics Department, Institute for Solar Energy Research Hamelin (ISFH), Emmerthal, Germany | [2]Inorganic Chemistry - Analytics, Department of Chemistry, Paderborn University, Paderborn, Germany | [3]Institute of Electronic Materials and Devices, Leibniz University Hannover, Hannover, Germany

020114-009

Acknowledgments

This work was funded by the state of Lower Saxony in the project **NextGenPV** funded by zukunft.niedersachsen, the joint science funding program of the Lower Saxony Ministry of Science and Culture and the Volkswagen Foundation under grant no ZN4271 and the Federal Ministry for Economic Affairs and Energy (BMWE) under grant number FKZ 03EE1098B (**2PowerPero**). The responsibility for the content of this publication lies with the authors.

V. B. thanks the Deutsche Bundesstiftung Umwelt for financial support via a scholarship.

J. V. thanks M. Löhning for the measurements of the SEM cross sections and PD Dr. Hans Egold for fruitful discussion.

Supported by:

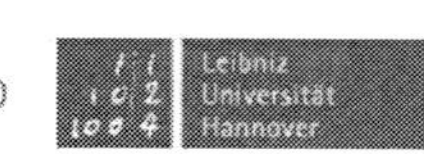

Federal Ministry for Economic Affairs and Energy

zukunft. **niedersachsen**

on the basis of a decision by the German Bundestag

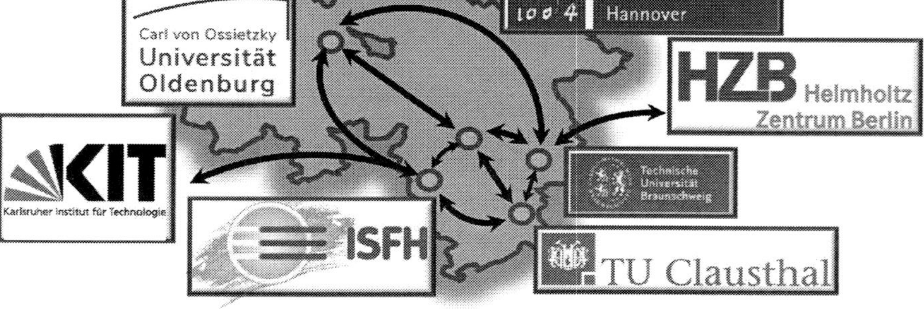

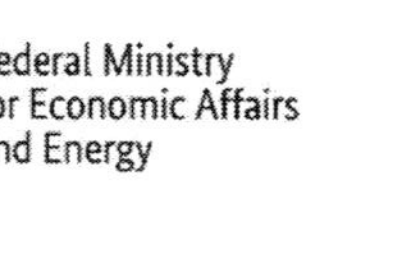

Aging of MeO-2PACz – *JV* curves

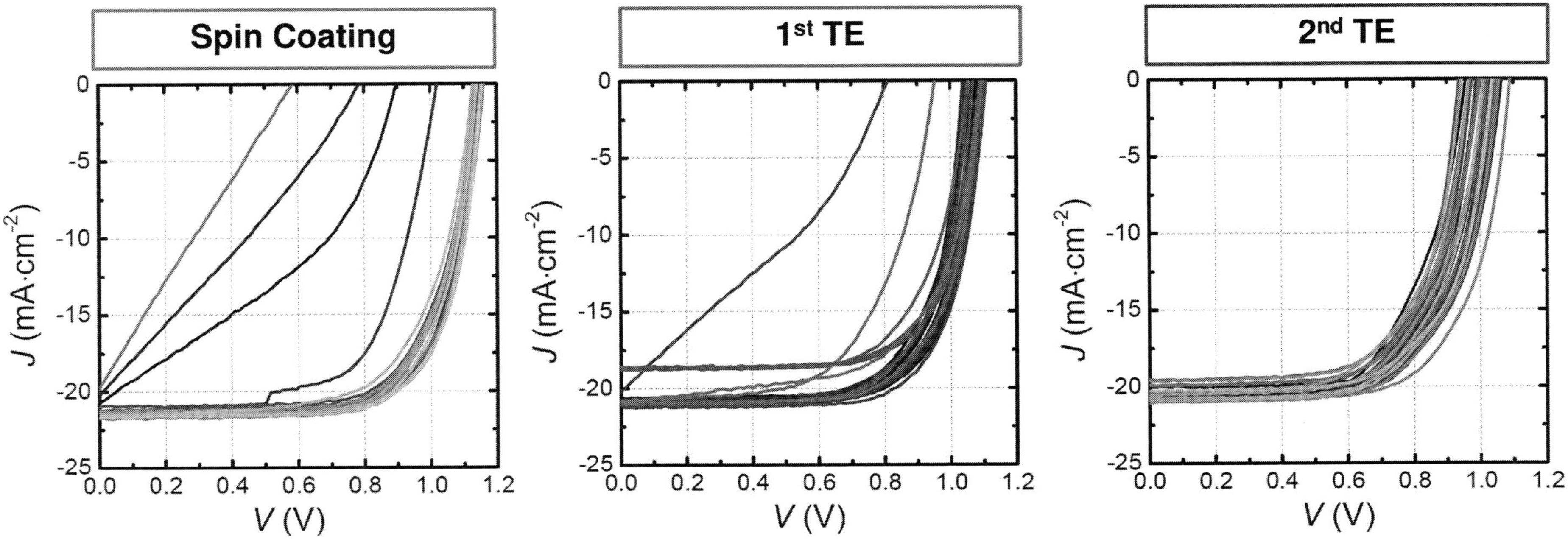

020114-011

Aging of MeO-2PACz – hysteresis

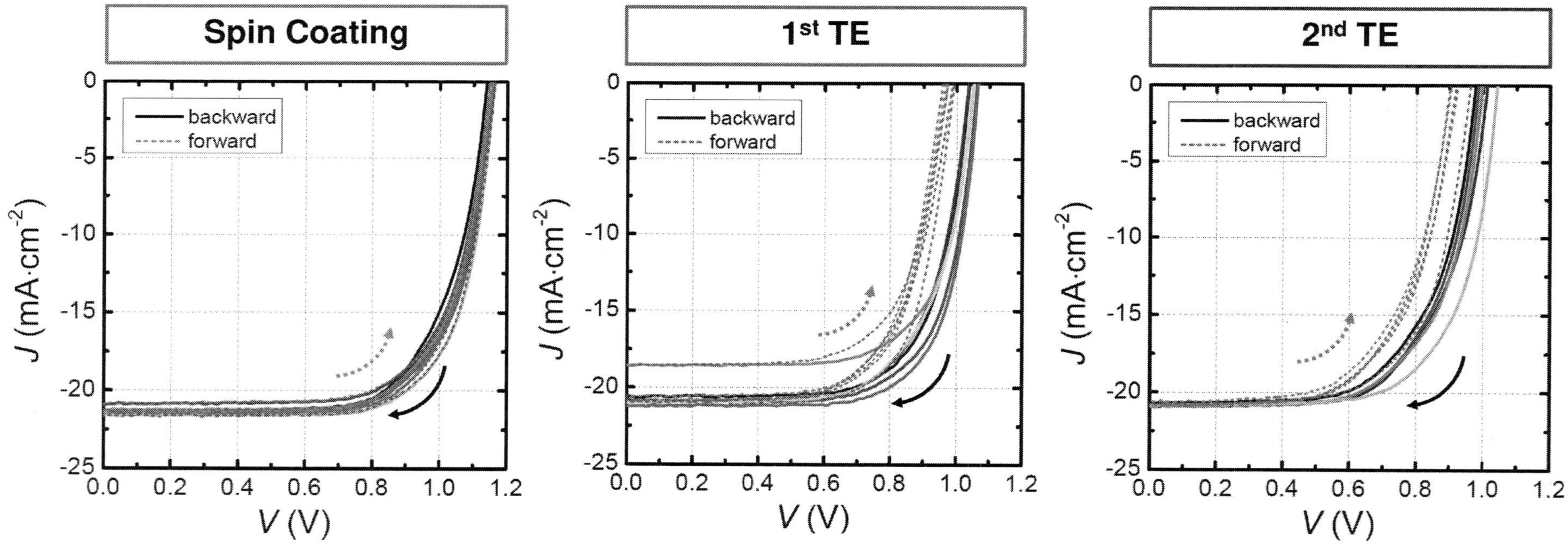

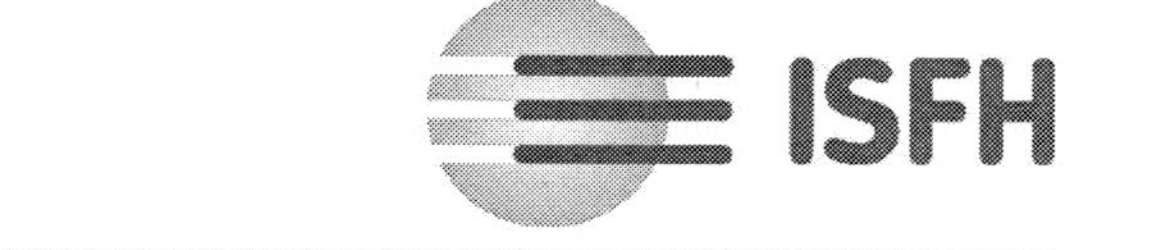

Aging of MeO-2PACz – *JV* results after 306 days

- Devices after 306 days of storage under N_2 in the dark

- Only devices that originally worked

- SC devices degraded most

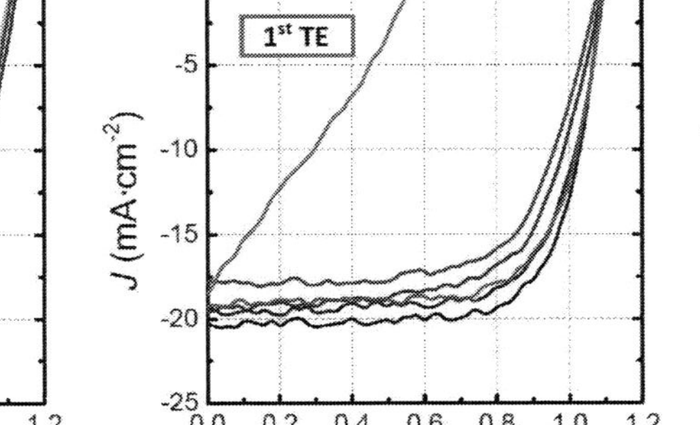

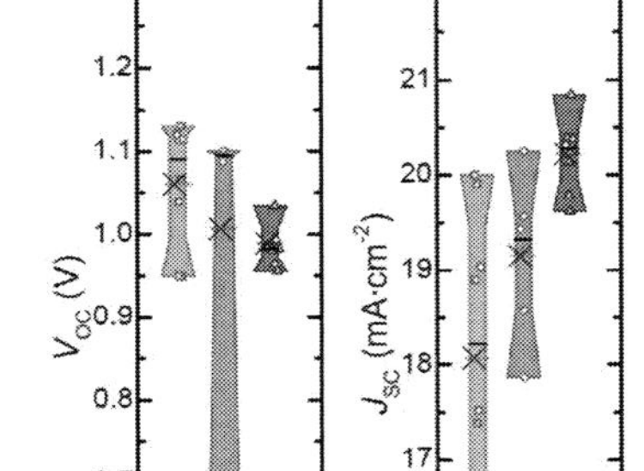
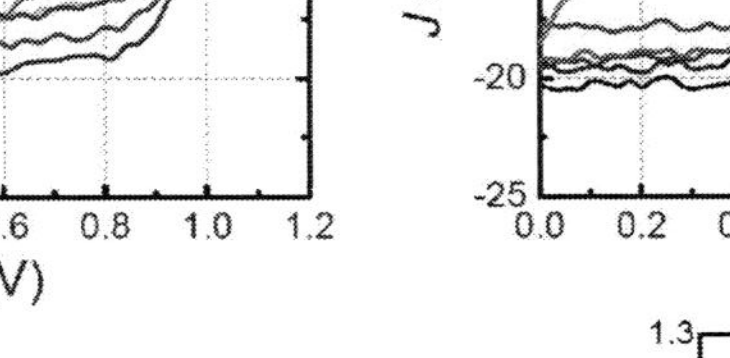

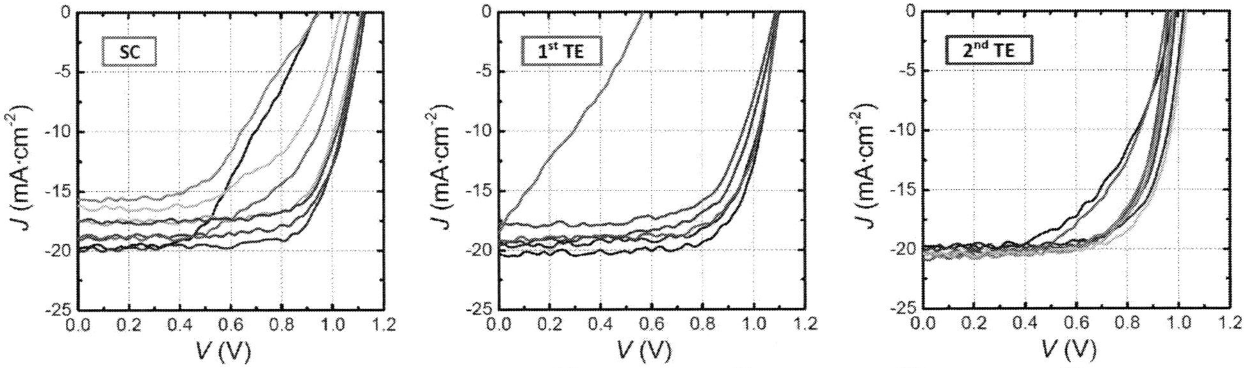

Method [a]	V_{OC} (mV)	J_{SC} (mA·cm^{-2})	*FF* (%)	η (%)
SC	1060 (1130)	18.1 (20.0)	61.9 (72.1)	12.0 (16.0)
1st TE	1007 (1099)	19.2 (20.3)	61.6 (71.5)	12.5 (15.9)
2nd TE	989 (1034)	20.2 (20.8)	65.4 (70.2)	12.8 (14.1)

[a] arithmetic means shown, maximum values in brackets

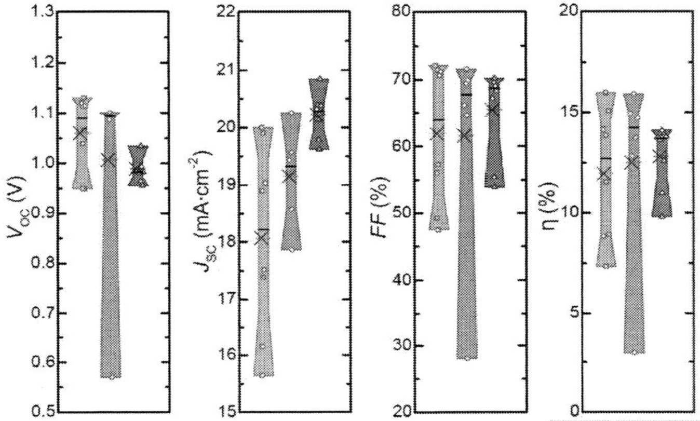

020114-013

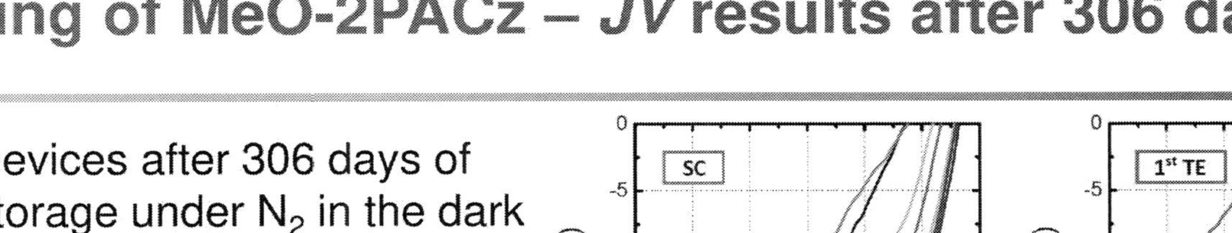

Thickness variation of MeO-2PACz – *JV* curves

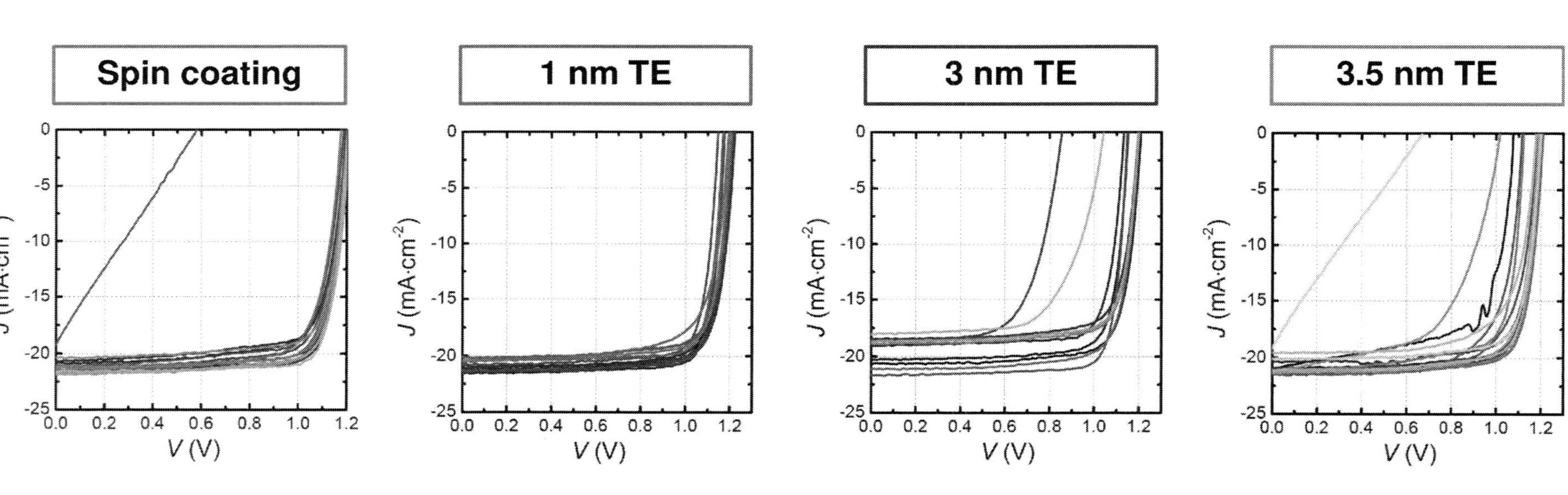

020114-014

Thickness variation – hysteresis

ISFH

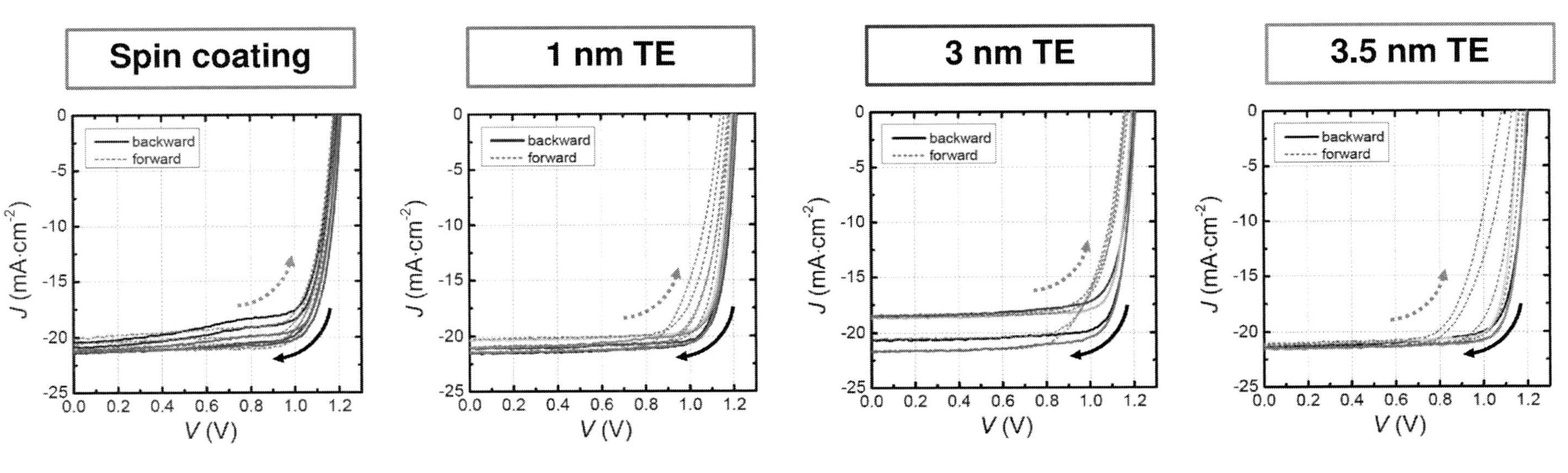

020114-015

Thickness variation – *JV* results after 257 days

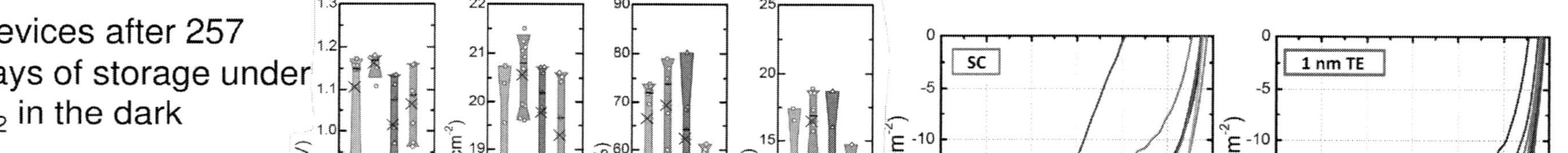

- Devices after 257 days of storage under N_2 in the dark

- Only devices that originally worked

- 1 nm TE least degraded

Method [a]	V_{OC}	J_{SC}	FF	η
	(mV)	(mA·cm^{-2})	(%)	(%)
SC	1106 (1172)	17.6 (20.7)	66.5 (73.9)	12.8 (17.4)
1 nm TE	1163 (1181)	20.6 (21.5)	69.3 (79.0)	16.4 (18.9)
3 nm TE	1015 (1135)	19.8 (20.7)	62.3 (80.3)	12.5 (18.7)
3.5 nm TE	1065 (1160)	19.3 (20.6)	57.5 (61.2)	11.9 (14.7)

[a] arithmetic means shown, maximum values in brackets

EQE and absolute PL

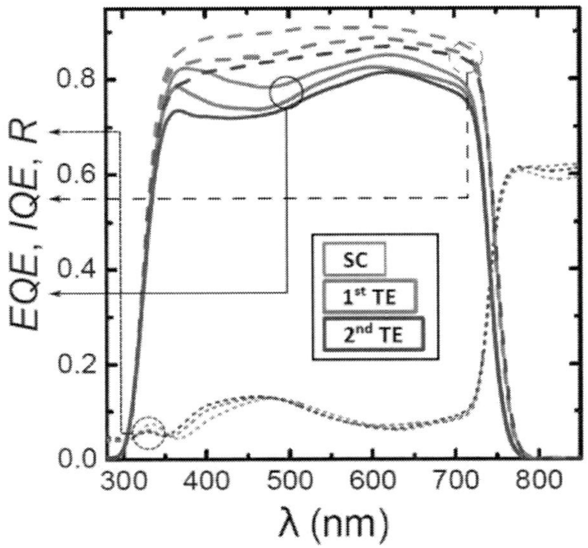

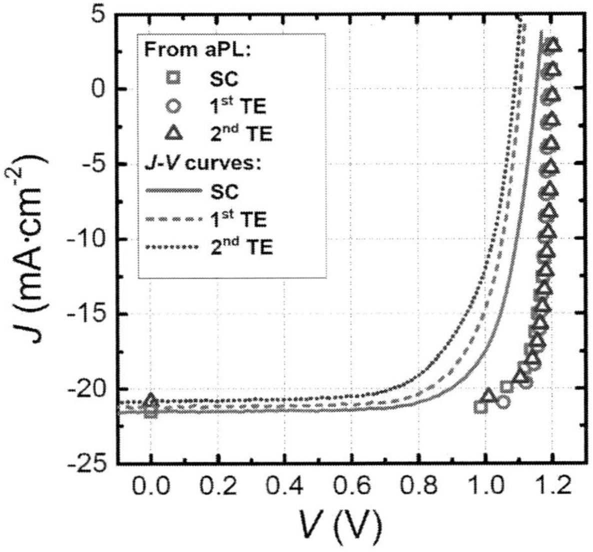

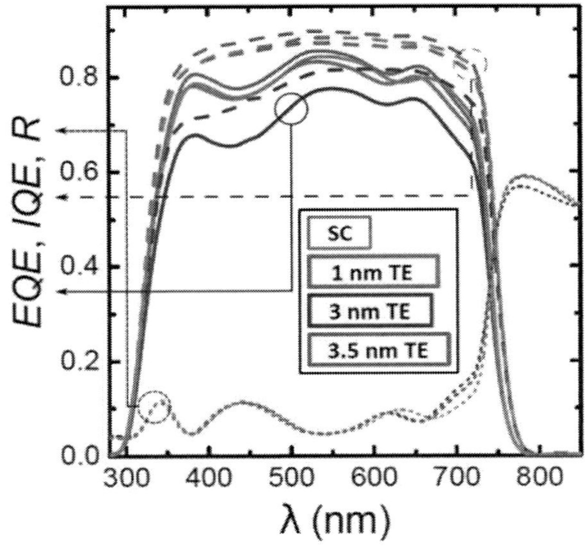

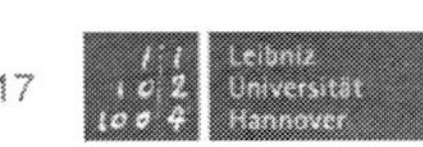

EQE and absolute PL

MeO-2PACz aging

Method	$J_{SC,EQE}$ (mA·cm^{-2})	PLQY (%)	E_{loss} (meV)	Shunt rate
SC	18.9	2.06	99.75	31/32 (97%)
1st TE	18.3	1.98	100.77	27/32 (84%)
2nd TE	17.9	2.63	93.47	29/32 (91%)

MeO-2PACz thickness variation

Method	$J_{SC,EQE}$ (mA·cm^{-2})	PLQY (%)	E_{loss} (meV)	Shunt rate
SC	18.5	1.28	112.07	17/20 (85%)
1 nm TE	18.1	0.93	120.25	15/20 (75%)
3 nm TE	16.6	1.19	113.85	11/16 (69%)
3.5 nm TE	18.7	0.93	120.17	17/20 (85%)

Leibniz Universität Hannover

020114-018

SEM cross sections

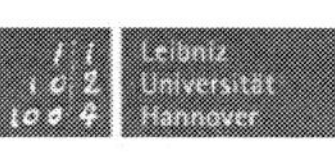

MeO-2PACz aging

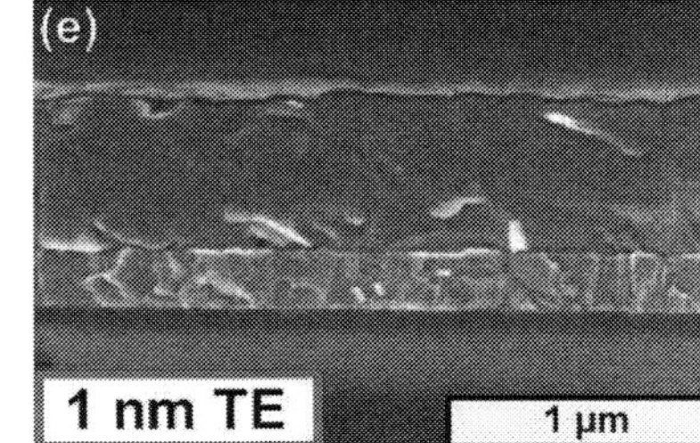

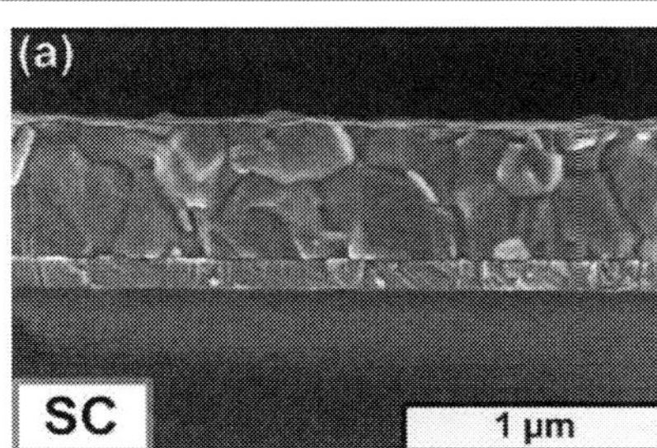

MeO-2PACz thickness variation

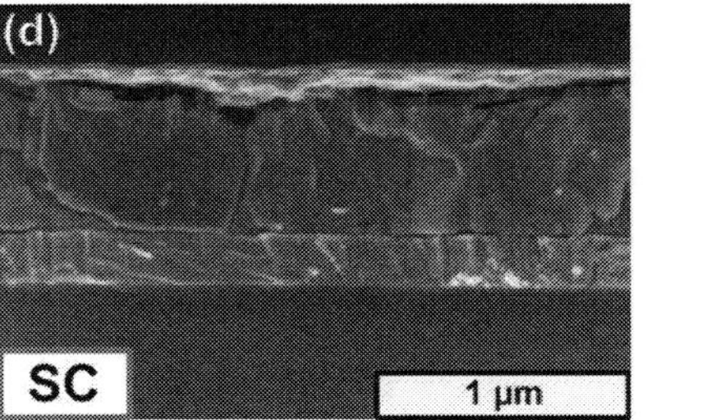

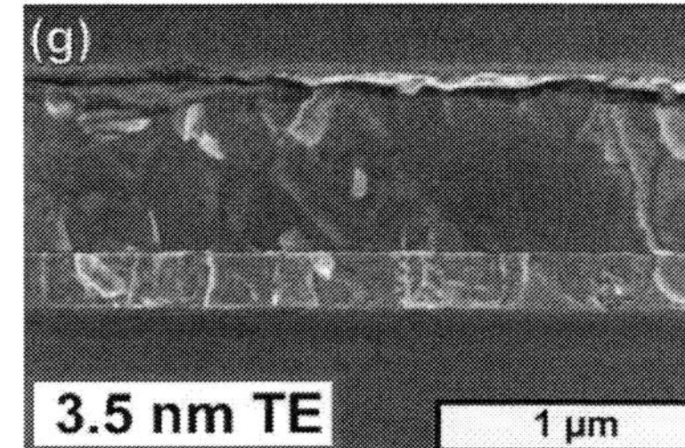

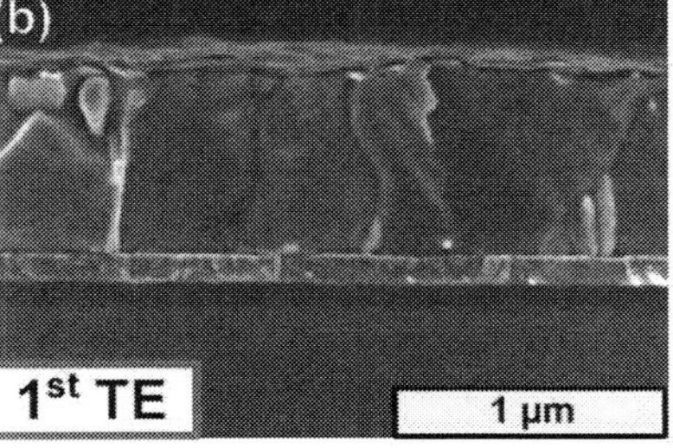

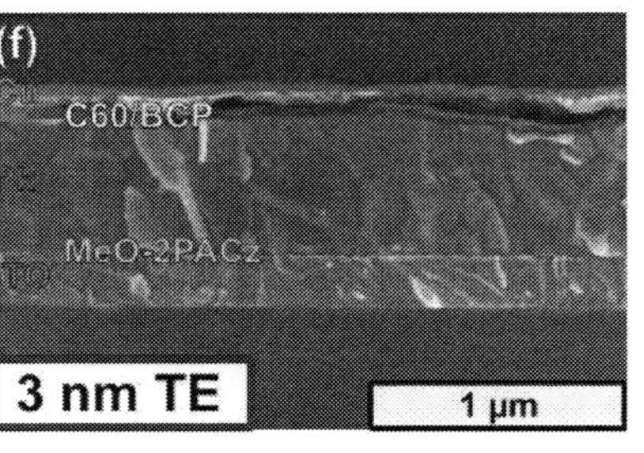
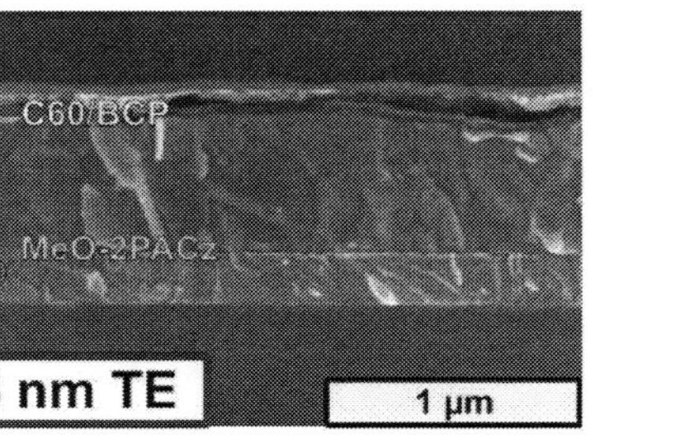

020114-019

XRD Pk after storage in N_2

MeO-2PACz aging after 306 days

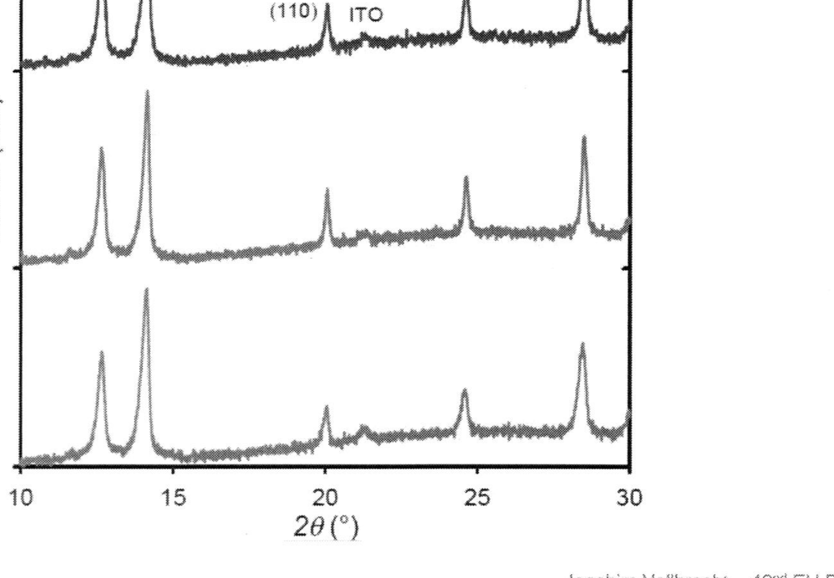

MeO-2PACz thickness var. after 257 days

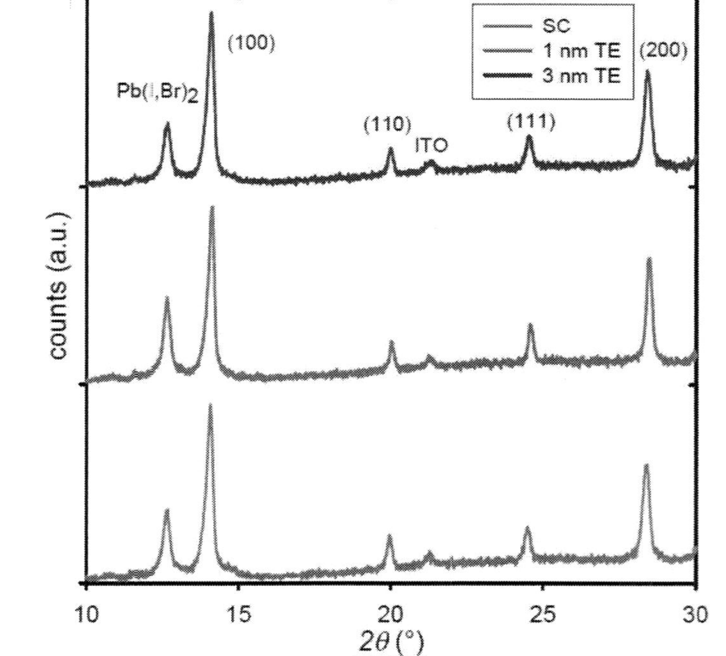

020114-020

This presentation was selected by the Sc. Committee of the EU PVSEC 2025 for submission of a full paper to one of the EU PVSEC's collaborating peer-reviewed journals.

OUTDOOR PERFORMANCE AND DEGRADATION ANALYSIS OF INVERTED PEROVSKITE SOLAR CELLS

°Makoto Konagai[1], Hayato Okawa [1], Ryousuke Ishikawa[1], Masatoshi Yanagida [2], Yasuhiro Shirai [2]
[1]Advanced Research Laboratories, Tokyo City University, [2]National Institute for Materials Science (NIMS)

ABSTRACT:
Perovskite solar cells were evaluated under two installation conditions: fixed at a south-facing tilt of 35° and mounted on a 2-axis tracking system. Significant performance degradation was observed during the high-temperature periods of July and August, with conversion efficiencies declining from 20–22% to 8–10%. Comparison between fixed-angle and tracking installations indicated that cells on the 2-axis system began to degrade one to two months earlier. Both J-V curve tracing and maximum power point tracking (MPPT) methods were employed, and although the sample size was limited, MPPT measurements appeared to induce slightly less degradation than J-V tracing. Three years of outdoor measurements revealed that the most critical degradation factor was elevated cell temperature during summer, accompanied by structural changes in the perovskite layer. Post-degradation analyses were conducted using optical microscopy, X-ray diffraction (XRD), and cross-sectional scanning electron microscopy (SEM). Severely degraded cells exhibited high-resistance layers in the cross-sections. Accelerated indoor degradation tests using a solar simulator with heating reproduced similar degradation phenomena, confirming the key role of temperature in device deterioration.

Keywords: Perovskite solar cell, Degradation, Outdoor performance

1 INTRODUCTION

The conversion efficiency of perovskite solar cells has improved remarkably in recent years.[1–3] Moreover, large-area module production has already commenced in several industries. Despite these advances, the widespread deployment of perovskite solar cells for power generation requires a reliable demonstration of long-term stability over 20–30 years. The degradation phenomena of perovskite solar cells have been comprehensively summarized in previous studies.[4–7]

To address this issue, our group has been systematically investigating the outdoor operational stability of perovskite solar cells and elucidating their degradation mechanisms to promote their practical implementation in power generation. This study presents detailed results from outdoor power generation tests conducted over a three-year period, beginning in September 2022, at Tokyo City University. Furthermore, post-degradation evaluations and analyses of the devices are discussed.

For large-area modules, the initial fill factor (FF) is frequently low, which complicates the evaluation of early-stage degradation. To circumvent this, we employed small-area (≈ 1 cm²) cells with high initial efficiencies of 20–23% and an initial FF of approximately 0.8.

One of the major challenges in the development of perovskite solar cells is the identification of degradation pathways.[8–11] To date, there have been no reports on the observation of degraded perovskite solar cells using optical microscopy, nor on the detection of charge-up phenomena induced by high-resistance layers under high-magnification SEM. In this study, such post-degradation analyses are introduced as they provide essential insights for developing strategies to mitigate thermally induced degradation, particularly under summer operating conditions.[12–15]

2 AIM AND APPROACH

The perovskite solar cells employed for outdoor measurements were fabricated by the National Institute for Materials Science (NIMS) and possessed the following device structure: glass/ITO/NiO$_x$/perovskite/C60/BCP/Ag (Fig. 1).[16] Each substrate had dimensions of 5 cm × 5 cm and contained four cells, each with an active area of 1.26 cm². The initial power conversion efficiencies (PCEs) were in the range of 20–23%. To enhance durability, the devices were encapsulated with glass on both sides.

Outdoor testing was performed under two installation conditions: (i) fixed mounting with a south-facing tilt angle of 35°, and (ii) installation on a 2-axis solar tracking system. Performance evaluation included comparison of current–voltage (J-V) curve tracing and maximum power point tracking (MPPT) methods.[17] Furthermore, efficiencies measured at noon on clear days were compared with the corresponding daily average values. To investigate seasonal degradation effects, particularly during the summer when device deterioration was most pronounced, additional tests were conducted using a UV-cut filter.[18]

The degradation phenomena of perovskite solar cells have been extensively documented in the literature, with multiple degradation pathways identified. In our three-year outdoor stability study, we found that the most critical degradation factor was the rise in cell temperature during summer, which was accompanied by structural changes in the perovskite layer. Notably, cells installed on the 2-axis tracking system exhibited accelerated degradation compared to those fixed at a 35° tilt.

To elucidate the underlying mechanisms, degraded

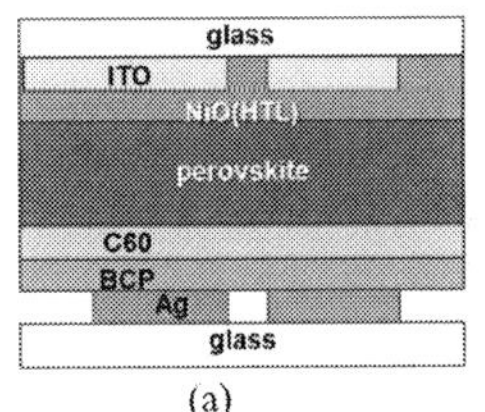

Figure 1: Structure of the sample used in the measurement. (a) Cross-sectional structure, (b) Sealed cell

10.4229/EUPVSEC2025/2DO.7.1
020115-001

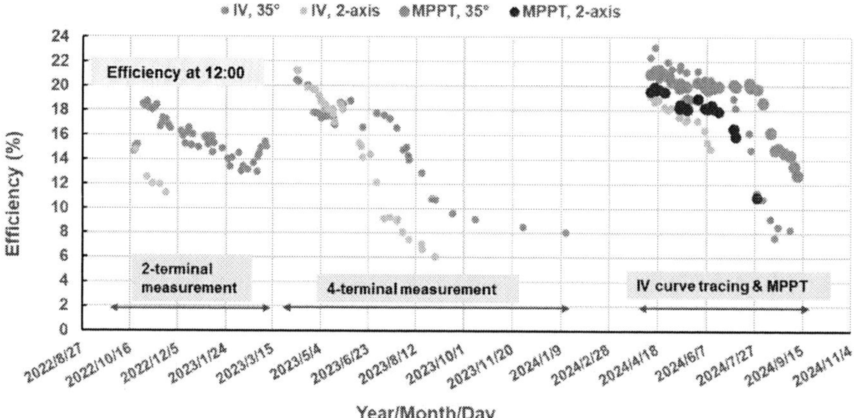

Fig.2 Outdoor power generation characteristics of perovskite solar cells from 2022 to 2024. Conversion efficiency values are based on measurements at 12:00 under solar irradiance conditions of approximately 100 mW/cm². Only reverse scan values are shown

cells were examined using optical microscopy, X-ray diffraction (XRD), and cross-sectional scanning electron microscopy (SEM). In severely degraded devices, high-resistance interfacial layers were clearly identified in the cross-sectional analyses.

To reproduce these phenomena under controlled conditions, accelerated degradation tests were performed indoors using a solar simulator combined with external heating. The results demonstrated that heating the cells to approximately 70 °C induced degradation behaviors analogous to those observed in outdoor environments.

3 EXPERIMETAL RESULTS

3.1 Summary of three-year measurement results

Figure 2 presents the outdoor power generation characteristics measured over a three-year period. All samples exhibited degradation, which was most pronounced during the summer months. In 2023, new devices were introduced in April and evaluated using a four-terminal measurement configuration. These samples exhibited initial efficiencies exceeding 20% with a fill factor of approximately 0.8. However, significant deterioration was observed during the high-temperature periods of July and August. Although a UV-cut filter was installed in July, its effect on suppressing degradation was negligible.

A comparison between fixed-angle (35° tilt) and 2-axis tracking configurations revealed that devices on the tracking system exhibited earlier degradation, typically by one to two months. Beginning in April 2024, MPPT measurements were conducted in parallel with conventional J-V curve tracing, owing to concerns that J-V curve measurements might contribute to degradation. Nevertheless, despite the limited number of samples, both methods indicated a comparable extent of degradation.

3.2 Comparative evaluation of degradation methods

Although reliability assessments and the identification of degradation mechanisms in perovskite solar cells remain at an early stage, numerous degradation pathways have already been reported. Among them, it has been suggested that J-V curve tracing may induce degradation due to the electric field applied across the junction. In this study, both J-V curve tracing and MPPT method were employed for performance evaluation, and the results were systematically compared. Under the MPPT protocol, J-V curve measurements were limited to three times per day.

Figure 3 compares the outcomes of MPPT and J-V measurements. MPPT continuously tracked the maximum power point, whereas J-V curves were recorded only at 11:00, 12:00, and 13:00 JST each day. The results demonstrate that both conversion efficiency and fill factor exhibited gradual degradation beginning in April, with accelerated deterioration observed during July and August when cell temperatures exceeded 50 °C. In addition, hysteresis—initially negligible—was found to increase progressively over time.

Although no temperature correction was applied, the conversion efficiency decreased from an initial value of approximately 20% to 10–15% by the end of August. While the sample size was limited, the results suggest that devices evaluated under the MPPT protocol exhibited slightly reduced degradation compared with those measured primarily by J-V curve tracing.

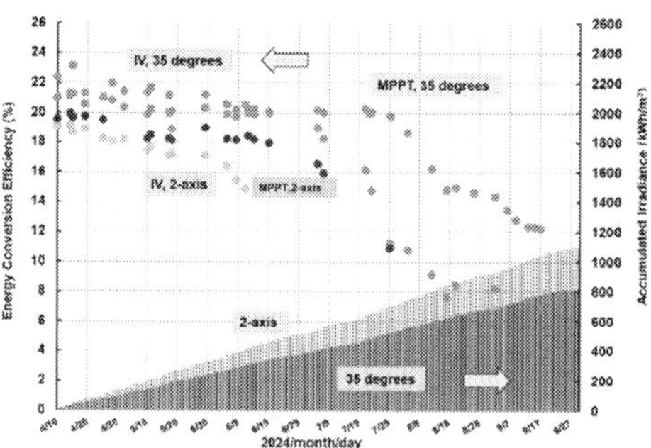

Fig.3 Comparison between I-V Curve Tracing and MPPT measurements (Measurement period: April–September 2024)

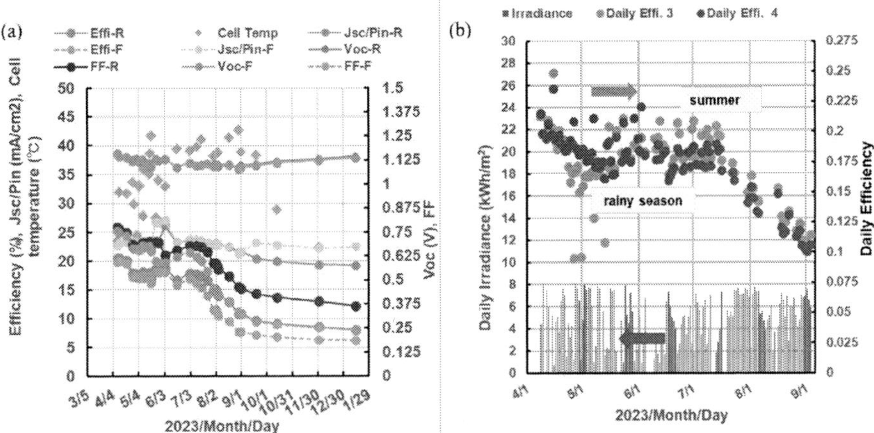

Fig.4 Comparison of (a) 12:00 conversion efficiency trends and (b) daily average efficiency trends.

3.3 Daily average efficiency

Figure 4 compares the conversion efficiency measured at 12:00 by J-V curve tracing with the corresponding daily average efficiency. For the 12:00 data, only measurements under an irradiation intensity of approximately 100 mW cm^{-2} were considered, while daily averages were plotted only for days with a total solar irradiance exceeding 5 kWh/m^2. In perovskite solar cells, the fill factor often appears larger under low-irradiance conditions, even after degradation. By restricting the analysis to data collected under sufficiently high irradiance, both measurement methods yielded consistent results.

4 DISCUSSIONS

4.1 Estimating cell temperature during operation

When evaluating the outdoor performance of perovskite solar cells, one of the most critical parameters is the cell operating temperature. However, accurately determining the junction temperature of perovskite solar cells encapsulated between glass plates is challenging, owing to the low thermal conductivity of both glass and the perovskite absorber. Ideally, precise measurement would require encapsulating either a temperature sensor or a calibrated, thin silicon reference cell alongside the device.

In the present study, the measurement system initially employed placed the temperature sensor on the exterior surface of the encapsulated cell, preventing accurate monitoring of the internal cell temperature. To address this limitation, the cell temperature was instead estimated from the I_{sc}–V_{oc} relationship obtained during outdoor measurements (Fig. 5). Although numerous reports on perovskite solar cell degradation exist, relatively few have investigated their temperature characteristics under outdoor operating conditions, as undertaken in this study.

For crystalline Si and GaAs solar cells, the junction temperature during operation can generally be estimated from the I_{sc}–V_{oc} relationship, provided that the temperature dependence of the dark current (I_d–V_d characteristics) is measured indoors. In contrast, for perovskite solar cells, measuring I_d–V_d characteristics at elevated temperatures (70–100 °C) is problematic due to concerns about accelerated degradation under such conditions. Therefore, in this study, the junction temperature during outdoor operation was estimated using the temperature coefficient (within the range of –1.6 to –2.0 mV/K obtained from separate temperature-dependent measurements),[20] this corresponds to a cell temperature rise of ~56 °C. Thus, the cell temperature was estimated to increase from ~14 °C in the early morning to ~70 °C at 14:00. A similar analysis for June 8 yielded a maximum cell temperature of ~78 °C.

For the cell fixed at a 35° tilt, the maximum cell temperature was estimated at ~70 °C. The higher temperature observed in the 2-axis tracking device is attributed to its peak irradiance (~1.1 kW/m^2, ~10% higher than that of the fixed installation) and daily accumulated irradiance (~30% higher).

These results indicate that 2-axis tracking accelerates perovskite solar cell degradation through a combined effect of increased irradiance and elevated operating temperature, compared with fixed-tilt installations.

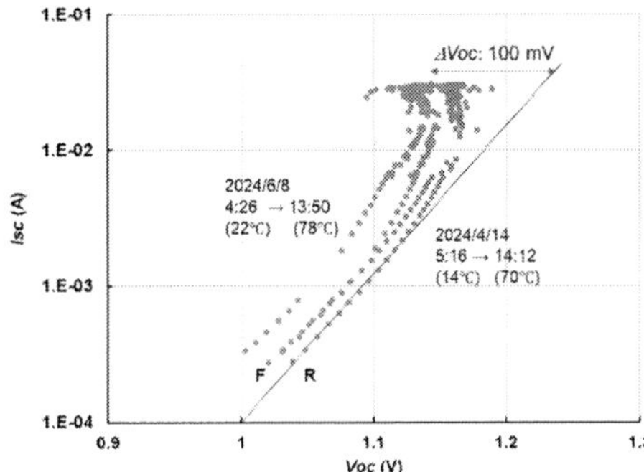

Fig.5 I_{sc}–V_{oc} plot of a perovskite solar cell mounted on a 2-axis tracker. On June 8th, the cell temperature was estimated to have reached a maximum of 78 °C.

4.2 SEM observation after deterioration

The degradation phenomena of perovskite solar cells have been extensively reported in the literature, with causes such as ion migration and elemental diffusion at interfaces identified. Results from the three-year outdoor measurements presented in this study indicate that the most critical factors driving degradation are elevated cell

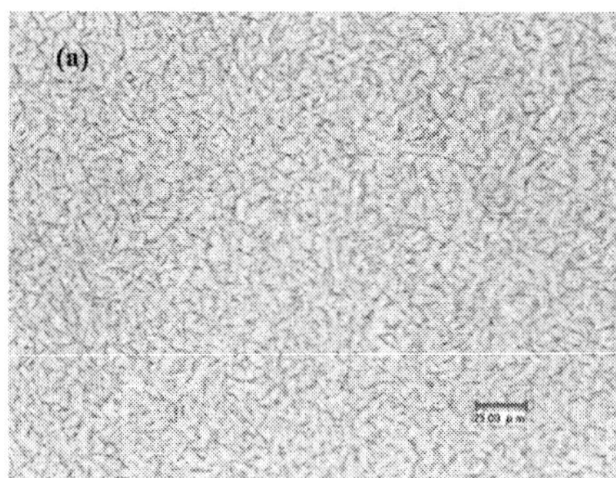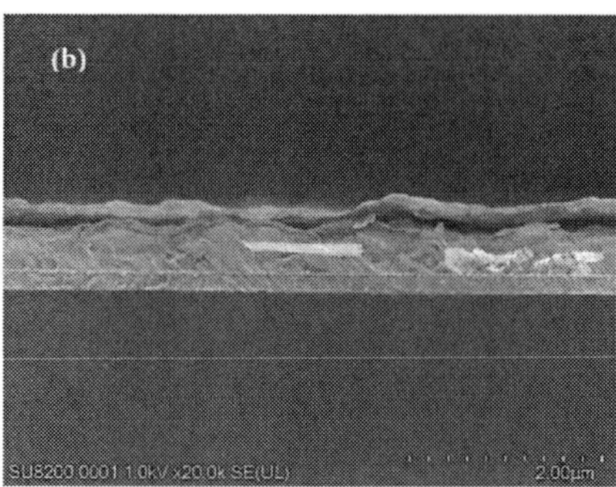

Fig.6 Structural changes in degraded samples:
(a) OM image observed through the glass substrate (contrast adjusted).
(b) Cross-sectional SEM image. White regions indicate high-resistance layers.

temperatures during summer and the resulting structural changes in the perovskite layer.

To further elucidate the underlying mechanisms, surface observations were conducted using optical microscopy (OM), cross-sectional analyses were performed with SEM, and XRD measurements were carried out. Cross-sectional SEM images of severely degraded cells revealed the formation of high-resistance layers (Fig. 6). Although these layers did not produce significant peaks in XRD, they are likely associated with the formation of the δ-phase.

4.3 Indoor Accelerated Degradation Tests

To reproduce these degradation phenomena under controlled conditions, accelerated indoor tests were performed using a solar simulator with external heating. Heating the cells to approximately 70 °C induced degradation behaviors comparable to those observed in outdoor measurements.

5 SUMMARY

In conclusion, although multiple factors contribute to the degradation of contemporary perovskite solar cells, the present study demonstrates for the first time that high-resistance layers emerge at elevated operating temperatures. This phenomenon is likely associated with phase transitions from the α-phase to the δ-phase. Further confirmation through XRD and transmission electron microscopy (TEM) is required to substantiate this interpretation.

ACKNOWLEDGEMENT

This work was supported by the Priority Research Project of Tokyo City University, Japan.

References
[1] T. Miyasaka, A. Kojima, K. Teshima, Y. Shirai, *J Am Chem Soc* 2009, *131*, 6050.
[2] N. G. Park, *Materials Today* 2015, *18*, 65.
[3] M. A. Green, E. D. Dunlop, M. Yoshita, N. Kopidakis, K. Bothe, G. Siefer, X. Hao, J. Y. Jiang, *Progress in Photovoltaics: Research and Applications* 2025, *33*, 3.
[4] T. Matsui, T. Yamamoto, T. Nishihara, R. Morisawa, T. Yokoyama, T. Sekiguchi, T. Negami, *Advanced Materials* 2019, DOI 10.1002/adma.201806823.
[5] J. Zhuang, J. Wang, F. Yan, *Review on Chemical Stability of Lead Halide Perovskite Solar Cells*, Springer Nature Singapore, 2023.
[6] D. B. Khadka, M. Yanagida, Y. Shirai, *Solar Energy Materials and Solar Cells* 2025, *281*, DOI 10.1016/j.solmat.2024.113319.
[7] S. Baumann, G. E. Eperon, A. Virtuani, Q. Jeangros, D. B. Kern, D. Barrit, J. Schall, W. Nie, G. Oreski, M. Khenkin, C. Ulbrich, R. Peibst, J. S. Stein, M. Köntges, *Energy Environ Sci* 2024, *17*, 7566.
[8] M. Jošt, B. Lipovšek, B. Glažar, A. Al-Ashouri, K. Brecl, G. Matič, A. Magomedov, V. Getautis, M. Topič, S. Albrecht, *Adv Energy Mater* 2020, *10*, DOI 10.1002/aenm.202000454.
[9] M. Konagai, H. Okawa, R. Ishikawa, M. Yanagida, Y. Shirai, *Proc. of the 34th International Photovoltaic Science and Engineering Conf. (PVSEC-34)* 2023, 222.
[10] V. Paraskeva, M. Norton, A. Livera, A. Kyprianou, M. Hadjipanayi, E. Peraticos, A. Aguirre, S. Ramesh, T. Merckx, R. Ebner, T. Aernouts, A. Krishna, G. E. Georghiou, *ACS Energy Lett* 2024, 5081.
[11] M. Khenkin, H. Köbler, M. Remec, R. Roy, U. Erdil, J. Li, N. Phung, G. Adwan, G. Paramasivam, Q. Emery, E. Unger, R. Schlatmann, C. Ulbrich, A. Abate, *Energy Environ Sci* 2023, *17*, 602.
[12] G. Hodes, *Science (1979)* 2013, DOI 10.1126/science.1245473.
[13] M. Saliba, T. Matsui, K. Domanski, J.-Y. Seo, A. Ummadisi, M. Saliba, T. Matsui, K. Domanski, J.-Y. Seo, A. Ummadisingu, S. M. Zakeeruddin, J.-P. Correa-Baena, W. R. Tress, A. Abate, M. Grätzel, *Science (1979)* 2016, *354*.
[14] T. Haeger, R. Heiderhoff, T. Riedl, *J Mater Chem C Mater* 2020, *8*, 14289.
[15] M. Nakamura, I. Takenaka, T. Mabuchi, C. Nishiyama, K. Tada, T. Bessho, H. Segawa, *ACS Appl Energy Mater* 2022, *5*, 10409.

[16] M. Yanagida, T. Nakamura, T. Yoshida, D. B. Khadka, Y. Shirai, K. Miyano, *Jpn J Appl Phys* 2023, *62*, SK1054.

[17] L. Cojocaru, S. Uchida, K. Tamaki, P. V. V. Jayaweera, S. Kaneko, J. Nakazaki, T. Kubo, H. Segawa, *Sci Rep* 2017, *7*, 1.

[18] M. B. Islam, M. Yanagida, Y. Shirai, Y. Nabetani, K. Miyano, *ACS Omega* 2017, *2*, 2291.

[19] S. Charan, M. Konagai, K. Takahashi, *J Appl Phys* 1979, *50*, 963.

[20] T. Moot, J. B. Patel, G. McAndrews, E. J. Wolf, D. Morales, I. E. Gould, B. A. Rosales, C. C. Boyd, L. M. Wheeler, P. A. Parilla, S. W. Johnston, L. T. Schelhas, M. D. McGehee, J. M. Luther, *ACS Energy Lett* 2021, *6*, 2038.

IPVF

Strategies for quasi-2D perovskite integration in p-i-n solar cells

Anna Capitaine, Hugo Le Bossenec, Marion Provost, Alexandra Levtchenko, Daniel Ory, Jean Rousset

EUPVSEC 2025

2D/3D Heterojunctions for increased efficiency and stability

- **Ammonium cations** are the most universal strategy for increasing efficiency

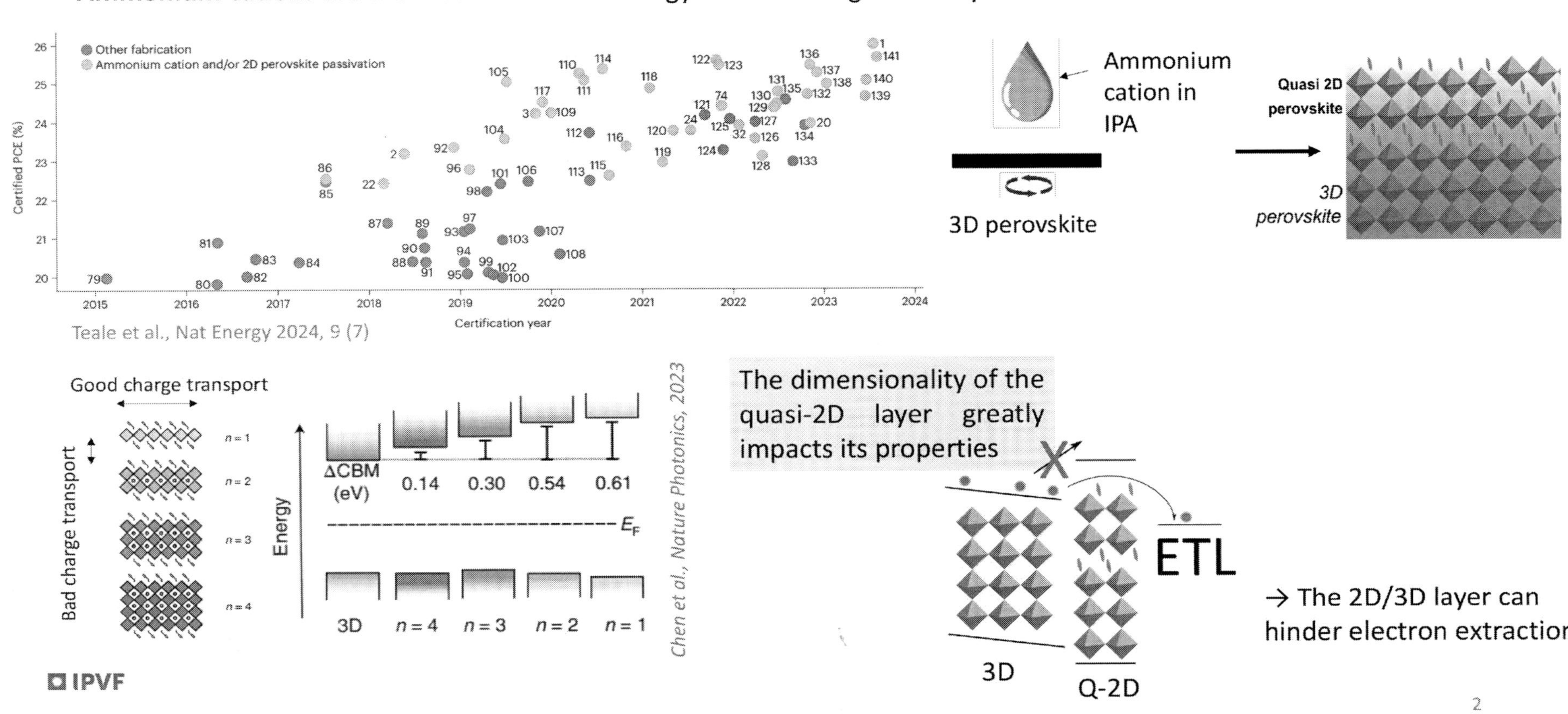

IPVF

Strategies for quasi-2D perovskite integration in p-i-n solar cells

Promising "2D cations"

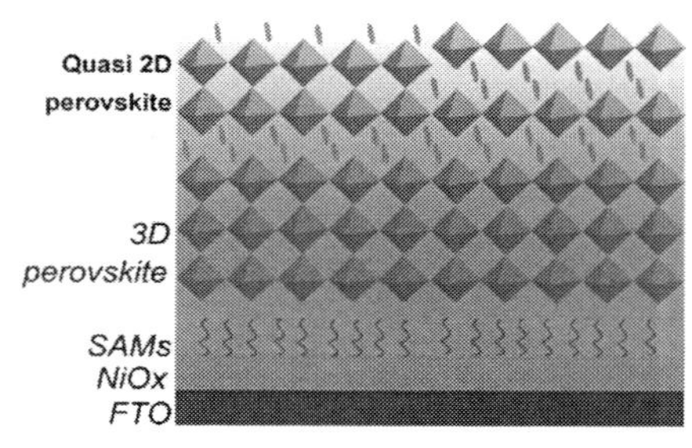

Phenethyl-ammonium derivatives (4F-)PEA$^+$

Butyl-ammonium derivatives BA$^+$

Strategy 1

Li et al., Advanced Materials, 2023

Strategy 2

Liu et al., Advanced Energy Materials, 2023

Strategy 3

Strategy 4

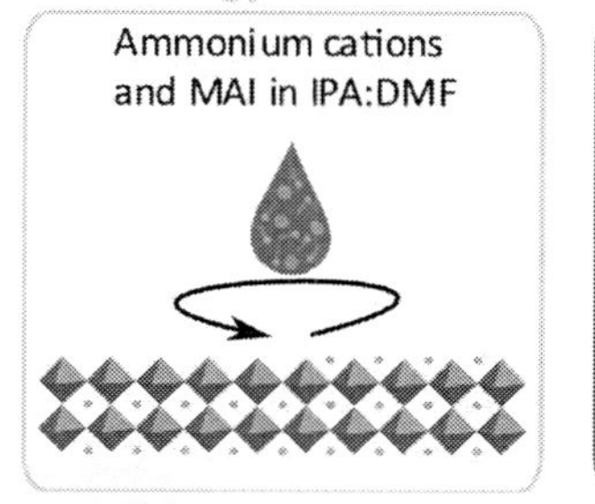

Huang et al., Energy and Environmental Science, 2023

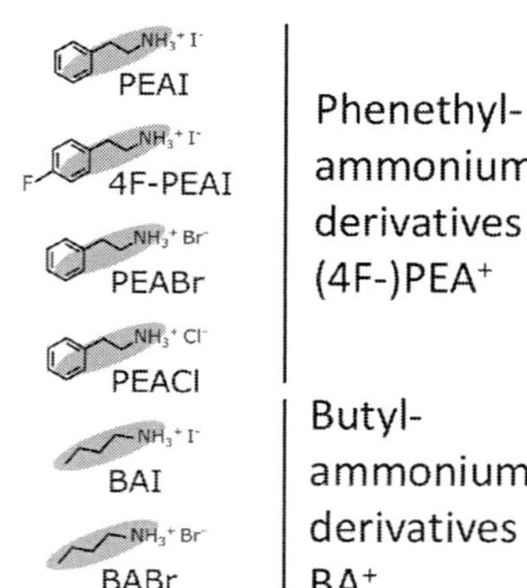

IPVF

3

What is the most promising strategy ?

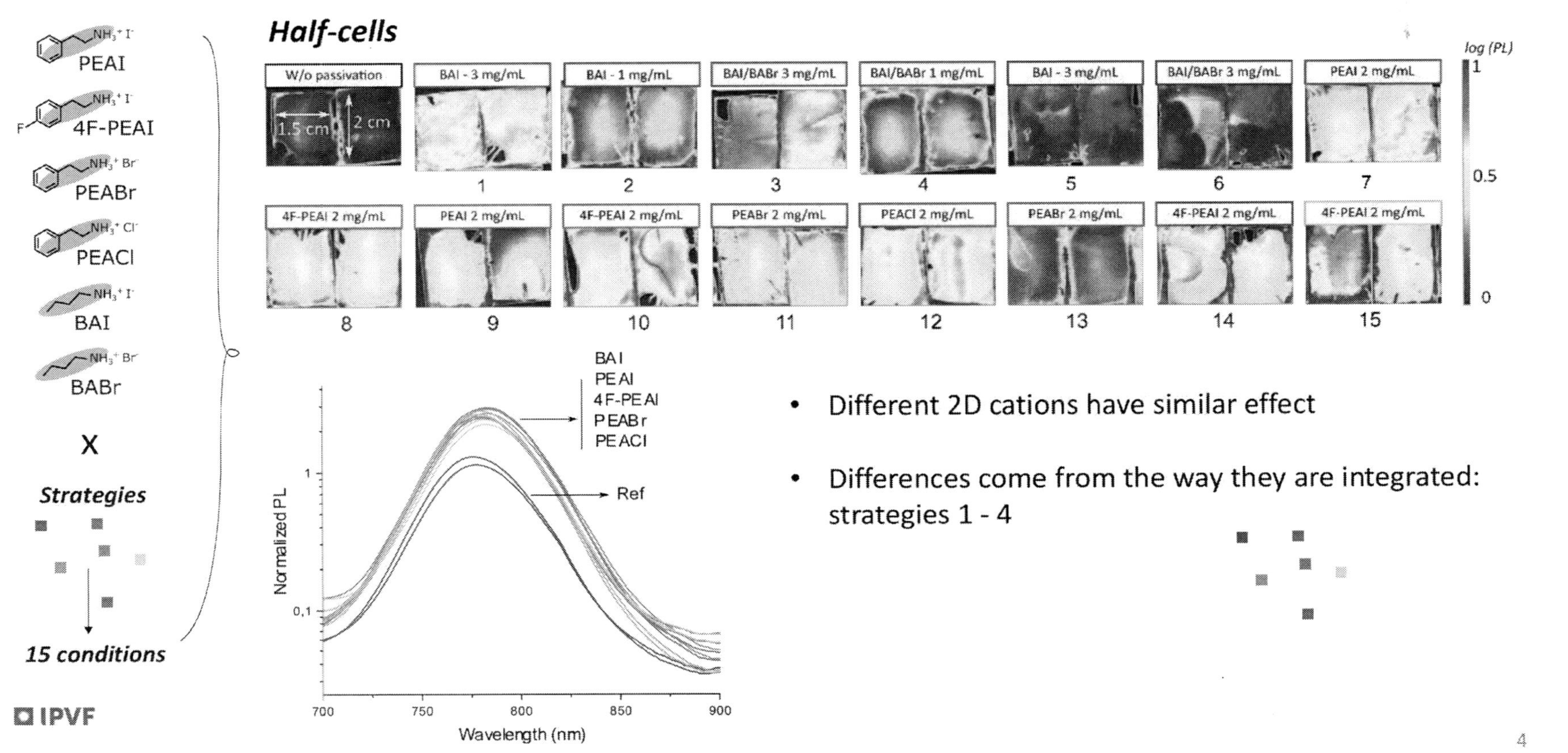

- Different 2D cations have similar effect

- Differences come from the way they are integrated: strategies 1 - 4

What is the most promising strategy ?

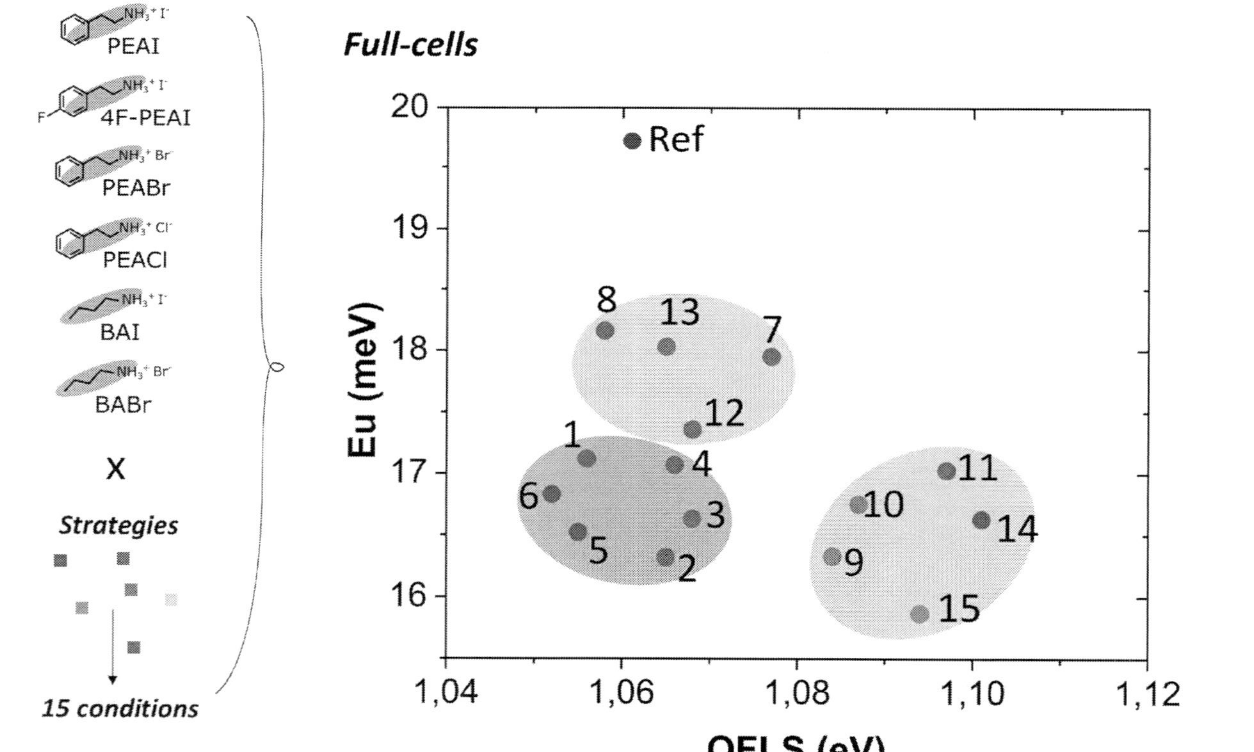

020116-005

What is the most promising strategy ?

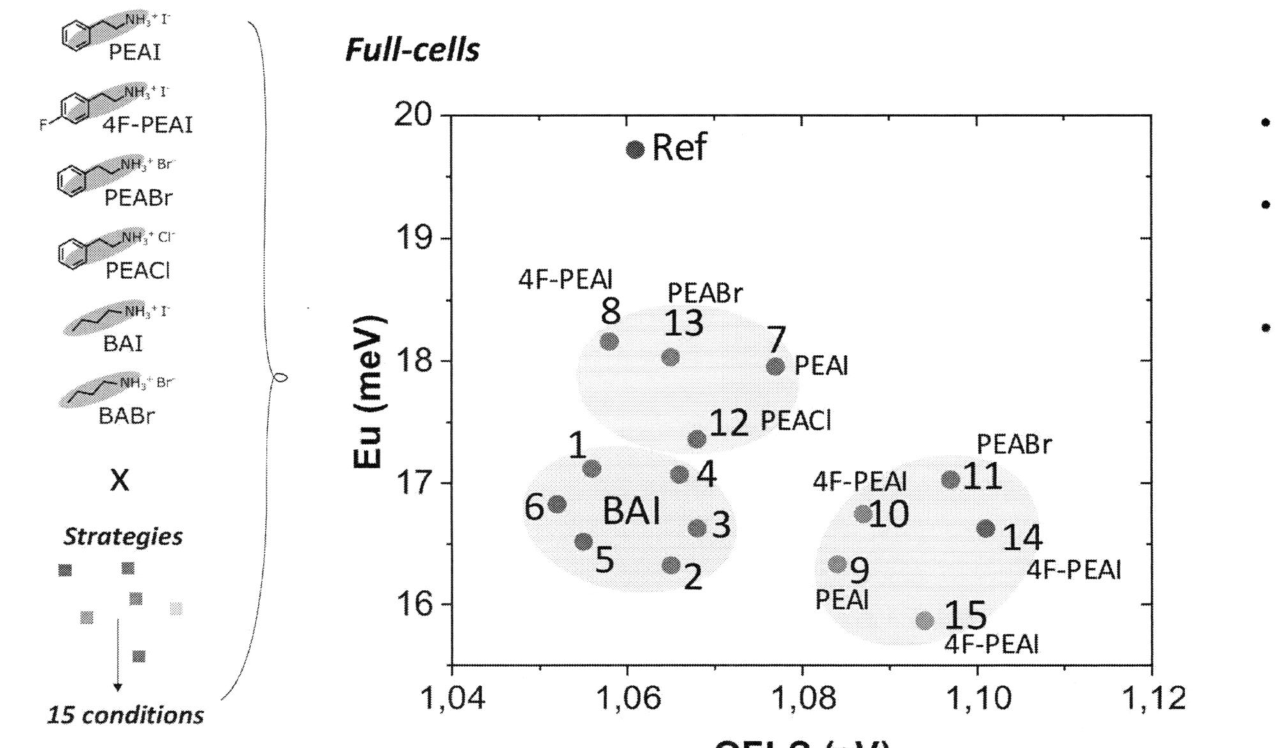

- QFLS up to **+ 40 meV**

- All strategies enable to reduce Urbach Energy (Eu)

- Best passivations – **low Eu and high QFLS** – are achieved with (4F)-PEA$^+$ derivatives thanks to solvent engineering solutions or addition of additives

Additives and solvent engineering strategies allow for 2D-phases of higher dimensionality

- 10 mg/mL 4F-PEAI for all (concentration x5) to characterize quasi-2D phases

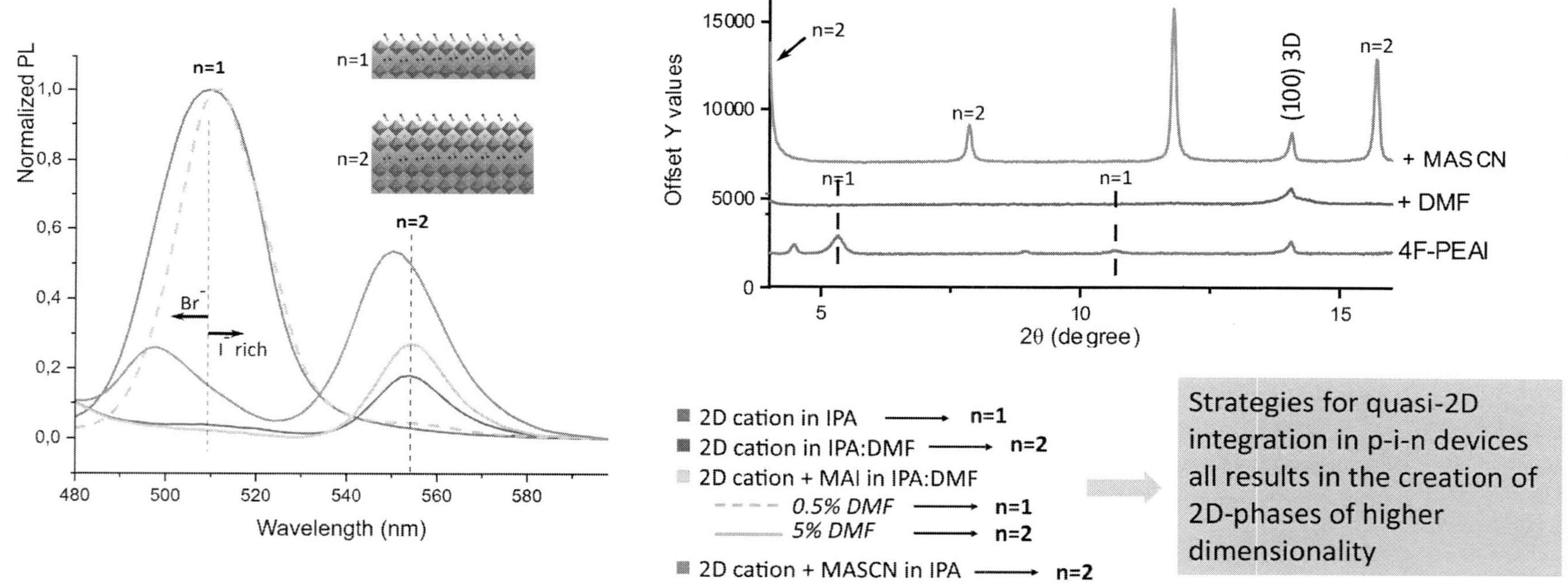

IPVF

Increasing performance and stability with quasi-2D phases remains a challenge

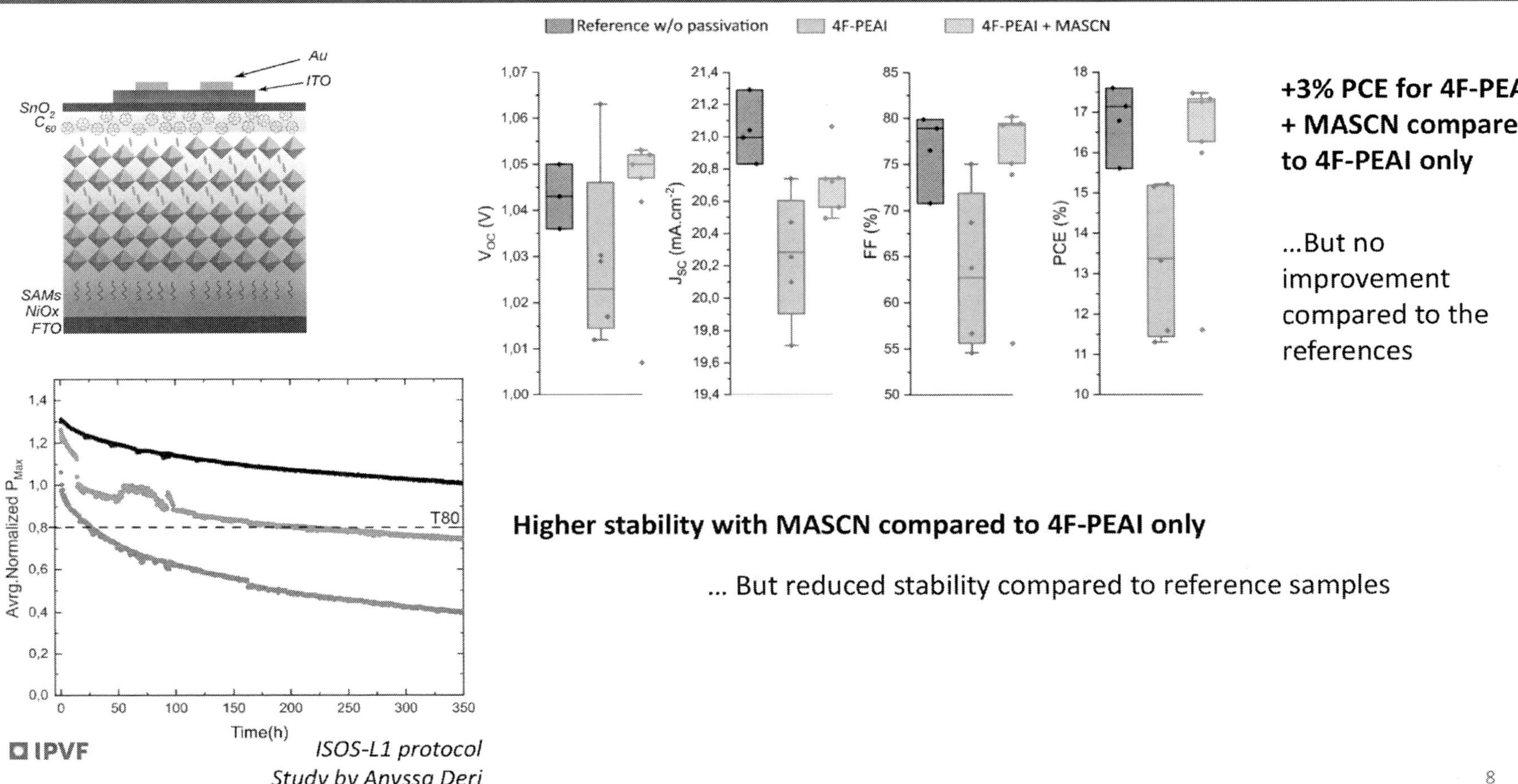

+3% PCE for 4F-PEAI + MASCN compared to 4F-PEAI only

...But no improvement compared to the references

Higher stability with MASCN compared to 4F-PEAI only

... But reduced stability compared to reference samples

How to control quasi-2D phases formation for enhanced performance ?

Quasi-2D phases form by intercalation in the 3D perovskite structure

And or by **PbI$_2$ conversion**

$$2\ (4F\text{-}PEAI) + PbI_2 \rightarrow (4F\text{-}PEA)_2 PbI_4 \qquad n=1$$

$$2\ (4F\text{-}PEAI) + (n\text{-}1)\ FAI + n\ PbI_2 \rightarrow (4F\text{-}PEA)_2 (FA)_{n-1} Pb_n I_{(3n+1)} \qquad n>1$$

More control

- With **slot-die coating** all the solution remains on the substrate

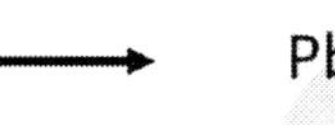

Slot-die head direction

Substrate

PbI$_2$ conversion + Slot-die coating
=
Stoichiometric approach

1 PbI$_2$ evaporation on 3D perovskite

2 PbI$_2$ conversion by slot-die coating

□ IPVF

PbI_2 conversion into quasi-2D perovskite by slot-die coating

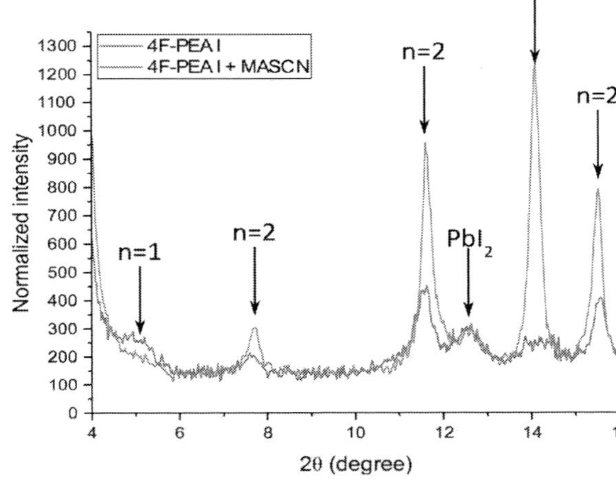

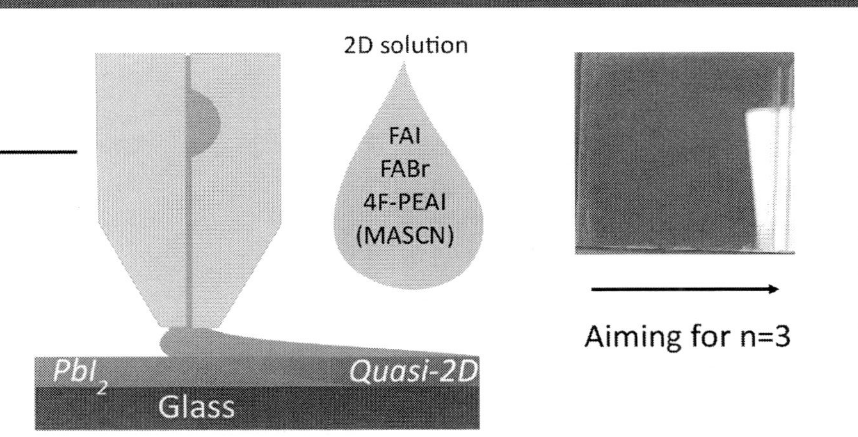

- PbI_2 almost complete conversion

- More n=2 and >2 phases when adding MASCN

PbI$_2$ conversion into quasi-2D perovskite by slot-die coating

Work by Hugo Le Bossenec

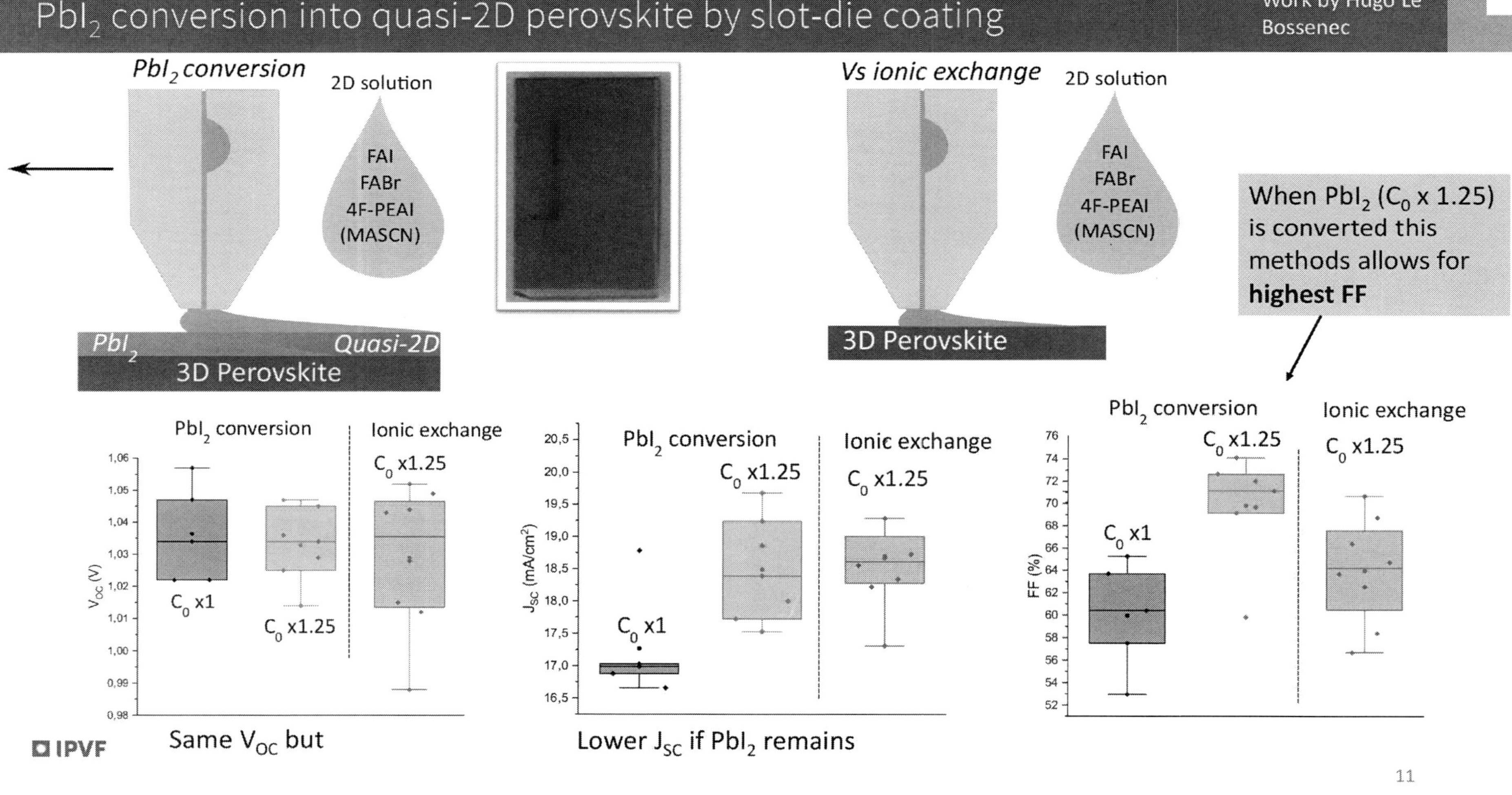

PbI_2 conversion into quasi-2D perovskite by slot-die coating

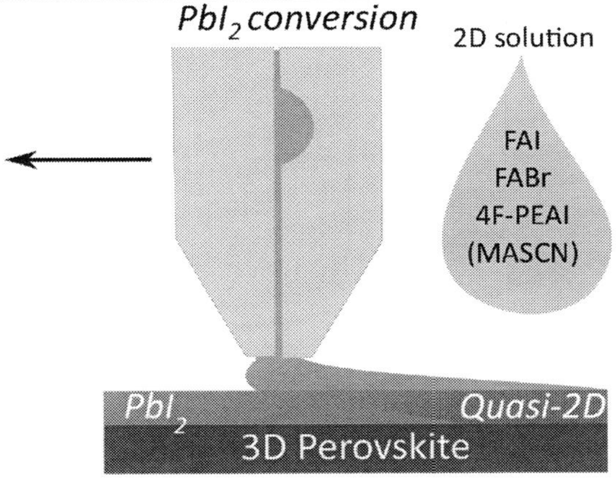

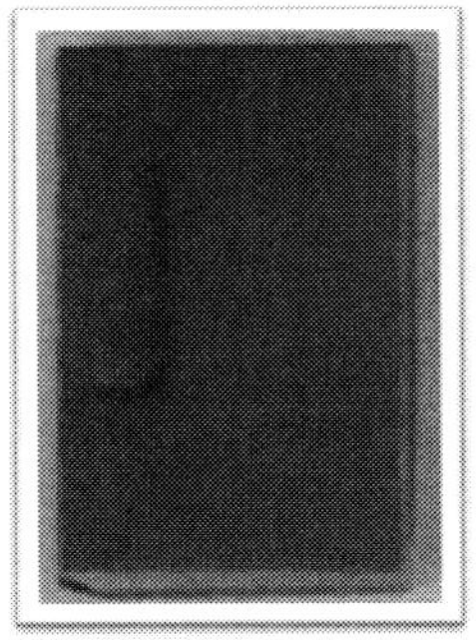

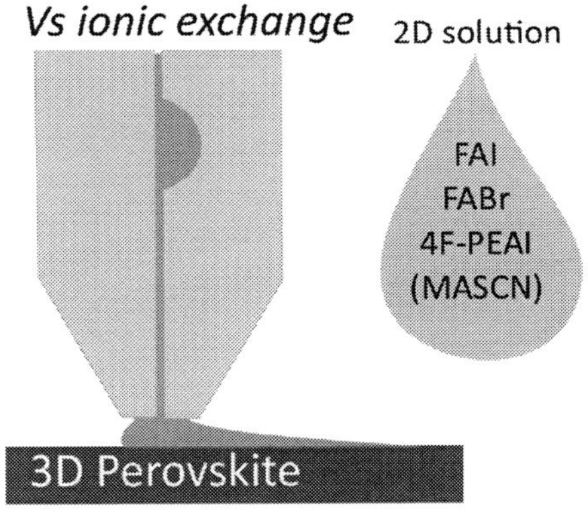

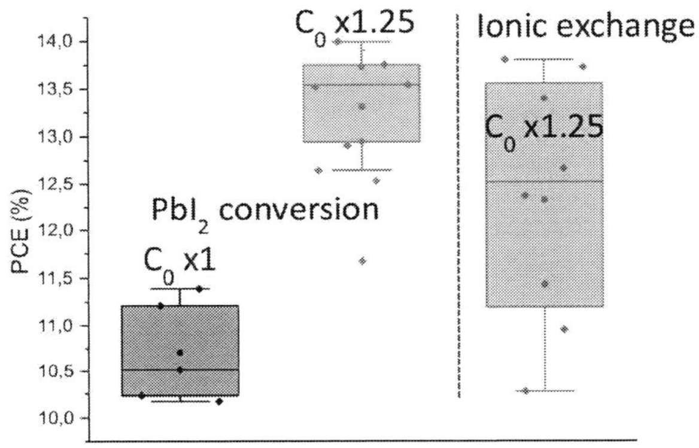

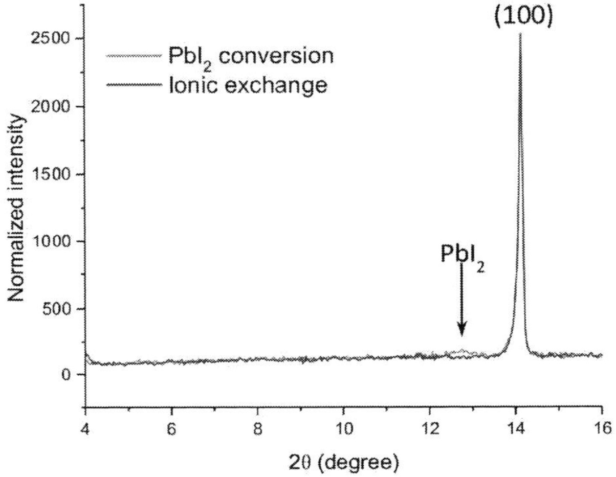

- Almost complete PbI_2 conversion

- **No traces of 2D phases:** penetration of 2D cations deeper than the PbI_2 template

Conclusion and perspectives

Spin coating

- Strategies developed for 2D cations integration in p-i-n solar cells lead to **n=2 rather than n=1 2D phases**

- Still, improving device performance and stability with a quasi-2D interface **remains a challenge despite their passivation effect** (QFLS, Eu)

PbI_2 evaporation and conversion by slot-die coating

- Quasi-2D perovskite can be formed by PbI_2 conversion by slot-die coating: increased FF

- Stable n>2 quasi-2D phases on top of 3D perovskite remains a challenge even with a stoichiometric reaction

    ⟶ Difficult to take advantage of quasi-2D properties with mono-ammoniums

Thank you for your attention

◻ IPVF

INNOVATIVE APPROACH TO BISMUTH-ANTIMONY-IODIDE DOUBLE PEROVSKITE PV ABSORBERS VIA ANION EXCHANGE AND SOLID-STATE REACTIONS

Oleksandr Stroyuk[1], Oleksandra Raievska[1], Sachin Kinge[2], Jens Hauch[1,3], Christoph J. Brabec[1,3]
[1]Forschungszentrum Jülich GmbH, Helmholtz-Institut Erlangen Nürnberg für Erneuerbare Energien
(HI ERN), 91058 Erlangen, Germany, o.stroyuk@fz-juelich.de
[2]Materials Engineering Division, Toyota Motors Europe, sachin.kinge@toyota-europe.com
[3]Friedrich-Alexander-Universität Erlangen-Nürnberg, Materials for Electronics and Energy Technology (i-MEET),
Martensstrasse 7, 91058 Erlangen, Germany, christoph.brabec@fau.de

ABSTRACT: This work focuses on the development of advanced synthesis protocols for lead-free $Cs_2AgBi(Sb)Br_6$ perovskites and their conversion into lower-bandgap $Cs_2AgBi(Sb)I_6$ perovskite PV absorbers by using an innovative combination of mild anion exchange with a solid-state reaction between intermediate iodide derivatives. High-throughput robot-assisted experimentation is applied for the optimization of the synthesis conditions, targeting the highest yields of $Cs_2AgBi(Sb)I_6$ perovskites (ca. 90 mass%) with the lowest bandgap (1.78 eV). We provide new insights into the pathways, mechanisms, and dynamics of the formation of iodide double perovskites, reporting stable lead-free double iodide perovskites crystallized in a non-conventional tetragonal symmetry.
Keywords: double perovskites; anion exchange; solid-state reaction; tetragonal perovskites

1 INTRODUCTION

The unprecedentedly successful and fast development of lead-halide-based solar cells stimulates parallel research aimed at the discovery of alternative metal-halide perovskite and perovskite-inspired materials with comparably high photovoltaic (PV) efficiency, but superior to lead-halide absorbers in terms of lower toxicity and higher stability [1,2]. These studies focused on several classes of lead-free perovskites, particularly on stable $Cs_2AgBiBr_6$ (CABB) double perovskite currently showing power conversion efficiencies of ca. 3% [3]. Further progress in this direction is expected from iodide-based analogs with lower bandgaps, such as Cs_2AgBiI_6 (CABI); however, the synthesis of iodide double perovskites is associated with many challenges, including instability of precursors and unreliable structural and compositional control over the products [4].

In the present work, we develop an innovative approach to mixed-halide $Cs_2Ag(Bi,Sb)BrI_5$ (CABSBI) double perovskites from $Cs_2AgBi(Sb)Br_6$ (CABSB) perovskites using a two-stage approach. On the first stage, CABSB is converted into mixtures of $CsAg_2I_3$ and $Cs_3(Bi,Sb)_2(Br,I)_9$ intermediates by mild anion exchanges (AE). The second stage of thermal annealing results in a solid-state reaction and formation of stable tetragonal double CAB(S)BI perovskites. The conditions of the two-stage process are optimized using high-throughput robot-assisted experimentation [5,6], yielding CABSBI perovskites with bandgaps below 1.8 eV, promising for indoor PV and multijunction architectures.

2 SYNTHESES AND CHARACTERIZATIONS

2.1 Syntheses

Microcrystalline $Cs_2AgBi_xSb_{1-x}Br_6$ samples were produced by mixing two precursor solutions at room temperature (RT) in open-atmosphere conditions. Precursor #1 combined x mL of 1.0 M $BiBr_3$ solution in 5.0 M aqueous HBr, $(1-x)$ mL of 1.0 M $SbCl_3$ solution in 5.0 M HBr, 1.0 mL of 8.9 M aqueous HBr, and 5.0 mL 2-propanol. Precursor #2 was prepared from 1.0 mL of 1.0 M aqueous $AgNO_3$ solution, 1.2 mL deionized water, 0.25 mL of 25 wt.% aqueous NH_4OH solution, 0.55 mL of 4.0 M aqueous Cs acetate solution, and 5.0 mL of 2-propanol.

The CABSB samples were brought into contact with water/2-propanol solutions of NaI (AE solution). In a typical procedure, 1 mmol of CABSB was mixed with 5.0 mL of 2-propanol in a 25-mL glass vial, capped with a Parafilm layer, subjected to intense magnetic refluxing for 15 min, and an AE solution was added (10 mL of 2-propanol and 2.0 mL of 4.0 M aqueous NaI solution).

All products were subjected to purification. For this aim, as-prepared suspensions were centrifuged at 1500 rpm for 2 min, the supernatant was removed, and 10.0 mL of 2-propanol was added to form a homogeneous suspension, which was subjected to centrifugation, and the purification process was repeated twice.

The as-prepared AE products (AE-CABSBI) were subjected to thermal annealing in air. For this, the microcrystalline AE-CABSBI was distributed as a thin uniform layer on a glass substrate and annealed on an open-air heating plate at varied T for 10 min.

The PV properties of CABB were characterized in planar solar cells with a titania electron transport layer (ETL) and P3HT as a hole transport layer (HTL). A CABB ink (0.5 M) in dimethylsulfoxide (DMSO) was used to form absorber layers. The ETL was formed by spin-coating of Ti(IV) tetraisopropoxide solution in HCl on preliminary cleaned ITO substrates, followed by calcination in air at 460 °C for 30 min. Then, the CABB film was spin-coated and the freshly deposited film was placed under vacuum to evaporate DMSO, then annealed in air at 250 °C for 10 min. Afterwards, a layer of P3HT HTL is spin-coated, and gold back electrodes were deposited by vacuum evaporation through a mask to form six-pixel cells.

2.2 Characterizations

Powder X-Ray diffraction (XRD) patterns were registered using a Panalytical X'pert powder diffractometer with copper K_α radiation. The XRD patterns were subjected to a Rietveld refinement procedure using MAUD software (version 2.99).

Scanning electron microscopic (SEM) imaging and energy-dispersive X-Ray spectroscopic (EDX) analysis were performed using a JEOL JSM-7610F Schottky field emission microscope operating under 15-20 kV and equipped with an X-Max 80 mm2 silicon drift detector

(Oxford Instruments) and AZtec nanoanalysis software.

Reflectance spectra were recorded using a BlackComet spectrometer (StellarNet Inc.) and a 75-W Xenon lamp (Thorlabs) as an excitation source. The spectra were registered with an optical Y-fiber probe in an identical geometry for samples and a scattering reference (ultra-pure $BaSO_4$, Alfa-Aesar). The reflectance spectra were transformed into absorption spectra using the Kubelka-Munk formula and the reference.

The J-V characteristics of CABB-based solar cells were measured using a Botest source measurement unit under AM1.5G illumination provided by an Oriel Sol 1A solar simulator (Newport) under ambient conditions.

3 RESULTS AND DISCUSSION

3.1 Advanced synthesis of bromide perovskites

The conventionally adopted synthesis of CABB double perovskite from a mixture of CsBr, AgBr, and $BiBr_3$ suffers from several drawbacks, including high light sensitivity of AgBr, low solubility of Cs_2AgBr_3 intermediate, and the requirements of using concentrated HBr (48%) and heating at ca. 100 °C. As a more practical alternative, we report a milder and more controlled protocol, where CABB forms at the interaction of two water/2-propanol precursor solutions containing Cs acetate and $AgNO_3$ (precursor 1), and $BiBr_3$ in 5% HBr (precursor 2). The protocol yields single-phase microcrystalline stoichiometric CABB double perovskite (Figure 1a,c,e) at RT with no additional thermal treatments, at the lowest reported HBr concentration. It can be scaled up to multi-gram synthesis and adapted to form other bromide perovskites, in particular, $Cs_2AgBi_xSb_{1-x}Br_6$, $Cs_3Bi_2Br_9$, and Cs_2AgBr_2.

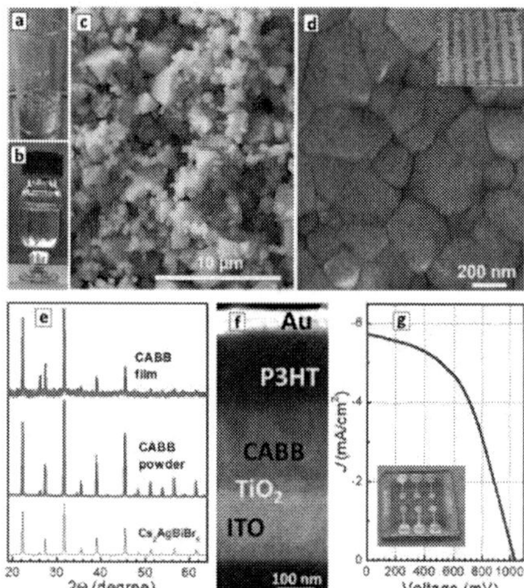

Figure 1: (a-e) Photographs of CABB powder (a), ink (b), and film (insert in (d)). (c-e) SEM images (c,d), and XRD patterns (e) of CABB powder (c) and film (d). In (e), the red line represents Rietveld's refinement. (f,g) Cross-sectional SEM image/scheme (f), J-V curve (g), and photograph (insert in (g)) of a CABB-based solar cell

The CABB powder dissolves spontaneously at RT in DMSO, forming a stable 0.5 M ink (Fig. 1b) that, after the spin-coating and annealing (250 °C), converts into a transparent nanocrystalline CABB film (Fig. 1d,e).

The CABB films were tested as PV absorbers in solar cells with TiO_2 and P3HT as electron- and hole-transport layers, respectively (Fig. 1f), showing a champion power conversion efficiency of 2.89% (Fig. 1g, J_{sc} = 5.73 mA/cm^2, V_{oc} = 1035 mV, and a fill factor FF of 49%).

3.2 Anion-exchange conversion of CAB(S)B

Similar to our recent reports [6, 7], we developed a mild anion-exchange-based approach for converting bromide perovskites into corresponding iodides using NaI as an iodide source. Interaction of CABB with NaI results in a "red" shift of absorption band edge (Figure 2a) and the formation of a bi-phase mixture of $Cs_3Bi_2I_9$ (CBI) double salt and $CsAg_2I_3$ (CAI) perovskite (Fig. 2b,c).

Similarly, AE-driven transformation of $Cs_2AgBi_{0.5}Sb_{0.5}Br_6$ (CABSB) perovskite was found to result in a mixture of $Cs_3(Bi_{0.5}Sb_{0.5})_2I_9$ (CBSI) and CAI phases. In both cases, CAI crystals reveal a distinct morphology, needle-like crystals (AE-driven conversion of CABB) or larger polygons (AE-driven transformation of CABSB), strongly different from the morphology of the CBI (CBSI) phase (Fig. 2d,e).

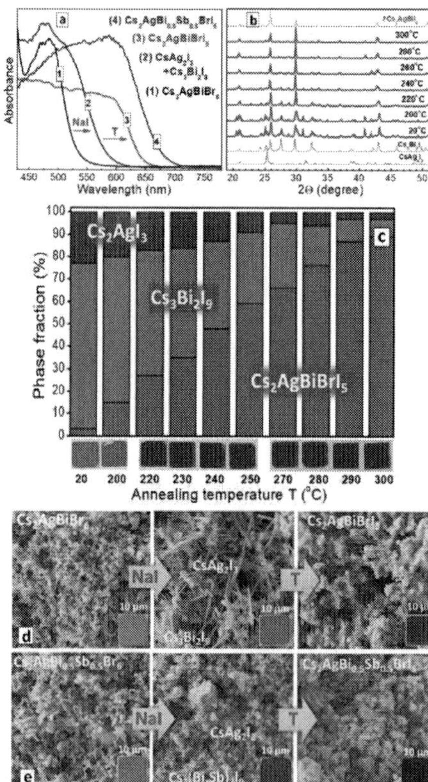

Figure 2: (a) Absorption spectra of CABB, CBI+CAI, and final CABBI and CABSBI perovskites; (b,c) evolution of the powder X-ray diffractogram of CBI+CAI mixture (b) and (c) phases distribution upon annealing at different temperatures; (d,e) SEM images of CABB (d) and CABSB (e) as well as corresponding AE products and final CABBI and CABSBI perovskites

Annealing of the CBI+CAI mixture at 200-300 °C results in the conversion of these intermediates into a new compound that was identified by the Rietveld refinement of XRD patterns and EDX analysis as tetragonal $Cs_2AgBiBrI_5$ (CABBI) double perovskite (symmetry group *I4m*, lattice parameters $a = b = 8.3825$ Å and $c = 11.8451$ Å).

The CABBI phase is present as a minor component even at 20 °C, its content growing with annealing temperature, reaching 85-86% at 290-300 °C (Fig. 2c). The powder XRD and SEM analyses clearly show the annealing-induced disappearance of the CAI phase and formation of tightly aggregated microcrystalline CABBI (CABSBI) products (Fig. 2d,e) of a solid-state reaction that can be presented by a brutto-equation:

$$Cs_3Bi_2I_9 + CsAg_2I_3 = 2Cs_2AgBiI_6$$

with ca. 5-20% of iodide sites still occupied with Br⁻.

This reaction results in a considerable red shift of the absorption band edge reaching ca. 650 nm for CABBI and ca. 680 nm for CABSBI (Fig. 2a).

3.3 High-throughput screening of CABSBI perovskites

Considering that $Cs_2AgBi_{0.5}Sb_{0.5}BrI_5$ perovskite showed a much lower bandgap as compared to CABBI, we performed a high-throughput screening of CABSBI perovskites using the previously reported robot-assisted methodology [5, 6]. At that, Bi/Sb and I/Br ratios were varied simultaneously, while conditions of AE and thermal annealing were varied for every composition to achieve the maximal yield of CABBI with the minimal bandgap.

Figure 3a shows exemplary sample arrays produced at varied Sb fractions and NaI content, revealing the low-bandgap domain at excess iodide and mixed Bi-Sb compounds. It is noteworthy that no changes in spectral properties were observed for a similar sample array with $Cs_3(Bi,Sb)_2Br_9$ double salts subjected to the AE with NaI (Fig. 3b). These observations provide additional evidence of the formation of low-bandgap products in a solid reaction between CBI and CAI.

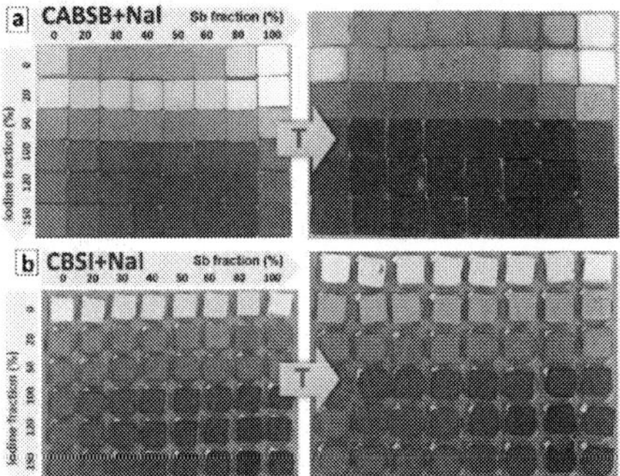

Figure 3: Photographs of sample arrays produced by high-throughput AE of CABSB perovskites (a) and CBSI double salts with varied Sb fraction and relative NaI content before (left panels) and after (right panels) annealing at 290 °C

It was found that the lowest bandgaps of CABSBI perovskites can be reached for AE performed at 133% excess NaI in the reaction mixture with respect to the stoichiometric amount necessary for the complete Br-to-I

substitution, the AE duration of 10 min, the annealing T of 290-300 °C, and annealing duration of 10-15 min, for Sb fractions between 45 and 75%.

The evolution of spectral properties of CABSBI perovskites and formation of the lowest bandgap domain can be tracked by comparing the compositional bandgap maps before (Figure 4a) and after the annealing (Fig. 4b).

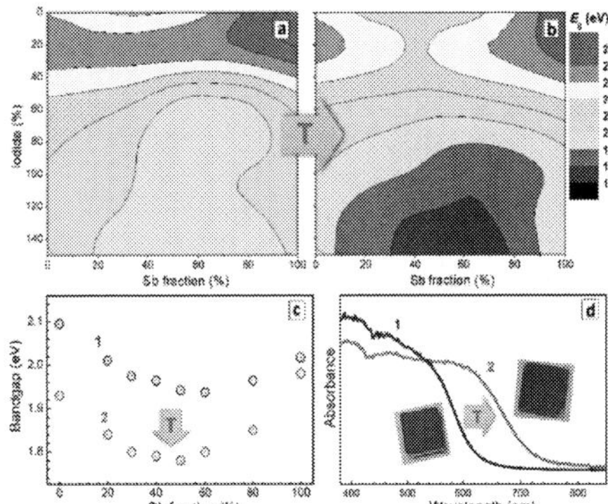

Figure 4: (a,b) Compositional bandgap maps for CABSB+NaI sample array before (c) and after (d) annealing at 290 °C. (c) Bandgap of CABSBI perovskites before (1) and after annealing (1), produced in optimized conditions, versus nominal Sb fraction. (d) Absorption spectra and photographs of the optimal CABSBI sample before (curve 1) and after annealing (curve 2)

Figure 4c additionally illustrates the bandgap dependence on the Sb fraction for the samples produced in optimal conditions. The lowest indirect bandgap of 1.78 eV was observed for CABSBI with 50%Sb, corresponding to the absorption band edge at ca. 730 nm (Fig. 4d). This value falls in the range typically expected for wide-bandgap components of tandem solar cells (ca. 1.8 eV), showing promise for multi-junction and indoor PV applications.

The conversion of optimized microcrystalline CABSBI perovskites into transparent films and their potential as PV absorbers in solar cells are currently being investigated.

4 CONCLUSION

We report an advanced general synthesis of lead-free bromide compounds that yield CABB double perovskite showing ca. 2.9% efficiency as a PV absorber in single-junction solar cells, as well as mixed Bi-Sb double perovskites with controllably varied Bi/Sb ratios.

Anion exchange of CABB (CABSB) with NaI as an iodide source results in bi-phase products composed of CBI (CBSI) double salts and CAI perovskites that can react upon thermal treatment and transform into tetragonal CABBI (CABSBI) double perovskites with ca. 20% of residual bromide. A high-throughput optimization of the conditions of anion exchange and the following thermal solid-state reaction between CBSI and CAI yielded stable CABSBI perovskites with the lowest bandgap of 1.78 eV. The potential of these compounds as PV absorbers is currently under evaluation.

References
[1] I. López-Fernández, D. Valli, C.Y. Wang, S. Samanta, T. Okamoto, Y.T. Huang, K. Sun, Y. Liu, V.S. Chirvony,

A. Patra, et al., Adv. Funct. Mater., 34 (2024) 2307896.
[2] S. Zhang, G. Liu, B. Teng, S. Ji, CrystEngComm, 27 (2025) 3416.
[3] H. Lei, D. Hardy, F. Gao, Adv. Funct. Mater., 31 (2021) 2105898.
[4] K.T. Kluherz, S.T. Mergelsberg, J.J. De Yoreo, and D.R. Gamelin, Chem. Mater., 35 (2023) 5699.
[5] O. Stroyuk, O. Raievska, M. Daum, J. Hauch, C.J. Brabec, J. Mater. Chem. C, 12 (2024) 8705.
[6] O. Stroyuk, O. Raievska, S. Kinge, J. Hauch, and C.J. Brabec, Mater. Adv., 2025, doi: 10.1039/D5MA00479A.
[7] O. Stroyuk, O. Raievska, A. Barabash, R.W. Hooper, V.K. Michaelis, J. Hauch, C.J. Brabec, J. Mater. Chem. C, 12 (2024) 533.

EU PVSEC 2DO.8.3

Innovative Approach to $Cs_2Ag(Bi,Sb)(Br,I)_6$ Double Perovskites via Anion Exchange and Solid-State Reactions

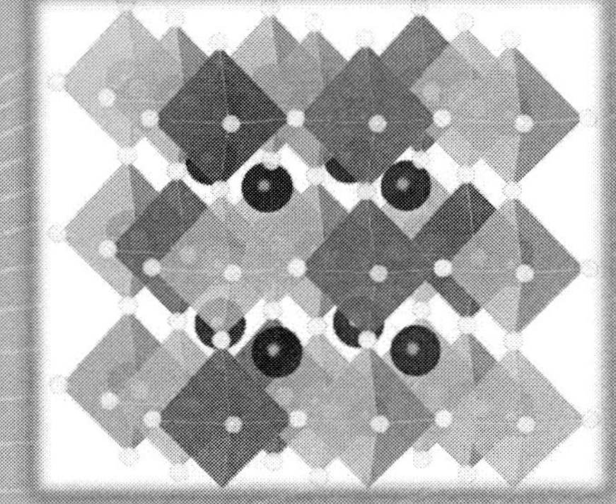

HI ERN Helmholtz Institut Erlangen Nürnberg, D-91058 Erlangen, Immerwahrstraße 2

2025-09-25 ||| **Dr. Oleksandr Stroyuk** ||| Team High Throughput Materials and Devices

part of
JÜLICH Forschungszentrum

in cooperation with
FAU FRIEDRICH-ALEXANDER UNIVERSITÄT ERLANGEN-NÜRNBERG
HZB Helmholtz Zentrum Berlin

020118-001

Double halide perovskites produced by anion exchange

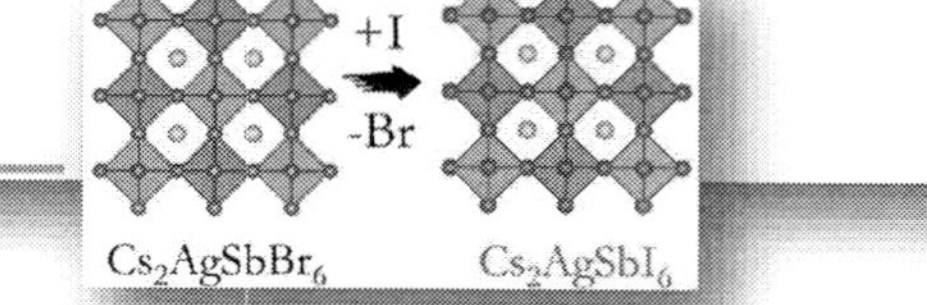

Regular perovskites

Double perovskites

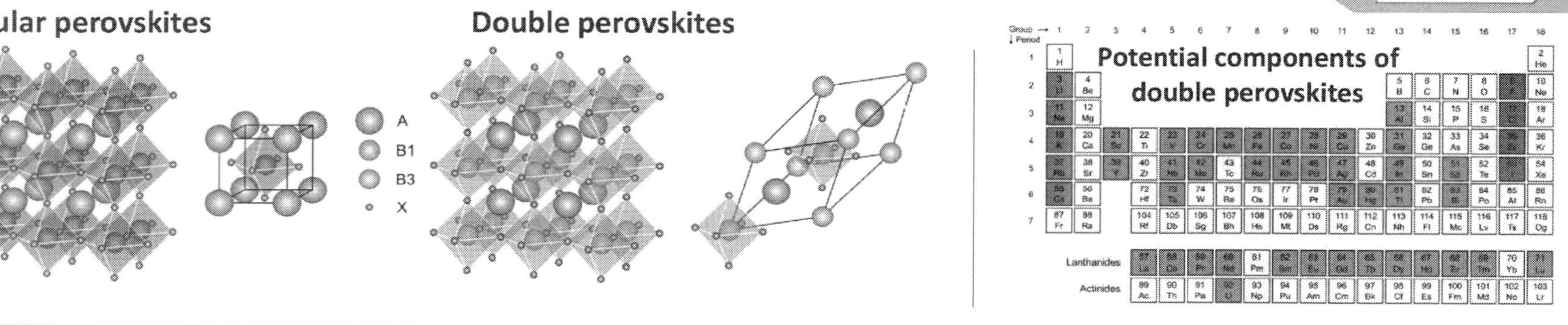

Potential components of double perovskites

Structure and Stability of the Iodide Elpasolite, Cs_2AgBiI_6

Kyle T. Kluherz, Sebastian T. Mergelsberg, James J. De Yoreo, and Daniel R. Gamelin*

Cite This: *Chem. Mater.* 2023, 35, 5699–5708   Read Online

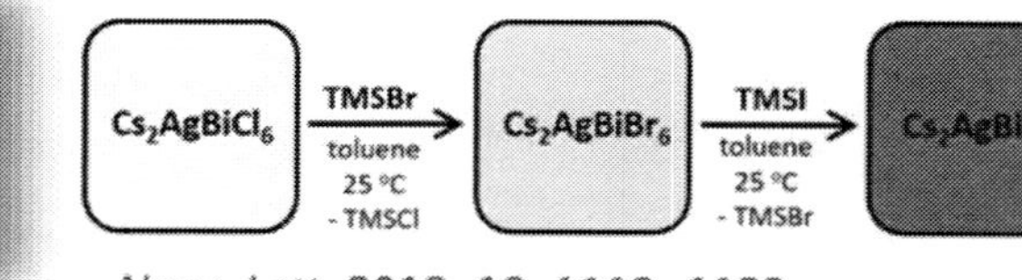

Nano Lett. 2018, 18, 1118–1123

$$2Cs_2AgBiI_6 \rightarrow Cs_3Bi_2I_9 + 2AgI + CsI$$

Tetragonal (I4-m)

Cs_2AgSbI_6 Nanocrystals: a New Air-Stable Iodide Double-Perovskite (Elpasolite) Semiconductor

Faris Horani and Daniel R. Gamelin*

Cite This: *J. Am. Chem. Soc.* 2025, 147, 16552–16559

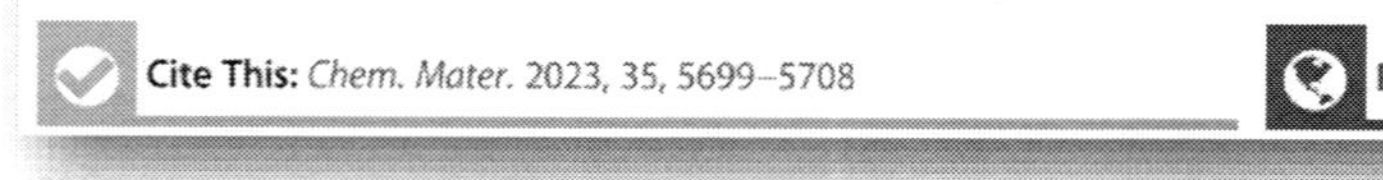

High-throughput screening of halide materials

High-throughput workflows

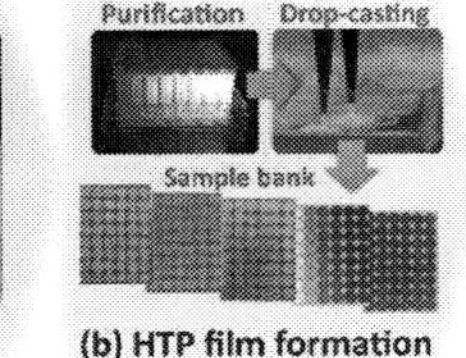

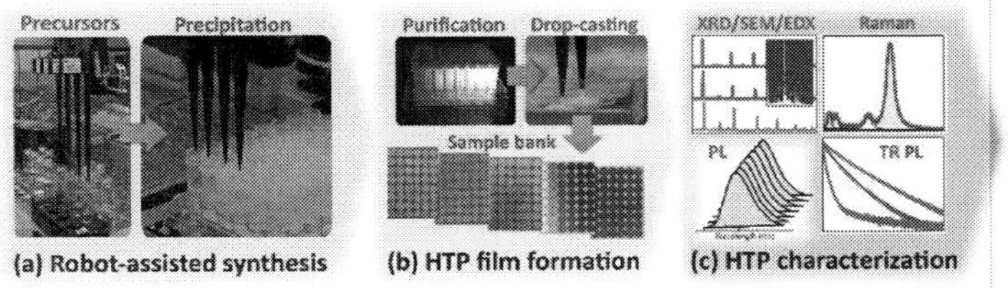

Mater. Res. Bull., 2024, 49, 1284

Lead-free double halide perovskites

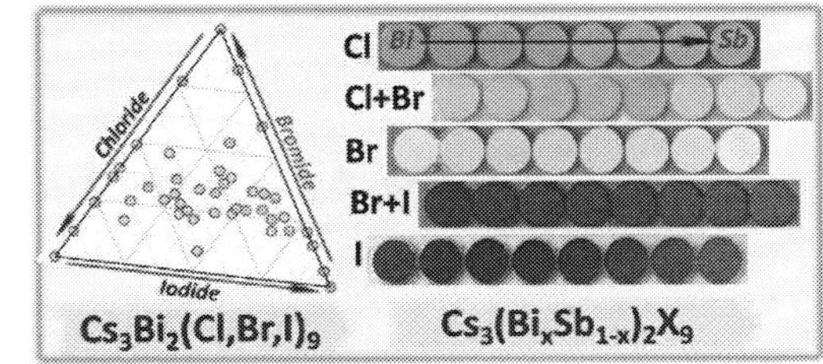

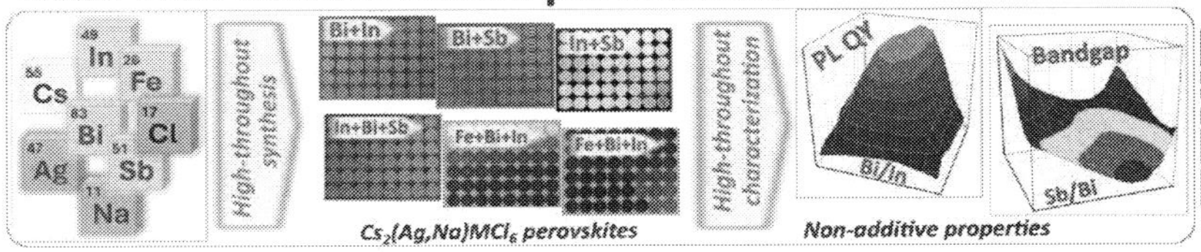

J. Mater. Chem. C, 2024, 12, 8705

Vacancy-ordered perovskites

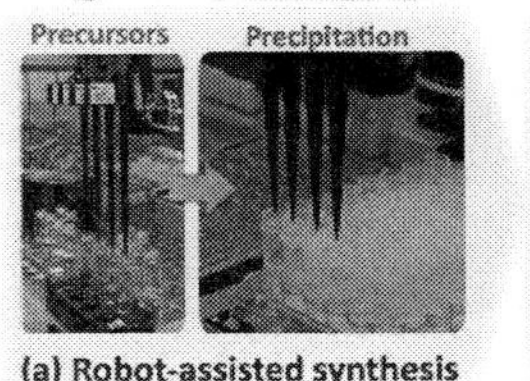

J. Mater. Chem. C, 2025, 13, 2303

Perovskite-like materials

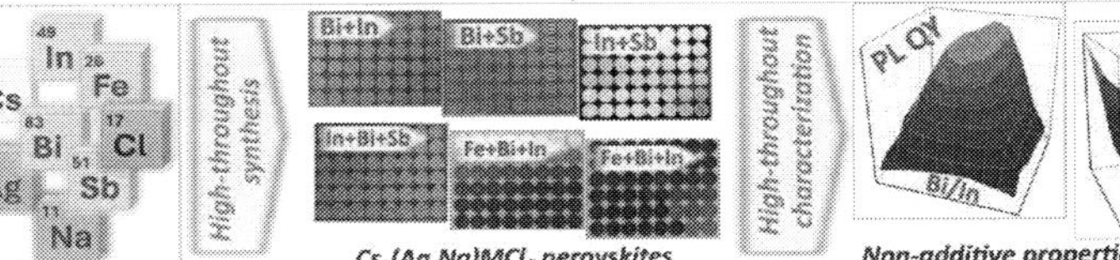

Mater. Adv., 2025, 6, 4847

High-entropy double perovskites

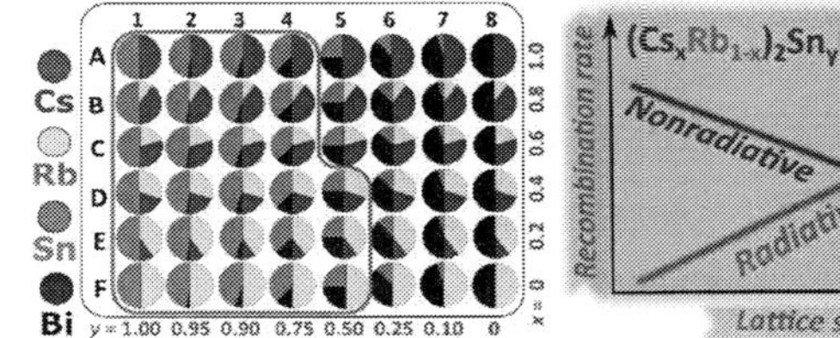

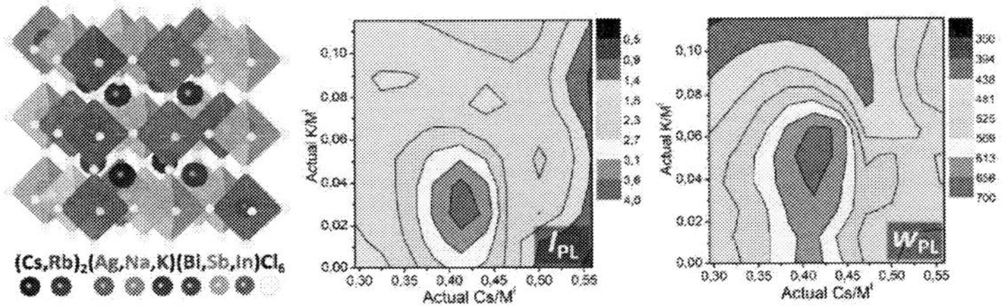

In preparation

Starting with $Cs_2AgBiBr_6$ (CABB)

High-Throughput Screening of Environmentally Stable Lead-Free Halide Perovskites for PV

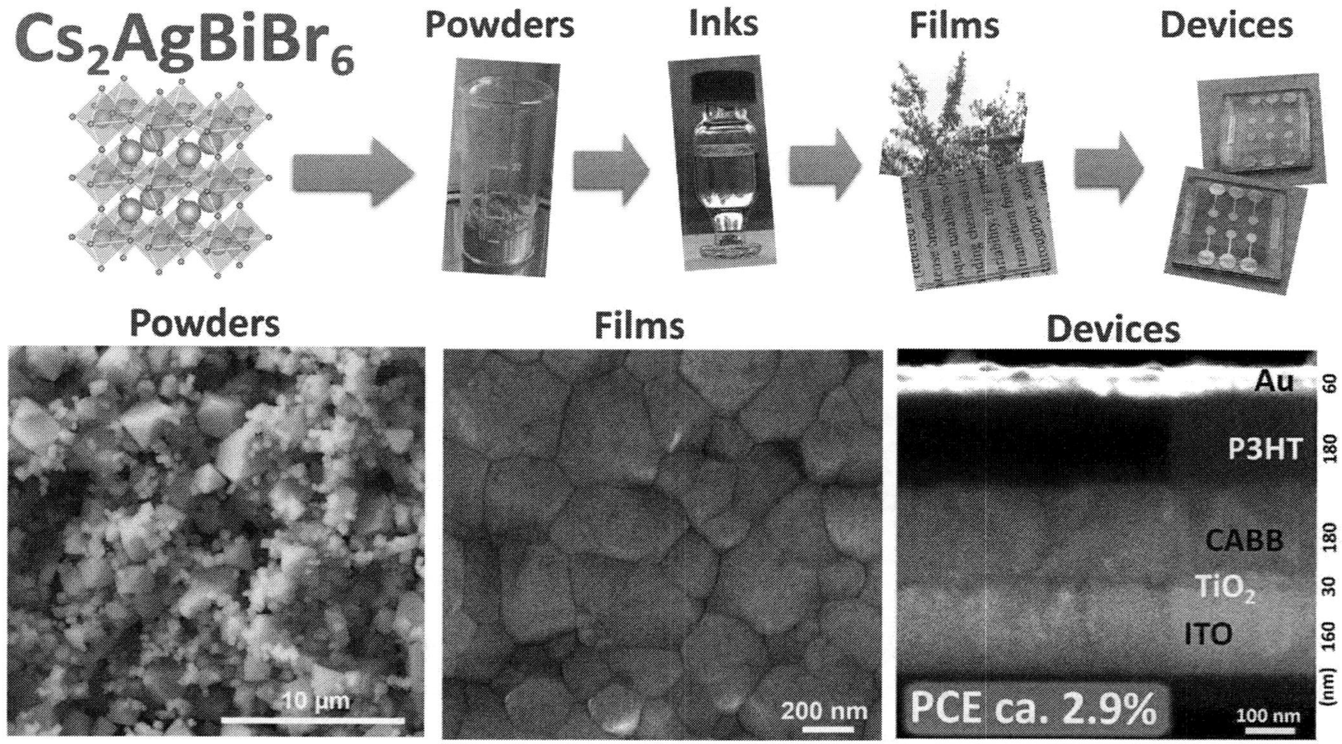

4

Conversion of cubic $Cs_2AgBiBr_6$ into tetragonal $Cs_2AgBi(Br,I)_6$

SEM images

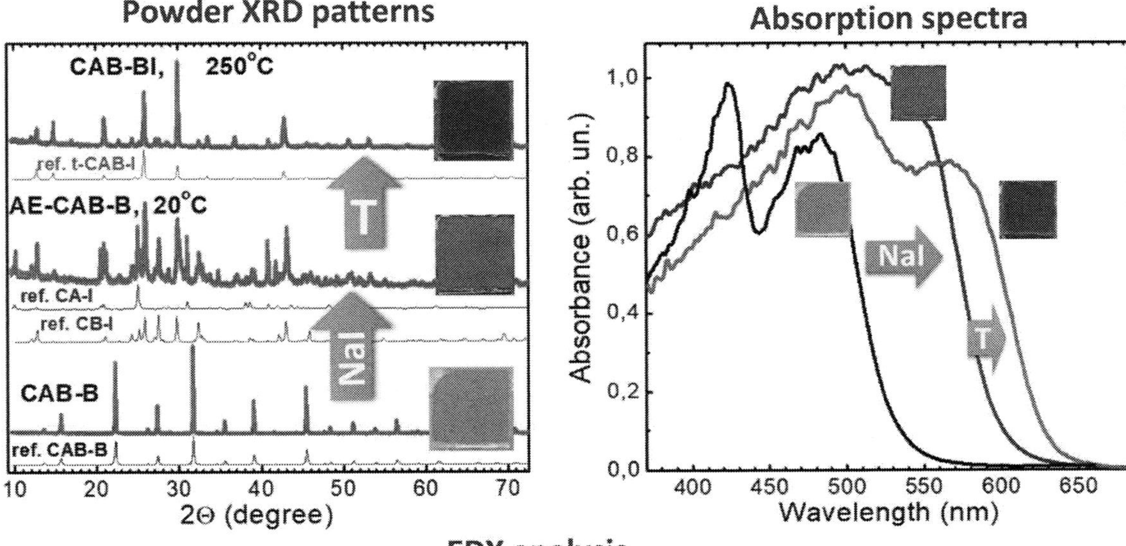

Powder XRD patterns

Absorption spectra

EDX analysis

Sample ID		X = Br+I		X/M^{III}	X/Ag	Cs/M^{III}	Cs/Ag	Formal composition
		Br, %	I, %					
CAB-B		100	0	6.0	6.0	2.2	1.8	$Cs_2AgBiBr_6$
AE of CAB-B	Site #1	20	80	4.6	-	1.5	-	$Cs_3Bi_2(Br_{0.20}I_{0.80})_9$
	Site #2	5	95	-	1.4	-	0.6	$CsAg_2I_3$
CAB-BI, 250 °C		20	80	6.1	6.1	2.0	2.0	$Cs_2AgBi(Br_{0.2}I_{0.8})_6$
CAB-BI, 300 °C		12	88	6.1	5.7	2.1	2.0	$Cs_2AgBi(Br_{0.12}I_{0.88})_6$

Proofs for the solid-state reaction between $Cs_3Bi_2I_9$ and $CsAg_2I_3$

$$Cs_2AgBiBr_6 \xrightarrow{\text{NaI}} Cs_3Bi_2I_9 + CsAg_2I_3 \xleftrightarrow{?} Cs_2AgBiI_6$$

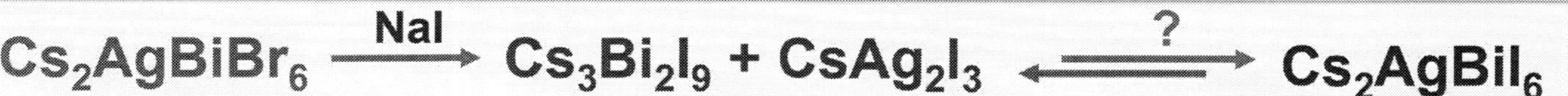

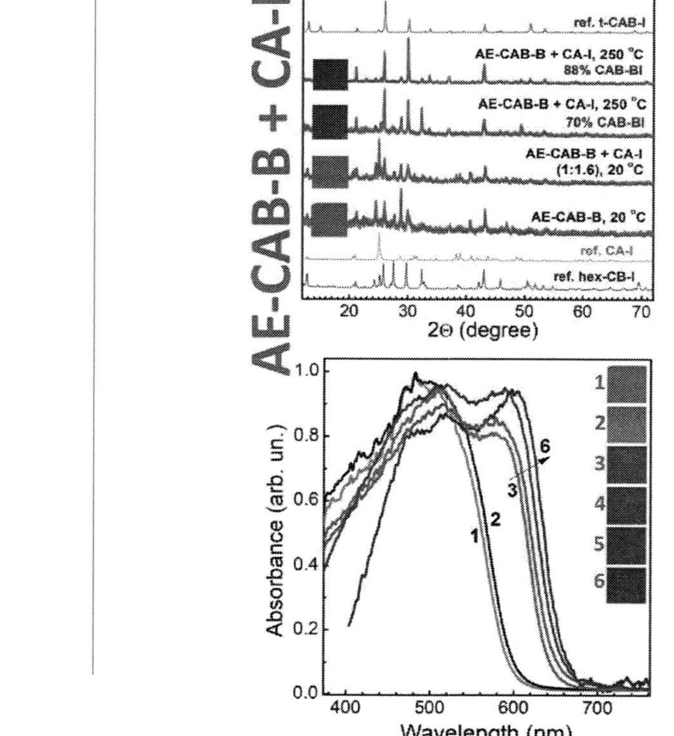

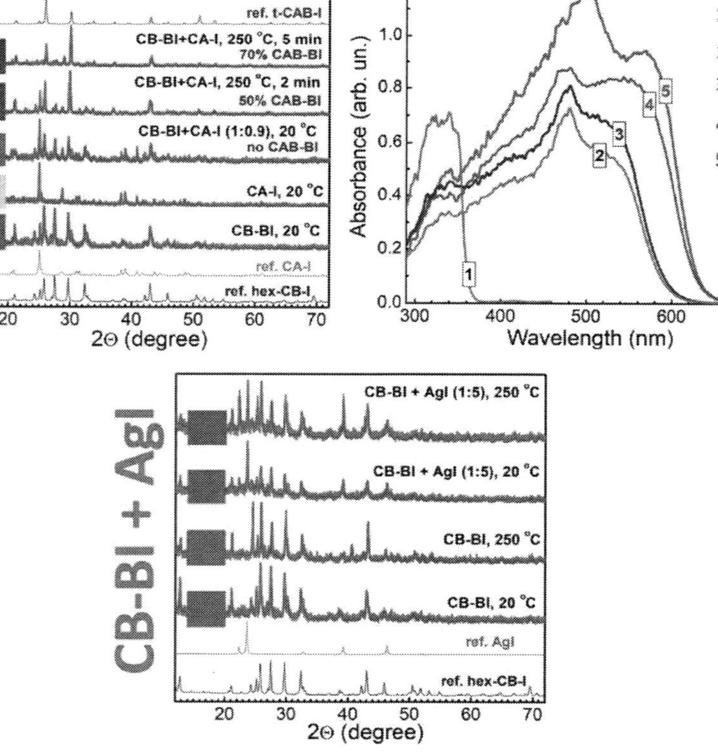

Optimization of the to-stage synthesis of $Cs_2AgBi(Br,I)_6$ perovskites

Optimizing anion exchange...

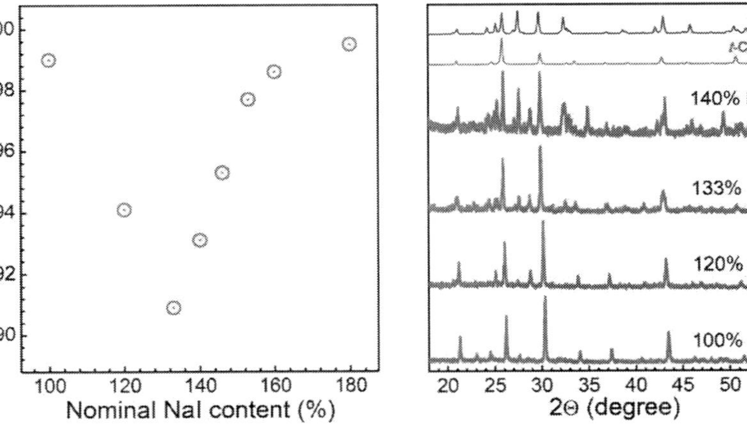

NaI content, %	CAB-BI fraction, wt.%	V_{CAB-BI}, $Å^3$	Actual iodide fraction in CAB-BI, %
100	95	806	60
120	85	826	70
133	65	845	82
140	15	851	88
150	5	858	92
160	0	-	-

Optimizing solid-state reaction...

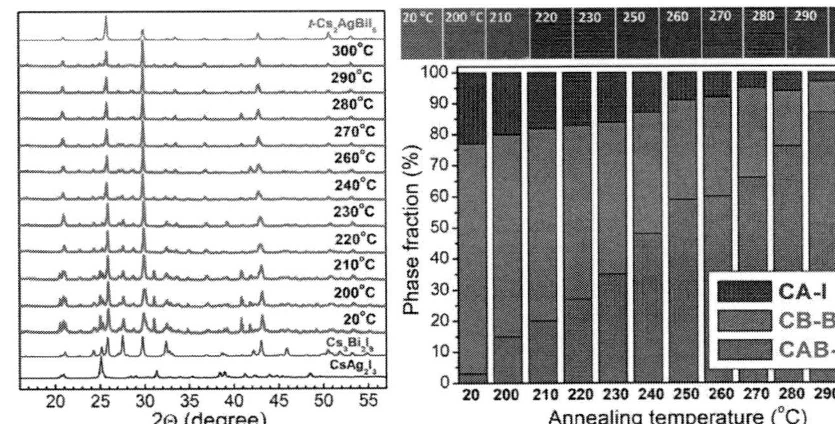

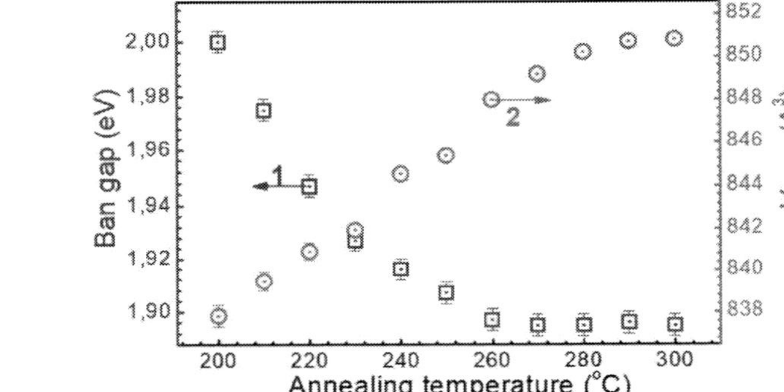

020118-007

Universal character of the two-stage route to iodide perovskites

Combinatorial syntheses

$$Cs_2AgBiBr_6 + CsAg_2I_3 + CsAgBr_2$$

Anion exchange + T

$$Cs_2AgBi(Br_yI_{1-y})_6$$

More complex precursors

$$Cs_2Ag(Bi_xSb_{1-x})Br_6 + CsAg_2I_3$$

Anion exchange + T

$$Cs_2Ag(Bi_xSb_{1-x})(Br,I)_6$$

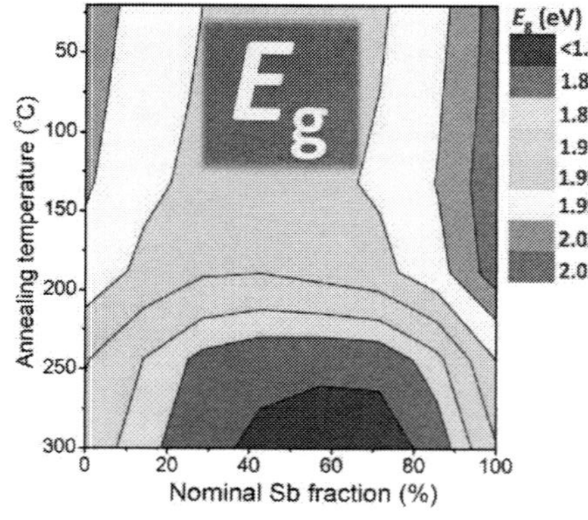

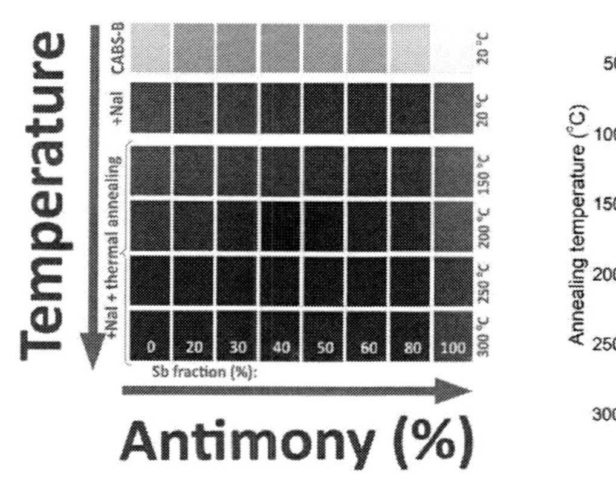

Conversion of $Cs_2Ag(Bi,Sb)Br_6$ into tetragonal $Cs_2Ag(Bi,Sb)(Br,I)_6$

$$Cs_2Ag(Bi_{0.5}Sb_{0.5})Br_6 \xrightarrow[\text{RT}]{\text{NaI}} Cs_3(Bi_{0.5}Sb_{0.5})_2(Br,I)_9 + CsAg_2I_3 \xrightarrow{T} t\text{-}Cs_2Ag(Bi_{0.5}Sb_{0.5})(Br,I)_6$$

(i) Cs-Ag-(Bi,Sb)-Br   **(ii) Anion exchange with NaI**   **(iii) Thermal annealing**

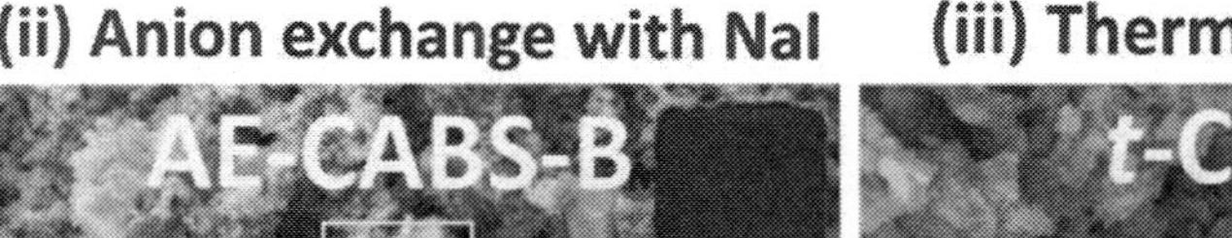

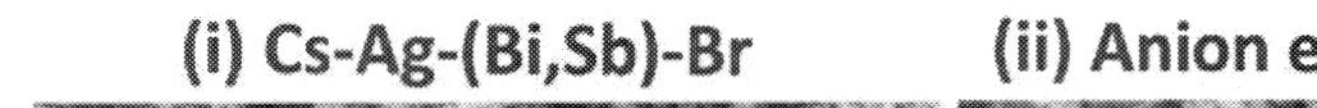

Absorption spectra

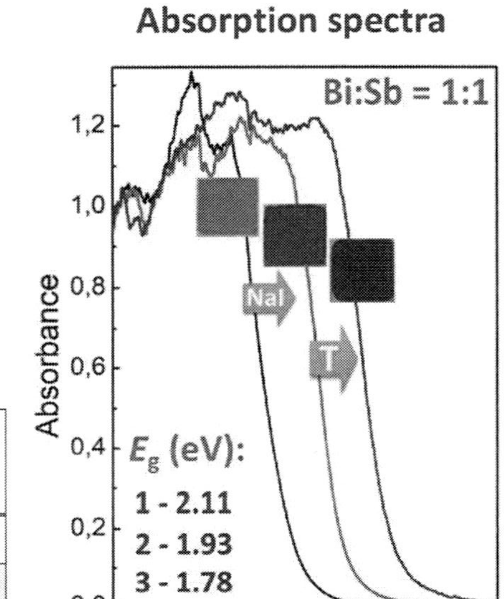

EDX analysis

Sample ID		X = Br+I		X/M^{III}	X/Ag	Cs/M^{III}	Cs/Ag	Bi/M^{III}	Formal composition
		Br, %	I, %						
CABS-B, nom. Bi:Sb=1:1		100	0	5.7	5.6	2.1	2.0	0.48	$Cs_2Ag(Bi_{0.5}Sb_{0.5})Br_6$
AE of CABS-B	Site #1	22	78	4.6	-	1.5	-	0.52	$Cs_3(Bi_{0.5}Sb_{0.5})_2(Br_{0.22}I_{0.78})_9$
	Site #2	3	97	-	1.5	-	0.6	-	$CsAg_2I_3$
CABS-BI, Bi:Sb=1:1, 300 °C		12	88	5.8	0.9	1.6	1.8	0.49	$Cs_2Ag(Bi_{0.5}Sb_{0.5})(Br_{0.12}I_{0.88})_6$

Summary

 A two-stage approach to stable tetragonal $Cs_2AgBi(Br,I)_6$ perovskites (more than 80% I) is developed, based on mild anion-exchange conversion of bromide precursors and open-air annealings

 The solid-state reaction between intermediary products, $Cs_3Bi(Sb)_2I_9$ and $CsAg_2I_3$, is proven and optimized

 The approach is universal and can be applied to (i) more complex mixtures of precursors and (ii) to more complex precursors, in particular, to produce tetragonal $Cs_2AgBi_xSb_{1-x}(Br,I)_6$ perovskites (ca. 90% I) with bandgaps below 1.8 eV

 Developing protocols for the formation of uniform and transparent films of tetragonal iodide double perovskites + PV tests

Thank you

for attention!

Contact info:
Dr. Oleksandr Stroyuk, Forschungszentrum Jülich GmbH,
Helmholtz-Institut Erlangen Nürnberg für Erneuerbare Energien (HI ERN),
Erlangen, Germany, e-mail: o.stroyuk@fz-juelich.de

INVESTIGATING THE 3-DIMENSIONAL STRUCTURE OF METALLIC FILLER PARTICLES IN ELECTRICALLY CONDUCTIVE ADHESIVES

S. Großer[1], A. Müller[1], R. Göckeritz[1], T. Nitsche[2], D. Buckland[2], G. Galbiati[2], B. Jäckel[1]
[1] Fraunhofer CSP, Otto-Eißfeldt-Straße 12, 06120, Halle (Saale), Germany
[2] Henkel AG & Co. KGaA, Henkelstr. 67, 40589, Düsseldorf, Germany

ABSTRACT: Electrically conductive adhesives (ECAs) are emerging interconnection materials whose performance hinges on a continuous three-dimensional metal filler network. Understanding the 3D microstructure is essential for predicting percolation, optimizing filler loading, and ensuring reliable, low-temperature interconnects. 2D analyses miss critical connectivity and distribution details that govern current paths. We present a 3D characterization of the metallic filler network in ECAs using focused ion beam–scanning electron microscopy (FIB-SEM) slice-and-view. The study aims to illuminate the 3D microstructure, enabling prediction of percolation, optimization of filler loading, and assessment of reliable, low-temperature interconnects. A voxel-based reconstruction from aligned 2D slices assigns phase labels (metal vs. resin) and color values to visualize the network and its interfaces, allowing explicit identification of connected and non-connected metal filler particles, which is crucial because macroscopic current conduction relies on a continuous metal network bridging 2 contact interfaces. The metal filler fraction in the resin matrix for 3D (volume) and for 2D (slice) data can be tested and showed a comparable value for the apparent ECA. Variations were found on microscopic scales which average out fast. Segmentation distinguishes connected clusters from isolated fillers, estimate in-plane needed current distances, noting that non-connected particles near sample edges can be artifacts that must be excluded from interpretation.
Keywords: Characterization, 3D microstructure, percolation, ECA, interconnection

1 Introduction

An increasing economic pressure and high silver demand is driving the reduction of silver consumption in PV with remarkable improvements towards the limit for cells and interconnections [1, 2]. Silver-containing interconnection materials are a promising option for temperature-sensitive high-efficiency solar cell modules which require adapted low-temperature interconnection processes in manufacturing [3]. Beside e.g. bismuth-based solder alloys, electrically conductive adhesives (ECAs) are an alternative already used for contact formation in interconnections [4]. Typically, ECAs in PV consists at least in part of expensive silver (Ag). The urgent need to realize material savings and achieving upcoming higher requirements on low-temperature interconnection in ECAs imply a strong demand on material improvement which can only be achieved by an understanding through detailed material analysis. Currently, the experimental access of these conductive networks in ECAs is very limited and based dominantly on 2-dimensional cross-sections. For structural understanding, low-filled ECAs appear to lack a continuous conductive network in two dimensions, yet electrical conduction is sustained by the three-dimensional connectivity of filler particles along the contact material [5]. From the microstructural point of view the metallic filler network forms multiple conduction pathways, each contributing to the total conduction. Consequently, the conductivity of ECAs depends on the arrangement of the metal filler particles.

We tested and applied our approach to data acquisition, processing, and reconstruction to characterize the metallic network of an exemplary ECA in greater detail using modern FIB-SEM, a technique developed more than 40 years ago [6]. The visualization of the metallic network, the metal volume fraction in the contact, the distribution of metal along the contact area, and the identification of low- and high-metal-filled regions, as well as non-contacted metal fillers, can be determined with our approach. The workflow for microstructure elucidation, data reconstruction, and analysis opens up a wide range of applications to improve ECAs and related processes with

high relevance. The aim of this work is to enhance the ability to determine the detailed microstructure of ECAs used in photovoltaic applications. Our results show that this approach provides detailed visualization of the metallic network, including the metal volume fraction in the contact, the distribution of metal along the contact area, and the identification of low- and high-metal-filled regions in the ECA, enabling the detection of isolated metal fillers without a conduction path to the metal contact.

2 Experimental

For testing, evaluation and demonstration of the experimental approach the requirements on the sample under test are low. An acrylic-based ECA has been used and manually stencil printed on a $Sn_{60}Pb_{40}$-coated 4 mm wide copper ribbon, usually used in PV for cross connection, offering a wide ECA contact. An equal ribbon has been placed on top and gently pressed down by a sheet of silicone membranes weight. Curing takes place on a hot plate at 150 °C for 30 min, guaranteeing a fully cured ECA. After curing a cross-section has been prepared by a metallographic preparation, shown in Figure 1. The thickness of the cured ECA layer was around 128 μm at the position of investigation.

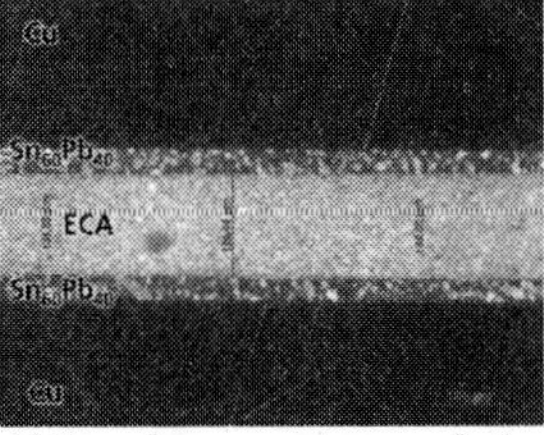

Figure 1: Light microscopy image of the symmetric ribbon/ECA/ribbon sample cross-section.

The workflow for slice and view technique on the material system was tested and evaluated by means of Focused Ion Beam and Scanning Electron Microscopy methodology with different instruments (ZEISS NVision

40 Crossbeam Ga-FIB-SEM and Thermo Scientific Helios 5 Hydra UX Crossbeam multi species plasma FIB). Within the 3-dimensional volume of an ECA (including the interface to the solder contact interface) a sequence of multiple cross-sections was prepared by FIB (using Xe-ion beam at 30 kV) and recorded by SEM which delivered a large dataset from the inspected volume. This dataset has been reconstructed as well as evaluated by means of the Avizo 3D software.

3 Results

From the measured sequence of 2D slices a 3D reconstruction depicts a voxel volume. Each voxel was assigned to a phase label and gray/color value to represent the present material and interface in the three-dimensional structure. This is shown for the dataset in Figure 2 whereas the solder interface is at the bottom and the ECA is on top. By the black arrow in z-direction the direction of the intended current flow direction (to opposite solder contact) is indicated. The resin is set as transparent allowing the unobstructed view on fillers in the near and far background. Metal phases are colored in blue. The 3D volume can be rotated in different arbitrary directions to provide a view on and inspect the metallic network arrangement.

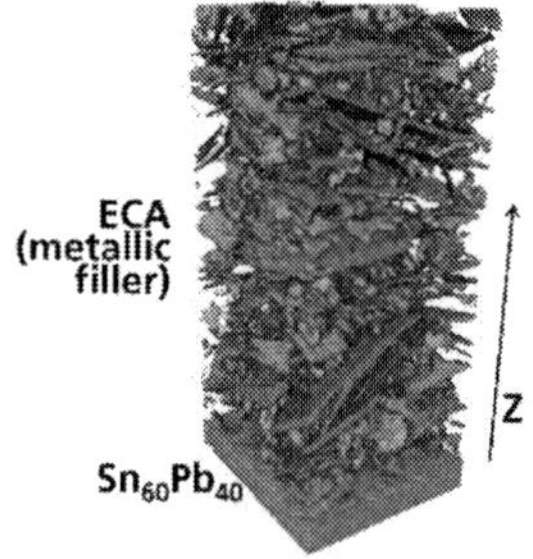

Figure 2: ECA dependent 3D-reconstruction of the metallic filler network (resin transparent).

3.1 From 2D-images to volume phase fraction of metallic filler

In 2D images the image information represents a section through the clusters and particles. By increasing the dimensionality to 3-dimensions the information content increases and results in a complex representation of fillers covering each other (see Figure 2). By using the attributed phase information one can determine absolute and relative volume fractions of metal and resin in an ECA. In the present case the analyzed volume of $10824\ \mu m^3$ exhibits relative volume fractions of $V_{filler,\ 3D} = 12$ vol% for the metal and $V_{resin,\ 3D} = 88$ vol% for the resin.

Due to the massive number of particles in a volume information of position and arrangement of single fillers, filler clusters or filler types are hard to collect. One suitable representation to mitigate self-covering was the sublayer-sectioning of the volume as shown in Figure 3. A layer separation with a layer thickness range (smaller than large particles) allows the screening of different positions in the volume but still give information about the shape of the particles. The benefit can be clearly seen in Figure 3 where on the left-hand side a 2D cross-section image is "connected" to the 3D-sublayer. The sublayer is visually

less dense packed and reveals the shape, position and direction of single fillers as well as their arrangement. This information exceeds the limited 2D-representation and enables the screening of the volume. The sample under test exhibited Ag-fillers with different shapes and sizes of flakes and nuggets. Some larger flake-shaped fillers are flat, others are bent. Flakes have a high aspect ratio in contrast to nugget-shaped fillers therefore their orientation is expected crucial to bridge large distances in Z. Extended flakes were found in different direction but empirically seem to be less likely to be aligned with their long axis in Z direction. Nugget-shaped fillers have been found as single particles or as clusters in proximity to flakes. The data representation allows the screening for separated fillers. These fillers or small clusters are surrounded by resin and therefore are electrically isolated with no contribution to the current conduction. The inspected volume exhibited only a neglectable number of isolated fillers but exclusively nugget shaped. Fillers cropped by the edge of the 3D-volume were not considered.

Figure 3: 2D-image (black/gray) and adjacent 3D-layer (blue) of the metallic filler network

The screening of the volume gives valuable access to the present arrangement of the fillers in the sample, expose the filler interconnection, bent and direction in a flexible and qualitative way. Quantifications of arrangement characteristics need different approaches as described in the next passage.

3.2 Testing the metallic filler network on cluster formation

The electrical conductivity in the metal filler network depends on their arrangement to touching or at least very near particles which enable electron transfer. Electron transfer must be feasible from one electrode at the bottom to the other electron on the top. In our representation in Figure 2 it corresponds with the Z-direction. Please note, the upper electrode was not included in the measured volume due to the high ECA thickness. Nevertheless, the investigated Z-range (depth) is representative for typical ECA contact thickness in PV. Clusters are formed in 3-dimensions which infer current flow contribution in in-plane (X-Y plane) to electrode.

The investigated volume of Figure 2 has an in-plane area of $305\ \mu m^2$ (X-Y plane). By means of a segmentation algorithm metal clusters in the volume have been determined. To prove non-connected metal fractions in the volume in $V_{filler,\ 3D}$ the specific cluster of electrode and electrode touching fillers must be excluded. Figure 4a) demonstrates the result in the volume representation. Different colors represent independent clusters. In contrast to Figure 2 the volume representation is less densely packed notable by strong reduced metal amount. In our calculation, 7 % of the total metal amount is not connected to the lower electrode which corresponds to an absolute value of $V_{non-connected\ filler,\ 3D} = 0.8$ vol%. However, the approach is lacking in information on the virtual cut of particles at the volume edge. The data gives no information if the edge particles are connected to the electrode through the cropped structure. However, by e.g. visual screening of the data (like shown in Figure 3) clusters can be identified which do not touch the edge, indicating that within the inspected volume only a neglectable amount of filler were not connected to the electrode. Consequently, $V_{non-connected\ filler,\ 3D}$ must be much lower than 0.8 vol% resulting in the conclusion that for the used ECA an area of 305 μm^2 is supposed to be sufficient.

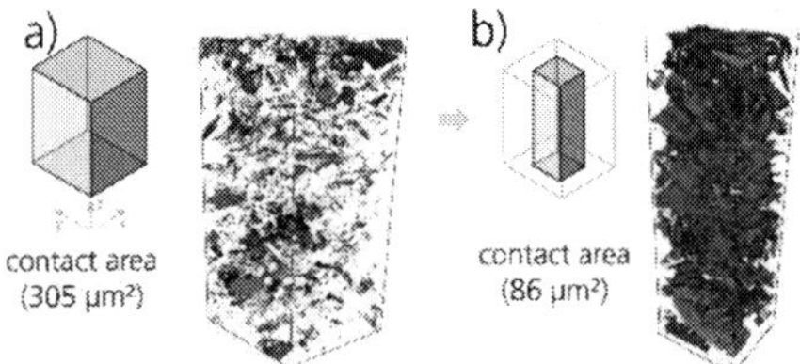

Figure 4: Schematic and reconstructed 3D model of filler and filler clusters, which are non-connected to the solder electrode for 2 different contact areas of the same dataset.

To approximate the minimum requirement of contact area a reduction of the volume under analysis was tested. An inner part of the same volume will be used to perform the cluster analysis whereas the outer part of the structure will be cropped. If cropping of connections between fillers appears then an increase of clusters number will increase, which are not connected to the lower electrode. A reduction of the volume in-plane area by around 73% have been tested representing a contact area of 86 μm^2 (8.9 μm x 9.7 μm). Figure 4 shows the schematic of the approach as well as the resulting separated cluster representation. One can clearly observe an increase in the non-connected cluster number by comparison with the full area equivalent of 305 μm^2 (17.2 μm x 17.7 μm). In the particular case we found the massive increase in non-connected metal fraction $V_{non-connected\ filler,\ 3D}$ from 7 % (305 μm^2) to 90 % (86 μm^2). By microstructural inspection the root cause has been identified in a low dense volume part near the lower solder electrode, shown in Figure 5 by the red dashed line as a guide to the eye. This gap separates all metal above from the connection. Anyhow the connection is provided on larger length but is limited on smaller length for 3D structured materials. From the investigated position an approximated length for connection in X-Y plane is supposed to be in the range of 10 to 18 μm. It is likely the microstructure sized gap exists on this specific position. Without the gap the length for connection in X-Y plane is expected to be lower for the present sample.

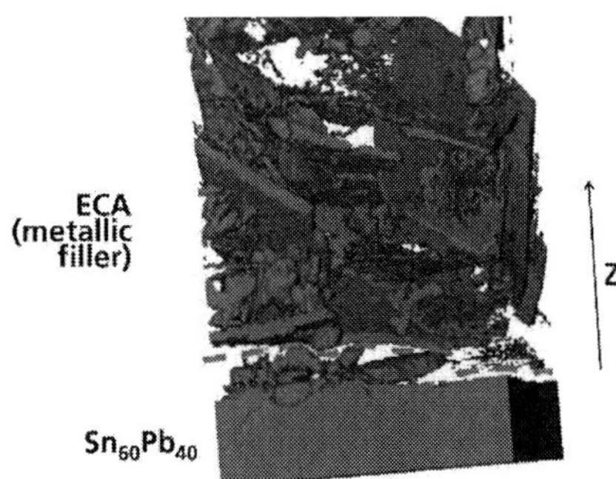

Figure 5: 3D-reconstruction of the metallic filler network of the contact area reduced sub-volume. A depletion of filles is indicated by a dashed-red line as guide for the eye.

3.3 Proofing microstructure relation of 2D to 3D

Interestingly, the found gap in Figure 5 is roughly in plane with the X-Y electrode surface plane. Therefore, an evaluation of metal fraction in the X-Y plane (2D) along the depth Z (1D) would indicate local variations in the (X-Y in plane) filler content. In 2D images the metal fraction $A_{filler,\ slice}$ represents the area fraction of metal on the total image area, at which 0 % is pure resin and 100 % is complete metal. In Figure 6 the volume of Figure 2 (with 305 μm^2 contact area) has been evaluated and $A_{filler,\ slice}$ plotted in dependence of Z. At 0 μm is the interface to the lower solder electrode located. The values for $A_{filler,\ slice}$ vary from 4 % (minimum at 1.3 μm) to 27 % (maximum at 18 μm). By calculation of the mean value of A_{filler}, taking all points along Z into account, a value of $A_{filler,\ mean} = (11.7 \pm 3.5)$ % results. This statistic value is in consistency with the calculated voxel-based metal fraction of $V_{filler,\ 3D} = 12$ vol%, on the present sample and on the investigated length of Z. On smaller length microstructural variations can take place. Within the inspected volume the minimum in $A_{filler,\ slice}$ correlates with the gap found in Figure 5, as expected. The validity of the interpretation is limited to reduced metal content in respect to the investigated plane and not very meaningful to depletions which are tilted or arbitrary formed in reference to the slice plane.

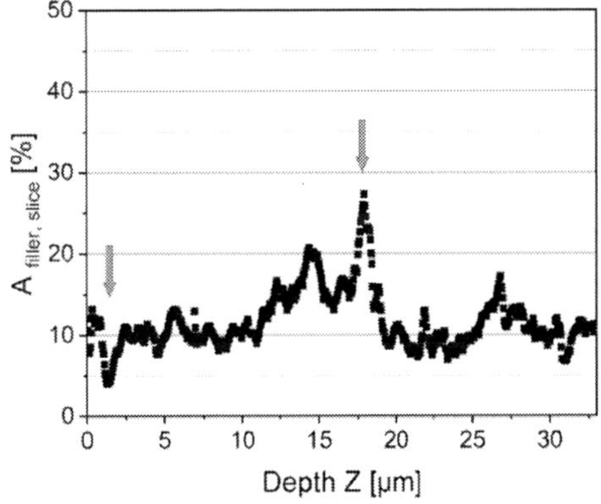

Figure 6: Area fraction of the metal $A_{filler,\ slice}$ in the (X-Y plane) in dependance of the depth Z. Minimum and maximum value are indicated by an arrow.

Nevertheless, the analysis of metal area fractions is an approach to approximate the very local metal volume fraction but needs sufficient data input to draw conclusion of local metal volume fractions.

4 Summary

This study presents a three-dimensional characterization of the metallic filler network in electrically conductive adhesives (ECAs) using focused ion beam - scanning electron microscopy (FIB-SEM) slice-and-view to reveal the continuous metal pathways that govern percolation, filler loading, and interconnect reliability. By reconstructing voxel-based 3D volumes from 2D SEM images and assigning phase labels to metal and resin, the work enables explicit visualization of connected versus isolated metallic filler particles and their interfaces, providing a direct link between microstructure and macroscopic impact to conductivity (qualitatively). In the examined volume, the 3D metal fraction is about 12 vol%, with variations on micron scales that average out. Segmentation distinguishes connected clusters from non-connected fillers, although edge artifacts near sample boundaries must be excluded from interpretation. Fillers that remain non-conductive to the network do not improve conduction and raise material costs. The analysis also demonstrates that local 2D metal fractions, when viewed across the depth of the contact, corroborated by the 3D results but also reveal microstructural metal density variations. The proposed technique and approach offer a practical route to be used for assessing how formulation changes influence network formation and conductance pathways, as well as the reliability of ECA interconnections in photovoltaic applications.

Acknowledgement
The authors like to thank Denise Ulm for supporting the preparation. Financial support from the Federal Ministry for Economic Affairs and Energy within the funded project "IndiFiduell" (FKZ: 03EE1185) is gratefully acknowledged.

References
[1] V. Cattaneo, J. Mast, I. Hackenhaar, S. Nardone, S. Scheerlinck, J. Mertens, J. Dewulf, Resources, Conservation and Recycling, 224 (2025) DOI:10.1016/j.resconrec.2025.108562
[2] M. Kronsbein, L. Böck, K. Dyhr, T. Rößler, N. Willenbacheret, Solar Energy Materials and Solar Cells, 287 (2025) DOI: 10.1016/j.solmat.2025.113603
[4] M. De Bastiani, M. Babics, E. Aydin, A. Subbiah, L. Xu, S. De Wolf, Solar RRL, 6, 3 (2021) DOI: 10.1002/solr.202100493
[4] International Technology Roadmap for Photovoltaics ITRPV) - 2024 Results, VDMA (2025)
[5] I. Devoto Acevedo, R. Wells, S. Großer, K. Wienands, D. Rudolph, A. Halm, R. Gottschalg, D. Tune, Progress in Photovoltaics: Research and Applications. (2024) DOI: 10.1002/pip.3787
[6] J. Melngailis, J., J. Vac. Sci. Technol. B, 5 (1987) 469-495. DOI: 10.1116/1.583937

Investigating the 3-dimensional structure of metallic filler particles in electrically conductive adhesives

Fraunhofer Center for Silicon Photovoltaics CSP

S. Großer[1], A. Müller[1], R. Göckeritz[1], T. Nitsche[2], D. Buckland[2], G. Galbiati[2], B. Jäckel[1]

[1] Fraunhofer CSP, Germany

[2] Henkel AG & Co. KGaA, Germany

3AV.1.1

Electrically conductive adhesives (ECA) are emerging interconnection materials [1]. ECA rely on a 3D metal filler network. Understanding the 3D microstructure is key to predict percolation, optimize loading, and ensure reliable, low-temperature interconnects [2,3].

Challenge: 2D analyses miss the 3D arrangement, losing details on metal fraction, connectivity, and filler distribution along the contact.

Task: Use FIB-SEM slice-and-view to reconstruct the 3D microstructure in the ECA contact, creating a dataset to visualize metal fraction, distribution, and isolated fillers to support formulation assessment.

Experimental Approach

- Method evaluation and demonstration on an arbitrary test system: electrically conductive adhesive (with Ag-filler) cured between $Sn_{60}Pb_{40}$ coated Cu ribbon
- Dual-beam Focused Ion Beam (FIB) / Scanning Electron Microscopy (SEM) instrument
- Slice-and-view technique (Sequential polishing and imaging) → sampling of a 3D volume
- Reconstruction of 3D microstructure

Fig 1: Cross section of ECA test sample (light microscopy)

3D reconstruction of the metallic filler network

From aligned sequence of 2D slices a 3D reconstruction depicts a voxel volume. Each voxel was assigned to a phase label and gray/color value to represent the present material and interface in the three-dimensional structure.

- Phase label to expose metal
  - Metall (set opaque)
  - Resin (set transparent)
- Color
  - Uniform for metallic part
- Visualization
  - Rotation
  - Sectioning

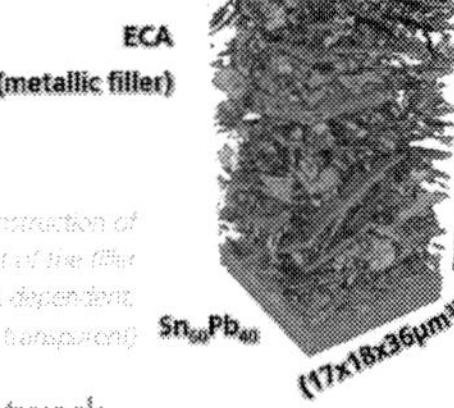

Fig 2: 3D reconstruction of metallic part of the filler network (ECA dependent, resin transparent)

Analysis of the 3-dimensional filler network

From 2D to volume phase fraction of metallic filler

3D cross-section images increase the information depth. From the 3D-microstructure, considering a 2-phase system of metal filler and resin, the volume fraction was calculated (solder-based interface layer excluded).

- Distribution of all fillers in resin matrix
- Metal content in volume
  - $V_{filler,\ 3D} = 12$ vol% (1.781 µm³)
  - $V_{resin,\ 3D} = 88$ vol% (9.043 µm³)

Fig 3: 2D-image and adjacent 3D-layer of the metallic filler network

Approaches to test the metallic filler network on cluster formation

Particle clusters (touching fillers) conduct the current. Segmentation of metallic parts was used to identify clusters. Same local dataset was analyzed.

- Expose of (to $Sn_{60}Pb_{40}$) non-connected filler clusters
  - Metall (opaque if non-connected)
  - Metall (transparent if connected)
  - Color (Cluster dependent)
- Test: Reduction of $Sn_{60}Pb_{40}$ interface area

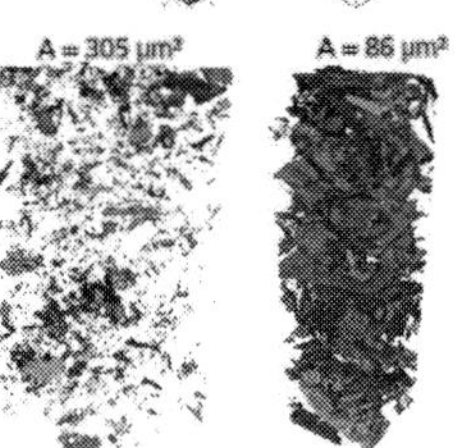

Non-connected filler fraction (to solder interface)

Contact area	Fraction (relative)
305 µm²	7 %*
86 µm²	90 %

Fig 4: Non-connected metallic part of the same filler network for 2 different contact areas

- Tested ECA with negligible* fraction of non-connected fillers
- Reduction of surface area exhibits increase of non-connected fillers → length of in-plane current paths in the network (range of 10 µm – 18 µm) in x and y
- *) Artifacts through edge effect (virtually cropped particles must be considered)

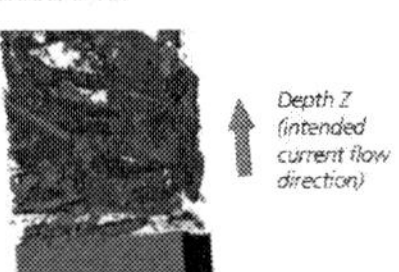

Fig 5: Visible cluster interruption near the interface but reduced dataset with 86 µm² area)

Validation microstructure relation between 2D to 3D

Determination of the filler area fraction A_{filler} from 2D images along the z-axis (depth).

- Assessment on µm scale (slice) and statistically in dataset (mean)
  - $A_{filler,\ slice} = 4$ % (min) – 27 % (max)
  - $A_{filler,\ mean} = (11.7 \pm 3.5)$ %
- Area and volume filler fraction in same range: $A_{filler,\ mean} \approx V_{filler,\ 3D}$

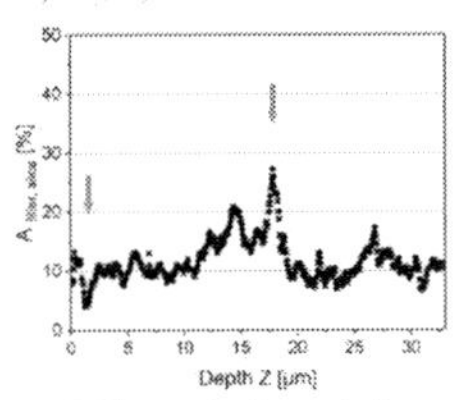

Fig 6: Filler area fraction vs depth (z-axis)

Summary

- 3D ECA network from FIB-SEM slice-and-view uncovers filler network and depth-dependent metal fraction.
- 3D view outperforms 2D for connectivity and quantitative insights.
- Identifies connected vs. non-connected fillers and rough estimate required in-plane current length.
- Outlook: Application to other ECAs

Contact

Dr. Stephan Großer
Tel. +49 345 5589-5112
stephan.grosser@csp.fraunhofer.de

Otto-Eissfeldt-Strasse 12
06120 Halle (Saale), Germany
www.csp.fraunhofer.de

1 International Technology Roadmap for Photovoltaics (ITRPV) - 2024 Results, VDMA (2025)
2 I. Devoto Acevedo et al., „The effects of increasing filler loading on the contact resistivity of interconnects based on silver–epoxied conductive adhesives and silver metallization pastes" Progress in Photovoltaics: Research and Applications. (2024) DOI: 10.1002/pip.3787
3 M. Kronsbein et al., „Less is more: Enabling low-filled electrically conductive adhesives for shingled solar cell interconnection using the capillary suspension concept" Solar Energy Materials and Solar Cells, 287 (2025) DOI: 10.1016/j.solmat.2025.113603

Financial support by the Federal Ministry for Economic Affairs and Energy funded project »IndiFiduell« (FKZ: 03EE1185B and 03EE1185C) is gratefully acknowledged

INVESTIGATION ON DIFFERENT BYPASS DIODES FOR SHADE RESISTANT PV-MODULES

Jens Froebel[1], Matthias Pander[1], Bengt Jaeckel[1], Andreas Maixner[2], Pouya Pourshafi[2], A. Bakhtiari[2], Hamed Hanifi[2]
[1]Fraunhofer-Center for Silicon-Photovoltaics (CSP), Halle (Saale), Germany
[2]AESOLAR, Koenigsbrunn, Germany
*Contact: +49 345 5589 5213, jens.froebel@csp.fraunhofer.de

ABSTRACT: The SegmentPV project focuses on developing photovoltaic modules for residential buildings, addressing challenges such as partial and dynamic shading through a collaboration between AESOLAR and the Fraunhofer Center for Silicon Photovoltaics (CSP). The design process encompasses various aspects, including the selection of the bill of materials (BOM), lamination processes, types of photovoltaic (PV) cells, interconnections, and bypass diodes. To understand the electrical, thermal, and structural requirements and challenges, this study investigates a selection of state-of-the-art and alternative bypass diodes. A primary goal is to determine the diode parameters essential for creating a digital twin, specifically a SPICE model, to simulate partial shading effects.

Partial shading of a single PV cell can lead to substantial power losses in the entire substring connected in series. For example, older designs with 60 cells and three substrings may suffer a 33% power loss if one cell is shaded, whereas modern butterfly designs reduce this to one-sixth of the module's power. This research explores various string designs to further minimize losses, requiring a detailed examination of bypass diode requirements, including I-V characteristics, power losses, reverse breakdown voltage, thermal behavior, and form factors for in-laminate designs. Alternatives to conventional Schottky diodes, such as silicon diodes, field-effect diodes, and active bypass diodes, are also evaluated.

Ten different diodes suitable for bypass applications were selected. Four-point measurements using a programmable source meter were conducted to determine I-V characteristics, with temperature-dependent I-V curve tracing performed on a subset. Diode parameters, including saturation current (Is), ideality factor (n), and series resistance (Rs), were extracted, and their temperature dependencies in the Shockley equation were characterized. The results provide insights for robust diode characterization and highlight temperature dependencies critical for accurate simulations.

Keywords: Bypass diodes, Characterization, PV modules

1 INTRODUCTION

Bypass diodes are key protection and performance elements in photovoltaic modules. In standard PV modules they are connected in anti-parallel across cell sub-strings (typically 18–24 cells) and provide an alternative current path in the event of partial shading, soiling or cell mismatch. The aim of the SegmentPV Project is to further subdivide the module to further increase its resistance to shading. One key objective is to identify optimal bypass diodes for residential photovoltaic modules that are resistant to recurring shading. This involves conducting electrical and thermal characterizations of various diode devices. The diodes were measured using a four-point connection setup at high speed to prevent self-heating, and additionally in a climate chamber from -40°C to 125°C to assess temperature behavior. Diode parameters were extracted from the data using a Python-based fitting algorithm, enabling simulations of shading scenarios that account for both partial shading and temperature variations. Standard SPICE simulations are limited because they apply a global temperature to all circuit components, so temperature-dependent modeling requires enhancements.

A measurement protocol was developed to evaluate and characterize potential bypass diodes, focusing on accurately capturing current-voltage behavior as a function of temperature. Measurements spanned a wide range from -40°C to 125°C, covering extreme operational conditions for PV modules. This approach provides a deeper understanding of the temperature-dependent behavior of these semiconductor components.

This paper presents an overview of state-of-the-art and alternative bypass diodes for use in solar modules. A robust measurement setup for diode characterization is described, and temperature-dependent diode parameters for simulations are extracted. The findings contribute to improving shade-resistant PV module designs by minimizing power losses and enhancing reliability.

Different Diode technologies are analyzed. This investigation includes:

Schottky Diodes: Based on a metal-semiconductor junction. They are widely used as BPDs because they offer low losses during forward conduction and enable fast switching. However, they may exhibit higher leakage current at high temperatures or reverse voltages.

Silicon Diodes (PN Junction): Standard silicon diodes with a PN junction. They are robust and have low leakage current but are less commonly used as BPDs due to higher losses.

Super Barrier Diodes (SBR): A hybrid technology that combines Schottky-like properties with PN advantages. They offer a balance of low forward voltage and low leakage current, making them more efficient than pure Schottky diodes.

Smart Diodes (Active Bypass Diodes): Active components, often MOSFET-based, that switch intelligently. They behave like "ideal diodes" with minimal losses and are particularly advantageous in partial shading scenarios due to their dynamic adjustment.

Conventional solar modules utilize junction boxes to house and connect Schottky bypass diodes, which typically have cylindrical or large rectangular form factors. To enhance thermal dissipation, these junction boxes are often filled with a potting compound. For subdivision of the module with the normal concept additional wiring and holes in the backsheet or rear glass would be required. Therefore, direct integration of the bypass diodes in the laminate is desirable. This approach requires diodes with a thin, compact form factor to ensure compatibility with the laminated structure and maintain module efficiency.

2 MATERIALS AND METHODS

2.1 Samples

Twelve solar module bypass diodes were selected, including alternative technologies. For scientific and product development purposes, brands and models were anonymized as P01 to P12, with addendums (e.g., s11) denoting specific samples on boards. Passive diodes included hot spot free, super barrier rectifiers, silicon, and Schottky types; active diodes were smart bypass diodes. Typically, six to eight samples per type were measured to statistically account for variations.

2.2 IV Characterization setup

The emphasis was on examining forward characteristics, including diode voltage and power consumption. The reverse breakdown voltage was verified, and diodes are slated for continuous stress testing in a subsequent work package. Forward characteristic curves were used to derive diode parameters such as saturation current (Is), ideality factor (n), and series resistance (Rs).

Test samples were measured in a climate chamber over a temperature range of -40°C to 125°C (limited from an initial plan of -45°C to 150°C due to technical constraints) to derive temperature-dependent parameters. Determining reverse breakdown voltage proved challenging without specialized equipment, as small currents at high voltages can damage the diodes. For instance, a typical -70 V breakdown at 100 mA equates to 7 W of load. The source meter used was limited to -40 V to +40 V, so only a minimum reverse breakdown of -40 V could be confirmed with our setup. Laboratory power supplies were inadequate for fine current adjustments, and prolonged testing caused heating that altered parameters.

The measurement setup involved soldering all diodes onto carriers designed for four-point measurements. Cross-connectors served as contacts to maximize solder area and minimize series resistance. Typically, six to eight diodes were mounted per test carrier to reduce the statistical impact of defects and errors. A high-accuracy programmable source meter measured IV-curves, with fast sweeps starting at low power to avoid heating.

For measurement of the temperature behavior in a climate chamber, individual carriers per diode were prepared with four-wire connections (Figure 1). Before measurement at a specific temperature the conditions are stabilized for at least 15 min.

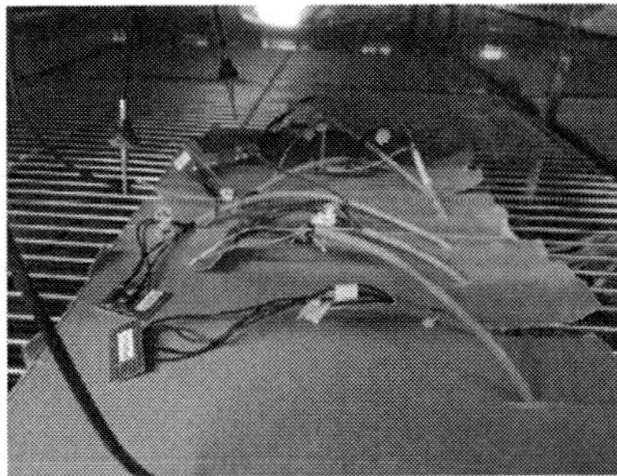

Figure 1: Specimen soldered on a PCB to realize a 4-point-measurement inside a climate chamber

2.3 Extraction of diode characteristic parameters

A Python-based fitting algorithm was developed to analyze measurement data and determine Shockley equation parameters. The Shockley equation [1] without series resistance is:

$$I_D = I_0 \left(e^{\frac{V_D}{nV_T}} - 1 \right) \text{ with } V_T = \frac{kT}{q} \qquad (1)$$

Including series resistance (Rs):

$$I_D = I_0 \left(e^{\frac{V_D - I_D R_S}{nV_T}} - 1 \right) \qquad (2)$$

Where I_D represents the diode current, I_0 is the saturation current, V_D is the applied voltage, R_S is the series resistance, n is the ideality factor, and V_T is the thermal voltage.

The saturation current I_0 (also known as reverse saturation current) in Shockley's equation is highly dependent on temperature T. This dependency arises mainly from the temperature dependence of the intrinsic carrier concentration in semiconductors, which is exponentially related to the band gap E_g. A common empirical function used to describe this dependency is:

$$I_0(T) = I_0(T_0) \left(\frac{T}{T_0} \right)^{\frac{m}{n}} \exp \left[\frac{E_g}{nk} \left(\frac{1}{T_0} - \frac{1}{T} \right) \right] \qquad (3)$$

In this equation, T represents the current absolute temperature, T_0 is the reference temperature, E_g is the bandgap energy of the semiconductor, k is the Boltzmann constant, and n is the ideality factor, m is a saturation current exponent. [1][2]

3 RESULTS

3.1 Room temperature IV characteristics

At room temperature (25°C), IV characteristics were measured for all diode types. As an overview of all specimen the IV-curve at 25°C is plotted in Figure 2.

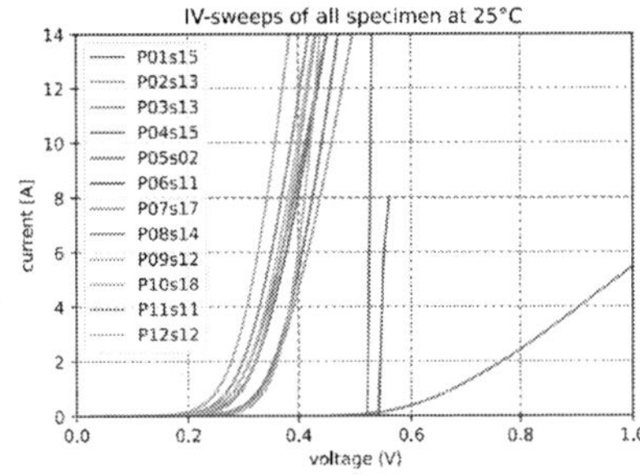

Figure 2: overview of IV-curves for all specimen at 25°C

Forward voltage drop (VD) aids in estimating power losses during conduction. Schottky Diodes (P07, P08, P09, P10, P12) and Super Barrier Rectifier (P02, P03, P04) show quite similar behaviour with around 0.4 +/- 0.05 V at 8 A, which would result in a power dissipation of 2.8 … 3.6 W. The silicon based super flat diode (P05) has a much higher Forward Voltage at around 1.2 V at 8.0 A (9.6 W). The active Bypass Diodes (P06, P11) however work like switches – and were not examined here furthermore.

Reverse behavior could not be characterized beyond -40 V, but diodes functioned reliably up to this point.

The extracted parameters, are shown in Table 1. Active BPD (P06 and P11) behaved as switched circuits and were not fitted to the Shockley model at room temperature. Parameters varied across types: forward voltages (VD) ranged from approximately 0.3 V to 0.7 V, saturation currents spanned orders of magnitude, ideality factors were near 1 for Schottky types and higher for silicon, and series resistances were generally low ($1.93\ m\Omega$ to $56.12\ m\Omega$).

Table 1: extracted diode parameters of the measurement

Sample	Type	Rs[mΩ]	Is(25°C)	n
P01	HS Free*	5.96	1.52E-05	1.15
P02	SBR**	4.3	1.66E-04	1.12
P03	SBR	5.4	7.80E-05	1.11
P04	SBR	6.09	6.36E-05	1.17
P05	Silicon	56.12	1.77E-06	1.82
P06	Active BPD	No measurement		
P07	Schottky	7.05	5.36E-06	1.05
P08	Schottky	7.03	5.35E-05	1.1
P09	Schottky	5.19	7.11E-05	1.14
P10	Schottky	1.93	4.15E-06	1.07
P11	Active BPD	No measurement		
P12	Schottky	4.78	2.36E-05	1.07

*Hot Spot Free
**Super Barrier Rectifier

3.2 Temperature-dependent IV characteristics

Temperature-dependent measurements were performed on a subset, excluding the silicon diode (P05) (anode/cathode not populated) and active BPD (P06, P11) due to setup constraints. IV-curves showed shifts with temperature: higher temperatures reduced forward voltage and increased reverse leakage.

Figure 3 to Figure 7 give an overview of the measured data and specimen size and setup. For example, specimen P01s21 (Hot Spot Free) exhibited decreasing forward voltage with increasing temperature, consistent with semiconductor behavior. Similar patterns were observed across types, with graphs illustrating uniformity.

Figure 3: IV-curves and images of P01 (Hot Spot Free) specimen for multiple temperatures between -40°C and 125°C

P01
Hot Spot Free
Very small size, was
soldered onto a wire

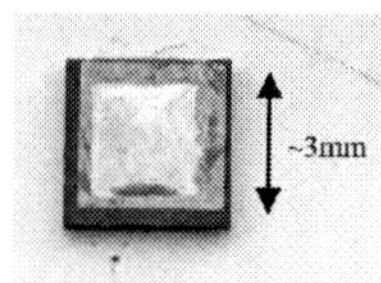

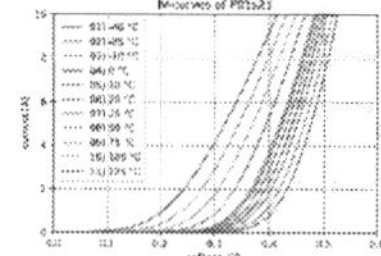

Figure 4: IV-curves and images of P02-P04 (SBR) specimen for multiple temperatures between -40°C and 125°C

P02
Super Barrier Rectifier

TO-277

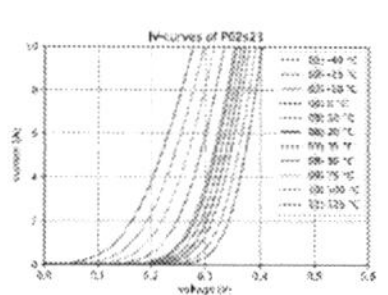

P03
Super Barrier Rectifier

TO-277

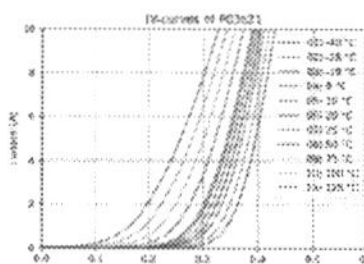

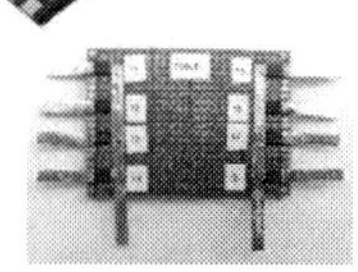

P04
Super Barrier Rectifier

POWERDI5SP

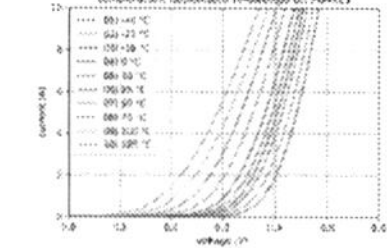

Figure 5: IV-curves and images of P05 (Silicon) specimen for multiple temperatures between -40°C and 125°C

P05
Flat Bypass Diode
Anode/Cathode were not
populated

These unpackaged
silicon diodes were
connected using
Electrically conductive
adhesive

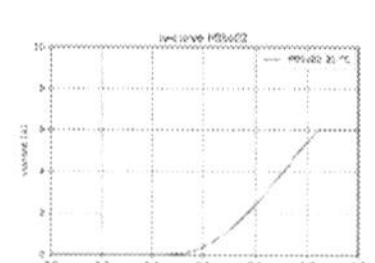

Figure 6: IV-curves and images of P07-P10 (Schottky Rectifier) specimen for multiple temperatures between -40°C and 125°C

P07
Schottky Rectifier

TO-277

P08
Schottky Rectifier

TO-277

P09
Schottky Rectifier

TO-277

P10
Schottky Rectifier

TO-263

P12
Schottky Rectifier

TO-277

Figure 7: IV-curve at room temperature and images of P06 and P11 (active bypass diodes) specimen

P06
Active BPD (smart Diode)
Was not in temperature test

D²PAK

P11
Active BPD
Was not in temperature test

TO-263

Saturation current (Is) showed exponential temperature dependence, varying by up to five orders of magnitude (log scale). Series resistance (Rs) displayed linear increases, while ideality factor (n) remained constant.

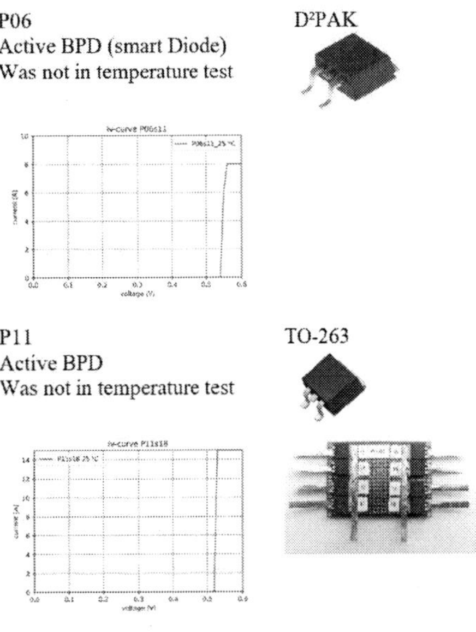

Figure 8: Temperature dependency of saturation current I_S on all Schottky Diodes. (log-axis for current)

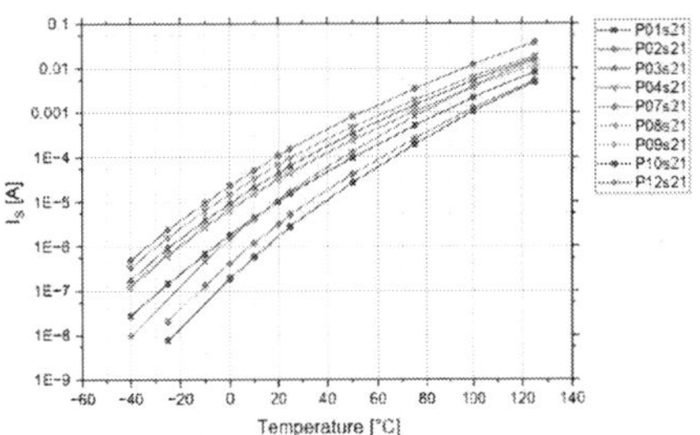

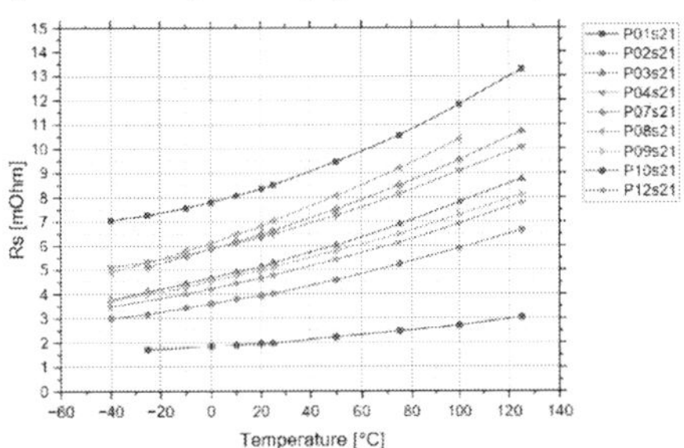

Figure 9: Temperature dependency of series resistance R_S

4 SUMMARY AND OUTLOOK

Selection of an appropriate bypass diode for a solar module application is driven by electrical and mechanical criteria: forward voltage at the expected operating current (dictating conduction losses), average and surge current capability under worst-case shading, reverse blocking voltage relative to substring open-circuit voltage, reverse leakage at elevated temperatures, thermal resistance and junction temperature limits, and avalanche robustness. Practical considerations like package form factor, pad layout, soldering/assembly effort, supply availability, and cost also influence the choice.

This study presents a robust test setup and procedure for characterizing bypass diode parameters, stressing the importance of low-resistance contacting and four-wire measurements. Passive diodes align with Shockley equation predictions:

a) Ideality factor n was constant and temperature-independent for each specimen.
b) Series resistance Rs showed linear temperature dependence.
c) Saturation current Is exhibited exponential temperature dependence, as per the formula.

These findings enhance SPICE modeling for temperature-varying conditions, as bypass diodes can reach 90°C or higher in operation if heat dissipation is poor. Passive diodes followed expected Shockley behavior, while active BPD acted as switches turning on at threshold voltages. Active diodes offer low-resistance paths but require careful integration.

Reverse breakdown at ~ -70 V is hard to measure without damage from small currents. Power losses, estimated from IV characteristics, are key for diode selection in PV designs.

Future work includes integrating these parameters into enhanced SPICE models for dynamic shading simulations, stress testing, and evaluating in-laminate designs. This will support SegmentPV's goal of higher-yield, reliable PV modules.

5 REFERENCES

[1] Tietze, U., Schenk, C., & Gamm, E. (2016). *Halbleiter-Schaltungstechnik* (15., überarbeitete und erweiterte Auflage). Berlin: Springer Vieweg. ISBN 978-3-662-48354-1

[2] H. T. Russell, Jr., "The SPICE diode model," in Rectifier Applications: Reference Manual and Handbook, HB214/D Rev. 2, Motorola Inc., Nov. 2001, pp. [page 47 .. 71].

6 ACKNOWLEDGEMENT

This publication was funded by the Federal Ministry for Economic Affairs and Climate Action in the project SegmentPV under grant number 03EE1180B. The findings herein reflect the work, and are solely the responsibility, of the authors.

SEGMENT PV
Segmented photovoltaic module

Investigation on Different Bypass Diodes for Shade Resistant PV-Modules

Jens Froebel[1], Matthias Pander[1], Bengt Jaeckel[1], Andreas Maixner[2], Pouya Pourshafi[2], A. Bakhtiari[2], Hamed Haniffi[2]
[1] Fraunhofer-Center for Silicon-Photovoltaics (CSP), Halle (Saale), Germany
[2] AESOLAR, Koenigsbrunn, Germany
Contact: jens.froebel@csp.fraunhofer.de

3AV.1.6

Introduction

This study is part of the project SEGMENT PV: Segmented photovoltaic module to achieve a higher energy yield and reliability with recurring partial shading. Sub-project: Characterization and reliability studies segment PV main components: solar cell and bypass diodes

We investigate a set of bypass diodes (BPD) suitable for solar application and with different technologies, such as Schottky, Silicon, switched Diodes (active BPD). The aim is to compare each properties and extract the diode parameters to create a SPICE simulation model.

Samples and measurement setup

* 12 solar bypass diodes are selected
* All diodes soldered onto a carrier enabling four-point measurements
* Cross-connectors used as contacts to maximize solder area and reduce series resistance
* Typically 6–8 specimens mounted per test carrier to mitigate defects and measurement errors statistically
* For climate chamber tests, one carrier per specimen was prepared with a 4-wire connection.
* A programmable source meter with high accuracy measures the IV-curves

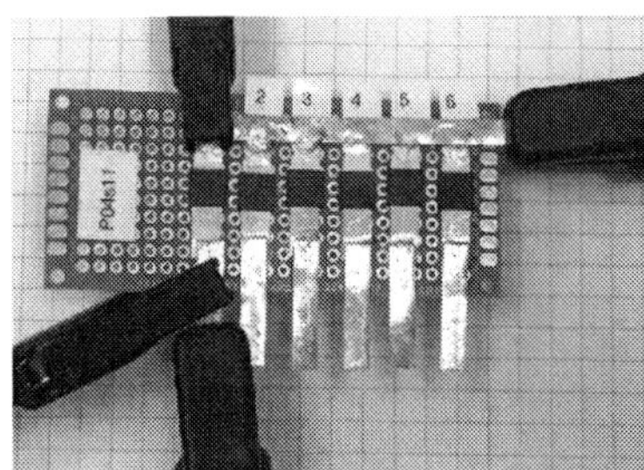

Fig 1. PCB carrier prepared with 6 diodes. Clamps for voltage and current sensing are in 4 wire connection

Deriving the diode parameters from IV-curves

* P06s11 and P11s11 are active BPD
* P05s02 is a silicon diode
* Fast IV-sweeps starting at low power to avoid heating
* A python script to fit the Shockley Equation was applied

Is Saturation Current, **Rs** Series Resistance, **n** emission coefficient were derived, **Rsh** Shunt Resistance is neglected

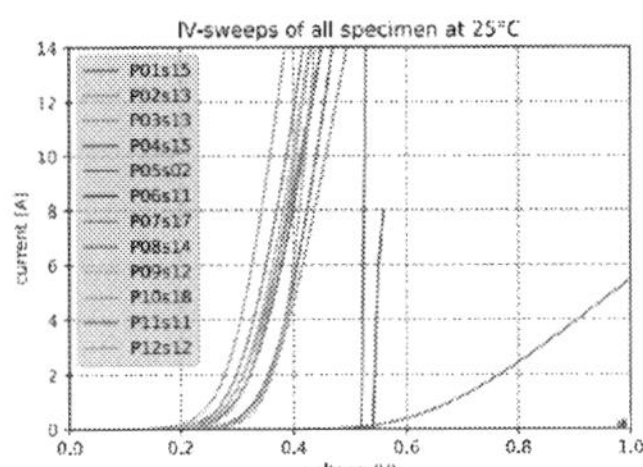

Fig 2. IV curves of all diode types at 25°C

A set of 12 Solar BPD were investigated, brand and model is anonymized.

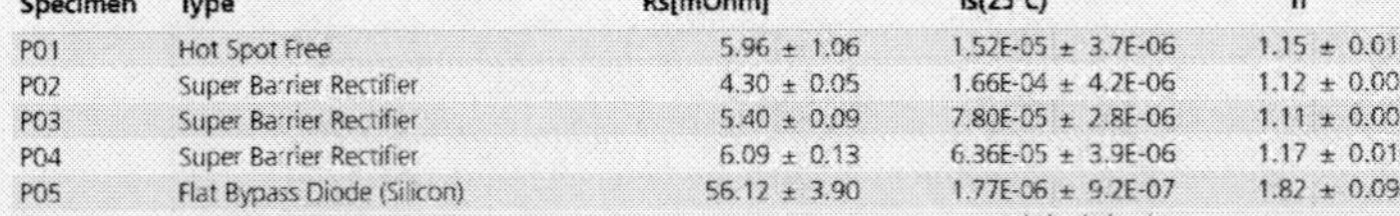

Specimen	Type	Rs[mOhm]	Is(25°C)	n
P01	Hot Spot Free	5.96 ± 1.06	1.52E-05 ± 3.7E-06	1.15 ± 0.0153
P02	Super Barrier Rectifier	4.30 ± 0.05	1.66E-04 ± 4.2E-06	1.12 ± 0.0058
P03	Super Barrier Rectifier	5.40 ± 0.09	7.80E-05 ± 2.8E-06	1.11 ± 0.0058
P04	Super Barrier Rectifier	6.09 ± 0.13	6.36E-05 ± 3.9E-06	1.17 ± 0.0100
P05	Flat Bypass Diode (Silicon)	56.12 ± 3.90	1.77E-06 ± 9.2E-07	1.82 ± 0.0985
P06	Active BPD (Smart Diode)		switched circuit	
P07	Schottky Rectifier	7.05 ± 0.04	5.36E-06 ± 1.3E-07	1.05 ± 0.0000
P08	Schottky Rectifier	7.03 ± 0.03	5.35E-05 ± 2.6E-06	1.10 ± 0.0000
P09	Schottky Rectifier	5.19 ± 0.08	7.11E-05 ± 4.5E-06	1.14 ± 0.0058
P10	Schottky Rectifier	1.93 ± 0.08	4.15E-06 ± 4.3E-07	1.07 ± 0.0058
P11	Active BPD (Smart Diode)		switched circuit	
P12	Schottky Rectifier	4.78 ± 0.07	2.36E-05 ± 1.6E-06	1.07 ± 0.0000

Temperature dependent behaviour

* A subset of specimen was IV-traced in a climate chamber at a wide range of temperature steps from -25°C up to 125°C
* Parameters Is, Rs, n were derived for every temperature
* Parameter n is a constant over the temperature

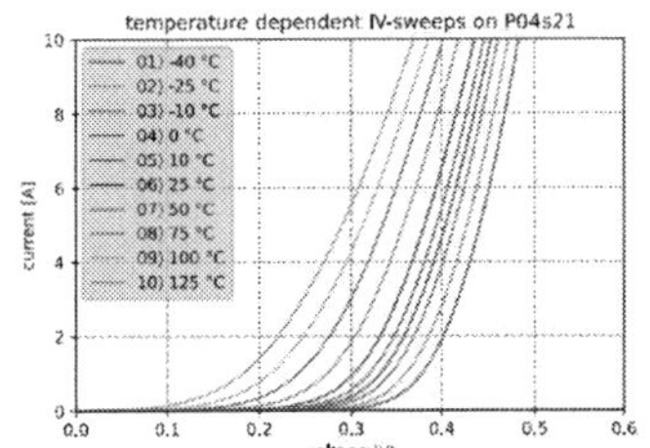

Fig 3. IV curves of all sweeps over the temperature range from -40°C to 125°C using specimen P04s21 as an example

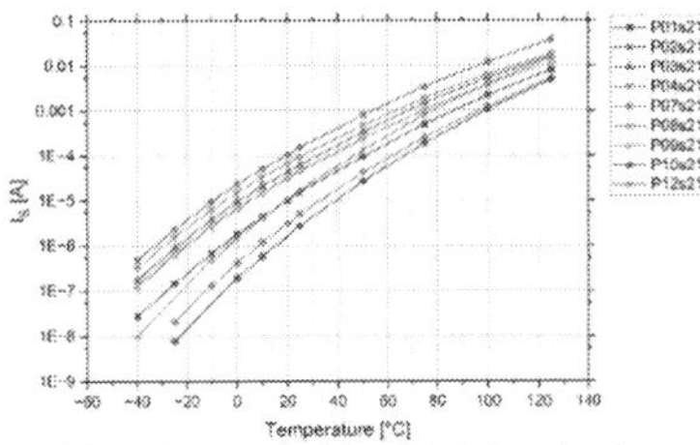

Fig 4. Saturation current Is of the selected subset of specimen. The values differ in a range of up to 5 orders of magnitude

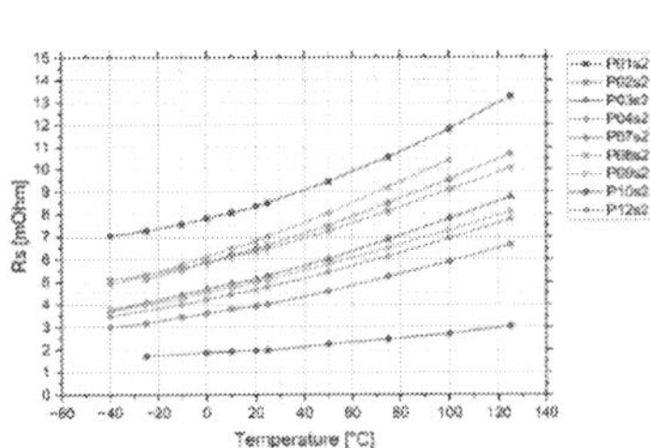

Fig 5. Series Resistance of the selected subset of specimen

Theory and formulae

* The Shockley Equation describes the characteristic of a diode at a temperature

$$I_D = IS \cdot \left[\exp\left(\frac{V_D}{N \cdot V_t} \right) - 1 \right] + GMIN \cdot V_D \quad \text{with} \quad V_t = \frac{k \cdot T}{q}$$

ID diode current; **VD** diode voltage; **IS** saturation current; **N** emission coefficient; **Vt** Temperature voltage; **GMIN** reciprocal of series resistance Rs; **K** Boltzmann constant; **T** Temperature; **q** elementary electron charge

* This enhances the simulation parameters under operation conditions because BPD can reach up to 90°C in normal operation and even higher when heat dissipation is insufficient by design of the PV module
* The results demonstrate that especially Is is highly temperature dependent and cannot be used as a constant for calculation or simulation [1]

$$IS(T) = IS(TNOM) \cdot \left(\frac{T}{TNOM} \right)^{XTI1N} \cdot \exp\left[\left(\frac{q \cdot EG}{N \cdot K} \right) \cdot \left[\frac{1}{TNOM} - \frac{1}{T} \right] \right]$$

TNOM nominal temperature; **XTI1N** IS temperature coefficient (SPICE); **EG** energy gap

Summary and Conclusion

* Test setup and procedure for robust characterization of characteristic parameters of bypass diodes presented
* It is very important to take good care of low-resistance contacting and 4-wire measurement
* Passives Diodes behave as expected and can be described by Shockley equation
* Active BPD act like switches that turn on at a threshold voltage
* Is is exponentially dependent on temperature
* Reverse breakdown voltage at approx. -70 Volts is hard to measure, a small current may already burn the specimen
* Power losses can be estimated from IV characteristics as part of selection process

Contact

Jens FROEBEL
PV Modules, Components
and Manufacturing
jens.froebel@csp.fraunhofer.de
Fraunhofer CSP
Otto-Eißfeldt-Str. 12
06120 Halle
www.csp.fraunhofer.de

In cooperation with our project partner AESolar

Project funded by the Federal Ministry for Economic Affairs and Energy in the project SegmentPV under grant number 03EE1180B.

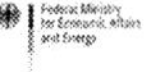

Literature: [1] H. T. Russell, Jr., "The SPICE Diode Model," in Rectifier Applications, ON Semiconductor, San Jose, CA, 4 Aug. 1991, ch. 3, pp. 49-71.

020122-001

OPTIMIZATION OF INFRARED SOLDERING PROCESS TO REDUCE THE TEMPERATURE INHOMOGENEITY IN SILICON SOLAR CELLS USING FINITE ELEMENT METHODS

Daniel Christopher Joseph*, Angela De Rose, Christian Reichel, Andreas J. Beinert, Holger Neuhaus
Fraunhofer Institute for Solar Energy Systems ISE, Heidenhofstrasse 2, 79110 Freiburg, Germany
*Corresponding author: e-mail to: daniel.christopher.joseph@ise.fraunhofer.de

ABSTRACT: A temperature-controlled infrared soldering process is becoming increasingly crucial for the successful integration of new solar cell technologies, such as silicon heterojunction and perovskite-silicon tandem solar cells. However, optimizing this process remains challenging due to temperature inhomogeneity and difficulties in accurate measurement. In this study, a Finite Element Method model, which can be easily adapted to different solar cell types, sizes and formats, is developed to reduce temperature inhomogeneity by systematically varying key process parameters, including the power supplied to the infrared emitters and the duration of the infrared radiation. A maximum temperature inhomogeneity, $\Delta T_C = 17$ K, is achieved for M6 silicon-heterojunction half solar cell, and $\Delta T_C = 15$ K, is achieved for M10 silicon-heterojunction half solar cell by identifying the optimum process parameters, which is a significant improvement from $\Delta T_C > 40$ K measured from conventional infrared soldering process. Thus, this research improves heating uniformity and minimizes the risk of overheating the solar cells.

Keywords: Finite element method, Infrared soldering, Photovoltaic modules, Radiative heat transfer, Interconnection, Tandem solar cells

1 INTRODUCTION

The emergence of new temperature-sensitive solar cell types, such as silicon heterojunction (SHJ) and perovskite-silicon tandem solar cells, along with new solder alloys, has made precise heating during the industrial infrared (IR) soldering process more critical than ever. In this process, the primary objective is to heat the solar cells above the liquidus temperature of the solder alloy to establish contact between the solder-coated copper wire and the metallization. However, limited control over the maximum temperature reached by the solar cells often results in overheating, particularly in the center of the cells. This overheating can cause damage to sensitive solar cell materials, such as IR radiation-induced degradation in SHJ solar cells [1] and heat-induced degradation in perovskite-based solar cells [2]. In addition to preventing damage, precise heating also offers an opportunity to reduce energy consumption by minimizing unnecessary overheating during the soldering process, thus lowering overall energy costs.

In previous work, a Finite Element Model (FEM) was developed to simulate the temperature distribution across solar cells during the IR soldering process using four IR emitters and two radiation pulses in an industrial stringer. The analysis revealed a temperature inhomogeneity of 27 K for SHJ M6 half-cell. This represents an improvement compared to the typical $\Delta T_C > 40$ K inhomogeneity observed in conventional industrial IR soldering processes. However, this non-uniform heating still resulted in overheating at the cell center, while the edges remained at relatively lower temperatures [3].

The aim of this research is to further optimize the IR soldering process for various solar cell types and sizes, with particular emphasis on minimizing temperature inhomogeneity to $\Delta T_C < 20$ K across the solar cells, using a FEM model. The FEM model has been developed based on an industrial stringer and is designed for direct application in optimizing the IR soldering process within industrial settings.

2 FEM MODEL

The FEM model developed using COMSOL Multiphysics 6.3 employed in this study builds upon our earlier work [3], where a comprehensive description of the material properties [4–6] and physics interfaces is provided. Here, only the key parameters and geometrical modifications are summarized. The tungsten filament temperature (T_F) is defined by the process parameters—input power (P_{IR}) and radiation pulse duration (t_{IR}). Based on T_F, the emitted radiation is calculated and coupled into the heat transfer and surface-to-surface radiation physics to determine the solar cell temperature (T_C). The initial cell temperature (T_0) corresponds to the experimentally measured value prior to IR heating. In the model, the silicon solar cell and the quartz tube are treated as semi-transparent surfaces, the reflector as an opaque surface, and the filament and down-holders as diffuse surfaces.

In our previous work, four IR emitters were used to heat half solar cells, generating two radiation pulses. The first pulse was only partially incident on the cell surface, while the second pulse covered the entire surface. This was primarily due to the smaller dimensions of the solar cell relative to the span of the four emitters, leading to temperature inhomogeneities exceeding 25 K [3]. This caused overheating of the solar cells in the center, in order to heat the edges beyond the liquidus temperature of the solder alloy.

The present work aims on optimizing the IR soldering process to minimize temperature inhomogeneities by identifying suitable process parameters while reducing the number of IR emitters. Through resource optimization, it was determined that three IR emitters are sufficient to heat the solar cells with a single radiation pulse, enabling both the cell and the interconnecting wires with solder alloy to exceed the liquidus temperature. Based on the geometrical model shown in Figure 1 where the half-cells are positioned centrally beneath the three IR emitters, the corresponding process parameters P_{IR} and t_{IR} were determined for M6 and M10 SHJ half-cells, with an emissivity of 0.7 obtained from in-situ measurements. Specifically, an M6 SHJ half solar cell (83 mm × 166 mm) with six busbars (BB), and a down-holder with six metal strips, and an M10 SHJ half solar cell (91 mm × 182 mm) with ten BB and a down-holder with nine metal strips, were modeled for the FEM simulation. To reduce computational complexity, a symmetry plane was applied perpendicular to the longer side of the solar cell. The ribbon consists of a round copper wire attached to the solar cell using solder alloy. The modeled configuration for M6 half-cell with the symmetry plane is illustrated in Figure 2.

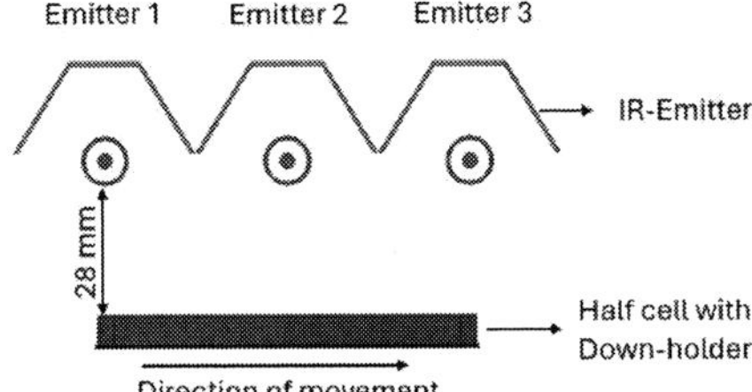

Figure 1: Geometry of the half-cell with down-holder positioned centrally beneath the three IR emitters during IR soldering, not to scale.

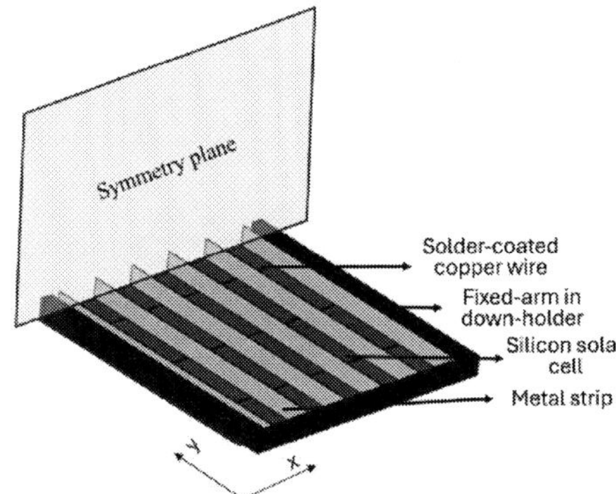

Figure 2: Modelled symmetric geometry of the M6 silicon half solar cell with solder-coated copper wire (ribbon) and the down-holder [3].

3   RESULTS AND DISCUSSION

For the M6 SHJ half-cell, the exposure time to IR radiation (t_{IR}) was initially set to 1.2 s, consistent with our previous study. The input powers of the three IR emitters (P_{IR1-3}) were varied for three different parameter cases, while the temperature of the heat plate below the emitters (T_{HP}) was fixed at 145 °C. The process parameters were chosen to achieve a minimum temperature of at least 190 °C, which is the liquidus temperature of the solder alloy used. These process parameters are summarized in Table I. To mitigate overheating in the central region of the solar cell, as identified in our earlier work, the input power of P_{IR2} was intentionally reduced. The resulting peak-temperature inhomogeneity values are provided in Table II, showing that the inhomogeneity is 20 K for all three cases, representing a good improvement compared to our previous works, which showed an inhomogeneity of more than 25 K [3].

Figure 3 shows the simulated temperature profile for case 3 with both maximum and minimum solar cell temperature. The temperature inhomogeneity (ΔT_C) is larger at the end of the IR-radiation pulse but starts to reduce after the radiation zone ends. The temperature, however, continues to increase for the next 0.8 s after the IR radiation pulse. This behavior arises because the IR lamps continue operating at a threshold power ($\approx$30%) as the solar cell continues to move on the transport belt after the IR radiation pulse, thereby contributing additional heating before the cooling phase begins. The inhomogeneity is thus measured at the maximum peak temperature (Peak $T_{C\_Max.}$), which in this case is at $t = 2$ s. The inhomogeneity is defined as the difference between maximum peak temperature (Peak $T_{C\_Max.}$) and the minimum temperature (Peak $T_{C\_Min.}$) measured at the same time instance of $t = 2$ s. Therefore, the inhomogeneity is measured at the end of the cycle duration of 2 s (divided into a radiation pulse of 1.2 s and the transport duration of 0.8 s)

Table I : Process parameters used in the FEM simulation for M6 SHJ half-cell for a radiation pulse duration $t_{IR} = 1.2$ s.

	Case 1	Case 2	Case 3
Initial solar cell temperature T_0 (°C)	125	125	125
Hot plate temperature T_{HP} (°C)	145	145	145
Power IR emitter 1 P_{IR1} (%)	85	80	80
Power IR emitter 1 P_{IR2} (%)	30	30	35
Power IR emitter 1 P_{IR3} (%)	85	80	80

Table II: Simulated solar cell temperature T_C for M6 SHJ half-cell for a radiation pulse duration $t_{IR} = 1.2$ s measured at $t = 2$ s.

	Case 1	Case 2	Case 3
Peak $T_{C\_Max.}$ (°C)	216	213	215
Peak $T_{C\_Min.}$ (°C)	196	193	195
ΔT_C (K)	**20**	**20**	**20**

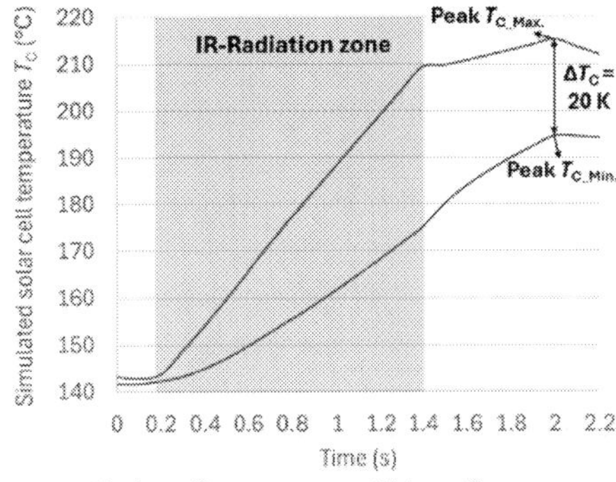

Figure 3: Simulated maximum (red) and minimum (blue) solar cell temperature T_C during IR soldering of SHJ M6 half-cell for case 3.

Based on these findings, and to efficiently use the additional heating after the IR pulse, the IR radiation duration was reduced to 1.0 s, while the input powers of P_{IR1} and P_{IR3} were slightly increased to compensate for the shorter pulse. The throughput, however, remains the same, as the transport time after the IR radiation is slightly increased from 0.8 s to 1 s, thus keeping the cycle time constant at 2 s. The corresponding process parameters and the resulting temperature inhomogeneity are listed in Tables III and IV, respectively. In the case 4, 5 and 6 similar inhomogeneity of 17-18 K is obtained. However, case 5 uses less power compared to the other two cases, to achieve ΔT_C = 17 K, maintaining the minimum temperature at a safe limit of at least 5 K above the liquidus temperature of 190 °C. The temperature distribution of the solar cell for case 5 at time t = 2 s, when the maximum temperature is reached, is shown in Figure 4. Further reduction was not possible since the minimum lamp power was constrained by the 30% threshold setting and the other parameter combinations resulted in either higher inhomogeneity or not heating beyond the liquidus temperature of the solder alloy.

Table III: Process parameters used in the FEM simulation for **M6** SHJ half-cell for a radiation pulse duration t_{IR} = 1 s.

	Case 4	Case 5	Case 6
Initial solar cell temperature T_0 (°C)	120	120	120
Hot plate temperature T_{HP} (°C)	145	145	145
Power IR emitter 1 P_{IR1} (%)	90	90	95
Power IR emitter 1 P_{IR2} (%)	35	30	30
Power IR emitter 1 P_{IR3} (%)	90	90	95

Table IV: Simulated solar cell temperature T_C for **M6** half-cell for a radiation pulse duration t_{IR} = 1 s measured at t = 2 s.

	Case 4	Case 5	Case 6
Peak $T_{C\_Max.}$ (°C)	217	215	218
Peak $T_{C\_Min.}$ (°C)	199	198	200
ΔT_C (K)	**18**	**17**	**18**

A similar set of experiments was conducted for the M10 SHJ half-cell. The investigated process parameters are summarized in Table V, and the corresponding temperature inhomogeneities are reported in Table VI. The temperature distribution of the solar cell for case 8 at time t = 2 s, when the maximum temperature is reached, is shown in Figure 5. Here, a minimum temperature inhomogeneity of ΔT_C = 15 K is achieved as the M10 half-cells have more area under the IR lamps compared to M6 half-cells, resulting in a slightly better temperature distribution. Thus, case 5 and case 8, with the same process parameters, results in minimum temperature inhomogeneity for both M6 and M10 SHJ half solar cells during the IR soldering process.

Table V: Process parameters used in the FEM simulation for **M10** SHJ half-cell for a radiation pulse duration t_{IR} = 1 s.

	Case 7	Case 8	Case 9
Initial solar cell temperature T_0 (°C)	120	120	120
Hot plate temperature T_{HP} (°C)	145	145	145
Power IR emitter 1 P_{IR1} (%)	90	90	95
Power IR emitter 1 P_{IR2} (%)	35	30	30
Power IR emitter 1 P_{IR3} (%)	90	90	95

Table VI: Simulated solar cell temperature T_C for **M10** half-cell for a radiation pulse duration t_{IR} = 1 s measured at t = 2 s.

	Case 7	Case 8	Case 9
Peak $T_{C\_Max.}$ (°C)	218	214	217
Peak $T_{C\_Min.}$ (°C)	202	199	201
ΔT_C (K)	**16**	**15**	**16**

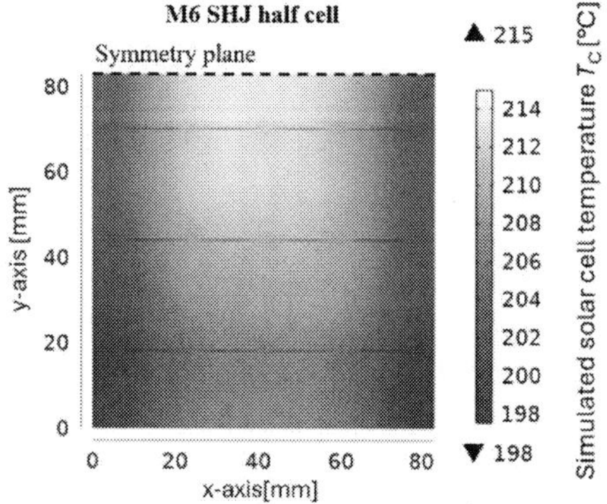

Figure 4: Simulated temperature distribution on the M6 half solar cell at t = 2 s for case 5 process parameters.

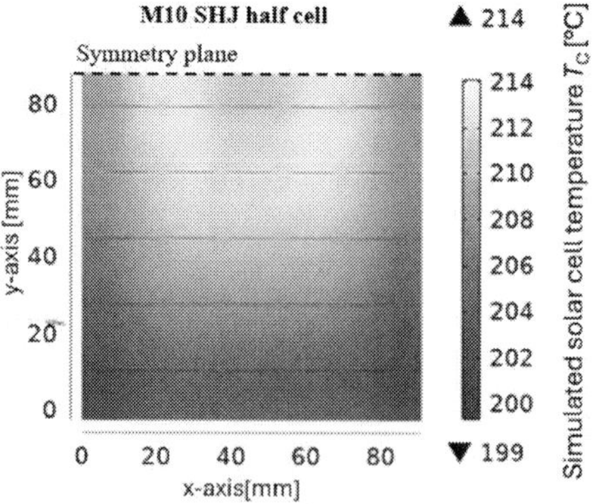

Figure 5: Simulated temperature distribution on the M10 half solar cell at t = 2 s for case 8 process parameters.

4 CONCLUSION

In summary, this research uses an FEM model to optimize the IR soldering process and minimize temperature inhomogeneity to $\Delta T_C < 20$ K . The study not only focuses on reducing temperature inhomogeneities but also helps in determining the maximum temperature reached during the IR soldering process, which is crucial for adapting the process to new solar cell technologies and sizes. A major adaption is to use only three IR emitters instead of four, which helps achieve the required heating with fewer resources. The second adaption is a variation of the process parameters - such as the power of the IR emitters P_{IR} and the duration of radiation t_{IR}, to determine the optimal values for the M6 and M10 SHJ half solar cell, achieving a temperature inhomogeneity of 17 K and 15 K respectively. Thus, the robust FEM model has been effectively used to determine the optimal process parameter that helps reduce inhomogeneity during the IR soldering process for M6 and M10 SHJ half solar cell. The model can be easily adapted to other solar cell types and sizes. Additionally, the FEM model will also be applied to compute thermomechanical stress during the cooling phase following the IR soldering process, providing a comprehensive framework for optimizing the interconnection process.

5 ACKNOWLEDGEMENT

The authors would like to thank the German Federal Ministry for Economic Affairs and Climate Action for the financial support within the project "Quelle" (Grant number 03EE1172E). The authors would further like to thank Teamtechnik Industrieausrüstung GmbH and Ceramicx ltd. for supporting with the infrared emitter characteristics.

6 REFERENCES

[1] A. De Rose, C. Rosado Alberdi, and A. Kraft, "Influence of IR Soldering Profile on Industrial Silicon Heterojunction Solar Cells," p. 536-540, 2022, doi: 10.4229/WCPEC-82022-3CO.4.3.

[2] G. Divitini, S. Cacovich, F. Matteocci, L. Cinà, A. Di Carlo, and C. Ducati, "In situ observation of heat-induced degradation of perovskite solar cells," *Nat Energy*, vol. 1, no. 2, 2016, doi: 10.1038/nenergy.2015.12.

[3] D. C. Joseph, A. De Rose, D. Eberlein, O. Parlayan, B. Grübel, A. J. Beinert, H. Neuhaus, "Investigation of temperature homogeneity during infrared soldering of silicon solar cells using the finite element method," *EPJ Photovolt.*, vol. 16, p. 9, 2025, doi: 10.1051/epjpv/2024052.

[4] Y. S. Touloukian and D. P. DeWitt, *Thermophysical Properties of Matter - The TPRC Data Series. Volume 7. Thermal Radiative Properties - Metallic Elements and Alloys*, 1970. Accessed: July 2025.

[5] M. Zhao, Z. Zhou, M. Zhong, J. Tan, Y. Lian, and X. Liu, "Thermal shock behavior of fine grained W–Y 2 O 3 materials fabricated via two different manufacturing technologies," *Journal of Nuclear Materials*, vol. 470, pp. 236–243, 2016, doi: 10.1016/j.jnucmat.2015.12.042.

[6] F. Hu and S. Lucyszyn, "Modelling Miniature Incandescent Light Bulbs for Thermal Infrared 'THz Torch' Applications," *J Infrared Milli Terahz Waves*, vol. 36, no. 4, pp. 350–367, 2015, doi: 10.1007/s10762-014-0130-8.

Optimization of Infrared Soldering Process to Reduce the Temperature Inhomogeneity in Silicon Solar Cells using Finite Element Methods

D. C. Joseph , A. De Rose, C. Reichel, A. J. Beinert and H. Neuhaus
Fraunhofer Institute for Solar Energy Systems ISE, Heidenhofstr. 2, 79110 Freiburg, Germany
daniel.christopher.joseph@ise.fraunhofer.de | www.ise.fraunhofer.de/module-fem

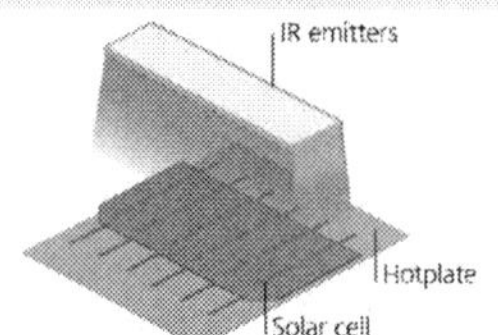

Motivation

- Precise heating of solar cells during the industrial infrared (IR) soldering process is critical for new solar cell technologies to prevent overheating and cell damage [1,2,3]

- Experimentally measured temperature inhomogeneity for an industrial IR soldering process exceeds 40 K for Silicon Heterojunction (SHJ) solar cells

- Previous simulation work reduced the temperature inhomogeneity to 27 K for SHJ half-cells using two radiation pulses from the four pre-heating IR emitters in an industrial stringer [4]

- Aim of this work: Optimize the infrared soldering process to minimize the temperature distribution inhomogeneity to $T_C < 20$ K on the half solar cell with optimum resources using a finite element method (FEM) model

Fig. 1: IR emitters heating the solar cell during the IR soldering process.

Method

- Experimentally validated FEM model adapted from our previous work that computes the radiative heat transfer for entire IR soldering process including the influence of hotplate [4]

- Single radiation pulse from three IR emitters is sufficient to achieve the required temperature on a half-cell

- Radiation pulse duration (t_{IR}) and the power of the IR emitter (P_{IR}) are systematically varied to determine the temperature inhomogeneity

- Two different sizes of Silicon Heterojunction (SHJ) half solar cells are used: M6 with six busbars and M10 with ten busbars

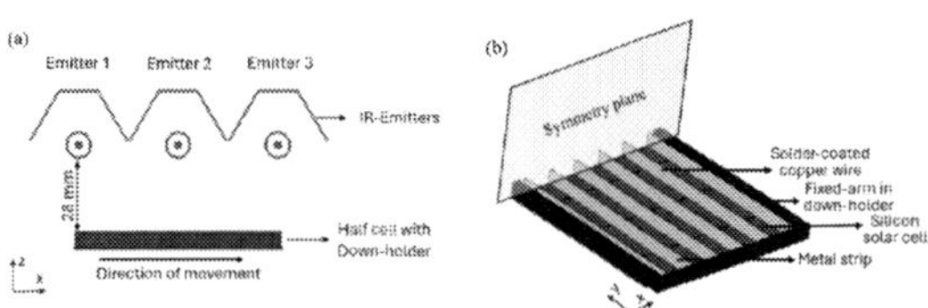

Fig. 2: (a) Half-cell with down-holder positioned centrally beneath the three IR emitters during IR soldering, not to scale. (b) Modelled symmetric geometry used in the FEM simulation [4].

- Industrial IR soldering process heats the solar cells with a radiation pulse duration of 1.2 to 1.3 seconds

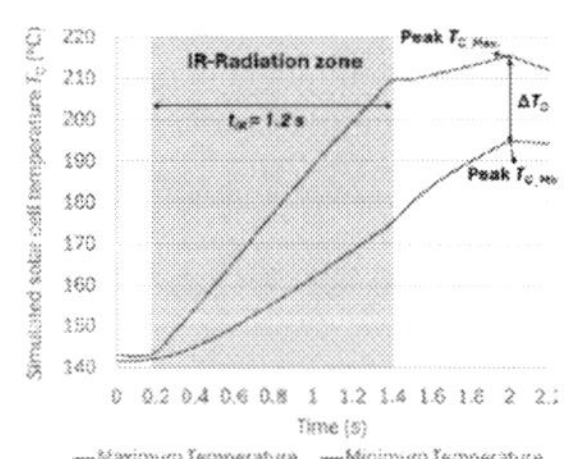

- Temperature slightly increases after the IR radiation pulse as IR emitters continue to emit radiation at threshold power ($\approx$ 30%)

- Inhomogeneity is measured at the peak maximum temperature ($t = 2$ s), as shown in the figure

Fig. 3: Simulated maximum (red) and minimum (blue) solar cell temperature T_C of SHJ M6 half-cell with the industrial process radiation pulse duration $t_{IR} = 1.2$ s

Results

- Shorter radiation pulse duration helps in decreasing the inhomogeneity

- Radiation pulse duration $t_{IR} = 1$ s is determined to be sufficient to heat the solar cells

- Optimized power of the IR emitters 1, 2 and 3 for both M6 and M10 SHJ half-cells to achieve low inhomogeneity:

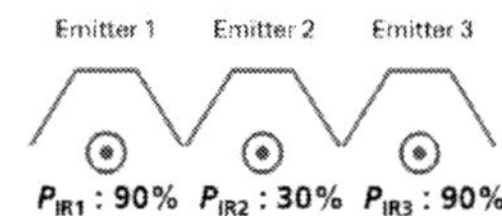

$P_{IR1} : 90\%$ $P_{IR2} : 30\%$ $P_{IR3} : 90\%$

Table 1: Simulated temperature T_C for SHJ half-cell for a radiation pulse duration $t_{IR} = 1$ s measured at peak T_{C_Max} ($t = 2$ s).

Solar cell size	Peak $T_{C\_Max.}$ (°C)	Peak $T_{C\_Min.}$ (°C)	ΔT_C (K)
M6 half-cell	215	198	17
M10 half-cell	214	199	15

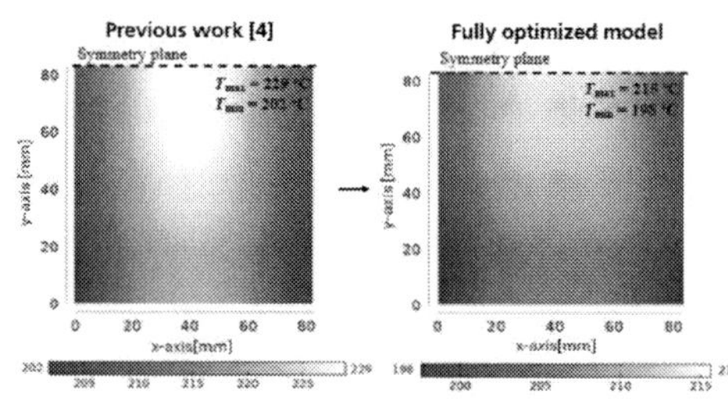

Fig. 4: M6 SHJ half-cell simulated temperature distribution T_C on: (left) partially optimized with 27 K inhomogeneity from previous work [4], (right) fully optimized M6 SHJ half-cell with 17 K inhomogeneity.

- **Reasons for inhomogeneity on the edges**: (a) shading of radiation because of the down-holder (b) inhomogeneity of IR emitters in y direction

Summary

- FEM model is precisely developed using the influential process parameters: radiation pulse duration (t_{IR}) and the power of the IR emitter (P_{IR})

- Optimum process parameters have been identified to reduce the inhomogeneity on M6 and M10 SHJ half solar cells

- Inhomogeneity has been reduced from more than 40 K (measured for industrial IR soldering process) to 17 K and 15 K on M6 and M10 SHJ half cells, respectively

- Easy to adapt to new solar cell sizes and technologies

Contact information

Daniel C. Joseph
Finite Element Methods – Module Technology
daniel.christopher.joseph@ise.fraunhofer.de
Fraunhofer Institute for Solar Energy Systems ISE
www.fraunhofer.de

1. A. J. Beinert, P. Romer, M. Heinrich, J. Aktaa, and H. Neuhaus, "Thermomechanical design rules for photovoltaic modules," Progress in Photovoltaics, vol. 31, no. 12, pp. 1181–1193, 2023, DOI 10.1002/pip.3624
2. M. Hertl, D. Weidmann, and J.-C. Lecomte, Microelectronics and Packaging Conference, 2009. EMPC 2009. European, 2009
3. A. De Rose, C. Rosado Alberdi, A. Kraft, "Influence of IR Soldering Profile on Industrial Silicon Heterojunction Solar Cells", 8th World Conference on Photovoltaics, p. 536–540, 2022, DOI: 10.4229/WCPEC-82022-3C0.4.3
4. D. C. Joseph, A. De Rose, D. Eberlein, O. Parlayan, B. Grübel, A. J. Beinert, H. Neuhaus, "Investigation of temperature homogeneity during infrared soldering of silicon solar cells using the finite element method," EPJ Photovolt., vol. 16, p. 9, 2025, doi: 10.1051/epjpv/2024052.

020124-001

Supported by:
Federal Ministry for Economic Affairs and Climate Action

on the basis of a decision by the German Bundestag

This research was funded by German Federal Ministry for Economic Affairs and Climate Action under the project "Quelle" (Grant number 03EE1172E).

PERFORMANCE EVALUATION OF A NEW DESIGN PHOTOVOLTAIC MODULE WITH REDUCED SELF-SHADING.

Pouya Pourshafi[1], Andreas Maixner[1], Hamed Hanifi[1*]
[1] AESOLAR, Messerschmittring 54, Koenigsbrunn, Germany
*Corresponding Author: h.hanifi@ae-solar.com

ABSTRACT: Photovoltaic (PV) systems are a key component of renewable energy, yet their extensive land requirements can limit deployment, particularly in agricultural regions. With decreasing module costs and rising land prices, combining energy generation with farming activities has become increasingly attractive. Vertical bifacial PV modules enable dual land use by allowing crop cultivation and machinery access. However, such vertical setups of bifacial modules often suffer from self-shading caused by junction boxes, frames, and cabling, which diminishes energy output. AESOLAR has addressed this challenge by redesigning module interconnections and relocating junction boxes and cables to the edges, while an optimized frame minimizes rear-side shading. This study evaluates the performance of the redesigned module against a standard half-cell module using a Python-SPICE simulation that incorporates shading from junction boxes, frames, and cables. Results indicate that mitigating self-shading can boost energy yield by up to 3.21%, lowering the levelized cost of electricity. Additionally, simulations across various geographic locations show that regions with higher solar irradiation benefit most from the improvements. These findings improve the practicality of vertical bifacial PV systems, enabling efficient solar energy production with agricultural activities.

1 INTRODUCTION

The role of photovoltaic (PV) energy in the global energy mix has expanded considerably in recent years. In 2023, PV represented 74% of newly installed renewable capacity worldwide [1]. With a levelized cost of energy (LCOE) at 0.044 USD/kW, which is significantly lower than fossil fuels, PV has become an economically viable and environmentally sustainable energy source [2].

Extensive land use is a major limitation that PV faces. Meanwhile, a surging global population heightens food production demands, requiring more farmland and intensifying land competition, particularly in fertile regions like Europe [3], [4]. According to German market data, PV module prices have fallen 97% over the past 24 years, while land prices have more than tripled [5].

The increasing gap between the declining cost of photovoltaic technology and the rising price of agricultural land accentuates the importance of dual-use land strategies. Agrivoltaics integrate agriculture and photovoltaic energy on shared land, resulting in enhanced land efficiency [6], [7]. To accelerate the deployment of agrivoltaics, it is essential to minimize structural costs to enhance accessibility and reduce the LCOE [8]. One effective strategy for achieving this is through vertical mounting, which helps to lower initial investments and, consequently, the LCOE in agrivoltaics [9]. Bifacial modules, which can capture energy from both sides, are particularly well-suited for vertical installations [10]. Research has highlighted the advantages of East-West oriented bifacial modules in various conditions, including elevated latitudes [11], [12] and desert regions facing soiling issues [13], [14].

Bifacial solar modules face rear-side shading challenges. According to [15], [16], junction box positioning can block up to 45% of light on impacted cells, thereby diminishing module energy yield.

In 2023, AESOLAR company unveiled the "TERRA" PV module, engineered for agrivoltaic applications to minimize self-shading from the junction box and frame, enhancing overall yield. This article aims to precisely evaluate the performance of this PV module compared to standard modules.

2 METHODOLOGY

2.1 New module design

The TERRA module utilizes half-cell TOPCon technology, providing high resistance to wind and snow and enhanced bifaciality by minimizing rear-side shading. Redesigned for durability, it improves performance in vertical installations, ensuring it withstands over 20 years of environmental stress [17]. Conventional PV modules experience rear-side shading from frames, junction boxes, and cables (**Figure 1a**), which decreases energy gain. TERRA overcomes these limitations through an innovative interconnection layout and optimized junction box placement (**Figure 1b**), thereby reducing self-shading and improving overall energy yield.

This paper presents a summarized version of our recent study. A more detailed and extended version of this work has been published in Renewable Energy [18], where comprehensive analyses and additional results are provided.

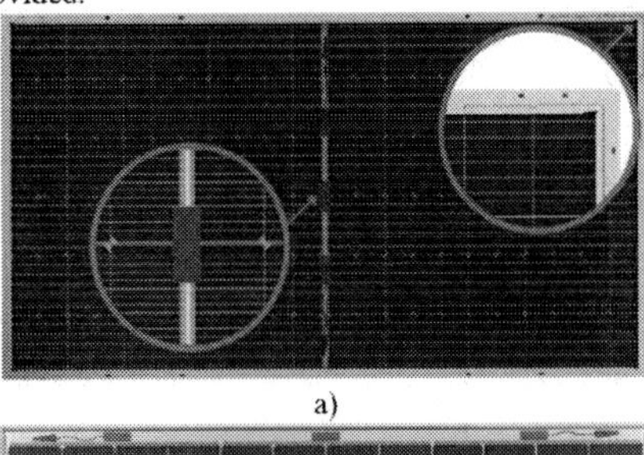

a)

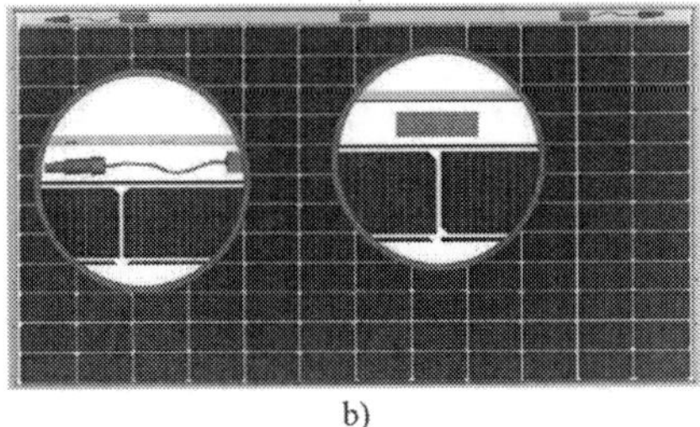

b)

Figure 1: Rear view of: a) Standard module, b) TERRA with new design and reduced self-shading

2.2 SPICE MODEL

Accurate models are essential for comparing the energy yield of TERRA to that of standard modules. While traditional simulation tools are useful for system-level analysis, they often fail to accurately capture the effects of shading and performance at the cell level. In this study, we employ a SPICE-based model to simulate photovoltaic (PV) modules, allowing for a detailed evaluation of thermal and electrical losses. The model has been developed and thoroughly tested by Hanifi et al. [19].

Both modules, rated at 420 W with 108 cells, are modeled in SPICE. Each bifacial cell is represented by two parallel cells, and the one-diode approach ensures a balance between simplicity and accuracy. The key parameters and their assumed values are listed in **Table 1**.

Table 1: List of key parameters used in the model

Parameter		Value
Nominal power of modules	P [W]	420W
Number of cells	n	108
Cell size	S [mm^2]	16562
Series resistance	R_S [Ω]	0.00436
Shunt resistance	R_{Sh} [Ω]	1000
Bifaciality	B_f [%]	85

2.3 Shading area

In standard modules, 12 cells are shaded by junction boxes, and one cell per side is shaded by cables during vertical installation. As shown in **Figure 1**, all cells around the rear side of the module are impacted by frame shading. All shading elements are measured and imported to the model. By contrast, TERRA's updated design—with optimized junction box placement and slightly wider glass—eliminates self-shading, ensuring uniform irradiance across all 108 cells.

Relocating the junction box to the edge of the module presented some manufacturing challenges, especially with the gluing process at the top corner and the framing. These issues were addressed by adjusting the module dimensions and incorporating an inactive area. Since customers prioritize energy yield (kWh) over efficiency, we optimized the edge distances for better performance. This resulted in a slightly larger module area and a minor reduction in efficiency.

2.4 Python script

While SPICE provides detailed analysis, it processes only one input step at a time, defined as front irradiance, rear irradiance, and temperature. Each iteration produces an output file with parameters such as maximum power. Calculating annual energy yield requires hourly inputs for all 8760 hours. Consequently, performing simulations across multiple locations and conditions is time-consuming.

To overcome SPICE's computational limits, a Python-based framework was developed to automate simulations and calculate energy yield. The workflow includes three steps: 1) preparing input data in an Excel file containing 8,760 hourly values of front irradiance, rear irradiance, and temperature. 2) A SPICE model defining circuit parameters and shading assumptions simulates I-V characteristics in steady-state. 3) A Python script updates the netlist for each hour, executes SPICE, and generates output files containing I–V curves and key parameters. The script extracts maximum power (P_max) from all

outputs, compiles results into Excel, and sums hourly values to determine annual energy yield. This integration enables efficient comparison of TERRA and standard modules. The overall simulation workflow is illustrated in the flowchart shown in **Figure 2**.

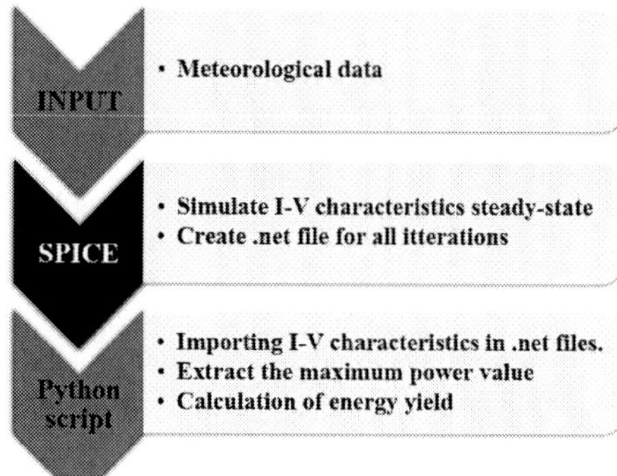

Figure 2: A step-by-step Python-based framework integrating SPICE simulations for hourly energy yield calculation

3 RESULTS

3.1 South-faced vs. vertical East-West

Figure 3 illustrates the difference in the energy production patterns of the TERRA module in vertical east–west and south-facing installations, based on meteorological data from Athens. In the east–west configuration, the module receives more irradiance during the morning and late afternoon hours, leading to higher energy production in these periods compared to the south-facing installation. However, around noon, the south-facing module benefits from stronger vertical radiation, resulting in greater energy generation. A detailed comparison of the two configurations shows annual energy yields of 752 kWh for the vertical east–west installation and 785 kWh for the south-facing installation. Although the east–west orientation results in approximately 4–5% lower total yield, it provides a broader daily generation profile.

3.2 Terra vs. Standard

Both TERRA modules and standard modules (with 108 cells and a power output of 420 W) were modeled, differing only in rear-side self-shading. **Figure 4** illustrates the hourly energy output for both types of modules over the course of a year. In the morning, the output is similar for both, as the front side primarily captures irradiation. However, in the afternoon, the rear side becomes more significant. In this period, self-shading negatively impacts the performance of the standard module, while TERRA achieves up to 7% higher output in the evening.

Figure 5 presents a month-by-month comparison of the energy production of the TERRA module versus that of the standard module in Athens. The primary axis illustrates the absolute monthly energy output for both modules, while the secondary axis quantifies the relative difference in energy production between the TERRA and standard modules for each month. The results show that the TERRA module consistently outperforms the standard module, achieving an energy gain ranging from 3.07% to 3.56%. This variation shows how the impact of self-shading mitigation changes with the seasons.

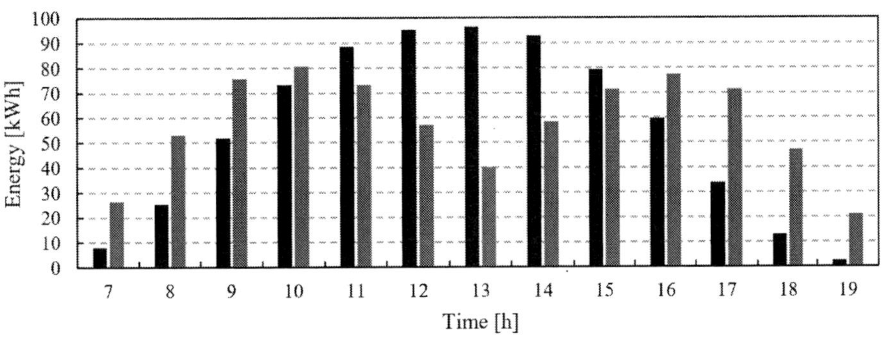

Figure 3: Annual energy production per hour of vertical E-W and south-faced (tilt=30º) installation of TERRA in Athens, For both installations, ground albedo = 0.2, height from ground = 1 meter, bifaciality factor = 85%, and the temperature is equal to the hourly temperature of Athens.

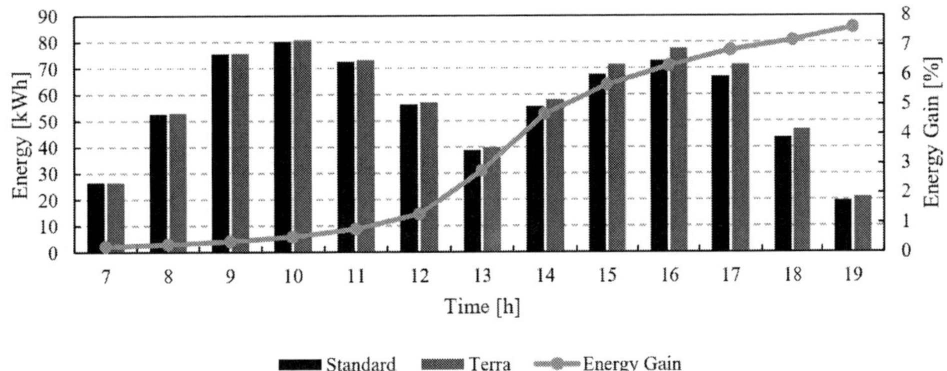

Figure 4: Annual hourly energy production of TERRA and standard modules with vertical E–W installation in Athens, The secondary axis represents TERRA's hourly energy gain relative to the standard module.

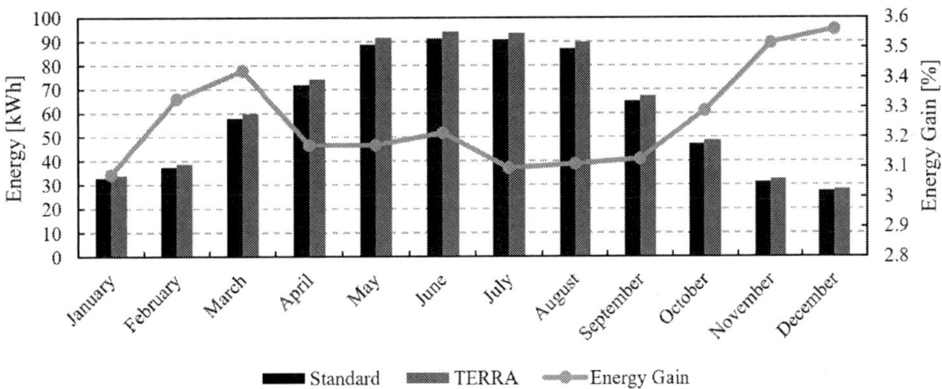

Figure 5: Monthly comparison of energy production between TERRA and the Standard module in Athens. The secondary axis indicates the difference in energy production for each month, showing that TERRA provides an energy gain ranging from 3.07% to 3.56%.

3.3 Global investigation

The model results indicate that the TERRA module delivers superior performance in sunny locations such as Athens. To validate these findings, the analysis was extended to additional cities with diverse meteorological conditions. By incorporating variations in solar radiation, temperature, and atmospheric effects, the robustness of the model predictions was thoroughly evaluated. The detailed results for each location are presented in **Figure 6**, while the overall workflow is shown in **Figure 2**. Meteorological data from each city, combined with the base SPICE model, served as inputs for the simulations. Following the procedure described in Section 2.4, a Python script was used to compute the annual energy output of both modules for each city. Finally, the difference in yearly energy production between TERRA and the standard module was determined for several locations.

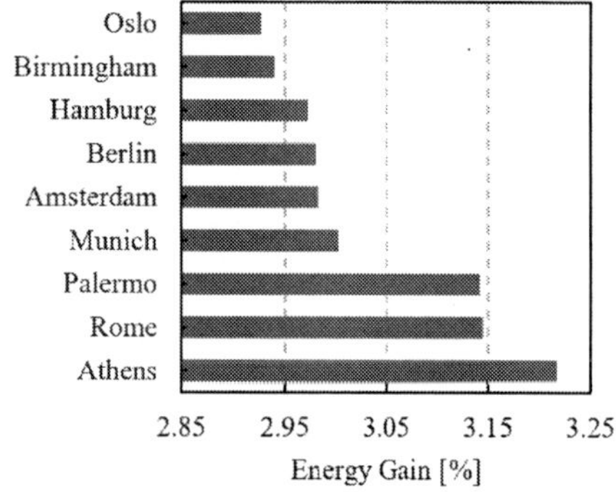

Figure 6: Energy yield differences between TERRA and standard modules across European cities. TERRA demonstrates an energy gain of 2.94% to 3.22%. Higher gains were observed in locations with greater solar irradiance.

4   CONCLUSIONS

The results of this study highlight the advantages of the TERRA module in vertical installations. To examine these benefits, both TERRA and standard modules were modeled using SPICE, with each design comprising 108 cells and a total power output of 420 W. The main difference between the two modules is the rear-side self-shading present in the standard module. While the SPICE model generates output for a single operating point, assessing annual energy production requires consideration of 8,760 operating points. To tackle this challenge, a Python script was developed to automate the SPICE simulations and calculate energy output with hourly resolution. This framework processes the hourly irradiance incident on the module surfaces and the cell temperature as inputs, enabling an accurate estimation of the energy yield.

Based on meteorological data for Athens, the TERRA module achieves approximately 3.217% higher energy yield in vertical installations compared to the standard module. This demonstrates the potential of the new design to enhance performance under real conditions. Extending the analysis to additional cities offers valuable insights for both researchers and investors, supporting more informed decision-making. As represented in **Figure 6**, the results consistently confirm the superior performance of the TERRA module across multiple locations. Its design makes it particularly effective for applications such as solar-powered fencing, photovoltaic noise barriers, agrivoltaics, and urban environments with limited space.

5   REFERENCES

[1] R. Alfaro-Pelico, "IRENA (2024), World Energy Transitions Outlook 2024: 1.5°C Pathway, International Renewable Energy Agency," 2024. [Online]. Available: www.irena.org

[2] Technology Collaboration Programme by International Energy Agency Photovoltaic Power Systems Programme PVPS Task 1 Strategic PV Analysis and Outreach. 2024. [Online]. Available: www.iea-pvps.org

[3] M. Trommsdorff, M. Hopf, O. Hörnle, M. Berwind, S. Schindele, and K. Wydra, "Can synergies in agriculture through an integration of solar energy reduce the cost of agrivoltaics? An economic analysis in apple farming," Appl Energy, vol. 350, p. 121619, Nov. 2023, doi: 10.1016/j.apenergy.2023.121619.

[4] M. Barragán Sánchez-Lanuza, I. Lillo-Bravo, G. Egea, and J. M. Delgado-Sanchez, "Spectral irradiance, ground and crop dynamic reflectance: Key determinants in predicting photocurrent for agrovoltaic systems," Energy Convers Manag, vol. 312, p. 118572, Jul. 2024, doi: 10.1016/j.enconman.2024.118572.

[5] Fraunhofer Ise, "Agrivoltaics: Opportunities for Agriculture and the Energy Transition." [Online]. Available: www.ise.fraunhofer.de

[6] S. Amaducci, X. Yin, and M. Colauzzi, "Agrivoltaic systems to optimise land use for electric energy production," Appl Energy, vol. 220, pp. 545–561, Jun. 2018, doi: 10.1016/j.apenergy.2018.03.081.

[7] A. Garrod, S. N. Hussain, and A. Ghosh, "The technical and economic potential for crop based agrivoltaics in the United Kingdom," Solar Energy, vol. 277, p. 112744, Jul. 2024, doi: 10.1016/j.solener.2024.112744.

[8] M. Trommsdorff et al., "Combining food and energy production: Design of an agrivoltaic system applied in arable and vegetable farming in Germany," Renewable and Sustainable Energy Reviews, vol. 140, p. 110694, Apr. 2021, doi: 10.1016/j.rser.2020.110694.

[9] K.-W. Hwang and C.-Y. Lee, "Estimating the Deterministic and Stochastic Levelized Cost of the Energy of Fence-Type Agrivoltaics," Energies (Basel), vol. 17, no. 8, p. 1932, Apr. 2024, doi: 10.3390/en17081932.

[10] T. M. Mahim, A. H. M. A. Rahim, and M. M. Rahman, "Review of Mono- and Bifacial Photovoltaic Technologies: A Comparative Study," IEEE J Photovolt, vol. 14, no. 3, pp. 375–396, May 2024, doi: 10.1109/JPHOTOV.2024.3366698.

[11] S. Guo, T. M. Walsh, and M. Peters, "Vertically mounted bifacial photovoltaic modules: A global analysis," Energy, vol. 61, pp. 447–454, Nov. 2013, doi: 10.1016/j.energy.2013.08.040.

[12] M. R. Khan, A. Hanna, X. Sun, and M. A. Alam, "Vertical bifacial solar farms: Physics, design, and global optimization," Appl Energy, vol. 206, pp. 240–248, Nov. 2017, doi: 10.1016/j.apenergy.2017.08.042.

[13] M. Kivambe, A. Abdallah, B. Figgis, G. Scabbia, M. Abdelrahim, and J. Lopez-Garcia, "Assessing vertical east-west bifacial photovoltaic systems in desert environments: Energy yield and soiling

mitigation," Sep. 01, 2024, Elsevier Ltd. doi: 10.1016/j.solener.2024.112835.

[14]   U. Bin Qasim, M. H. Riaz, and H. Imran, "Investigation of soiling effects for east/west vertical bifacial and north/south tilted monofacial photovoltaic farms," Energy & Environment, vol. 35, no. 6, pp. 2991–3009, Sep. 2024, doi: 10.1177/0958305X221143410.

[15]   A. González-Moreno, D. Mazzeo, A. Dolara, E. Ogliari, and S. Leva, "Outdoor Performance Comparison of Bifacial and Monofacial Photovoltaic Modules in Temperate Climate and Industrial-like Rooftops," Applied Sciences, vol. 14, no. 13, p. 5714, Jun. 2024, doi: 10.3390/app14135714.

[16]   R. O. Yakubu, L. D. Mensah, D. A. Quansah, and M. S. Adaramola, "A systematic literature review of the bifacial photovoltaic module and its applications," The Journal of Engineering, vol. 2024, no. 8, Aug. 2024, doi: 10.1049/tje2.12421.

[17]   H. Hanifi et al., "Optimum PV module interconnection layout and mounting orientation to reduce inhomogeneous soiling losses in desert environments," Solar Energy, vol. 203, pp. 267–274, Jun. 2020, doi: 10.1016/j.solener.2020.04.025.

[18]   P. Pourshafi, A. Maixner, A. Bakhtiari, and H. Hanifi, "Performance analysis of a novel photovoltaic module design for vertical applications: Mitigate self-shading of bifacial modules," Renew Energy, vol. 256, p. 124186, Jan. 2026, doi: 10.1016/j.renene.2025.124186.

[19]   H. Hanifi, C. Pfau, M. Turek, and J. Schneider, "A practical optical and electrical model to estimate the power losses and quantification of different heat sources in silicon based PV modules," Renew Energy, vol. 127, pp. 602–612, Nov. 2018, doi: 10.1016/j.renene.2018.04.060.

PERFORMANCE EVALUATION OF A NEW DESIGN PHOTOVOLTAIC MODULE WITH REDUCED SELF-SHADING

Pouya Pourshafi[1*], Andreas Maixner[1], Hamed Hanifi[1]

1 AESOLAR, Messerschmittring 54, 86343 Koenigsbrunn, Germany
*Corresponding author: p.pourshafi@ae-solar.com

MOTIVATION

- Photovoltaics' key challenge: substantial land usage.
- As PV costs drop, optimal installation becomes less critical.
- Smart choice: Vertical agrivoltaics.
- Major challenge:
  - Self-shading on the rear side.
- TERRA, a new module designed by AESOLAR.

SUMMARY

- A new PV design with no self-shading from junction boxes, frame, or cables on the rear side is developed to maximize the bifaciality at the module level.
- The new module(TERRA) achieves an energy gain of 2.94–3.22% over a standard module across European cities, with higher gain in energy yield in regions of higher solar irradiance.
- The new design with elimination of self-shading achieves a higher energy yield in all locations, which can be a factor in reducing the Levelized cost of electricity.

TERRA shows up to 3.21% higher energy yield compared to standard butterfly design modules when vertically mounted.

METHODOLOGY

Module designs

Standard module

- Self-shading:
  - junction box
  - Frame
  - cabling

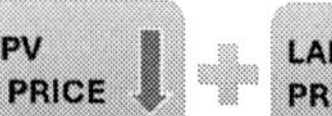
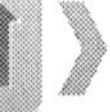

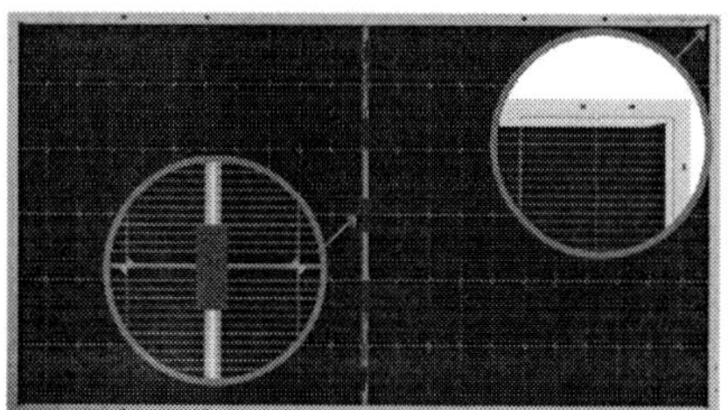

Figure 1: Rear view of a standard module, highlighting the self-shading elements.

TERRA module

- TERRA removes self-shading on the rear-side by redesigning the circuit:
  - No self-shading from junction boxes cables, and frame.

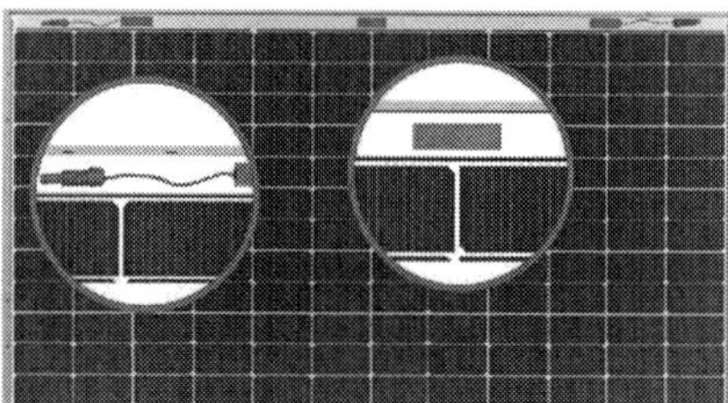

Figure 2: Rear view of a TERRA, highlighting the modifications made to eliminate self-shading.

PERFORMANCE ANALYSIS:

- Model:
  - IV characteristics: SPICE model based on Hanifi et al.[1]
  - Energy yield: Developed an hourly-scale Python model.
- Modules:
  - 108 cells, 420W
  - Same electrical characteristics
- Self-shading of standard module is included.

INPUT
- Meteorological data

SPICE
- Simulate I-V characteristics steady-state
- Create .net file for all itterations

Python script
- Importing I-V characteristics in .net files.
- Extract the maximum power value
- Calculation of energy yield

RESULTS

- Average hourly energy yield over the year shows: In the afternoon, direct rear-side illumination accentuates the effect of removing self-shading. Afternoon hours: TERRA shows an energy yield gain of up to 7.6% higher than the standard module.

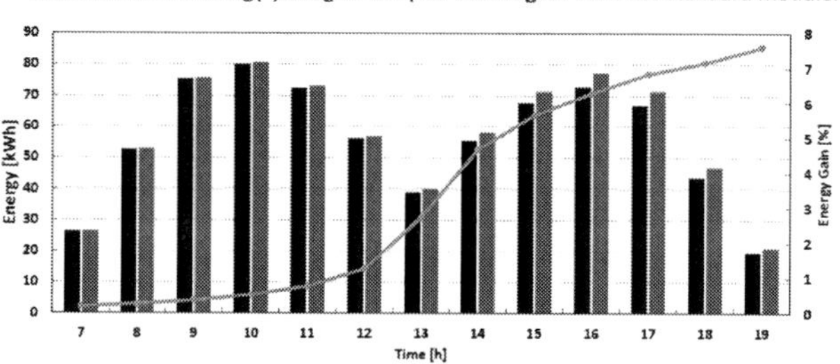

Figure 3: Annual average hourly energy production based on meteorological data from Athens. The secondary axis shows TERRA's energy gain relative to the standard module.

- Figure 4 shows that the TERRA module produces 3.07–3.56% more energy than the standard module across different months.

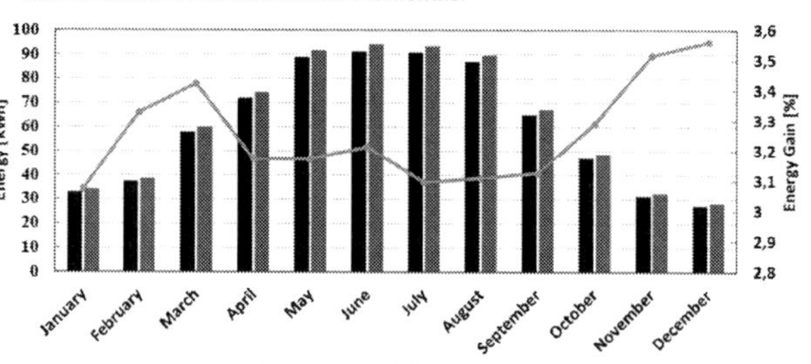

Figure 4: Monthly average annual energy production using meteorological data from Athens. The secondary axis indicates TERRA's energy gain compared to the standard module.

- Investigation in various cities demonstrates that TERRA offers enhanced yield performance by effectively mitigating self-shading.

Figure 5: Energy yield differences between TERRA and standard modules across European cities. TERRA demonstrates an energy gain of 2.94% to 3.22%, with higher gains observed in locations with greater solar irradiance.

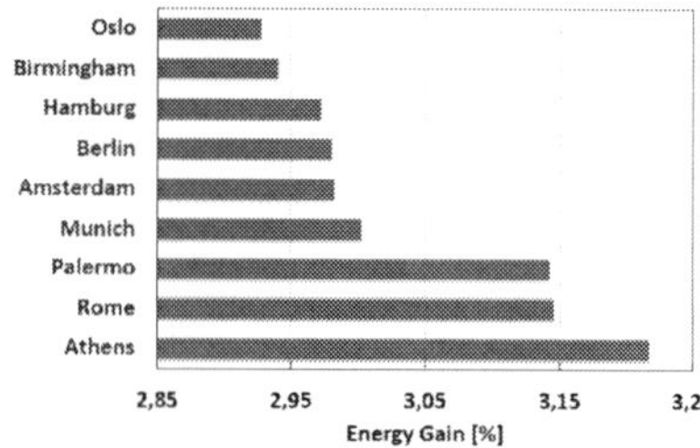

[1] H. Hanifi et al. "Reduced Shading Effect of Half-Cell Modules - Measurement and Simulations," EUPVSEC, Hamburg, 2015

MATERIALS ASSESSMENT FOR PV-T MODULES THERMAL PERFORMANCE IMPROVEMENT

Author(s): L. Cano[1]*, R. Simón-Allué[1], R. Villén[1], Y. Lara[1], I. Guedea[1]
Company / Institute(s): [1]ENDEF
Address(es): *lucia.cano@endef.com

ABSTRACT: Photovoltaic-thermal (PV-T) collectors integrate solar thermal and photovoltaic technologies into a single system, enabling simultaneous production of electricity and heat. The efficiency of PV-T collectors is directly linked to effective heat transfer through the system layers, which impacts overall thermal and electrical performance. This study evaluates the role of adhesives, the attachment media between the photovoltaic (PV) panel and the heat exchanger (HX); and insulating materials, which constitute the back-side of the PV-T panel, in optimizing heat transfer and improving the efficiency of PV-T collectors. Two small-scale prototypes were developed to test selected adhesives and insulations under real-world conditions. The investigation considers not only thermal performance but also economic feasibility, durability, and ease of manufacture. Final conclusions integrate experimental data with a one-dimensional Python simulation, identifying the most conductive adhesive and the most effective insulating material. The findings contribute to the development of a more efficient and cost-effective new PV-T collector design.
Keywords: Hybrid photovoltaic-thermal (PV-T) collector, adhesives, insulations, experimental testing, heat transfer modelling.

1 INTRODUCTION

Photovoltaic-thermal (PV-T) collectors combine solar thermal and photovoltaic technologies in a single panel, producing electricity and heat simultaneously. This hybrid technology may be used for diverse applications, such as pool heating, domestic hot water production, and heat production at low temperature for industrial processes (Herrando et al., 2014; Kalogirou & Tripanagnostopoulos, 2006). However, the temperature requirements of the final application also determine the most suitable PV-T collector type for each case (Herrando et al., 2014; Ramos et al., 2017). PV-T collectors usually have a photovoltaic (PV) laminate and an absorber or heat exchanger (HX), through which thermal energy is extracted.

This work aims to study the influence of different materials on the heat transfer along the PV-T collector, focusing on the impact of the attachment media between the PV panel and the absorber, as well as the back insulation of the PV-T modules.

PVT collector materials have direct impact on heat transfer through layers and, therefore, are related to the energy performance of the PV-T collector (Abdelrazik et al., 2018; Michael et al., 2015; Zhang et al., 2012). Thermal performance is conditioned by the heat transfer between the PV and the HX, as well as by keeping the PV-T panel isolated to avoid ambient losses (Herrando et al., 2019; Joshi & Dhoble, 2018). Moreover, PV panels reduce its performance ratio operating at high temperatures. Extracting heat to the heat exchanger also raises the electrical performance (Dubey et al., 2013; Rawat et al., 2017).

The final objective of the study is to assess the most adequate materials for a new PV-T collector design, in order to maximize the heat transfer through all the layers and, in consequence, its thermal and electrical efficiency. Economic and durability aspects will be additionally considered in the assessment, as well as each material's handling, especially for adhesives, in order to facilitate the PV-T collector manufacturing as much as possible.

2 EXPERIMENTAL SETUP DESCRIPTION

2.1 Prototypes

Two small-scale prototypes are prepared and evaluated in order to determine the suitability of the materials in terms of heat transfer and insulation performance.

A range of materials (both adhesives and insulations) have been reviewed and two sets have been selected for the testing. Apart from the costs, which have been used for both; application modes, ease of handling during manufacturing and thermal conductivity (ranged between 0.18 to 3.40 W/m·K) have been used as criteria for choosing adhesives, while insulations have been selected based on the thermal insulation properties (from 0.025 to 0.037 W/m·K), their physical characteristics and handling. **Table I** describes each prototype and its tested materials.

Each prototype consists of a PV panel with four test probes made of the material to be tested along with the absorber, each one sized 30x30 cm. Each prototype has the same layer structure (PV panel, adhesive, absorber, insulation and backsheet). **Figure 1** shows Prototype 1 disposition in detail.

Prototype 1 tests four back insulations, with the PV attached to the HX with the same adhesive, while Prototype 2 tests four adhesives, maintaining the same insulation. Both prototypes contain a glass-glass PV panel (unglazed PV with a laminated glass in place of the tedlar backsheet). The PV panel incorporates N-type and TOPCon cell technology, with 600 Wp of maximum power and a 22.21% of efficiency at STC.

Table I: Prototypes 1 and 2 description

Prototype 1 - Insulations		
Probe	Thickness (m)	Thermal conductivity (W/m·K)
1	0.025	0.037
2	0.025	0.032
3	0.025	0.025
4	0.030	0.025
Prototype 2 - Adhesives		
Probe	Thickness (m)	Thermal conductivity (W/m·K)
5	0.00013	0.16
6	0.00013	0.18
7	0.0002	1.5
8	0.002	3.4

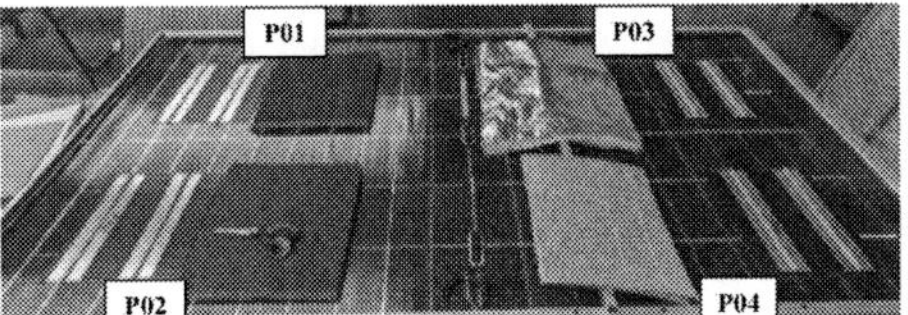

Figure 1: Prototype 1 design and assembly

2.2 Test procedure

In order to measure and analyse heat transfer performance, temperature sensors are placed in each prototype. Only heat transfer due to solar radiation is being taken into account; thus, thermal and electrical circuits are disconnected. Experimental tests are performed in Zaragoza, Spain (latitude 41.716), during winter months. Prototypes are tested under natural conditions, exposed to a quasi-constant solar in-plane irradiance between 300-420 W/m² (horizontal). Panels are placed in horizontal 120 cm height benches.

Pt100 temperature sensors are distributed in each layer to measure every prototype: two under the PV laminate, two between the absorber and the insulation for each probe, one in the back side of the insulation for each probe. Therefore, each prototype counts with 15 precision probes (described in **Figure 2**). An additional methacrylate layer is added to the probes to fasten the assembly of all the materials and ensure a proper contact between components.

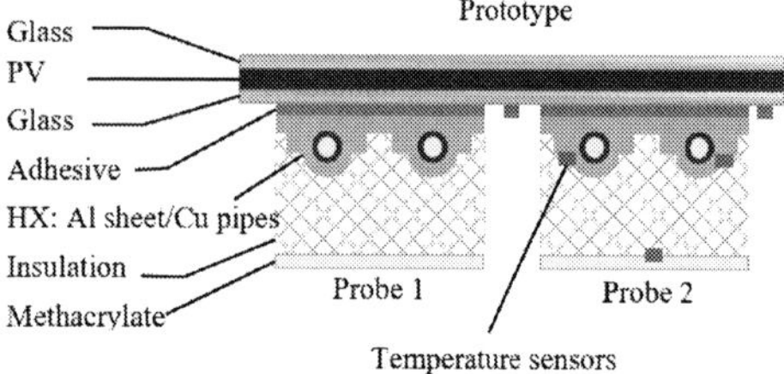

Figure 2: Prototype layers and temperature sensors distribution

Environmental data (irradiance, ambient temperature and wind speed) are also measured (see **Table II**) and registered with a frequency of 1 min in a PLC Modicon 241. Each test is performed at least for 2 days with similar weather conditions and 4 days in total. The test starts when the panel is exposed to sun and lasts at least one hour. The first 30-40 minutes of exposure are intended to allow the prototypes to acclimatize until they become stable. All temperature sensors measured the same value before exposing the panel to the sun.

Table II: Instrumentation and sensors

Physical property	Sensor model	Range	Precision
Temperature	Pt100	-50-400 °C	± 0.05 °C
Irradiance	Pyranometer, LP-PYRA-03 AC	0-2000 W/m²	± 0.025 W/m²
Wind velocity	4.3303.22.007, Thies Clima	0-50 m/s	± 0.3 m/s

2.3 One-dimensional simulation

One-dimensional model is developed using Python for simulating temperatures in each layer of the PV-T collector and prototypes. This simulation is intended to be validated with the experimental data, in order to implement it in a more complex model for estimating PV-T panel efficiency and both electrical and thermal productions.

Figure 3 shows the PV-T layer configuration and the energy flows considered.

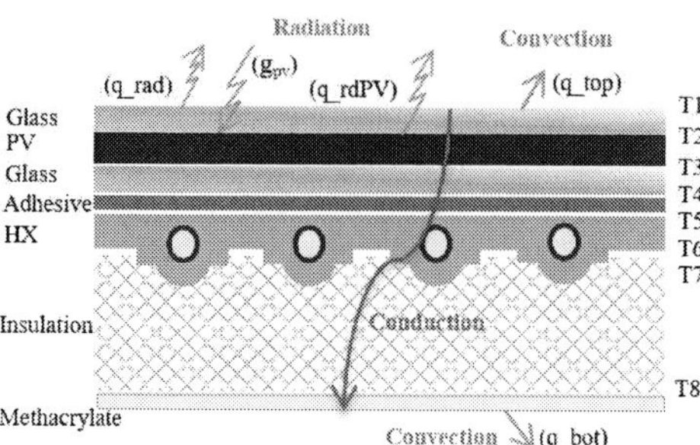

Figure 3: PV-T collector layers and energy flows

The PV-T collector model is developed under the following assumptions:
- radiation absorption in the glass layer and the collector frame is negligible; (Agarwal & Garg, 1994; Herrando et al., 2019)
- the ambient temperature is uniform around the collector and heat losses from the PV panel frame and the borders of each probe are negligible (Cristofari et al., 2009; Notton et al., 2005);
- the PV cells and the thermal absorber are in perfect thermal contact; (Herrando et al., 2019)
- solar irradiance and wind speed are uniform over the collector surface area. (Herrando et al., 2019)

The model is run under steady-state conditions (Herrando et al., 2019; Zondag et al., 2003). Energy conservation equation is used for defining heat transfer through layers. In addition, there is no fluid running into the copper tubes so there is no thermal energy generated and the electric circuit of the PV panel is disconnected, so there is no electricity production. Above all these assumptions, boundary conditions for these equations are detailed below:

Top Layer. The main losses on the top of the PV-T collector are due to forced convection caused by wind (q_{top}, see eq. (2)) and radiation from the glass to the sky (q_{rad}, see eq. (3)). The convective heat transfer coefficient depends on wind velocity (v_{wind}) and various expressions are given in bibliography for its estimation. In previous works (Bhattarai et al., 2012; Notton et al., 2005; Rejeb et al., 2015) for similar applications, validated with experimental data, expression showed in eq. (1) provided accurate values. Initially, the model is based on this experimentally obtained h_{wind} approximation, but has been adjusted according to the results of the tests. Hence:

$$h_{wind} = 4,2 + 2,9 \cdot v_{wind} \quad (1)$$

$$q_{top} = h_{wind} \cdot (T_{glass} - T_{amb}) \quad (2)$$

$$q_{rad} = \varepsilon_{glass,long\lambda} \cdot \sigma \cdot (T_{glass}^{4} - T_{sky}^{4}) \quad (3)$$

where T_{glass} is the glass temperature in the above surface, T_{sky} is the sky temperature, which is calculated as $T_{sky} = 0.0552 \cdot T_{amb}^{1.5}$, with the ambient temperature (T_{amb}) in Kelvin, $\varepsilon_{glass,long\lambda}$ is the glass emissivity at long wavelengths and σ is the Stefan-Boltzmann constant ($\sigma = 5.67 \cdot 10^{-8}$ W/(m²·K⁴)) (Cristofari et al., 2009; Notton et al., 2005).

PV layer. The PV layer absorbs the fraction of the total solar irradiance (G_{inc}) that is not reflected by the glass (g_{PV}), calculated as:

$$g_{PV} = G_{inc} \cdot \tau_{g,short\lambda} \cdot \alpha_{PV,short\lambda} \quad (4)$$

where $\tau_{g,short\lambda}$ is the transmittance of the glass while $\alpha_{PV,short\lambda}$ is the absorptivity of the PV panel, both at short wavelengths (Tiwari & Sodha, 2006; Zondag et al., 2003).

The radiative heat flux emitted by the PV layer at long wavelengths, which is not absorbed by the glass, is lost to the environment. This radiative heat loss (q_{rdPV}) can be estimated as follows:

$$q_{rdPV} = \varepsilon_{PV,long\lambda} \cdot \tau_{g,long\lambda} \cdot \sigma \cdot \left(T_{PV}{}^4 - T_{sky}{}^4 \right) \quad (5)$$

where T_{PV} is the temperature of the PV layer. $\tau_{g,long\lambda}$ is the transmittance of the glass and $\varepsilon_{PV,long\lambda}$ is the emissivity of the PV layer, both for long wavelengths (Tiwari & Sodha, 2006; Zondag et al., 2003).

Back insulation layer. The main loss in the back layer of the PVT collector is due to forced convection caused by wind (q_{bot}, see eq. (6)), calculated similarly to q_{top}:

$$q_{bot} = h_{wind} \cdot (T_{metha} - T_{amb}) \quad (6)$$

where T_{metha} is the temperature in the bottom side of the methacrylate layer.

Heat conduction. For every layer, it is considered perfect thermal contact, which allows a heat flow from the hottest layers to the coolest, in contact with the ambient. For every layer, heat conduction equation is defined as:

$$q_{layer,a} = \frac{k_a}{\delta_a} \cdot (T_{a\_in} - T_{a\_out}) \quad (7)$$

where k_a is the thermal conductivity coefficient of the layer, δ_a corresponds to the thickness of each layer and T_{a_in} and T_{a_out} relay to the temperatures in the top and the bottom of each layer. The top temperature of each layer is the bottom of the one above, due to the assumptions made previously.

Introducing environmental data (wind velocity, irradiance and ambient temperature) in the one-dimensional model, temperatures in each layer and heat fluxes between them are obtained. Conduction, convection and radiation can be studied as well as the heat and energy losses to the ambient. For comparing both experimental and simulated temperatures, only results from the moment the system has stabilized onwards are considered.

The model also included T_{cell}, the theorical temperature of the PV cells (Hajji et al., 2014; Santos et al., 2022), calculated as:

$$T_{cell} = ((T_{NOCT} - 20) / 800) \cdot G_{inc} + T_{amb} \quad (8)$$

where T_{NOCT} is the nominal operating cell temperature, characteristic of each PV panel.

A statistics analysis is additionally performed in order to evaluate the numerical goodness of the simulation. The Percentage Error is calculated for the period in which panel temperature is already stabilized.

$$Percentage\ Error = \frac{|y_{exp} - y_{stm}|}{y_{exp}} \cdot 100 \quad (9)$$

Table III: Properties of the PVT collector layers

Layer	Parameter		Wavelengths	Value
Top layer	$\varepsilon_{g,short\lambda}$	Emissivity (-)	Short	0.05
	$\tau_{g,short\lambda}$	Transmittance (-)	Short	0.94
	$\varepsilon_{g,long\lambda}$	Emissivity (-)	Long	0.86
	$\tau_{g,long\lambda}$	Transmittance (-)	Long	0.06
PV layer	$\alpha_{PV,short\lambda}$	Solar absorption coefficient (-)	Short	0.95
	$\varepsilon_{PV,long\lambda}$	Emissivity (-)	Long	0.89

3 RESULTS AND DISCUSSION

Experimental tests have been conducted for **Prototype 1 and Prototype 2** to analyse the influence of the four insulations and four adhesive materials on heat transfer with a glass-glass PV. The results obtained provide qualitative information on the performance of each test sample. Figures containing the results are discussed below. Temperatures of the probes are represented in Celsius. Each Figure contains the collector absorber temperatures of each probe, simulated (solid lines) and experimental (dashed lines), as well as environmental (T_{amb}) and cell (T_{cell}) temperatures.

3.1 PV temperatures comparison

Both experimental and simulated results have been analysed firstly considering only the PV layers, taking temperatures from the free PV area where there are no heat exchanger nor material probes. **Figure 4** and **Figure 5** show experimental and simulated PV panel temperatures, as well as ambient temperature and theoretical PV cell temperature.

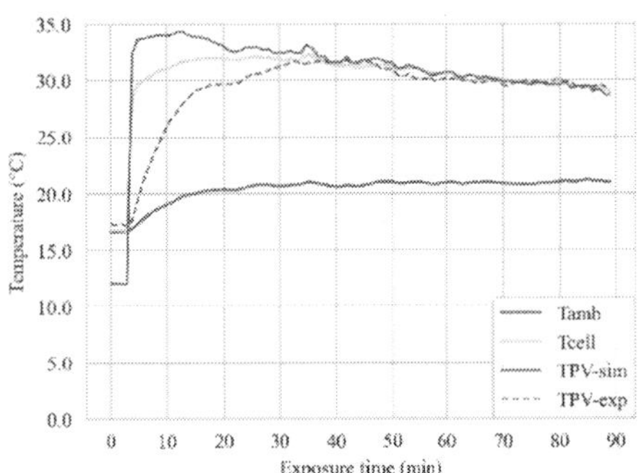

Figure 4: PV panel temperatures. Windless day

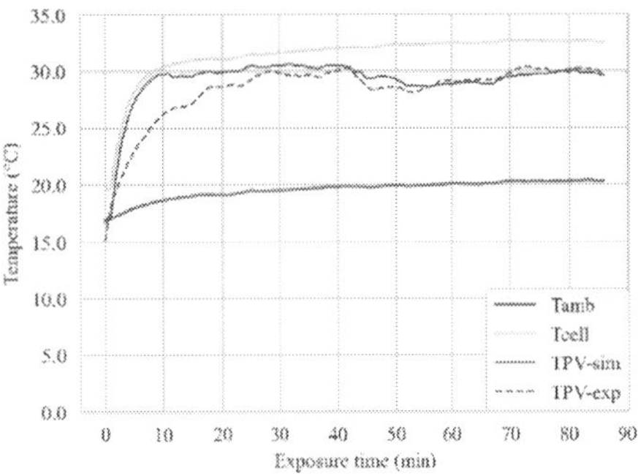

Figure 5: PV panel temperatures. Windy day

In these figures, simulated values do match experimental data, which means the one-dimensional simulation can reproduce experimental temperatures and heat transfer fluxes through the PV panel layers. However, it can be noticed that the simulated results do not match the first few minutes of the experimental tests, in which the panels are still acclimatizing. This is explained because the one-dimensional model has no inertia, unlike the experimental data, as it is performed under steady-state conditions.

It is significant to notice differences in the theoretical

temperature of the PV cells between windy and windless days. During windless or very low wind days T_{cell} matches both experimental and simulated PV temperatures once they are stabilized; however, this matching does not exist in windy days, where the T_{cell} is higher, due to the fact that T_{cell} definition does not take into account wind effect.

3.2 Insulating materials comparison

Small-scale tests were conducted for Prototype 1 in order to determine which insulation kept more heat inside the absorber.

Temperatures of the heat exchanger are represented for the four insulating materials (**Table I**). $T_{1\text{-exp}}$-$T_{4\text{-exp}}$ correspond with the mean of both temperature sensors placed inside the **heat absorber** (see **Figure 2**) for each probe. **Figure 6** shows results for a test performed with windless weather conditions while **Figure 7** shows results obtained during a windy day.

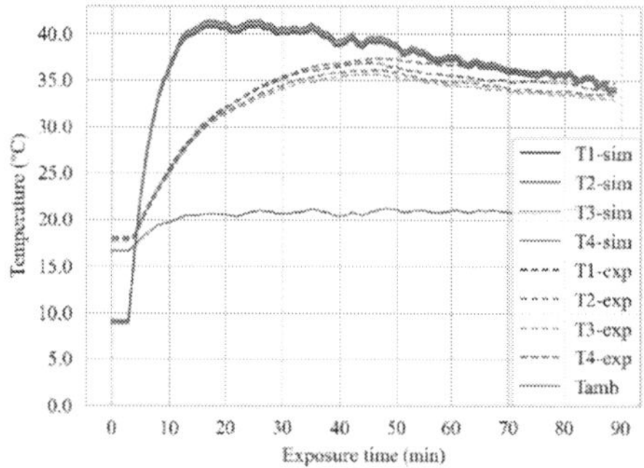

Figure 6: Prototype 1 heat absorber temperatures for each probe. Windless day

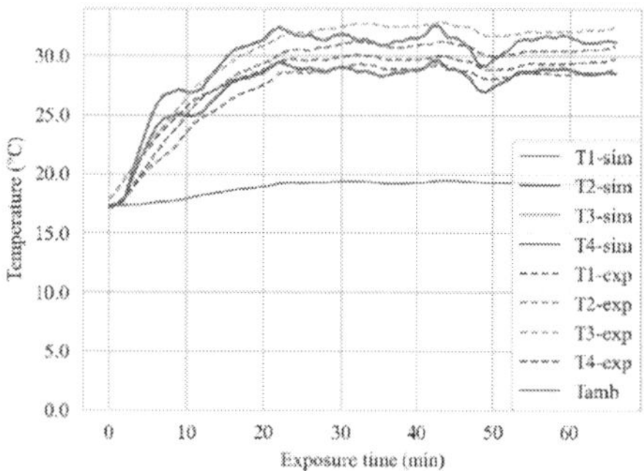

Figure 7: Prototype 1 heat absorber temperatures for each probe. Windy day

Experimental results reveal higher temperatures during windless days in probes 1 and 2, with a difference of 2,5 °C with probes 3 and 4; while this difference between probes is barely noticeable for simulated results.

On the contrary, on windy days (more than 4 m/s) probes 3 and 4 are the ones reaching higher temperatures during experimental tests. Moreover, temperature differences between probes are bigger (~ 5 °C). This can be explained because wind affects to the results and alters heat transfer depending not only on wind speed, but also direction and prototype orientation. Probes 1 and 2 are being penalized due to their orientation and location in the panel. Observing results from different windy days based

on wind direction and the location of the probes in the panel, it is conclusive that the assumption of wind speed being uniform over the collector surface area is not valid. A new model for wind speed over a flat-plate surface has been designed for recalculate the convective heat losses due to the wind in the entire surface of the PV-T collector, considering probes distribution and prevailing wind. This new convective heat transfer coefficient has been included as an enhancement of the first simulation approach. The results of this new model show two distinct curves for the probes facing the wind directly (1 and 2, more affected by the wind) and indirectly (3 and 4, less affected) (**Figure 7**). This differentiation fits better with the experimental data.

As in the PV temperatures, the one-dimensional simulation can predict quantitatively thermal changes, heat fluxes and layer temperatures, although simulated data do not reproduce the first minutes of experimental data, in which real temperature sensors have inertia and a period of acclimatation. Moreover, the simulation is considerably sensitive to radiation and wind, whose changes are straight reflected on simulated results.

Overall, insulating materials contained in probes 1 and 2 have better heat performance, reaching higher temperatures during windless days.

3.3 Adhesive materials comparison

The following **Figure 8** and **Figure 9** show results obtained from adhesives small-scale tests (Prototype 2) for low and high wind speed respectively. Temperatures ($T_{5\text{-exp}}$-$T_{8\text{-exp}}$) represent the mean temperature inside the **heat absorber**, for each material (Probes 5-8, **Table I**).

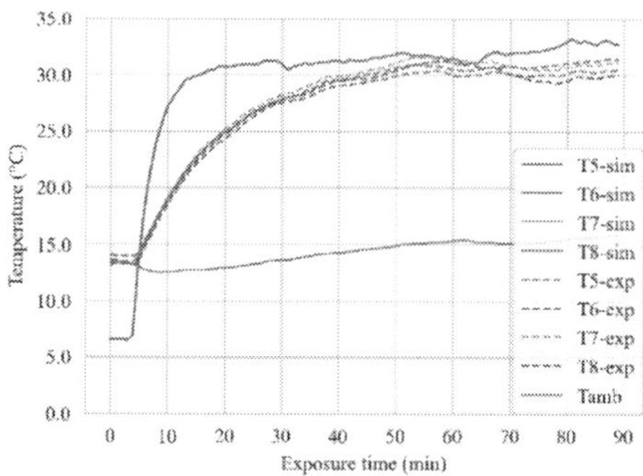

Figure 8: Prototype 2 heat absorber temperatures for each probe. Windless day

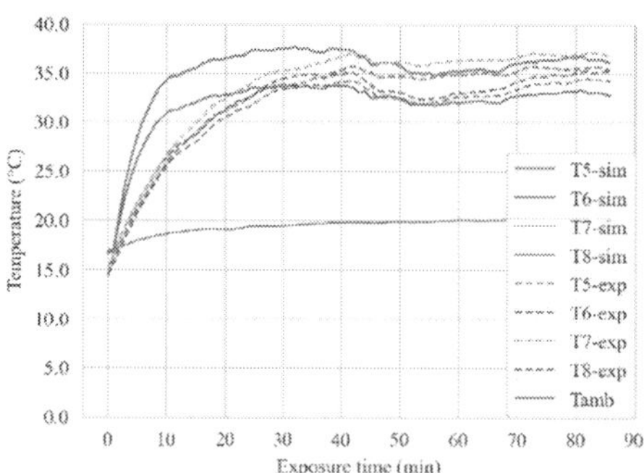

Figure 9: Prototype 2 heat absorber temperatures for each probe. Windy day

Figure 8 shows differences of less than 2 °C between probes during a windless day test, while for a windy day test in **Figure 9**, the differences of temperature between probes are higher, around 5 °C. As it happened with insulating material tests, temperature results on windy days are more affected by the wind depending on probe location, regarding the wind direction, in the adhesive's comparison tests.

Probe 7 and probe 8 reach higher temperatures in both tests. Probe 8 attaching media is a thermal paste with higher conductivity; however, its handling and applicability were a disadvantage against the double-face adhesive of probe 7.

As in the previous sections, the one-dimensional simulation can predict quantitatively layer temperatures and heat transfer, although simulated data do not reproduce the inertia of the temperature sensors. The simulation remains sensitive to radiation and wind, with the improvements included.

Overall, differences between adhesives during windless days, when results are not affected by probe location regarding wind distribution above flat-plate, are not as significant as in the insulating material tests. Heat transfer depends on the thickness and thermal conductivity of materials, in particular for adhesives, where the thicknesses are very low, no appreciable differences are measured in the experimental tests. Other criteria, as ease of handling, prices, sustainability and lifetime are taken into account for choosing the ideal adhesive for the PV-T design.

3.4 Numerical assessment of 1D simulation

Percentage Error has been calculated in order to evaluate numerically the assessment of the one-dimensional model, comparing simulated results with the experimental values measured.

Table IV shows this indicator obtained for each scenario. In all the comparison tests, a Percentage Error of less than 8.0 % is obtained, so it can be concluded that the one-dimensional simulation is capable of predict reliable numerical data within that measurement range.

Table IV: Average Percentage Error values for each comparison test.

	Windless days	Windy days
PV	1.5 %	1.3 %
Prototype 1		
Probe 1	2.9 %	2.5 %
Probe 2	1.4 %	1.3 %
Probe 3	7.3 %	2.6 %
Probe 4	6.6 %	3.4 %
Prototype 2		
Probe 5	6.1 %	4.1 %
Probe 6	6.6 %	2.3 %
Probe 7	3.6 %	2.4 %
Probe 8	4.2 %	1.8 %

4 CONCLUSIONS

Following conclusion can be resumed from this work:
- The experimental study shows no significant differences between adhesives, but does show between insulations.
- Insulations in probe 1 and 2 are chosen because of the experimental results during windless days and its ease of installation and handling.
- Experimental results are highly dependent of the wind direction and the location of the probe in the panel. Forced heat convection in flat plate should be studied and taken into account in future studies or experiments.
- The one-dimensional simulation can reproduce experimental temperatures and heat transfer fluxes through the PV-T panel layers.
- The Percentage Error between simulated and experimental data remains under 8.0% in every comparison test.

5 ACKNOWLEDGEMENTS

This work was undertaken in the framework of CRETE VALLEY project, funded by the European Union's *Horizon Europe* research and innovation program through grant agreement No 101136139.

6 REFERENCES

Abdelrazik, A. S., Al-Sulaiman, F. A., Saidur, R., & Ben-Mansour, R. (2018). A review on recent development for the design and packaging of hybrid photovoltaic/thermal (PV/T) solar systems. *Renewable and Sustainable Energy Reviews*, 95(December 2017), 110–129. https://doi.org/10.1016/j.rser.2018.07.013

Agarwal, R. K., & Garg, H. P. (1994). Study of a Photovoltaic-Thermal system - Thermosyphonic solar water heater combined with solar cells. *Energy Conversion and Management*, 35(7), 605–620.

Bhattarai, S., Oh, J., Euh, S., Krishna, G., & Hyun, D. (2012). Simulation and model validation of sheet and tube type photovoltaic thermal solar system and conventional solar collecting system in transient states. *Solar Energy Materials and Solar Cells*, 103, 184–193. https://doi.org/10.1016/j.solmat.2012.04.017

Cristofari, C., Notton, G., & Canaletti, J. L. (2009). Thermal behavior of a copolymer PV/Th solar system in low flow rate conditions. *Solar Energy*, 83(8), 1123–1138. https://doi.org/10.1016/j.solener.2009.01.008

Dubey, S., Sarvaiya, J. N., & Seshadri, B. (2013). Temperature dependent photovoltaic (PV) efficiency and its effect on PV production in the world - A review. *Energy Procedia*, 33, 311–321. https://doi.org/10.1016/j.egypro.2013.05.072

Hajji, M., Naimi, S. E., Hajji, B., & El Hafyani, M. L. (2014). A comparative study between two structures of hybrid photovoltaic/thermal (PV/T) collectors for water pumping systems. *Proceedings of 2014 International Renewable and Sustainable Energy Conference, IRSEC 2014*, 235–240. https://doi.org/10.1109/IRSEC.2014.7059745

Herrando, M., Markides, C. N., & Hellgardt, K. (2014). A UK-based assessment of hybrid PV and solar-thermal systems for domestic heating and power: System performance. *Applied Energy*, 122, 288–309.

Herrando, M., Ramos, A., Zabalza, I., & Markides, C. N. (2019). A comprehensive assessment of alternative absorber-exchanger designs for hybrid PVT-water collectors. *Applied Energy*, 235(July 2018), 1583–

1602. https://doi.org/10.1016/j.apenergy.2018.11.024

Herrando, M., Wang, K., Huang, G., Otanicar, T., Mousa, O. B., Agathokleous, R. A., Ding, Y., Kalogirou, S., Ekins-Daukes, N., Taylor, R. A., & Markides, C. N. (2023). A review of solar hybrid photovoltaic-thermal (PV-T) collectors and systems. In *Progress in Energy and Combustion Science* (Vol. 97). Elsevier Ltd. https://doi.org/10.1016/j.pecs.2023.101072

Joshi, S. S., & Dhoble, A. S. (2018). Photovoltaic - Thermal systems (PVT): Technology review and future trends. *Renewable and Sustainable Energy Reviews, 92*(September 2017), 848–882. https://doi.org/10.1016/j.rser.2018.04.067

Kalogirou, S. A., & Tripanagnostopoulos, Y. (2006). Hybrid PV/T solar systems for domestic hot water and electricity production. *Energy Conversion and Management, 47*(18–19), 3368–3382. https://doi.org/10.1016/j.enconman.2006.01.012

Michael, J. J., Iniyan, S., & Goic, R. (2015). Flat plate solar photovoltaic-thermal (PV/T) systems: A reference guide. *Renewable and Sustainable Energy Reviews, 51*, 62–88. https://doi.org/10.1016/j.rser.2015.06.022

Notton, G., Cristofari, C., Mattei, M., & Poggi, P. (2005). Modelling of a double-glass photovoltaic module using finite differences. *Applied Thermal Engineering, 25*(17–18), 2854–2877. https://doi.org/10.1016/j.applthermaleng.2005.02.008

Ramos, A., Guarracino, I., Mellor, A., Alonso-Álvarez, D., Childs, P., Ekins-Daukes, N. J., & Markides, C. N. (2017). Solar-Thermal and Hybrid Photovoltaic-Thermal Systems for Renewable Heating. In *Grantham Institute* (Issue 22). www.imperial.ac.uk/grantham/publications

Rawat, R., Lamba, R., & Kaushik, S. C. (2017). Thermodynamic study of solar photovoltaic energy conversion: An overview. *Renewable and Sustainable Energy Reviews, 71*(October 2015), 630–638. https://doi.org/10.1016/j.rser.2016.12.089

Rejeb, O., Dhaou, H., & Jemni, A. (2015). Parameters effect analysis of a photovoltaic thermal collector: Case study for climatic conditions of Monastir, Tunisia. *Energy Conversion and Management, 89*, 409–419. https://doi.org/10.1016/j.enconman.2014.10.018

Santos, L. D. O., De Carvalho, P. C. M., & Filho, C. D. O. C. (2022). Photovoltaic Cell Operating Temperature Models: A Review of Correlations and Parameters. *IEEE Journal of Photovoltaics, 12*(1), 179–190. https://doi.org/10.1109/JPHOTOV.2021.3113156

Tiwari, A., & Sodha, M. S. (2006). Performance evaluation of hybrid PV/thermal water/air heating system: A parametric study. *Renewable Energy, 31*(15), 2460–2474. https://doi.org/10.1016/j.renene.2005.12.002

Zhang, X., Zhao, X., Smith, S., Xu, J., & Yu, X. (2012). Review of R&D progress and practical application of the solar photovoltaic/thermal (PV/T) technologies. *Renewable and Sustainable Energy Reviews, 16*(1), 599–617. https://doi.org/10.1016/j.rser.2011.08.026

Zondag, H. A., de Vries, D. W., van Helden, W. G. J., van Zolingen, R. J. C., & van Steenhoven, A. A. (2003). The yield of different combined PV-thermal collector designs. *Solar Energy, 74*(3), 253–269. https://doi.org/10.1016/S0038-092X(03)00121-X

Materials assessment for PV-T modules thermal performance improvement

Author(s): L. Cano[1*], R. Simón-Allué[1], R. Villén[1], Y. Lara[1], I. Guedea[1]
[1]ENDEF

*Corresponding author:
lucia.cano@endef.com

The efficiency of PV-T collectors is directly linked to effective heat transfer through the system layers, which impacts overall thermal and electrical performance. This study evaluates the role of adhesives, the attachment media between the photovoltaic (PV) panel and the heat exchanger (HX); and insulant materials, which constitute the back-side of the PV-T panel. Two small-scale prototypes were developed to test selected adhesives and insulants under real-world conditions.

Approach

Prototypes

Two sets of four adhesives **and four** insulating materials were selected for the testing. Two prototypes were assembled.

Prototype 1 - Insulations			Prototype 2 - Adhesives		
Probe	Thickness (m)	Thermal conductivity (W/m·K)	Probe	Thickness (m)	Thermal conductivity (W/m·K)
1	0.025	0.037	5	0.00013	0.16
2	0.025	0.032	6	0.00013	0.18
3	0.025	0.025	7	0.0002	1.5
4	0.030	0.025	8	0.002	3.4

Figure 1. Prototype 1 design and assembly

Experimental setup

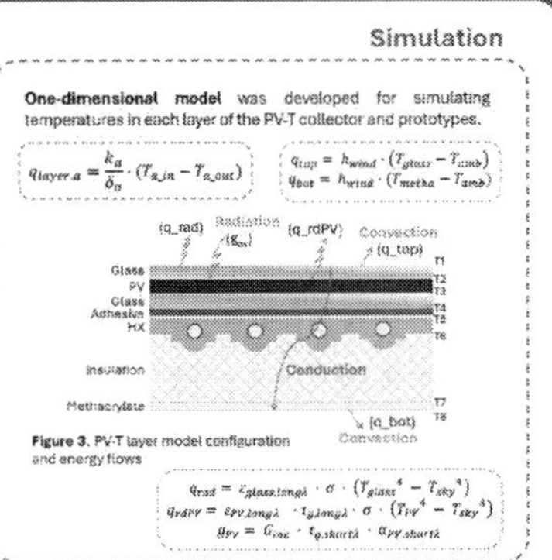

Figure 2. Prototype layers and temperature sensors distribution

Experimental tests were performed in **Zaragoza**, Spain, during winter months. Panels were placed in horizontal.

Objective of the study: **measuring temperatures in the heat exchanger to compare materials.**

Simulation

One-dimensional model was developed for simulating temperatures in each layer of the PV-T collector and prototypes.

$$q_{layer\ a} = \frac{k_a}{\delta_a} \cdot (T_{a\_in} - T_{a\_out})$$

$$q_{top} = h_{wind} \cdot (T_{glass} - T_{amb})$$

$$q_{bot} = h_{wind} \cdot (T_{metha} - T_{amb})$$

Figure 3. PV-T layer model configuration and energy flows

$$q_{rad} = \varepsilon_{glass\,longi} \cdot \sigma \cdot (T_{glass}^4 - T_{sky}^4)$$

$$q_{rdPV} = \varepsilon_{PV\,longi} \cdot \varepsilon_{gl\,longi} \cdot \sigma \cdot (T_{PV}^4 - T_{sky}^4)$$

$$q_{PV} = G_{inc} \cdot \varepsilon_{g\,shortl} \cdot \alpha_{PV\,shortl}$$

Results and discussion

PV panel

The first approach of the one-dimensional model only considers the PV panel, excluding the heat exchanger and the material probes.

Windless/very low wind day

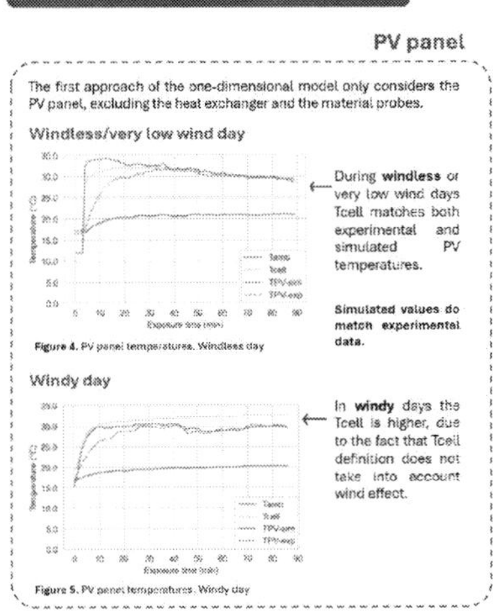

Figure 4. PV panel temperatures. Windless day

During **windless** or very low wind days Tcell matches both experimental and simulated PV temperatures.

Simulated values do match experimental data.

Windy day

Figure 5. PV panel temperatures. Windy day

In **windy** days the Tcell is higher, due to the fact that Tcell definition does not take into account wind effect.

Simulation numerical assessment

	Windless days	Windy days
PV	1.5 %	1.3 %
Prototype 1		
Probe 1	2.9 %	2.5 %
Probe 2	1.4 %	1.3 %
Probe 3	7.3 %	2.6 %
Probe 4	6.5 %	3.4 %
Prototype 2		
Probe 5	6.1 %	4.1 %
Probe 6	6.6 %	2.3 %
Probe 7	3.6 %	2.4 %
Probe 8	4.2 %	1.8 %

$$\%Error = \frac{|y_{exp} - y_{sim}|}{y_{exp}} \cdot 100$$

Percentage Error of less than 8.0 % is obtained in every test.

The 1D model is capable of predict reliable numerical data within that measurement range.

Insulating materials

Windless/very low wind day

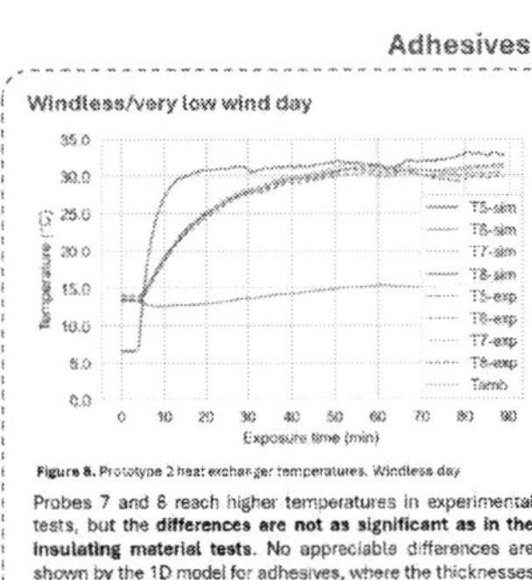

Figure 6. Prototype 1 heat exchanger temperatures. Windless day

Experimental results reveal higher temperatures in **probes 1 and 2.**

Windy day

New wind speed model implemented*

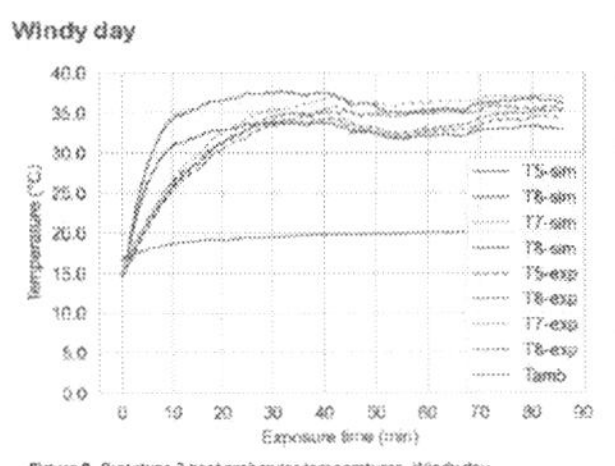

Figure 7. Prototype 1 heat exchanger temperatures. Windy day

Wind affects to the results and **alters heat transfer** depending not only on wind speed, but also direction and prototype orientation. Probes 1 and 2 are being penalized. A **new model** for wind speed over a **flat-plate surface** has been designed for recalculate the convective heat losses of the PV-T collector*.

Adhesives

Windless/very low wind day

Figure 8. Prototype 2 heat exchanger temperatures. Windless day

Probes 7 and 8 reach higher temperatures in experimental tests, but the **differences are not as significant as in the insulating material tests.** No appreciable differences are shown by the 1D model for adhesives, where the thicknesses are very low.

Windy day

Figure 9. Prototype 2 heat exchanger temperatures. Windy day

The simulation remains sensitive to radiation and wind, with the improvements included.

Conclusions

1. The experimental study shows **no significant differences** between adhesives, but does show between insulations.

2. Insulations in **probe 1 and 2** are chosen because of the experimental results during windless days and its ease of installation and handling.

3. Experimental results are highly dependent of the wind direction and the location of the probe in the panel. **Forced heat convection in flat plate** should be studied and taken into account in future studies or experiments.

4. The one-dimensional simulation can **reproduce** experimental temperatures and heat transfer fluxes through the PV-T panel layers.

5. The **Percentage Error** between simulated and experimental data remains under 8.0% in every comparison test.

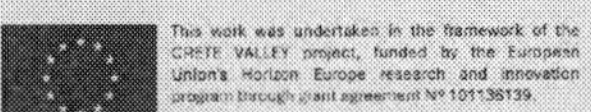

This work was undertaken in the framework of the CRETE VALLEY project, funded by the European Union's Horizon Europe research and innovation program through grant agreement Nº 101136139.

EVALUATING REPAIR TECHNIQUES FOR C-SI PV MODULES: SPOT-WELDING

Jorge Rabanal-Arabach [1,3*], Sonia Beltran-Condori [1*], Natalia Videla-Magnata [1,3], Katalina Rojas-Henríquez [1],
Andreas Schneider [2], Edward Fuentealba-Vidal [1,3]

[1] University of Antofagasta, Av Angamos 601, 1270300 Antofagasta, Chile.
[2] University of Applied Sciences Gelsenkirchen, Germany.
[3] Solar Energy Research Center, Tupper 2007, 8370451 Santiago, Chile.
* email: jorge.rabanal@uantof.cl, sonia.beltran.condori@ua.cl

ABSTRACT: Extending the operational life of photovoltaic (PV) modules is essential for sustainable energy transitions and waste reduction and repairing them is one option to achieve this aim. This study focuses on crystalline silicon (c-Si) modules affected by failures inside the junction box (jbox), where overheated solder joints often interrupt current flow. We explored spot-welding with nickel plates as an alternative to traditional soldering. Three welding strategies are considered through digital simulations to evaluate ease of application and reliability, and the most promising is applied experimentally: horizontal placement with a double-folded plate. The PV modules are assessed before and after repair using current–voltage curves, series resistance measurement, and thermal imaging under direct current injection. The intervention of the jbox successfully restored conductivity and power output, with no evidence of hot-spot formation. Post-repair performance is within ±5% of reference modules in terms of power output, without a significant change in the series resistance of the modules under test, supporting second-life use. The findings confirm spot-welding as a robust and lead-free repair method that contributes to circular economy practices in the PV sector.
Keywords: Photovoltaics, modules, junction box, repair, bussing, ribbons, spot-welding

1 INTRODUCTION

The rapid global expansion of photovoltaic technologies highlights the need for effective strategies to extend module lifetimes [1, 2]. With the increasing number of PV systems reaching their mid-life stage, repair and refurbishment provide cost-efficient alternatives to premature disposal [3, 4, 5, 6, 7, 8]. In particular, second-life applications are gaining traction as a sustainable approach that aligns with circular economy principles. However, to date most of the related standards focus on the quality qualification for fabrication or for recycling of this type of solar devices, and only few research publications focus on its repair.

Fault diagnosis frameworks, often guided by international standards such as IEC 60904, IEC 61215, and IEC 62446, along with IEA PVPS methodologies, allow classification of modules by the type and severity of degradation. Previous large-scale studies on crystalline silicon (c-Si) modules have shown that failures are not uniformly distributed but frequently localized in components such as the junction box (jbox), frame, connectors, or backsheet.

A recurrent issue inside the jbox is the deterioration of tin solder joints that connect bussing ribbons to the main electrical busbar. Overheating can cause melting, leading to disconnections and reduced power output. To overcome these limitations, alternative interconnection strategies are needed. Spot-welding using nickel plates has emerged as a potential solution due to nickel's mechanical resilience, corrosion resistance, and stable electrical properties.

This work investigates the feasibility of spot-welding as a repair method for bussing ribbon disconnections. Our study evaluates three welding layouts, compares their practicality, and experimentally validates the most effective technique. Electrical and thermal assessments before and after repair provide insight into the reliability of the restored modules and their suitability for continued service.

2 METHODOLOGY

The study develops and applies an experimental repair strategy for PV modules, targeting damaged bussing ribbons inside the jbox through spot-welding with nickel plates. Nickel is selected as the interconnection material due to its high conductivity and resistance to corrosion. Figure 1 provides a schematic view of a typical jbox, indicating key components such as diodes, busbars, and bussing ribbons.

To identify the most practical configuration, three welding approaches are digitally simulated: (1) vertical placement of two nickel plates covering the busbar, (2) horizontal folding of the ribbon secured by a single plate, and (3) a variation of the second approach using a double-folded plate to strengthen the weld and increase the contact area. The experimental methodology consisted of three main steps. First, modules with faulty junction boxes (devices under test, DUTs) are identified and characterized through baseline testing by measurements of I–V curves and electrical resistance. Second, the spot-welding repair is performed. Finally, post-repair evaluation included repeat I–V and resistance testing, complemented by hot-spot detection using infrared thermography.

2.1 Baseline Testing

The objective of this step is to assess the pre-repair condition of the bussing ribbons and depict the exiting faults: I-V curves and electrical resistance. The latter is determined using the four-wire Kelvin method under dark conditions to ensure accurate detection of conductivity anomalies. Probes are placed at points A (common), B, C, and D according to Figure 1, corresponding to measurements across one substring (1/3), two substrings (2/3), and the full cell matrix (3/3). A test voltage of (2.00 ± 0.02) V_{DC} is applied and the current and voltage recorded to later calculate the series resistance.

Current–voltage curves are obtained with a portable tracer under natural sunlight, following IEC 60904-1 guidelines. All measurements are performed directly on the bussing ribbons inside the jbox, as the external cables are disconnected from the DUT circuit.

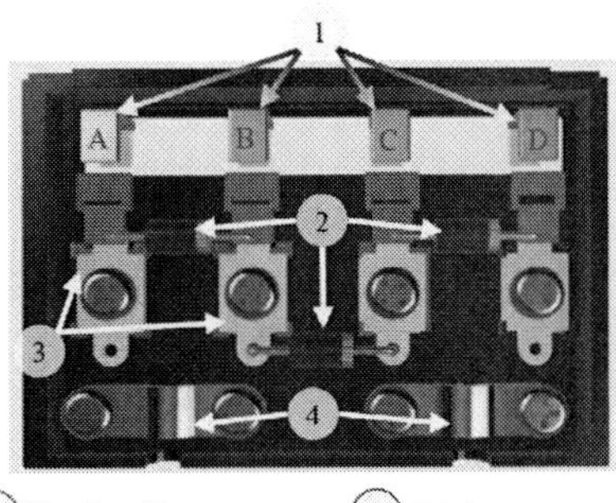

1 — Bussing ribbons
2 — Diodes
3 — Internal connections base
4 — External electrical conductor entrance

Figure 1: Scheme of a jbox from the DUTs.

2.2 Repair Implementation

To restore electrical continuity, the bussing ribbons are repaired using spot-welding with nickel plates. Nickel alloys are chosen because they combine resistance to electrical and thermal stress with ease of welding [3]. The repair protocol involved four sequential steps, from opening and preparing the junction box to completing the final welds, as shown in Figure 2. While three possible welding approaches are considered, only the "horizontal welding reinforced with a double-folded plate" is implemented across all modules, as it offered the most reliable and straightforward solution.

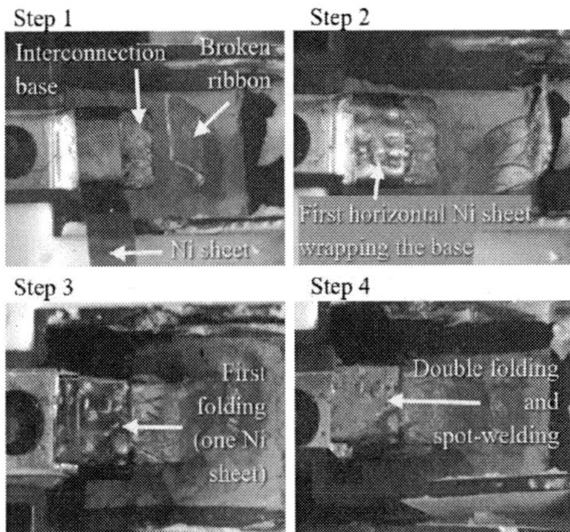

Figure 2: Implementation of broken outgoing ribbon refurbishment into a jbox.

2.3 Post-repair Evaluation

After repair, modules are re-characterized but this time measures are taken at their outer connections (MC4 terminals). Electrical recovery is validated by comparing I–V and resistance values before and after welding. Additionally, infrared thermography, as shown in Figure 3, is used to monitor local heating during direct current injection at near-nominal operating conditions. Images are recorded at 15 s and 60 s to track short-term thermal evolution.

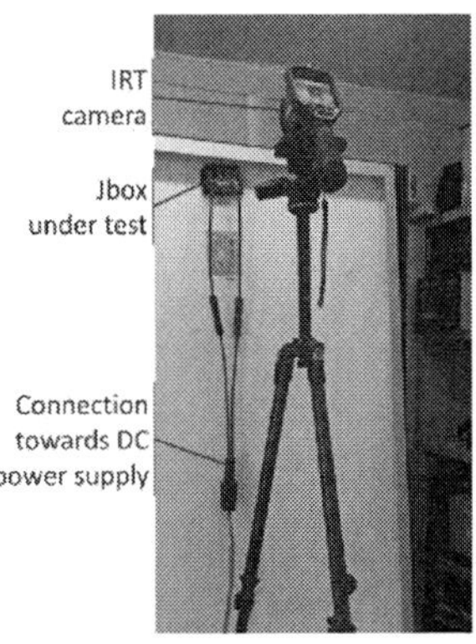

Figure 3: Experimental setup for hot-spot assessment.

3 RESULTS AND DISCUSSION

Post-repair analysis reveals that electrical resistance remained essentially unchanged across all DUTs, indicating that the spot-welding process does not introduce additional series resistance. Instead, the repair enhances electrical continuity, with improvements evident at both the substring scale and across the full module. Figure 4 presents the average electrical resistance measured across the devices under test (DUTs), alongside a reference group of 11 healthy PV modules (R_ref), whose mean value and associated error bars are shown for comparison (full module only). Pre-repair measurements are represented by circles, while post-repair results are indicated by triangles. The labels "1/3," "2/3," and "3/3" correspond to the fraction of the cell matrix evaluated: "1/3" refers to measurements between points B and A in Figure 1, "2/3" between points C and A, and "3/3" between points D and A.

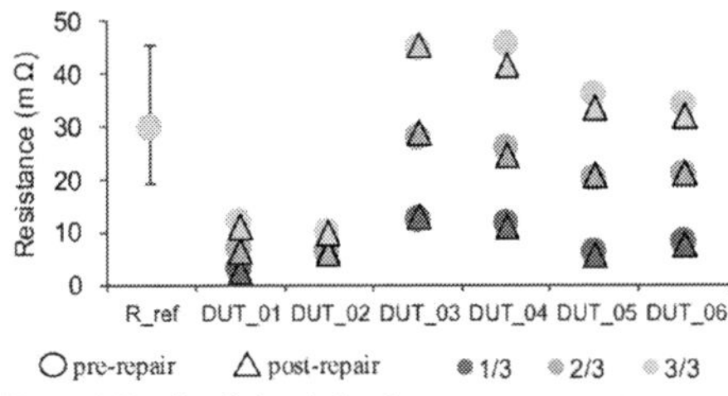

Figure 4: Results of electrical resistance measurements

No hot-spot formation is detected in any of the repaired modules. Under controlled ambient conditions of (20 ± 2) °C, junction box temperatures ranged between 24 °C and 26 °C, with a maximum rise of 2 K. These variations fall well within the safe operational range for PV modules.

Module power output is assessed before and after refurbishment in accordance with IEC 60904-1, using natural sunlight under clear-sky conditions. Pre-repair measurements are obtained by directly contacting the bussing ribbons inside the junction box, as no current is available at the external MC4 terminals due to the fault. After repair, power is measured conventionally through the outer MC4 connectors. The results, summarized in Table I, show that the repair process successfully restores module functionality. It should be noted that pre-repair power values could only be acquired internally from the jbox, highlighting the loss of output through the external connectors prior to restoration.

Table I: Comparison of Power Output before and after repair.

DUT	Pre-repair Power (W)	Post-repair Power (W)	Rel. Dif. (%)
P_ref	290 ± 15	--	--
DUT_01	294	280	−5
DUT_02	276	271	−2
DUT_03	279	265	−5
DUT_04	279	268	−4
DUT_05	282	286	1
DUT_06	287	289	1

4 CONCLUSION

The results of this study confirm that spot-welding with a double-folded nickel plate is a practical and effective method for repairing localized bussing ribbon failures in PV module junction boxes. This approach restores electrical functionality and power output while avoiding the use of toxic materials such as lead. Compared with conventional tin soldering, spot-welding offers improved reliability by minimizing the risk of future disconnections caused by solder melting under thermal stress.

Although the restored power output did not fully reach the original pre-failure values, the deviation is within 5%, which remains acceptable for second-life applications where minor performance losses are tolerable.

By offering a lead-free and mechanically stable alternative to soldering, spot-welding supports sustainable module management and contributes to the circular economy. Expanding the sample size in future work will further validate its reliability for large-scale refurbishment.

5 ACKNOWLEDGEMENTS

This work was supported by the Solar Circular fase2 project (CORFO 23BP-251214), the ANID/FONDEF/IDEA project ID24I10478, and the Chilean Solar Energy Research Center (SERC Chile) under Grant ANID/FONDAP/1523A0006. The authors gratefully acknowledge the support provided by the Master's Program in Solar Energy at the University of Antofagasta.

6 REFERENCES

[1] H. Mirletz, S. Ovaitt, S. Sridhar and T. Barnes, "Circular economy priorities for photovoltaics in the energy transition," *PLoS ONE*, vol. 17, no. 9, p. e0274351, 2022.

[2] J. Rabanal-Arabach, E. Fuentealba-Vidal, J. Astudillo-Ledezma, S. Beltran-Condori, A. Taquichiri, J. Tapia-Jelcic, D. Muñoz, A. Schneider, M. Riquelme-Zambrano and I. Jamett-Aranda, "Procedure Proposal to Determine PV Module Status for Its Second Life Application," in *EU PVSEC 2023*, 2023.

[3] G. Beaucarne, G. Eder, E. Jadot, Y. Voronko and W. Mühleisen, "Repair and preventive maintenance of photovoltaic modules with degrading backsheets using flowable silicone sealant," *Progress in Photovoltaics*, vol. 30, no. 8, pp. 1045-1053, 2021.

[4] Y. Voronko, G. Eder, C. Breitwieser, W. Mühleisen, L. Neumaier, S. Feldbacher, G. Oreski and N. Lenck, "Repair options for PV modules with cracked backsheets," *Energy Science and Engineering*, vol. 9, no. 9, pp. 1583-1595, 2021.

[5] Y. Kawano, J. Chantana, Y. Kuroda, K. Hirose and T. Minemoto, "Development of repairing technique for interconnection of silicon photovoltaic modules using an induction heating system," *Solar Energy*, vol. 261, pp. 55-62, 2023.

[6] M. Tas and W. van Shark, "Experimental repair technique for glass defects of glass-glass photovoltaic modules – A techno-economic analysis," *Solar Energy Materials and Solar Cells*, vol. 257, p. 112397, 2023.

[7] F. Rosillo, M. Nieto-Morone, J. Benavides Esteva, F. Soriano, S. Temprano, C. González and M. d. C. Alonso-García, "Repairing ribbon bus bar interruptions in photovoltaic modules using non-intrusive interruption location," *Renewable Energy*, vol. 223, p. 120012, 2024.

[8] M. B. Nieto-Morone, F. Rosillo, M. Muñoz-García and M. d. C. Alonso-García, "Enhancing photovoltaic module sustainability: Defect analysis on partially repaired modules from Spanish PV plants," *Journal of Cleaner Production*, vol. 461, p. 142575, 2024.

EVALUATING REPAIR TECHNIQUES FOR C-SI PV MODULES: SPOT-WELDING

Jorge Rabanal-Arabach[1,3], Sonia Beltrán-Condori[1], Natalia Videla-Magnata[1,3], Katalina Rojas-Henriquez[1], Andreas Schneider[2], and Edward Fuentealba-Vidal[1,3]

[1]Universidad de Antofagasta, Av. Angamos 601, 1270300 Antofagasta, Chile.
[2]University of Applied Sciences Gelsenkirchen, , Neidenburger Str. 43, 45897 Gelsenkirchen, Germany.
[3]Solar Energy Research Center, Tupper 2007, 8370451 Santiago, Chile.

INTRODUCTION

The diagnosis of PV modules health status and the repair of its anomalies are mandatory to enable a second life of such devices. However, to date most of the related standards focus on the quality qualification for fabrication or for recycling of this type of solar devices, and only few research publications focus on its repair [1-5]. This study assess the repair of broken soldering in jboxes due to overheating. To address this, spot-welding using nickel plates was proposed for bussing ribbons. DC current was injected into repaired modules to evaluate thermal behavior and detect hot spots.

RESULTS

Post-repair resistance measurements (△) show a slight but consistent decrease compared to pre-repair values (○) at all substring positions
(1/3=B-A, 2/3=C-A, 3/3=D-A),
with reference values from 11 undamaged modules confirming the trend (Fig. 1).

Power measurement (IEC 60904-1) confirms the effectiveness of the repair, showing pre-repair characterization limited to bus ribbon access (no MC4 output) and restored functionality after repair (Fig. 2).

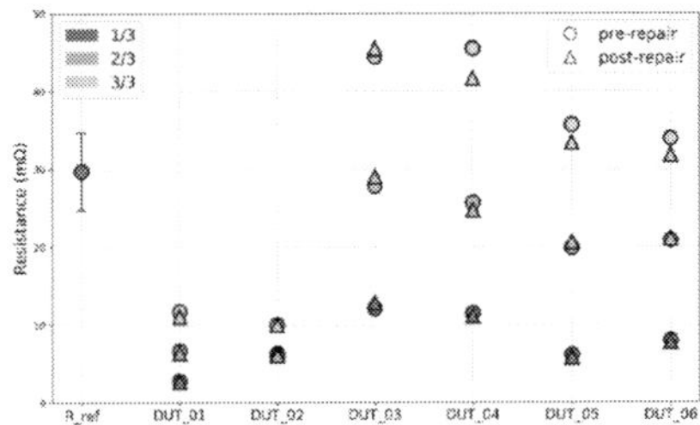

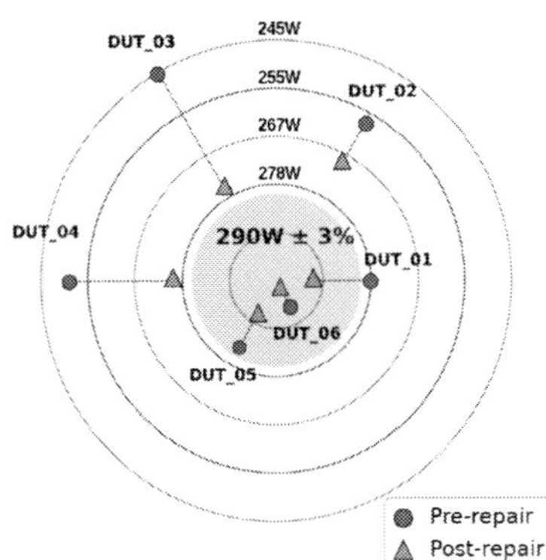

Fig. 2. Comparisson of power output before and after repair.

Zero hot-spots post-repair.
Jbox temps stable (24–26)°C, Δ≤2K) under (20±2)°C ambient temp.
IRT shows in average minimal ΔT: +0.9K after 15s and +0.5K after 60s. All within safe limits.

CONCLUSION

The double-folded nickel plate spot-welding technique provides an effective, lead-free solution for repairing bussing ribbons in PV modules, restoring electrical performance with only a ~5% deviation in power output. The method offers a safer alternative to tin soldering, supports second-life applications, and contributes to circular economy strategies in the PV sector. While further validation with larger sample sets is needed, the results confirm spot-welding as a practical approach to refurbishing damaged junction box connections.

REFERENCES

[1] R. Avery and G. Moe, Guidelines for the welded fabrication of nickel alloys, The Nickel Institute, 2018.
[2] G. Beaucarne et al., Prog. Photovolt., 30(8), pp. 1045-1053, 2021.
[3] Y. Voronko et al., Energy Sci. Eng., 9(9), 1583-1595, 2021.
[4] H. Mirletz et al., PLoS ONE, 17(9), pp. e0274351, 2022.
[5] J. Rabanal-Arabach et al., EU PVSEC, 2023.
[6] Y. Kawano et al., Solar Energy, 261, pp. 55–62, 2023.
[7] M. Tas and W. van Shark, Sol. Energy Mater. Sol. Cells, 257, pp. 112397, 2023.
[8] F. Rosillo et al., Renew. Energy, 223, pp. 120012, 2024.
[9] M. B. Nieto-Morone et al., J. Clean. Prod., 461, pp. 142575, 2024.

METHODOLOGY

PV modules with abnormal voltage variation (ΔV > 5 V) were selected

Jbox were opened to access internal connections

① Electrical conductor entrance
② Diodes
③ Internal connection base
④ Bussing ribbons

Silicone covering the bussing ribbons was removed using dedicated tools

Nickel strips were manually positioned over the bussing ribbons

Spot welding was applied to secure the nickel strips

Repaired terminals were connected to a power supply and monitored with IRT

① Jbox under test
② Connection towards DC power supply
④ IRT camera

Tests at 9A and 50V were performed for 15 s and 60 s

15 s

60 s

This work was supported by Solar Circular fase2 project under Grant CORFO 23BP-251214, by the project ANID/FONDEF/IDEA ID24110478, and by the Chilean Solar Energy Research Center (SERC Chile) under Grant ANID/FONDAP/1523A0006.

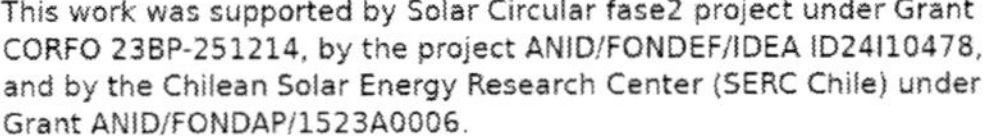

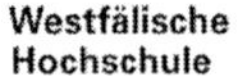

THERMALLY CONDUCTIVE FILLER PARTICLE MIXED SILICONE LAYER TO PROVIDE HEAT DISSIPATION FUNCTIONALITY TO C-SI SOLAR CELL MODULES WITHOUT ENCAPSULANTS

Yasushi Sobajima[1], Kouzen Wakazono[1], Keisuke Ohdaira[2]
[1]Gifu Univ., [2]JAIST
*Y. Sobajima, sobajima.yasushi.b2@f.gifu-u.ac.jp

ABSTRACT: To ensure stable photovoltaic conversion performance, reducing the operating temperature of encapsulant-free solar cell modules (novel solar cell module). We have developed a method to improve heat dissipation in this novel solar cell module structure by using a high-density mixture of highly thermally conductive filler material in silicone, arranged in sheet form at the bottom substrate of the cell. In this study, we explored ways to improve heat dissipation: incorporating AlN particles, creating through-holes in the substrate, and filling these holes with silicone material. Additionally, an AlN/silicone layer was applied to curved modules with increased cell area, demonstrating the effectiveness of this approach.
KEYWORDS: c-Si cell, novel module structure, thermally conductive filler, AlN, MgO, Heat dissipation effect

1 INTRODUCTION

The adoption of crystalline silicon (c-Si) solar cell modules continues to increase each year. Solar cell modules must withstand weather conditions and mechanical stress, which is why structures using encapsulants are now commonly employed. [1-3] However, this design makes recycling difficult due to the strong adhesion of the encapsulant. To support the ongoing large-scale adoption of next-generation solar cell modules, there is a clear need for significantly improved recyclability. S. Shimpo et al. have proposed a novel structure that does not use encapsulants [4]. This novel structure, through eliminating encapsulants, this structure can enhance the recyclability of solar modules. The novel module is formed by enclosing it within a lower substrate, installing the cells, and covering the top with a transparent material, with the substrate or cover providing mechanical strength. It is hypothesized that this will improve traditional solar module designs by reducing potential induced degradation (PID) phenomena [4].

However, novel structure still faces challenges such as component selection, achieving mechanical strength in large-area modules, increasing incident light intensity, and maintaining long-term performance stability. One key issue is suppressing internal temperature rise during the photoelectric conversion process. Since the band gap of c-Si is small, a decrease in cell efficiency due to a decrease in V_{OC} caused by temperature rise can occur during operation [5, 6].

We have demonstrated that SiO_X containing high thermal conductivity filler particles is effective for heat dissipation in encapsulated c-Si modules [7]. Recently, we transitioned from using SiO_X to silicone, which enables the formation of a strong sheet structure. This change has helped establish a more durable, robust sheet. Additionally, replacing MgO thermal conductive filler with AlN was considered, since white AlN provides higher thermal conductivity.

In this study, we applied silicone mixed with highly thermally conductive AlN particles (AlN/silicone) to a novel solar cell module structure to investigate improvements in heat dissipation performance. We also examined substrate enhancements, specifically the effect on heat dissipation when vertical through-holes were added to the substrate.

2 EXPERIMENTAL DETAILS

2.1 Method for preparing silicone material with thermally conductive filler

The silicone used in this study is a commercially available product with a proven track record as an encapsulant for c-Si solar cell modules. The raw material for this silicone is liquid, and mixing the two components begins curing through a chemical reaction. Like other encapsulants, silicone has low thermal conductivity. In this study, particles of a thermally conductive filler were mixed into this liquid silicone and cured, resulting in a material with improved thermal dissipation in both vertical and horizontal directions. Figure 1 shows how thermal conduction paths form in silicone by adding AlN thermally conductive particles. When heat is generated from the bottom during device operation, it spreads through the highly conductive material toward cooler areas. If AlN particle is present in enough quantity to create a continuous chain, the high temperature can easily spread throughout the entire material. Naturally, this efficiency in thermal conduction is expected to change depending on the amount of filler material, the formation of chains, and the adhesion strength.

In this study, a mixture of MgO or AlN particles, ranging from 250 to 500 mg, was used per 1 ml of silicone, which was blended from two liquids in a 1:1 ratio. The particle-mixed silicone was allowed to diffuse for 30 minutes before being applied over the entire substrate surface. The silicone thickness could be adjusted by varying the volume of liquid applied. The desired thickness was achieved by changing the number of application passes. After applying a single coat of silicone solution, the substrate was cured by drying at 80°C for 1 hour in air. To evaluate the thickness per application and the transverse thermal conductivity of the fabricated silicone material, cross-sectional scanning electron microscope (SEM) images and surface thermography

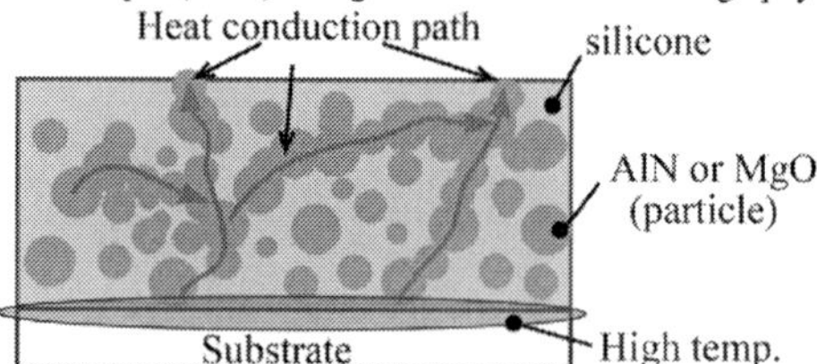

Figure 1: Schematic diagram of thermal conduction pathways in AlN/silicone containing AlN particles as highly thermally conductive fillers

Figure 2: Novel module structure using small area c-Si cells (15 x 15 mm²)

2.2 Structure and fabrication method of novel c-Si solar cell modules

The structure of the novel solar cell module in this study is shown in Figure 2. The module size is 50 mm square, and the upper transparent cover material uses EagleXG glass (0.7 mm thick). The substrate is made of gray PVC and was manufactured using the laboratory's 3D printer. The c-Si cells installed in the module were commercially available cells cut into 15 mm squares using a diamond cutter. The backside of these cells contains silicone (MgO/silicone or AlN/silicone) combined with thermally conductive filler particles. To improve thermal conductivity between the c-Si cell, a commercially available thermal conductive film that covers the cell area is applied. The structure with through holes on the substrate was designed on a PC and manufactured using a 3D printer. To accurately measure this module's heat dissipation performance, the interior must be sealed. When measuring temperature rise caused by light irradiation, the substrate and glass were bonded with quick-drying silicone putty and measured in a tightly sealed environment. Moreover, when using through-holes, heat dissipation occurs through these holes. Therefore, the holes were filled with AlN/silicone material before use. During this filling process, trapped air bubbles could reduce the module's heat dissipation ability. To prevent this, the filling was performed multiple times to thoroughly remove all air bubbles.

2.3 Continuous light irradiation experiment

The change in *J-V* characteristics of c-Si solar cell modules with AlN/silicone was measured as a function of continuous light irradiation (AM 1.5, 100 mW/cm²) time up to 3 hours. Since directly measuring the temperature inside the solar module during continuous operation is difficult, the temperature in the novel module was estimated based on the temperature characteristics of the c-Si solar cell [6]. This study estimated the module's internal temperature rise caused by light irradiation by measuring the change in V_{OC} (ΔV) from immediately after the start to 180 minutes of continuous light exposure. The ΔV of the conventional structure without AlN/silicone (ΔV_S) was used as a reference, and the ΔV of the measured samples (ΔV_F), along with the temperature characteristics of c-Si solar cells in Ref. [6], were used to calculate the estimated temperature difference (ΔT), which indicates the heat dissipation effect of AlN/silicone, using the following formula.

$$\Delta T = \frac{\Delta V_S - \Delta V_F}{\alpha}$$

ΔT(°C): Estimated temperature difference
ΔV_F(V): The V_{OC} change values from immediately after
    light irradiation starts to 180 min later when
    AlN/silicone-coated module is applied
ΔV_S(V): The ΔV_F of the silicone-uncoated module
α (V/°C): The temperature coefficient of V_{OC} in c-Si cells
    (α is calculated from data in Ref. [6])

The magnitude of ΔT was used to evaluate the heat dissipation performance under each condition. Measurements were taken indoors under light irradiation at room temperature, with no cooling fan used to regulate the module's internal temperature. Additionally, materials with low thermal conductivity were used at the module installation points to suppress heat transfer from the substrate to the outside.

3 RESULTS AND DISCUSSION

3.1 Thermally conductive material AlN/silicone and MgO/silicone

Using thermography images, the surface heat dissipation of a glass substrate coated with MgO/silicone was observed. The glass used was flat and measured 20 × 20 mm² (EagleXG). As shown in Figure 3(a), since the glass itself has low thermal conductivity, almost no heat diffusion was observed even when a heat source was placed at one end of the glass. However, when MgO/silicone (Figure 3(b)) or AlN/silicone (Figure 3(c)) was applied to the glass surface, uniform thermal conductivity spread laterally from the heat source. This shows that silicone materials exhibit lateral thermal diffusion characteristics when they contain an appropriate amount of thermally conductive filler particles.

Figure 3: Surface thermographic images of samples without (EagleXG flat glass) (a), 5 times layer applications of AlN/silicone (b), and MgO/silicone (c).

3.2 Evaluation of surface thermal conductivity

Samples with varying numbers of layers were fabricated on flat glass substrates, and their thickness was evaluated using cross-sectional SEM images. Figure 4 shows the change in thickness with the number of layers. The figure indicates that, for all materials, thickness steadily increases as the number of layers grows. The solution used to make the materials contained 250 to 500 mg of thermally conductive filler per 1 ml of silicone solvent. The figure shows that each layer of the fabricated silicone material was about 60 μm thick, regardless of the type of particles added. This thickness is significantly greater than in the SiO$_X$ case shown in the

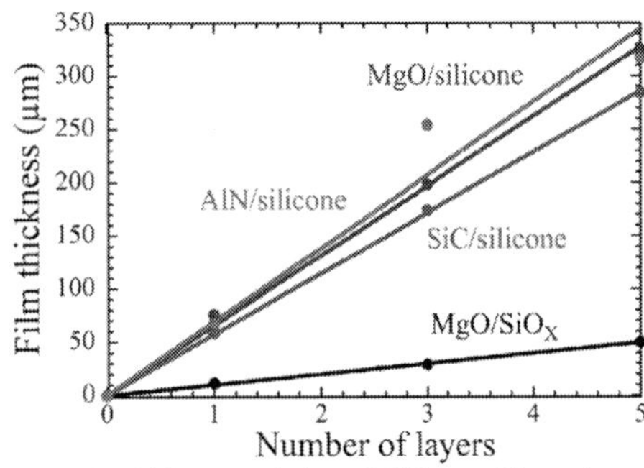

Figure 4: Thickness variation of different silicone layers with the number of coatings

figure. The difference in thickness is likely due to variations in the solute's viscosity and volatility.

3.3 Heat dissipation effect of different solutions

Figure 5 shows the estimated internal temperature rise within the module for different types of heat-conductive filler materials. In these heat dissipation experiments, the same c-Si material was used for all tests. First, when using the novel module alone, the decrease in V_{OC} after light exposure began was significantly larger compared to c-Si modules made with conventional vacuum lamination and EVA encapsulants (not shown in the Figure). As indicated by the temperature characteristics of c-Si solar cells discussed earlier, assuming the entire V_{OC} decrease is due to an internal temperature rise, this suggests that the novel module heats up more easily than the conventional design. In all cases, the reduction in V_{OC} levels reaches equilibrium after 180 minutes of light exposure. This study focused on the values at the start of light irradiation and after 180 minutes of continuous exposure. Furthermore, in case (a) without coating and case (b) without transparent silicone (i.e., without incorporating the heat-conductive filler material), no change was observed, including any variation over the course of light exposure. This demonstrates that silicone alone does not contribute to improving heat dissipation performance.

Furthermore, in cases (c) and (d), where the entire substrate is coated with silicone containing thermally conductive filler material, the reduction in V_{OC} after 180 minutes of light irradiation is smaller compared to cases (a) and (b). Additionally, when using AlN particles with high thermal conductivity, the reduction in V_{OC} due to light irradiation is further suppressed compared to using MgO particles. Calculating the estimated temperature difference DT for cases (c) and (d) based on case (a) yields values of 8.9°C and 11.5°C, respectively, indicating high heat dissipation performance regardless of the particle type used.

Note that the heat dissipation capacity of each silicone material depends on the concentration of the thermally conductive filler and the material's thickness. This trend remains consistent whether MgO/SiO_X is used in a general module structure with encapsulants [7] or MgO/silicone is applied to a novel module structure. However, no significant change was observed in small-area c-Si modules at various AlN densities for AlN/silicone. The latent heat dissipation ability of AlN particles is expected to be very high. Based on the reasons mentioned above, the conditions used in this study for MgO/silicone and AlN/silicone involve applying three coats (approximately 200 μm thick) over the entire substrate surface and using at least 250 mg of particles per 1 ml of silicone to ensure

Table I: The estimated temperature difference (ΔT) between conditions without AlN/silicone coating (Fig. 7(a)) and those with surface coating (b) or filling of the through hole by AlN/silicone (diameter 2.0 mmφ ((c) in the Figure, 4.0 mmφ (d) and 10 mmφ ((e), respectively).

	ΔT (°C)
(b) Fully covered by AlN/silicone (3 layers)	9.78
(c) Fill the 2.0 mm diameter through-hole with AlN/silicone	12.0
(d) In the case of 4.0 mm diameter	12.5
(e) In the case of 10 mm diameter	12.2

proper heat dissipation. These conditions are crucial to effectively facilitate heat dissipation from the thermally conductive filler particles.

3.4 Application of through-holes on substrates and investigation into improved heat dissipation performance

In our previous research, we confirmed that applying heat dissipation materials across the entire surface while ensuring lateral heat dissipation performance achieves sufficient thermal results. However, for modules larger than 1m², this approach is inefficient for dissipating heat generated at the cell center. Furthermore, in novel modules designed for airtightness, it remains uncertain whether heat dissipation mechanisms can be incorporated at the module edges or sides.

This section analyzed the improvement of performance by adding through-holes in the substrate and filling these areas with heat dissipation material as a solution to the problems. Complex structures immediately increase costs, so it is preferable to use through-holes with the lowest possible density and simplest structure in actual modules. As a first step to assess the maximum heat dissipation performance achievable with this structure, a through-hole was drilled across the entire substrate.

The diameter of the through-holes used throughout the module substrate for 15mm² cells was varied during fabrication, and all holes and the entire surface were filled with AlN/silicone (250 mg/ml). Figure 6 shows the change in V_{OC} over continuous light exposure time when using these substrates. Furthermore, Table 1 presents the results obtained by deriving ΔT using a function derived from the data in Fig. 6. As a result, using through holes enhances heat dissipation performance by approximately 2°C or more compared to covering the entire heat dissipation material. Additionally, the heat dissipation performance does not improve significantly even when varying the through-hole diameter. Therefore, while using through

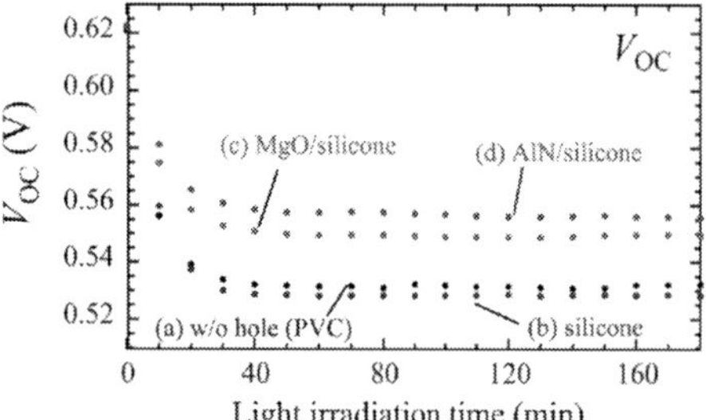

Figure 5: Effect of different thermally conductive filler materials in silicone layers on V_{OC} changes

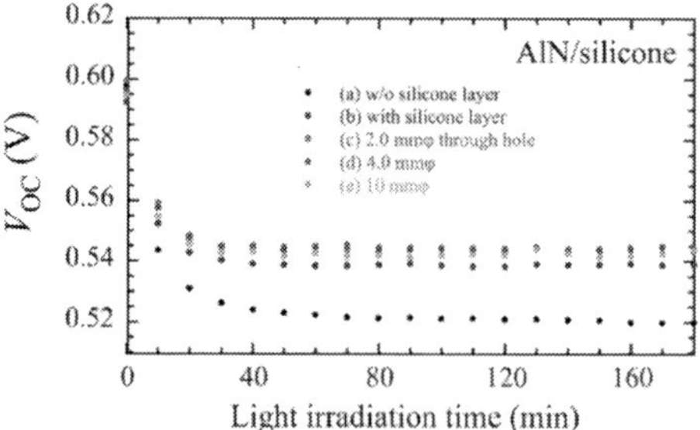

Figure 6: Reduction of V_{OC} through a novel c-Si module structure under continuous light irradiation

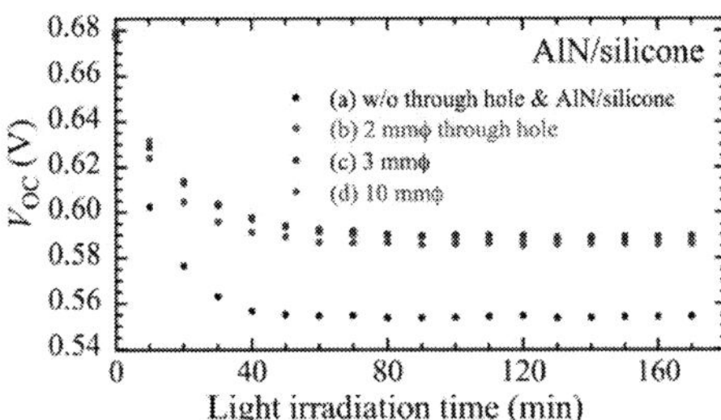

Figure 7: Effect of substrate through-hole diameter on heat dissipation effect in curved-surface modules using large-area cells (52 x 28mm²)

holes provide some improvement in heat dissipation, the extent of this improvement is not greatly affected by the size of the through holes. These results demonstrate the high heat dissipation performance of AlN particles, indicating that sufficient heat dissipation can be achieved without applying through-holes across the entire surface, at least for this particle size. The substrate thickness used in this study was 5.0 mm, and the raw material PVA has low thermal conductivity, similar to PC. Further improvement in heat dissipation performance is expected by reducing the substrate thickness within the range that ensures mechanical strength.

3.5 Evaluation of applicability to curved surface shapes with expanded cell area

AlN/silicone has demonstrated sufficient heat dissipation in small-area cells of 15 mm². For large-area novel module structures, switching the cover material from traditional glass to transparent PC is being considered to realize curved-shaped modules. To assess the usefulness of this silicone in such applications, a curved prototype was made after increasing the cell size to 28 x 52 mm². Through-holes of different diameters were drilled in each substrate, filled with AlN/silicone (250 mg/ml), and the surface was also coated with this silicone. The top cover is 2.0 mm thick PC material. After sealing the components with silicone putty, thermal performance was tested. The results, shown in Figure 8, indicate that effective heat dissipation was achieved regardless of through-hole diameter when filled with AlN/silicone. This silicone material demonstrates good heat dissipation across different cell areas and module shapes. However, increasing the area relative to smaller modules causes the ΔT values in Table 2 to tend to rise, indicating that the module's internal temperature increases as the area expands. This may be due to the internal structure of the module being in early development, possibly providing more space than small-area modules, which suggests room for improvement through design modifications. Even in these cases, the new through-hole AlN/silicone-filled structure shows significant heat dissipation benefits, and

Table II: Estimated temperature difference (ΔT) between conditions without AlN/silicone coating (a) and various through-hole diameters in the substrate in the case of Fig. 7 with increasing cell area (52 x 28 mm²).

	ΔT (°C)
(b) Fill the 2.0 mm diameter through-hole with AlN/silicone	16.7
(c) In the case of 3.0 mm diameter	18.0
(d) In the case of 10 mm diameter	17.4

further enhancements could be made by integrating it into module design.

4 CONCLUSIONS

This study examined the adoption of AlN/silicone and a method for creating through-holes in the entire substrate to fill them with AlN/silicone, aiming to enhance the heat dissipation performance of innovative solar cell modules. AlN/silicone shows higher thermal conductivity than MgO/silicone because it contains AlN particles with superior thermal properties. The through-hole AlN/silicone filling structure showed better heat dissipation compared to simply covering the substrate surface. Furthermore, this method remained effective even when the area was expanded. By ensuring thermal conductivity in the vertical direction, it significantly improved heat dissipation performance, overcoming the decline observed with previous structures that relied only on lateral conduction as the area increased.

5 ACKNOWLEDGEMENT

This research was commissioned by NEDO and funded by the General Incorporated Foundation International Club.

6 REFERENCES

[1] A.W. Czanderna, F. J Pern, Solar Energy Materials and Solar Cells (1996) 101-181.
[2] Oliveira MCC, Cardosa ASA, Viana MM, Lins VFC, Solar Energy Materials and Solar Cells 81 (2018) 2299-2317.
[3] G. Oreski, G.M. Wallner, Solar Energy 79 (2005) 612-617.
[4] S. Shimpo, H. T. C. Tu, K. Ohdaira, Jpn. J. Appl. Phys. 62, SK1039 (2023).
[5] E. Radziemska, E. Klugmann, Energy Conversion and Management 43 (2002) 1889-1900.
[6] E. Radziemska, Renewable Energy 28 (2003) 1-12.
[7] E. Shimokata, Y. Sobajima, K. Ohdaira, A. Masuda, Proc. of EUPVSEC 2024 (2024) 3AV.1.15, 020148-001-004.

ULTRASONIC CHARACTERIZATION OF ETHYLENE-VINYL ACETATE IN GLASS-GLASS-MODULES

Christopher Bruce Konu, Rico Meier
HTW Berlin - University of Applied Sciences, Wilhelminenhofstr. 75a Berlin, 12459, Germany
Christopher.Konu@HTW-Berlin.de

ABSTRACT: The encapsulant properties, particularly in modules with passivated emitter and rear cells (PERC) and silicon heterojunction (SHJ) configurations, are increasingly pivotal for long-term reliability. Optimal processing conditions for the encapsulant are therefore essential; however, manufacturers often prioritize reduced lamination times to increase throughput, which can lead to incomplete cross-linking and unconsumed reaction starters, potentially resulting in degradation modes such as accelerated aging, cell breakage, delamination, corrosion, and local inhomogeneities. Traditional destructive characterization methods, such as differential scanning calorimetry, Soxhlet extraction, or Shear testing, yield limited insights into the local material properties across the module. Since glass-glass (G–G) modules are gaining a large market share, also due to their bifacial capabilities, preparing samples for traditional characterization techniques has become even more cumbersome and costly. This study proposes a novel non-destructive ultrasonic approach to characterize EVA in G-G modules, extending techniques previously developed for the glass-backsheet configuration. By analyzing frequency-dependent time-of-flight measurements through the samples during lamination, we established a quantitative correlation with the lamination progression. A comparison with results from mechanical shear tests showed the potential of the method for non-destructive evaluation of adhesion strength. Furthermore, the method revealed new insights into the lamination process, including the time-of-flight dynamics during the different stages of lamination. This research, therefore, offers a pathway for in-situ lamination process surveillance and optimization to enhance production yields and reliability, ultimately reducing the levelized cost of energy.

Key Words: Ultrasonic Characterization, Lamination Monitoring, Glass-Glass Modules, In-situ Process Control

1 INTRODUCTION

1.1 The Critical Role of the Encapsulant for Photovoltaic Module Reliability

The long-term reliability and performance of photovoltaic (PV) modules are intrinsically linked to the quality of the lamination process. Within this process, the degree of cross-linking in the encapsulants (in this case, Ethylene-Vinyl Acetate (EVA)) is a paramount factor, governing critical module properties such as adhesion strength, resistance to moisture ingress, and resilience against thermomechanical stress.
Suboptimal lamination conditions resulting in incomplete or non-uniform EVA cross-linking initiate a cascade of degradation modes. While often electrically undetectable in initial performance tests, these deficiencies manifest severely in the field, leading to premature power degradation and an increased Levelized Cost of Energy (LCOE) [1]. This issue is crucial as manufacturers are trying to shorten lamination times to boost output, but cannot risk producing modules that will not last for their required 25-year lifespan [2], [3].

1.2 Degradation Modes from Cross-linking Deficiencies

The failure mechanisms stemming from inadequate cross-linking are well-documented:
Delamination: Reduced adhesion at critical interfaces (glass-EVA, EVA-cell) promotes layer separation, facilitating moisture ingress and increasing optical losses. This is a primary failure mode repeatedly observed in field-aged modules [4].
Corrosion: A not fully-crosslinked EVA layer provides an insufficient barrier against humidity, accelerating corrosion of cell metallization and busbars, which are observable as snail trails, discoloration, and increased series resistance [2]. Moisture ingress, often through degraded encapsulant or backsheets, is a key initiator of these secondary processes [5], [6].
Cell Fractures: Inhomogeneous curing can create localized stress concentrations, enhancing the propagation of microcracks into cell breakage, especially under thermomechanical load [7].
Potential-Induced Degradation (PID): PID occurs when voltage stress drives leakage currents through the encapsulant. Lower cross-linking density reduces EVA volume resistivity, increasing PID susceptibility and causing power loss and potential hot spots [8].

1.3 The Industrial Challenge: Limitations of Current Quality Control

The PV industry predominantly relies on destructive, offline techniques for quality assurance of the lamination process. The standardized Soxhlet extraction method, while considered a reference for determining gel content, is laborious and time-consuming, not suited for a production environment where quick quality management decisions are necessary [9]. Similarly, Differential Scanning Calorimetry (DSC) provides precise measurements of the cross-linking progress (the DSC degree of cross-linking), but is inherently unsuitable for in-line module inspection due to its destructive nature [10]. Shear tests, while indicative of adhesion strength, are also destructive and localized. Consequently, a critical technological gap exists for a non-destructive evaluation (NDE) method capable of quantifying EVA quality in situ and in real-time to enable closed-loop process control.

1.4 Potential of Ultrasonic Methods

Ultrasound has emerged as a promising NDE technique for polymers, leveraging the fact that during the cross-linking process, the material's viscoelastic properties are altered, which in turn affect acoustic wave propagation parameters such as velocity and attenuation [11].

Ultrasonic wave propagation depends on the mechanical properties of the material. A change in storage modulus during cross-linking can be observed as a change in longitudinal sound velocity [12]. The longitudinal sound velocity c_L can (when boundary effects can be neglected, such as in an infinite medium) be described by the equation

$$c_L = \sqrt{\frac{C_{ij}}{\rho}}, \tag{1}$$

where C_{ij} represents the elastic tensor of the sound-transmitting material. In isotropic materials, it corresponds to the elastic modulus (Young's modulus) Y and ρ is the density of that material.

Previous studies have demonstrated correlations between ultrasonic parameters and the cross-linking state of EVA [9]. This work continues the ultrasonic approach and transfers the previously developed methodology to glass-glass modules.

2 EXPERIMENTAL APPROACH

2.1 High-Temperature Ultrasound Transducer Design

Standard ultrasonic transducers are unsuitable for the elevated temperatures encountered in the PV lamination process, which mostly exceeds 140°C. Furthermore, their typical dimensions limit their integration potential in standard laminators. To overcome these limitations, custom transducers were designed and fabricated in-house. A high-temperature piezoceramic disc element served as the active component. Electrical contact was established by bonding insulated, high-temperature coaxial cables to the disc's electrodes using a thermally stable conductive epoxy. This assembly was then encased and sealed within a custom-machined aluminum housing. The aluminum housing acts as mechanical support and can also be heated by electric heating pads glued to its backside.

2.2 Sample Preparation

To imitate the structure of a commercial photovoltaic module, a simplified glass-encapsulant-glass configuration was utilized. Square float glass plates measuring 40 mm x 40 mm x 2 mm were thoroughly cleaned and dried before lamination. Sheets of EVA encapsulant foil from Vista Solar were cut to dimensions matching the glass.

The laminate stack (glass-EVA-EVA-glass) was assembled in a clean, dry environment and represents the core layered structure of a glass-glass PV module around the solar cells.

2.3 In-Situ Ultrasonic Monitoring of the Lamination Process

The setup was designed to perform non-destructive, in-situ ultrasonic transmission measurements throughout the entire lamination cycle. The prepared glass-EVA-glass sample was placed between two custom-made ultrasonic transducers and coupled to them via high-temperature ultrasonic gel. This complete assembly, as shown in Figure 1, was then housed within a temperature-controlled vacuum chamber. Before initiating the thermal cycle, the

chamber was evacuated to a vacuum pressure of 0.003 mbar absolute (stated limit of the pump) to eliminate air gaps and prevent the formation of bubbles.

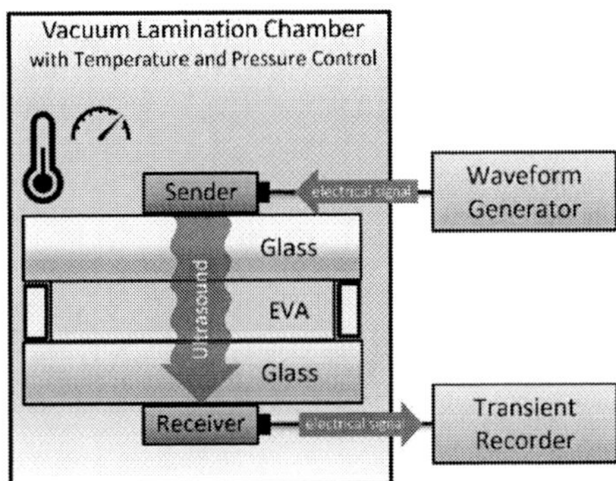

Figure 1. Ultrasound transmission setup for real-time monitoring of the lamination process.

A representative lamination cycle was then executed: The sample was heated from room temperature to a temperature of 140°C. This temperature was maintained for an hour, a duration expected to be sufficient for completing the cross-linking reaction, and then cooled to 60°C. Throughout the entire thermal cycle, encompassing the ramp-up, dwell, and cool-down phases, a high-frequency ultrasonic chirp was continuously transmitted through the sample as indicated in Figure 1. The receiving transducer captured the transmitted ultrasonic signal and converted it to an electric signal, which was recorded by a transient recorder at regular two-second intervals.

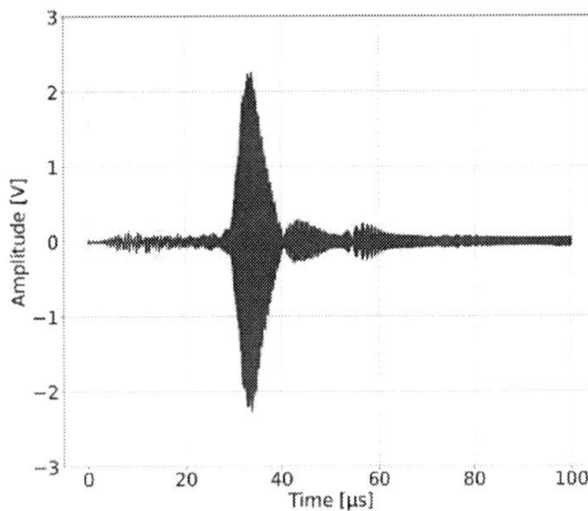

Figure 2. Typical ultrasonic waveform (time-signal) recorded during lamination.

A second lamination cycle was applied afterwards on the same sample to distinguish the effects of permanent changes, e.g., cross-linking or rearrangement of the polymer fibers (which should only occur once), and heating.

Additionally, a thermal cycling experiment was conducted on a separate, identically prepared sample, by repeatedly running cooling-heating cycles between 140 °C and 80°C. Ultrasonic time-of-flight (ToF) was again continuously measured throughout these cycles.

2.4 Frequency Selection of the Ultrasonic Excitation Signal

The excitation signal was optimized by selecting an appropriate thickness for the piezoelectric disk and exciting it with an electric chirp. Higher frequencies demonstrated an increased sensitivity to variations in the thin EVA layer; however, they also exhibited greater absorption, which consequently limited the signal-to-noise ratio. To achieve a balance between sensitivity and detectability, we employed a 100 µs linear chirp that spanned from 1 to 20 MHz for excitation. Spectral analysis (Fast Fourier Transform (FFT)) revealed a prominent spectral peak at 6.5 MHz (see Fig. 2 and Fig. 3), upon which our evaluation was focused.

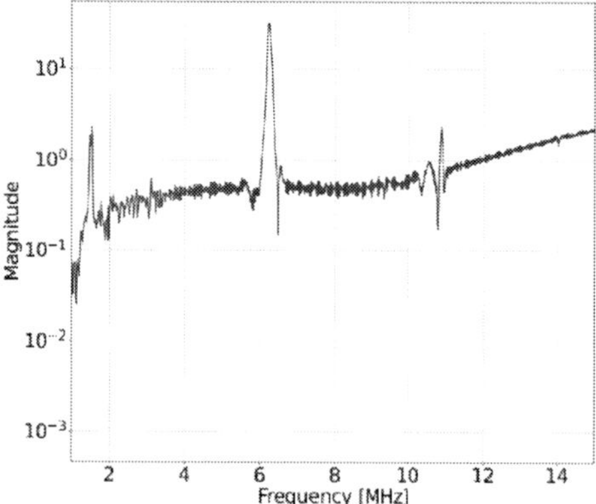

Figure 3. Amplitude spectrum of the recorded time signal (Fig. 2).

2.5 Determination of Changes in Time-of-Flight

A precise determination of the changes in Time-of-Flight (ToF) was crucial for tracking small changes in sound velocity during lamination. The signal processing methodology, outlined in Figure 4, consists of the following steps:

First, the recorded waveform $V(t, t_{rec})$, called the time signal, was captured by a transient recorder. The recorded time signal has a length of 100 µs, and was recorded every 2 s. The corresponding time of the recording is denoted as t_{rec} in Figure 4.
The waveform before lamination was used as a reference signal $R(t)$ at a well-known temperature. The time shift $dToF$ will later be calculated with respect to that reference signal (Figure 4, top-left).

To enhance the signal-to-noise ratio and select a specific acoustic mode, both the raw signal $V(t, t_{rec})$ (Fig. 4a) and the reference signal $R(t)$ (Fig. 4b) were filtered using identical bandpass filters (here from 5.6 MHz to 6.6 MHz), resulting in the filtered signals $V'(t, t\,rec)$ (Fig. 4c) and $R'(t)$ (Fig. 4d). The core of the $dToF$ calculation relied on a cross-correlation analysis. The cross-correlation function $M_{VR}(dt, t_{rec})$ was computed for each recorded time signal by shifting the filtered reference signal $R'(t + dt)$ by a constant dt and multiplying it by the filtered signal $V'(t, t_{rec})$.

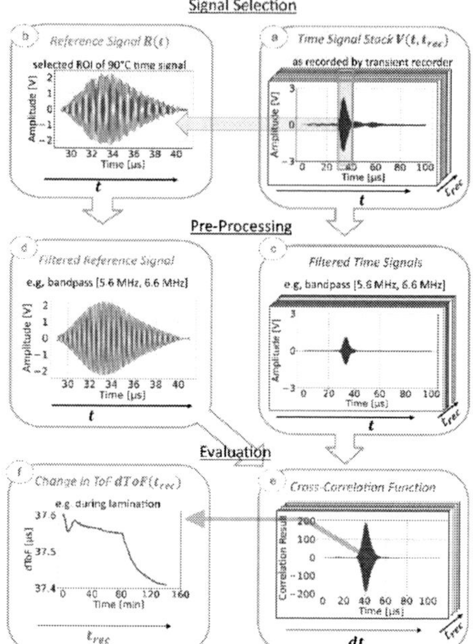

Figure 4. Overview of the $dToF$ determination method.

This product is then summed up over each datapoint of the complete signal by

$$M_{VR}(dt, t_{rec}) := \sum V^*(t, t_{rec})R^*(t + dt) \qquad (2)$$

This procedure is repeated for all dt in an interval from 0 to 100 µs. The plot of all those sums (correlation result) vs. dt is represented in Fig. 4e. The time shift dt that maximizes the cross-correlation result corresponds to the Change in Time-of-Flight $dToF(t_{rec})$, for that specific recording time t_{rec} relative to the reference signal. Figure 4f shows all the evaluated dToFs during the lamination process.

2.5 Shear Testing for Evaluation of the Adhesion Strength

To compare the acoustic properties to adhesion parameters, shear tests were performed using a specially designed shear wedge, illustrated in Figure 5.
Multiple glass/EVA/glass laminates were prepared under different lamination conditions: at 80°C, 100°C, 120°C, and 140°C (with peak-temperature holding times of 1, 5, 20, 40, and 60 minutes).
The laminates were arranged within the shear wedges, with one glass sheet securely clamped in the lower wedge and the other in the upper wedge. A universal testing machine applied a compressive force on the assembly, pressing the upper wedge downward. Due to the geometry of the wedges, the lower wedge was displaced horizontally, thereby subjecting the EVA layer between the two glass sheets to shear loading. A load cell measured the applied force, and force-displacement curves were recorded for each sample. To ensure statistical relevance, three samples were tested for each lamination condition.

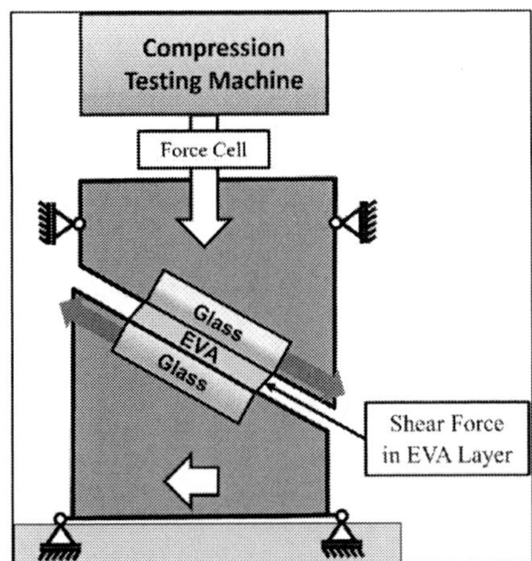

Figure 5. Shear test experimental setup

The shear strength of the EVA interface was then calculated from the maximum recorded force using the standard relation:

$$\tau_{shear} = \frac{F_{Max}}{A}, \qquad (3)$$

where τ_{shear} denotes the shear strength, F_{Max} the maximum force when failure occurred, and A the area of the sheared EVA layer. The shear strength was then compared to the acoustic measurements.

3 RESULTS AND DISCUSSION

3.1 In-Situ Ultrasonic Characterization of EVA Lamination and Our Interpretation

With our custom setup, we were able to monitor the lamination process of the previously mentioned Glass-EVA-Glass samples with ultrasound in real-time. The ToF of the 6.5 MHz acoustic longitudinal wave mode was utilized as the primary metric to track the structural and chemical transformations within the polymer. The recorded ToF data over the entire process, spanning two full thermal cycles, is presented in Figure 6. The process can be distinctly segmented into five key phases, each correlating to a specific physical or chemical phenomenon.

Phase I: Initial Compression and Air Expulsion (0 min - 6 min)
The process begins with an immediate and sharp decrease in ToF. This initial drop corresponds directly to the application of pressure and the onset of heating.
Mechanically, the applied vacuum pressure leads to an outgas of entrapped air from the interstitial spaces between the EVA and the adjacent glasses. The rising temperature softens the EVA, allowing it to conform and compress under the applied load. This compaction reduces the effective acoustic path length and increases the material density, both of which contribute to a decrease in Time-of-Flight.

Phase II: Melting and Structural Transformation (6 min - 16 min)
As the temperature approaches and surpasses the melting point of the EVA (around 70 to 80°C) [13], a pronounced

reversal in the ToF trend is observed, characterized by a significant increase. This critical phase is governed by two primary mechanisms:
1. Polymer Melting and Softening: The crystalline regions within the EVA melt, and the polymer transitions into a low-viscosity molten state. Hence, the modulus of elasticity drops drastically, as well as the speed of sound (see eqn. 1), which can be seen as an increase in ToF.
2. Moisture Evaporation: The heat out-gases residual moisture and solvents within the polymer. The presence of these small, scattered gas pockets significantly scatters and attenuates the ultrasonic signal and further delays the observed peak in ToF [14].

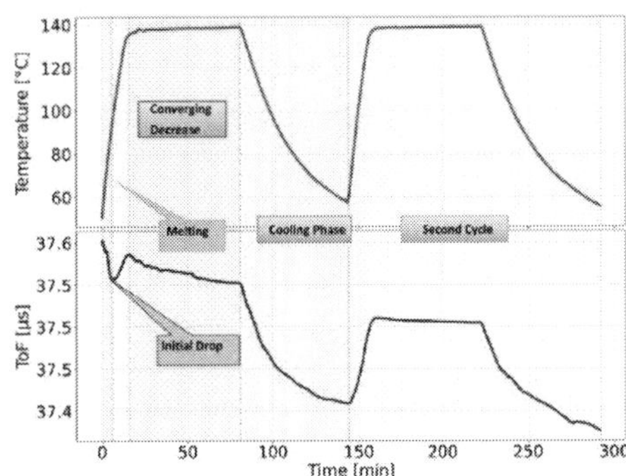

Figure 6. Evaluated Time-of-Flight (ToF) of the ultrasonic waves travelling through the sample during the lamination process. The data reveals five distinct phases: (I) Initial Drop, (II) Melting, (III) Cross-Linking and Stabilization, (IV) Cooling Phase, and (V) Second Cycle.

Phase III: Realignment, Cross-Linking and Network Formation (16 min – 121 min)
Following the melting phase, the ToF begins a steady, converging decrease throughout the remainder of the high-temperature plateau. This trend signifies a gradual and sustained increase in sound velocity. This phenomenon is directly attributed to structural changes such as the realignment of the polymer fibers and/or the peroxide-initiated cross-linking reaction. As covalent bonds form between adjacent polymer chains, a three-dimensional network structure is created. This network drastically increases the rigidity and structural integrity of the polymer melt [9]. The growing cross-link density progressively raises the elastic modulus, which in turn increases the sound velocity, resulting in a stable, reduced ToF. The convergence of the signal indicates the fiber realignment and reaction approaching completion.

Phase IV: Cooling Phase (121 min - 222 min)
Upon initiation of the cooling cycle by floating the chamber with room-temperature air, a further sharp decrease in ToF was recorded. As the temperature drops below the EVA melting regime (about 80 °C), molecular mobility of the polymer chains is reduced as crystallites reform. The material transitions from a rubbery melt to a semi-crystalline solid, leading to stiffening of the encapsulant, accompanied by a significant increase in its elastic modulus [15]. This thermo-physical stiffening during cooling leads to a continuous increase in sound velocity, observed as a decrease in ToF, consistent with previous ultrasound measurements of EVA cure and cooling behavior [9].

Phase V: Second Cycle and Structural Stability (222 min - 42 min)

A second thermal cycle was applied afterwards to the laminated sample. The ToF profile in this cycle is significantly different. It is a rather flat function at peak temperature without the pronounced, decreasing slope indicating the realignment/cross-linking progression, showing only reversible changes in ToF that mirror the temperature-induced changes in the elastic properties. A slight offset before and after the cycle is attributed to a slight displacement of the transducer when floating the setup with air.

The absence of the initial drop and realignment/cross-linking slope provides critical insight. The lamination process is almost complete after the first cycle. The reorientation of the fibers, the chemical (cross-linking) and physical (air expulsion) transformations are irreversible and permanent. The polymer network formed is stable and does not further cross-link or degrade upon re-heating. The small, almost reversible change confirms that the ultrasonic response is now fully dominated by the temperature dependence of the elastic constant of the solidified, cross-linked polymer.

3.2 Ultrasonic Monitoring of Thermal Cycling

For further confirmation of our interpretation, thermal cycling tests were carried out on unlaminated samples in order to stepwise laminate the samples during the process. The simultaneous ultrasonic and temperature measurements recorded over 250 minutes are presented in Figure 7. The sample was repeatedly cycled between 80 °C and 140 °C. The change in time-of-flight closely tracks each temperature cycle, increasing during heating and decreasing during cooling due to the thermoelastic softening and stiffening of the polymer.

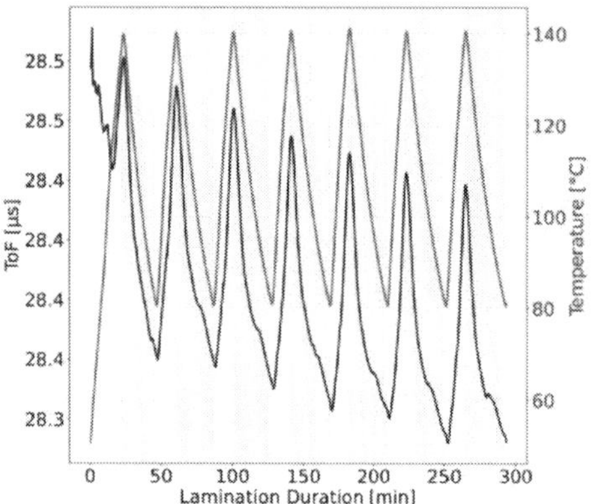

Figure 7. Time-of-Flight (ToF) evolution during successive EVA lamination cycles at temperatures between 80°C and 140°C, with the cooling phases marked blue.

As seen in our previous measurement (Figure 6), the ToF exhibits an indication of the different phases of the lamination process: A sharp initial drop in ToF during the first minutes of the first cycle aligns with the previously observed effects of compression, air expulsion, and early heating, reflecting densification of the EVA layer (Phase I). In the following temperature cycles between 80°C and 140°C, despite the temperature-induced softening and

hardening of the polymer during temperature change, an overall reduction in ToF can be observed. The decrease progressively continues with each cycle until it converges. This trend indicates ongoing material evolution, primarily attributed to realignment and cross-linking of the EVA fibers. Each cycle drives further network formation, increasing rigidity and sound velocity, consistent with the converging ToF reduction observed in the earlier monitoring experiment in Figure 6 (Phase III). The lamination experiment confirms that even under repeated thermal cycling, irreversible changes in the acoustic properties of the polymer continue to accumulate, providing a quantitative measure of progressive realignment/cross-linking and densification across cycles.

Furthermore, we evaluated the slope of the change in ToF with respect to temperature in each cooling phase (Figure 7). This quotient $dTof/T$ is a material-dependent parameter dependent on the structure and composition of the sample. In Figure 8, we can identify a similar behavior as we have previously seen for the ToF in Phase III (of Figures 6) and Figure 7, with a general downward trend and a convergence at the later cycles. Even though it is a different parameter, the observation can be attributed to the same origin. The continuing reduction is a result of the ongoing reorientation and cross-linking of the EVA fibers in each temperature cycle. The convergence in the later cycles indicates that the material changes are almost completed at this point, and the curing process is cumulative and irreversible.

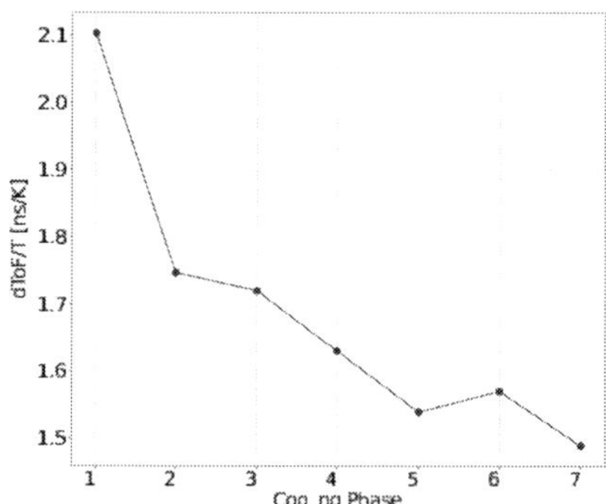

Figure 8. During the cooling phases (blue areas in Fig. 7) the ToF is proportional to temperature. The proportionality constant of each cycle is plotted here for each cooling phase.

3.3 Adhesion Testing

For comparison, mechanical shear tests were performed on laminates prepared with lamination durations capturing the critical phases of the process, as defined by the ToF and temperature profiles in Figure 6.

Samples from the early stages of the process (Phase I, Phase II) exhibited consistently low shear strength. Conversely, as the ToF decreases in Phase III, which we attributed to advancing fiber reorientation, cross-linking, and polymer network formation, achieved significantly higher shear strength, which increases as the cross-linking progresses. After the test, all samples showed a delamination of the EVA from the glass, and never a rupture within the EVA layer. This clearly shows that the dominant failure mode was driven by adhesion failure.

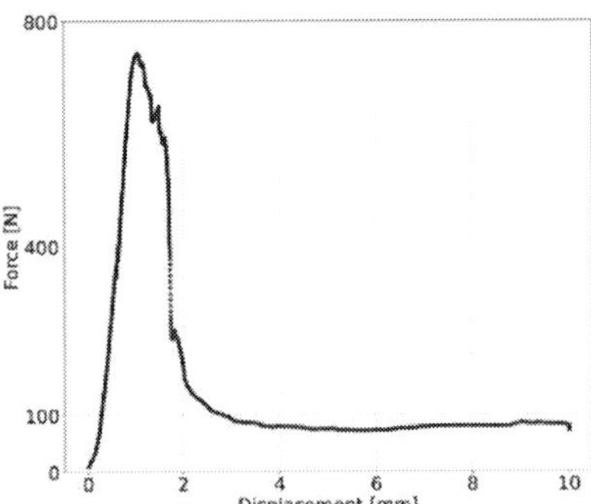

Figure 9. The measured force in dependence on the vertical displacement of the upper wedge recorded by a universal testing machine while performing the shear test (on an 80-minute laminated sample).

There is some statistical scatter in the shear strength data in Figure 10, which can be attributed to small variations during sample preparation and interfacial defects.

The samples were small (1 cm x 1 cm) and manually prepared. Small shifts of the glass during lamination could not be completely avoided and affected the shear strength. Larger samples would decrease the influence of those small variations but would also require higher shear forces, which would increase the probability of glass failure. So instead, to address that scatter, we decided on a more statistical analysis. The overarching trend is unambiguous: the development of mechanical adhesion strength closely follows the irreversible downward drift of the ToF baseline and thus the cross-linking progression. This indicates that the in-situ and non-destructively evaluated ultrasonic time-of-flight could be used as a promising and reliable indicator for the evolution of the adhesion state.

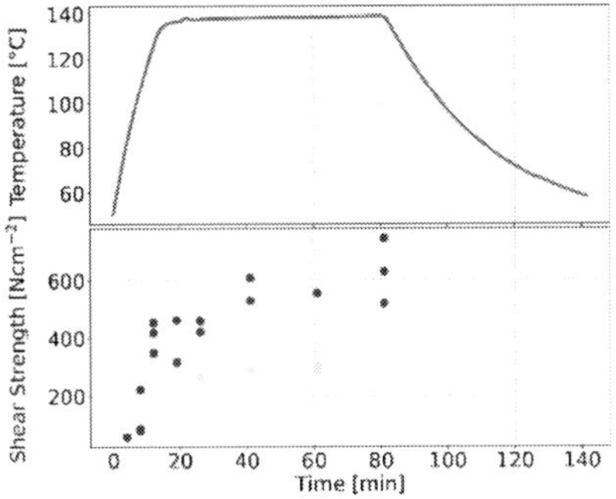

Figure 10. Shear tests show an increase in shear strength with lamination duration.

4 CONCLUSIONS

This study demonstrates that high-frequency longitudinal ultrasound can be utilized as a powerful tool for in-situ monitoring of the lamination process of glass-glass photovoltaic modules. The time-of-flight (ToF) of ultrasonic signals provides a real-time, non-destructive metric, sensitive to structural and chemical changes in the EVA encapsulant, successfully capturing five distinct lamination process phases: initial compression and air

expulsion, melting and moisture evaporation, fiber realignment/cross-linking and network formation, cooling and solidification.

The irreversible decrease in ToF during the high temperature phase of the lamination process was identified as a key indicator of polymer network formation, showing strong correlation with adhesion as validated through shear tests, which confirmed increasing adhesion strength with extended lamination time. Thermal cycling experiments on unlaminated samples revealed that the ultrasonic response comprises reversible thermoelastic variations during heating and cooling, superimposed on a progressive, irreversible decrease in ToF caused by permanent material changes, including cross-linking and densification of the EVA layer.

The consistent correlation between ultrasonic and mechanical adhesion measurements shows the robustness and reliability of this technique and the potential for non-destructive, real-time quantification of the lamination progression. This paper provides a strong foundation for the successful industrial implementation of an in-line ultrasonic monitoring tool, ensuring reliable quality control of the lamination process in PV manufacturing.

5. ACKNOWLEDGEMENTS

This work was generously supported by Franz-W. Aumund-Stiftung. We also thank Michael Wendt and his colleagues from Fraunhofer CSP for fruitful discussions and for providing EVA material. Finally, we thank Finn Ole Peterson and Leon Necat from HTW Berlin for sample preparation and setup optimization.

6. REFERENCES

[1] D. C. Jordan, S. R. Kurtz, K. VanSant, and J. Newmiller, "Compendium of photovoltaic degradation rates," *Progress in Photovoltaics: Research and Applications*, vol. 24, no. 7, pp. 978–989, Jul. 2016, doi: 10.1002/pip.2744.

[2] D. Wu *et al.*, "Influence of Lamination Conditions of EVA Encapsulation on Photovoltaic Module Durability," *Materials*, vol. 16, no. 21, Nov. 2023, doi: 10.3390/ma16216945.

[3] M. C. C. de Oliveira, A. S. A. Diniz Cardoso, M. M. Viana, and V. de F. C. Lins, "The causes and effects of degradation of encapsulant ethylene vinyl acetate copolymer (EVA) in crystalline silicon photovoltaic modules: A review," Jan. 01, 2018, *Elsevier Ltd.* doi: 10.1016/j.rser.2017.06.039.

[4] A. Kaan Öz, C. Herzog, C. Wellens, D. E. Mansour, M. Heinrich, and A. Kraft, "The Impact of the Lamination Process on the Adhesion Properties at the Glass-Encapsulant Interface and Damp Heat Stability of PV Modules," *38th European PV Solar Energy Conference and Exhibition, 6-10 September 2021*.

[5] O. K. Segbefia, A. G. Imenes, and T. O. Sætre, "Moisture ingress in photovoltaic modules: A review," Aug. 01, 2021, *Elsevier Ltd.* doi: 10.1016/j.solener.2021.06.055.

[6] M. Baiamonte, C. Colletti, A. Ragonesi, C. Gerardi, and N. T. Dintcheva, "Durability and Performance of Encapsulant Films for Bifacial Heterojunction Photovoltaic Modules," *Polymers (Basel)*, vol. 14, no. 5, Mar. 2022, doi: 10.3390/polym14051052.

[7] M. Sander, S. Dietrich, M. Pander, M. Ebert, and J. Bagdahn, "Systematic investigation of cracks in encapsulated solar cells after mechanical loading," 2013. doi: 10.1016/j.solmat.2012.12.031.

[8] M. Aghaei et al., "Review of degradation and failure phenomena in photovoltaic modules," May 01, 2022, *Elsevier Ltd.* doi: 10.1016/j.rser.2022.112160.

[9] W. Stark and M. Jaunich, "Investigation of Ethylene/Vinyl Acetate Copolymer (EVA) by thermal analysis DSC and DMA," *Polym Test*, vol. 30, no. 2, pp. 236–242, Apr. 2011, doi: 10.1016/j.polymertesting.2010.12.003.

[10] C. Hirschl et al., "Determining the degree of crosslinking of ethylene vinyl acetate photovoltaic module encapsulants - A comparative study," *Solar Energy Materials and Solar Cells*, vol. 116, pp. 203–218, 2013, doi: 10.1016/j.solmat.2013.04.022.

[11] R. Meier, I. M. Slauch, and M. I. Bertoni, "Ultrasonic Characterization of Ethylene Vinyl Acetate (EVA) Crosslinking for Quality Assurance and Lamination Process Control," *Proc. of the 50th IEEE Photovoltaic Specialists Conference (PVSC)*, pp. 1–5, 2023.

[12] M. Jaunich and W. Stark, "Monitoring the vulcanization of rubber with ultrasound: Influence of material thickness and temperature," *Polym Test*, vol. 28, no. 8, pp. 901–906, Dec. 2009, doi: 10.1016/j.polymertesting.2009.08.006.

[13] R. Kuwahara et al., "Crystallization and hardening of poly(ethylene-co-vinyl acetate) mouthguards during routine use," *Sci Rep*, vol. 7, Mar. 2017, doi: 10.1038/srep44672.

[14] K. Ono, "A comprehensive report on ultrasonic attenuation of engineering materials, including metals, ceramics, polymers, fiber-reinforced composites, wood, and rocks," Apr. 01, 2020, *MDPI AG.* doi: 10.3390/app10072230.

[15] J. Dutta and K. Naskar, "Investigation of morphology, mechanical, dynamic mechanical and thermal behaviour of blends based on ethylene vinyl acetate (EVA) and thermoplastic polyurethane (TPU)," *RSC Adv*, vol. 4, no. 105, pp. 60831–60841, 2014, doi: 10.1039/c4ra07823c.

Ultrasonic Characterization of Ethylene-Vinyl Acetate in Glass-Glass-Modules

__Christopher Bruce Konu[1]__, Rico Meier[1]

[1] University of Applied Sciences – HTW Berlin, Wilhelminenhofstr. 75a, D-12459 Berlin, Germany

MOTIVATION

Optimal processing of the EVA encapsulant during lamination is crucial to ensuring long-term photovoltaic (PV) module reliability and performance, preventing failures such as:

* Delamination compromising structural integrity.
* Humidity ingress leading to metallization corrosion.
* Local inhomogeneities causing property variations and failures [1].

Challenges

Traditional methods for evaluating EVA quality (Differential Scanning Calorimetry, Dynamic Mechanical Analysis, Peel Tests) are:

* Destructive, time-consuming, and costly.
* Limited to small selected samples and unable to monitor the lamination process of all modules in real time.

Goals

This study aims to:

* Develop a real-time ultrasonic method for EVA quality monitoring in glass-glass modules during lamination.
* Understand how polymer networks and additives influence ultrasound propagation during lamination.
* Adapt the method for various module designs and encapsulants.

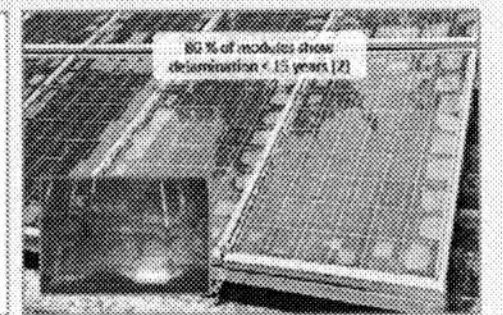

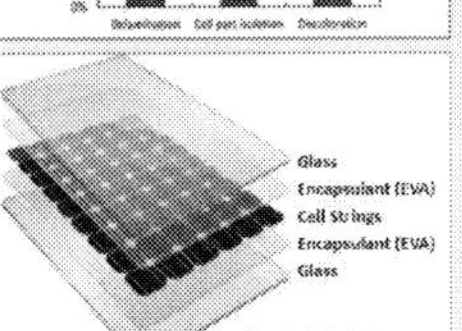

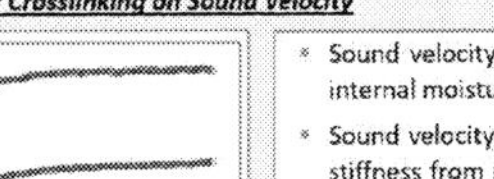

THEORETICAL BACKGROUND

Speed of Sound in Solid Materials

__The longitudinal speed of sound c_L depends on elastic modulus C_{ij} and density ρ.__

$$c_L = \sqrt{\frac{C_{ij}}{\rho}}$$

The Impact of Crosslinking on Sound Velocity

* Sound velocity decreases as a result of initial melting or initial internal moisture evaporating during heating.
* Sound velocity increases with lamination time due to increasing stiffness from polymer network formation, then converges once the network is fully formed.
* Higher frequencies result in higher sound velocities without affecting the overall shape of the graph [5].

RESEARCH METHODOLOGY

Ultrasonic Characterization

Ultrasound waves are transmitted through the sample, received by a transducer on the opposite side, then amplified and recorded.

Adhesion Testing

Laminated samples are shear tested in a 45° fixture. The force required for adhesion failure is recorded for each sample.

Change in Time-of-Flight Determination

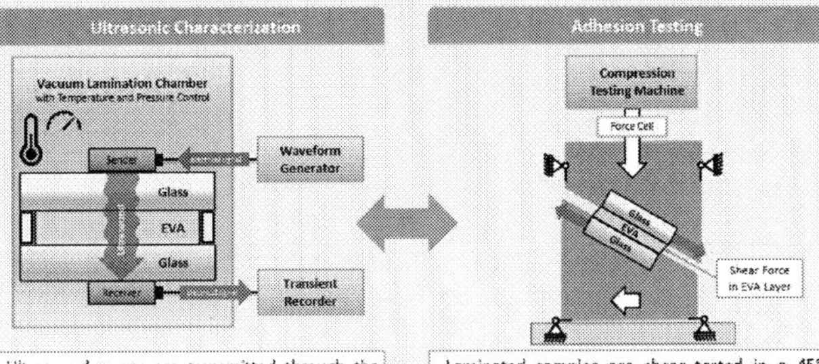

RESULTS

Samples were laminated at 140°C and 0.3 Pa absolute pressure for one hour and then cooled by room temperature air at atmospheric pressure. This cycle was repeated. Ultrasound transmission data was recorded in real-time. Samples at different stages of lamination were removed and shear tested.

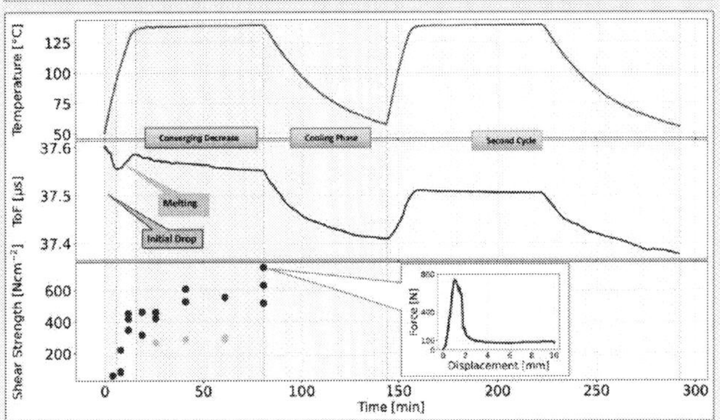

Ultrasound-Characterization:

* __Initial drop in ToF (0...6 min):__ corresponds to thickness reduction as air is expelled and sample compresses under pressure and heat while softening.
* __Melting onset (6...16 min):__ ToF increases as a result of EVA softening, melting and moisture evaporation during heating. Sound velocity drops due to the lower moduli of elasticity at higher temperatures.
* __Converging Decrease (16...121 min):__ ToF decreases and stabilizes, indicating increased sound velocity from crosslinking due to the growth of a stiffened polymer network.
* __Cooling Phase (121...222 min):__ Decrease in ToF due to the increase in elastic moduli at lower temperatures
* __Second cycle (222...429 min):__ Shows only minor irreversible changes, indicating that structural changes in first cycle were almost completed.

Adhesion Testing:

* High differences in delamination shear strength between the samples due to sample variations, local properties and occasional glass breakage → statistical analysis required
* Overall, the critical shear stress for delamination (shear strength) increased with lamination time.

CONCLUSION AND OUTLOOK

The evaluation of high-frequency longitudinal ultrasound transmitted through the thickness of solar glass-glass modules allowed for the identification of irreversible changes in the encapsulant's properties during lamination. This is a promising step towards the industrial realization of an ultrasonic technique for in-line polymer characterization during PV module manufacturing. Shear tests, while statistically scattered, confirmed the expected increase in shear strength with longer lamination durations.

Next Steps

__Comparing Ultrasonic Results to In-depth Polymer Analysis:__

* __Dynamic Mechanical Analysis (DMA):__ Mechanical characterization of the temperature-dependent elastic-viscoplastic material properties
* __Differential Scanning Calorimetry (DSC):__ Precise identification of melting points, crosslinking temperatures and progress.
* __Soxhlet Extraction (SE):__ Determination of gel content and crosslinking progress

__Polymer Variation__

* Characterization of the influence of different additives (adhesion promoters, crosslinking agents). Decoupling of adhesion and crosslinking behavior and their ultrasonic fingerprint.
* Transfer of the method to new polymers e.g. Polyolefin Elastomers (POE) or polymer coatings

__Polymer Ageing__

* Characterization of the ultrasonic properties during polymer ageing under different environmental stressors (UV, heat, humidity)

ACKNOWLEDGEMENTS

This work was generously supported by _Franz-W. Aumund-Stiftung_. We also thank Michael Wendt and his colleagues from Fraunhofer CSP for fruitful discussions and for providing EVA material. Finally, we thank Finn Ole Peterson and Leon Necat from HTW Berlin for sample preparation and setup optimization.

REFERENCES

1. Meier, R., Slauch, I. M., Bertoni, M. I. (2023). _Ultrasonic Characterization of Ethylene Vinyl Acetate (EVA) Crosslinking for Quality Assurance and Lamination Process Control._ Proc. of the 50th IEEE Photovoltaic Specialists Conference (PVSC), 1-5.
2. Wohlgemuth, J., Silverman, T., Miller, D. C., McNutt, P., Kempe, M., Deceglie, M.,(2015). _Evaluation of PV module field performance._ IEEE 42nd Photovoltaic Specialist Conference. PVSC 2015. Institute of Electrical and Electronics Engineers Inc., Dec. 2015.
3. Polverini, D., Alfieri, F., Spiliotopoulos, C., and Arcipowska, A. (2024). _Towards a recyclability index for photovoltaic modules: Methodology, challenges and policy implications._ Progress in Photovoltaics: Research and Applications, 10.1002/pip.3781.
4. Dodd, N., Espinosa Martinez, M.D.L.N., Van Tichelen, P., Peeters, K. and Soares, A. (2020). _Preparatory study for solar photovoltaic modules, inverters and systems,_ EUR 30468 EN, Publications Office of the European Union, Luxembourg, 2020, JRC122431.
5. Stark, W., Jaunich, M., Bohmeyer, W., Lange, K. (2012). _Investigation of the crosslinking behavior of ethylene vinyl acetate (EVA) for solar cell encapsulation by rheology and ultrasound._ Polymer Testing, 31(7), 904-908.

COMPARISON OF DIFFERENT ECAs APPLIED TO PK/SI TANDEM SOLAR CELLS IN A MINI-MODULE CONFIGURATION

F. Mouhoubi [1], V. Barth[1], S. Berson[1]
[1] Univ. Grenoble Alpes, CEA Liten, Campus INES, Le Bourget du Lac, France.
Contact: felicia.mouhoubi@cea.fr

Context and motivations

- High efficiency: perovskite-silicon tandem cells outperform conventional cells
- Key limitation: degradation under humidity, oxygen and temperature exposure
- Current progress in the field:

→ **Qcells**: Record 28 ± 1.5% (M10 commercial module, 330 cm²).
→ **Fraunhofer & Oxford PV**: Certified module, 25% efficiency.
→ **Trina Solar**: Large-area module (3.1 m²), 808 W output, TÜV SÜD certified [a,b,c]

Objectives

❖ **Apply ECAs** as an interconnection solution
❖ **Assess compatibility** with PK–Si tandem solar cells
❖ **Evaluate electrical & mechanical properties**
❖ **Assess stability** during dark aging and thermal cycling

Goal → Enable stable and reliable interconnection of perovskite-silicon tandem solar cell by mitigating degradation during this step and beyond

Materials & Methods

- **Mini-modules:** Perovskite–silicon tandem solar cells (two architectures) + Silicon solar cells with tandem FS materials
- **Active area:** 8.5 cm²
- **Metallization:** Silver screen-printed, cured at ultra-low-temperature

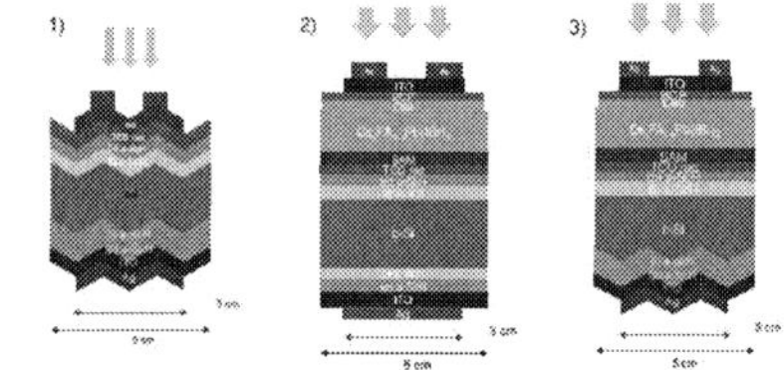

Fig 1. cell schematics used for interconnection and encapsulation

- **Encapsulation:** TPO with edge sealant
- **Architecture:** Glass–glass

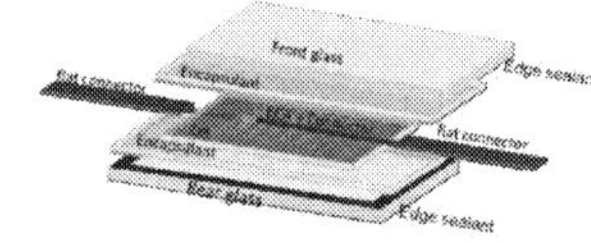

Fig 2. Schematic view and an image of a tandem mini-module

- **Approach:** Test ultra-low-temperature ECAs (<150 °C) for interconnection

ECA	Matrix	% Ag
A1 ref	Acrylate	~55
A2	Acrylate	~90
A3	Acrylate	~46
E1	Epoxy	~40
[illegible]	[illegible]	[illegible]

A1 reference: single junction & tandem

- **Evaluation:**
  - Compare behavior of cells interconnected with different ECAs
  - Evaluate **electrical** properties and **stability**
    - **Environmental stability testing:**
      - Dark storage over several days
      - Thermal cycling (TC)

Results

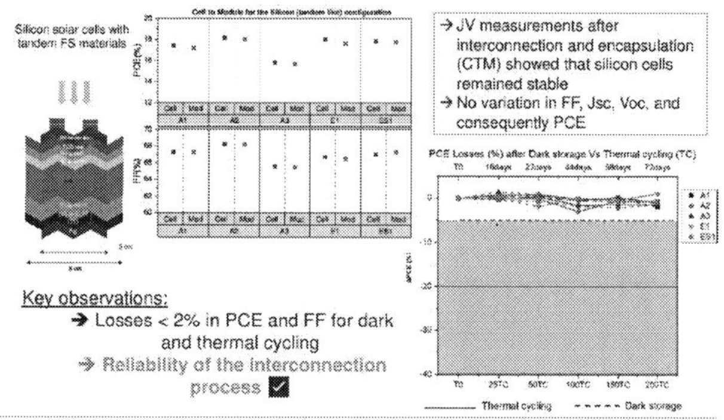

→ JV measurements after interconnection and encapsulation (CTM) showed that silicon cells remained stable
→ No variation in FF, Jsc, Voc, and consequently PCE

Key observations:
→ Losses < 2% in PCE and FF for dark and thermal cycling
→ Reliability of the interconnection process ✓

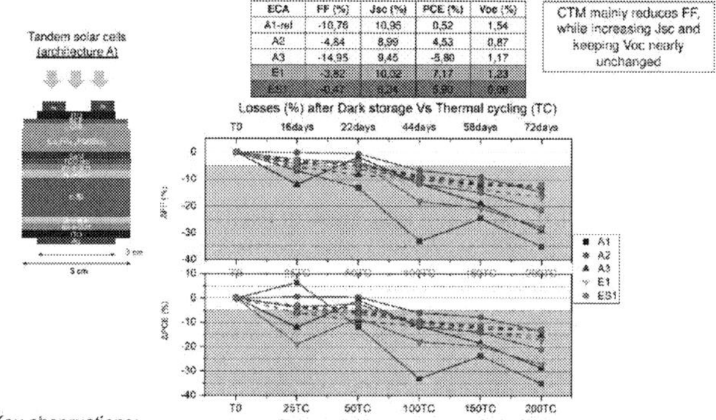

ECA	FF (%)	Jsc (%)	PCE (%)	Voc (%)
A1-ref	-10,76	10,95	0,52	1,54
A2	-4,84	8,99	4,53	0,87
A3	-14,95	9,45	-5,80	1,17
E1	-3,82	10,02	7,17	1,23
[illegible]	-0,47	6,24	5,90	0,06

CTM mainly reduces FF, while increasing Jsc and keeping Voc nearly unchanged

Key observations:
→ PCE losses > 10% for most modules
- « A1 ref » loses 35% of PCE & FF after 200 TC cycles
- « A2 » loses less than 15% of PCE and FF after 200 TC cycles and dark storage
→ Degradation of the top cell under both dark storage and thermal aging
→ Interconnection affects the cell, reducing its performance

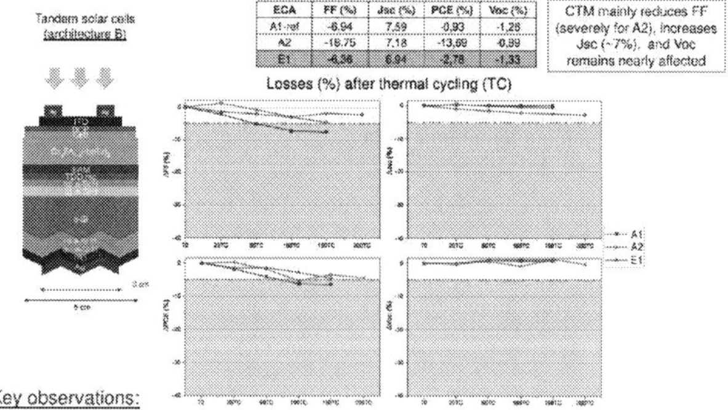

ECA	FF (%)	Jsc (%)	PCE (%)	Voc (%)
A1-ref	-6,94	7,59	-0,93	-1,26
A2	-18,75	7,18	-13,69	-0,89
E1	-6,36	6,94	-2,78	-1,33

CTM mainly reduces FF (severely for A2), increases Jsc (~7%), and Voc remains nearly affected

Key observations:
A1: FF drops → PCE loss
→ Due to top cell degradation and interconnection instability
A2: Jsc & FF losses
→ Caused by partial top cell degradation and current mismatch in tandem
E1: FF loss only → PCE loss < 5%
→ Most suitable ECA at this stage

Conclusion

- Ultra-low-temperature ECA interconnection ensures reliable and stable module assembly.
- **Tandem modules** show that top cell degradation and interconnection quality strongly affect performance.
- Some modules remain stable with minimal PCE loss (<5%) under thermal cycling.
- Correlation between ECA properties and module performance is under investigation, highlighting the importance of formulation and module architecture for long-term stability and performance.

a) Bhambhani, A. *Fraunhofer ISE & Oxford PV Achieve 25% Tandem Module Efficiency.* TaiyangNews. https://taiyangnews.info/fraunhofer-ise-oxford-pv-achieve-25-tandem-module-efficiency
b) *US/Trinasolar Develops World's First 800W+ Tandem Module. Ushering in a New Era.* Trinasolar. https://static.trinasolar.com/us/resources/newsroom/Worlds-First-800W-Tandem-Module
c) *Qcells Achieves World Record Efficiency for Commercially Scalable Perovskite-Silicon Tandem Solar Cell - Qcells North America.* https://us.qcells.com/blog/qcells-tandem-cell-world-record-efficiency

020134-001

EU PVSEC
22 — 26
September
BEC
Bilbao Exhibition Centre
Bilbao
Spain
EU PVSEC 2025
42nd European Photovoltaic Solar Energy Conference and Exhibition
030001-001

Conference Highlights

Robert Kenny
European Commission Joint Research Centre
EU PVSEC Technical Programme Chair

EU PVSEC
FACTS & FIGURES | Presentations
EU PVSEC 2025
EU PVSEC Programme -
Distribution of
Presentations per Type
CONFERENCE PLENARIES & ORALS
349
CONFERENCE VISUALS
562
OPENING & CLOSING
6
1000+
PRESENTATIONS
4
PANEL DISCUSSIONS WITH
29
PANELISTS
PARALLEL EVENTS
110
INDUSTRY SUMMIT
44

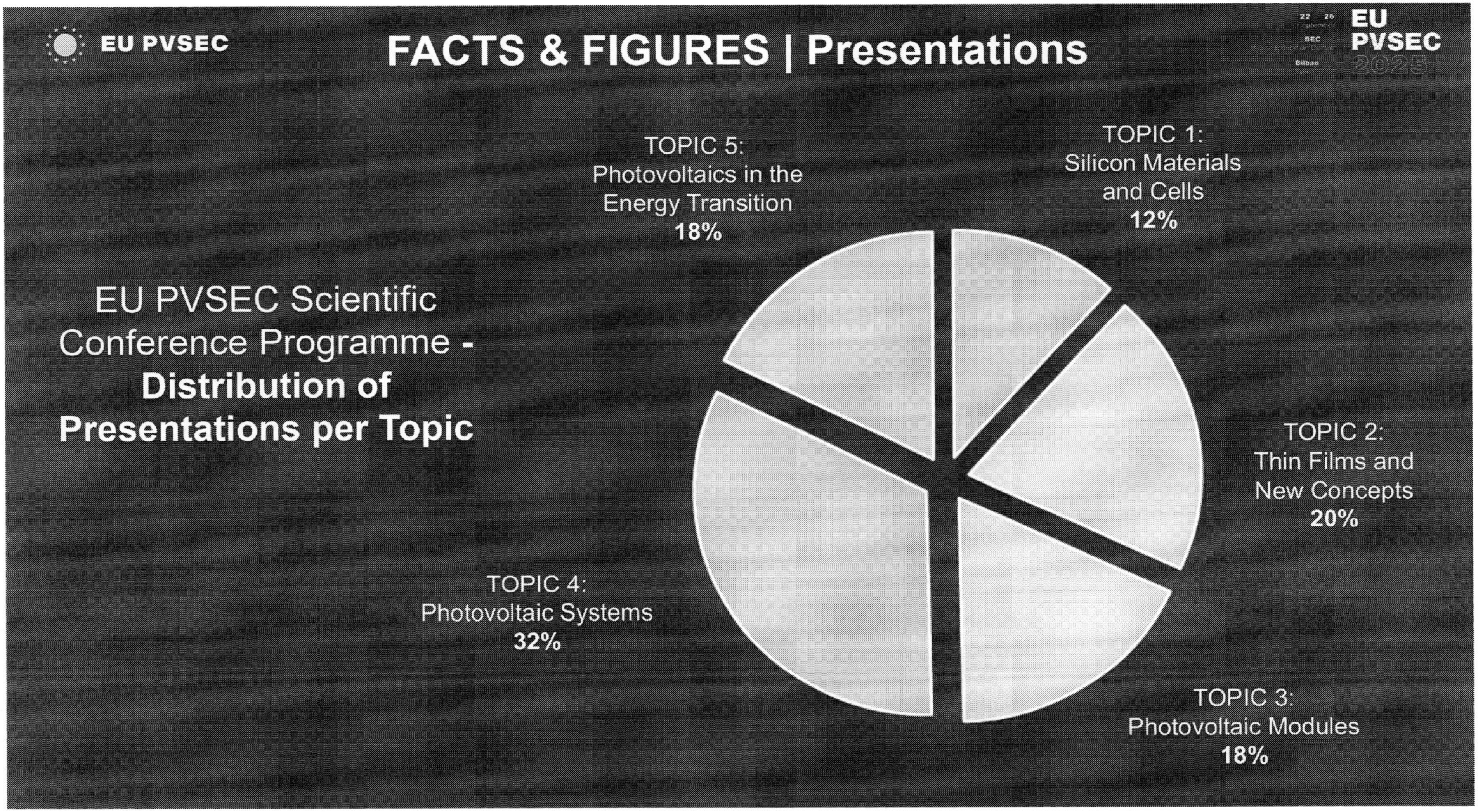

EU PVSEC
FACTS & FIGURES | Presentations
EU PVSEC 2025
EU PVSEC Scientific Conference Programme - Distribution of Presentations per Topic
TOPIC 5:
Photovoltaics in the Energy Transition
18%
TOPIC 1:
Silicon Materials and Cells
12%
TOPIC 2:
Thin Films and New Concepts
20%
TOPIC 3:
Photovoltaic Modules
18%
TOPIC 4:
Photovoltaic Systems
32%
030001-005

FACTS & FIGURES | Participants

Participants by Countries
Top 10

No	Country	Participants
1	Germany	310
2	Spain	270
3	France	108
4	Italy	90
5	The Netherlands	76
6	South Korea	67
7	Switzerland	62
8	Japan	55
9	Belgium	44
10	Norway	35

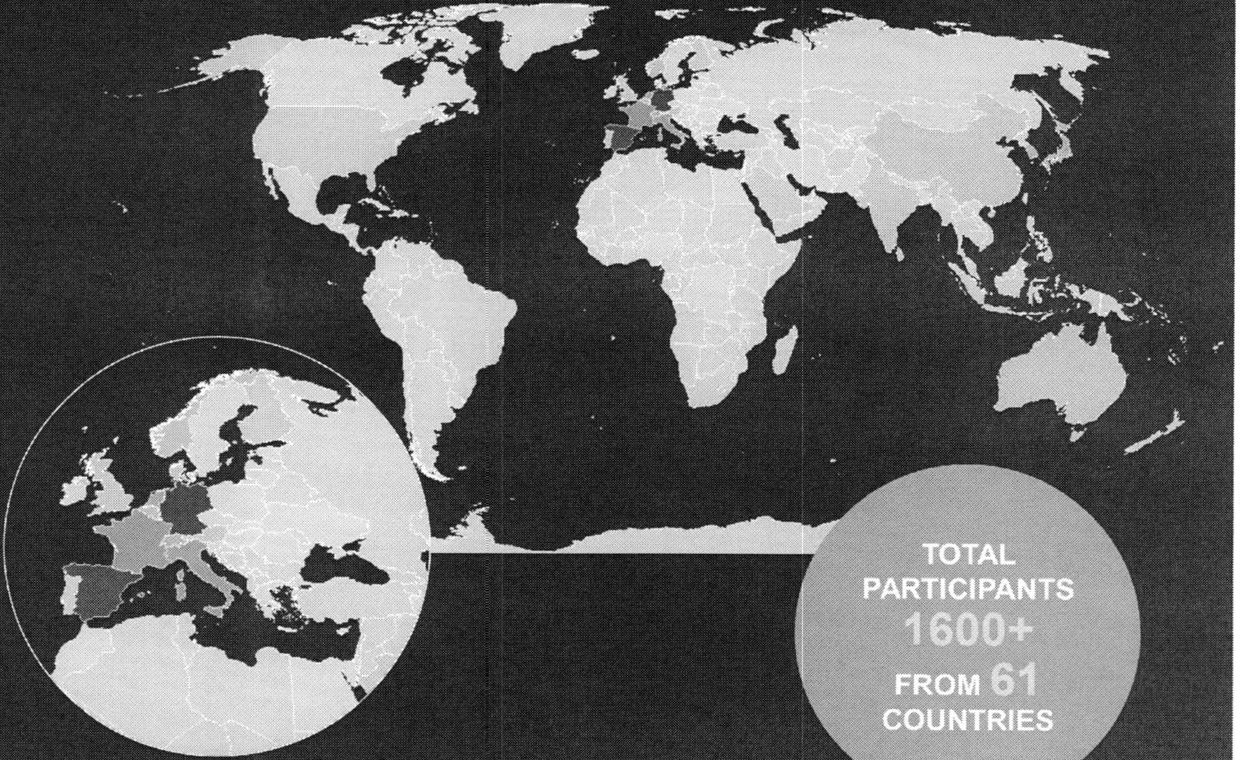

Plenary Session "PV Everywhere"
OPENING
Monday, 22 Sept. 2025
Welcome Messages
Carlos DEL CAÑIZO
jon DE GREGORIO
Gaëtan MASSON
Key Note Speech "The Dual Face of Global Solar Growth"
Becquerel Prize Ceremony
Moderated Panel Discussion "Solar in Turbulent Times: Global Dynamics and the Way Forward"
Torsten BRAMMER

EU PVSEC
PANEL DISCUSSIONS
22 26
BEC
Bilbao
EU PVSEC
2025

BO.13 Reliability and Bankability in PV
"The rapid developments of PV technology require increased attention to be paid to reliability testing."

CO.7 Challenges and Opportunities of PV up to 2030
"PV Technology is already reliable and cost effective, and even though improvements are welcome, key blockages are storage and grid strengthening. AI and robotics are essential to meet the scale of developments needed."

DO.13 Scalability and Manufacturability Prospects in Europe for New Technologies
"The prospects for reaching the 30GW target for PV module manufacturing in Europe were discussed and policy measures proposed."

030001-008

EU
PVSEC
2025

CONFERENCE

KEY MESSAGES

Cross-cutting themes emerged throughout the programme, showcasing how solar technologies can be applied everywhere, from traditional to emerging fields.

- Sustainability and circularity remain central, with research focused on reducing material use, such as replacing silver with copper, and advancing end-of-life management of modules.

- Ensuring long-term stability and predictable energy yield is equally essential, with studies of degradation mechanisms such as UVID carried out.

- The role of AI across the PV value chain is rapidly expanding, from design to operations and maintenance, including drone applications.

CONFERENCE

TOPIC 1: SILICON MATERIALS AND CELLS

Enhancements in IV measurement procedures

- Michael Rauer, Fraunhofer ISE: 1AO.4.5 *Universal Contacting Approaches for the Characterization of Solar Cells*
- Shuai Nie, UNSW: 1AO.4.6 *Contact-Free J-V: a Simple Technique for Universal State-of-the-Art Solar Cells*

Replacement of critical by sustainable materials:

- Reduced Ag consumpion e.g. by replacing by Cu (plating)
- In-free SHJ solar cells and Pero-Si tandems

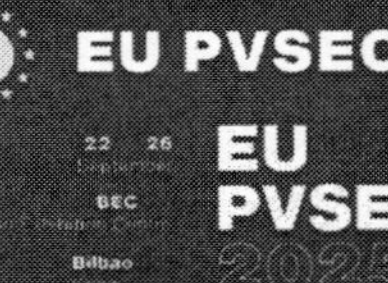

CONFERENCE

TOPIC 1: SILICON MATERIALS AND CELLS

Great advance in understanding of UV induced degradation and Hydrogen related degradation

- Excellent PLENARY by Bram Hoex (presenting for Muhammad Umair Khan), UNSW: 1CP.3.5 *Understanding the Root Cause of UV-Induced Degradation in TOPCon and PERC Solar Cells*

Further high quality orals:

- Christina Hollemann, ISFH: 1AO.4.2 *Mitigating UV-Induced Degradation: Impact of PECVD and PEALD AlOx Layers Deposited in a Tube-Type Direct Plasma-Enhanced Chemical Vapor Deposition System*
- Hugo Lajoie, CEA: 1AO.4.3 *New Insights on UV-Induced Degradation of SHJ Solar Cells*
- Byungsul Min, ISFH: 1BO.3.6 *UV Stable Passivation Stack with Plasma-Enhanced Atomic Layer Deposition of Aluminum Oxide from an Industrial Tube-Type Direct Plasma-Enhanced Chemical Vapor Deposition System*
- Wolfram Kwapil, Fraunhofer ISE: 1AO.5.6 *Impact of Illumination on Solar Cell Properties: Insights into Atomic Hydrogen Release*

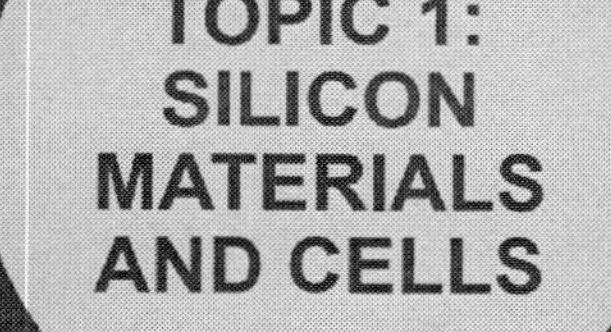

CONFERENCE

Advances in TOPCon and SHJ technology → Pushing the Limits of Performance

- Fantastic keynote lecture (PLENARY) on heterojunction solar cells by Dr. Guangtao Yang, Trina: 1CP.1.1 *Silicon Surface and Interface Study for >27% Efficient SHJ Solar Cell*
  - Deep insight into technological aspects eg. influence of rear side polishing on cell performance
  - Very high efficiencies for both-sides contacted HJT > 27%
  - Issues with CAPEX, sustainibility (Ag, In)
  - Pero-Si tandem cells on large area and modules

Late News Presentation on 27.8% efficient back contact silicon solar cells by Hua Wu, Longhi: 1DO.9.1 *Hybrid Interdigitated Back Contact Silicon Solar Cells with Superior Efficiency*

Late News Presentation as TOPCon for Bottom Solar Cells in Pero-Si Tandem devices by Jana Polzin-Isabelle Polzin, Fraunhofer ISE: 1DO.9.3 *Silicon Solar Cells – From High Efficiency Single-junction to Bottom Cells in Two-Terminal Perovskite-Silicon Tandem Devices*

CONFERENCE

TOPIC 1: SILICON MATERIALS AND CELLS

Further high quality orals:

- Hua Wu, Longhi: 1DO.9.1 *Hybrid Interdigitated Back Contact Silicon Solar Cells with Superior Efficiency*
- Daming Chen, Trina: 1AO.5.1 *Large Area i-TOPCon Solar Cells with 25.9% Record Efficiency*
- Maysa Sarsour, UNSW: 1AO.6.1 *Evaluating Silicon Heterojunction Solar Cell Stability under Industrial Illuminated Hydrogenation Conditions*

Bottom cell optimization for Pero-Si tandems

CONFERENCE

**TOPIC 2:
THIN FILMS
AND NEW
CONCEPTS**

A lot of focus on the long-term stability improvement and upscaling of tandem devices based on a variety of materials (hence not only pero-Si).

Many companies (e.g. Hanwha Q-cells, Oxford PV, Microquanta Seminconductor, Jinko Solar, Longi, etc. non-exhaustive list) presented impressive results on industrial size single-junction pero modules and pero-based tandem modules. A highlight here was the plenary talk from Hanwha Q-cells showing a record large area (M10) pilot-scale Pk/Si tandem cell of 28.6% efficiency.

CONFERENCE

**TOPIC 2:
THIN FILMS
AND NEW
CONCEPTS**

In the field of pero-Si tandems, there is clearly more focus on improving the stability of the tandem devices than before with many contributions doing in-depth investigations into the different degradation mechanisms that can occur in pero-Si tandems.

In this respect, 2DO9.5 presented a consensus statement about reliability testing of perovskite-based tandems that is endorsed by specialists worldwide from both industry and research and presents a kind of minimum that should be done in terms of testing and reporting concerning the stability and lifetime of perovskite-based tandem devices.

More and more advanced characterization methods for perovskite and perovskite - silicon tandem solar cells are being used, hyperspectral imaging methods identify non-uniformities by layer for processing development.

CONFERENCE

Another clear trend is that pero-TOPCon cells are nearing the same record efficiencies as pero-Heterojunction cells. A highlight talk here was the certified 34.22% efficiency perovskite/ topcon tandem solar cell(1cm2) by Jinko Solar 2CO2.1

Another highlight was the 30.5% triple junction pero/pero/silicon cell by EPFL (2CO2.3)

In the field of perovskite single junction devices, 2DO.7.3 showed perovskite devices with remarkable reliability, withstanding 4 years of outdoor exposure. The degradation mechanism is attributed to the diurnal behaviour, also verified and replicated with indoor experiments.

2AO3.6 investigated experimental degradation and recovery of perovskite solar cells, improving the comprehension of instability's dynamics, to extend the lifetime of devices.

CONFERENCE

TOPIC 2:
THIN FILMS
AND NEW
CONCEPTS

In the field of compound semiconductors, there were many presentations on alternative materials for perovskite in tandems. In this way, first monolithic (AgCu)(InGa)Se2 on Si tandem cells were demonstrated as well as 16.1% semitransparent Ag doped Cu(InGa)S2 sulfide top cells.

An exciting highlight in this field was 2BO8.2 in which UPC Barcelona achieved 18% efficiency under indoor lighting for kesterite solar cells with alkali doping

EU PVSEC
22 26 September
BEC
Bilbao Spain

EU
PVSEC
2025

CONFERENCE

TOPIC 3:
PHOTOVOLTAIC
MODULES

"Reliable packaging to Maximize the energy yield from high efficiency cells"

big theme: Optimizing module materials and packaging for long lifetime and predictable energy yield from high efficiency cells. The industry and research community are moving quickly to assess and improve reliability.

• Understanding, accelerated testing, and mitigating UV-ID in n-type cells and modules

• How do you develop accelerated tests for constantly changing BOMs - new encapsulants, new metallization, thinner glass, and high efficiency cells

030001-018

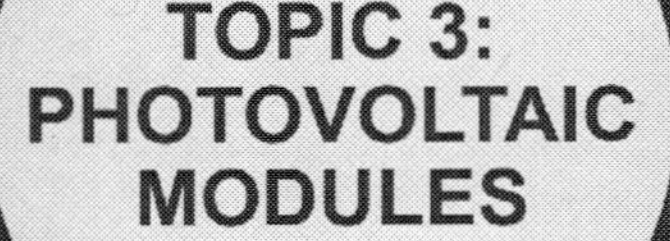

CONFERENCE

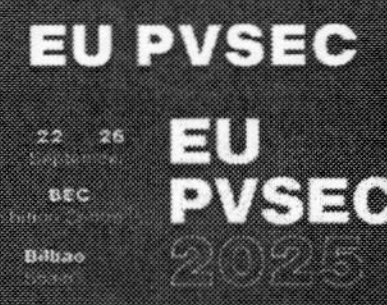

- Degradation and metastability in packaged perovskite tandems - understanding energy yield and realistic degradation rates

- Characterization out of the lab and into the field and factory - accurate outdoor performance, online quality control measurements for encapsulant cross linking

- Reducing silver content and metallization temperatures - reliability of low temperature and low silver metallization

- Developing glass qualification requirements to minimize breakage

CONFERENCE

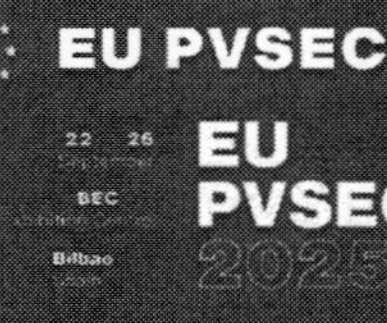

Advances in O&M of PV systems

(4CV.1) focuses on fault detection, cleaning optimization, soiling (and snow 4CO.8), UAV for autonomous monitoring and digital twin.

Data driven and AI based O&M (4CO.9) including a medicine-like workflow in Autonomous multi-AI agent system for health monitoring: a fully automated O&M pipeline with field robotics (4CO.9.4 D. Moser, EURAC)

PV Everywhere from space to agricultural applications like integration in vineyards (Mo, Opening plenary) and many other **integrated options** as we have seen throughout the week. On Thursday (4DO.4) agriPV, noise barriers and floating integrated systems. AgriPV technologies (4DO.2), BIPV

PV needs solar energy. **Solar resource and forecasting** (Mo, 4AO.7-9 & Tu 4BV.3). Shortly IEA PVPS T16 will publish minute irradiance data, some including GT over 220 stations worldwide with. Same format and quality controlled. (*Worldwide solar radiation measurement database with quality-control added value*, Anne Forstinger CSP Services, 4AO.7.1)

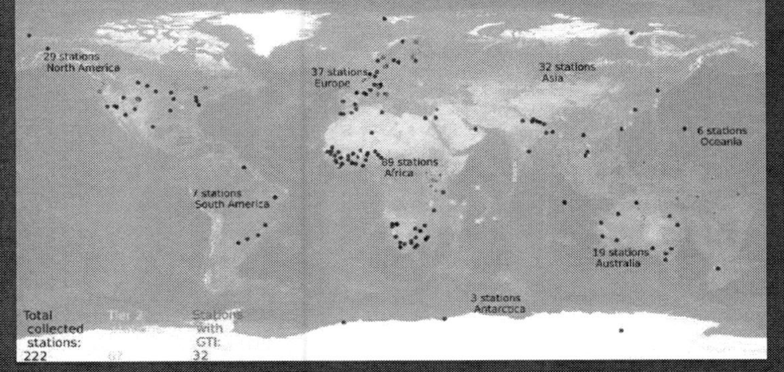

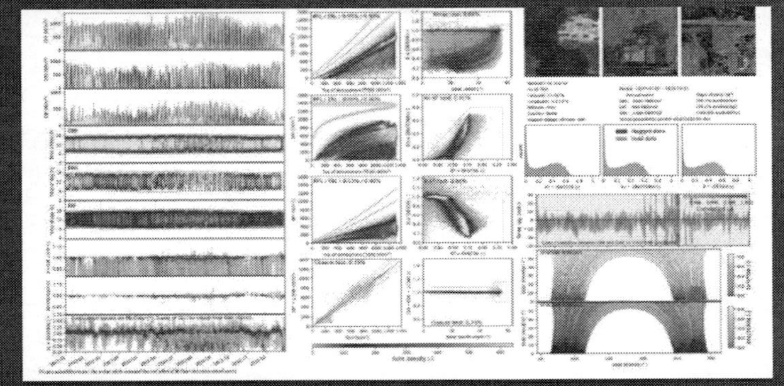

(4BV.3). Poster winner 4BV.3.12 *Advancing Very Short-Term Solar Irradiance Forecasting in Africa: A Low-Cost Sky Imaging and Machine Learning-Based Approach*, implications for PV deployment and grid integration (Martin Ansong, KIT). Runner-up 4BV.3.25 *Evaluating the Suitability of Köppen-Geiger Climate Classifications for Photovoltaic Systems: Micro-climate Analysis and Risk Assessment Maps*, with worldwide distribution of humidity related risk assessment for PV performance (Pavan Kumar Panda, Anhalt University of Applied Sciences).

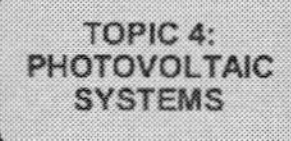

Integrated PV

BIPV (4BO.16) examples of coloured modules (which was main topic of the poster session along with fire concerns of BIPV, 4BV.4), lightweight solutions (4BO.5) and modelling partial shading effects 4BO.17.1, *Modelling partial shading at the cell level on PV modules,* Jean-Paul Calin, ENSTA) and 4BO.17.3, *Comparing the energy yield and degradation rates of smart PV modules compared to conventional PV system designs in shaded urban scenario's,* Youri Blom, TU DELF.

AgriPV 4DO.2 the room was fully packed showing the interest in the topic. 5 talks were on new ways of sharing light (2 spectral splitting before the PV conversion, 2 semitransparent PV modules both c-Si and CdTe, 1 on downshifting encapsulate) + 1 new AgrivPV like application with Algae instead of crops.

4DO.4 also included AgriPV and **Others types of integration like noise barriers and floating.** In addition to performance other aspects like (*Hydrological and ecological effects on floating PV,* Konstantin Ilgen, FHO ISe) have been highlighted this week

4DO4.2

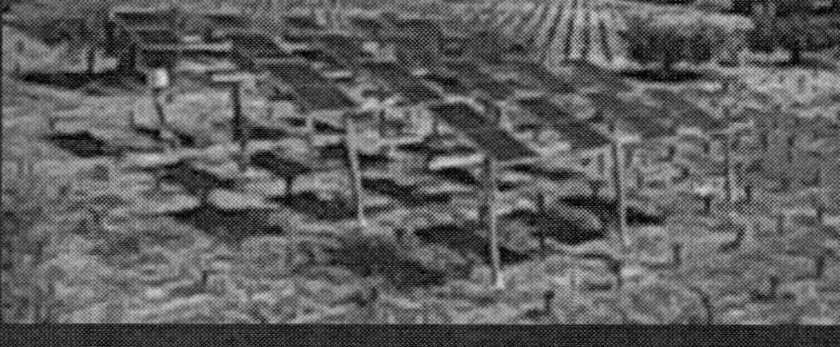

BOS and tracking systems (4DO.1) focused on backtracking strategies and terrains with complex topography.

4DO.1.4

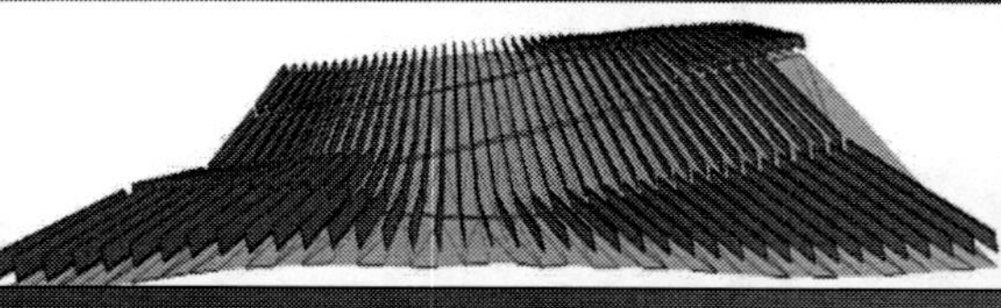

CONFERENCE

TOPIC 4: PHOTOVOLTAIC SYSTEMS

Reliability of PV systems

Several presentations focused long-term monitored degradation, failure modes and degradation modes identification techniques (non-destructive, aerial images, AI-based)

4BO.6.1 *Three decades, three climates: insights and lessons on PV reliability.* Good BOM offer very high reliability in power production, with 30-35 years old modules showing 0.24% degradation rate per year.

4BO.6.3 *Non-destructive detection of water ingress in solar modules using NIR spectroscopy* (Oleksandr Mashkow HI ERN) proved near-infrared absorption (NIRA) technique to detect water ingress in modules in the field, which correlated with the module degradation.

4BO.7.2 *Robust PV performance loss rate calculation for high latitudes* (Lauri Karttunen, Meteo Inst Helsinki) and 4BO.7. 3 *Detailed analysis of degradation rates of operating PV assets in tropical climate conditions* (Xioaqi Xu, Seris Singapore) Performance loss rates reported for high latitudes and tropics based on solid data sets. PLR in the tropics -1.4%/year

4DO.3.6 PV system design and assessment highlighted how inverter safety issues are extremely important and how more research about inverter safety and reliability is needed.

EU PVSEC
22 26
September
BEC
Bilbao
Spain
EU PVSEC
2025
CONFERENCE
TOPIC 5:
PHOTOVOLTAICS
IN THE ENERGY
TRANSITION
Main topics of interest :
• Flexibility
• Artificial intelligence
• EoL management
030001-024

CONFERENCE

5.1 Grid Integration and Flexibility Enablers (2 sessions)

- Smoothing effect related to different orientations of PV systems in a given area allows 10 to 15% additional hosting capacity of the distribution grid compared to the conservative calculation that consists in summing the AC power. Such accurate calculation enabled by high resolution large area images and LIDAR and induces therefore very low costs.

5.2 Sustainability of PV (4 sessions)

- New inventories LCI and LCA for emerging technologies even though lack of data for perovskites, LCA showing a way for low environmental Impacts with technology improvement and localisation. / Technological improvements will contribute to the reduction of environmental Impact / Grid Efficiency has an Impact on the environmental Footprint.

- Manufacturing optimization / Reuse & recycling: results from the perspective of economic performance – would it convince manufacturer to consider it if economic benefit ?

- EoL Management /recycling -> emerging field attracting lots of activities / mainly EU projects (EVERPV / ICARUS / QASAR) – highlight on polymer, interesting question came up and to be debated for the next decade: is it worth it to consider polymer (EVA/ backsheet) recycling ?

- Major progress in methodology and indicators to assess sustainable design & circularity and improve transparency recyclability index, technical recyclability, digital passport)

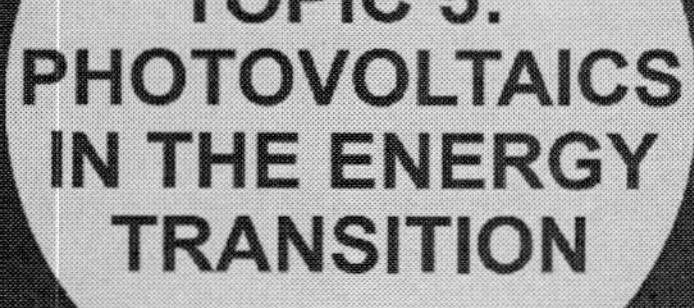

CONFERENCE

5.3 Scenarios for Renewables, Policy, Global Challenges (1 session)

- wide scope of contributions on the way to massive, medium- to long-term PV deployment -> should not be taken for granted despite positive projections since there can be limiting factors such as public acceptance / regulatory restrictions and effect of climate change

5.4 Costs, Economics, Finance and Markets (1 session)

- Annual installed capacity over 400 GWp / total cumulative installed capacity worldwide over 2.1 TWp / Clear mismatch between PV module installations rate worldwide and PV module production rate leading to bunch of inventories and drastically reduced prices.

5.6 Societal Challenges; Citizens' Participation, Awareness (1 session)

- data and analysis in gender aspects are emerging in PV! (poster session) + Highlight on innovation in education! On example that targets students & skilled workers -> mobile Lab for advanced experimental training PV-related to bring skills and characterization tools everywhere.

PARALLEL
EVENTS
Collaborat Network
Diversity
Prejudice
Justifica
Change
Needs — Profile Match
Avoid Blind Spots
Job cost?
Integration
Lack of Attraction
Resilience (People + Company)
Creativity
Different Communica
Internal Friction
More effort

PARALLEL EVENTS

- Perovskite Innovation Roundtable: Driving EU Leadership in Perovskite Innovation
- Women in PV presents: Leading with Inclusion – Embracing the 6 Traits of Inclusive Leadership
- Unlocking the Potential of Integrated Photovoltaic Systems - European R&D Approach
- Why Do PV Plants Perform Lower than Expected? (Estimating losses by backtracking algorithms in undulating terrain & Analysis of the loss chain and identification of deviations from initial expectations)
- PV Made in the EU: How Do Companies Die and How Can They Thrive?

22 — 26
September
BEC
Bilbao Exhibition Centre
Bilbao — Spain
EU
PVSEC
2025
42nd European
Photovoltaic Solar Energy
Conference and Exhibition
GEOPOLITICS & PV MANUFACTURING CHALLENGES
EXHIBITION
FORUM
INDUSTRY
SUMMIT
The road to a
sustainable future

Industry Summit Opening (session I)

Session Title: Solar PV production in Europe - the way forward

Moderators: Begoña Molinete, Walburga Hemetsberger

Key Takeaway:

This session discussed the state of play of European manufacturing projects and whether there is enough European support. It was clear that political support is further lacking – only 3 Member States have developed schemes to support European manufacturing. While the Net Zero Industry Act is helpful to diversify supplies, it will not particularly support European manufacturing.

All panellists agreed that apart from further policy support (financing, derisking) collaboration is the way forward.

EU PVSEC

EU PVSEC 2025

INDUSTRY SUMMIT

Session II
Session Title: International corporations in the light of changing geopolitics
Moderators: Radovan Kopecek, Puzant Baliozian

Key takeaway:
EU machine builders are still supporting mostly Indian but also US and EU projects with their technology and expertise. The major arguments for choosing EU tech are quality, training, support and low OPEX.

Session III
Session Title: PV Systems: How do we get the produced electricity in Europe into the grid?
Moderators: Catarina Augusto, Peter Fath

Key Takeaway:
Hybrid PV + storage systems (co-located or distributed) are essential for integrating PV into electricity grids. Storage adds flexibility and stabilizes the grid, making it a cornerstone of resilient energy systems; while the technology is mature, scalable and bankable revenue models remain the key gap for widespread deployment.

LIST OF EXHIBITORS
(in alphabetical order)

Company name	Country
2nd Cycle FlexCo	Austria
9-Tech	Italy
Avalon ST / Pasan	Switzerland
BASQUENERGY Cluster	Spain
Becquerel Institute	Belgium
ECOPROGETTI	Italy
EKIENERGY	Spain
ESMC Pavilion	Belgium
Eternal Sun I WAVELABS	The Netherlands
EU PVSEC Startup Pavilion	
European Commission JRC	Italy
exateq	Germany
FLUXiM AG	Switzerland
G2V Optics	Canada
GALEA	Spain
halm elektronik	Germany
HighLine Technology	Germany
IEA PVPS	
Innovations in Optics, Inc.	United States of America
ISC Konstanz	Germany
LAB14	Germany
MBJ Solutions	Germany
Mondragon Assembly	Spain
Nagase Chemtex America	United States of America
NEO Messtechnik Holding	Austria
ODTÜ GÜNAM	Türkiye
Phoenixolar	China
PSE Instruments	Germany
PVsyst	Switzerland
RCT Future	Germany
RCT Solutions	Germany
RENA	Germany
ReNewPV-CA21148 / 5GSOLAR	Estonia
SALD B.V.	The Netherlands

SCIPRIOS	Germany
SEMILAB	Hungary
SINGULUS TECHNOLOGIES	Germany
Sinton Instruments	United States of America
SOLAR MATERIALS	Germany
SolarNL	The Netherlands
Soli Tek R&D	Lithuania
TAMURA ELSOLD	Germany
TECNALIA	Spain
The Netherlands Pavilion	The Netherlands
TNO	The Netherlands
University of the Basque Country	Spain
Vector Energy	Spain
VON ARDENNE	Germany
WCPEC-9	South Korea
WIP Renewable Energies	Germany
ZSW	Germany

We thank the EU PVSEC 2025 Sponsors

Platinum

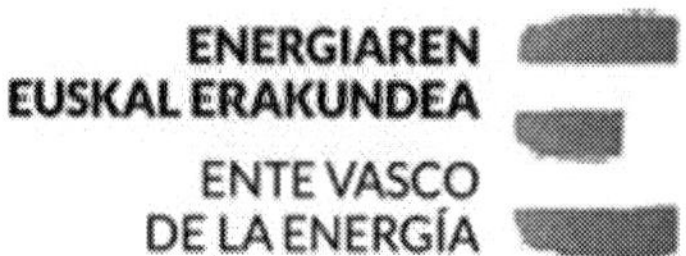

Gold

Silver

Bronze

AUTHORS OF EU PVSEC 2025 PROCEEDINGS PAPERS

Aghamohammadi, Amirhossain   020356
Amirkabir University of Technology, Tehran, Iran

Aguirre, Aranzazu   020064
Hasselt Unversity, Genk, Belgium

Ahmadi, Mehdi   020066
CNR-IMM, Catania, Italy

Aiello, Andrea   020255
ACCA Software, Cosenza, Italy

Aimé, Jérémie   020217, 020311
CEA / INES, Le Bourget-du-Lac, France

Aissa, Brahim   020042, 020075, 020108, 020109, 020146, 020147
QEERI, Doha, Qatar

Aizpurua, Jon   020139
Tecnalia, Donostia - San Sebastián, Spain

Akbayrak, Serdar   020020
Necmettin Erbakan University, Konya, Türkiye

Akram, M. Waqar   020164
Hohai University, Changzhou, China

Al Katrib, Mirella   020116
IPVF, Palaiseau, France

Alam, Habeel   020394
Lancaster University, Lancaster, United Kingdom

Alberts, Vivian   020229
DEWA, Dubai, United Arab Emirates

Albuquerque, Daniel P.   020464
Centre for New Energy Technologies, Sacavém, Portugal

Alet, Pierre-Jean   020238, 020544
CSEM, Neuchâtel, Switzerland

Alexandris, Nikos   020210
European Commission JRC, Ispra, Italy

Alfieri, Felice   020497
Viegand Maagøe, Copenhagen, Denmark

Ali, Adnan   020147
QEERI, Doha, Qatar

Allen, Vince   020048
SunDrive Solar, Kurnell, Australia

Alloji, Esma   020020
Necmettin Erbakan University, Konya, Türkiye

Almeida Silva, José   020565
University of Évora, Évora, Portugal

Almuneau, Guilhem   020074
LAAS-CNRS, Toulouse, France

Alonso, Ricardo   020197, 020198, 020353, 020358
TECNALIA, Derio, Spain

Alonso-Montesinos, Joaquín   020100
University of Almeria, Almeria, Spain

Alonso-Montesinos, Joaquín University of Almería, La Cañada de San Urbano, Spain	020336
Álvarez Hervás, José Domingo University of Almería, La Cañada de San Urbano, Spain	020336
Alvarez, José CNRS, Gif-sur-Yvette, France	020040, 020058
Álvarez, Marta CENER, Sarriguren, Spain	020300
Álvarez-Pérez, Guillem IPVF, Palaiseau, France	020062
Alvaro Høye, Ingar Solkraft Sør, Øyslebø, Norway	020443
Alves e Silva, Kiane UPM, Madrid, Spain	020439, 020535, 020567, 020575
Amaro e Silva, Rodrigo University of Lisbon, Lisbon, Portugal	020490
Amatriain, Irati CENER, Sarriguren, Spain	020392
Anamiati, Gaetana GreenPowerMonitor a DNV company, Barcelona, Spain	020448, 020481
Anaya, Julian University of Valladolid, Valladolid, Spain	020191, 020205
Ancillao, Andrea Polytechnic University of Turin, Turin, Italy	020079
Anderlini, Alessandro Coveme, Gorizia, Italy	020155
Andersen, Nanna L. DTU, Roskilde, Denmark	020250
Andersen, Nanna Lysgaard DTU, Roskilde, Denmark	020306
Andrade-Arvizu, Jacob IREC, Barcelona, Spain	020094
Andreozzi, Federico University of Rome Tor Vergata, Rome, Italy	020494
Anefnaf, Ikram University of Verona, Verona, Italy	020093
Ansong, Martin KIT, Eggenstein-Leopoldshafen, Germany	020272
Antognini, Luca PVsyst, Geneva, Switzerland	020196
Antoine, C. IMDEA Nanoscience Institute, Madrid, Spain	020508
Antón, Ignacio UPM, Madrid, Spain	020209, 020246, 020257, 020453, 020459
Antonucci, Daniele Eurac Research, Bolzano, Italy	020551

Apostoleris, Harry   020487
EPRI, Dubai, United Arab Emirates

Arakawa, Hayato   020436
NIED, Shinjo, Japan

Aranguren, Gerardo   020289, 020353
UPV/EHU, Bilbao, Spain

Arbaretaz, Sebastien   020317
CEA INES, Le Bourget-du-Lac, France

Ardissone, Bastien J. J.   020396
PV Lighthouse, Coledale, Australia

Arduino, Daniele   020079
Polytechnic University of Turin, Turin, Italy

Ariolli, Daniela Maria Godinho   020325
BayWa r.e, Rome, Italy

Ariza Camacho, Maria Jesus   020100
University of Almeria, Almería, Spain

Armstrong, Alona   020394
Lancaster University, Lancaster, United Kingdom

Arribat, Mathieu   020074
LAAS-CNRS, Toulouse, France

Arrizabalaga, Igor   020139
Tecnalia, Donostia - San Sebastián, Spain

Artegiani, Elisa   020057, 020089, 020093
University of Verona, Verona, Italy

Arumughan, Jayaprasad   020569
ISC Konstanz, Konstanz, Germany

Asaa, Shu-Ngwa   020393
imo-imomec, Genk, Belgium

Ascencio-Vásquez, Julián   020371
Univers, Courbevoie, France

Askins, Steve   020209, 020257
UPM, Madrid, Spain

Assaid, El Mahdi   020171
University of Chouaib Doukkali, El Jadida, Morocco

Aste, Niccolò   020249
Polytechnic University of Milan, Milan, Italy

Astigarraga, Alexander   020226
Eurac Research, Bolzano, Italy

Athienitis, Andreas   020248
Concordia University, Montreal, Canada

Aurrekoetxea, Olaia   020302
TECNALIA, Saint Sebastian, Spain

Awadallah, Carlos   020536
Wattkraft, Madrid, Spain

Azkona, Nekane   020055, 020097, 020153, 020287
UPV/EHU, Bilbao, Spain

| Azzopardi, Brian
FIR, Birkirkara, Malta | 020318, 020334, 020520 |
| Azzopardi, Carmel
FIR, Birkirkara, Malta | 020334 |

Babich, Francesco Eurac Research, Bolzano, Italy	020551
Babics, Maxime CEA / INES, Le Bourget-du-Lac, France	020217
Babin, Markus DTU, Roskilde, Denmark	020249, 020250, 020306, 020477
Bachour, Dunia A. QEERI, Doha, Qatar	020275, 020278
Bachour, Dunia QEERI, Doha, Qatar	020291
Baderiya, Naman MARIN, Wageningen, The Netherlands	020390
Badosa Franch, Jordi Polytechnic Institute of Paris, Palaiseau, France	020214
Baeck, Pieter-Jan Flemish Institute for Technological Research (VITO), Genk, Belgium	020511
Bai, Jianbo Hohai University, Changzhou, China	020164
Bailache, Simon CSTB, Marne-la-Vallée, France	020303
Bakhtiari, Afshin AESOLAR, Koenigsbrunn, Germany	020121
Balafoutis, Athanasios T. CERTH, Athens, Greece	020464
Bald, Juan AZTI, PASAIA, Spain	020514
Baldacchino, Alex J. UNSW, Sydney, Australia	020065
Baležentienė, Skirmantė The Applied Research Institute for Prospective Technologies, Vilnius, Lithuania	020380
Baležentis, Algirdas The Applied Research Institute for Prospective Technologies, Vilnius, Lithuania	020380
Ballif, Christophe CSEM, Neuchâtel, Switzerland	020467
Ballif, Christophe EPFL, Neuchâtel, Switzerland	020251
Bandaru, Narendra Aarhus University, Aarhus, Denmark	020039, 020043, 020104

Bang, Ole   020043
Technical University of Denmark, Copenhagen, Denmark

Barakel, Damien   020188
Toulon University, Marseille, France

Baraket, Mira   020039
ATLANT 3D, Taastrup, Denmark

Baranek, Philippe   020060
EDF R&D, Palaiseau, France

Barchi, Grazia   020485, 020489, 020544
Eurac Research, Bolzano, Italy

Bardizza, Giorgio   020181
TÜV Rheinland Italia, Milan, Italy

Bardizza, Giorgio   020208
TÜV Rheinland Solar, Cologne, Germany

Bardizza, Giorgio   020144
TÜV Rheinland, Cologne, Germany

Barguès, Anna   020505
Becquerel Institute France, Lyon, France

Barguès, Anna   020558
Becquerel Institute, Brussels, Belgium

Barnscheidt, Verena   020063, 020114
ISFH, Emmerthal, Germany

Barretta, Chiara   020325
PCCL, Leoben, Austria

Barrionuevo, Bruno   020464
CERTH, Athens, Greece

Barroso, João   020565
University of Évora, Évora, Portugal

Barrou, Alexis   020467
CSEM, Neuchâtel, Switzerland

Barrutia, Laura   020446, 020536
UPM, Madrid, Spain

Barth, Vincent   020134
CEA / INES, Le Bourget-du-Lac, France

Barth, Vincent   020019
CEA, Le Bourget-du-Lac, France

Barth, Vincent   020226
CEA/ INES, Le Bourget-du-Lac, France

Bartholomäus, Martin   020346
DTU, Roskilde, Denmark

Bartolo, Brian   020334
FIR, Birkirkara, Malta

Basta, Beata   020068
Roltec, Poznań, Poland

Basta, Marek   020068
Roltec, Poznań, Poland

Battisti, Kurt	020255
A-Null Development, Vienna, Austria	
Bauhuis, Gerard	020067
Radboud University, Nijmegen, The Netherlands	
Baumann, Kerstin	020470
bifa Umweltinstitut, Augsburg, Germany	
Baumann, Sara	020063
ISFH, Emmerthal, Germany	
Baumann, Ulrike	020006
ISFH, Emmerthal, Germany	
Baur, Carsten	020246
European Space Agency, Noordwijk, The Netherlands	
Beaucarne, Guy	020384
Dow Silicones Belgium, Seneffe, Belgium	
Becker, Carl	020331
DLR, Almería, Spain	
Behrensdorff Poulsen, Peter	020037
DTU, Lyngby, Denmark	
Beinert, Andreas J.	020123
Fraunhofer ISE, Freiburg, Germany	
Bejat, Timea	020225, 020500
CEA, Le Bourget-du-Lac, France	
Belawadi, Aditya Girish	020231
Fraunhofer ISE, Freiburg, Germany	
Belferkous, Brahim Anis	020325
PCCL, Leoben, Austria	
Bellmann, Martin	020495, 020510
SINTEF, Trondheim, Norway	
Bellvert, Eduard	020139
Tecnalia, Donostia - San Sebastián, Spain	
Beltran-Condori, Sonia	020129, 020417
University of Antofagasta, Antofagasta, Chile	
Belzunce, María Jesús	020514
AZTI, PASAIA, Spain	
Bendix, Peter	020388
Next2Sun Technology, Dillingen, Germany	
Bengoechea, Jaione	020181, 020300
CENER, Sarriguren, Spain	
Bermudez Benito, Veronica	020146
QEERI, Doha, Qatar	
Bermudez-Garcia, Anderson	020246
Thales Alenia Space, Cannes, France	
Berrian, Djaber	020492
Belectric, Kolitzheim, Germany	
Berson, Solenn	020134
CEA / INES, Le Bourget-du-Lac, France	

Besson, Pierre 020373
INES, Le Bourget-du-Lac, France

Betak, Juraj 020241
Solargis, Bratislava, Slovakia

Bettucci, Ottavia 020077
University of Milano-Bicocca, Milan, Italy

Bhardwaj, Shashank 020515
TU Delft, Delft, The Netherlands

Bhatnagar, Shrey 020367
Nextracker, Fremont, United States of America

Biard, Yves 020303
SemperStyl, Eragny, France

Bieber, Lisa-Marie 020195
Fraunhofer ISE, Freiburg, Germany

Bilitu, Eddie 020393
Hasselt University, Hasselt, Belgium

Binani, Ashish 020225
TNO, Petten, The Netherlands

Binetti, Simona 020093
University of Milano Bicocca, Milan, Italy

Binetti, Simona 020087
University of Milano-Bicocca, Milan, Italy

Blakesley, James 020293
National Physical Laboratory, Teddington, United Kingdom

Blanc, Philippe 020291
MINES Paris, Nice, France

Blanco Aguiar, Adrián 020243
ieco.io, Vigo, Spain

Blieske, Ulf 020141
University of Applied Science Cologne, Cologne, Germany

Blieske, Ulf 020140
University of Applied Sciences Cologne, Cologne, Germany

Blstak Catlosova, Katarina 020274
Solargis, Bratislava, Slovakia

Blum, Niklas 020235, 020237, 020239
DLR, Almería, Spain

Boccardi, Roberto 020039
DTU, Copenhagen, Denmark

Boccardi, Roberto 020037
DTU, Lyngby, Denmark

Boccardi, Roberto 020028
DTU, Roskilde, Denmark

Boddaert, Simon 020302, 020303
CSTB, Marne-la-Vallée, France

Bokalič, Matevž 020047, 020319
University of Ljubljana, Ljubljana, Slovenia

Bolink, Henk J. 020226
University of Valencia, Paterna, Spain

Bonal, Victor 020085
UAM, Madrid, Spain

Bonnet, Martin 020141
University of Applied Science Cologne, Cologne, Germany

Bonnet-Eymard, Bénédicte 020251
CSEM, Neuchâtel, Switzerland

Borgers, Tom 020225
IMEC, Genk, Belgium

Borgna, Luciano 020369
BFH, Burgdorf, Switzerland

Borie, Benjamin 020039
ATLANT 3D, Taastrup, Denmark

Borowski, Peter 020307
Avancis, Munich, Germany

Borriello, Aniello 020378
ENEA, Portici, Italy

Borzi, Giovanni 020019
Enginsoft, Padua, Italy

Bosch, Elina 020252, 020543, 020564, 020573
Becquerel Institute, Brussels, Belgium

Bosma, Theo 020571
DNV, Arnhem, The Netherlands

Bothe, Karsten 020236
ISFH, Emmerthal, Germany

Bou-Nassif, Liliane 020338
CETHIL, Villeurbanne, France

Bouchier, Daniel 020058
CNRS, Palaiseau, France

Bouguerra, Sara 020156, 020294, 020389, 020393
imec, Genk, Belgium

Bourdin, Vincent 020406
CNRS, Paris, France

Bourgeois, Antoine 020102
SERIS, Singapore, Singapore

Bovesecchi, Gianluigi 020494
University of Rome Tor Vergata, Rome, Italy

Brabec, Christoph J. 020117
HI ERN, Erlangen, Germany

Bradford, David Roy 020077
Newcastle University, Newcastle upon Tyne, United
Kingdom

Brailovsky, Peter Henri 020475
Fraunhofer ISE, Freiburg, Germany

Braña, Alejandro F. 020508
Autonomous University of Madrid, Madrid, Spain

Brandstätter, Andreas   020227
Lenzing Plastics, Lenzing, Austria

Braun, Christian   020457
Luxembourg Institute of Science and Technology, Esch-sur-Alzette, Luxembourg

Brecl, Kristijan   020269, 020319
University of Ljubljana, Ljubljana, Slovenia

Bredemeier, Dennis   020240
Leibniz University Hannover, Hannover, Germany

Breitenbücher, Marian   020225
Highline Technologies, Freiburg, Germany

Brendel, Rolf   020006, 020008, 020236, 020240, 020260, 020482
ISFH, Emmerthal, Germany

Brendstrup Møller, Clara Bolette   020028
DTU, Roskilde, Denmark

Bretzel, Tamara   020195
Fraunhofer ISE, Freiburg, Germany

Breyer, Christian   020479
LUT University, Lappeenranta, Finland

Brito, Miguel   020457
University of Lisbon, Lisbon, Portugal

Brivio, Elisabetta   020462
RSE, Milan, Italy

Brockmann, Lukas   020063
ISFH, Emmerthal, Germany

Brodnicke, Linda   020296
ETH, Zurich, Switzerland

Brueckner, Emanuel   020063
ISFH, Emmerthal, Germany

Bründlinger, Roland   020369
AIT, Vienna, Austria

Brun, Gonzalo   020414, 020517
ENDEF, Zaragoza, Spain

Bruno, Maddalena   020452
Fraunhofer ISE, Freiburg, Germany

Buceta, Alicia   020300
CENER, Sarriguren, Spain

Bucher, Christof   020179, 020322, 020359, 020369, 020386
BFH, Burgdorf, Switzerland

Buchholz, Florian   020035, 020225, 020569
ISC Konstanz, Konstanz, Germany

Buchmann, Johanna   020309
Berlin University of Applied Sciences, Berlin, Germany

Buck, Thomas   020033
ISC Konstanz, Konstanz, Germany

Calin, Jean-Paul   020251
ENSTA Paris, Palaiseau, France

Çalışkan Arslan, Meriç   020006, 020135
Kalyon PV, Ankara, Türkiye

Caluori, Philip   020455
Virtual Vehicle, Graz, Austria

Camara, Assa   020274
Solargis, Bratislava, Slovakia

Cambarau, Werther   020139
Tecnalia, Donostia-San Sebastián, Spain

Campana, Pietro Elia   020381
Mälardalen University, Västerås, Sweden

Campos Guzman, Laura   020331
DLR, Almería, Spain

Cancro, Carmine   020378
ENEA, Naples, Italy

Canesse, Auriane   020196
PVsyst, Geneva, Switzerland

Cañizo, Carlos   020097
IES-UPM, Madrid, Spain

Cano, Francisco J.   020139
Tecnalia, Donostia - San Sebastián, Spain

Cano, Lucía   020127
ENDEF, Zaragoza, Spain

Cánovas, Enrique   020508
IMDEA Nanoscience Institute, Madrid, Spain

Cao, Han   020263
SERIS, Singapore, Singapore

Capitaine, Anna   020116
IPVF, Palaiseau, France

Cappelle, Jan   020329, 020351
KU Leuven, Ghent, Belgium

Capron, Guillaume   020217
CEA / INES, Le Bourget-du-Lac, France

Carballo López, José Antonio   020336
University of Almería, La Cañada de San Urbano, Spain

Cardenas, Luis Alejandro   020339, 020546
National University of Colombia, Bogotá, Colombia

Carmo, Paulo   020304, 020420
University of Évora, Évora, Portugal

Carrasco, Luis Miguel   020439, 020535, 020567
UPM, Madrid, Spain

Carrillo Mejía, Luis   020279
District University of Bogotá, Bogotá, Colombia

Carrillo, Rafael E.   020238
CSEM, Neuchâtel, Switzerland

Carroy, Perrine   020226
CEA/ INES, Le Bourget-du-Lac, France

Carstens, Justus   020003
ISC Konstanz, Konstanz, Germany

Cartenì, Fabrizio   020378
University of Naples Federico II, Naples, Italy

Casappa, Michele   020087
National Research Council, Parma, Italy

Casasola Paesa, Marta   020389
Hasselt University, Diepenbeek, Belgium

Castilla Nieto, María del Mar   020336
University of Almería, La Cañada de San Urbano, Spain

Castillo Patton, Daniel Jason   020326
Enertis Applus+, Madrid, Spain

Castro, Luis Guilherme   020530
Casa dos Ventos, Fortaleza, Brazil

Castro, Rui   020464
University of Lisbon, Lisbon, Portugal

Castro-Gallardo, Fernando   020417, 020422
University of Antofagasta, Antofagasta, Chile

Cavaco, Afonso   020304, 020565
University of Évora, Évora, Portugal

Cebecauer, Tomas   020274
Solargis, Bratislava, Slovakia

Çekerek, Gamze   020006
Kalyon PV, Ankara, Türkiye

Celik, Duygu   020551
WIP Renewable Energies, Munich, Germany

Çeliktaş, Melih Soner   020559
Ege University, İzmir, Türkiye

Centazzo, Massimo   020006
EnPV, Karlsruhe, Germany

Centeno Brito, Miguel   020421, 020490
University of Lisbon, Lisbon, Portugal

Cereceda, Eneko   020055, 020097, 020153, 020287
UPV/EHU, Bilbao, Spain

Ceretti, Mattia   020204
SUPSI, Mendrisio, Switzerland

Cesar, I.   020405
TNO, Petten, The Netherlands

Ceuppens, Ignas   020302
BUILD'UP, Aarschot, Belgium

Chatterji, Nithin   020071
SVNIT, Surat, India

Chen, Daniel   020048
SunDrive Solar, Kurnell, Australia

Chen, Syh-Homg
ITRI, Hsinchu, Taiwan
020161

Chen, Xiang
Hohai University, Changzhou, China
020111

Cheung, Kak Pong
Kiel University of Applied Sciences, Kiel, Germany
020313

Chhapia, Gaurang
Belectric, Kolitzheim, Germany
020492

Chiba, Takahiro
Hokkaido University of Science, Sapporo, Japan
020436

Chichignoud, Guy
13Institut Polytechnique De Grenoble, Grenoble, France
020495

Chicote, Beatriz
Mondragon University, Arrasate-Mondragon, Spain
020289

Chiesa, Matteo
Khalifa University, Abu Dhabi, United Arab Emirates
020487

Chini de Freitas, Felipe
PUCRS, Porto Alegre, Brazil
020023

Cho, Yunae
KIER, Daejeon, South Korea
020045

Choi, Kwan Bum
SERIS, Singapore, Singapore
020102

Chouder, Aissa
University of M'sila, M'sila, Algeria
020301

Chowdhury, Gofran
3E, Brussels, Belgium
020276, 020544

Christ, Anja
ISFH, Emmerthal, Germany
020063

Chrkavy, Daniel
Solargis, Bratislava, Slovakia
020262

Chueh, Wei-Lo
TSEC, Hsinchu, Taiwan
020021

Ciesla, Alison
UNSW, Sydney, Australia
020065

Cirimele, Vincenzo
University of Bologna, Bologna, Italy
020314

Clausing, Roland
ISFH, Emmerthal, Germany
020063, 020114

Clochard, Laurent
Nines Photovoltaics, Dublin, Germany
020031

Clochard, Laurent
Nines Photovoltaics, Dublin, Ireland
020007

Clyncke, Jan
PV CYCLE, Brussels, Belgium
020472, 020513

Coşkun, Özlem
Kalyon PV, Ankara, Türkiye
020006, 020027, 020225

Colberts, Fallon   020389
Zuyd University, Heerlen, The Netherlands

Colin, Hervé   020217, 020262
CEA / INES, Le Bourget-du-Lac, France

Collin, Stéphane   020074
C2N, Palaiseau, France

Colwell, Jack   020048
SunDrive Solar, Kurnell, Australia

Comak, Mertcan   020003
ISC Konstanz, Konstanz, Germany

Connolly, James Patrick   020058, 020060
CNRS, Gif-sur-Yvette, France

Cordeiro, Diogo   020464
EDP, Lisbon, Portugal

Cornago, Iñaki   020392
CENER, Sarriguren, Spain

Cornaro, Cristina   020494
University of Rome Tor Vergata, Rome, Italy

Correa, Guillermo   020412
Gonvarri MS R&D, Corvera - Asturias, Spain

Correia, Joana   020565
University of Évora, Évora, Portugal

Couderc, Romain   020217, 020311, 020546
CEA / INES, Le Bourget-du-Lac, France

Coutel, John   020244
SOLAÏS, Valbonne, France

Cowan, Don   020230
Kiwa PI Berlin, Hudson, United States of America

Cox, Joel D.   020250
SDU Climate Cluster, Odense, Denmark

Cox, Joel D   020306
SDU Climate Cluster, Odense, Denmark

Coz, Pier Luigi   020246
European Space Agency, Noordwijk, The Netherlands

Crespo, Carolina   020490
University of Lisbon, Lisbon, Portugal

Cristiane Pan, Aline   020548
UFRGS, Tramandaí, Brazil

Cristóbal, Ana Belén   020491, 020535, 020575
UPM, Madrid, Spain

Crozier McCleland, Jacqueline   020185, 020344
Nelson Mandela University, Port Elizabeth, South Africa

Cuadra, Juan Manuel   020318
CENER, Sarigurren, Spain

Cui, Jindan   020320, 020525
Tokyo University of Science, Tokyo, Japan

Culot, Dominique
Dow Silicones Belgium, Seneffe, Belgium
020384

Curon, Jonathan
Dow Silicones Belgium, Seneffe, Belgium
020384

Cusenza, Maria Anna
RSE, Milan, Italy
020466

D. Pinto, Luciana
Federal University of Rio de Janeiro, Rio de Janeiro, Brazil
020090

Daenen, Michael
imec, Genk, Belgium
020156, 020389, 020393

Dagla, Anastasia
3E, Brussels, Belgium
020276

Dahle, Arne
Norsun, Oslo, Norway
020225, 020495

Dahlioui, Dounia
University of Agder, Grimstad, Norway
020443

Dalibor, Thomas
Avancis, Munich, Germany
020307

Dalla Maria, Enrico
Eurac Research, Bolzano, Italy
020485

Dalla Torre, Francesco
Applied Materials, Treviso, Italy
020010

Dalmazzone, Didier
ENSTA Paris, Palaiseau, France
020251

Damon, Keanu
7SecondSolar, Cape Town, South Africa
020382

Danelli, Andrea
RSE, Milan, Italy
020462, 020466

Darsene Dimd, Berhane
SINTEF, Trondheim, Norway
020270

Das, Gourab
RCT Solutions, Konstanz, Germany
020005, 020222, 020463

Dasilva-Villanueva, Nerea
UPM, Madrid, Spain
020014, 020501, 020508

Daßler, David
Fraunhofer CSP, Halle, Germany
020313

Daßler, David
Fraunhofer IMWS, Halle, Germany
020355

Daume, Darwin
pvnode, Rosenheim, Germany
020361

Davidsen, Rasmus Schmidt
Aarhus University, Aarhus, Denmark
020028, 020039, 020043

De Almeida, Laura
LAAS-CNRS, Toulouse, France
020074

De Biasio, Martin 020504
Silicon Austria Labs, Villach, Austria

De Blasi, Mariam 020378
Enel Green Power, Pisa, Italy

de Graaf, Gertjan J. 020405
TNO, Petten, The Netherlands

de Groot, Koen M. 020405
TNO, Petten, The Netherlands

De Gruijter, Alvaro 020254
Eurac Research, Bolzano, Italy

de Jong, Minne M. 020169, 020425
TNO, Eindhoven, The Netherlands

De Jong, Richard 020156, 020294, 020389
imec, Genk, Belgium

de l`Epine, Mélodie 020252, 020505, 020543, 020564
Becquerel Institute France, Lyon, France

de l`Epine, Melodie 020225, 020334, 020520, 020558
Becquerel Institute, Brussels, Belgium

de l`Epine, Melodie 020570
IEA PVPS Task 1, Lyon, France

de la Casa Higueras, Juan 020269
University of Jaén, Jaén, Spain

de la Viuda, Eva 020205
University of Valladolid, Valladolid, Spain

de Meatza, Iratxe 020495
CIDETEC, San Sebastián, Spain

De Rose, Angela 020123
Fraunhofer ISE, Freiburg, Germany

De Rose, Jonas 020010
Fraunhofer ISE, Freiburg, Germany

Debastiani Benato, Betina 020019
AMIRES, Prague, Czech Republic

Deepti, 020563
SRM University, Sonipat, India

Del Campo, Valeria 020311
Federico Santa María Technical University, Valparaiso, Chile

del Cañizo, Carlos 020014, 020501, 020507, 020508
UPM, Madrid, Spain

Del Pero, Claudio 020249
Polytechnic University of Milan, Milan, Italy

Del Pozo, Alberto 020197, 020198
TECNALIA, Derio, Spain

del Prado Santamaria, Rodrigo 020191, 020376
DTU, Roskilde, Denmark

del Ser, Javier 020358
UPV/EHU, Bilbao, Spain

Dittrich, Arne   020240
ISFH, Emmerthal, Germany

Dizier, Antoine   020373
INES, Le Bourget-du-Lac, France

Djeukeu, Ivanol Jaurece   020050
halm elektronik, Frankfurt am Main, Germany

Dobreva, Petja   020193
University of Namibia, Windhoek, Namibia

Dörenkämper, Maarten   020169
TNO, Eindhoven, The Netherlands

Dörn, Markus   020255
A-Null Development, Vienna, Austria

Doi, Minh Thong   020317
CEA INES, Le Bourget-du-Lac, France

Domínguez, César   020209, 020246, 020257
UPM, Madrid, Spain

Donadello, Alessandro   020485, 020489
Edyna, Bolzano, Italy

Donėlienė, Jolanta   020157
Applied Research Institute for Prospective Technologies,
Vilnius, Lithuania

Donoso, José   020570
UNEF, Madrid, Spain

Doppler, Christian   020455
Virtual Vehicle, Graz, Austria

dos Reis, Givaldo   020348
University of São Paulo, São Paulo, Brazil

dos Santos, Jeremias   020409
University of Évora, Évora, Portugal

Doucet, Jean-Baptiste   020074
LAAS-CNRS, Toulouse, France

Dovesi, Roberto   020060
Academy of Sciences of Turin, Torino, Italy

Driesse, Anton   020211, 020293, 020452
PV Performance Labs, Freiburg, Germany

Duarte, Dorivaldo   020418, 020565
University of Evora, Évora, Portugal

Dubois, Sebastien   020034
University Grenoble Alpes, Le Bourget-du-Lac, France

Dubravskij, Piotr   020157
Applied Research Institute for Prospective Technologies,
Vilnius, Lithuania

Dubravskij, Piotr   020380
Modern E-Technologies, Vilnius, Lithuania

Duerinckx, Filip   020064, 020225
Hasselt Unversity, Genk, Belgium

Düz, Cansel   020135
Kalyon PV, Ankara, Türkiye

Dullweber, Thorsten   020006, 020007, 020008, 020225
ISFH, Emmerthal, Germany

Dunlop, Ewan D.   020173, 020210, 020213
European Commission JRC, Ispra, Italy

Dupon, Olivier   020294
imec, Genk, Belgium

Dupuis, Julien   020188
EDF R&D, Moret Loing Orvanne, France

Dutykh, Denys   020338
Khalifa University, Abu Dhabi, United Arab Emirates

Duzellier, Sophie   020073
University of Toulouse, Toulouse, France

Dypvik Sødahl, Elin   020340
IFE, Kjeller, Norway

Ebert, Matthias   020426
Fraunhofer CSP, Halle, Germany

Ebert, Matthias   020355
Fraunhofer IMWS, Halle, Germany

Ebner, Rita   020318, 020334, 020521
AIT, Vienna, Austria

Echeverria, Oihane   020139
Tecnalia, Donostia - San Sebastián, Spain

Eder, Gabriele C.   020160, 020162, 020249, 020500, 020504
OFI, Vienna, Austria

Eelma, Tonis   020302
IBS, Tartu, Estonia

Efthymiou, Venizelos   020544
EPL Technology Frontiers, Dhali, Cyprus

Egan, Renate   020048
UNSW, Sydney, Australia

Egido, Miguel-Ángel   020407
UPM, Madrid, Spain

Eidtmann, Maximilian   020385
ZHAW, Winterthur, Switzerland

Eijgelaar, Marcel   020571
DNV, Arnhem, The Netherlands

Eikelboom, Erik   020225
Futurasun, Citadella, Italy

Einhaus, Roland   020312
ZSW, Stuttgart, Germany

Eisenacher, Matthias   020141
University of Applied Science Cologne, Cologne, Germany

Eiternick, Stefan   020004, 020052
Fraunhofer CSP, Halle (Saale), Germany

Ekins-Daukes, Nicholas J.   020065
UNSW, Sydney, Australia

El Ainaoui, Khadija   020171
Green Energy Park, Benguerir, Morocco

El mrabet, Yasmine   020171
Green Energy Park, Benguerir, Morocco

Elgaili, Mohamed   020166
QEERI, Doha, Qatar

Elhamaoui, Said   020171
Green Energy Park, Benguerir, Morocco

Ellis, Hanna   020213
European Commission JRC, Ispra, Italy

Engelen, Tine   020389
Hasselt University, Diepenbeek, Belgium

Erber, Alexander   020386
BFH, Burgdorf, Switzerland

Eryılmaz, Hande   020521
ODTÜ-GÜNAM, Ankara, Türkiye

Escudero, Ana   020414
IaSol, Zaragoza, Spain

Esmailifar, Seyyed Majid   020335, 020356, 020374, 020375
Amirkabir University of Technology, Tehran, Iran

Espinosa, Nieves   020497, 020506
University of Murcia, Murcia, Spain

Essam T. Mohammed, Sarah   020546
EU SOLARIS, Almeria, Spain

Esteras, Miguel   020358
TECNALIA, Derio, Spain

Eyhorn, Steffen   020369
Fraunhofer ISE, Freiburg, Germany

Fabel, Yann   020235, 020237, 020239
DLR, Almeria, Spain

Fabris, Francesca   020225
Futurasun, Citadella, Italy

Faes, Antonin   020251
CSEM, Neuchâtel, Switzerland

Falangas, Alexandros   020210
TRASIS International, Brussels, Belgium

Fang, Xue   020525
Tokyo University of Science, Tokyo, Japan

Fano, Vanesa   020055, 020097, 020153, 020287
UPV/EHU, Bilbao, Spain

Farhat, Mohammad   020428
Australian University, Kuwait City, Kuwait

Farina, Andrea   020066
CNR-IFN, Milan, Italy

Farrias-Basulto, Guillermo   020101
HZB, Berlin, Germany

Fath, Moritz   020463
RCT Solutions, Konstanz, Germany

Fath, Peter   020005, 020463
RCT Solutions, Konstanz, Germany

Fava, Henrique   020565
University of Évora, Évora, Portugal

Feichtner, Markus   020255
Sonnenkraft Energie, St. Veit/Glan, Austria

Feichtner, Markus   020160
Sonnenkraft Energy, St. Veit/Glan, Austria

Feldbacher, Sonja   020136, 020500
PCCL, Leoben, Austria

Feldhof, Anne Maren   020522
University of Applied Science Cologne, Cologne, Germany

Fernandes, Cláudia   020464
Centre for New Energy Technologies, Sacavém, Portugal

Fernández Solas, Álvaro   020331
DLR, Almería, Spain

Ferrando, Jorge   020226
University of Valencia, Paterna, Spain

Ferreira, Catarina G.   020250
SDU Climate Cluster, Odense, Denmark

Ferreira, Catarina   020306
SDU Climate Cluster, Odense, Denmark

Ferrero, Sergio   020079
Polytechnic University of Turin, Turin, Italy

Feuerherdt, Niels   020309
Berlin University of Applied Sciences, Berlin, Germany

Fialho, Luis   020203, 020254, 020261, 020304, 020403, 020409, 020418, 020420, 020565
Eurac Research, Bolzano, Italy

Figueroa, Andrés   020339
National University of Colombia, Bogotá, Colombia

Fischer, Stefan   020495
SGL Carbon, Meitingen, Germany

Fleischanderl, Martin   020136
voestalpine Stahl, Linz, Austria

Fleury, Perine   020513, 020521
Biosphere Solar, Delft, The Netherlands

Flouchi, Imane   020171
Green Energy Park, Benguerir, Morocco

Fodor, Nikoletta   020521
SolarPower Europe, Brussels, Belgium

Fontani, Daniela   020066
CNR-INO, Florence, Italy

Forster, Jacob   020135
Fraunhofer ISE, Freiburg, Germany

Forstinger, Anne   020331
CSP Services, Cologne, Germany

Franch, Jordi Badosa   020406
Ecole Polytechnique, Palaiseau, France

Franchi, Daniele   020077
CNR-ICCOM, Sesto Fiorentino, Italy

Franquet, Erwin   020259, 020428
Côte d'Azur University, Nice, France

Frasson, Nicola   020019
Applied Materials, San Biagio di Callalta, Italy

Freer, Solomon   020396
PV Lighthouse, Coledale, Australia

Freitag, Marina   020077
Newcastle University, Newcastle upon Tyne, United
Kingdom

Freund, Timo   020312
EnBW, Karlsruhe, Germany

Friansyah, Rizal   020376
DTU, Roskilde, Denmark

Friesen, Gabi   020160, 020249, 020574
SUPSI, Mendrisio, Switzerland

Friesen, Thomas   020249
Megasol Energie, Deitingen, Switzerland

Fritz Muñoz, Benjamín   020099
UPV, Valencia, Spain

Froebel, Jens   020121, 020142, 020192, 020223
Fraunhofer CSP, Halle, Germany

Frontini, Francesco   020249, 020253
SUPSI, Mendrisio, Switzerland

Fuentealba-Vidal, Edward   020129, 020311, 020342, 020417, 020422
University of Antofagasta, Antofagasta, Chile

Füreder-Kitzmüller, Friedrich   020136
voestalpine Stahl, Linz, Austria

Fuertes Marrón, David   020014, 020501, 020507, 020508
UPM, Madrid, Spain

Fuertes, David   020097
IES-UPM, Madrid, Spain

Furnari, Alessandro   020010
Enel Green Power, Catania, Italy

Fuß, Michael   020206
MBJ Solutions, Ahrensburg, Germany

Gabor, Andrew M. BrightSpot Automation, Boulder, United States of America	020166
Gaete, Martin University of Antofagasta, Antofagasta, Chile	020311
Gafert, Michael AIT, Vienna, Austria	020369
Gageot, Tristan CEA / INES, Le Bourget-du-Lac, France	020040
Gainza, Eusebio ALLOTARRA, Allo, Spain	020392
Galarza, Alejandra IPVF, Palaiseau, France	020461
Galbiati, Giuseppe Henkel, Düsseldorf, Germany	020119, 020218
Galdikas, Algirdas Applied Research Institute for Prospective Technologies, Vilnius, Lithuania	020157
Galiana, Beatriz Charles III University of Madrid, Madrid, Spain	020085
Galiazzo, Marco Applied Materials, San Biagio di Callalta, Italy	020019
Gall, Stefan HZB, Berlín, Germany	020101
Gallmetzer, Sandra Eurac Research, Bolzano, Italy	020261, 020509
Galparsoro, Ibon AZTI, PASAIA, Spain	020514
Gamarra, Ana Rosa CIEMAT, Madrid, Spain	020502
Ganter, Alissa ETH, Zurich, Switzerland	020296
Gaona García, Elvis Eduardo District University of Bogotá, Bogotá, Colombia	020279
Garabetian, Thomas SolarPower Europe, Brussels, Belgium	020551
García Campos, Enrique University of Almería, La Cañada de San Urbano, Spain	020336
García, Fernando UC3M, Madrid, Spain	020326
García, Sonia Tecnalia, Donostia - San Sebastián, Spain	020139
García-Cañas, Alejandro IMDEA Nanoscience, Madrid, Spain	020257
García-Salinas, María José University of Almeria, Almería, Spain	020100

Garcia-Sanchez, Almudena 020246, 020257
UPM, Madrid, Spain

Garg, Vivek 020069, 020071, 020081
SVNIT, Surat, India

Garraín, Daniel 020502
CIEMAT, Madrid, Spain

Gasse, Hugues 020073
University of Toulouse, Toulouse, France

Gassner, Anika 020160, 020162, 020500, 020504
OFI, Vienna, Austria

Gatti, Cesare 020541
PedersoliGattai, Milan, Italy

Gattu, Apoorva 020003
ISC Konstanz, Konstanz, Germany

Gautier, Damien 020505
Becquerel Institute, Brussels, Belgium

Gauvin, Xavier 020302
Bouygues Construction, Saint-Quentin-en-Yvelines, France

Ge, Hua 020249
Concordia University, Montreal, Canada

Gebhardt, Paul 020195
Fraunhofer ISE, Freiburg, Germany

Geerligs, L. J. 020030
TNO, Petten, The Netherlands

Gehrlein, Janek 020522
University of Applied Science Cologne, Cologne, Germany

Geier, Jutta 020234
PCCL, Leoben, Austria

Geml, Fabian 020031
University of Konstanz, Constance, Germany

Genovese, Maria 020378
Enel Green Power, Pisa, Italy

Georghiou, George E. 020534
University of Cyprus, Nicosia, Cyprus

Germani, Simone 020302
CEI, Milan, Italy

Getsiou, Maria 020181
Directorate General for Research and Innovation, Brussels,
Belgium

Geymayer, Lukas 020136
voestalpine Stahl, Linz, Austria

Ghahremani, Amirreza 020335, 020374
Amirkabir University of Technology, Tehran, Iran

Ghennioui, Abdellatif 020171
Green Energy Park, Benguerir, Morocco

Ghosh, Saptak 020519
CSTEP, Bengaluru, India

Girardi, Pierpaolo
RSE, Milan, Italy
020462, 020466

Giroux-Julien, Stephanie
CNRS, Villeurbanne, France
020338

Gissler, Antoine
EDF R&D, Palaiseau, France
020060

Göckeritz, Robert
Fraunhofer CSP, Halle, Germany
020119

Gohil, Hardik
RCT Solutions, Konstanz, Germany
020222

Gomes de Venuto, Vitor
PUCRS, Porto Alegre, Brazil
020025

Gomez Trillos, Juan Camilo
DLR, Oldenburg, Germany
020482

Gomez-Lazaro, Emilio
University of Castilla-La Mancha, Albacete, Spain
020562

Gonnella, Gabriella
Eurac research, Bolzano, Italy
020249, 020254

González Pérez, Sara
ULL, San Cristóbal de La Laguna, Spain
020151

González Rodríguez, Brais
University of Vigo, Vigo, Spain
020243

González, Miguel Ángel
University of Valladolid, Valladolid, Spain
020205

González-Díaz, Benjamín
ULL, San Cristóbal de La Laguna, Spain
020151

Goraya, Baljeet Singh
Fraunhofer ISE, Freiburg, Germany
020475

Gordillo, Gerardo
National University of Colombia, Bogotá, Colombia
020110

Gordon, Ivan
imec, Genk, Belgium
020521

Gottschalg, Ralph
Anhalt University of Applied Sciences, Köthen, Germany
020158

Gottschalg, Ralph
Fraunhofer CSP, Halle, Germany
020056, 020201, 020229, 020233, 020284, 020574

Govaerts, Jonathan
imec, Genk, Belgium
020019

Gracia Amillo, Ana María
CENER, Pamplona, Spain
020211

Gracia Amillo, Ana María
CENER, Sarigurren, Spain
020318

Gracia Amillo, Ana María
CENER, Sarriguren, Spain
020181, 020365, 020366, 020497

Gregory, Geoffrey
EnPV, Karlsruhe, Germany
020006

Greslou, Olivier   020551
CSTB, Bussy-Saint Georges, France

Grommes, Eva-Maria   020522, 020523
University of Applied Science Cologne, Cologne, Germany

Grosser, Stephan   020119, 020142, 020218
Fraunhofer CSP, Halle, Germany

Grünsteidl, Stefan   020307
Avancis, Munich, Germany

Gruginskie, Natasha   020067
Radboud University, Nijmegen, The Netherlands

Guedea, Isabel   020127, 020517
ENDEF, Zaragoza, Spain

Gülsoy, Eren Cihan   020521
METU, Ankara, Türkiye

Gümüs Çiftci, Burcu   020027
Kalyon PV, Ankara, Türkiye

Guerra, Gerardo   020448, 020481
GreenPowerMonitor a DNV company, Barcelona, Spain

Guidetti, Giulia   020541
Green Horse Advisory, Milan, Italy

Guillemoles, Jean François   020062
IPVF, Palaiseau, France

Guillevin, Nicolas   020225
TNO, Petten, The Netherlands

Gunbas, Gorkem   020113
ODTÜ-GÜNAM, Ankara, Türkiye

Gupta, Akshit   020551
Eurac Research, Bolzano, Italy

Gutierrez, Jose Ruben   020055, 020097, 020153, 020287
UPV/EHU, Bilbao, Spain

Gutjahr, Astrid   020030
TNO, Petten, The Netherlands

Haaland, Petry Kristine Nøttum   020476
NTNU, Trondheim, Norway

Haase, Felix   020063
ISFH, Emmerthal, Germany

Hadiwidjaja, Stella   020102
SERIS, Singapore, Singapore

Hadjipanayi, Maria   020064
University of Cyprus, Nicosia, Cyprus

Haedrich, Ingrid   020195, 020231
Fraunhofer ISE, Freiburg, Germany

Hämmer, Matthias   020470
bifa Umweltinstitut, Augsburg, Germany

Hafidi, Elias 020511
Inflights BV, Brussels, Belgium

Hagemann, Elizabeth M. 020416
Nelson Mandela University, Port Elizabeth, South Africa

Hallais, Géraldine 020058
CNRS, Palaiseau, France

Halle, Lasse 020359
BFH, Burgdorf, Switzerland

Hallensleben, Carina 020220
TAMURA-ELSOLD, Ilsenburg, Germany

Halm, Andreas 020218, 020220, 020221
ISC Konstanz, Konstanz, Germany

Halme, Janne 020249
Aalto University, Espoo, Finland

Hamada, Toshiyuki 020190
Osaka Electro-Communication University, Osaka, Japan

Hammer, Annette 020239
DLR, Oldenburg, Germany

Hamouda, Frederic 020058
CNRS, Palaiseau, France

Hanifi, Hamed 020121, 020125, 020137, 020223
AESOLAR, Koenigsbrunn, Germany

Hansen, Per-Anders 020017, 020503
Institute for Energy Technology, Kjeller, Norway

Harit, Amit Kumar 020064
Hasselt Unversity, Genk, Belgium

Harrison, Samuel 020225
CEA, Le Bourget-du-Lac, France

Hashem, Ahmad 020056, 020201
Anhalt University of Applied Sciences, Köthen, Germany

Hategan, Sergiu Mihai 020283
West University of Timisoara, Timisoara, Romania

Hauch, Jens 020117, 020149, 020150
HI ERN, Erlangen, Germany

Hauer, Martin 020255
Bartenbach, Vienna, Austria

Haverkamp, Helge 020008
centrotherm international, Blaubeuren, Germany

Hee Lee, Sang 020045
KIER, Daejeon, South Korea

Heidrich, Robert 020233
Fraunhofer CSP, Halle, Germany

Heikkinen, Kyösti 020423
VTT Technical Research Centre of Finland, Oulu, Finland

Heiser, Moritz 020230
Kiwa PI Berlin, Berlin, Germany

Helbig, Matthias ISC Konstanz, Konstanz, Germany	020220
Helten, David CSP Services, Cologne, Germany	020331
Hennig, Carsten saferay holding, Berlin, Germany	020313, 020355
Hennig, Patrick Kiel University of Applied Sciences, Kiel, Germany	020313
Heras, Jesús Wattkraft, Madrid, Spain	020536
Hermle, Martin Fraunhofer ISE, Freiburg, Germany	020475
Hernández Mora, Johann Alexander District University of Bogotá, Bogotá, Colombia	020279, 020441
Hernández, Jaime J. IMDEA Nanoscience, Madrid, Spain	020257
Hernández, Johann Francisco José de Caldas District University, Bogota, Colombia	020526
Herodotou, Panayiotis University of Cyprus, Nicosia, Cyprus	020534
Herrera Leon, Fernando Augusto National University of Colombia, Bogotá, Colombia	020339, 020546
Herrero, Leire Tecnalia, Donostia - San Sebastián, Spain	020139
Herrero, Rebeca UPM, Madrid, Spain	020209, 020453, 020459
Herrmann, Werner TÜV Rheinland Solar, Cologne, Germany	020208
Herteleer, Bert KU Leuven, Ghent, Belgium	020329, 020351
Herteleer, Bert SUPSI, Mendrisio, Switzerland	020574
Hessler-Wyser, Aïcha EPFL, Neuchâtel, Switzerland	020251
Heydari, Azim Eurac Research, Bolzano, Italy	020485
Hinken, David ISFH, Emmerthal, Germany	020236
Hladys, Bertrand CEA, Grenoble, France	020010
Hoex, Bram UNSW, Sydney, Australia	020065
Hofer, Leo BFH, Burgdorf, Switzerland	020322
Hoffmann, Erik EnPV, Karlsruhe, Germany	020006

Hogan Almeida, Rita	020535, 020567
UPM, Madrid, Spain

Hollemann, Christina	020008
ISFH, Emmerthal, Germany

Holovský, Jakub	020107
Czech Technical University, Prague, Czech Republic

Honrubia-Escribano, Andrés	020562
University of Castilla-La Mancha, Albacete, Spain

Hopp, Tobias	020384
Sunman Energy, Frankfurt, Germany

Horn, Jonas	020050
halm elektronik, Frankfurt am Main, Germany

Horta, Pedro	020304, 020403, 020409, 020418, 020420,
University of Évora, Évora, Portugal	020565

Hosatte, Mikaël	020068
SEGTON Advanced Technology, Versailles, France

Hoß, Jan	020004, 020035
ISC Konstanz, Konstanz, Germany

Hossain, Mohammad Istiaque	020042, 020075, 020108, 020109, 020146,
QEERI, Doha, Qatar	020147

Hou, Yi	020102
SERIS, Singapore, Singapore

Hsiao, Pei-Chieh	020048
UNSW, Sydney, Australia

Hsieh, Cho Fan	020083, 020161, 020163
ITRI, Hsinchu, Taiwan

Hu, Shuaifeng	020226
University of Oxford, Oxford, United Kingdom

Huang, Chris	020048
SunDrive Solar, Kurnell, Australia

Huang, Gan	020272
KIT, Eggenstein-Leopoldshafen, Germany

Huang, Lu-Jan	020425
TNO, Leiden, The Netherlands

Huang, Tzu-Yen	020096
National Synchrotron Radiation Research Center, Hsinchu,
Taiwan

Hügi, Matthias	020322
BFH, Burgdorf, Switzerland

Huemer, Martin	020227
University of Linz, Linz, Austria

Huerta, Hugo E.	020286, 020400
TUAS, Turku, Finland

Hüttl, Bernd	020361
Coburg University of Applied Sciences, Coburg, Germany

Hulik Jansova, Marketa
Solargis, Bratislava, Slovakia
020274

Hung, Tzu Han
ITRI, Taipei City, Taiwan
020552

Hutterer-Tik, Thomas
Watt Analytics, Vienna, Austria
020347

Hwang, Hye-Mi
KIER, Daejeon, South Korea
020324, 020357, 020561

Iglesias, Unai
Tecnalia, Donostia - San Sebastián, Spain
020139

Ikeda, Kazuaki
AIST, Koriyama, Japan
020436

Infante, Paulo
University of Évora, Évora, Portugal
020420

Isabella, Olindo
TU Delft, Delft, The Netherlands
020515

Ishikawa, Ryousuke
Tokyo City University, Setagaya, Japan
020106, 020115

Iwaszko, Victorien
ROSI Solar, Saint-Martin-d'Hères, France
020495

Izquierdo-Roca, Victor
IREC, Barcelona, Spain
020094

J. N. Soares, Guillermo
Federal University of Rio de Janeiro, Duque de Caxias,
Brazil
020090

Jacob, Julieu
METABUILD, Berlin, Germany
020302

Jacobs, Ayesha
Zutari, Cape Town, South Africa
020382

Jaeckel, Bengt
Fraunhofer CSP, Halle, Germany
020056, 020119, 020121, 020140, 020142,
020175, 020192, 020201, 020223, 020229

Jäger Waldau, Arnulf
European Commission, Rome, Italy
020570

Jäger, Philip
ISFH, Emmerthal, Germany
020006

Jäggi, Adrian
BFH, Burgdorf, Switzerland
020179

Järventausta, Pertti
Tampere University, Tampere, Finland
020445

Jaffré, Alexandre
CNRS, Gif-sur-Yvette, France
020058

Jahn, Ulrike
Fraunhofer CSP, Halle, Germany
020521, 020574

Jahn, Ulrike   020355
Fraunhofer IMWS, Halle, Germany

Jahreis, Sophia   020142, 020192
Fraunhofer CSP, Halle, Germany

Jakomin, Roberto   020090
Federal University of Rio de Janeiro, Duque de Caxias,
Brazil

Jakubik, Martin   020274
Solargis, Bratislava, Slovakia

Jakuza, Paola   020089
University of Padova, Padova, Italy

Jalkh, Judy   020455
Virtual Vehicle, Graz, Austria

Jandl, Ralf   020204
FFHS, Zurich, Switzerland

Jankovec, Marko   020197
University of Ljubljana, Ljubljana, Slovenia

Jaworczak, Kamil   020402
Technology Innovation Institute, Abu Dhabi, United Arab
Emirates

Jensen, Adam R.   020267
DTU, Kongens Lyngby, Denmark

Jeong, Jungi   020323
K-water, Daejeon, South Korea

Jeong, Kyung Taek   020045
KIER, Daejeon, South Korea

Jeong, Minsoo   020045
KIER, Daejeon, South Korea

Jeronimo, Pedro   020010
CEA, Grenoble, France

Jiang, Zonghan   020158, 020201
Anhalt University of Applied Sciences, Köthen, Germany

Jimenez, Maria   020302
Onyx Solar, Avila, Spain

Jimeno, Juan Carlos   020055, 020097, 020153, 020287, 020289,
UPV/EHU, Bilbao, Spain   020353

Jo, Hyunsik   020323
K-water, Daejeon, South Korea

Job, Enzo   020231
Fraunhofer ISE, Freiburg, Germany

Johnson, Mark Robert   020546
Institut Laue-Langevin (ILL), Grenoble, France

Joo, Dongmyoung   020449
KETI, Wonmi-gu, South Korea

Jooss, Wolfgang   020005, 020222, 020463
RCT Solutions, Konstanz, Germany

Joseph, Daniel Christopher   020123
Fraunhofer ISE, Freiburg, Germany

Joshi, Deepak   020069, 020081
SVNIT, Surat, India

Joss, David   020359, 020369, 020386
BFH, Burgdorf, Switzerland

Jouini, Anis   020034
ECM Technologies, Grenoble, France

Jouttijärvi, Sami   020286, 020298, 020398
University of Turku, Turku, Finland

Joziak, Roman   020230
Kiwa PI Berlin, Berlin, Germany

Ju, Young-Chul   020324, 020357, 020561
KIER, Daejeon, South Korea

Jugo, Josu   020437
UPV/EHU, Leioa, Spain

Junge, Sebastian   020008, 020482
ISFH, Emmerthal, Germany

Kaaya, Ismail   020156, 020294, 020389, 020393
imec, Genk, Belgium

Kähler, Jan-Dirk   020482
Centrotherm International, Blaubeuren, Germany

Kahraman, Mert   020027
Kalyon PV, Ankara, Türkiye

Kainz, Konrad   020430
AIT, Vienna, Austria

Kaiser, Martin   020215
Fraunhofer ISE, Freiburg, Germany

Kaizuka, Izumi   020570
RTS Corporation, Tokyo, Japan

Kajari-Schröder, Sarah   020063
ISFH, Emmerthal, Germany

Kallioharju, Kari   020444, 020445
TUAS, Tampere, Finland

Kalliojärvi, Heidi   020194
Tampere University, Tampere, Finland

Kalshetty, Mahesh   020519
CSTEP, Bengaluru, India

Kaltenbach, Thomas   020195
Fraunhofer ISE, Freiburg, Germany

Kamphues, Joshua   020031
University of Konstanz, Constance, Germany

Kandiyoti-Eskenazi, Selin   020467
CSEM, Neuchâtel, Switzerland

Kang, Min Gu   020045
KIER, Daejeon, South Korea

Kapetanovic, Viktor   020367
Nextracker, Fremont, United States of America

Karhu, Juha   020286
Finnish Meteorological Institute, Helsinki, Finland

Kari, Thøger   020191, 020376
DTU, Roskilde, Denmark

Karimy, Hedayatullah   020052
Fraunhofer CSP, Halle (Saale), Germany

Karttunen, Lauri   020298, 020398
University of Turku, Turku, Finland

Kasper, Ruth   020167, 020232
University of Applied Sciences Cologne, Cologne, Germany

Katouli, Tannaz   020195
Fraunhofer ISE, Freiburg, Germany

Kaufmann, Kai   020355
DENKweit, Halle, Germany

Kawabata, Rudy   020092
PUC-Rio, Rio de Janeiro, Brazil

Kemp, Linda   020390
MARIN, Wageningen, The Netherlands

Kenchington, Ian   020225, 020474, 020558
Becquerel Institute, Brussels, Belgium

Kenny, Robert   020210
European Commission JRC, Ispra, Italy

Khan, Abeer Ali   020513
First Solar, Mainz, Germany

Khosravi, Arash   020381
Mälardalen University, Västerås, Sweden

Kikkert, Benjamin W. J.   020405
TNO, Petten, The Netherlands

Kilickaya, Seda   020020
ODTÜ-GÜNAM, Ankara, Türkiye

Kim, Jin-Hong   020449
KETI, Wonmi-gu, South Korea

Kim, Jun-Tae   020249
Kongju National University, Chungnam, South Korea

Kim, Kihwan   020112
KIER, Daejeon, South Korea

Kim, Seok Won   020449
KETI, Wonmi-gu, South Korea

Kim, Yong-Jin   020045
KIER, Daejeon, South Korea

Kinge, Sachin   020117
Toyota Motors Europe, Brussels, Belgium

Kitamura, Ibuki   020190
Osaka Electro-Communication University, Osaka, Japan

Kitzberger, Gregor   020136
voestalpine Stahl, Linz, Austria

Kivambe, Maulid   020166
QEERI, Doha, Qatar

Kizukuri, Rihoko   020220
TAMURA-ELSOLD, Ilsenburg, Germany

Kladas, Anastasios   020329, 020351
KU Leuven, Ghent, Belgium

Kleider, Jean-Paul   020040, 020058
CNRS, Gif-sur-Yvette, France

Kleissl, Jan   020528
University of California, San Diego, United States of
America

Klengel, Robert   020355
Fraunhofer IMWS, Halle, Germany

Klenk, Markus   020385
ZHAW, Winterthur, Switzerland

Klos, Christine   020510
Buhck Re.Energy, Hamburg, Norway

Kluska, Sven   020019
Fraunhofer ISE, Freiburg, Germany

Klute, Carola   020355
Fraunhofer IMWS, Halle, Germany

Knausdorf, Christian   020361
Coburg University of Applied Sciences, Coburg, Germany

Ko, Seok-whan   020561
KIER, Daejeon, South Korea

Ko, Suk Whan   020324, 020357
KIER, Daejeon, South Korea

Koc, Timurhan   020376
DTU, Roskilde, Denmark

Koduvelikulathu, Lejo Joseph   020035, 020068
ISC Konstanz, Konstanz, Germany

Koduvelikulathu, Lejo   020003
ISC Konstanz, Konstanz, Germany

Köntges, Marc   020206
ISFH, Emmerthal, Germany

Koepge, Ringo   020142, 020192
Fraunhofer CSP, Halle, Germany

Koester, Lukas   020203, 020261, 020325
Eurac Research, Bolzano, Italy

Kohlenberg, Heike   020063
ISFH, Emmerthal, Germany

Kohno, Tohru   020186
Hitachi, Tokyo, Japan

Kolahi, Mohammad   020356, 020375
University of Isfahan, Isfahan, Iran

Konagai, Makoto   020106, 020115
Tokyo City University, Setagaya, Japan

Kono, Toru   020484
Hitachi, Kokubunji, Japan

Konu, Christopher Bruce   020132
HTW Berlin, Berlin, Germany

Kopecek, Radovan   020569
ISC Konstanz, Konstanz, Germany

Kopp, Nils   020220
TAMURA-ELSOLD, Ilsenburg, Germany

Korkmaz Arslan, Melisa   020020
ODTÜ-GÜNAM, Ankara, Türkiye

Korpås, Magnus   020476
NTNU, Trondheim, Norway

Kortetmäki, Aki   020444, 020445
TUAS, Tampere, Finland

Koskela, Juha   020444, 020445, 020554
Tampere University, Tampere, Finland

Kossen, Eric J.   020030
TNO, Petten, The Netherlands

Kowalski, Julia   020237
RWTH, Aachen, Germany

Kräling, Ulli   020215
Fraunhofer ISE, Freiburg, Germany

Kraft, Thomas M.   020423
VTT Technical Research Centre of Finland, Oulu, Finland

Krainer, Diana Maria   020430
AIT, Vienna, Austria

Krasilnikov, Inga   020379
Tel Aviv University, Tel Aviv, Israel

Krever Lopes, Bruno   020023
PUCRS, Porto Alegre, Brazil

Kribus, Abraham   020379
Tel Aviv University, Tel Aviv, Israel

Krishnan, Sasikumar   020361
Coburg University of Applied Sciences, Coburg, Germany

Kroon, Jan   020225
TNO, Petten, The Netherlands

Kuan, Ta-Ming   020021, 020053
TSEC, Hsinchu, Taiwan

Kubicek, Bernhard   020281, 020318, 020334, 020347, 020430
AIT, Vienna, Austria

Kucuk, E. Busra   020030
TNO, Petten, The Netherlands

Kuczyńska-Łażewska, Anna   020498, 020499
Gdansk University of Technology, Gdansk, Poland

Kühne, Philip   020240
Leibniz University Hannover, Hannover, Germany

Kuhrmann, Bernd   020206
MBJ Solutions, Ahrensburg, Germany

Kujansivu, Eino   020554
Solarigo Systems, Pirkkala, Finland

Kumar, Gaurav   020563
MERI College of Engineering and Technology,
Bahadurgarh, India

Kumar, Sagarika   020402
Technology Innovation Institute, Abu Dhabi, United Arab
Emirates

Kumar, Saurabh   020563
PTB, Braunshweig, Germany

Kuo, Cheng-Wen   020021, 020053
TSEC, Hsinchu, Taiwan

Kurtulus, Gunes   020556
ODTU GUNAM, Ankara, Türkiye

Kuruganti, Vaibhav V.   020033
ISC Konstanz, Konstanz, Germany

Kurz, Hannes   020136
voestalpine Stahl, Linz, Austria

Kusch, Alexander   020361
Coburg University of Applied Sciences, Coburg, Germany

Kuzhagaliyeva, Nursulu   020402
Technology Innovation Institute, Abu Dhabi, United Arab
Emirates

Kuznicki, Zbigniew T.   020013, 020068
SEGTON Advanced Technology, Versailles, France

Kwiatkowski, Jerzy   020551
NAPE, Warsaw, Poland

Kyranaki, Nikoleta   020156
Hasselt University, Genk, Belgium

Kyranaki, Nikoleta   020393
Hasselt University, Hasselt, Belgium

Kyranaki, Nikoleta   020294
imec, Genk, Belgium

Kyratsi, Theodora   020495
University of Cyprus, Nicosia, Cyprus

L. Andersen, Nanna   020477
DTU, Roskilde, Denmark

L. Souza, Patrícia   020090
Federal University of Rio de Janeiro, Rio de Janeiro, Brazil

Lachowicz, Agata   020039
CSEM, Neuchâtel, Switzerland

Lahr, Simon   020388
Next2Sun Technology, Dillingen, Germany

Lahr, Simon   020411
Next2Sun, Dillingen, Germany

Lajunen, Antti   020400
University of Helsinki, Helsinki, Finland

Lambertz, Andreas   020233
FZJ, Jülich, Germany

Lamblot, Hervé   020302
Sunstyle, Paris, France

Lamghari, Fouad   020402
Fujairah Research Centre, Fujairah, United Arab Emirates

Lamminaho, Jani   020250, 020306
SDU Climate Cluster, Odense, Denmark

Landaas, Christian   020495
Northern Silicon, Meråker, Norway

Landberg, Lars   020448
DNV Denmark, Hellerup, Denmark

Landberg, Lars   020481
DNV Denmark, Hellerup, Spain

Landes, Dieter   020361
Coburg University of Applied Sciences, Coburg, Germany

Landová, Lucie   020107
Czech Technical University, Prague, Czech Republic

Lansade, David   020073
University of Toulouse, Toulouse, France

Lappalainen, Kari   020194, 020528, 020537
Tampere University, Tampere, Finland

Lara, Yolanda   020127, 020414, 020517
ENDEF, Zaragoza, Spain

Larionova, Yevgeniya   020006, 020007, 020225
ISFH, Emmerthal, Germany

Låstad, Jonas   020011
NTNU, Trondheim, Norway

Laurens-Berge, Clarisse   020034
University Grenoble Alpes, Le Bourget-du-Lac, France

Laurikėnas, Paulius   020353
Solitek, Vilnius, Lithuania

Lauwaert, Johan   020064
Ghent University, Ghent, Belgium

Lazaro-Castrillon, Luna   020085
IO-CSIC, Madrid, Spain

Le Bossenec, Hugo   020116
IPVF, Palaiseau, France

Le Brun, Anton   020096
Australian Nuclear Science and Technology Organisation,
Lucas Heights, Australia

Lechón, Yolanda   020502
CIEMAT, Madrid, Spain

Ledesma, Javier R.   020337
UPM, Madrid, Spain

Ledesma, Javier   020446
UPM, Madrid, Spain

Lee, Chun-Wei   020021
TSEC, Hsinchu, Taiwan

Lee, Hyunju   020046
Meiji University, Kanagawa, Japan

Lee, Jieun   020323
K-water, Daejeon, South Korea

Lee, Jin-Seok   020324, 020357, 020561
KIER, Daejeon, South Korea

Legarrea, Aritz   020365
CENER, Sarriguren, Spain

Lelievre, Jean-Francois   020373
INES, Le Bourget-du-Lac, France

Lelong, Benoit   020373
Cythelia Energy, La Motte-Servolex, France

Leloux, Jonathan   020262
LuciSun, Villers-la-Ville, Belgium

Lenain, Philippe   020495
benkei, Lyon, France

Lennon, Alison   020048
UNSW, Sydney, Australia

Lenz, Markus   020226
School of Life Sciences FHNW, Muttenz, Switzerland

Lenzmann, Frank   020019
TNO Energy Transition, Petten, The Netherlands

Leone, Sander   020405
Novar, Rotterdam, The Netherlands

Leonforte, Fabrizio   020249
Polytechnic University of Milan, Milan, Italy

Leopold, Ulrich   020457
Luxembourg Institute of Science and Technology, Esch-sur-
Alzette, Luxembourg

Levrat, Jacques   020251, 020467
CSEM, Neuchâtel, Switzerland

Levtchenko, Alexandra   020116
IPVF, Palaiseau, France

Lewandowski, Simon   020073
University of Toulouse, Toulouse, France

Leza, Baurin 020412
Gonvarri MS R&D, Corvera - Asturias, Spain

Lezaca, Jorge 020239
DLR, Oldenburg, Germany

Li, Xinyang 020222
RCT Solutions, Konstanz, Germany

Li, Yung-Chih 020021
TSEC, Hsinchu, Taiwan

Li, Yuxuan 020001
East China University of Science and Technology,
Shanghai, China

Libal, Joris 020218, 020474
ISC Konstanz, Konstanz, Germany

Lichtenberger, Janine 020430
AIT, Vienna, Austria

Lițiu, Andrei Vladimir 020551
EPB Center, Rotterdam, The Netherlands

Lin, Shih-Chieh 020021
TSEC, Hsinchu, Taiwan

Lindahl, Johan 020486, 020532
Becquerel Sweden, Knivsta, Sweden

Linder, Johannes 020492
Belectric, Kolitzheim, Germany

Lindfors, Anders 020286
Finnish Meteorological Institute, Helsinki, Finland

Lindig, Sascha 020371
Univers, Courbevoie, France

Linke, Jonathan 020004, 020035, 020225
ISC Konstanz, Konstanz, Germany

Linß, Volker 020033
VON ARDENNE, Dresden, Germany

Lipovšek, Benjamin 020047
University of Ljubljana, Ljubljana, Slovenia

Lippke, Benjamin 020180, 020230
Kiwa PI Berlin, Berlin, Germany

List-Kratochvil, Emil 020101
HZB, Berlin, Germany

Litrico, Grazia 020010
Enel Green Power, Catania, Italy

Liu, Cui 020001
East China University of Science and Technology,
Shanghai, China

Liu, Dongyang 020063
ISFH, Emmerthal, Germany

Liu, Han-Chang 020350
ITRI, Tainan, Taiwan

Lossen, Jan   020003, 020035
ISC Konstanz, Konstanz, Germany

Louwen, Atse   020203, 020226, 020261, 020509, 020546
Eurac Research, Bolzano, Italy

Louwen, Atse   020316
RISE, Boras, Sweden

Lu, Huan-Wu   020161
ITRI, Hsinchu, Taiwan

Lu, Matthew   020230
Kiwa PI Berlin, Shanghai, China

Lucea, Aingeru   020197, 020198
TECNALIA, Derio, Spain

Lüdemann, Marius   020233
Fraunhofer CSP, Halle, Germany

Luís, Margarida   020421
University of Lisbon, Lisbon, Portugal

Lustoza de Souza, Patricia   020092
UFRJ, Rio de Janeiro, Brazil

Ly, Moussa   020023, 020025
PUCRS, Porto Alegre, Brazil

Lyubenova, Teodora   020210
European Commission JRC, Ispra, Italy

M. Bazilio, Willian   020092
PUC-Rio, Rio de Janeiro, Brazil

M. S. Kawabata, Rudy   020090
Pontifical Catholic University of Rio de Janeiro, Rio de
Janeiro, Brazil

M. Torelly, Guilherme   020090
Pontifical Catholic University of Rio de Janeiro, Rio de
Janeiro, Brazil

Ma Lu, Silvia   020381
Mälardalen University, Västerås, Sweden

Ma, Xiang   020011
SINTEF, Oslo, Norway

Macé, Philippe   020225, 020252, 020474, 020505, 020543,
Becquerel Institute, Brussels, Belgium   020558, 020573

Mack, Sebastian   020031
Fraunhofer ISE, Freiburg, Germany

Madsen, Morten   020250, 020306
SDU Climate Cluster, Odense, Denmark

Mahmood, Aysha   020265, 020376
DTU, Roskilde, Denmark

Maixner, Andreas   020121, 020125, 020137, 020223
AESOLAR, Koenigsbrunn, Germany

Maiz, Alexander   020437
UPV/EHU, Vitoria-Gasteiz, Spain

Majak, Martyna   020068
Roltec, Poznań, Poland

Makrides, George   020534
University of Cyprus, Nicosia, Cyprus

Malarkannan, Lavanya   020210
National Physical Laboratory, Teddington, United Kingdom

Malcorps, Philippe   020276
3E, Brussels, Belgium

Malik, Stephanie   020313
Fraunhofer CSP, Halle, Germany

Malik, Stephanie   020355
Fraunhofer IMWS, Halle, Germany

Maliutina, Kristina   020141
University of Applied Science Cologne, Cologne, Germany

Malo, Javier   020209
UPM, Madrid, Spain

Mancini, Simone   020425
TNO, Eindhoven, The Netherlands

Mandiola, Gotzon   020514
AZTI, PASAIA, Spain

Manganiello, Patrizio   020389
Hasselt University, Diepenbeek, Belgium

Manganiello, Patrizio   020294
imec, Genk, Belgium

Manito, Alex   020348
University of São Paulo, São Paulo, Brazil

Manochehrian, Rasoul   020539
Frankfurt University of Applied Sciences, Frankfurt am
Main, Germany

Manzolini, Giampaolo   020261
Polytechnic University of Milan, Milan, Italy

Maqsood, Ayman   020101
HZB, Berlin, Germany

Marangis, Demetris   020534
University of Cyprus, Nicosia, Cyprus

Marcos-Castro, Ana   020297
CIEMAT, Madrid, Spain

Marechal, Philippe   020217
CEA / INES, Le Bourget-du-Lac, France

Marí Soucase, Bernabé   020099
UPV, Valencia, Spain

Markert, Jochen   020231
Fraunhofer ISE, Freiburg, Germany

Marquardt, Cornelia   020063
ISFH, Emmerthal, Germany

Marteau, Baptiste ECM Technologies, Grenoble, France	020034
Martín Rueda, Javier UPM, Madrid, Spain	020535
Martín, Francisco José UPM, Madrid, Spain	020459
Martín, Francisco UPM, Madrid, Spain	020209
Martín-Chivelet, Nuria CIEMAT, Madrid, Spain	020297
Martín-Rueda, Javier UPM, Madrid, Spain	020337, 020363
Martínez González, Mario Enertis Applus+, Madrid, Spain	020326
Martinez, Juan Ignacio Becquerel Institute Spain, San Sebastian, Spain	020252
Martinez, Oscar University of Valladolid, Valladolid, Spain	020191, 020205
Martínez-Barbeito, María ieco.io, Vigo, Spain	020243
Maruyama, Rodrigo P. University of São Paulo, São Paulo, Brazil	020154, 020348
Marzo, Aitor University of Granada, Granada, Spain	020311, 020546
Mashkov, Oleksandr HI ERN, Erlangen, Germany	020149, 020150, 020377
Massaro, Lorenzo PedersoliGattai, Milan, Italy	020541
Masson, Gaëtan Becquerel Institute, Brussels, Belgium	020474, 020558, 020564, 020573
Masson, Gaëtan IEA PVPS Task 1, Brussels, Belgium	020570
Mateos, Yeray UPV/EHU, Bilbao, Spain	020055, 020153
Maturi, Laura Eurac Research, Bolzano, Italy	020249, 020254, 020551
Mayer-Ullmann, Philipp AIT, Vienna, Austria	020430
Mazzoleni, Stefano University of Naples Federico II, Naples, Italy	020378
McIntosh, Keith R. PV Lighthouse, Coledale, Australia	020396
McNab, Shona UNSW, Sydney, Australia	020065
Meereboer, Martijn Energyra, Westknollendam, The Netherlands	020225

Meier, Rico   020132
HTW Berlin, Berlin, Germany

Meixner, Michael   020050
halm elektronik, Frankfurt am Main, Germany

Mekhaldi, Bouchra   020406
Ecole Polytechnique, Palaiseau, France

Melges de Andrade, Adnei   020154
University of São Paulo, São Paulo, Brazil

Melino, Francesco   020314
University of Bologna, Bologna, Italy

Mellone, Celeste   020541
Green Horse Advisory, Rome, Italy

Menard, Lionel   020291
MINES Paris, Nice, France

Mencaraglia, Denis   020058
CNRS, Gif-sur-Yvette, France

Menchaca, Iratxe   020514
AZTI, PASAIA, Spain

Mendes Ferreira Gomes, Amanda   020548
UFSC, Florianopolis, Brazil

Mendikoa, Iñigo   020514
Tecnalia, BRTA, Derio, Spain

Meneghini, Matteo   020089
University of Padova, Padova, Italy

Ménézo, Christophe   020317
LOCIE, Le Bourget-du-Lac, France

Menghini, Mariela   020508
IMDEA Nanoscience Institute, Madrid, Spain

Mercade Ruiz, Pau   020448, 020481
GreenPowerMonitor a DNV company, Barcelona, Spain

Merino, Amanda   020040
CEA / INES, Le Bourget-du-Lac, France

Merino, José Manuel   020085
UAM, Madrid, Spain

Mermoud, André   020196
PVsyst, Geneva, Switzerland

Merodio, Pablo   020337
UPM, Madrid, Spain

Mertens, Jan   020389
imec, Genk, Belgium

Mertens, Verena   020006, 020008
ISFH, Emmerthal, Germany

Meßmer, Marius   020031
Fraunhofer ISE, Freiburg, Germany

Messmer, Tobias   020218, 020221, 020225
ISC Konstanz, Konstanz, Germany

Messner, Christian   020369
AIT, Vienna, Austria

Mettner, Larissa   020063, 020114
ISFH, Emmerthal, Germany

Meusel, Manuel   020052
Fraunhofer CSP, Halle (Saale), Germany

Meyer, Kevin   020260
ISFH, Emmerthal, Germany

Meza, Carlos   020318, 020334, 020426, 020520
Anhalt University of Applied Sciences, Köthen, Germany

Mezzasalma, Frédéric   020217
CEA / INES, Le Bourget-du-Lac, France

Micha, Daniel   020092
CEFET/RJ, Petrópolis, Brazil

Michael, Poland   020193
Nelson Mandela University, Port Elizabeth, South Africa

Miclea, Paul-Tiberiu   020233
Fraunhofer CSP, Halle, Germany

Midtgård, Ole-Morten   020476
NTNU, Trondheim, Norway

Miettunen, Kati   020286, 020298, 020398
University of Turku, Turku, Finland

Migan-Dubois, Anne   020406
CNRS, Gif-sur-Yvette, France

Mignonac, Alexandre   020217
CEA / INES, Le Bourget-du-Lac, France

Mignonac, Alexandre   020334
CEA, Cadarache, France

Mignonac, Alexandre   020318
CEA, Saint-Paul-Lez-Durance, France

Miguel Laborda, María   020414
IaSol, Zaragoza, Spain

Mihailetchi, Valentin Dan   020033
ISC Konstanz, Konstanz, Germany

Mihailetchi, Valentin   020225
ISC Konstanz, Konstanz, Germany

Mihaylov, Blago   020210
European Commission JRC, Ispra, Italy

Milani, Emanuele   020495
Marelli Europe, Venaria Reala, Italy

Milesi, Frédéric   020068
CEA, Grenoble, France

Min, Byungsul   020008, 020482
ISFH, Emmerthal, Germany

Mirandona López, Haritz   020432, 020434
Sunveon, Madrid, Spain

Miró-Llorente, Marta   020094
IREC, Barcelona, Spain

Misra, Prashant   020429
NISE, Gurugram, India

Miszczuk, Andrzej   020068
Roltec, Poznań, Poland

Mittag, Max   020137
Fraunhofer ISE, Freiburg, Germany

Mittal, Ankit   020318
AIT, Vienna, Austria

Mittelman, Gur   020379
Afeka Tel-Aviv Academic College of Engineering, Tel
Aviv, Israel

Mizushima, Io   020028
IPU P/S, Virum, Denmark

Mizushima, Io   020037
IPU, Virum, Denmark

Mngomezulu, Ndumiso   020344
PVinsight, Port Elizabeth, South Africa

Mo, Alvin   020065
UNSW, Sydney, Australia

Mockeviciute-Azzopardi, Austeja   020334
FIR, Birkirkara, Malta

Moe Nygård, Magnus   020340
IFE, Kjeller, Norway

Moehlecke, Adriano   020023, 020025
PUCRS, Porto Alegre, Brazil

Mohammadi, Mohammad Hossein   020037, 020104
Aarhus University, Aarhus, Denmark

Mollier, Stéphane   020262
CEA / INES, Le Bourget-du-Lac, France

Moltke, Asbjørn   020043
Technical University of Denmark, Copenhagen, Denmark

Mondaca-Cuevas, Gino   020422
University of Antofagasta, Antofagasta, Chile

Monokroussos, Christos   020181
TÜV Rheinland Shanghai, Shanghai, China

Monokroussos, Christos   020144, 020208
TÜV Rheinland, Shanghai, China

Monteiro Martins, Filipa   020317
Galp Energia, Lisbon, Portugal

Montes, Carlos   020151
ITER, Granadilla de Abona, Spain

Montoya, Josefa   020311
University of Antofagasta, Antofagasta, Chile

Morabito, Floriana   020066
CNR-IFN, Milan, Italy

Moradi Sizkouhi, Amirmohammad   020356, 020375
Concordia University, Montreal, Canada

Moradi Zavie Kord, Soroush   020400
University of Helsinki, Helsinki, Finland

Morales, Sergio   020491
UPM, Madrid, Spain

Morantes Quintana, Giobertti Raul   020551
Eurac Research, Bolzano, Italy

Mordvinkin, Anton   020233
Fraunhofer CSP, Halle, Germany

Moreda, Guillermo P.   020407
UPM, Madrid, Spain

Morin, Claire   020551
SolarPower Europe, Brussels, Belgium

Morisset, Audrey   020068
CSEM, Neuchâtel, Switzerland

Morlier, Arnaud   020156
Hasselt University, Genk, Belgium

Morlier, Arnaud   020294, 020389
imec, Genk, Belgium

Mortazavifar, Leila   020056, 020158, 020201, 020284
Anhalt University of Applied Sciences, Köthen, Germany

Moruno, Ricardo   020209, 020453
UPM, Madrid, Spain

Mosel, Frank   020015
PVA TePla, Wettenberg, Germany

Moser, David   020573
Becquerel Institute Italy, Trento, Italy

Moser, David   020316
Becquerel Institute, Bolzano, Italy

Moser, David   020254
Bequerel Institute, Trento, Italy

Moser, David   020203, 020226, 020261, 020325, 020485,
Eurac Research, Bolzano, Italy   020489, 020546

Mouhoubi, Felicia   020134
CEA / INES, Le Bourget-du-Lac, France

Müllejans, Harald   020208, 020213
European Commission JRC, Ispra, Italy

Müller, Alexander   020119
Fraunhofer CSP, Halle, Germany

Müller, Larissa   020523
University of Applied Sciences Cologne, Cologne, Germany

Mugica, Maikel   020139
Tecnalia, Donostia - San Sebastián, Spain

Mujovi, Fahradin   020251
CSEM, Neuchâtel, Switzerland

Mukherjee, Srijani CEA / INES, Le Bourget-du-Lac, France	020338
Mukhtar, Mariyam University of Verona, Verona, Italy	020057
Mulder, Peter Radboud University, Nijmegen, The Netherlands	020067
Muller, Matthew NREL, Denver, United States of America	020314
Munkhammar, Joakim Uppsala University, Uppsala, Sweden	020532
Muñoz Cerón, Emilio University of Jaén, Jaén, Spain	020269
Muñoz, Delfina CEA / INES, Le Bourget-du-Lac, France	020040, 020311, 020546
Muñoz, Delfina CEA, Le Bourget-du-Lac, France	020521
Muñoz, Delfina CEA/ INES, Le Bourget-du-Lac, France	020226
Muñoz, Ildefonso CENER, Sarriguren, Spain	020365, 020366, 020392
Muñoz, Jesús Ángel UCM, Madrid, Spain	020508
Muñoz-García, Miguel-Ángel UPM, Madrid, Spain	020407
Murano, Giovanni ENEA, Ispra, Italy	020551
Murillo, Asier CENER, Sarriguren, Spain	020497
Musembi, Robinson J. University of Nairobi, Nairobi, Kenya	020272
Nabipouor, Mohammad Anhalt University of Applied Sciences, Köthen, Germany	020426
Nagel, Henning Fraunhofer ISE, Freiburg, Germany	020475
Nakamura, Kyotaro Toyota Technological Institute, Nagoya, Japan	020046
Nanno, Ikuo Nanno Energy Research Center, Yamaguchi, Japan	020190
Nargelienė, Viktorija Center for Physical Sciences and Technology (FTMC), Vilnius, Lithuania	020157
Narsi Patel, Hitarth SVNIT, Surat, India	020069
Narvarte, Luis UPM, Madrid, Spain	020337, 020446, 020491, 020535, 020536, 020567, 020575

Nascimento, Lucas   020377
Solar Energy Research Laboratory Fotovoltaica/ UFSC,
Florianópolis, Brazil

Nasebandt, Lasse   020063
ISFH, Emmerthal, Germany

Nasser, Hisham   020226
ODTÜ-GÜNAM, Ankara, Türkiye

Naveiro, José Manuel   020414
ENDEF, Zaragoza, Spain

Nazififard, Mohammad   020259, 020428
Côte d'Azur University, Nice, France

Nejim, Ahmed   020058
SILVACO, St. Ives, United Kingdom

Nel, Paul   020382
7SecondSolar, Cape Town, South Africa

Nelson, Jenny   020394
Imperial College London, London, United Kingdom

Neuba, Adam   020114
Paderborn University, Paderborn, Germany

Neuber, Viola   020031
Fraunhofer ISE, Freiburg, Germany

Neuhaus, Holger   020123, 020140
Fraunhofer ISE, Freiburg, Germany

Neumaier, Lukas   020504
Silicon Austria Labs, Villach, Austria

Neussl, Vassilissa   020318, 020430
AIT, Vienna, Austria

Neykova, Neda   020107
Czech Technical University, Prague, Czech Republic

Nezhad, Mahyar   020230
Kiwa PI Berlin, Hudson, United States of America

Nguyen, Viet Xuan   020008
centrotherm international, Blaubeuren, Germany

Nicolet-dit-Félix, Kléber   020251
EPFL, Neuchâtel, Switzerland

Nicot-Senneville, Zoltan   020102
SERIS, Singapore, Singapore

Nielsen, Michael P.   020065
UNSW, Sydney, Australia

Nissen, Hauke   020313
Wattmanufactur, Galmsbüll, Germany

Nitsche, Tobias   020119, 020218
Henkel, Düsseldorf, Germany

Nobre, André M.   020263
PV Doctor, Singapore, Singapore

Noels, Serge   020472
PV CYCLE, Brussels, Belgium

Noh, Yong-Su 020449
KETI, Wonmi-gu, South Korea

Nold, Sebastian 020461
Fraunhofer ISE, Freiburg, France

Nold, Sebastian 020475
Fraunhofer ISE, Freiburg, Germany

Nordboe, Eirik 020495
Fiven Norge, Lillesand, Norway

Norde Santos, Fernanda 020331
DLR, Almería, Spain

Nouri, Bijan 020235, 020237, 020239
DLR, Almería, Spain

Nova, David 020339
National University of Colombia, Bogotá, Colombia

Núñez, Rubén 020209, 020453
UPM, Madrid, Spain

Núñez-Osorio, Alessia 020100
University of Almeria, Almeria, Spain

Nurmesjärvi, Antti 020423
VTT Technical Research Centre of Finland, Oulu, Finland

Nussbaumer, Hartmut 020385
ZHAW, Winterthur, Switzerland

Nyang'onda, Thomas N. 020272
University of Nairobi, Nairobi, Kenya

Obeidavi, Sahereh 020361
Coburg University of Applied Sciences, Coburg, Germany

Oberbeck, Lars 020461
TotalEnergies OneTech, Paris, France

Oberegger Filippi, Ulrich 020551
Eurac Research, Bolzano, Italy

Ocaña, Luis Manuel 020151
ITER, Granadilla de Abona, Spain

Ockert, Ajka 020312
EnBW, Karlsruhe, Germany

Odilio dos Santos, Daniel 020548
UFSC, Florianopolis, Brazil

Öhgren, Gustav 020532
Becquerel Sweden, Knivsta, Sweden

Öttl, Christian 020347
Watt Analytics, Vienna, Austria

Öz, Aksel Kaan 020135
Fraunhofer ISE, Freiburg, Germany

Özden, Talat 020226
ODTÜ-GÜNAM, Ankara, Türkiye

Ory, Daniel   020116
EDF, Palaiseau, France

Osman, Alaa   020006
ISFH, Emmerthal, Germany

Osuna, Jose Antonio   020358
MAGTEL, Córdoba, Spain

Osvald, Oliver   020274
Solargis, Bratislava, Slovakia

Otaegi, Aloña   020055, 020097, 020153, 020287
UPV/EHU, Bilbao, Spain

Otnes, Gaute   020169
Institute for Energy Technology, Kjeller, Norway

Otto, Nicolas   020101
HTW, Berlin, Germany

Otto, William   020390
MARIN, Wageningen, The Netherlands

Ou, Chao-Wei   020350
National Chin-Yi University of Technology, Taichung,
Taiwan

Ovaitt, Silvana   020314
NREL, Denver, United States of America

Ovaitt, Silvana   020574
NREL, Golden, United States of America

Oviedo Hernandez, Guillermo   020325
BayWa r.e, Rome, Italy

Ozer, Shay   020379
Agricultural Research Organization, Rishon LeZion, Israel

P. Pires, Maurício   020090
Federal University of Rio de Janeiro, Rio de Janeiro, Brazil

Pabiou, Herve   020338
CETHIL, Villeurbanne, France

Pabst, Elena   020312
ZSW, Stuttgart, Germany

Paiva, Lúcio   020530
Casa dos Ventos, Fortaleza, Brazil

Palais, Olivier   020188
Toulon University, Marseille, France

Palitzsch, Wolfram   020225, 020495
LuxChemTech, Freiberg, Germany

Palomino, Laura   020491, 020535
UPM, Madrid, Spain

Pamir Aly, Shahzada   020229
DEWA, Dubai, United Arab Emirates

Pamula, Bindu   020069
SVNIT, Surat, India

Panda, Pavan Kumar   020284
Anhalt University of Applied Sciences, Köthen, Germany

Pandar, Matthias   020229
Fraunhofer CSP, Halle, Germany

Pander, Matthias   020121, 020142, 020175, 020192, 020218,
Fraunhofer CSP, Halle, Germany   020223, 020232

Panduri, Fabio   020322
BFH, Burgdorf, Switzerland

Pantoja, Jaime   020526
Francisco José de Caldas District University, Bogota,
Colombia

Papantoni, Veatriki   020482
DLR, Oldenburg, Germany

Paraficz, Danuta   020204
FFHS, Zurich, Switzerland

Paraskeva, Vasiliki   020064
University of Cyprus, Nicosia, Cyprus

Pardo, Eduardo   020414
Tecnova, Almeira, Spain

Parfeniukas, Karolis   020039
ATLANT 3D, Taastrup, Denmark

Parion, Jonathan   020064
Hasselt Unversity, Genk, Belgium

Park, Hyeonwook   020112
KENTECH, Naju-Si, South Korea

Parmar, Richa   020429
NISE, Gurugram, India

Parra, Johan   020406
Ecole Polytechnique, Palaiseau, France

Parra, Johan   020214
Polytechnic Institute of Paris, Palaiseau, France

Parrilla, Carlos G.   020402
Fujairah Research Centre, Fujairah, United Arab Emirates

Pascual Gallego, Valero   020407
UPM, Madrid, Spain

Pasquier, Mathis   020451
DTU, Roskilde, Denmark

Passaro, Marcello   020513
Sunzest Solar, Rotterdam, The Netherlands

Patel, Dharm   020355
Fraunhofer IMWS, Halle, Germany

Paul, Ananta   020250, 020306
SDU Climate Cluster, Odense, Denmark

Paulescu, Marius   020283
West University of Timisoara, Timisoara, Romania

Paviet-Salomon, Bertrand 020068, 020467
CSEM, Neuchâtel, Switzerland

Payno, David 020085, 020094
UAM, Madrid, Spain

Pearce, Pheobe 020065
UNSW, Sydney, Australia

Peche, René 020468, 020495
bifa Umweltinstitut, Augsburg, Germany

Pehlivanli, Ezgi 020521
METU, Ankara, Türkiye

Peibst, Robby 020006, 020063, 020114
ISFH, Emmerthal, Germany

Pelfort Ojer, Marta 020241
Solargis, Bratislava, Slovakia

Pelland, Sophie 020211
Natural Resources Canada, Varennes, Canada

Pelle, Martina 020249, 020254
Eurac Research, Bolzano, Italy

Peña-Bermudez, Julian 020110
University of the Caribbean, Santo Domingo, Dominican
Republic

Peng, Cheng-Yu 020350
National Chin-Yi University of Technology, Taichung,
Taiwan

Pera, David 020457
Luxembourg Institute of Science and Technology, Esch-sur-
Alzette, Luxembourg

Perani, Martina 020204
FFHS, Zurich, Switzerland

Peraticos, Elias 020064
University of Cyprus, Nicosia, Cyprus

Pereda, Ainhoa 020198, 020358
TECNALIA, Derio, Spain

Pereira Fialho, Luis Andre 020509
Eurac Research, Bolzano, Italy

Pereira, Sara 020403, 020418, 020565
University of Évora, Évora, Portugal

Pérez García, Manuel 020336
University of Almería, La Cañada de San Urbano, Spain

Pérez, Ernesto 020339
National University of Colombia, Bogotá, Colombia

Pérez, Jairo 020412
Gonvarri AgroTech, Corvera - Asturias, Spain

Pérez, Jorge 020412
Gonvarri AgroTech, Corvera - Asturias, Spain

Pérez, Luis 020412
Gonvarri MS R&D, Corvera - Asturias, Spain

Perez, Richard	020494
University at Albany, Albany, United States of America

Perez-Astudillo, Daniel	020275, 020278, 020291
QEERI, Doha, Qatar

Pérez-García, Manuel	020100
University of Almeria, Almería, Spain

Pérez-Rodríguez, Alejandro	020085, 020094
IREC, Barcelona, Spain

Pernas, Tomás	020412
Gonvarri AgroTech, Corvera - Asturias, Spain

Pernau, Thomas	020008
centrotherm international, Blaubeuren, Germany

Perrin, Marion	020544
Energy Pool, Le Bourget-du-Lac, France

Pervan, Nikolina	020136, 020234
PCCL, Leoben, Austria

Pcter Amalathas, Amalraj	020107
University of Jaffna, Jaffna, Sri Lanka

Peter, Kristian	020569
ISC Konstanz, Konstanz, Germany

Peters, Ian Marius	020230, 020263
Forschungszentrum Jülich, Erlangen, Germany

Peters, Ian Marius	020149, 020150, 020377, 020574
HI ERN, Erlangen, Germany

Petersons, Karlis	020250, 020306
Stensborg, Roskilde, Denmark

Petkovski, Emil	020571
DNV, Arnhem, The Netherlands

Petzschmann, Jonas	020312
ZSW, Stuttgart, Germany

Pfau, Jan Hendrik	020240
Leibniz University Hannover, Hannover, Germany

Pfeiffer, Oliver	020141
University of Applied Science Cologne, Cologne, Germany

Pfeiffer, Oliver	020140
University of Applied Sciences Cologne, Cologne, Germany

Philipp, Daniel	020215, 020231
Fraunhofer ISE, Freiburg, Germany

Pierro, Marco	020489, 020494
Eurac Research, Bolzano, Italy

Pieters, Bart E.	020180
FZJ, Jülich, Germany

Pieterse, Marco	020495
Chemconserve, Bussum, The Netherlands

Pietralunga, Silvia Maria	020066
CNR-IFN, Milan, Italy

Pietsch, Veith   020331
Aquila Capital, Hamburg, Germany

Pilat, Eric   020311
CEA / INES, Le Bourget-du-Lac, France

Pilat, Eric   020317
CEA INES, Le Bourget-du-Lac, France

Pillai, Akhildev   020558
Becquerel Institute, Brussels, Belgium

Pinheiro, Philippe   020457
Luxembourg Institute of Science and Technology, Esch-sur-
Alzette, Luxembourg

Pinho Almeida, Marcelo   020348
University of São Paulo, São Paulo, Brazil

Pinto, Cristina Leyre   020497
CENER, Sarriguren, Spain

Pinto, Luciana   020092
UFRJ, Rio de Janeiro, Brazil

Pitaval, Sébastien   020244
SOLAÏS, Valbonne, France

Pitz-Paal, Robert   020237, 020331
DLR, Cologne, Germany

Plakhotnyuk, Maksym   020039
ATLANT 3D, Taastrup, Denmark

Platero Gaona, Carlos A.   020332
UPM, Madrid, Spain

Plaza, Caroline   020543, 020564, 020573
Becquerel Institute France, Lyon, France

Polacchi, Cristina   020509, 020513
Eurac Research, Bolzano, Italy

Polo, Jaime   020300
CENER, Sarriguren, Spain

Polo, Jesús   020297
CIEMAT, Madrid, Spain

Polverini, Davide   020181
Directorate General for Internal Market, Industry,
Entrepreneurship and SMEs, Brussels, Belgium

Polverini, Davide   020497
European Comission, Brussels, Belgium

Pongthanacharoenkul, Nattapark   020230
Kiwa PI Berlin, Berlin, Germany

Poortmans, Jef   020064
Hasselt Unversity, Genk, Belgium

Popescu, Lacramioara   020068
ISC Konstanz, Konstanz, Germany

Pospischil, Maximilian   020225
Highline Technologies, Freiburg, Germany

Poulsen, Peter B.   020039
DTU, Copenhagen, Denmark

Poulsen, Peter B.   020250, 020265, 020267, 020376, 020451
DTU, Roskilde, Denmark

Poulsen, Peter Behrensdorff   020028, 020306, 020346
DTU, Roskilde, Denmark

Pourshafi, Pouya   020121, 020125, 020137
AESOLAR, Koenigsbrunn, Germany

Pozza, Cristian   020551
Eurac Research, Bolzano, Italy

Prakash, Jai   020429
NISE, Gurugram, India

Prando, Davide   020485, 020489
Edyna, Bolzano, Italy

Prasad, Manjunath   020225
ISC Konstanz, Konstanz, Germany

Pravettoni, Mauro   020402
Technology Innovation Institute, Abu Dhabi, United Arab
Emirates

Preis, Pirmin   020003
ISC Konstanz, Konstanz, Germany

Preu, Ralf   020475
Fraunhofer ISE, Freiburg, Germany

Preuschoff, Jonas   020101
HTW, Berlin, Germany

Protti, Alexander Aguilar   020140
Fraunhofer ISE, Freiburg, Germany

Protti, Alexander   020137
Fraunhofer ISE, Freiburg, Germany

Provost, Marion   020116
IPVF, Palaiseau, France

Puel, Jean Baptiste   020062
IPVF, Palaiseau, France

Puertas López, Antonio Manuel   020100
University of Almeria, Almeria, Spain

Puttock, Claire   020367
Nextracker, Fremont, United States of America

Queste, Samuel   020068
Marie and Louis Pasteur University, Besançon, France

Quiroz, Mónica   020328
Qualifying Photovoltaics, Madrid, Spain

R. Ledesma, Javier   020363
UPM, Madrid, Spain

Rabanal Arabach, Jorge   020183
University of Antofagasta, Antofagasta, Chile

Rabanal-Arabach, Jorge   020129, 020342, 020417, 020422
University of Antofagasta, Antofagasta, Chile

Rabiei, Hossein   020063
ISFH, Emmerthal, Germany

Rachdi, Lazhar   020035, 020068
ISC Konstanz, Konstanz, Germany

Radzevicius, Aurimas   020225
Valoe Cells, Vilnius, Lithuania

Rafiee, Hossein   020539
Frankfurt University of Applied Sciences, Frankfurt am
Main, Germany

Raginskis, Justinas   020380
Kaunas University of Technology, Kaunas, Lithuania

Raievska, Oleksandra   020117, 020149
HI ERN, Erlangen, Germany

Rajan, S. Prithivi   020262
LuciSun, Villers-la-Ville, Belgium

Rajkiewicz, Katarzyna   020551
NAPE, Warsaw, Poland

Rakotoniaina, Jean Patrice   020311
CEA / INES, Le Bourget-du-Lac, France

Ramachandran Nair, Jishnu   020233
Fraunhofer CSP, Halle, Germany

Ramesh, Santhosh   020389
imec, Genk, Belgium

Ramírez Ledesma, Javier   020535
UPM, Madrid, Spain

Ramirez, S.   020396
PV Lighthouse, Coledale, Australia

Rampino, Stefano   020087
National Research Council, Parma, Italy

Ramspeck, Klaus   020050
halm elektronik, Frankfurt am Main, Germany

Ranisch, Tadeus   020101
HTW, Berlin, Germany

Ranta, Samuli   020286, 020400
TUAS, Turku, Finland

Ranta, Samuli   020298, 020398
Turku University of Applied Sciences, Turku, Finland

Raposo, Mauro   020565
University of Évora, Évora, Portugal

Ratnagiri, Abhinav   020367
Nextracker, Fremont, United States of America

Raugewitz, Annika   020063, 020114
ISFH, Emmerthal, Germany

Raval, Mehul   020005, 020222, 020463
RCT Solutions, Konstanz, Germany

Razanajao, Aina   020244
SOLAÏS, Valbonne, France

Razi, Umair   020085
IREC, Barcelona, Spain

Recart, Federico   020097
UPV/EHU, Bilbao, Spain

Redondo Cuevas, Marta   020332
UPM, Madrid, Spain

Redondo, Juan Manuel   020209
UPM, Madrid, Spain

Rehan, Muhammad   020112
KIER, Daejeon, South Korea

Rehman, Anees ur   020111, 020164
Hohai University, Changzhou, China

Reichart, Hannah   020167, 020232
University of Applied Sciences Cologne, Cologne, Germany

Reichel, Christian   020123, 020137, 020140
Fraunhofer ISE, Freiburg, Germany

Reichle, Julian   020005, 020222, 020463
RCT Solutions, Konstanz, Germany

Reinders, Angele   020253
TU Eindhoven, Eindhoven, The Netherlands

Reindl, Thomas   020263
SERIS, Singapore, Singapore

Reis, Luiz Filipe   020530
Casa dos Ventos, Fortaleza, Brazil

Rémondeau, Paul   020251
EPFL, Neuchâtel, Switzerland

Renard, Charles   020058
CNRS, Palaiseau, France

Rende, Fedele   020255
ACCA Software, Cosenza, Italy

Rennhofer, Marcus   020180, 020281, 020318, 020334, 020347,
AIT, Vienna, Austria   020430

Rentsch, Jochen   020475
Fraunhofer ISE, Freiburg, Germany

Rerat, Michel   020060
IPREM, Pau, France

Reshef, Liad   020379
Agricultural Research Organization, Rishon LeZion, Israel

Revol, Inès   020074
LAAS-CNRS, Toulouse, France

Reyal, Jean-Pierre   020303
SemperStyl, Eragny, France

Riaño, Sandra
TECNALIA, Derio, Spain 020197, 020358

Richards, Bryce S.
KIT, Karlsruhe, Germany 020272

Riechelman, Stefan
PTB, Braunschweig, Germany 020181

Riechelmann, Stefan
PTB, Braunschweig, Germany 020177, 020199, 020211

Riedel-Lyngskær, Nicholas
DTU, Roskilde, Denmark 020451

Rienäcker, Michael
ISFH, Emmerthal, Germany 020063

Rindert, Sören
Kiwa PI Berlin, Berlin, Germany 020230

Ríos Moral, Lucía
UCM, Madrid, Spain 020501

Ríos-Ledesma, Felipe
UPM, Madrid, Spain 020446

Ripke, Melanie
ISFH, Emmerthal, Germany 020006

Riva, Roland
CEA, Le Bourget-du-Lac, France 020495

Rivas Rodríguez, José Manuel
Enertis Applus+, Madrid, Spain 020326

Robledo, Jesús
LuciSun, Villers-la-Ville, Belgium 020262

Rodríguez Lucas, Delia
EkiLabs, Boston, United States of America 020407

Rodríguez Plaza, José Luis
Autonomous University of Madrid, Madrid, Spain ... 020508

Rodríguez Rodríguez, Araceli
UCM, Madrid, Spain 020501

Rodríguez Salazar, David Leonardo
District University of Bogotá, Bogotá, Colombia .. 020441

Rodríguez, Araceli
UCM, Madrid, Spain 020508

Rodríguez, Diego Julián
Francisco José de Caldas District University, Bogota, Colombia ... 020526

Rodríguez, Isabel
IMDEA Nanoscience, Madrid, Spain 020257

Rodriguez, Sonia Maria
UPV/EHU, Leioa, Spain 020289

Rodríguez, Velia
UPV/EHU, Bilbao, Spain 020097

Rodríguez-Conde, Sofía
Enertis Applus+, Madrid, Spain 020326

Rudzikas, Matas   020380
The Applied Research Institute for Prospective
Technologies, Vilnius, Lithuania

Rüther, Ricardo   020377
Solar Energy Research Laboratory Fotovoltaica/ UFSC,
Florianópolis, Brazil

Rüther, Ricardo   020548
UFSC, Florianopolis, Brazil

Ruf, Manuel   020455
Robert Bosch, Stuttgart, Germany

Ruiz Donoso, Elena   020331
DLR, Almeria, Spain

S. Sousa, Graciana   020090
Federal University of Rio de Janeiro, Rio de Janeiro, Brazil

Safarian, Jafar   020011
NTNU, Trondheim, Norway

Sah, Dheeraj   020039
Aarhus University, Aarhus, Denmark

Sahin, Hasret   020479
LUT University, Lappeenranta, Finland

Saito, Kimihiko   020106
Tokyo City University, Setagaya, Japan

Salem, Mohammad   020428
Australian University, Kuwait City, Kuwait

Salerno, Giorgia   020077
University of Milano-Bicocca, Milan, Italy

Salis, Fabio   020541
Iberdrola, Rome, Italy

Salvador, Antonio   020358
MAGTEL, Córdoba, Spain

Sample, Tony   020213
European Commission JRC, Ispra, Italy

Samuolienė, Giedrė   020380
The Lithuanian Research Centre for Agriculture and
Forestry, Kaunas, Lithuania

San José, Luis Javier   020209, 020453
UPM, Madrid, Spain

Sánchez de León Peque, Miguel   020243
ieco.io, Vigo, Spain

Sanchez Garcia, Alfredo   020270
SINTEF, Trondheim, Norway

Sanchez, Hugo   020056, 020158, 020284
Anhalt University of Applied Sciences, Köthen, Germany

Sanchez, Jesus   020437
UPV/EHU, Vitoria-Gasteiz, Spain

Sanchez, Laura 020437
UPV/EHU, Leioa, Spain

Sánchez, Yudania 020085
IREC, Barcelona, Spain

Sanchez-Friera, Paula 020412, 020513, 020521
Solkeys, Gijón, Spain

Sanchez-Ruiz, Alain 020437
UPV/EHU, Vitoria-Gasteiz, Spain

Sansavini, Giovanni 020296
ETH, Zurich, Switzerland

Sansoni, Paola 020066
CNR-INO, Florence, Italy

Santamaría Fernández, Susanna 020249
TECNALIA, Derio, Spain

Santamaría-Sancho, Juan 020363
UPM, Madrid, Spain

Santos, Jose Domingo 020197, 020198, 020358
TECNALIA, Derio, Spain

Santos, Rodrigo 020530
Casa dos Ventos, Fortaleza, Brazil

Sanz Martinez, Asier 020546
Tecnalia, Bilbao, Spain

Sanz, Asier 020514
Tecnalia, BRTA, Derio, Spain

Sanz, Asier 020197
TECNALIA, Derio, Spain

Sanz-Cuadrado, Cristina 020575
UPM, Madrid, Spain

Sanz-Saiz, Carlos 020297
CIEMAT, Madrid, Spain

Sarafijanovic-Djukic, Natasa 020204
FFHS, Regensdorf, Switzerland

Saretti, Angelica 020301
Polytechnic University of Bari, Bari, Italy

Sarkadi, Monika 020569
ISC Konstanz, Konstanz, Germany

Sauer, Thomas 020140
EXXERGY, Gräfelfing, Germany

Saura, Juan Antonio 020506
University of Murcia, Murcia, Spain

Savisalo, Tuukka 020225
Valoe, Mikkeli, Finland

Saw, Min Hsian 020402
Technology Innovation Institute, Abu Dhabi, United Arab
Emirates

Saxena, Anmol Ratan 020429
NIT, Delhi, India

Sayed, Abdullah Abu   020180, 020230
Kiwa PI Berlin, Berlin, Germany

Scaltrito, Luciano   020079
Polytechnic University of Turin, Turin, Italy

Scerri, Kenneth   020334
University of Malta, Msida, Malta

Schading, Steve   020443
University of Agder, Grimstad, Norway

Schäfer, Aysim   020388
Next2Sun Technology, Dillingen, Germany

Schäfer, Sebastian   020539
Frankfurt University of Applied Sciences, Frankfurt am
Main, Germany

Schenk, Paul   020192
Fraunhofer CSP, Halle, Germany

Schermer, John   020067
Radboud University, Nijmegen, The Netherlands

Scherret, Jacqueline   020255
A-Null Development, Vienna, Austria

Schifferegger, Raffael   020162
OFI, Vienna, Austria

Schimanke, Sabrina   020006
ISFH, Emmerthal, Germany

Schirmer, Yoko   020101
HTW, Berlin, Germany

Schläger, Christian   020240
Leibniz University Hannover, Hannover, Germany

Schlatmann, Rutger   020101
HTW, Berlin, Germany

Schmidt Davidsen, Rasmus   020037, 020104
Aarhus University, Aarhus, Denmark

Schnaus, Dominik   020237
TUM, Garching, Germany

Schneider, Andreas   020129, 020183
University of Applied Sciences Gelsenkirchen,
Gelsenkirchen, Germany

Schneider, Astrid   020255
TU Wien, Vienna, Austria

Schneider, Friedrich   020482
LPKF SolarQuipment, Suhl, Germany

Schneider, Marc Gabriel   020522
University of Applied Science Cologne, Cologne, Germany

Schneiderlöchner, Eric   020033
VON ARDENNE, Dresden, Germany

Schnierer, Branislav   020262
Solargis, Bratislava, Slovakia

Schönau, Maximilian   020361
Coburg University of Applied Sciences, Coburg, Germany

Schönau, Maximilian   020544
smartblue, Munich, Germany

Schönheits, Markus   020468, 020470
bifa Umweltinstitut, Augsburg, Germany

Schranz, Christian   020255
TU Wien, Vienna, Austria

Schrempf, Michael   020199
PTB, Braunschweig, Germany

Schrijvers, Patrick   020390
MARIN, Wageningen, The Netherlands

Schröter, Nick   020142
Fraunhofer CSP, Halle, Germany

Schubert, Martin C.   020475
Fraunhofer ISE, Freiburg, Germany

Schubnel, Baptiste   020238
CSEM, Neuchâtel, Switzerland

Schüler, Marc Andre   020388
Next2Sun Technology, Dillingen, Germany

Schüler, Marc Andre   020411
Next2Sun, Dillingen, Germany

Schueler, Nadine   020015
Freiberger Instruments, Freiberg, Germany

Schulte-Huxel, Henning   020008, 020260
ISFH, Emmerthal, Germany

Schultz, Christof   020101
HTW, Berlin, Germany

Schulz, Philip   020060
IPVF, Palaiseau, France

Schulze, Achim   020361
Rosenheim Technical University of Applied Sciences,
Rosenheim, Germany

Schulze, Patricia S.C.   020475
Fraunhofer ISE, Freiburg, Germany

Schwenke, Almut   020495
SGL Battery Solutions, Meitingen, Germany

Sciuto, Marcello   020010
Enel Green Power, Catania, Italy

Scognamiglio, Alessandra   020541
ENEA, Naples, Italy

Scognamiglio, Alessandra   020378
ENEA, Portici, Italy

Sedaghat, Ahmad   020428
Australian University, Kuwait City, Kuwait

Seiffert, Christoph   020169
Institute for Energy Technology, Kjeller, Norway

Seiffert, Daniela   020008
centrotherm international, Blaubeuren, Germany

Seitz, Matthias   020468
bifa Umweltinstitut, Augsburg, Germany

Selj, Josefine H.   020169
Institute for Energy Technology, Kjeller, Norway

Senno, Maximiliano Alejandro   020226
University of Valencia, Paterna, Spain

Senturk, Bilge   020556
ODTU GUNAM, Ankara, Türkiye

Setien, Eneko   020198
TECNALIA, Derio, Spain

Šetkus, Arūnas   020157
Center for Physical Sciences and Technology (FTMC),
Vilnius, Lithuania

Shaaban, Ahmed   020402
Technology Innovation Institute, Abu Dhabi, United Arab
Emirates

Shah, Syed Fawad Ali   020112
KENTECH, Naju-Si, South Korea

Shanmugam, Raphael   020218, 020220
ISC Konstanz, Konstanz, Germany

Sharma, Rajesh Kumar   020071, 020081
SVNIT, Surat, India

Sharma, Sushma   020563
SRM University, Sonipat, India

Shen, Xinyi   020226
University of Oxford, Oxford, United Kingdom

Shen, Zhenjue   020001
YIST, Jiangyin, China

Shin, Donghyeop   020112
KIER, Daejeon, South Korea

Shin, Woo Gyun   020324, 020357
KIER, Daejeon, South Korea

Shin, Woo-gyun   020561
KIER, Daejeon, South Korea

Shirai, Yasuhiro   020115
NIMS, Tsukuba, Japan

Shirazi, Elham   020544
University of Twente, Enschede, The Netherlands

Shishavan, Amir Asgharzadeh   020367
Nextracker, Fremont, United States of America

Shishido, Hirotaka   020106
Tokyo City University, Setagaya, Japan

Shochet, Ofer   020225
Copprint, Jerusalem, Israel

Shyong, Yung-Jen   020163
ITRI, Hsinchu, Taiwan

Sicot, Lionel   020217
CEA / INES, Le Bourget-du-Lac, France

Sidler, Anika   020226
School of Life Sciences FHNW, Muttenz, Switzerland

Siebert, Michael   020206
ISFH, Emmerthal, Germany

Siefer, Gerald   020246
Fraunhofer ISE, Freiburg, Germany

Sierra, Daniel   020491
UPM, Madrid, Spain

Sigounis, Anna-Maria   020248, 020249
Concordia University, Montreal, Canada

Søiland, Anne-Karin   020495
ReSiTec, Kristiansand, Norway

Silva, José A.   020304, 020409, 020420
University of Évora, Évora, Portugal

Silva, José   020403
University of Évora, Évora, Portugal

Silvestre, Santiago   020301
UPC, Barcelona, Spain

Simeunovic, Jelena   020238
CSEM, Neuchâtel, Switzerland

Simón-Allué, Raquel   020127, 020414, 020517
ENDEF, Zaragoza, Spain

Singh, Ravi   020571
DNV, Arnhem, The Netherlands

Sinha, Amish Kumar   020463
RCT Solutions, Konstanz, Germany

Sinopoli, Alessandro   020042
QEERI, Doha, Qatar

Sivaramakrishnan Radhakrishnan, Hariharsudan   020064
Hasselt Unversity, Genk, Belgium

Sivaramakrishnan, Hariharsudan   020225
IMEC, Genk, Belgium

Snaith, Henry   020226
University of Oxford, Oxford, United Kingdom

Søndenå, Rune   020503
Institute for Energy Technology, Kjeller, Norway

Sobajima, Yasushi   020131
Gifu University, Gifu, Japan

Soler Toledo, Denet   020509
University of Antofagasta, Antofagasta, Chile

Solomon, Asfaw A.   020479
LUT University, Lappeenranta, Finland

Stowhas-Villa, Alejandro   020422
Federico Santa María Technical University, Valparaiso,
Chile

Stoyanova Lyubenova, Teodora   020173
European Commission JRC, Ispra, Italy

Sträter, Hendrik   020211
PTB, Braunschweig, Germany

Strey, Jessica   020063, 020114
ISFH, Emmerthal, Germany

Strömberg, Rich   020472
University of Alaska, Fairbanks, United States of America

Stroyuk, Oleksander   020185
HI ERN, Erlangen, Germany

Stroyuk, Oleksandr   020117, 020149, 020150
HI ERN, Erlangen, Germany

Suárez Sánchez, Sergio   020326
Enertis Applus+, Madrid, Spain

Subasi, Dilara Maria   020475
Fraunhofer ISE, Freiburg, Germany

Sudbury, Ben A.   020396
PV Lighthouse, Coledale, Australia

Suemitsu, Issei   020484
Hitachi, Kokubunji, Japan

Suhonen, Riikka   020423
VTT Technical Research Centre of Finland, Oulu, Finland

Sulca, Kabir Paúl   020191, 020205
University of Valladolid, Valladolid, Spain

Svatos, Jan   020250
DTU, Roskilde, Denmark

Sylla, David   020063
ISFH, Emmerthal, Germany

Syre Wiig, Marie   020340
IFE, Kjeller, Norway

Szarek, Magda   020298, 020398
University of Turku, Turku, Finland

Taghipour Kani, Ghaem   020335, 020374
Amirkabir University of Technology, Tehran, Iran

Takahashi, Kanji   020106
Tokyo City University, Setagaya, Japan

Talvi, Micke   020528
Tampere University, Tampere, Finland

Tanahashi, Tadanori   020436
AIST, Koriyama, Japan

Tang, Kai   020011
SINTEF, Trondheim, Norway

Tang, Torben   020028
IPU P/S, Virum, Denmark

Tang, Torben   020037
IPU, Virum, Denmark

Tayebjee, Murad J. Y.   020065
UNSW, Sydney, Australia

Taylor, Nigel   020210
European Commission JRC, Ispra, Italy

Tellez Rodriguez, Eduardo   020230
Kiwa PI Berlin, Berlin, Germany

Teppe, Andreas   020005
RCT Solutions, Konstanz, Germany

Terheiden, Barbara   020031
University of Konstanz, Constance, Germany

Terrados, Cristian   020205
University of Valladolid, Valladolid, Spain

Thakur, Dhruv Singh   020071, 020081
SVNIT, Surat, India

Theocharides, Spyros   020371
Univers, Courbevoie, France

Thomas, Jean   020169
Ciel et Terre, Lille, France

Thorning, Jacob K.   020267, 020283
DTU, Roskilde, Denmark

Thorsteinsson, Sune   020039
DTU, Copenhagen, Denmark

Thorsteinsson, Sune   020037
DTU, Lyngby, Denmark

Thorsteinsson, Sune   020028, 020249, 020250, 020265, 020306,
DTU, Roskilde, Denmark   020477

Timofte, Tudor   020218, 020221
ISC Konstanz, Konstanz, Germany

Ting, San-Yu   020161, 020163
ITRI, Hsinchu, Taiwan

Tissier, Corentin   020238
CSEM, Neuchâtel, Switzerland

Tönies, Alexandra   020523
University of Applied Sciences Cologne, Cologne, Germany

Tomšič, Špela   020047
University of Ljubljana, Ljubljana, Slovenia

Tong, Yongfeng   020108, 020109
QEERI, Doha, Qatar

Topič, Marko   020047, 020269, 020319
University of Ljubljana, Ljubljana, Slovenia

Torabi, Narges   020089
University of Verona, Verona, Italy

Torelly, Guilherme 020092
PUC-Rio, Rio de Janeiro, Brazil

Torre, Gorka 020437
UPV/EHU, Leioa, Spain

Torres Aguilar, Moira Itzel 020214
CentraleSupélec, Gif-sur-Yvette, France

Torres Aguilar, Moira Itzel 020406
CNRS, Gif-sur-Yvette, France

Torres Silva, Nicole 020546
ATAMOSTEC, Santiago, Chile

Torres, Oscar 020110
National University of Colombia, Bogotá, Colombia

Tosi, Irene 020037
IPU, Virum, Denmark

Tran Caliste, Thu Nhi 020546
European Synchrotron Radiation Facility (ESRF), Grenoble,
France

Treberspurg, Christoph 020255
Treberspurg und Partner Ziviltechniker, Vienna, Austria

Treberspurg, Martin 020255
Treberspurg und Partner Ziviltechniker, Vienna, Austria

Trefzer, Aaron 020135
Fraunhofer ISE, Freiburg, Germany

Trifiletti, Vanira 020087
University of Milano-Bicocca, Milan, Italy

Trigo-Gonzalez, Mauricio 020342, 020422
University of Antofagasta, Antofagasta, Chile

Tsai, Min-An 020053, 020083, 020161, 020163
ITRI, Hsinchu, Taiwan

Tsanakas, Ioannis (John) A. 020262
CEA / INES, Le Bourget-du-Lac, France

Tsanakas, Ioannis (John) A. 020544
CEA, Le Bourget-du-Lac, France

Tsanakas, Ioannis (John) 020546
CEA / INES, Le Bourget-du-Lac, France

Tsanakas, Ioannis (John) 020317
CEA INES, Le Bourget-du-Lac, France

Tsanakas, Ioannis (John) 020513, 020521
CEA, Le Bourget-du-Lac, France

Tsanakas, Ioannis 020217, 020338
CEA / INES, Le Bourget-du-Lac, France

Tsanakas, Ioannis 020500
CEA, Le Bourget-du-Lac, France

Tsanakas, John A. 020311
CEA / INES, Le Bourget-du-Lac, France

Tseberlidis, Giorgio 020093
University of Milano Bicocca, Milan, Italy

Tseberlidis, Giorgio   020087
University of Milano-Bicocca, Milan, Italy

Tsoi, Konstantin   020113
ODTÜ-GÜNAM, Ankara, Türkiye

Tsombou, Francois M.   020402
Fujairah Research Centre, Fujairah, United Arab Emirates

Tsuno, Yuki   020436
AIST, Koriyama, Japan

Tsunoda, Jun   020484
Hitachi, Kokubunji, Japan

Tsunoda, Jun   020186
Hitachi, Tokyo, Japan

Tulinski, Lona   020385
ZHAW, Winterthur, Switzerland

Tune, Daniel   020220, 020221, 020225
ISC Konstanz, Konstanz, Germany

Turcu, Mircea   020063
ISFH, Emmerthal, Germany

Turek, Marko   020004, 020052
Fraunhofer CSP, Halle (Saale), Germany

Ueda, Yuzuru   020320, 020525
Tokyo University of Science, Tokyo, Japan

Ujvari, Gusztav   020318, 020430
AIT, Vienna, Austria

Ulbikaitė, Vaidvilė   020157
Applied Research Institute for Prospective Technologies,
Vilnius, Lithuania

Ulbikas, Juras   020225
Protechnology, Vilnius, Lithuania

Ulyashin, Alexander G.   020011
SINTEF, Oslo, Norway

Unsur, Veysel   020020
ODTÜ-GÜNAM, Ankara, Türkiye

Urban, Harald   020255
TU Wien, Vienna, Austria

Useni, Yannick   020393
University of Lubumbashi, Lubumbashi, Congo (DRC)

Uzuner, Bahri Eren   020113
ODTÜ-GÜNAM, Ankara, Türkiye

Väisänen, Kaisa-Leena   020423
VTT Technical Research Centre of Finland, Oulu, Finland

Vaicikauskas, Viktoras   020157
Center for Physical Sciences and Technology (FTMC),
Vilnius, Lithuania

Valaski, Rogério   020090
National Institute of Metrology Quality and Technology,
Rio de Janeiro, Brazil

Valencia, Felipe   020342, 020546
AtamosTec, Santiago, Chile

Vallerotto, Guido   020209, 020246, 020257
UPM, Madrid, Spain

van Aken, Bas B.   020405
TNO, Petten, The Netherlands

van der Heide, Arvid   020472
imec, Genk, Belgium

van der Zee, Friso F.   020405
Wageningen University and Research, Wageningen, The
Netherlands

Van Dyck, Rik   020225
IMEC, Genk, Belgium

van Dyk, E. Ernest   020193, 020416
Nelson Mandela University, Port Elizabeth, South Africa

van Dyk, Ernest E.   020344
Nelson Mandela University, Port Elizabeth, South Africa

Van Overstraeten, Julien   020543
Becquerel Institute France, Lyon, France

Van Overstraeten, Julien   020252
Becquerel Institute, Brussels, Belgium

vanBaal, Rene   020492
Belectric, Kolitzheim, Germany

Vanhanen, Tuomas   020225
Valoe, Mikkeli, Finland

Vargas, Renzo   020348
University of São Paulo, São Paulo, Brazil

Varney, Valérie   020522
University of Applied Science Cologne, Cologne, Germany

Varney, Valérie   020523
University of Applied Sciences Cologne, Cologne, Germany

vas Dyk, Ernest   020185
Nelson Mandela University, Port Elizabeth, South Africa

Vasconcelos, Letícia   020530
Casa dos Ventos, Fortaleza, Brazil

Vavilkin, Tatjana   020302
Soltech, Genk, Belgium

Vázquez Adán, Alejandra   020501
UCM, Madrid, Spain

Vázquez, A.   020508
UCM, Madrid, Spain

Veas, Christian   020136, 020234
PCCL, Leoben, Austria

Vecino, Fernando Román   020346
DTU, Roskilde, Denmark

Veerman, Sebastian   020035
ISC Konstanz, Konstanz, Germany

Vega de Seoane, José Maria   020252
Becquerel Institute Spain, San Sebastian, Spain

Vega de Seoane, Jose   020546
Becquerel Institute, Brussels, Belgium

Vega-Herrera, Jorge   020342
University of Antofagasta, Antofagasta, Chile

Vehus, Tore Sandnes   020443
University of Agder, Grimstad, Norway

Veirman, Jordi   020203, 020226, 020254
Eurac Research, Bolzano, Italy

Velasco, Angel   020367
Nextracker, Fremont, United States of America

Veludo, Jorge   020317
Galp Energia, Lisbon, Portugal

Veneri, Alessandro   020093
University of Verona, Verona, Italy

Vergura, Silvano   020301
Polytechnic University of Bari, Bari, Italy

Verlinden, Pierre   020001
YIST, Jiangyin, China

Vermang, Bart   020064
Hasselt Unversity, Genk, Belgium

Vernay, Christophe   020244
SOLAÏS, Valbonne, France

Vero, Giuseppe   020301
Polytechnic University of Bari, Bari, Italy

Veronese, Elisa   020513
Eurac Research, Bolzano, Italy

Veurman, Welmoed   020063
ISFH, Emmerthal, Germany

Viani, Lucas   020326
Enertis Applus+, Madrid, Spain

Vicente-Laiglesia, Pablo   020181
European Climate, Infrastructure and Environment
Executive Agency, Brussels, Belgium

Vidal de Oliveira, Aline   020377
Solar Energy Research Laboratory Fotovoltaica/ UFSC,
Florianópolis, Brazil

Vidal, Beatriz Muñoz   020414
IaSol, Zaragoza, Spain

Vidal-Fuentes, Pedro   020094
IREC, Barcelona, Spain

Videla-Magnata, Natalia	020129
Universidad de Antofagasta, Antofagasta, Chile	
Videla-Magnata, Natalia	020417
University of Antofagasta, Antofagasta, Chile	
Vilches, Anna Morales	020388
Next2Sun Technology, Dillingen, Germany	
Villalonga Palou, Joan Tomás	020432, 020434
Sunveon, Madrid, Spain	
Villén, Raúl	020127, 020414, 020517
ENDEF, Zaragoza, Spain	
Villodas, Aritz	020198
TECNALIA, Derio, Spain	
Vincent, Laetitia	020058
CNRS, Palaiseau, France	
Vincent, Robin	020196
PVsyst, Geneva, Switzerland	
Viorel Spataru, Sergiu	020191
DTU, Roskilde, Denmark	
Viriyaroj, Bergpob	020298
Aalto University, Espoo, Finland	
Viti, Valeria	020541
Legance, Milan, Italy	
Vitoshkin, Helena	020379
Agricultural Research Organization, Rishon LeZion, Israel	
Vögeli, Pascal	020385
ZHAW, Winterthur, Switzerland	
Vogt, Malte R.	020515
TU Delft, Delft, The Netherlands	
Vogt, Thomas	020482
DLR, Oldenburg, Germany	
Vollbrecht, Joachim	020063, 020114
ISFH, Emmerthal, Germany	
Voltan, Alessandro	020010
Applied Materials, Treviso, Italy	
von Friedeburg, Christoph	020557
CF Energy Research-Consulting-Operation, Berlin, Germany	
Voronko, Yuliya	020162, 020249
OFI, Vienna, Austria	
Vorster, Frederik J.	020193, 020344, 020416
Nelson Mandela University, Port Elizabeth, South Africa	
Vorster, Frederik	020185
Nelson Mandela University, Port Elizabeth, South Africa	
Vuillon, Laurent	020338
CNRS, Chambery, France	

Vulic, Natasa 020296
Univesity of Applied Arts and Sciences Northwestern
Switzerland, Muttenz, Switzerland

Vumbugwa, Monphias 020185, 020193, 020344
Nelson Mandela University, Port Elizabeth, South Africa

Waibel, Christoph 020511
Flemish Institute for Technological Research (VITO), Genk,
Belgium

Wakabayashi, Ryo 020484
Hitachi, Kokubunji, Japan

Wakazono, Kouzen 020131
Gifu University, Gifu, Japan

Wallner, Gernot M. 020227
University of Linz, Linz, Austria

Walpita, Harsha 020169
University of Oslo, Kjeller, Norway

Walsh, Yoselyn 020520
Costa Rica Institute of Technology, Cartago, Costa Rica

Wambach, Karsten 020468, 020470
bifa Umweltinstitut, Augsburg, Germany

Wang, Chia-Chen 020549
ITRI, Hsinchu, Taiwan

Wang, Shuo 020286, 020400
TUAS, Turku, Finland

Wang, Tzuya 020549
ITRI, Hsinchu, Taiwan

Wang, Xiaolin 020381
Mälardalen University, Västerås, Sweden

Wannenwetsch, Jann 020312
EnBW, Karlsruhe, Germany

Wargocki, Pawel 020551
DTU, Roskilde, Denmark

Waschl, Alfred 020255
buildingSMART, Vienna, Austria

Weber, Thomas 020180, 020230
Kiwa PI Berlin, Berlin, Germany

Weeber, Arthur W. 020515
TU Delft, Delft, The Netherlands

Wei, Wenpeng 020484
Hitachi, Kokubunji, Japan

Weihs, Philipp 020281
BOKU, Vienna, Austria

Weinrich, Frank 020177
PTB, Braunschweig, Germany

Weiß, Marius 020361
Coburg University of Applied Sciences, Coburg, Germany

Wellens, Christine   020135
Fraunhofer ISE, Freiburg, Germany

Whyatt, Duncan   020394
Lancaster University, Lancaster, United Kingdom

Wienands, Karl   020218, 020220, 020221
ISC Konstanz, Konstanz, Germany

Wiesenfarth, Maike   020246
Fraunhofer ISE, Freiburg, Germany

Wietler, Tobias   020063
ISFH, Emmerthal, Germany

Wilbert, Stefan   020235, 020237, 020239, 020331
DLR, Almería, Spain

Willers, Guido   020201
Fraunhofer CSP, Halle, Germany

Wilson, Helen R.   020249
Fraunhofer ISE, Freiburg, Germany

Winter, Renate   020063
ISFH, Emmerthal, Germany

Winter, Stefan   020177, 020181
PTB, Braunschweig, Germany

Wirtz, Wiebke   020260
ISFH, Emmerthal, Germany

Witkowska, Agnieszka   020498
Gdansk University of Technology, Gdansk, Poland

Wittmer, Bruno   020196
PVsyst, Geneva, Switzerland

Wolf, Andreas   020031
Fraunhofer ISE, Freiburg, Germany

Wong, Craig   020230
Kiwa PI Berlin, Berlin, Germany

Wu, Li-Guo   020021
TSEC, Hsinchu, Taiwan

Wu, Yu   020030
TNO, Petten, The Netherlands

Wyss, Philippe   020068
CSEM, Neuchâtel, Switzerland

Xiong, Weizhen   020320
Tokyo University of Science, Tokyo, Japan

Xu, Jiahui   020001
YIST, Jiangyin, China

Xu, Wenhao   020144, 020208
TÜV Rheinland, Shanghai, China

Xu, Xiaoqi   020263
SERIS, Singapore, Singapore

Xu, Yu   020263
SERIS, Singapore, Singapore

Xuereb, Steven   020180, 020230
Kiwa PI Berlin, Berlin, Germany

Yadav, Shivendra   020071, 020081
SVNIT, Surat, India

Yamaguchi, Yosuke   020484
Hitachi, Kokubunji, Japan

Yanagida, Masatoshi   020115
NIMS, Tsukuba, Japan

Yanar, T. Meriç   020027
Kalyon PV, Ankara, Türkiye

Yang, Donggeon   020323
K-water, Daejeon, South Korea

Yang, Hyoung-Kyu   020449
KETI, Wonmi-gu, South Korea

Yde, Leif   020250, 020306
Stensborg, Roskilde, Denmark

Ye, JiaYi   020102
SERIS, Singapore, Singapore

Yerci, Selcuk   020113
ODTÜ-GÜNAM, Ankara, Türkiye

Ylikunnari, Mari   020423
VTT Technical Research Centre of Finland, Oulu, Finland

Ylinen, Marko   020444
Satakunta University of Applied Sciences, Pori, Finland

Ylipaino, Juho   020444, 020445, 020554
TUAS, Tampere, Finland

Yılmaz, Büşra   020521
Kameleon Solar, Roosendaal, The Netherlands

Yordadov, Georgi   020389
imec, Diepenbeek, Belgium

Younes, Kareem   020487
Khalifa University, Abu Dhabi, United Arab Emirates

Yu, Cheng-Yeh   020021, 020053
TSEC, Hsinchu, Taiwan

Yu, Shusen   020406
Ecole Polytechnique, Palaiseau, France

Yuan, Xiao   020001
YIST, Jiangyin, China

Yun, Jae Ho   020112
KENTECH, Naju-si, South Korea

Zaimi, Mhammed   020171
University of Chouaib Doukkali, El Jadida, Morocco

Zanatta Britto, João Victor   020025
PUCRS, Porto Alegre, Brazil

Zanesco, Izete   020023, 020025
PUCRS, Porto Alegre, Brazil

Zaror, Yasmin   020225
WIP - Renewable Energies, Munich, Germany

Zarzalejo, Luis F.   020237, 020331
CIEMAT, Madrid, Spain

Zekri, Atef   020146
QEERI, Doha, Qatar

Zerafa, Steve   020334
PIXAM, Msida, Malta

Zhang, Geng   020001
Jolywood (ShanXi) Solar Technology, Taiyuan, China

Zhang, Jingwei   020111
Hohai University, Changzhou, China

Zhang, Kai   020233
FZJ, Jülich, Germany

Zhang, Wenjing   020001
YIST, Jiangyin, China

Zhang, Wuai   020101
HZB, Berlin, Germany

Zhang, Yating   020144, 020208
TÜV Rheinland, Shanghai, China

Zhou, Qilin   020102
SERIS, Singapore, Singapore

Zhu, Junjie   020017
Institute for Energy Technology, Kjeller, Norway

Ziaullah, Abdul Wahab   020278, 020291
QEERI, Doha, Qatar

Zilles, Roberto   020154, 020348
University of São Paulo, São Paulo, Brazil

Zimmermann, Iwan   020116
IPVF, Palaiseau, France

Zubillaga, Oihana   020139
Tecnalia, Donostia - San Sebastián, Spain

Zugasti, Eugenia   020334
CENER, Pamplona, Spain

Zugasti, Eugenia   020300
CENER, Sarriguren, Spain

Zwahlen, Theo   020369
BFH, Burgdorf, Switzerland

KEYWORDS OF EU PVSEC 2025 PROCEEDINGS PAPERS

Antireflection	020001
Antisoiling	020402
AOD	020278
Appearance	020250
Aquatic Ecosystem	020418
Architecture	020255
Arid Regions	020402
AROMP	020141
Artificial Intelligence	020544
Artificial Intelligence (AI)	020356, 020375
Artificial Neuronal Network	020342
Automation	020275
Autonomous Aerial Monitoring (AAM)	020356, 020375
Azimuth	020532

Back Contact	020006
Back Contact Solar Cell	020218
Backsheet	020151
Backsheet Degradation	020377
Backsheets	020150
Backtracking	020363
Backtracking 3D	020434
Backtracking Strategies	020434
Balancing Market Bid Planning	020525
Basin Test	020390
Battery	020429
Battery Energy Management	020490
Battery Energy Storage System	020490
Battery Energy Storage Systems	020492
Bifacial	020066, 020106, 020210, 020287, 020396, 020407
Bifacial Efficiency	020081
Bifacial Module	020379
Bifacial Modules	020181
Bifacial Photovoltaic	020443
Bifacial PV Modules	020154
Bifacial Technology	020342
Big Data	020328
Bio-based Polymers	020141

BIPV	020250, 020260, 020300, 020302, 020304, 020306
BIPV Modelling	020297
BIPV Shading	020297
Bishop Model	020056
Bogotá	020441
Boron Diffusion	020025
BSF Sheet Resistance	020025
Buffer Layers	020087
Building Attached Photovoltaics	020477
Building Energy Efficiency	020259
Building Information Modelling (BIM)	020255
Building Integrated Photovoltaics (BIPV)	020255
Building Integrated PV (BIPV)	020303
Building Renovation	020551
Building-Integrated	020252
Building-Integrated Photovoltaics	020254, 020257, 020477, 020556
Building-Integrated Photovoltaics (BIPV)	020192, 020551
Building-integrated PV	020298
Buried Contact (BC)	020037
Business Models	020564
Bussing	020129
Bypass Diode	020455
Bypass Diodes	020121, 020153
c-Si	020300
c-Si Cell	020131
Cable Layout Optimisation	020382
Calibration	020215
CAMS	020291
Catadioptric Concentrator	020246
CBTS	020069
Cd-free	020087
CdTe	020499
Cell Efficiency	020060
Cell Interconnection	020218
Ceramic	020300
Chalcogenides	020085

Characteristics Addition	020081
Characterization	020050, 020119, 020121, 020151, 020166, 020459
CIGS	020097
CIGS/Perovskite Solar Cell	020104
Circular Economy	020141, 020504, 020510, 020517
Circularity	020470, 020472, 020507, 020517
Citizen Participation	020491, 020575
Clay	020300
Clean Firm Power	020487
Clean Transportation	020428
Cleaning	020332
Cleaning Frequency	020348
Cleaning Optimization Asset Management	020339
Clear-sky	020278
Clear-Sky Detection	020340
Climate Change	020402
Climate-dependent Degradation	020150
Climate-responsive Design	020259
Climate-Specific PV O&M	020546
Cloud Detection	020267
Clustering	020243
Co-Extruded EPE	020135
Co-Visibility	020244
Collective Self-consumption	020490
Color Stability	020254
Colored Photovoltaics	020556
ColorFoil	020306
Comfort	020302
Compact Furnace	020025
Comparative Life Cycle Assessment (LCA)	020303
Competitiveness	020573
Compliance	020444
Composite Encapsulant	020139
Composites	020498
Computational Efficiency	020432
Computer Vision	020336, 020511
COMSOL	020104

Energy Management System	020534
Energy Management System (EMS)	020536
Energy Performance Directive	020477
Energy Performance of Buildings
Directive (EPBD)	020551
Energy Poverty	020564
Energy Rating	020173, 020177, 020211
Energy Sharing	020564
Energy Storage	020428, 020487, 020534
Energy Testing	020171
Energy Transition	020479, 020537, 020541
Energy Yield	020175, 020181, 020210, 020286, 020318, 020443, 020453
Energy Yield Estimation	020294
Energy Yield Overestimation	020363
Energy Yield Simulations	020262
Environmental Impact	020418
Environmental Psychology	020523
Epitaxial Lateral Overgrowth	020058
Epoxy Bonding	020092
Epoxy–Fiberglass	020417
EROI	020479
ET	020522
Etching	020007, 020031
EU-LAC Collaboration	020546
Eurocode	020167
EV Charging	020428
Evaporation	020015
Experimental Testing	020127
Exports	020563

Facade-Integrated Photovoltaics
(FIPV)	020192
Facade-mounted PV	020359
Failures	020328
Fault Analysis	020217
Fault Clustering	020351
Fault Detection	020337, 020346, 020353, 020375, 020511
Fault Signatures	020351
Field Measurements	020377

Field Performance	020183
Finite Element Analysis	020048
Finite Element Method	020123
Fire Safety	020359
First-principles	020060
Flexibility	020390
Flexible Modules	020304
Flexible PV	020423
Flexible Solar Cells	020090
Flexible Substrate	020090
Floating photovoltaics	020169, 020348
Floating PV	020390, 020418
Fluorescence	020149
Fluoropolymer Materials	020151
Food-Energy Yield	020394
Football Stadiums	020309
Force-Field Analysis	020556
Forecasting	020336
Four-terminal	020066
Frequency Containment Reserve	020571
Fresnel Lens Concentrator	020246
GaAs/Si	020092
Gapless Layup	020221
Gapless Stringing	020221
Gel Content	020135
Generative AI	020164
Geospatial PV Analytics	020340
GHI	020291
Glare	020244
Glass Beads	020227
Glass Breakage	020230, 020231
Glass Cracking	020154
Glass Stress	020167
Glass-Free Laminate	020417
Glass-Glass Modules	020132
Glass-like Alumina	020001
Global Warming Assessments	020477
Graph Neural Network	020338

Irregular Terrain	020434
ISOS Protocols	020064
IV	020346
I–V and EL	020417
I–V Curve Emulation	020369
IV Data	020510
IV Testing	020050
IWO/SiO2 Stack	020046
Junction Box	020129
KPI	020302
Laboratory Measurements	020386
Laboratory Practices	020100
Lamination Monitoring	020132
Land Use	020398, 020543
Land Use Requirements	020476
Landscape	020549
Large Language Model	020544
Large-Size PV Modules	020161
Laser Processing	020023
Laser-grooved BC Technology	020037
LCA	020464, 020468, 020499, 020515
LCOE	020304
LCOE Reduction	020358
LCOH	020426
Lessons Learned	020567
Levelized Cost of Electricity	020482
Li-ion Batteries	020536
LID	020215
LiDAR	020262
Life Cycle Assessment	020511
Life Cycle Impact Assessment	020479
Life-Cycle Assessment	020559
Lifetime Financial Analysis	020367
Light Emitting Diodes	020067
Light Soaking	020010
Light Trapping (LT)	020104

Lightweight	020384
Long-Term Degradation Rate	020181
Low Intensity Low Temperature (LILT)	020246
Low-Cost Sky Imager	020272
Low-energy Secondary Generation and Multiplication	020013
Luminescence	020206
Machine Learning	020337, 020342, 020355, 020434, 020510, 020522
Machine Learning (ML)	020317
Machine Learning Model	020279
Manufacturing	020007, 020558
Market	020570
Market Potential	020252
Market Uptake	020556
Market Value	020539
Mask	020031
Mass Production	020021
Material Classification	020504
Material Qualification	020574
Maximum Power Line	020449
Maximum Power Point Tracking	020437, 020449
McClear	020278
Mechanical Load Test	020167
Mechanical Loads	020231
Mediterranean Climate PV Performance	020334
Metal Recovery	020501, 020508
Metallization	020020, 020028
Metastability	020215
MgO	020131
Micro-Concentrator Optics	020257
Microalgae	020378
Microclimate	020403, 020565
Microinverter	020386
Minimum Sustainable Price	020482
Mismatch	020056, 020396
Mismatch Losses	020432
Mitigation strategies	020573

O&M   020328
Off-grid Photovoltaic System   020441
Open-source   020446
Operating Conditions   020194
Operation and Maintenance   020358, 020371
Operations and Maintenance   020340
Optical Characterisation   020140
Optimal Capacity of Battery Storage   020539
Optimization   020534
Optoelectrical Properties   020071
Optoelectronic Properties   020060
Organic Solar Cells   020096
Organizational Factors   020523
Orientation Methods   020532
Orientation Smoothing Effect   020486
Outdoor   020307
Outdoor Performance   020115
Outdoor Performance Monitoring   020192
Output Power Control   020449
Overhead PV   020400

Palm   020199
Partial Safety Concept   020167
Partial Shading   020153, 020193, 020223, 020243, 020422, 020455
Passivating Contacts   020006, 020008
Patterning   020007
PCB   020055
PECVD   020008, 020040
Peer-comparison   020320
PERC   020171, 020482
PERC PV Modules   020229
Percolation   020119
Performance   020193, 020229, 020307
Performance Analysis   020287
Performance Evaluation   020320
Performance Impact   020367
Performance Indicator   020194
Performance Losses   020314
Performance Modelling   020319

Performance Ratio	020289, 020319, 020353, 020407
Performance Stability	020139
Perovskite	020106
Perovskite Degradation	020064
Perovskite Outdoor	020064
Perovskite Solar Cell	020115
Perovskites	020060, 020505, 020558
Photobioreactors	020378
Photoluminescence	020205
Photonic-nanostructure	020104
Photovoltaic	020171, 020244, 020332, 020346, 020398, 020407, 020421, 020445, 020534, 020544, 020548, 020575
Photovoltaic (PV)	020563, 020570
Photovoltaic (PV) Modules	020164
Photovoltaic (PV) Plants	020356, 020375
Photovoltaic (PV) Systems	020320
Photovoltaic Encapsulation	020141
Photovoltaic Energy	020409, 020420
Photovoltaic Inverter Testing	020369
Photovoltaic Manufacturing	020043
Photovoltaic Module	020499
Photovoltaic Module Inspection	020191
Photovoltaic Modules	020123, 020183, 020335, 020374
Photovoltaic Performance	020371
Photovoltaic Power	020528
Photovoltaic Power Estimation	020342
Photovoltaic Power Modeling	020528
Photovoltaic Power Production	020537
Photovoltaic Production	020336
Photovoltaic Shading Systems	020259
Photovoltaic Solar Energy	020100
Photovoltaic System	020265, 020279, 020449
Photovoltaic System Monitoring	020334
Photovoltaic Systems	020243, 020267, 020287, 020289, 020337, 020339, 020353, 020437, 020439, 020444, 020492, 020536, 020554
Photovoltaics	020066, 020068, 020087, 020094, 020129, 020210, 020309, 020358, 020376, 020486, 020495, 020517, 020532, 020535, 020571
Photovoltaics Failures	020328

Pinholes	020028
Plane-of-Array Irradiation	020348
pLCA	020515
Plug and Play Photovoltaics	020386
Plug-In Photovoltaics	020386
Policy Impacts	020309
Pollution Variables	020279
POLO BJ	020482
Poly Si	020021
Poly-Si	020008, 020035
Polyaniline	020498
Polymer Degradation	020149, 020150
Polymer Properties	020157
Polynomial Surface	020525
Polysilicon	020006, 020031
PolyZEBRA	020035
Positional Effects	020416
Potential-Induced Degradation	020265
Power Fluctuations	020528
Power Loss	020201
Power Optimizers	020359
Power Output Prediction	020338
Power Reserve	020571
Power System Balancing	020554
Predictive Modelling	020317
Production	020050
Profitability	020388
PSC	020083
Public Buildings	020562
Pump Controllers	020429
PV	020252
PV and Buildings	020301
PV Architecture	020453
PV Array Simulator Assessment	020369
PV Degradation	020217, 020329
PV Digital Twin	020319
PV Fault Diagnosis	020351
PV Fire Performance	020359
PV Integration	020139

PV KPI	020329
PV Modelling	020201
PV Module	020139, 020175, 020177, 020199, 020217
PV Module Modeling	020196
PV Module Performance	020215
PV Module Reliability	020151, 020217
PV Modules	020121, 020206, 020231, 020429, 020470
PV Output Estimation	020329
PV Performance	020317
PV Power Variability	020241
PV Recyclability Index	020497
PV Recycling	020011
PV Self-consumption	020567
PV Simulation	020363, 020412, 020446
PV Simulation Tools	020297
PV Sizing	020426
PV System	020515
PV System Design	020382
PV Systems	020217, 020311, 020317, 020539, 020546
PV Test Stand	020318
PV Waste	020507
PV-Career Orientation	020569
PV-Module Reliability	020167
PVC-PMMA Blends	020090
PVsyst	020196
PVT	020301

Qatar	020291
Quality Assurance	020344
Quality Control	020135, 020283
Quality Infrastructure	020563
Quantitative	020188
QuantumATK	020071

Radiative Heat Transfer	020123
Raman Spectroscopy	020150
Rapid Shutdown	020359
Rated Energy Yield	020140
Ray Tracing	020396

Silicon	020007, 020058, 020097, 020468, 020495, 020501, 020507, 020508, 020515
Silicon Heterojunction	020040
Silicon Heterojunction Cell	020046
Silicon Kerf	020495
Silicon Photovoltaics	020144
Silicon Solar Cell	020001, 020013, 020023
Silicon Solar Cells	020006, 020068
Silicone	020384
Silver Recovery	020498
Simulation	020255, 020301
Simulation Acceleration	020243
Single-Axis Tracker Reliability	020314
Sizing Optimization	020530
Smart City	020420
Smart Energy System	020544
Smart Inverter IV Tracing	020361
SMARTS2	020278
Social Cognitive Career Theory (SCCT)	020569
Social Housing	020564
Social Innovation	020575
Social Risks	020505
Socio-Economics	020476
Software Tool	020183
Soil	020403, 020565
Soiling	020311, 020332, 020339, 020361
Soiling Loss Modeling	020317
Soiling Losses	020311, 020348
Soiling Mitigation	020311
Solar	020188, 020276
Solar Array Simulator Evaluation	020369
Solar Cell	020007, 020053, 020083
Solar Cells	020090, 020501, 020508
Solar Energy	020526
Solar Glass	020140
Solar Irradiance	020286
Solar Irradiance Forecasting	020267
Solar Irradiation	020412

Solar Mandate	020551
Solar Modules	020157
Solar Panel Reliability	020154
Solar Photovoltaic Technology	020569
Solar Photovoltaics	020479, 020564
Solar Power	020571
Solar Power Plant	020539
Solar PV	020476, 020549, 020552, 020559, 020573
Solar PV Systems in Buildings	020562
Solar Radiation	020275, 020283
Solar Railways	020421
Solar Resource Variability	020241
Solar Silicon	020011
Solar Water Pumping System	020429
Solder Paste	020220
Solid-State Reaction	020117
Solvent Additives	020096
Soxhlet Extraction	020135
Space	020053
Spatial Planning Integration	020552
Spatio-Temporal Analysis	020338
Spectral Composition	020416
Spectral Irradiance	020283
Spectral Mapping	020149
Spectroscopy	020227
Spectrum Splitting	020379
Stability	020096
Stakeholder Analysis	020556
Stall Detection	020314
Stance Detection	020522
Standardisation	020472
Standards	020211, 020444
STC Parameters	020183
Storage	020429, 020535
Storage Effect	020215
Storage System	020539
Stress Profile	020355
Structural Electronics	020423
Structuring	020031

Thermal Effects   020416
Thermal Image   020193
Thermal Stress   020153, 020260
Thermally Conductive Filler   020131
Thermomechanical Test   020497
Thermophotonics   020067
Thin Film   020071, 020180
Thin Films   020069, 020087
Thin-film   020094
Thin-Film Devices   020067
Thin-Film Solar Cells   020085
Tilt   020532
TOPCon   020010, 020021, 020028, 020031, 020037
TOPCON PV Modules   020229
Tracking Irradiation Gain   020363
Tracking Systems   020402
Transparency   020574
Transparent Conducting Oxide   020046
Tree Shading   020294

UAV-Based Monitoring   020335, 020374
Ultrasonic Characterization   020132
Ultraviolet Fluorescence   020158
Ultraviolet-Fluorescence Imaging   020185
Urban Planning   020420, 020526
Urban Shadowing   020457
Utility-Scale Photovoltaics   020348
Utility-Scale Solar PV   020382
UV Exposure   020229
UV Fluorescence   020166
UV Instability   020229
UV Laser Annealing   020079
UV Laser Scribing   020043
UV-Vis Spectroscopy   020081

Vacuum Refining   020011
Vacuum Thermal Evaporation   020558
Vacuum-Assisted Processing   020079
Validation   020390

Value Chain	020505
Vehicle Integrated Photovoltaics (VIPV)	020459
Vehicle-Integrated Photovoltaics	020453, 020457
Vehicle-Integrated Photovoltaics (VIPV)	020422
Vertical Bifacial PV	020262
Vertical PV	020388, 020400
Very Short-term Solar Forecasting	020272
Vibration Durability	020417
VIPV	020417, 020455
Virtual Power Plant	020554
Virtual Power Plants	020535
Visual inspection	020169, 020185
Water Quality	020418
Weather Station	020371
Weather Variables	020279
Wet Etching	020028
Yield	020180, 020307, 020396
YOLO Classifiers	020335, 020374
ZnSnO	020085

WIP – Renewable Energies
Sylvensteinstr. 2
81369 Munchen
Germany

ISBN 979-8-3313-2987-7